MINNEAPOLIS-MOLINE
SHOP MANUAL MM-201

Avery Models ■ A ■ R ■ V

Minneapolis-Moline Models

■ BF ■ BG ■ GTA ■ GTB ■ R ■ U ■ UT ■ V ■ ZA ■ ZT

Minneapolis-Moline Models ■ GB ■ UB ■ ZB

Minneapolis-Moline Models

■ 335 ■ 445 ■ Jet Star ■ Jet Star Two ■ Jet Star Three

■ 4 Star ■ 4 Star Super ■ U-302

Minneapolis-Moline Models

■ UB Special ■ UTS Special ■ 5 Star ■ M5 ■ M504 ■ M602

■ M604 ■ M670 ■ M670 Super

Minneapolis-Moline Models

■ G-VI ■ G-705 ■ G-706 ■ G-707 ■ G-708 ■ G-900 ■ G-950

■ G-1000 ■ G-1000 Vista ■ G-1050 ■ G-1350

Massey-Ferguson ■ MF95 (after SN 17300000) ■ MF97

I&T
SHOP SERVICE

Information and Instructions

This shop manual contains several sections each covering a specific group of wheel type tractors. The Tab Index on the preceding page can be used to locate the section pertaining to each group of tractors. Each section contains the necessary specifications and the brief but terse procedural data needed by a mechanic when repairing a tractor on which he has had no previous actual experience.

Within each section, the material is arranged in a systematic order beginning with an index which is followed immediately by a Table of Condensed Service Specifications. These specifications include dimensions, fits, clearances and timing instructions. Next in order of arrangement is the procedures paragraphs.

In the procedures paragraphs, the order of presentation starts with the front axle system and steering and proceeding toward the rear axle. The last paragraphs are devoted to the power take-off and power lift systems. Interspersed where needed are additional tabular specifications pertaining to wear limits, torquing, etc.

HOW TO USE THE INDEX

Suppose you want to know the procedure for R&R (remove and reinstall) of the engine camshaft. Your first step is to look in the index under the main heading of ENGINE until you find the entry "Camshaft." Now read to the right where under the column covering the tractor you are repairing, you will find a number which indicates the beginning paragraph pertaining to the camshaft. To locate this wanted paragraph in the manual, turn the pages until the running index appearing on the top outside corner of each page contains the number you are seeking. In this paragraph you will find the information concerning the removal of the camshaft.

I&T Shop Service

P.O. Box 12901, Overland Park, KS 66282-2901
Phone: 800-262-1954 Fax: 800-633-6219
itshopmanuals.com

January, 2002
October, 2004
May, 2007

MINNEAPOLIS-MOLINE

Minneapolis-Moline Models

■ GTA ■ GTB ■ R ■ U ■ UT ■ ZA ■ ZT (Page 2)

Avery Models

■ A ■ R ■ V (Page 60)

Minneapolis-Moline Models

■ BF ■ BG ■ V (Page 60)

Previously contained in I & T Shop Service Manual No. MM-2A

SHOP MANUAL
MINNEAPOLIS-MOLINE

MODELS GTA-GTB

SERIES R-U-ZA-ZT

IDENTIFICATION

Tractor serial number is stamped on a plate which is riveted to right side of transmission housing.

Engine serial number is stamped on a plate which is riveted to right side of crankcase.

AXLE TYPE
Adjustable: RTE - UTE - ZAE - ZTE
Non-Adjustable: GTA - GTB - RTS - UTS - ZAS - ZTS

TRICYCLE TYPE
Double Wheel: RTU - UTU - ZAU - ZTU
Single Wheel: RTN - UTN - ZAN - ZTN

CANE TYPE
Extra Reduction Chain Drive: UTC

BEGINNING TRACTOR SERIAL NUMBERS

Model	GTA	GTB	RT	RTE	RTN	RTS	RTU	UT	UTC	UTE
1940			402,201					312,451		
1941			405,576					314,893		
1942	162,001		407,951					316,501		
1943	162,301		408,826					317,702		
1944	162,303		409,358					318,163		
1945	162,660		410,748					321,102		
1946	162,870		413,755					325,231		
1947	163,220	164,001	416,545					329,752		
1948		164,179		0,044,800,001	0,034,800,001		0,014,800,001	337,418	0,154,800,001	
1949		0,164,900,001		0,044,900,001	0,034,900,001	0,024,900,001	0,014,900,001		0,154,900,011	
1950		0,165,000,001		0,045,000,001	0,035,000,001	0,025,000,001	0,015,000,001			
1951		01,601,864		00,400,205	00,300,094	00,200,301	00,102,156		01,500,101	04,300,001
1952		01,603,399		00,400,282		00,200,402	00,103,973		01,500,181	04,300,112
1953		01,604,890		00,400,283		00,200,552				04,300,262
1954		01,605,973					00,104,824		01,500,266	04,300,265
1955										

Model	UTN	UTS	UTU	ZAE	ZAN	ZAS	ZAU	ZTN	ZTU	ZTS
1940								567,155	567,155	610,685
1941								568,755	568,755	611,088
1942								570,822	570,822	611,343
1943								571,422	571,422	611,447
1944								572,968	572,968	611,966
1945								575,713	575,713	612,486
1946								576,814	576,814	612,886
1947								578,014	578,014	613,086
1948		0,124,800,001	0,114,800,001					581,815	581,815	
1949		0,124,900,001	0,114,900,001	0,094,900,001	0,084,900,001	0,074,900,001	0,064,900,001			
1950	0,385,000,001	0,125,000,001	0,115,000,001	0,095,000,001	0,085,000,001	0,075,000,001	0,065,000,001			
1951	03,800,102	01,203,851	01,105,384	00,900,374	00,800,239	00,700,481	00,605,436			
1952	03,800,205	01,207,139	01,110,118	00,900,577	00,800,443	00,701,286	00,609,940			
1953		01,210,571		00,900,998	00,800,619	00,701,911				
1954		01,213,220	01,113,450							
1955										

INDEX (By Starting Paragraph)

Minneapolis-Moline Model "GTB"

**Minneapolis-
Moline
"R"**

**Minneapolis-
Moline
"U"**

**Minneapolis-
Moline
"Z"**

CONDENSED SERVICE DATA

MODEL OR SERIES	GTA	GTB	R	U	ZA	ZT
GENERAL						
Engine Make	Own	Own	Own	Own	Own	Own
Engine Model	LE	403A	EE	*283A	206B	RE
Cylinders	4	4	4	4	4	4
Bore—Inches	4⅝	4⅝	3⅝	4¼	3⅝	3⅝
Stroke—Inches	6	6	4	5	5	4½
Displacement—Cubic Inches	403	403	165	283	206	185.8
Compression Ratio		5.4	6.2	6.2	6.2	5.75
Compression Ratio		4.3	5.0	4.4	4.7	4.70
Pistons Removed From:			——Above: See paragraphs 82 and 83——			
Main Brgs. Adjustable (Except KEC)	No	No	No	No	No	No
Main Brgs. Adjustable (KEC)				Yes		
Rod Brgs. Adjustable (Except KEC)	No	No	No	No	No	No
Rod Brgs. Adjustable (KEC)				Yes		
Cylinder Sleeves	No	No	No	No	No	No
Forward Speeds	4	5	4	5	5	5
Main Bearings, Number of	3	3	2	3	3	2
Generator & Starter Make			——Delco-Remy——			
TUNE-UP						
Firing Order	1-3-4-2	1-3-4-2	1-3-4-2	1-3-4-2	1-3-4-2	1-3-4-2
Valve Tappet Gap—Inlet (Hot)	0.008	0.008	See ZT	0.008	0.008	††
Valve Tappet Gap—Exhaust (Hot)	0.010	0.010	See ZT	0.010	0.010	††
Valve Face Angle	45°	45°	45°	45°	45°	45°
Valve Seat Angle	45°	45°	45°	45°	45°	45°
Ignition Distributor Make			——Delco-Remy——			
Ignition Distributor Model	1111718	1111718	1111711	1111718	1111711	1111711
Ignition Magneto Make			——Fairbanks-Morse——			
Ignition Magneto Model	FMO4B4	FMO4B4	FMK4B4	FMO4B4	FMK4B4	FMK4B4
Breaker Gap—Distributor	0.020	0.020	0.020	0.020	0.020	0.020
Breaker Gap—Magneto	0.020	0.020	0.020	0.020	0.020	0.020
Distributor Timing—Retard			——See Paragraph 146——			
Distributor Timing—Full Advance			——See Paragraph 146——			
Magneto Impulse Trip Point			——See Paragraph 145——			
Magneto Lag Angle	35°	35°	25°	35°	25°	25°
Magneto Running Timing			——See Paragraph 145——			
Flywheel Mark Indicating:						
Magneto Impulse Trips			——See Paragraph 145——			
Magneto Running Timing			——See Paragraph 145——			
Distributor Retard Timing			——See Paragraph 146——			
Distributor Full Adv. Timing			——See Paragraph 146——			
Spark Plug Make			——Champion or AC——			
Model for Gasoline (Champion)	O Comm.	O Comm.	J8	O Comm.	J8	J8
Model for Gasoline (AC)	73 Comm.	73 Comm.	45 Comm.	73 Comm.	45 Comm.	45 Comm.
Model for Low Octane (Champ.)	1 Comm.	1 Comm.	8 Comm.	1 Comm.	8 Comm.	8 Comm.
Model for Low Octane (AC)	75 Comm.	75 Comm.	86 Comm.	75 Comm.	86 Comm.	86 Comm.
Electrode Gap	0.025	0.025	0.025	0.025	0.025	0.025
Carburetor Make			——Marvel-Schebler——			
Model			——Refer To Carburetor——			
Float Setting			——¼" For TSX; 2" For TTX——			
Engine No Load rpm		1210	1650	1400	1650	1650
Engine Loaded rpm	1075	1100	1400	1275	1500	1500
Belt Pulley Loaded rpm	650	627	933	727	786	786
Belt Pulley No Load rpm		690	1100	800	865	865
P.T.O. Loaded rpm	526	495	560	575	615	615
SIZES—CAPACITIES—CLEARANCES						
(Clearance in thousandths)						
Crankshaft Journal Diameter Front	2.9115	2.9115	Roller	2.9115	Roller	Ball
Crankshaft Journal Center	2.9115	2.9115	——	2.9115	2.750	†3.2495
Crankshaft Journal Diameter Rear	2.9115	2.9115	3.000	2.9115	3.000	Ball
Crankpin Diameter	2.750	2.750	2.625	2.577	2.625	2.625
Camshaft Journal Diameter Front	3.308	3.308	1.24655	3.308	1.24655	1.24655
Camshaft Journal Diameter Center	3.2755	3.2755	1.24655	3.2755	1.24655	1.24655
Camshaft Journal Diameter Rear	1.9965	1.9965	1.24655	1.9965	1.24655	1.24655
Piston Pin Diameter	1.250	1.250	0.9995	1.250	0.9995	0.9995
Valve Stem Diameter	7/16	7/16	11/32	7/16	11/32	11/32
Compression Ring Width	3/16	3/16	1/8	5/32	1/8	1/8
Oil Ring—Width	1/4	1/4	3/16	1/4	3/16	3/16
Plain Main Brgs., Diam. Clearance	1.5-4	1.5-4	1.5-3	1.5-4	1.5-3.5	†1-3
Rod Brgs., Diam. Clearance	1.5-3	1.5-3	1.5-3	1.5-3	1.5-3	1.5-3
Piston Skirt Clearance	3.5-4.5	3.5-4.5	2.5-4.5	3.5-5.5	2.5-4.5	2.5-4.5
Crankshaft End Play	2-6	2-6	2-6	2-6	3-4	4-6
Camshaft Bearing Clearance	8 Max.	8 Max.	7 Max.	8 Max.	7 Max.	7 Max.
Cooling System—Gallons	7	12	3½	6	3¾	3½
Crankcase Oil—Quarts	9	9	7	9	7	7
Trans. & Diff.—Quarts	52	52	18	52	28	28

*Used on late production. Early models used KEC and KEF. Refer to engine section of this manual for details.
†Applies to oil collar. ††Refer to paragraph 81A.

FRONT SYSTEM
(TRICYCLE TYPE)

PEDESTAL (FRONT SUPPORT) & COMPONENTS

The support or pedestal unit of tri-cycle type models can be overhauled without removing the unit from the tractor.

Models RTN-ZAN-ZTN

1. **WHEEL BEARINGS AND AXLE.** The two wheel axle shaft bearings can be renewed after removing two clamp bolts from lower end of fork. Each wheel bearing is individually adjusted by means of nut (25—Fig. MM1) so as to remove all end play and yet permit wheel to rotate freely.

2. **FORK, EXTENSION SHAFT, BEARINGS AND SECTOR.** To remove these parts, proceed as follows: Remove wheel and hub assembly, and hood, radiator and grille assembly. Remove starting crank extension shaft and upper bearing cover (18).

Remove wheel fork to extension shaft retaining cap screw (26), cap screw (34) and large washer (33) from upper end of extension shaft as shown in Fig. MM2. Remove cover plate (19—Fig. MM1) from support by placing large washer under the head of one of the radiator retaining cap screws and turning the screw into one of the threaded holes of the cover plate. Using the head of the screw as a fulcrum, pry under the washer with a suitable bar until the cover plate, upper bearing and cage (30) are removed.

To remove the extension shaft from fork, place two pieces of "2x4" blocks on top of support and bridge these with two steel bars. Screw a long ⅝ inch threaded stud into extension shaft and place a washer and nut on the threads. Screw the nut down against the steel bars until the shaft extension is pulled out of the wheel fork.

3. With the shaft extension removed as per paragraph 2, the wheel fork can be driven or preferably pushed out of the sector as shown in Fig. MM3. The steel bars are placed under the deck of the support and push is obtained by a puller screw, nut and washer reacting against top of fork and undersides of steel bars. The wheel fork bearing and felt seal can be renewed at this time.

When reassembling the parts to front support it will be necessary to center the cover plate (19—Fig. MM1) to insure correct alignment of upper bearing cone (32) before tightening the cover plate retaining screws as shown in Fig. MM4. All of the support bearings are adjusted by turning the upper cap screw (34—Fig. MM1). The bearings should be adjusted to a slight drag.

4. **STEERING SECTOR AND WORM.** To remove the steering gear sector which is keyed to the wheel fork, proceed as outlined in paragraphs 2 and 3. To remove the steering gear worm and shaft, proceed as follows: Drive pin out of steering worm shaft universal joint. Loosen socket head set screw which locks the worm adjusting plug (nut) and unscrew the plug. Rotating the worm, thread same and out of mesh with the sector.

Adjust worm shaft bearings with adjusting plug to remove all end play and yet permit worm shaft to rotate freely.

5. **R & R SUPPORT ASSEMBLY.** To remove the pedestal (front support) assembly, first remove hood, radiator and grille. Support front as-

Fig. MM2—Removing cap screw (34) and washer (33) from top of RTN fork extension shaft. Models ZAN and ZTN are similar.

Fig. MM1—Exploded view of models RTN, ZAN and ZTN front support (pedestal) and associated parts.

18. Bearing cover	27. Washer
19. Housing cover plate	28. Housing
20. Lower bearing cup	29. Fork extension
21. Cone	shaft
22. Retainer washer	30. Upper bearing cage
23. Felt oil seal	31. Upper bearing cup
24. Wheel fork	32. Cone
25. Adjusting nuts	33. Washer
26. Cap screw	34. Cap screw

Fig. MM3—Pressing the wheel fork out of the steering sector on models RTN, ZAN and ZTN.

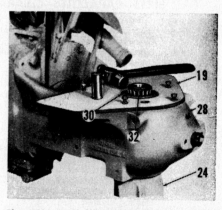

Fig. MM4—Models RTN, ZAN and ZTN support housing cover plate is centered before tightening, by centering the upper bearing cone.

sembly and engine separately and remove bolts retaining front assembly to engine. It will be necessary to slightly raise engine so that pedestal can clear crankshaft pulley.

Model UTN

6. **WHEEL BEARINGS AND AXLE.** To renew or adjust the wheel axle bearings, follow the procedure outlined in paragraph 1.

7. **FORK, BEARINGS AND SECTOR.** To remove these parts, proceed as follows: Raise and support front portion of tractor and remove wheel and hub assembly. Remove hood, radiator and grille assembly. Slide pedestal forward on pedestal supports, drive crankpin out of crank lower shaft and remove the sprocket housing cover, lower sprocket and chain. Drive the tapered pin out of the upper sprocket and shaft as in Fig. MM5 and remove the sprocket.

Remove cover from pedestal. Release pressure from spring by removing cotter pin from the crank extension shaft and withdraw crank extension shaft, spring and washer.

Remove nut and washer (9—Fig. MM6) from fork, and, using a piece of pipe slipped over threads of the wheel fork as shown in Fig. MM7, drive the fork and lower bearing cone unit down and out of sector. Bearing cage (14—Fig. MM6) can now be removed from the housing.

Reinstall parts by reversing the removal procedure and tighten nut (8) to obtain a slight amount of bearing drag.

8. **STEERING SECTOR AND WORM.** To remove the steering gear sector, which is keyed to the wheel fork, proceed as outlined in paragraph

7. To remove the steering worm and shaft, proceed as follows: Drive the pin out of the steering worm shaft universal joint, loosen the socket head set screw which locks the worm adjusting plug (nut) and unscrew the plug.

Steering worm can now be turned out of housing as shown in Fig. MM8.

Adjust the worm shaft bearings with adjusting plug (16) to remove all end play and yet permit same to rotate freely.

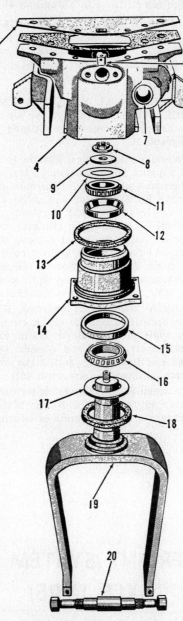

Fig. MM6—Exploded view of model UTN pedestal and associated parts. The taper roller bearings are carried in bearing cage (14).

1. Housing cover	12&15. Bearing cups
4. Housing	13. Cork seal
7. Expansion plug	14. Bearing cage
8. Nut	17. Washer
9. Washer	18. Felt seal
10. Washer	19. Fork
11&16. Bearing cones	20. Axle

9. **R & R SUPPORT ASSEMBLY.** To remove the pedestal (front support) assembly, follow the general procedure given in paragraph 5.

Models RTU-ZAU-ZTU

10. **VERTICAL SPINDLE AND WHEEL AXLE.** The wheel spindle (axle) and block assembly (11—Fig. MM9) can be removed as shown in Fig. MM10 by using a suitable puller, after removing the front wheel and hub assemblies, and the spindle block retaining nut.

10A. To remove axle & spindle (5—Fig. MM9), proceed as follows: Support front of tractor and remove hood, radiator and grille assembly. Remove pedestal cover, starting crank extension and front wheel and hub assemblies.

10B. Unscrew spindle shaft bearing adjusting nut (10) from lower side of pedestal after first removing the lock screw for same. Working through opening in top of pedestal, remove steering gear sector retaining nut. Using a piece of pipe as a drift, bump the vertical spindle down and out of the

Fig. MM7—Using a piece of pipe to protect threads of vertical shaft when driving the shaft out of RTU pedestal. The same procedure is used on models UTN, UTU, ZAU and ZTU.

3. Washer	5. Shaft or fork
4. Nut	17. Sector

Fig. MM8—Removing the steering gear worm from model RTU pedestal. Other tricycle and the adjustable axle models are similar.

13. Bearing cones	15. Worm
14. Set screw	16. Adjusting nut

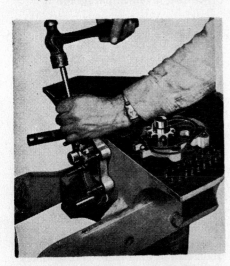

Fig. MM5—Removing crank sprocket assembly from models UTE, UTN and UTU pedestal.

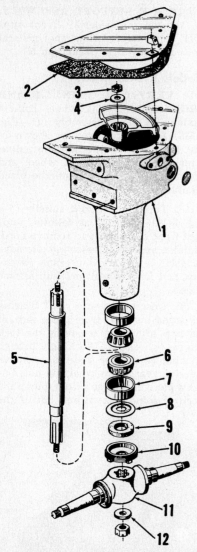

Fig. MM9—Exploded view of model UTU pedestal and related parts. Other dual wheel tricycle models are similar.

1. Pedestal	7. Cup
2. Gasket	8. Retainer
3. Nut	9. Felt seal
4. Washer	10. Adjusting nut
5. Spindle	11. Axle
6. Cone	12. Washer

sector as shown in Fig. MM7. Vertical spindle bearing cups and cones can be renewed at this time.

Adjust vertical spindle bearings to a slight drag by turning adjusting nut (10—Fig. MM9) and then locking the adjustment with the socket head set screw.

11. STEERING SECTOR AND WORM. To remove the steering gear sector proceed as outlined in paragraph 10A. Steering gear worm and shaft overhaul and adjustment procedures are similar to the models which are outlined in paragraph 4.

12. R & R SUPPORT ASSEMBLY. To remove the pedestal (front support) unit, follow the procedure outlined in paragraph 5.

Model UTU

13. VERTICAL SPINDLE AND WHEEL AXLE. To remove the wheel axle assembly, proceed as outlined in paragraph 10.

To remove the vertical spindle, raise and support front portion of tractor and remove wheel and hub assemblies. Remove hood, radiator and grille assembly. Slide pedestal forward on pedestal supports, drive crankpin out of crank lower shaft and remove the sprocket housing cover, lower sprocket and chain. Drive the tapered pin out of the upper sprocket and shaft as in Fig. MM5 and remove the sprocket.

Remove cover from pedestal. Release pressure from the crank extension shaft and withdraw crank extension shaft, spring and washer. For balance of disassembly, follow the procedure outlined in paragraph 10B.

Reassemble in reverse order and tighten adjusting nut (10—Fig. MM9) to obtain a slight amount of bearing drag.

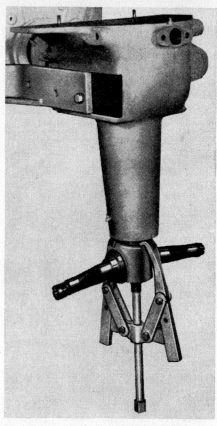

Fig. MM10—Removing horizontal axle from dual wheel tricycle type tractors.

14. STEERING SECTOR AND WORM. To remove the steering sector, proceed as outlined in paragraph 13. The steering gear worm and shaft overhaul and adjustment procedures are similar to the models which are outlined in paragraph 4.

15. R & R SUPPORT ASSEMBLY. To remove the pedestal (front support) assembly, follow the general procedure given in paragraph 5.

FRONT SYSTEM (AXLE TYPE)

STEERING KNUCKLES AND ARMS
Models GTA-GTB-RTS-UTS-ZAS-ZTS

20. To remove steering knuckles (9 —Fig. MM15), first remove knuckle pin retaining pin by bumping same rearward and out of axle member. Using a drift, bump knuckle pin (7) **down**, forcing lower expansion plug (6) out of knuckle; then, bump knuckle pin **up** forcing upper expansion plug out of knuckle and knuckle pin from axle and knuckle.

The bronze knuckle pin bushings (8) supplied for service, require final sizing after installation to provide a 0.006-0.008 diametral clearance for the knuckle pin.

Install thrust bearing (13) between underside of axle and steering knuckle with word "Thrust" or "Timken" facing up.

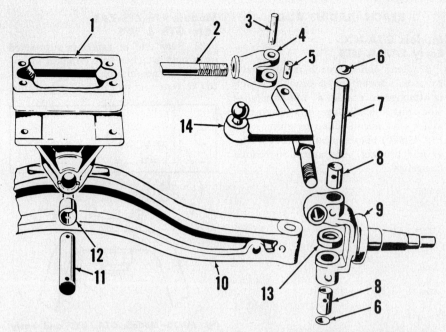

Fig. MM15—Model ZAS front axle assembly. Other non-adjustable axle models are similar, the differences of which are evident after an examination of the unit. Install bearing (13) with "Timken" or "Thrust" mark facing up.

1. Axle support	6. Expansion plug	11. Axle king (pivot) pin
2. Tie rod	7. Knuckle pin	12. King pin bushing
3. Clevis pin	8. Knuckle pin bushing	13. Knuckle thrust bearing
4. Tie rod end	9. Knuckle	14. Steering knuckle arm
5. Clevis pin bushing	10. Axle	(left)

Model UTC

21. To remove steering knuckles, first remove front wheel and hub assemblies. Remove knuckle steering arms (1—Fig. MM16) from tops of knuckle pins. Remove bolts and nuts from lower end of steering knuckle and remove knuckle from knuckle pin. Extract Woodruff keys from knuckle pin and withdraw pin from top of axle. Knuckle pin bushings in axle can be driven out and new ones installed. Clearance between knuckle pin and bushing should be 0.005 -0.006.

Reassembly is reverse of disassembly. Install thrust bearing between knuckle and underside of axle with word "Timken" facing up. Adjust up-and-down play of knuckle pin by positioning knuckle on pin.

Models RTE-UTE-ZAE-ZTE

22. The steering arm (14—Fig. MM17) retains the knuckle to the spindle, and removal of the arm will release the knuckle from the axle spindle.

The old bushings can be pressed or driven out of knuckle by removing the one inch pipe plug in lower side of knuckle and using a drift.

The knuckle spindle bronze service bushings (11) require final sizing after installation to provide a 0.006-0.008 clearance between spindle and bushing.

TIE RODS

Models So Equipped

23. On GTA, ZAS and early production GTB models, the steering knuckle arms are bushed for the clevis type tie rod ends. The bronze type bushings for service require final sizing after installation to provide a free fit.

The procedure for renewing the automotive type tie rod ends as used on the UTS and late production GTB models is evident after an examination of the unit.

Tie rod ends on other models are of the ball and socket type with renewable, screwed-in ball studs.

Toe-in of approximately ¼ inch is adjusted by varying the tie rod length.

KING (PIVOT) PIN

Models GTA-GTB-RTS-UTC-UTS-ZAS-ZTS

24. The axle main member king (pivot) pin (11—Fig. MM15) and/or bushing (12) can be removed after supporting front portion of tractor and removing king pin retaining cotter pins. Service bushings require final sizing to provide a 0.003-0.005 diameter clearance. When installing a new bushing, make certain bushing lubrication hole registers with hole in axle main member.

Models RTE-UTE-ZAE-ZTE

24A. Axle main member king (pivot) pins can be removed after supporting front portion of tractor and removing center steering arm from vertical shaft. Remove king pin retaining cotter pins to release king pins and axle main member.

King pin bushings (7—Fig. MM17) can be renewed at this time.

VERTICAL SHAFT AND/OR BUSHINGS

Models RTE-UTE-ZAE-ZTE

25. The front support housing is similar to the support housing as used on models RTN, UTN, ZAN and ZTN. However, the components which comprise the steering system (vertical shaft, center steering arm, vertical shaft housing) are different.

The procedure for renewing the vertical shaft (17—Fig. MM17) and/or bushings (4) is as follows: With the axle main member removed as outlined in paragraph 24A, remove the hood, radiator and grille assembly. On model UTE, move pedestal forward. On all models, remove pedestal cover and starting crank extension shaft. Remove the steering gear sector retaining nut and bump the vertical

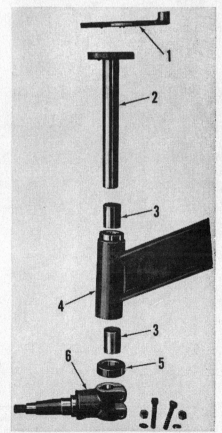

Fig. MM16—Exploded view of model UTC steering knuckle.

1. Steering arm	4. Axle
2. Knuckle pin	5. Thrust bearing
3. Knuckle bushing	6. Knuckle

shaft down and out of sector and vertical shaft housing. The vertical shaft bushings can be renewed after removing the vertical shaft housing (5).

STEERING SECTOR AND WORM
Models RTE-UTE-ZAE-ZTE

26. To remove the steering sector, proceed as outlined in paragraph 25. The steering gear worm and shaft overhaul and adjustment procedures are similar to the models which are outlined in paragraph 4.

REACH (RADIUS ROD)
Models GTA-UTC-Early GTB & UTS

27. Rear end of reach is supported by a ball socket on a bracket which is attached to engine at the transmission split line. Clearance between ball and socket is controlled by shims (6—Fig. MM20) between ball socket washer and bracket. Add shims to reduce clearance.

Models RTS-ZTS-ZAS-Late GTB & UTS

28. Rear end of reach is supported on a bolt attached to a bracket at engine and transmission split line. Bushing in rear end of reach is renewable.

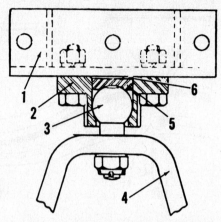

Fig. MM20—Models GTA, UTC and early production GTB and UTS reach (radius) rod pivot.

1. Bracket   4. **Reach**
2. Socket   5. Socket washer
3. Ball   6. Adjusting shims

STEERING GEAR

29. For information on the worm and sector type steering gear, refer to the appropriate preceding paragraphs: For models RTN, ZAN and ZTN, refer to paragraphs 2, 3 and 4; for model UTN, paragraphs 7 and 8; models RTU, ZAU, ZTU, paragraphs 10, 10A, 10B and 11; model UTU, paragraphs 13 and 14; models RTE, UTE, ZAE and ZTE, refer to paragraphs 25 and 26.

For other models, refer to the appropriate paragraphs which follow:

Model GTA

30. **ADJUSTMENT.** To adjust worm shaft bearings, loosen set screw (13—Fig. MM21) and turn plug (20), by rotating the column jacket (18), clockwise until all end play is removed but gear does not bind. No adjustment is provided for gear backlash.

Adjusting screws (2) and (4) are used to position gear bracket (7) in relation to worm shaft (19) and cross shaft (29). Adjustment of these screws is required when steering gear is disassembled. See the following paragraph for adjustment procedure.

31. **OVERHAUL.** Complete assembly cannot be removed as a unit. Proceed as follows: Loosen set screw (13—Fig. MM21), remove the column bracket retaining cap screws and turn jacket (18) counterclockwise until adjusting plug (20) is free of the bracket (7). Remove cap screws and column

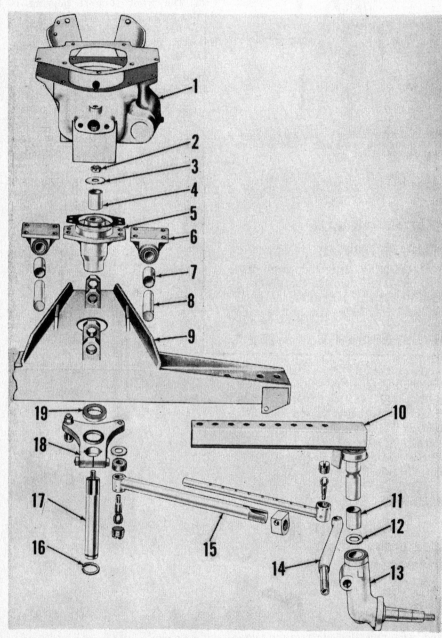

Fig. MM17—Exploded view of model ZAE pedestal and axle assembly. Models RTE, UTE and ZTE are similar.

1. **Housing**
2. Nut
3. Washer
4&7. Bushings
5. Shaft housing
6. King pin bearing
8. King pin
9. Axle center
10. Axle extension
11. Bushing
12. Washer
13. Knuckle
14. Steering arm
15. Tie rod tube
16. Snap ring
17. **Vertical shaft**
18. Center steering arm
19. Washer

bracket (12) and remove column and worm assembly. Remove transmission cover. Remove steering arm from cross shaft (29) and pin (27) from collar (26). Remove set screw (9) from the sector (10) and withdraw cross shaft through the left side of transmission case.

The collar and sector can be removed through the top of the transmission case. To remove the bracket from the transmission case after the worm and sector have been removed, remove nut (8) and lockwasher from the upper adjusting screw (4) and withdraw the bracket through the top of the transmission case.

To remove the worm gear (21) from the worm shaft, remove lower bearing snap ring (23) and bearing (22) and gear pin, then pull gear off shaft. If worm gear has been loose on its shaft, renew the Woodruff key (30) as well as the pin.

To reassemble, install the bracket (7) on the upper adjusting screw (4). Start the cross shaft (29) into the

transmission case and place the collar (26) on the cross shaft. Place the sector (10) in the bracket with its set screw (9) up and start cross shaft through the bracket. With the set screw one spline forward of the spline on the cross shaft which would align with the steering arm split line, slide the cross shaft into the sector.

Reinstall pin (27) in the collar and tighten the sector set screw. Place the transmission cover in position. Install worm shaft assembly through the cover and screw the jacket clockwise until all end play is removed from worm shaft but without causing binding of the worm shaft bearings. With the transmission cover and the column bracket (12) in their correct positions, turn steering wheel through its range and feel for any binding.

If binding exists it will be necessary to move bracket (7) forward. The bracket adjusting screws can be reached through the clutch housing opening after removing the bottom inspection plate.

To move the bracket forward: Loosen locknut (3) and back off the lower adjusting screw (2); then loosen center nut (6) on the upper adjusting screw (4) and tighten the rear nut (8) against the bracket. Turn the lower adjusting screw back in until it contacts the bracket and tighten the locknut.

To move the bracket rearward: Loosen screw (2), rear nut (8) on the upper adjusting screw (4) and tighten center nut (6) against the bracket. It may be necessary, in order to have sufficient threads of the upper adjusting screw through the bracket, to loosen the upper adjusting screw locknut (5) and turn the screw farther into the transmission case. After the bracket is positioned on the upper adjusting screw, turn the lower adjusting screw back in until it contacts the bracket and tighten the locknut. Two or three adjustments may be required to obtain a satisfactory bracket setting.

Fig. MM21—Sectional views of model GTA steering gear assembly. Screws (2) and (4) are accessible through the clutch housing.

1. Transmission case
2. Bracket lower adjusting screw
3. Locknut
4. Bracket upper adjusting screw
5. Locknut
6. Center nut
7. Gear bracket
8. Bracket rear nut
9. Sector set screw
10. Sector gear
11. Transmission cover
12. Column bracket
13. Lock screw
14. Jacket tube seal
15. Worm shaft seal
16. Column upper bushing
17. Felt retainer
18. Column jacket
19. Worm shaft
20. Adjusting plug
21. Worm
22. Thrust bearing
23. Snap ring
24. Steering arm
25. Cross shaft seal
26. Cross shaft collar
27. Collar retaining pin
29. Cross shaft
30. Woodruff key

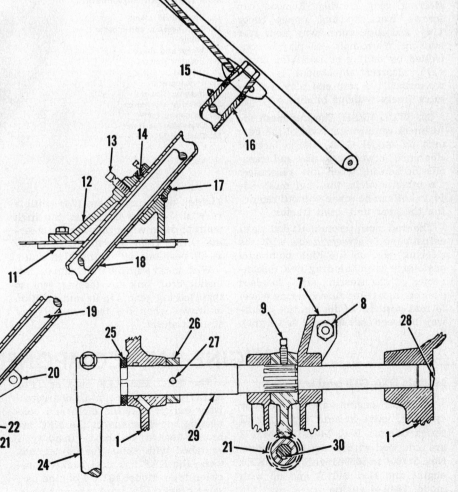

**Models GTB-RTS-UTC-
UTS-ZAS-ZTS**

32. **ADJUSTMENT**. Before adjusting
the Ross worm (cam) and lever type
steering gear unit, disconnect drag
link from steering gear arm to remove any load from gear and permit
locating mid-position. Model ZTS
lever is of the single stud type; whereas, other models are of the dual stud
type.

33. **WORMSHAFT (CAM) END
PLAY.** Two types of wormshaft bearing adjustments are used on these
steering gears. The enclosed (jack-
eted) type of gear as used on model
ZTS is provided with a threaded adjusting plug while the open shaft type
as used on other models is provided
with shims under the housing cap.

34. **Adjusting Plug Type.** Refer to
Fig. MM22. Loosen steering column
support and adjusting plug lock screw.
Turn adjusting plug clockwise to reduce end play. All end play must be
removed from camshaft, but shaft
should rotate freely.

35. **Shim Type.** Refer to Fig. MM23.
Loosen clamp bolt on clamp (15) and
slide dust shield (26) away from
steering gear housing. Remove cap
screws from housing upper cover
(16), and slide same away from gear
housing. Wormshaft end play is controlled by adding or removing shims
(17). Correct adjustment is when
wormshaft has zero end play, yet rotates freely without binding.

36. **STUD MESH.** The stud mesh adjustment requires removal of the gear
unit on model GTB due to lack of
clearance between gear unit and transmission housing when unit is installed.
On other models, the stud mesh adjustment can be made without removing the gear unit from tractor.

The stud mesh (cross shaft end play)
adjustment is always made with the
steering gear on the high point and
preferably with the drag link disconnected at the steering arm. To place
gear on high point, turn steering wheel
to mid-position of its rotation (half-
way between full left and full right).

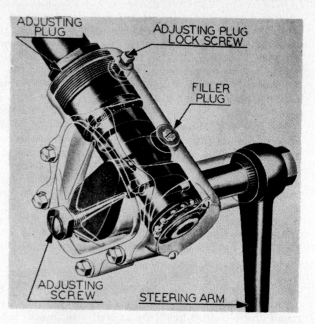

Fig. MM22 — Model ZTS
Ross single stud steering
gear unit.

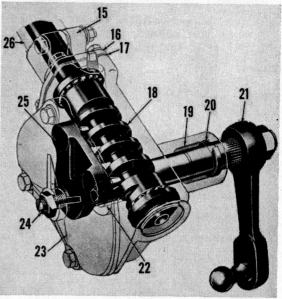

Fig. MM23 — Ross steering
gear assembly. Shims (17)
control worm shaft bearings
adjustment. Screw (24) controls stud mesh adjustment.

15. Dust shield clamp
16. Gear housing upper cover
17. Shims
18. Worm and shaft
19. Bushing (outer)
20. Oil seal
21. Steering arm
22. Bushing (inner)
23. Housing side cover
24. Adjusting screw
25. Cross shaft & lever
26. Dust shield

Tighten adjusting screw (24) until a
very slight drag is felt at the high
point position when rotating the steering wheel. Gear should rotate freely
at all positions off of the high point.

With mesh adjustment complete, reinstall drag link to steering arm so
that steering gear is in its mid-position
of travel when the front wheels are
straight ahead.

37. **OVERHAUL.** Remove gear unit
from tractor. Procedure for disassembly is readily evident from an examination of Figs. MM22 or 23. The bronze
service bushings (19 & 22) for the
lever shaft require final sizing after
installation to provide a 0.0005-0.0025
diametral clearance between shaft
and bushing. Lip of oil seal (20)
should face wormshaft.

ENGINE AND COMPONENTS

Models GTA-GTB and U Series

40. These engines are of the four
cylinder, valve-in-head type. The U
series tractors Nos. 540001 to 543153
are equipped with model KEC engine,
Nos. 544001 to 565985 with model KEF
engine and Nos. 640751 and up with
model 283A-4 engine.

The KEC and KEF engines (Fig.
MM30) are identical in all characteristics except that the main and connecting rod bearings in the KEC are
bronze-backed, babbitt-lined type,
equipped with shims for adjustment,
while the KEF has steel-backed, precision type. Model 283A-4 engine uses
same crankshaft, crankcase and bear-

ings as model KEF, but cylinders are
cast in pairs of two as is also the cylinder head. GTA tractors are equipped
with model LE engine which, although
larger, is similar in construction to
model 283A-4 engine. The 403A engine used in model GTB and shown
in Figs. MM31 & 32 is similar to the
LE engine.

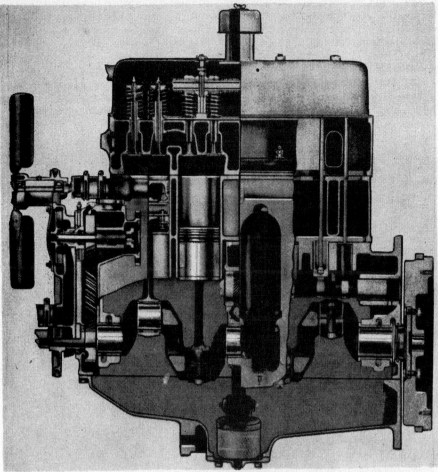

Fig. MM30—Model KEC 283 cubic inch engine used in U series tractors. Model KEF engine is similar except bearings are precision insert type. Model 283A-4 engine is similar to the KEF except that cylinder block is cast in pairs of two. Model LE engine used in the GTA tractor is similar to the 283A-4 engine except that it is larger having 403 cubic inch displacement.

R And ZT Series

41. Engines used in ZT series, shown in Fig. MM34, and R series Fig. MM33 are the same in general characteristics, differing only in size and crankshaft details. They are side-valve type of construction with horizontal valves (2) actuated directly by long rocker arms (3) operated by a gear driven camshaft in left side of crankcase.

Cylinders are cast in removable blocks of two; the cast-iron pistons (5) operating directly in the cast-iron, sleeveless cylinders. A one piece cylinder head is attached to the right side of engine. The crankcase is one-piece construction with a large removable cover on the left side. The crankshaft has two main bearings.

R series tractors have a roller bearing (13) at the front and a precision shell-type removable plain bearing (7) at the rear; ZT series tractors have single-row ball bearings at both front and rear as shown in Fig. MM34. A vertical shaft (16—Fig. MM33) driven from front of camshaft drives magneto (or distributor) (19) mounted on top of crankcase, and oil pump (11) mounted under front of crankcase.

A transverse shaft driven from a spiral gear on the camshaft between the fourth and fifth cams drives a fly-ball-type governor mounted on right

Fig. MM31—Model GTB engine, side sectional view. Twin-blocks and heads are retained to crankcase by long studs.

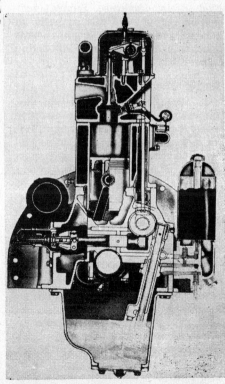

Fig. MM32—Model GTB engine, front sectional view. Piston and connecting rod assemblies can be removed from above or below as outlined under ROD AND PISTON UNITS.

or opposite side of crankcase. A plain bearing fan (18) and packless water pump (17) mounted on front of engine are driven by belt from crankshaft pulley (15).

Oil under pressure is delivered to connecting rod bearings via drilled passages (6) in the crankshaft, to governor drive and magneto drive through metered passages and to rocker arms and valves by drip tubes (1). Oil under pressure is supplied also to the rear main bearing on the R series tractors.

ZA Series

42. The ZA series engine is similar to the ZT series, except the crankshaft is supported in three main bearings as shown in Fig MM35. The front bearing is a straight roller type; whereas, the center and rear main bearings are of the slip-in precision type.

R&R ENGINE

Model GTA

50. Remove hood. Disconnect fuel line, throttle control rod, oil gauge line and wires at starting motor, generator and magneto. Remove drag link, block up front end of transmission and support engine in a chain hoist. Remove bolts and nuts retaining engine to transmission and separate tractor halves. Remove radiator hoses and fan and, if engine is to be disassembled, drain crankcase. Support rear end of engine base side supports on horses, remove front engine mount bolts and lift engine out of engine base.

Model GTB

51. Drain cooling system and disconnect upper and lower radiator hoses. Remove hood and radiator. Disconnect drag link, fuel line at carburetor, generator wires at generator, battery cable at starter, throttle and choke rod at carburetor, drag link, head light wires, ignition coil wire at coil, and oil pressure gage line. Remove coolant temperature gage sending unit. Remove reach (radius) rod. Working through clutch compartment hand-hole, remove cap screws retaining clutch to flywheel.

Support engine and transmission housing separately. Remove bolts retaining engine and main frame to transmission housing, and pull engine forward to release clutch and clutch shaft from flywheel. Support front axle assembly and main frame. Remove engine to main frame bolts. Engine can now be removed from engine base.

Two bolts, ⅝ inch x 10 inches can be used to serve as guides when reconnecting engine and frame assembly to transmission housing.

R And ZT Series

52. The engine and clutch can be removed as a unit. Remove hood, fuel tank and front fuel tank saddle, disconnect fuel and oil lines, throttle control rod, light and magneto wires and clutch rod from shifter shaft arm. On Standard models remove drag link and on Standard models after serial No. 411940 remove steering gear.

On other models drive out pin connecting steering worm shaft to universal joint and disconnect shaft.

Fig. MM33—Cross section view of engine used in R series tractors.

1. Oil drip tube for valve mechanism
2. Intake valve
3. Rocker arm
4. Rocker arm shaft retaining nut
5. Piston
6. Crankshaft oil passage
7. Rear main bearing
8. Rear oil seal
9. Rear bearing cage
10. Oil screen
11. Oil pump
12. Oil filter
13. Front main bearing
14. Front oil seal
15. Crankshaft pulley
16. Magneto or distributor and oil pump drive shaft
17. Water pump
18. Fan hub
19. Distributor or magneto

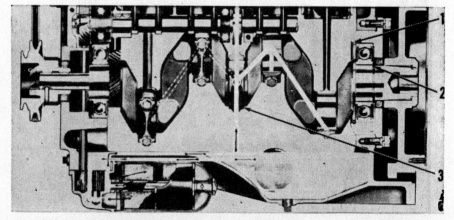

Fig. MM34—Cross section view of crankshaft installation in ZT series tractor engine. Cylinder and valve system is similar to the R series engine.

1. Rear main bearing outer race snap ring   2. Rear main bearing inner race snap ring   3. Oil collar

Drain cooling system and if engine is to be disassembled, drain crankcase. Remove radiator hoses and with engine supported, remove cap screws holding pedestal or radiator support to crankcase and remove entire front assembly as a unit. Support rear half of tractor, remove bolts holding engine to transmission and remove engine from rear half of tractor.

U Series

53. Remove hood. Disconnect fuel line, throttle control rod, oil gauge line and wires at starting motor, generator, spark plugs, magneto and headlamps. On Standard models remove drag link; on other models drive out pin retaining steering worm shaft to universal joint.

Block up front end of transmission and support engine on chain hoist. Remove cap screws retaining engine to transmission and separate tractor halves. Remove radiator hoses and, if engine is to be disassembled, drain crankcase. Remove frame bars from engine (and front axle reach from flywheel housing on Standard models) and pedestal; then, while steadying assembly, remove front wheels, pedestal and radiator as a unit.

ZA Series

54. Drain cooling system and disconnect upper and lower radiator hoses. Remove hood and radiator. Disconnect battery cable at starter, throttle rod at carburetor, steering shaft universal joint or drag link, carburetor fuel line, choke control at carburetor, generator wires at generator, ignition coil wire at coil, head light wires, and oil pressure gage line. Remove coolant temperature gage sending unit, and wiring harness clips from water manifold. Remove cap screws retaining throttle linkage and bracket from under hydraulic reservoir. Disconnect hydraulic pressure lines at reservoir. Remove reach (radius) rod from models so equipped.

Support the engine and transmission housing separately. Remove bolts retaining front support to engine. Slightly raise front portion of engine to provide removal clearance to front support from crankshaft pulley and roll front support assembly away from engine. Remove bolts retaining engine to transmission housing and pull engine forward to release clutch shaft.

Two guide bolts ⅝ inch x 10 inches can be used as guides when reconnecting the engine to the transmission.

Fig. MM35—Cut-a-way view of ZA series engine. The crankshaft front main bearing is of the straight roller type; whereas, the center and rear main bearings are of the slip-in precision type.

CYLINDER HEAD

U Series (Except 283-A Engine)

55. To remove cylinder head, remove hood and side panels. Remove upper radiator hose, water manifold and air cleaner. Disconnect fuel line and throttle control rod from carburetor. Remove the cylinder head cover, oil tubes and rocker arms and shafts. Remove cylinder head nuts and cylinder head. Reverse removal procedure to install head. Tighten head nuts from center outward and to a torque of 125-130 ft.-lbs. on camshaft side and 105-110 ft.-lbs. on exhaust manifold side.

Models GTA-GTB-U Series (With 283-A Engine)

56. The engines are equipped with two cylinder heads. To remove one cylinder head, first remove hood and drain cooling system. Remove upper radiator hose, water manifold, and air cleaner. Disconnect throttle control rod and fuel line from carburetor, and remove exhaust and inlet manifold. (To remove both cylinder heads for gasket renewal, it is not necessary to remove the manifolds.) Remove cylinder head rocker cover, oil lines, and rocker arms and shafts assembly. Remove cylinder head retaining nuts and lift cylinder head from engine.

Long studs, which are threaded into upper crankcase, pass through cylinder block and head to retain same in position. When reinstalling cylinder head, tighten water, and inlet and exhaust manifolds before tightening cylinder block and head hold down nuts on camshaft side of engine to 115-120 ft.-lbs., and head hold down nuts on exhaust manifold side of engine to 95-100 ft.-lbs. torque for models GTA and GTB. For the U series, use the torque values which are specified in paragraph 55.

R-ZA-ZT Series

57. Cylinder head is located on right side of engine and can be removed for carbon removal and valve work. Drain cooling system, remove air cleaner and bracket and disconnect governor linkage and fuel line. Remove cap screw holding carburetor spacer to manifold and remove carburetor, carburetor spacer and air inlet pipe. Remove retaining nuts and remove cylinder head. To install, reverse removal procedure. Tighten cylinder head retaining nuts in sequence shown in Fig. MM37 and to a torque of 50-55 ft.-lbs.

VALVES AND SEATS
All Models

58. Tappets should be set hot to 0.008 for the inlet and 0.010 for the exhaust. (Refer to paragraph 81A.) Inlet valves seat directly in cylinder head or cylinder block and are not interchangeable with exhaust valves which are equipped with seat inserts. Exhaust valve seat inserts are supplied for service. Both inlet and exhaust valves have a face and seat angle of 45 degrees. Desired seat width is 3/32 inch. Seats may be narrowed, using 20 degree and 70 degree cutters. Check the valve stem diameter against the values listed below.

GTA-GTB-U Series.....0.4335-0.4345
R-ZA-ZT Series........0.3405-0.3415

Engines may be equipped with valve rotators; in which case, refer to Standard Units Section for maintenance procedure.

VALVE GUIDES AND SPRINGS
All Models

59. The inlet and exhaust valve guides are interchangeable and can be pressed or driven into position using a piloted driver which is 0.002 smaller than bore of guide. Ream the guides after installation to provide a valve stem-to-guide clearance of 0.0015-0.0035.

60. Intake and exhaust valve springs are interchangeable in any one model. Renew springs which are rusted, distorted or do not meet the following test specifications.

Free length
  GTA-GTB-U Series .....$4\frac{1}{16}$ inches
  R-ZA-ZT Series ....$1\frac{29}{32}$ inches
Test load (lbs.) @ length (inches)
  GTA-GTB-U Series ....80-85 @ $2\frac{1}{2}$
  R-ZA-ZT Series ......53-59 @ $1\frac{13}{64}$

VALVE TAPPETS
(CAM FOLLOWERS)
Models GTA-GTB-U Series

61. The barrel (cylindrical) type tappets (cam followers) operate directly in machined bores of upper crankcase. Tappets are supplied in standard size only and should have a clearance of 0.0005-0.002 in the case bores. Any tappet can be removed after removing either the camshaft or the cylinder block or blocks. This procedure is necessary because the holes for long push rods in the cylinder block are too small to permit withdrawal of the tappets.

ROCKER ARMS
Models GTA-GTB-U Series

62. Rocker arms and shaft assembly can be removed after removing hood, valve cover and rocker arm shaft support retaining nuts. Rocker arm valve contacting surface can be refaced, but original radius must be maintained and face must be parallel to rocker arm shaft. Desired clearance between rocker arm bushing and the 0.966-0.967 diameter shaft is 0.001-0.003. Rocker arm bushings are not supplied for service except on model GTA and U series prior to 55y649. Renew rocker arm, bushing and/or shaft if clearance exceeds 0.008.

Fig. MM37—Cylinder head tightening sequence for the R, ZA and ZT series.

Adjust rocker tappets hot to 0.008 for inlet and 0.010 for exhaust.

R-ZA-ZT Series

63. Each cylinder is equipped with a separate pair of rocker arms and rocker arm shaft. To remove a pair of rocker arms and shaft, proceed as follows: Rotate crankshaft until both valves of the cylinder are closed. Remove cylinder side cover and nut retaining rocker arm shaft to cylinder block. Both rocker arms (inlet and exhaust), shaft and rocker arms retainer are removed as an assembly.

New rocker arm bronze bushings require final sizing after installation to provide a clearance of 0.001-0.0015 for the 0.810-0.811 diameter shaft. If clearance exceeds 0.008, renew shaft and/or bushing.

Cam contacting surface of rocker arm can be refaced but must be kept parallel to rocker arm shaft. Valve contacting screws must contact valve stems squarely; if not, make certain rocker arm shaft is properly seated, then correct any misalignment by bending the rocker arm.

Adjust rocker tappets hot to 0.008 for the inlet and 0.010 for the exhaust on late style camshafts and refer to paragraph 81A for tappet gap on old style shafts.

VALVE TIMING
All Models

64. Valves are correctly timed when mark "1" on camshaft gear is in mesh with mark "1" on crankshaft gear as in Fig. MM41 on GTA, GTB and U series and as in Fig. MM42 on R, ZA and ZT series.

Inlet valve opens 4 degrees (9/16 inch) after the mark "DC 1-4" on GTA, GTB and U series; 11 degrees (1⅜ inches) after "DC 1-4" on the R, ZA and ZT series. The flywheel is not marked to indicate inlet valve opening, so it will be necessary to affix a mark to same.

To check valve timing when engine is assembled, adjust inlet tappet of number one cylinder to 0.004 more than normal operating clearance. Next, in-

Fig. MM38—Sectional view of intake valve installation on R, ZA and ZT series engines, showing valve seat centered on valve face. Exhaust valves have renewable seats.

Fig. MM36—Tighten models GTA-GTB and U series cylinder head hold down nuts in the sequence shown. Rocker arm oil connections are shown at (34).

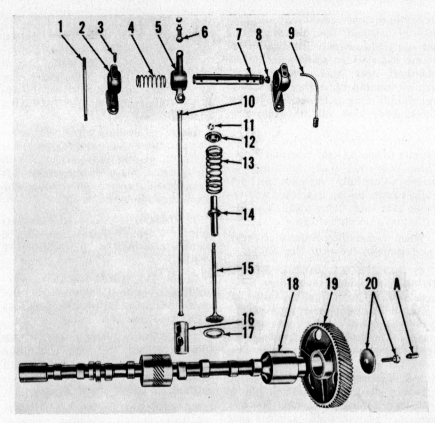

Fig. MM39—Camshaft, valves and related parts as used on model GTB. Model GTA and U series are similar. Valve seat inserts (17) are used for the exhaust valves only. Screw (A) located in front face of timing gear case cover controls camshaft end play.

A. Camshaft end play adjusting screw
1. Shaft support stud
2. Shaft support
3. Rocker arm shaft retaining screw
4. Rocker arm shaft spring
5. Rocker arm
6. Adjusting screw
7. Rocker arm shaft
8. Plug
9. Rocker arm oil line
10. Push rod
11. Valve spring keepers (split cone)
12. Valve spring seat
13. Valve spring
14. Valve guide
15. Valve
16. Cam follower
17. Exhaust valve seat insert
18. Camshaft
19. Camshaft gear
20. Retaining washer & cap screw

sert a 0.004 feeler gage between rocker arm and valve stem. Crank engine over slowly until a slight resistance occurs when trying to withdraw feeler gage. At this time, inlet valve is just starting to open, and the affixed flywheel mark should be in register with or not more than ¼ inch either way from the index. Timing marks are viewed through clutch compartment hand hole port located in left side of transmission housing. Reset inlet valve tappet to operating gap.

TIMING GEAR COVER

Models GTA-GTB And U Series

65. The timing gear cover is also the water pump body. Removal of this cover will expose only the camshaft gear. To remove timing gear cover, remove hood, fan assembly, crankshaft pulley and water pump cover.

Bump Groov pin (33) out of water pump impeller as shown in Fig.

Fig. MM42—R, ZA and ZT series engines with side cover removed. Mesh "1" marks on camshaft and crankshaft gears.

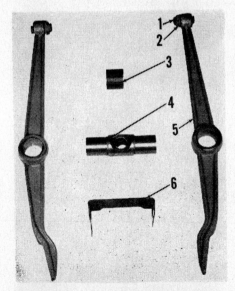

Fig. MM40—Exploded view of R, ZA and ZT series rocker arms for one cylinder.

1. Adjusting screw
2. Locknut
3. Bushing
4. Shaft
5. Rocker arm
6. Retaining spring

Fig. MM41—Models GTA, GTB and U series engine with timing gear case cover removed. Mesh "1" marks on crankshaft and camshaft gears. Mesh "O" marks on camshaft and accessory gears. Allen screw (27) retains accessory drive shaft sleeve (28).

19. Camshaft gear
22. Water pump to cylinder manifold hose
23. Lubrication tube to accessory shaft bushing
25. Crankshaft front oil seal
26. Accessory shaft
27. Allen screw
28. Accessory shaft sleeve
30. Timing gear case

MM45. Remove impeller which is left-hand threaded by rotating same in clockwise direction. Loosen water pump outlet hose (pump to water manifold) and pump inlet hose (radiator to pump) and remove timing case cover retaining cap screws. Refer to Fig. MM41. For method of removing timing gear case refer to paragraph 68.

Camshaft end play is controlled by a thrust screw (A), located in front face of timing gear cover. To adjust, turn screw in until same contacts the camshaft gear retaining cap screw; then, retract screw ½ turn.

TIMING GEARS
Models GTA-GTB And U Series

66. Timing drive of three helical gears consists of the crankshaft gear, camshaft gear, water pump and ignition (battery or magneto) unit drive gear. The accessory drive gear shaft also drives the hydraulic lift unit pump.

When reinstalling either the camshaft gear, crankshaft gear, and/or accessory shaft gear, mesh "1" mark on camshaft gear with an identical mark on crankshaft gear. Also mesh "O" mark on camshaft gear with an identical mark on accessory gear as shown in Fig MM41.

67. **CAMSHAFT GEAR.** To remove camshaft gear, remove timing gear cover as outlined in paragraph 65. Remove cap screw and washer from end of camshaft. Using a suitable puller attached to the gear, remove camshaft gear. When reinstalling gear, it is advisable to remove one of the crankcase inspection plates and buck up the camshaft. Mesh gears as shown in Fig. MM41.

68. **CRANKSHAFT GEAR.** To remove crankshaft gear, it is first nec-

essary to remove camshaft gear as previously outlined; then remove radiator and grille assembly. Straighten cap screw locks which are located under camshaft gear; then, remove these cap screws and remaining cap screws retaining timing gear case to cylinder block. Disconnect oil line from gear case.

Remove four cap screws retaining oil pan to timing gear case and loosen balance of oil pan retaining cap screws. Carefully separate oil pan gasket from timing gear case and remove gear case. Using a suitable puller, remove crankshaft gear.

When reinstalling crankshaft gear, mesh same as shown in Fig. MM41.

69. **ACCESSORY DRIVE SHAFT GEAR.** To remove accessory shaft gear (water pump, ignition unit, and hydraulic lift pump drive), proceed as follows: Remove camshaft gear as outlined in preceding paragraphs. Remove magneto or battery ignition unit, and cover plate or hydraulic lift pump at rear of accessory drive shaft. Bump accessory shaft rearward and out of gear and timing gear case. Remove accessory gear through camshaft gear opening located in front of gear case.

Accessory shaft bronze bushings and/or oil seal shown in Fig. MM87A can be renewed at this time. The front bushing and oil seal (95) are contained in a sleeve which is retained in position with an Allen screw, located at point (27—Fig. MM41). The other two bushings are pressed in the timing gear case and can be renewed without removing the case. Desired clearance between new bushings and shaft is 0.0015-0.003.

When reinstalling accessory shaft gear, mesh same as shown in Fig. MM41.

R-ZA-ZT Series

70. Timing drive of four helical gears consists of the crankshaft, camshaft, hydraulic (Uni-Matic) pump drive and oil pump drive gears. The latter gear which also drives the ignition unit is located forward of the camshaft gear.

When reinstalling either the camshaft and/or crankshaft gear, mesh the mark "1" on the camshaft gear with an identical mark on the crankshaft gear. Marks can be viewed when the crankcase side cover is off.

71. **CAMSHAFT GEAR.** Camshaft gear removal requires removal of camshaft as outlined in CAMSHAFT section.

72. **CRANKSHAFT GEAR.** Crankshaft gear removal requires removal of crankshaft as outlined in CRANKSHAFT section.

73. **IGNITION UNIT & OIL PUMP DRIVE GEAR.** To remove ignition unit and oil pump drive gear, it will be necessary to remove camshaft as outlined in CAMSHAFT section.

74. **HYDRAULIC PUMP DRIVE.** The hydraulic pump gear is a press fit to the hydraulic pump shaft and can be removed after removing the pump unit.

75. **IGNITION UNIT & OIL PUMP DRIVEN GEAR & SHAFT.** Shaft and gear assembly can be removed after removing the ignition unit, oil pump, pump gear and Woodruff keys; then, loosen thrust bushing retaining set screw (Fig. MM46) which is located

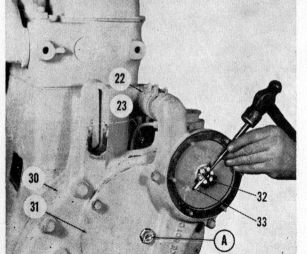

Fig. MM45 — Bumping Groov pin from water pump impeller on models GTA and GTB and U series. Impeller is left-hand threaded to accessory drive shaft. Adjust camshaft end play with screw (A).

A. Camshaft end play adjusting screw
22. Water pump to cylinder manifold hose
23. Lubrication tube to accessory shaft bushing
30. Timing gear case
31. Water pump body & timing gear case cover
32. Water pump impeller
33. Groov pin

Fig. MM46—The R, ZA and ZT series oil pump and ignition unit drive shaft bushing is retained by a set screw as shown.

on front face of crankcase and push shaft upward and out of crankcase. Shaft should have 0.001-0.0025 clearance in the shaft bushings.

Reassemble in reverse order, and with number one cylinder on compression stroke and flywheel mark "DC 1-4" aligned with pointer, mesh the gears as follows:

For magneto equipped engines, mesh oil pump and magneto drive shaft gear so that the magneto drive coupling slot is parallel with the engine crankshaft.

For battery ignition equipped engines, mesh oil pump and ignition unit drive shaft gear so that the ignition unit drive coupling slot is at right angles to the crankshaft center line.

CAMSHAFT
Models GTA-GTB-U Series

80. To remove camshaft, first remove timing gear cover (water pump body), as outlined in paragraph 65. Remove radiator, rocker arms and shafts assembly, push rods, governor, oil pan and oil pump. Block up and support cam followers; then, withdraw camshaft with camshaft gear through front of timing gear case.

Camshaft journals ride directly in three machined bores in the crankcase. Shaft journal sizes are: Front, 3.3075-3.3085; center, 3.275-3.276; rear, 1.996-1.997. Recommended clearance of camshaft journals in their bores is 0.0025-0.005. The maximum permissible clearance is 0.008 and when it exceeds this amount, it will be necessary to renew camshaft and/or crankcase or make-up and install bushings.

When reinstalling camshaft and gear assembly, mesh gears as shown in Fig. MM41. Adjust shaft end play by turning screw (A—Fig. MM45) in until same contacts screw head in shaft; then, retract screw (A) ½ turn.

R-ZA-ZT Series

81. To remove the camshaft, first remove engine crankcase side cover, valve covers, rocker arms and shafts, and camshaft bearing caps. See Fig. MM49.

Camshaft journals ride directly in three machined bores which are fitted with caps in the crankcase. Shaft journal sizes for all three journals are 1.2465-1.2470. Recommended clearance of camshaft journals in their bores is 0.0025-0.004. The maximum permissible clearance is 0.007 and when it exceeds this amount, it will be necessary to renew the camshaft and/or the crankcase.

Mesh "1" mark on camshaft gear with an identical mark on the crankshaft gear as shown in Fig. MM42. Reinstall camshaft journal bearing caps with the oil grooves UP as shown in Fig. MM49. Adjust camshaft end play by locating front bearing cap (provided with elongated holes) to crankcase to obtain a clearance of 0.003. Clearance is between bearing cap rear face and hub face of camshaft gear as shown in Fig. MM50.

81A. Tappet gap (hot) is 0.008 for the intake; 0.010 for the exhaust on engines equipped with latest style camshaft.

NOTE: ZT series tractors with engines prior to RE73108 and R series tractors with engines prior to EE-413963 were equipped with either a RE451 or RE451A camshaft and the intake tappet gap is 0.012 hot and the exhaust tappet gap is 0.014 hot. The late production RE451B camshaft can be installed on older production models and it is recommended that the late production RE108C (repair number RE5109) rocker arms be installed also. On all models that are either factory or field equipped with a RE451B camshaft the intake tappet gap is 0.008 hot and the exhaust tappet gap is 0.010 hot. On models prior to 1946, it is advisable to remove the engine side cover (crankcase cover) and check the camshaft part number before adjusting the tappets.

ROD AND PISTON UNITS
Models GTA-GTB-U Series

82. Piston and connecting rod assemblies are removed from above after removing cylinder head and oil pan.

The assemblies can also be removed from below in the following manner: Remove oil pan and rocker arms and shafts assemblies. Loosen cylinder block retaining bolts and block up cylinder blocks 1½ inches above crankcase surface using wood blocks; then, with crankshaft crankpins in a horizontal position, remove rod and piston assemblies from below.

Piston and connecting rod assemblies are installed with the rod correlation marks facing the camshaft. Tighten the connecting rod bolts to 80-85 ft.-lbs. torque.

R-ZA-ZT Series

83. Piston and connecting rod assemblies are removed from above after removing the cylinder head, cylinder block and crankcase side cover as shown in Fig. MM51.

Tighten the connecting rod cap screws to 60-65 ft.-lbs. torque.

PISTONS AND RINGS
All Models

90. Cast iron pistons are supplied in standard size, and oversizes of 0.030, 0.063 and 0.094 for models GTA and GTB and U series. Cast iron pistons in standard size, and oversize of 0.020 and 0.040 are supplied in deflector-

Fig. MM50—Measuring clearance between camshaft gear and camshaft front bearing on R, ZA and ZT series.

Fig. MM51—Lifting both cylinder blocks along with piston and connecting rod units from R, ZA and ZT series crankcase.

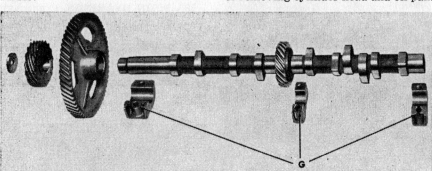

Fig. MM49—R, ZA and ZT series camshaft, gears and bearing caps. Bearing caps must be installed with groove "G" up.

head type for the R series tractors and flat-head type for ZA and ZT series tractors. Check pistons and bores against the values listed below.

Cylinder bore
 GTA-GTB 4.626-4.627
 R-ZA-ZT Series 3.6255-3.6265
 U Series 4.251-4.252
Piston skirt diameter
 GTA-GTB 4.6225
 R-ZA-ZT Series 3.622-3.623
 U Series 4.2465-4.2475
Maximum cylinder wear........0.008
Maximum ring side clearance...0.005

There are three compression rings and one oil control ring per piston. Install taper compression rings with the word "TOP" facing up. The scraper ring which has an undercut face is installed in the third groove with undercut down. Oil ring is installed with beveled edge facing up. Recommended end gap for all rings is 0.015-0.020 for all models except GTA where 0.025-0.035 should be provided for compression rings and 0.020-0.030 for the oil ring. Recommended side clearance is 0.0015-0.003 for the compression rings, and 0.001-0.0025 for the oil ring.

CYLINDER BLOCKS
Models GTA-GTB-U Series

NOTE: The KEC and KEF engines as used in early production U series tractors are of the single block design; whereas, the 283A-4 engine as used in late production U series tractors is of the twin-block design. The engines which are used in the GTA and GTB tractors are of the twin-block design, similar to the 283A-4 engine. In either case, however, the general removal procedure given in the following paragraph can be used.

91. To remove cylinder block or blocks, remove hood, rocker arms and shafts assembly, push rods and cylinder head and block retaining nuts. If only one block is to be removed on twin-block engines, unbolt the manifolds. It is not necessary to remove manifolds if both blocks are removed as a unit. Disconnect and slide water pump hose away from block and lift block or blocks off of crankcase. Cylinder blocks can be removed before or after removing connecting rod and piston assemblies. Block (or blocks) is retained to crankcase by long studs which pass through both block and cylinder head.

Cylinder block or blocks can be installed to crankcase while rod and piston assemblies are attached to crankshaft by lowering block over pistons, or by first attaching block to crankcase and then installing rod and piston assemblies from above.

R-ZA-ZT Series

92. To remove cylinder blocks, remove hood, valve cover, and rocker arms and shafts units. Disconnect governor linkage, fuel line & radiator hoses. Remove connecting rod bearing caps and cylinder block hold down nuts. Remove blocks, cylinder head and connecting rod and piston assemblies as a unit as shown in Fig. MM51.

If only one block is to be removed, also remove cylinder head, manifolds and water manifold; then remove cylinder block from crankcase as shown in Fig. MM52. When reinstalling cylinder blocks, assemble connecting rod and piston assembly to crankcase. Do not tighten cylinder block hold down nuts until head and manifolds have been tightened.

PISTON PINS
Models GTA-GTB-U Series

93. Model GTA and early production U series piston pins are locked in the piston boss by a set screw. Model GTB and late production U series piston pins are of the full floating type which are retained in the piston pin bosses by snap rings. The 1.2497-1.2500 diameter piston pins are available in standard size, and oversizes of 0.005 and 0.010.

Install piston pin bushing in rod so that oil hole in bushing registers with oil hole in top end of connecting rod.

Fit pins to a finger push fit in connecting rod and plain boss of piston and a hammer-tap fit in the set screw boss.

R-ZA-ZT Series

94. The 0.9994-0.9996 diameter floating type piston pins are retained in piston pin bosses by snap rings and are available in standard, as well as 0.005 oversize.

Install piston pin bushing in rod so that oil hole in bushing registers with

Fig. MM52—One cylinder block with piston and connecting rod units can be removed from R, ZA and ZT series crankcase without disturbing the other cylinder block.

oil hole in top end of connecting rod.

Pin should be fitted to a finger push fit (0.0003 clearance) in both rod and piston.

ROD BEARINGS
All Models Except U Series With KEC Engine

95. Connecting rod bearings are of the shimless, non-adjustable, slip-in, precision type, renewable after removing oil pan or side cover. When installing new bearing shells, be sure that bearing shell projection engages milled slot in rod and cap, and rod and cap correlation marks face toward camshaft side of engine. Bearings are available in 0.0025, 0.005, 0.020 and 0.040 undersize, as well as standard.

Check the bearings and crankshaft against the values listed below:
Crankpin diameter
 GTA-GTB 2.7495-2.750
 U Series 2.577-2.5775
 R-ZA-ZT Series 2.6245-2.6250
Running clearance 0.0015-0.003
Side clearance 0.002-0.006
Bolt torque (ft.-lbs.)
 GTA-GTB-U Series 80-85
 R-ZA-ZT Series 60-65

95A. NOTE: *New engines, using precision insert main and/or rod bearings, which have a letter "K" suffixed to model number have 0.0025 undersize crankpins; letter "F", 0.0025 undersize main bearing journals; letters "KF", 0.0025 undersize crankpins and main journals.*

U Series With KEC Engine

96. This engine model is equipped with shimmed, bronze-back, babbitt-lined bearings. Adjustment for wear is accomplished by varying the number of shims to provide 0.0015-0.003 clearance. New bearings must be checked with bluing, and if necessary, hand-scraped to obtain a proper fit. Refer to paragraph 95 for standard crankpin diameter and clearances.

CRANKSHAFT & BEARINGS
Models GTA-GTB-U Series

100. **MAIN BEARINGS.** Crankshaft main bearings are slip-in, precision shell type, which may be renewed from below after removing oil pan and bearing caps on all models except KEC engine, which is fitted with bronze-back, babbitt-lined bearings renewal of which requires crankshaft removal. Rear and center main bearing caps are marked "FRONT", and should be installed with marking toward front of engine. Precision type bearings are available in 0.0025, 0.005, 0.020 and 0.040 undersize as well as standard.

Bronze-back, babbitt-lined bearings can be adjusted for wear by varying the number of shims to provide 0.0015-0.004 clearance. New bearings should be checked by bluing and, if necessary, line-reamed or hand fit to crankshaft journals.

101. **CRANKSHAFT.** Crankshaft end play is controlled by rear main bearing. Recommended end play is 0.002-0.006.

To remove crankshaft, it is necessary to remove engine, oil pan, timing gear cover, timing gear case, oil pump, connecting rod bearing caps and flywheel.

Check crankshaft, crankpins and journals for wear, scoring and out-of-round condition against values listed below. Refer also to paragraph 95A.

Crankpin diameter
   GTA-GTB 2.7495-2.750
   U Series 2.577-2.5775
Main journal diameter.....2.911-2.912
   Running clearance 0.0015-0.004
Bolt torque (ft.-lbs.)
   Front 110-120
   Center & rear..............75-80

R Series

102. **MAIN BEARINGS.** Crankshaft is supported on two main bearings. Rear main is a slip-in, precision shell type removable without removing crankshaft. To remove rear main bearing, remove crankcase side cover, lock wire and rear main bearing cap screws and rear main bearing cap as in Fig. MM55. Bearing shells are available in Standard, 0.0025, 0.005, 0.020 and 0.040 undersize. Rear main bearing controls crankshaft end play of 0.002-0.006. Front main bearing is a straight roller type and removal necessitates crankshaft removal. Refer to paragraph 103 for procedure.

Fig. MM55—R series rear main bearing cap can be removed through side of crankcase.

103. **CRANKSHAFT.** To remove crankshaft it is necessary to remove the engine. Refer to paragraph 52 for procedure. Remove generator and fan drive pulley from crank jaw and turn crankshaft until socket screw in crank jaw lines up with slot in front oil seal. Remove socket screw and pull crank jaw with a suitable puller. Remove clutch and flywheel after marking flywheel so it will be reinstalled in the same position on crankshaft. Remove crankcase cover plate, connecting rod bearing caps and oil tube from rear main bearing cage.

If cylinder blocks are not to be removed, push pistons to top of cylinders so crankshaft will clear. If crankshaft only is to be removed, remove cap screws retaining rear main bearing cage to crankcase as shown in Fig. MM56 and withdraw crankshaft and rear bearing cage from crankcase. If front main bearing is to be removed it will be necessary to remove lock shown in Fig. MM57 and drive bear-

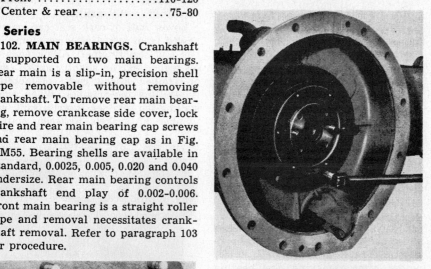

Fig. MM56—Removing R series rear main bearing cage retaining cap screws.

Fig. MM57—Series R engine, showing the front main bearing lock installation.

ing out towards rear of crankcase. Rear main bearing cage assembly can be disassembled by removing rear oil seal, bearing cap screws and bearing cap and slipping cage over crankshaft flange as in Fig. MM58.

Check crankshaft against the values listed below. Refer also to paragraph 95A.

Crankpin diameter 2.6245-2.6250
Rear journal diameter....2.9995-3.000
   Running clearance 0.0015-0.003
   End play 0.002-0.006
   Bolt torque ....55-60 ft.-lbs.

To reinstall, assemble front bearing to crankcase and rear bearing cage, bearing and rear oil seal to crankshaft. Install crankshaft in crankcase, aligning timing gear marks 1 as in Fig. MM42. Balance of reassembly is reverse of disassembly.

ZT Series

104. **MAIN BEARINGS.** Crankshaft is supported on two single-row ball bearings; the rear one, being retained in the case by a snap-ring, takes the crankshaft end play of 0.004-0.006. Replacement of bearings requires crankshaft removal as outlined in the following paragraph.

105. **CRANKSHAFT.** To remove crankshaft it is necessary to remove the engine. Turn crankshaft until socket screw in crank jaw is in line with slot in front oil seal. Remove socket screw and using a puller, remove generator-fan pulley and crank jaw. On engines using separate pulleys and crank jaw (after engine No. 52437) remove cap screws retaining pulleys to crank jaw, remove pulleys and turn crankshaft until socket screw in crank jaw lines up with slot in oil seal. Remove socket screw and pull crank jaw.

Remove crankcase side cover, valve side cover, rocker arms and connecting rod bearing caps and push pistons to top of cylinders. Remove camshaft following procedure given in para-

Fig. MM58—Removing R series rear main bearing cage from crankshaft.

graph 81. Remove oil tube from oil collar shown in Fig. MM60. Remove clutch and flywheel after marking flywheel so it will be reinstalled in the same position on crankshaft. Remove rear main bearing cage retaining cap screws and pull crankshaft, bearings and cage from rear of crankcase. Remove snap ring (2—Fig. MM61), from bearing cage and remove cage from bearing. Remove snap ring (4) from crankshaft. Bearings can then be pressed off crankshaft. Oil collar assembly can be disassembled and removed from crankshaft.

Diameter of oil collar journal on crankshaft is 3.249-3.250. Inside diameter of new oil collar is 3.251-3.252.

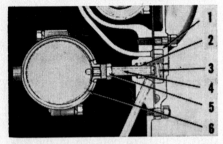

Fig. MM60—Sectional view of the ZT series crankcase, showing the crankshaft oil collar installation.

1. Crankcase side cover
2. Oil tube packing
3. Packing spring
4. Oil tube
5. Oil tube nut
6. Oil collar

Fig. MM61—Crankshaft, rear main bearing and associated parts as used on ZT series tractors.

1. Crankshaft
2. Outer race snap ring
3. Rear main bearing
4. Inner race snap ring
5. Bearing cage
6. Rear oil seal

Clearance between collar and journal must not exceed 0.008 for adequate oil supply to bearings. Collar width is 1¼ inches on engines up to No. 66470 incl. and 1⅛ inches after engine No. 66470. Reassembly is reverse of disassembly.

ZA Series

106. **MAIN BEARINGS.** The crankshaft center and rear journals are supported in two shimless, non-adjustable, slip-in, precision type main bearings; whereas, the front journal is supported in a roller type bearing.

Crankshaft end play 0.003-0.004 is controlled by the rear main bearing.

The center and rear main bearings can be renewed after removing the crankcase side cover, and are available in 0.0025, 0.005, 0.020, and 0.040 undersize as well as standard.

To renew the front main bearing, it will be necessary to remove the crankshaft, and using a suitable puller, remove bearing from shaft.

107. **CRANKSHAFT.** To remove crankshaft, it is necessary to remove the engine, crankcase side cover, starting crank jaw, fan pulley, flywheel, and camshaft. Working through crankcase side cover opening, disconnect oil line at rear bearing, and remove connecting rod bearing caps, and center main bearing cap. Remove rear main bearing cage retaining cap screws. Rotate crankshaft, until number 2 & 3 crank throws are facing crankcase opening, and pull crankshaft rearward until center journal is past center bearing bore; then, rotate shaft until number 1 & 4 crank throws are facing crankcase opening, and withdraw crankshaft and rear bearing housing. The front bearing can be renewed after removing the bearing lock. To remove rear bearing housing from crankshaft, remove crankshaft rear oil seal retainer and main bearing cap.

Check the crankshaft journals for wear, scoring and out-of-round condition against the values listed below. Refer also to paragraph 95A.
Crankpin diameter 2.6245-2.6250
Journal diameter
Front .... Roller
Center 2.7495-2.7500
Rear 2.9995-3.000
Running clearance 0.0015-0.0035
End play 0.003-0.004
Bearing cap bolt torque..55-60 ft.-lbs.

CRANKSHAFT OIL SEALS
Models GTA-GTB-U Series

110. **FRONT SEAL.** The felt type seal is contained in a bell-shaped metal retainer (25—Fig. MM62) which is pressed into timing gear case. Procedure for renewing the seal is evident after removing the radiator on models GTA and GTB and radiator and pedestal on U series.

111. **REAR SEAL.** The rear bearing crankshaft oil seal cork is of a two-piece type. The lower half (59—Fig. MM63) is contained in a retainer, and the upper half in a groove which is machined in the crankcase.

Lower half of cork seal can be renewed from below after removing oil pan and seal retainer. Allow ends of oil seal to extend slightly above edge of retainer. Renew corks (57) before reinstalling the retainer. When reinstalling the retainer, insert a sufficient number of gaskets between mating

Fig. MM63—Crankshaft rear oil seal and retainer assembly as used on model GTB and U series. Model GTA is similar.
(57) Cork seal, (58) Seal retainer, (59) Crankshaft rear oil seal

Fig. MM62—Model GTB crankshaft and related parts. Model GTA and U series are similar. Felt seal and retainer (25) can be renewed after removing crankshaft pulley. Crankshaft end play is controlled by rear main bearing (47).

25. Front oil seal
45. Flywheel
46. Clutch shaft pilot bushing
47. Rear main bearing
48. Crankshaft
49. Center main bearing
50. Front main bearing
51. Starting crank jaw
52. Crankshaft pulley
53. Spacer
54. Crankshaft gear
56. Starter ring gear

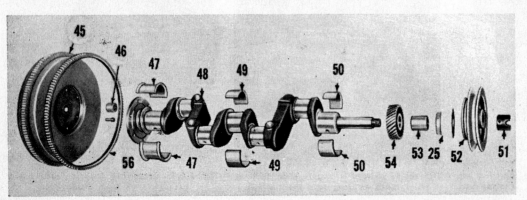

surfaces of crankcase and seal retainer so that retainer will protrude 0.005 beyond gasket surface of crankcase when retainer is bolted in position.

Oil seal upper half can be pulled out, and a new seal inserted from below after removing oil pan, retainer for lower seal and loosening main bearing caps.

R Series

112. **FRONT SEAL.** Crankshaft front oil seal is pressed into front of crankcase and renewal requires removal of radiator, pedestal, crank jaw and pulley. To remove the crank jaw, turn the crankshaft until socket screw in crank jaw lines up with slot in oil seal. Remove the socket screw, pull crank jaw with a suitable puller and remove seal from crankcase.

113. **REAR SEAL.** Crankshaft rear oil seal shown in Fig. MM58 is mounted on back end of rear main bearing cage and contacts flywheel flange on crankshaft. To renew seal, split the tractor as in clutch removal and remove clutch, flywheel and oil seal retaining screws. Refer to paragraph 117 for flywheel removal. Assemble new seal with sharp lip towards front of engine. Oil seal should be soaked in oil before assembling to engine.

ZA-ZT Series

115. **FRONT SEAL.** Crankshaft front oil seal is pressed into front of crankcase and renewal requires removal of radiator, pedestal, crank jaw and pulley.

116. **REAR SEAL.** The crankshaft rear oil seal can be renewed after detaching engine from transmission housing and removing flywheel. Install seal with lip of same facing the timing gears.

FLYWHEEL

All Models

117. The flywheel can be removed after separating engine from transmission as outlined in the clutch section and on the R series, removing the clutch from the flywheel. To install a new flywheel ring gear, heat same to approximately 500 deg. F. and install gear on flywheel with beveled edge of teeth facing front of engine.

CRANKCASE AND OIL PAN

Models GTA-GTB-U Series

120. Crankcase upper half is main supporting member between front pedestal and transmission case on the U series and is the main engine unit of both U series and GTA and GTB tractors. The crankshaft, camshaft, cam followers and oil pump are contained in the crankcase and are accessible for inspection by removing oil pan.

The oil pan is removable from below after removing cap screws retaining oil pan to crankcase, timing gear case and transmission case. On models so equipped, it is necessary to remove the reach from the transmission case and front axle to permit oil pan removal.

CRANKCASE AND SIDE COVER

R-ZA-ZT Series

121. The one-piece crankcase is main supporting member between front pedestal and transmission case. There is no removable oil pan; the case being provided with a large removable cover on the left side.

Removal of side cover provides accessibility to connecting rods and camshaft and on R series tractor to rear main bearing and on ZA series tractors, to center and rear main bearings.

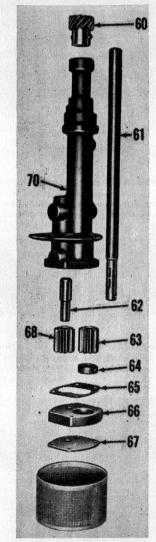

Fig. MM70—Model GTB oil pump. Model GTA and U series are similar. Shim gaskets (65) control end clearance of 0.002-0.006 between gears, and spacer plate (66).

60. Spiral drive gear	65. Shim gasket
61. Drive shaft	66. Spacer plate
62. Idler gear shaft	67. Cover
63. Pump drive gear	68. Idler gear
64. Thrust collar	70. Pump body

Be sure gasket is in good condition especially around oil passages. On ZT series tractors be sure oil seals and spring on oil collar assembly tube shown in Fig. MM60, are in perfect condition and positioned correctly. It is necessary to loosen the steering gear mounting bolts on RTS tractors after serial number 411940 to provide sufficient clearance for crankcase side plate removal. Refer to Power Lift, paragraph 311 or 320, for removal of power lift hydraulic pump.

OIL PUMP AND RELIEF VALVE

Models GTA-GTB-U Series

122. The gear type pump, shown in Fig. MM70, can be removed after removing oil pan. To disassemble pump, remove pump screen and cover plate (67). Bump pin from spiral drive gear (60) and remove gear. Withdraw drive shaft (61) and gear unit from pump body. Bump pin out of thrust collar, and remove collar. Gear (63) can now be removed from drive shaft, and idler gear (68) from idler gear shaft (62).

End clearance between pump body gears and plate (66) should be 0.002-0.006 and is controlled with shim gaskets (65). The recommended diametral clearance between gears and pump body is 0.001-0.004. Check pump drive shaft and its mating surface for wear.

The piston type relief valve (72-Fig. MM71) is located in oil filter

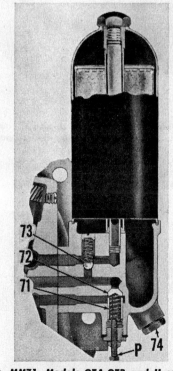

Fig. MM71—Models GTA-GTB and U series oil filter. Oil pressure is regulated with screw (P) which is located in filter base.

(P) Relief valve adjusting screw, (71) relief valve spring, (72) valve, (73) differential valve ball, (74) drain plug.

base, and is adjusted by means of an adjusting screw (P) to maintain a pressure of 25 psi at rated engine speed.

R-ZA-ZT Series

123. The oil pump is located externally at front of engine on underside of crankcase and is driven by the magneto and oil pump drive shaft which is driven by a gear at front end of camshaft. The pump can be removed from the engine as shown in Fig. MM72. The drive gear can be removed as shown in Fig. MM73.

The lower bushing (15—Fig. MM74) in the crankcase, is renewable from below after removing the oil pump and oil pump drive shaft. To remove oil pump drive shaft refer to Timing Gears, paragraph 75. Oil pump gear end clearance should be not less than 0.0015 or more than 0.004 and can be adjusted by varying number of shims shown in Fig. MM72. The recommended diametral clearance between the gears and pump body is 0.001-0.0025.

Oil pressure regulator is built into pump. It can be adjusted by removing cap nut (1—Fig. MM75) and gasket, loosening ring locknut (2) and adjusting spring tension by turning regulating screw (3) with a screwdriver inserted through locknut. Turn-

ing to right or clockwise increases oil pressure. Tighten locknut after making adjustment.

Some engines are equipped with oil pressure regulator shown in Fig. MM76 which has an external locknut (1) and regulating screw (2). Oil pressure should be 35 lbs. at 1200 to 1500 rpm, with engine and oil completely warmed.

Fig. MM74—R, ZA and ZT series engine sectional view, showing the ignition unit and oil pump drive shaft installation. The shaft bushings are shown at (15).

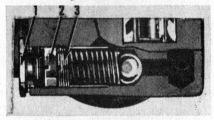

Fig. MM75—One type of oil pressure relief valve as used on the R and ZT series tractors. Refer also to Fig. MM76.

1. Cap nut
2. Ring lock nut
3. Regulating screw

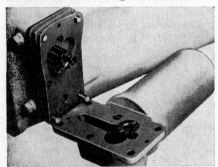

Fig. MM72—Underside of crankcase on R, ZA and ZT series, showing the oil pump removed.

Fig. MM73—Removing R, ZA and ZT series oil pump drive gear (5) from the ignition unit and oil pump drive shaft (4).

Fig. MM76—One type of oil pressure relief valve as used on the R, ZA and ZT series tractors. Refer also to Fig. MM75. The adjustment is made by loosening the lock nut (1) and turning adjusting screw (2).

CARBURETOR

All Models

125. Idling mixture adjustment is controlled by the needle valve nearest to the carburetor flange. Turning adjustment in to the right (clockwise) richens the mixture. Approximate setting is two turns open. Power mixture adjustment is controlled by the other needle valve. Turning adjustment in to the right (clockwise) leans the mixture. Approximate setting is two turns open. Float setting is ¼ inch for TSX and 2 inches for TTX.

GOVERNOR

ADJUSTMENT

All Models

126. Make certain that all governor linkage is free from binding at all points. To check linkage, pull throttle hand control back as far as it will go; then, raise governor control lever and release same. Governor control lever should return the carburetor throttle to closed position without any binding. Binding linkage can be corrected by shifting carburetor position on its studs.

To adjust governor, first adjust carburetor idle speed and mixture; then, with throttle hand control in full forward position, adjust screw (X—Fig. MM77) on governor, to obtain the recommended speeds which are listed later. Turning adjusting screw clockwise decreases engine speed; turning

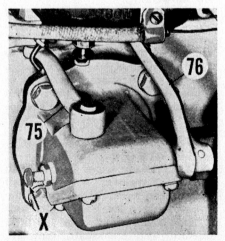

Fig. MM77 — Typical Minneapolis-Moline governor unit installation, showing the speed adjusting screw (x).

75. Speed control hand lever
76. Governor control lever

it counter-clockwise increases engine speed. When adjusting screw has been retracted to increase engine speed, push throttle hand control forward to contact new adjusting screw position.

Engine Load rpm
    GTA 1075
    GTB 1100
    R Series 1400
    U Series 1275
    ZA-ZT Series 1500

Belt Pulley Load rpm
    GTA 650
    GTB 627
    R Series 933
    U Series 727
    ZA-ZT Series 786

Engine No Load rpm
    GTB 1210
    R Series 1650
    U Series 1400
    ZA-ZT Series 1650

Belt Pulley No Load rpm
    GTB 690
    R Series 1100
    U Series 800
    ZA-ZT Series 865

R & R AND OVERHAUL
Models GTA-GTB-U Series

127. To remove governor, unscrew the governor to crankcase retaining cap screws and withdraw governor unit.

Before disassembling, mark governor housing (115—Fig. MM78) and cover (113) so that cover can be reinstalled in the correct position. Re-

move cover retaining screws and cover. Remove bearing retaining plate (102), and separate plate from governor housing. Remove plug from housing and bump pin (111) out of control lever arm and shaft (112), and remove control lever shaft as shown in Fig. MM79. Bump pin (109—Fig. MM78) out of speed control lever (75) and shaft (108) and remove shaft and speed adjusting arm (114). Ball (105) will roll out of governor shaft (119). Remove weight pins (93) and withdraw thrust thimble (104) from governor shaft. From governor, remove snap ring (118) and ball bearing (103). To remove weights (101), remove weight shafts (100).

Control arm shaft bushings (110) have an inside diameter of 0.374-0.375, and require final sizing after installation to provide a 0.0015-0.002 diametral clearance. Spring adjusting sleeve (117) should be a close fit in housing but should not bind. Check speed adjusting lever shaft (108) and mating surface in housing for wear. Diametral clearance in excess of 0.007 will require renewal of housing and/or lever shaft. Taper pin holes can be reamed with a No. 0 taper pin reamer for a tight fit of pins.

R-ZA-ZT Series

128. Remove governor from engine. Mark governor housing and cover so that cover can be reinstalled in the

correct position. Remove retaining screws and cover (113—Fig. MM80). Drive pin (109) out of speed adjusting lever (75) and remove shaft (108) and arm at lower end of shaft through housing. Drive taper pin out of control arm shaft and control arm (112) from inside of housing. Unhook spindle (106) from control arm and withdraw control arm lever (76) and shaft from housing. Drive grooved pin out of flyball rotor and remove pinion gear, shaft, and thrust washer. Remove rotor assembly. Remove hexagon head threaded pins (93) from governor weights (101) and withdraw thrust thimble (104) from rotor.

Fig. MM79—Bumping pin out of governor control arm and shaft on models GTA and GTB and U series.

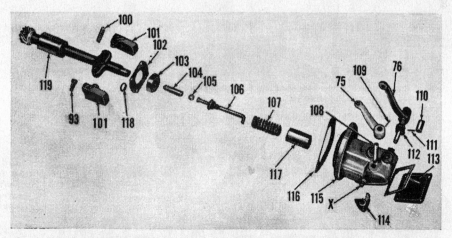

Fig. MM78—Exploded view of a typical governor as used on models GTA and GTB and U series.

X. Speed control adjusting screw	104. Thrust thimble	112. Control **arm**
75. Speed control hand lever	105. Thimble ball	113. Cover
76. Governor control lever	106. Spindle	114. Speed adjusting **arm**
93. Weight pin	107. Spring	115. Housing
100. Weight **shaft**	108. Speed adjusting lever shaft	116. Housing gasket
101. Weight	109. Speed adjusting lever pin	117. Spring adjusting sleeve
102. Bearing retainer plate	110. Control arm shaft bushing	118. Bearing snap ring
103. Housing bearing	111. Control arm pin	119. Rotor **shaft**

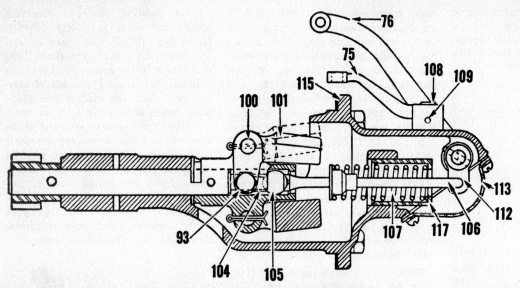

Fig. MM80 — Sectional view of governor unit as used on R, ZA and ZT series.

75. Speed control hand lever
76. Control lever
93. Weight pin
100. Weight shaft
101. Weight
104. Thrust thimble
105. Thimble ball
106. Spindle
107. Spring
108. Speed adjusting lever shaft
109. Speed adjusting lever pin
112. Control arm
113. Cover
115. Housing
117. Spring adjusting sleeve

Governor weights can be removed by removing cotter pins and weight shafts (100). Bushings for control arm shaft should be renewed when governor is overhauled. Spring adjusting sleeve (117) should be a close fit in housing, but should not bind. End play in governor shaft should be held to a minimum by thrust washers. To reassemble, reverse disassembly procedure.

COOLING SYSTEM

RADIATOR

All Models

129. The radiator assembly which has detachable upper and lower tank units can be removed after removing hood and disconnecting upper and lower hoses; then, removing the radiator retaining cap screws.

THERMOSTAT

Model GTA & R-U-ZA-ZT Series

130. Thermostat is located in top tank of radiator and can be removed after removing water inlet flange from top of radiator. Thermostats are supplied in two values; one for high compression engines opens at 170 degrees and one for low compression engines opens at 185 degrees. A special thermostat opening at 155 degrees is supplied for tractors using butane fuel and for tractors using alcohol in the radiator.

Model GTB

131. Thermostat is located in water outlet manifold elbow. Gasoline engines are equipped with thermostats which open at 150 deg. F. Distillate engines are equipped with thermostats which open at 175 deg. F. A special thermostat opening at 155 degrees is supplied for tractors using butane fuel and for tractors using alcohol in the radiator.

FAN ASSEMBLY

All Models

135. Procedure for removal and/or overhaul of the fan assembly is evident after an examination of the unit and reference to Figs. MM85, 86 or 87. The taper roller fan shaft bearings as used on some models should be adjusted to remove all end play, yet permit shaft to rotate freely.

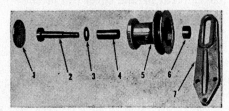

Fig. MM87—Exploded view of fan hub as used on R and ZT series tractors.

1. Hub-cover plate
2. Fan spindle
3. Thrust washer
5. Fan hub
6. Collar
7. Fan bracket

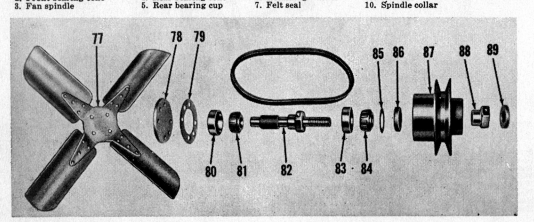

Fig. MM85—Exploded view of roller bearing fan hub used on GTA and U series tractors. Gaskets (8) control bearing adjustment.

1. Front bearing cup
2. Front bearing cone
3. Fan spindle
4. Rear bearing cone
5. Rear bearing cup
6. Retaining washer
7. Felt seal
8. Fan gasket
9. Fan hub
10. Spindle collar

Fig. MM86—Engine fan and shaft assembly as used on model GTB. The ZA series unit is similar. Shaft bearings are adjusted with shims (79) to provide shaft with zero end play.

77. Fan blades
78. Bearing retainer
79. Shim
80. Fan end bearing cup
81. Fan end bearing cone
82. Fan spindle
83. Rear bearing cup
84. Rear bearing cone
85. Retainer washer for felt
86. Fan hub felt
87. Fan hub
88. Collar (nut)
89. Clamp washer

WATER PUMP

Models GTA-GTB And U Series

The water pump body is integral with timing gear case cover.

140. **PUMP SEAL.** To renew water pump seal (90—Fig. MM87A or MM 88), proceed as follows: Remove fan belt and pump cover (91). Bump Groov pin (33) out of impeller and shaft, as shown in Fig. MM45, and remove impeller by rotating same in clockwise direction (left-hand thread). Impeller is threaded to shaft. Seal assembly is retained in impeller and can be renewed at this time without further pump disassembly. Check condition of seal contacting thrust surface which is the outer face of bushing and sleeve assembly (28—Fig. MM87A or MM88) and reface or renew if same is scored.

141. **PUMP BODY, ACCESSORY SHAFT AND/OR BUSHINGS.** To renew pump body (timing gear case cover), accessory shaft and/or bushings, proceed as follows: Remove timing gear cover as outlined in paragraph 65. Loosen Allen screw (27) (located left side of timing gear case) Figs. MM41 and MM89, and remove sleeve (28) which contains bushing (92) and oil seal (95). Remove magneto or battery ignition unit, and power lift pump;

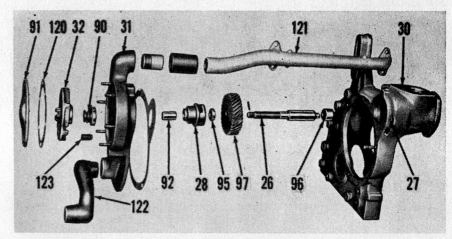

Fig. MM88—Water pump, accessory drive shaft, and timing gear case as used on models GTA and GTB and U series. Accessory shaft drive gear (97) can be removed after removing camshaft gear. Mesh "O" mark on accessory gear with identical mark on camshaft gear.

26. Accessory shaft	95. Oil seal
27. Allen screw	96. Bushing (rear)
28. Accessory shaft sleeve	97. Accessory shaft drive gear
30. Gear case	120. Cover gasket
31. Water pump body & timing gear case cover	121. Water outlet manifold
32. Water pump impeller	122. Water pump inlet elbow
90. Pump seal	
91. Pump cover	
92. Bushing (front)	

then, bump accessory shaft rearward and out of gear and timing gear case. Bushings (96—Fig. MM87A) which should have a 0.0015-0.003 diametral clearance between shaft and bushings can be renewed at this time.

When reinstalling accessory shaft gear, mesh same as shown in Fig. MM41.

R-ZA-ZT Series

142. **RESEAL AND OVERHAUL.** Remove fan belt. Remove bolts and nuts retaining water pump to water manifold and remove water pump. Water pump and water manifold can be removed as a unit by removing four cap screws retaining manifold to cylinder block.

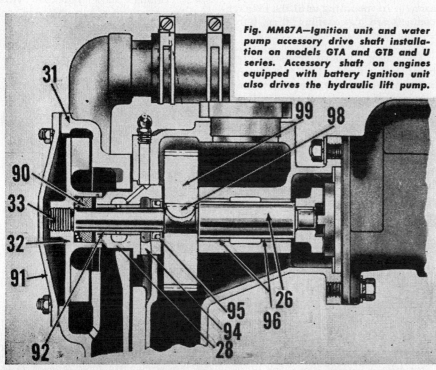

Fig. MM87A—Ignition unit and water pump accessory drive shaft installation on models GTA and GTB and U series. Accessory shaft on engines equipped with battery ignition unit also drives the hydraulic lift pump.

26. Accessory shaft	33. Groov pin	95. Oil seal
28. Accessory shaft sleeve	90. Water pump seal	96. Bushing (rear)
31. Water pump body and timing gear case cover	91. Pump cover	98. Woodruff key
	92. Bushing (front)	99. Accessory drive shaft gear
32. Impeller	94. Vent hole	

Fig. MM89—Accessory drive shaft sleeve (28) is retained in timing gear case with Allen screw (27) on models GTA and GTB and U series.

27. Allen screw	92. Bushing (front)
28. Shaft sleeve	95. Oil seal

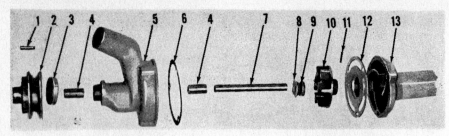

Fig. MM90—Exploded view of R, ZA and ZT series water pump.

1. Pulley pin
2. Pulley
3. Felt seal assembly
4. Bushing
5. Pump body
6. Gasket
7. Pump shaft
8. Thrust washer
9. Shaft seal
10. Impeller
11. Impeller pin
12. Baffle plate
13. Water manifold

MM90) from pulley (2) and shaft (7) and remove pulley. Pull impeller (10) and shaft from pump body (5). Thrust washer (8) and seal assembly (9) can be renewed at this time without further disassembly. Thrust surface contacted by thrust washer must be smooth and true.

If thrust surface is scored, it should be refaced or renewed. When installing bushings (4), register oil holes in bushings with grease reservoir in pump body.

143. If pump and manifold have been removed as a unit, remove bolts and nuts retaining pump to manifold and remove pump. Drive pin (1—Fig.

IGNITION AND ELECTRICAL SYSTEM

All Models

144. Engines are equipped with either Fairbanks-Morse magneto ignition or Delco-Remy battery ignition.

145. **MAGNETO TIMING.** Adjust breaker point opening to 0.020. Crank engine until number one cylinder is on compression stroke and flywheel mark "DC 1-4" aligns with pointer as in Fig. MM91. At this time, slot in accessory shaft magneto drive coupling should be in a horizontal position on models GTA and GTB and U series. On the R, ZA and ZT, the slot in the magneto drive shaft coupling should be parallel to the crankshaft.

If magneto drive coupling slot is not in correct position, the shaft will have to be retimed to camshaft. Refer to paragraph 69 for models GTA and GTB and U series, and paragraph 75 for R, ZA and ZT series.

Rotate magneto shaft in a direction opposite to normal rotation until magneto rotor disc segment is under number 1 cylinder contact of distributor cap, Fig. MM92; then install magneto to engine. The rotor disc is in this position when the white mark on the disc appears in distributor cap window. Mark flywheel at running timing index which is specified below. Rotate engine crankshaft in a counter-clockwise direction past this mark, but not far enough to engage impulse coupling, then slowly rotate engine in a clockwise direction until the affixed mark indexes with pointer. Loosen magneto retaining bolts and rotate same in its mounting until the breaker contacts are just opening; then, tighten mounting bolts.

To check impulse coupling trip point, mark flywheel at the impulse trip point which is specified below; then, rotate engine in clockwise direction until impulse trips for Nos. 1 or 4 cylinders at which time impulse trip point mark on flywheel should index with pointer. If mark does not index, check for a faulty coupling and/or for coupling of incorrect specifications.

Magneto Lag Angle (Degrees):
GTA-GTB-U Series 35
R-ZA-ZT Series 25

Magneto running timing in degrees and inches BTC:
GTA-GTB ....27° or 4 in.
R Series (H. Comp.).....17° or 2 in.
R Series (L. Comp.)...18° or 2⅛ in.
U Series (H. Comp.)...25° or 3½ in.
U Series (L. Comp.)...27° or 3¾ in.
ZA Series ....17° or 2 in.
ZT Series (H. Comp.)..16° or 1⅞ in.
ZT Series (L. Comp.)..18° or 2⅛ in.

Magneto impulse trip point in degrees and inches ATC:
GTA-GTB ....8° or 1⅛ in.
R Series (H. Comp.)......8° or 1 in.
R Series (L. Comp.)....7° or ⅞ in.
U Series (H. Comp.)...10° or 1½ in.
U Series (L. Comp.)....8° or 1 in.
ZA Series ....8° or 1 in.
ZT Series (H. Comp.)....9° or 1 in.
ZT Series (L. Comp.)....7° or ⅞ in.

146. **BATTERY IGNITION TIMING.** Adjust breaker point opening to 0.018-0.024. Mark flywheel for static timing index which is listed below. With the static timing mark indexed with pointer, number one cylinder on

Fig. MM91—Numbers 1 and 4 pistons are in top dead center position when flywheel mark "DC 1-4" is in register with the clutch housing pointer as shown.

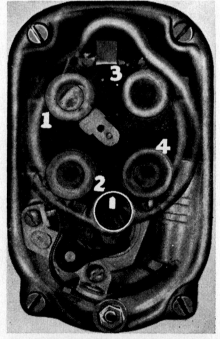

Fig. MM92—Magneto rotor segment is in firing position for number one cylinder when white mark on rotor disc is visible through distributor cap window as shown.

compression stroke, and rotor in the number one firing position, install distributor to engine. Next, rotate distributor until breaker points are just opening; then, lock distributor housing in this position.

To check running timing, mark flywheel running timing index which is listed below and use a timing light. This affixed mark should index within ⅛ inch with pointer at an engine no-load speed of at least 1250 rpm. If static timing is O.K. but running spark does not occur when specified, look for a malfunctioning distributor governor unit.

Distributor static timing index in degrees and inches ATC:

GTA .... 5° or ¾ in.

GTB .... 5° or ¾ in.

R Series (H. Comp.) ..... 8° or 1 in.

R Series (L. Comp.) ..... 7° or ⅞ in.

U Series (H. Comp.) ..... 7° or 1 in.

U Series (L. Comp.) .... 5° or ¾ in.

ZA Series .... 7° or ⅞ in.

ZT Series (H. Comp.) .... 9° or 1 in.

ZT Series (L. Comp.) ... 7° or ⅞ in.

Distributor running timing index in degrees and inches BTC:

GTA .... 27° or 4 in.

GTB .... 27° or 4 in.

R Series (H. Comp.) ..... 17° or 2 in.

R Series (L. Comp.) ... 18° or 2⅛ in.

U Series (H. Comp.) ... 25° or 3½ in.

U Series (L. Comp.) ... 27° or 3¾ in.

ZA Series .... 18° or 2⅛ in.

ZT Series (H. Comp.) .. 16° or 1⅞ in.

ZT Series (L. Comp.) .. 18° or 2⅛ in.

CLUTCH

The Minneapolis-Moline tractors which are covered in this section are equipped with over-center, toggle-action clutches.

ADJUSTMENT

Models GTA-GTB-Series U-ZA-ZT

150. **ADJUSTMENT.** With clutch compartment cover removed and transmission gear shift lever in neutral position, rotate engine crankshaft until lockpin (P), shown in Fig. MM-100, is accessible; then pull pin out as far as it will go. Place transmission gear shift lever in any gear; then, disengage clutch, and rotate adjusting yoke to the right (UP, when viewed through clutch compartment opening) to tighten clutch. Clutch should be tightened to a point where no slippage

will occur under full load, yet not so tight that difficulty is encountered when engaging the clutch. Be sure lock pin is firmly seated in one of the holes in the floating plate after completing the adjustment.

R Series

151. **ADJUSTMENT.** With clutch opening cover removed and gear shift in neutral, turn engine until latch button is accessible, as shown in Fig. MM-101, then push button in as far as it will go. Place gear shift in any gear, disengage clutch and turn adjusting ring to the left (**down,** when viewed through opening) to tighten clutch.

Clutch should be tightened to the point where no slippage will occur under full load, yet not so tight that difficulty is encountered going through the "center" position.

R & R AND OVERHAUL

Models GTA-GTB-Series U-ZA-ZT

152. To remove clutch unit, it is first necessary to perform a tractor split (detach engine from transmission) as outlined in paragraph 154. Disconnect actuating (clutch hand lever and shifter fork) rod. On GTA, loosen cap screws retaining shifter fork to shifter fork shafts and remove shafts and forks. On all models, remove nut and washer retaining clutch unit to clutch shaft, and using a puller attached as shown in Fig. MM104, pull clutch assembly forward until same is free from clutch shaft Woodruff key. Rotate clutch assembly on clutch shaft until sliding sleeve keyway is in line with the Woodruff key; then, remove clutch unit from shaft. If sleeve does

Fig. MM100—Adjusting over-center toggle-action type clutch as used on models GTA, GTB and U, ZA and ZT series. Pull lockpin (P) out as far as possible; then, rotate adjusting yoke to the right. (Up, when viewed through clutch compartment opening.)

Fig. MM101—Adjusting the over-center toggle-action type clutch as used on the R series. Push the latch button in as far as it will go; then, turn the adjusting ring to the left (down, when viewed through opening.)

not have a keyway remove toggle pins at clutch plate end to permit removal of Woodruff key and sleeve.

The GTB, U, ZA and ZT asbestos clutch brake plate (33—Fig. MM131) can be renewed at this time. The shifter yoke can be removed from sliding sleeve by removing bolts which join the two halves. Adjust diametral clearance of shifter yoke on sliding sleeve, by varying the number of shims (22—Fig. MM103) between yoke mating surfaces, to zero running clearance without permitting the yoke to bind when same is rotated.

To disassemble clutch unit, pull out adjusting lock pin and retract adjusting yoke and sleeve assembly, lift off floating plate and driving plate and remove release springs. Adjusting yoke, finger levers, lever links and sliding sleeve can be disassembled by removing snap rings and pins.

R Series

153. Split the tractor as outlined in paragraph 154. Mark cover, flywheel, pressure plate, levers and sliding sleeve so parts will be reinstalled in their same relative positions. Remove six cap screws retaining clutch to flywheel and remove cover assembly and driven plate. Note that driven plate is installed with baffle towards flywheel.

To remove pressure plate, remove release springs and lift off pressure plate and adjuster ring. With latch button depressed, adjuster ring can be screwed out of pressure plate. To disassemble sliding sleeve and lever assembly, remove pins retaining levers to cover plate and sliding sleeve.

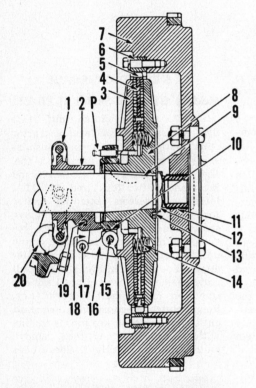

Fig. MM102—Over-center toggle-action type clutch as used in models GTA & GTB. The U, ZA and ZT series are similar.

P. Lockpin
1. Shifter ring
2. Sliding sleeve
3. Floating plate
4. Driving plate lining
5. Driving plate
6. Driving ring gear
7. Flywheel
8. Hub & back plate
9. Clutch shaft key
10. Adjusting yoke
11. Pilot bushing
12. Hub retaining nut
13. Lock washer
14. Release spring
15. Lever pin on adjusting yoke
16. Finger lever
17. Pin on lever link
18. Lever link
19. Link pin on sliding sleeve
20. Shifter yoke

Fig. MM104—Using a suitable puller attached as shown to remove clutch unit from clutch shaft on models GTA, GTB and U, ZA and ZT series.

Fig. MM103—Disassembled view of the clutch illustrated in Fig. MM102.

P. Adjusting lock pin
1. Shifter yoke
3. Floating plate
4. Driving plate lining
5. Driving plate
6. Driving ring gear
8. Hub & back plate
10. Adjusting yoke (complete)
14. Release spring
15. Lever pin on adjusting yoke
16. Finger lever
17. Pin on lever link
18. Lever link
21. Sliding sleeve and collar assembly
22. Yoke shim
23. Yoke bolt and nut
24. Lever pin snap ring
25. Lock pin spring
26. Finger pin snap ring

TRACTOR SPLIT
All Models

153A. A general procedure for splitting the tractor is given in the following paragraphs. Minor differences in construction are obvious after an examination of the unit.

154. **TRACTOR SPLIT.** Remove hood, disconnect fuel line at carburetor, throttle control and choke rod,

oil pressure gage line, ignition switch, generator wires at generator, battery cable at starter and coolant temperature gage sending unit. Disconnect drag link. Block up engine and transmission separately, using a traveling chain hoist or some other device for one section so that it can be moved independently from the other section. Working through clutch compartment

hand-hole, remove cap screws retaining clutch assembly to flywheel. Remove bolts retaining engine and main frame to transmission housing, and move transmission and rear axle unit away from engine and engine frame unit, as shown in Fig. MM106.

To facilitate joining transmission housing to engine unit, install two long pilot studs in housing as shown.

Fig. MM105—Clutch and transmission sliding gear shaft front bearing retainer as used on model GTB.

34. Bearing cover
63. Clutch & transmission sliding gear shaft
80. Oil seal
85. Lower countershaft front bearing retainer

Fig. MM107—Clutch adjusting yoke and sliding sleeve assembly for model GTB.

Fig. MM106—Tractor split (detach engine from transmission housing). Note long pilot studs installed in transmission housing to facilitate reconnecting both units.

FLYWHEEL SIDE

Join transmission housing to engine while entering clutch shaft into pilot bearing, and clutch driving plate splines into driving ring gear which is bolted to the flywheel. It may be necessary to back-off on the clutch adjusting sleeve to allow driving plate to center in driving ring gear. Balance of installation is reverse of disassembly.

Fig. MM108—Exploded view of R series clutch.

1. Driven plate	9. Lever pin
2. Pressure plate	10. Lever pin spacing
3. Adjuster ring	washer
4. Driving lug	11. Lever
5. Cover plate	12. Lever roller
6. Sliding sleeve	13. Latch pin and
7. Sleeve bushing	spring
8. Shifter ring	14. Release spring

TRANSMISSION AND CONNECTIONS

Model GTA

Refer to paragraph 180 for model GTB.

160. TRANSMISSION COVER. Cover can be removed after removing fuel tank, clutch housing cover, steering column and gear shifter shaft. Refer to Steering Gear, paragraph 31 for column removal procedure. Shifter shaft can be removed after removing pin (4—Fig. MM109) from shifter arm and shaft. Reassembly is reverse of disassembly.

161. SHIFTER YOKES (FORKS) AND SHAFTS. To remove forks and shafts, remove clutch housing cover. Remove pin (4—Fig. MM109) from shifter arm (11) and shifter shaft (9) and remove shaft and arm. Remove covers (1) and set screws from both sides of transmission case. Carefully remove pipe plugs (12) from top of shifter forks and remove detent springs (13). Slide fork shafts (7) and (8) out of housing while catching detent balls (14) as they roll out of each fork.

162. CLUTCH SHAFT. Clutch shaft removal requires splitting tractor and removing clutch. Refer to Clutch paragraphs 152 and 154 for procedure. Remove clutch brake snap ring (7—Fig. MM110), brake plate (6) and asbestos disc (5) from clutch shaft and clutch shaft bearing cover plate (4) from front of transmission case. Remove clutch housing and transmission housing covers. Remove oiling chain idler sprocket (13) and spindle (12) from bottom of transmission case and disengage chain from clutch shaft sprocket (2). Drive clutch shaft (8), bearing and bearing cage (3) out through front of transmission case.

Do not discard shim gaskets (11) from between bearing cage and transmission case as they control position of clutch shaft bevel gear in relation to the bevel gear on the power shaft. Bearing and bearing cage can be removed from clutch shaft after snap ring (10) is removed. Reassembly is reverse of disassembly. For adjustment of bevel gear mesh, refer to Bevel Gear Mesh, paragraph 166.

163. REVERSE IDLER GEAR. Idler gear and shaft (3—Fig. MM111) can be removed after removing transmission cover, transmission case reinforcing rod and left rear wheel from tractor. Remove pins from collars on reverse idler gear shaft and remove shaft locking set screw. Remove expansion plug from right end of reverse idler gear shaft and drive shaft out through the left side of case while

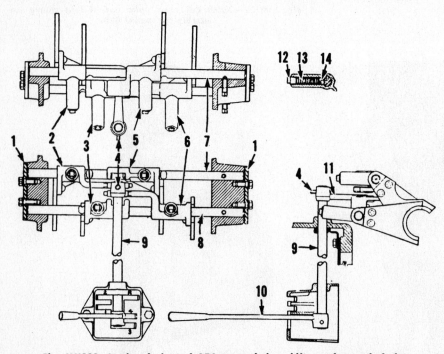

Fig. MM109—Sectional view of GTA transmission shifter yokes and shafts.

1. Shaft cover	6. Fourth speed yoke	10. Shift lever
2. First speed yoke	7. Front shaft	11. Shift shaft arm
3. Third speed yoke	8. Rear shaft	12. Pipe plug
4. Shaft pin	9. Shift shaft	13. Detent spring
5. Second and reverse yoke		14. Detent ball

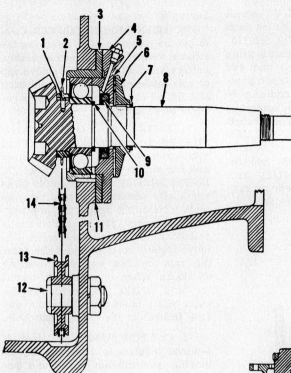

165. POWERSHAFT. Powershaft (12—Fig. MM113) can be removed after removing transmission and clutch housing covers, shifter forks and shafts, transmission case reinforcing rod, reverse idler gear and shaft and countershaft. For countershaft removal, refer to Countershaft, paragraph 164. Remove pulley or shaft cap (9—Fig. MM113) from right end of powershaft (12) and cover (7) from right bearing. Remove cover (16) from left bearing. Force powershaft assembly through left side of transmission case far enough to permit fourth speed sliding pinion (6) and right bearing to be removed from the powershaft. Withdraw powershaft through left side of

Fig. MM110—Sectional view of GTA clutch shaft installation.

1. Sprocket drive pin
2. Oiler sprocket
3. Bearing cage
4. Bearing cover
5. Clutch brake asbestos disc
6. Clutch brake thrust plate
7. Clutch brake snap ring
8. Clutch shaft
9. Oil seal
10. Bearing snap ring
11. Mesh adjusting shim
12. Idler sprocket spindle
13. Idler sprocket
14. Oiler chain

withdrawing gear and collars from top of case. The bushing in the reverse idler gear can be renewed, shaft size is 1.875. Reassembly is reverse of disassembly.

164. COUNTERSHAFT. Countershaft (7—Fig. MM112) can be removed after removing transmission cover, transmission case reinforcing rod, left rear wheel and reverse idler gear and shaft. Refer to paragraph 163 for reverse idler gear and shaft removal. Remove brake hand lever and brake band assembly from left side of transmission case. Remove cap screw and washer retaining brake drum (10 —Fig. MM112) to countershaft (7) and pull drum off shaft. Remove countershaft bearing cages (5) and (8).

Do not discard shims (6) as they control bearing adjustment. Drive countershaft out of right bearing cone and through countershaft gears and left side of case and withdraw gears from top of case. Left bearing cone can be pressed off shaft.

Reassembly is reverse of disassembly. Remove or add shims (6) between left bearing cage and case and right bearing cage and case to eliminate all bearing play and provide just a slight drag or pre-load on the bearings.

Divide shims between left and right bearings to maintain proper gear face contact on bull pinion gear (3) and differential bull gear. Make bearing adjustments with transmission reinforcing rod tightened into place.

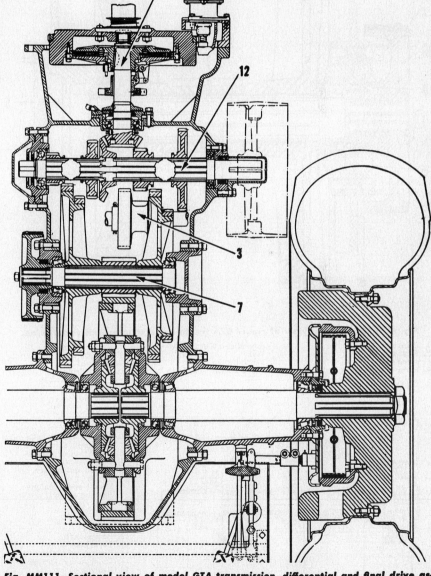

Fig. MM111—Sectional view of model GTA transmission, differential and final drive assembly.

3. Reverse idler gear and shaft	7. Countershaft	8. Clutch shaft	9. Powershaft

transmission case. Do not discard shims (2) from between left bearing cage (1) and case as they control backlash of the bevel gears.

166. BEVEL GEAR MESH. Add or remove shims (2—Fig. MM113) between left bearing cage and case to obtain a backlash of 0.006-0.008 between bevel gears. If clutch shaft or clutch shaft bearing, or powershaft or powershaft left side bearing, or bevel gear or transmission case is renewed, the tooth contact of the bevel gears should be checked by bluing after the

backlash has been adjusted. To correct a heavy toe contact on the clutch shaft gear, remove shims (11—Fig. MM110) from between the clutch shaft bearing cage and transmission case and add shims (2—Fig. MM113) between powershaft left bearing cage and case to re-establish backlash. To correct a heavy toe contact on the powershaft bevel gear, add shims (11—Fig. MM 110) between clutch shaft bearing cage and transmission case and remove shims (2—Fig. MM113) from between powershaft left bearing cage and case to re-establish backlash.

Series R

170. TRANSMISSION COVER. Cover can be removed after removing instrument panel and tool box assembly, battery and battery shelf. Remove cap screws retaining cover to transmission and lift off cover. Reinstallation is reverse of removal.

171. SHIFTER FORKS AND SHAFTS. To remove shifter forks and shafts, remove the transmission cover and the four retaining cap screws (A, B—Fig. MM115). To disassemble forks and shafts assembly, remove two cap screws retaining gear shift jaw separating bracket (gate) to shifter shafts rear bearing, and remove bracket. Remove detent springs and balls from the rear bearing and slide bearing off shafts. When reassembling, install the long springs (1¾ inches) in the outer shaft holes and the short one (1½ inches) in the center shaft hole.

172. CLUTCH SHAFT. Clutch shaft removal requires splitting tractor, removing transmission cover and removing belt pulley carrier unit. Refer to paragraph 154 for tractor splitting procedure. Remove cap screws retaining clutch shaft center bearing plate to clutch housing and remove plate as in Fig. MM116.

Remove clutch shaft ball bearing retaining clip from front of transmission case and using a soft drift, drive clutch shaft, bearing and shims out of front of case as in Fig. MM117. Do not discard shims as they control depth of mesh of the belt pulley bevel pinion gear.

Sliding gear shaft (mainshaft) pilot bearing can be removed from pocket in clutch shaft main drive gear. The belt pulley bevel pinion gear can be pressed off the clutch shaft and the clutch shaft bearing removed. Reassembly is reverse of disassembly. Refer to Belt Pulley, paragraph 293, for adjusting mesh of belt pulley bevel gears.

Bushing in center bearing plate should be reamed to 1.321-1.322 and oil seal installed with sharp lip towards transmission.

173. SLIDING GEAR SHAFT (MAINSHAFT). This shaft (6—Fig. MM120) can be removed after transmission cover, clutch shaft and power take-off assembly have been removed. Refer to paragraph 172 for clutch shaft removal and paragraph 303 for power take-off shaft removal. Remove the castellated nut and washer from rear end of sliding gear shaft, reinstall nut and drive shaft out of case with a soft drift as shown in Fig. MM119.

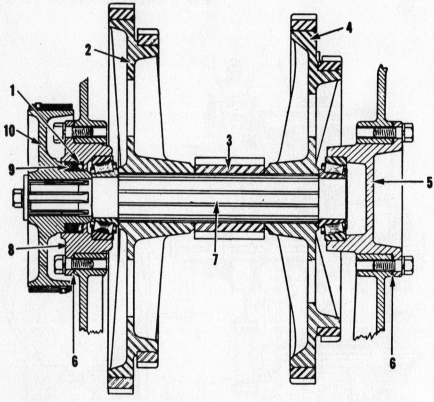

Fig. MM112—Sectional view of model GTA transmission countershaft installation.

1. Oil seal
2. First and third speed gear
3. Main (bull) pinion
4. Second and fourth speed gear
5. Bearing cage
6. Bearing adjusting shims
7. Countershaft
8. Bearing cage
9. Felt seal
10. Brake drum

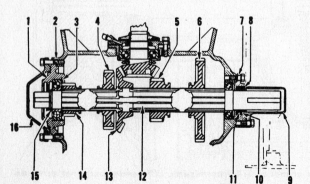

Fig. MM113—Sectional view of model GTA power shaft assembly.

1. Bearing cage
2. Gear mesh shim
3. Outer race snap ring
4. Third speed pinion
5. Second and reverse pinion
6. Fourth speed pinion
7. Transmission cover
8. Snap ring
9. Shaft cover
10. Felt seal
11. Oil seal
12. Powershaft
13. Bevel gear
14. First speed pinion
15. Inner race snap ring
16. Bearing cover

The constant mesh gear can be removed from the sliding gear shaft after removing either the sliding gears and constant mesh gear retaining snap ring or the bearing cone. The double roller bearing outer race (cup) can be removed from the transmission case after removing the retaining clip (8—Fig. MM120) by driving the race out towards the rear.

Reassembly is reverse of disassembly. Install constant mesh pinion (5)

with long part of hub towards rear of tractor. Install first speed sliding gear (3) with groove towards front, second speed—reverse sliding gear (2) and third—fourth speed sliding gear (1) with grooves toward rear.

174. REVERSE IDLER GEAR ASSEMBLY. Idler gear (4—Fig. MM121) can be withdrawn from left side of the transmission case after removing the retaining cap screws. Do not discard shim gaskets (3—Fig. MM121) from

between transmission case and reverse idler gear housing (carrier) as they control the backlash of the idler gear. To disassemble, drive retaining pin out of housing and remove gear shaft.

New shaft diameter is 1.247-1.248. Clearance between shaft and bushing should be 0.002-0.004. When renewing bushing, ream inside diameter to 1.250-1.251. Reassembly is reverse of disassembly. Adjust backlash between reverse idler gear and reverse gear of countershaft gear cluster to 0.006-0.008 by varying number of shims (3) between reverse idler gear housing and transmission case.

175. COUNTERSHAFT. Removal of the one-piece combination countershaft and main drive bevel pinion requires removing transmission sliding gear shaft (mainshaft), reverse idler gear assembly and differential. Refer to paragraph 173 for sliding gear shaft removal, paragraph 174 for reverse

Fig. MM115—Series R transmission with cover removed. "A" and "B" are cap screws retaining shifter shaft bearings to transmission case. "E" is cover plate giving access to P.T.O. shaft front bearing cover.

Fig. MM116—Removing R series clutch shaft center bearing plate.

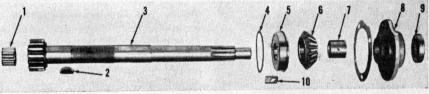

Fig. MM118—Exploded view of R series clutch shaft.

1. Sliding gear shaft pilot bearing
2. Bevel pinion key
3. Clutch shaft
4. Bevel pinion mesh adjusting shim
5. Shaft bearing
6. Belt pulley bevel pinion gear
7. Bushing
8. Center bearing plate
9. Oil seal
10. Bearing retaining clip

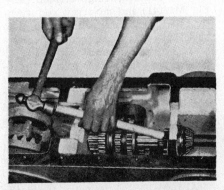

Fig. MM117—Driving R series clutch shaft assembly out front of transmission case. Shims behind bearing snap ring control mesh of belt pulley bevel gears.

Fig. MM119—R series sliding gear shaft (mainshaft) can be driven out as shown after the clutch shaft and power take-off shaft are removed.

Fig. MM121—Exploded view of R series reverse idler gear and carrier assembly.

1. Carrier
2. Shaft retaining pin
3. Backlash shim
4. Idler gear
5. Gear bushing
6. Gear shaft

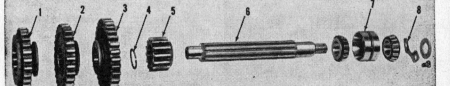

Fig. MM120—Exploded view of R series sliding gear shaft (mainshaft).

1. Third and fourth sliding gear
2. Second and reverse sliding gear
3. First speed sliding gear
4. Snap ring
5. Constant mesh pinion gear
6. Sliding gear shaft
7. Double row bearing cup
8. Cup retaining clip

idler gear assembly removal and to Differential, paragraph 206, for differential removal.

Pry sheet metal cover from front of countershaft bearing as in Fig. MM 124, and remove castellated nut and washer retaining countershaft to bearing cone. With snap ring pliers, remove snap ring from countershaft as in Fig. MM125; then using a soft drift, drive countershaft out towards the rear. Countershaft gear cluster, thrust washers, countershaft constant mesh gear and snap ring can be withdrawn from transmission case and countershaft from differential housing, as shown in Fig. MM126.

Countershaft front bearing cup can be pulled or driven out of front of case and rear cup out of rear of case. Shims located between countershaft bearing cups and transmission case should be retained for reassembly. On tractors prior to 407951, shims (5—Fig. MM-

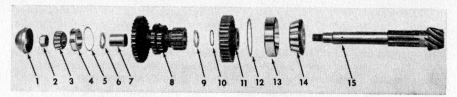

Fig. MM127—Exploded view of R series countershaft assembly.

1. Bearing cover
2. Countershaft nut adjusts bearings after 407950
3. Front bearing cone
4. Front bearing cup
5. Bearing cup shim (not used after number 407950)
6. Thrust washer
7. Gear bushing (2)
8. Gear cluster
9. Thrust washer
10. Snap ring
11. Constant mesh gear
12. Gear mesh adjusting shim
13. Rear bearing cup
14. Rear bearing cone
15. Countershaft and main drive pinion

Fig. MM124—Removing cover from front of R series countershaft bearing.

Fig. MM125—Removing snap ring from R series countershaft.

Fig. MM126—R series countershaft is withdrawn from differential housing and gears from transmission case.

127) located behind the front cup, and nut (2), control the countershaft bearing clearance; on later models, shims (5) are omitted and nut (2) controls the adjustment of the bearings. Shims (12), between the rear cup and transmission case, control the depth of mesh of the main drive bevel pinion. Adjust countershaft bearings to a slight pre-load. If mesh position of bevel pinion must be adjusted, do so by varying shims (12).

Model GTB And U-ZA-ZT Series

Care should be exercised when ordering parts for these transmissions as in some individual cases, different gears have been used during various periods of production.

180. **TRANSMISSION COVER.** Cover can be removed after removing the instrument panel, battery and battery shelf. Remove cap screws retaining cover to transmission case and lift off cover. Reinstallation is reverse of removal.

181. **SHIFTER RAILS AND FORKS.** Rails and forks can be removed after removing transmission cover, and four cap screws retaining shifter rail bearings (69 & 70—Fig. MM130) to transmission housing. Complete disassembly of rails and forks is self-evident after an examination and reference to Fig. MM130.

182. **SLIDING GEAR (CLUTCH) SHAFT.** The sliding gear (clutch) shaft (63—Fig. MM131) can be removed after "splitting" tractor as outlined in paragraph 154, and removing transmission cover, clutch, transmission shifter rails and forks, and clutch shifter fork.

Working through transmission housing clutch compartment, remove clutch brake plate (32—Fig. MM131 or 132) and asbestos disc (33) from clutch shaft. Remove clutch shaft ball bearing cover from front of transmission case; then, using a soft drift as in Fig. MM133, bump clutch shaft forward and out of transmission housing.

Remove sliding gear shaft gears out through top cover opening. Pocket bearing (52—Fig. MM131 or 132), can be renewed at this time from pocket in main drive bevel pinion shaft. Constant mesh gear (36) can be removed at this time after removing snap ring (82). To remove clutch shaft bearing (62) remove snap ring and press bearing off toward front end of shaft.

Reassembly is reverse of disassembly. Install constant mesh pinion (36) with long part of hub toward front of transmission. Install oil seal (80) with lip of same facing the rear.

183. **UPPER COUNTERSHAFT.** The upper countershaft (57—Fig. MM140 or 141) can be removed after removing clutch and sliding gear shaft (paragraph 182), and power take-off unit (paragraph 308).

MODEL GTB AND ZA, ZT AND LATE PRODUCTION U SERIES. Working through clutch compartment, remove front bearing retainer (61); then, working through the power take-off unit opening in rear of transmission case, bump upper countershaft forward and out of transmission housing. Gears, spacer, and countershaft rear bearing (double row ball) can be removed through top of housing.

EARLY PRODUCTION U SERIES. Working through clutch compartment, remove front bearing retainer (61—Fig. MM141) and cap screw and washer (KK). Separate gear spacer from back end of double gear and loop a piece of wire around snap ring (L) located between double gear and spacer. Pull snap ring out of countershaft as in Fig. MM142. Snap ring will be distorted in this operation and should be renewed on reassembly. Drive countershaft out through clutch housing by driving with a bar. Gears and rear bearing can be withdrawn through transmission case.

ALL MODELS. Reinstall the upper countershaft by reversing the removal procedure and on ZA and ZT series tractors, vary the number of shims

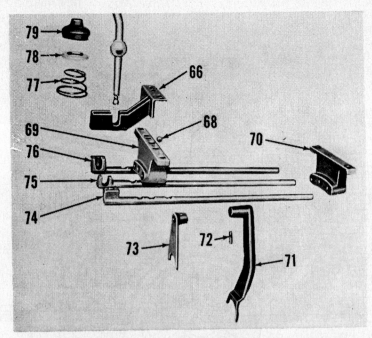

Fig. MM130—Exploded view of model GTB shifter rails and forks. The U series is similar, the differences of which are evident after an examination of the unit.

66. Gear shifter separating bracket
68. Detent ball
69. Rail bearing (rear)
70. Rail bearing (front)
71. 2nd & reverse fork
73. 1st, 3rd, 4th & 5th fork

74. 2nd & reverse rail
75. 3rd & 4th rail
76. 1st & 5th rail
77. Shifter ball spring
78. Spring seat
79. Shifter cap

(83—Fig. MM140) to provide a slight amount of pre-load for the taper roller bearings.

190. LOWER COUNTERSHAFT. The lower countershaft, Fig. MM150, can be removed after "splitting" trac-

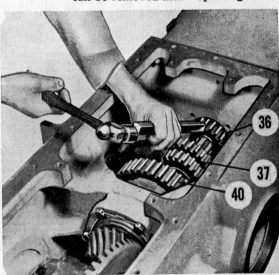

Fig. MM133—After removing clutch shaft front bearing retainer, use a soft drift to bump clutch and transmission sliding gear shaft forward and out of housing on model GTB and series U, ZA and ZT.

36. Constant mesh gear
37. 1st & 4th sliding gear

40. Main drive bevel pinion shaft and gear

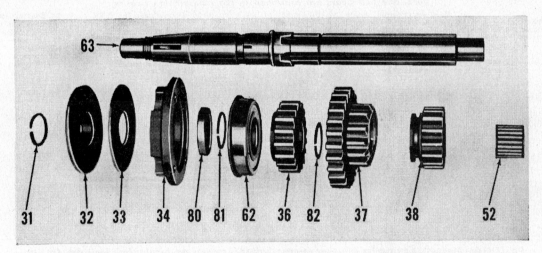

Fig. MM131—Model GTB clutch and transmission sliding gear shaft. The U series is similar.

31. Snap ring
32. Thrust brake plate
33. Asbestos brake disc
34. Bearing cover
36. Constant mesh gear

37. 1st & 4th sliding gear
38. 3rd & 5th sliding gear
52. Clutch shaft pocket bearing

62. Bearing (ball)
63. Sliding gear shaft
80. Oil seal
81. Snap ring
82. Snap ring

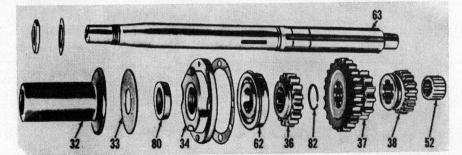

Fig. MM132—Series ZA clutch and sliding gear shaft. The ZT series is similar. Refer to legend under Fig. MM131.

tor (paragraph 154), and removing transmission cover, clutch unit, shifter rails and forks, clutch shaft, power take-off unit, upper countershaft, and belt pulley unit.

Working through transmission top cover opening, remove belt pulley drive gear positioning snap ring (91—Fig. MM151) from its groove and slide same rearward. Working through

clutch compartment, remove **four cap** screws from front bearing carrier (85 —Fig. MM150). Insert a split spacer, approximately 5¼ inches long, between sliding gear and belt pulley

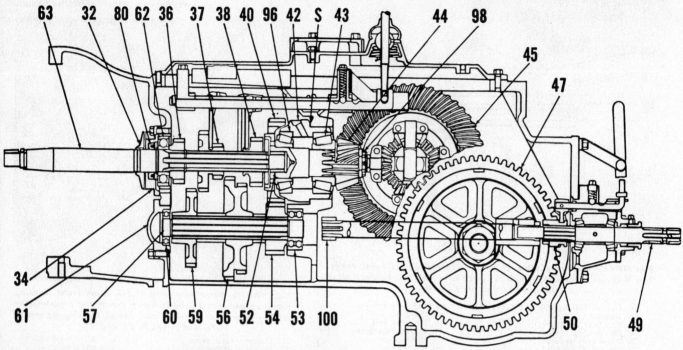

Fig. MM134—Model GTB transmission cross sectional view. Transmission shafts, bevel pinion and ring gear, differential unit, bull pinions, and bull gears are contained in the transmission housing.

S. Shims
32. Thrust brake plate
34. Bearing cover
36. Constant mesh gear (18 teeth)
37. 1st & 4th sliding gear
38. 3rd & 5th sliding gear

40. Main drive bevel pinion shaft & transmission gear
42. Bearing cage (bevel pinion shaft)
43. Bearing
44. Main drive bevel pinion
45. Bevel ring gear

47. Bull gear
49. PTO shaft
50. PTO clutch jaw
52. Pocket bearing
53. Ball bearing (rear)
54. Constant mesh gear (21 teeth)

56. Double gear (44 & 38 teeth)
57. Upper countershaft
59. Constant mesh gear (33 teeth)
60. Bearing (ball)
61. Bearing retainer

62. Bearing (ball)
63. Clutch & transmission sliding gear shaft
80. Oil seal
96. Bearing
98. Pinion retaining nut
100. PTO connecting shaft

Fig. MM140—Model GTB transmission upper countershaft (57) rotates on annular ball bearings. Late production U series tractors are similar. ZA series tractors are similar except taper roller bearings are used and spacer (55) is not used.

53. Ball bearing (rear)
54. Constant mesh gear
55. Spacer
56. Double gear
58. Spacer
59. Constant mesh gear
60. Ball bearing (front)
61. Bearing retainer
83. Gasket
84. Bearing retaining washer

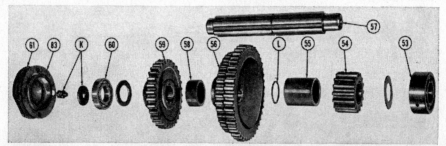

Fig. MM141—Exploded view of early production U series upper countershaft. Front bearing (60) is retained by washer and cap screw (K). The ZT series is similar except spacer (55) and washer and cap screw (KK) are not used. Refer to legend under Fig. MM140.

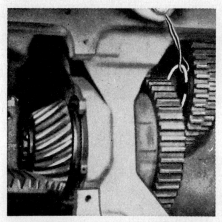

Fig. MM142—Using a looped wire to remove snap ring from early production U series upper countershaft.

drive gear as shown in Fig. MM152 to prevent damaging the gear teeth or bearing cone when bumping shaft forward. Working through differential compartment, bump lower countershaft forward and out of transmission housing. Remove gears, snap ring and rear bearing cone out through transmission top cover opening.

Shims (95—Fig. MM150) located between rear bearing cup (94) and bearing cup bore in transmission housing control mesh position of belt pulley drive gear (90).

Adjust lower countershaft bearings by varying number shims (86 & 87), interposed between transmission compartment forward wall and front bearing carrier (85) to provide a slight bearing pre-load of 0.001-0.003. If the lower countershaft and/or belt pulley drive gear are renewed, adjust belt pulley drive gear backlash of 0.006-0.008 as outlined in paragraph 288 under BELT PULLEY section.

191. **MAIN DRIVE BEVEL PINION AND SHAFT.** Main drive bevel pinion, constant mesh gear and shaft, and

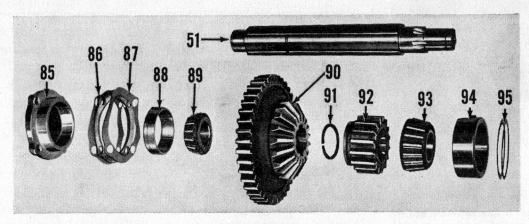

Fig. MM150—Model GTB transmission lower countershaft. Belt pulley drive gear (90) mesh position is controlled with shims (95) inserted between bearing cup (94) and bearing cup bore. Shims (86) and (87) control bearing adjustment. The U and ZA series are similar. The ZT series is similar except that gear (90) is a two piece unit.

51. Lower countershaft	88. Bearing cup	91. Snap ring	93. Bearing cone
85. Bearing retainer	89. Bearing cone	92. 2nd & reverse gear	94. Bearing cup
86 & 87. Shims & gasket	90. Constant mesh gear		95. Shim

Fig. MM151—Removing belt pulley unit drive gear positioning snap ring prior to removal of lower countershaft on model GTB. The U, ZA and ZT series are similar.

Fig. MM152—A spacer is installed between belt pulley drive gear and sliding gear when bumping transmission lower countershaft forward and out of housing on model GTB. The same procedure can be used on the U, ZA and ZT series.

40. Main drive bevel pinion shaft and gear	90. Constant mesh and belt pulley bevel drive gear	91. Snap ring
51. Lower countershaft		92. 2nd & reverse gear

Fig. MM155—Model GTB main drive bevel pinion shaft and gear, bevel pinion, and related parts. Shims (S) control bevel pinion mesh position. Series U, ZA and ZT are similar.

40. Main drive bevel pinion shaft and gear	41. Bearing cone	43. Bearing cone	97. Bearing cup
	42. Bearing cage (bevel pinion shaft)	44. Main drive bevel pinion	98. Pinion retaining nut
		96. Bearing cup	

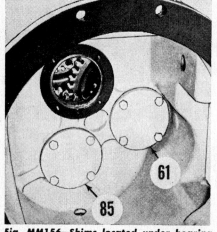

Fig. MM156—Shims located under bearing retainer (85) control lower countershaft bearing adjustment on model GTB. Series U, ZA and ZT are similar.

61. Upper countershaft front bearing retainer
85. Lower countershaft front bearing retainer

bearing cage assembly Fig. MM155 can be removed after "splitting" tractor, and removing other transmission shafts and gears as outlined in preceding paragraphs.

Remove safety wire and six cap screws retaining bearing cage (42) to transmission housing wall. A half-moon box wrench is best suited for this operation. The complete assembly (shaft, gears and bearing) can be withdrawn forward and out of transmission housing. Do not discard shims (S) located between bearing cage and transmission housing.

Pinion and ring gears are available only as matched pairs, and can be identified as such by etched numbers on both pinion and gear.

When reassembling, press pinion gear on pinion shaft; then, tighten pinion retaining nut (98) to 40-75 inch pounds torque so as to slightly preload the bearings. Install assembly so that the bearing cage oil reservoir is facing up. For bevel pinion gear mesh adjustment, refer to MAIN DRIVE BEVEL GEARS section, paragraph 215.

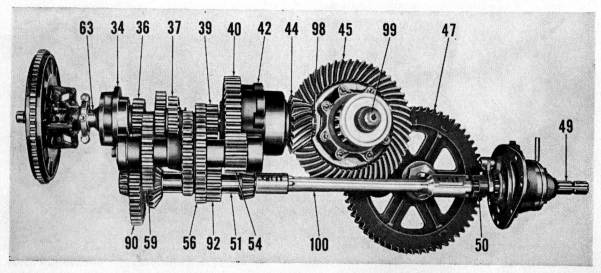

Fig. MM157—Model GTB clutch unit, transmission gears and shafts, bevel pinion and ring gear, differential unit, bull pinions, bull gears, and power take-off unit are contained in the transmission housing.

34. Bearing cover
36. Constant mesh gear (18 teeth)
37. 1st & 4th sliding gear
39. 3rd & 5th sliding gear
40. Main drive bevel pinion shaft and transmission constant mesh gear
42. Bearing cage (bevel pinion shaft)
44. Main drive bevel pinion
45. Main drive bevel ring gear
47. Bull gear
49. PTO shaft
50. PTO clutch jaw
51. Lower countershaft
54. Constant mesh gear (21 teeth)
56. Double gear (44 & 38 teeth)
59. Constant mesh gear (33 teeth)
63. Clutch & transmission sliding gear shaft
90. Constant mesh gear and integral belt pulley bevel drive gear
92. 2nd & reverse gear (21 teeth)
98. Bevel pinion retaining nut
99. Bull pinion & integral differential shaft
100. Connecting shaft from PTO to lower countershaft

Fig. MM160—Gears, shafts and bearings of U series transmission prior to number 327401. ZT series transmission is similar.

1. Main drive pinion shaft and constant mesh gear (42 teeth; 38 on Z)
2. First and fifth sliding gear (15 teeth; 14 on Z)
3. Sliding gear and clutch shaft
4. Third and fourth sliding gear

(22-26 teeth; 18-23 on ZTU-ZTN prior to 565135 and ZTS prior to 610389; 20-23 on later Z series)
5. Snap ring
6. Constant mesh gear (18 teeth; 16 on Z)

7. Clutch shaft bearing
8. Bearing cover
9. Upper countershaft (See Fig. MM141)
10. Lower countershaft (See Fig. MM150)

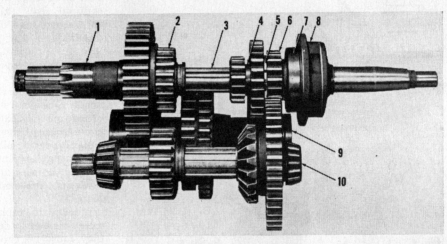

Fig. MM161—Gears, shafts and bearings of U series transmission after number 327400.

1. Main drive pinion shaft and constant mesh gear
2. Third and fifth sliding gear (20 teeth)
3. Sliding gear and clutch shaft

4. First and fourth sliding gear (14-25 teeth)
5. Snap ring
6. Constant mesh gear (18 teeth)

7. Clutch shaft bearing
9. Upper countershaft (See Fig. MM140)
10. Lower countershaft (See Fig. MM150)

DIFFERENTIAL AND FINAL DRIVE

DIFFERENTIAL

Model GTA

200. REMOVE AND REINSTALL. Remove transmission cover, support rear of tractor under the transmission case and remove both rear wheels. Remove the transmission reinforcing rod, support weight of bull gear and differential assembly on a chain hoist and remove both rear axle shaft and axle housing assemblies. Differential and bull gear assembly can then be lifted out of transmission housing.

To reinstall, reverse the removal procedure. Be sure bearing spacers (4—Fig. MM169) are in place when axle shaft and housing assemblies are reinstalled.

201. DISASSEMBLY AND REASSEMBLY. Remove eight bolts and nuts retaining differential case halves (3—Fig. MM169) to bull gear (1). Differential case halves can then be separated from the bull gear and pinions (14), pinion shafts (2) and side gears (13) can be removed. Reassem-

bly is reverse of disassembly. Side play of differential is controlled by the non-adjustable ball bearings.

R Series

205. BEARING ADJUSTMENT. Differential bearing adjustment is controlled by shims (2—Fig. MM170) between bearing cages (1) and transmission housing. Removing shims reduces bearing clearance. To make a bearing wear adjustment, support rear of tractor under transmission and remove left rear wheel.

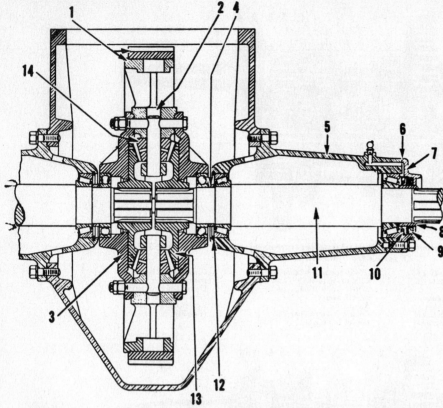

Fig. MM169—Sectional view of model GTA differential and rear axle assemblies.

1. Bull gear	10. Oil seal
2. Pinion shaft	11. Axle shaft
3. Differential case	12. Snap ring
4. Bearing spacer	13. Side gear
5. Axle housing	14. Pinion gear
6. Bearing adjusting shim	
7. Bearing cap	
8. Spacer	
9. Felt seal	

Do not discard shims from between bearing cages and transmission as they control differential bearing play and bevel ring gear (backlash). With bearing cages removed, differential unit can be withdrawn through top of transmission housing as shown in Fig. MM171.

To disassemble the unit, mark both halves of differential case so they can be reassembled in their original position. Remove eight bolts and nuts (7—Fig. MM170) joining the halves of the differential case and separate the two halves. Pinions (10), pinion shafts (12), side gears (9) and side gear thrust washers (8) can then be removed. If wear on pinion bushings or pinion shafts exceeds 0.005, they should be renewed. New pinion shaft diameter is 0.996-0.997. New bushings must be reamed, after being pressed into gear, to 1.000-1.001.

Install side gear thrust washers (8) with bevel edge towards the gear. Install oil seals (3) in bearing cages with sharp edge of seal towards differential.

Install differential by reversing the removal procedure. Reinstall bearing cages with same thickness of shims between each bearing cage and transmission case as was present at time of removal. If bearing play exists, remove shims from left bearing cage until all bearing play is eliminated but permitting differential to turn without binding. Be sure also that some backlash exists between teeth of the bevel gears.

If main drive pinion and ring gear were renewed during disassembly, they must be checked and adjusted for correct mesh. For mesh adjusting procedure, refer to Gear Mesh Adjustment, paragraph 215.

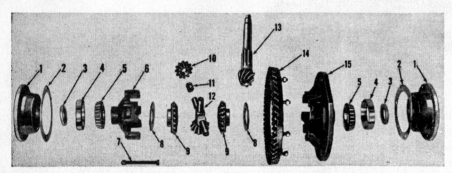

Fig. MM170—Exploded view of R series differential assembly.

1. Bearing cage	8. Side gear thrust washer	13. Main drive pinion and transmission countershaft
2. Shim	10. Pinion (4)	14. Main drive ring gear
5. Bearing cone	11. Pinion bushing	15. Cage (diff. case) (right side)
6. Cage (diff. case) (left side)	12. Pinion shaft (2)	
7. Cage bolt and nut		

Disconnect left brake linkage and remove cap screws retaining left rear axle housing to transmission housing. Withdraw left axle shaft and housing assembly from transmission being careful not to damage oil seal in differential bearing cage. Remove differential left bearing cage and remove required number of shims from between cage and transmission. Reinstall bearing cage and check bearing play.

Bearings should have no play but differential should not bind. NOTE: If removal of more than 0.004 thickness of shims is required to remove bearing play, remove the right axle

shaft and housing assembly and half the required thickness of shims from between the right bearing cage and transmission.

206. R & R AND OVERHAUL. Remove transmission cover, support rear of tractor under transmission and remove rear wheels. Disconnect brake linkage and remove cap screws retaining rear axle housings to transmission housing. Withdraw axle shaft and housing assemblies from transmission being careful not to damage oil seal in differential bearing cages. Remove differential bearing cages from transmission housing.

Fig. MM171—R series differential assembly is removed from transmission housing after rear axle housings and differential bearing cages are removed.

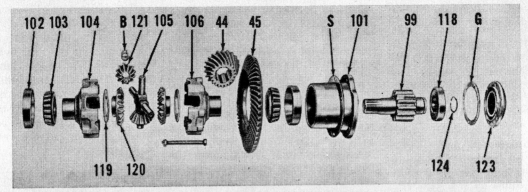

Fig. MM172—Model GTB main drive bevel ring gear, differential unit and bull pinions, exploded view. Shims (S) control differential carrier bearing adjustment, and bevel ring gear backlash. The U series is similarly constructed.

B. Bushing
G. Gasket
S. Shims
44. Main drive bevel pinion
45. Main drive bevel ring gear

99. Bull pinion & shaft
102. Bearing cup (differential carrier)
103. Bearing cone
104. Differential case (right)
105. Spider (pinion)

106. Differential case (left)
118. Bull pinion bearing
119. Thrust washer
120. Differential side gear
121. Differential pinion
123. Bearing retainer
124. Snap ring

GTB Model and U Series

207. BEARING ADJUSTMENT. Differential carrier bearing adjustment is controlled with shims (S—Fig. MM172 or 233) inserted between bearing cages and transmission housing. The same shims also control bevel ring gear and pinion backlash to the value as etched on both pinion and ring gear.

To adjust differential carrier bearings, first remove transmission top cover. Remove left brake assembly on U series and GTB models equipped with disc type brakes. Remove cap screws retaining left bearing cage to transmission housing and slide cage out far enough to permit removal of required thickness of shims to provide zero end play and yet permit differential unit to rotate without binding. Reinstall bearing cage and check bearing adjustment and backlash. If bearing adjustment is O.K. but backlash is .002 greater or less than value stamped on ring gear it will be necessary to adjust backlash by transferring shims from one side to the other until correct backlash is obtained.

208. R & R AND OVERHAUL. To remove differential unit, first remove transmission housing top cover, power take-off unit, paragraph 308, or transmission housing rear cover plate, and rear axle shaft and housing assemblies. Remove both brake assemblies from the U series and GTB models which are equipped with disc type brakes. Remove cap screws retaining differential bearing cages to transmission housing. Tilt lower end of left bull gear to the right and remove left differential bearing cage and bull pinion shaft (or sleeve) and left differential shaft on U series which are

equipped with continuous type power take-off. With the left bull gear in an upright position, tilt lower end of right bull gear to the left and remove right differential cage and bull pinion shaft.

Do not discard shims located between bearing cages and transmission housing. With bearing cages removed, the differential unit can be lifted out

through top opening of transmission housing.

Mark both halves of differential case. Remove bolts and nuts retaining both halves of differential case. Pinions (121—Fig. MM173), pinion spider (105), side gears (120) and side gear thrust washers (119) can then be removed. New pinion shaft diameter is 0.996-0.997. Service bushings for pin-

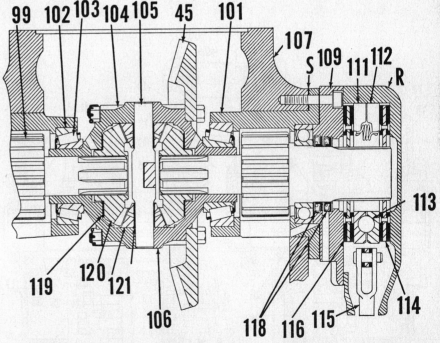

Fig. MM173—Model GTB differential, bevel ring gear, and bull pinions assembly as used on models equipped with disc type brakes. Models equipped with rear wheel brakes are similar in construction. The U series which are not equipped with continuous power take-off are similarly constructed except disc brakes are not used. Refer to Fig. MM233 for U series when equipped with continuous power take-off.

R. Brake housing cover & outer brake plate
S. Shims
45. Main drive bevel ring gear
99. Bull pinion & integral differential unit shaft
101. Bearing cage

102. Bearing cup
103. Bearing cone
104. Differential case (right)
105. Spider
106. Differential case (left)
107. Transmission housing
109. Brake plate (inner)
111 & 112. Brake actuating disc

113. Actuating disc ball
114. Brake disc
115. Brake actuating rod
116. Brake disc
118. Oil seal (2 used)
119. Thrust washer
120. Differential side gear

ions are to be sized after installation to an inside diameter of 1.000-1.001.

When reassembling differential unit, install side gear thrust washers (119) with bevel edge facing inward. On GTB models equipped with disc type brakes and all U series, install oil seal (118—Fig. MM173) with lip of same facing the differential.

Reinstall differential unit by reversing removal procedure. Reinstall differential bearing cages with same thickness of shims as was removed.

Check and adjust differential carrier bearings, as in paragraph 207 and mesh and backlash of main drive bevel gears as outlined in paragraph 215.

ZA-ZT Series

209. **BEARING ADJUSTMENT.** On ZT series and ZA series not equipped with continuous power take-off, the differential bearing adjustment is controlled with shims (2—Fig. MM180), which are inserted between both bearing cages and the transmission housing. On ZA series which are equipped with continuous power take-off, the differential bearing adjustment is controlled by shims (S—Fig. MM234)

which are located between the brake housing and the transmission case. These shims, also control bevel ring gear and pinion backlash to the value as etched on the gear.

To make a bearing adjustment, remove transmission cover. Remove the left brake assembly and cap screws retaining differential left bearing cage (or brake housing) to transmission housing and slide bearing cage (or housing) out far enough to permit removal of required thickness of shims. Retighten bearing cage (or housing) and check bearing play. Bearings should have no play, but differential should not bind.

210. **R & R AND OVERHAUL.** To remove differential unit, first remove transmission cover, power take-off unit, or rear cover plate, rear axle shaft and housing assemblies. Remove right and left hand brake assemblies. On ZT series and ZA series not equipped with continuous power take-off, remove differential side gear and bull pinion shaft bearing cages. On ZA series equipped with continuous power take-off, remove brake housings.

Tilt the bottom of the left bull gear to the right and remove the left bull pinion and differential side gear. Straighten up the left bull gear and tilt the bottom of the right bull gear to the left and remove the right differential side gear and bull pinion. Shims (2—Fig. MM180 or S—Fig. MM 234) control differential bearing end play and main drive bevel ring gear backlash.

Place a piece of wood (approximately 2½ inches wide) between back face of bevel ring gear and transmission housing. Working through the right hand opening in transmission housing, bump differential shaft out of the differential case. Lift the differential and bevel ring gear assembly out through transmission top cover opening.

To disassemble the differential unit, remove the two long bolts retaining differential bevel pinion shafts to differential case. Bump one pinion shaft through the cage, forcing the other pinion shaft out; then bump the first pinion shaft out. Differential pinion bronze bushing inside diameter is 1.000-1.001, with a shaft diameter of 0.996-0.997.

NOTE: Pinion gears as used on older models of the ZT series were not fitted with bushings. These gears can be replaced with the later, bushed type.

Differential shaft bushings (26—Fig. MM180), which are pressed in the integral differential side gear and bull pinion (or sleeve) can be renewed at this time.

Install oil seals (3) in bearing cages with lip of seal facing differential unit.

Reverse removal procedure. Reinstall bearing cages (or brake housings) with same thickness of shims between each bearing cage (or brake housing) and transmission as was removed. If bearing play exists, remove an equal thickness of shims from between each bearing cage (or brake housing) and transmission until all bearing play is eliminated, but being sure that sufficient backlash exists between teeth of the bevel gears.

If main drive pinion and ring gear, which are available only as matched pairs, were renewed; they must be checked and adjusted for correct mesh and backlash. For adjusting procedure, refer to paragraph 215.

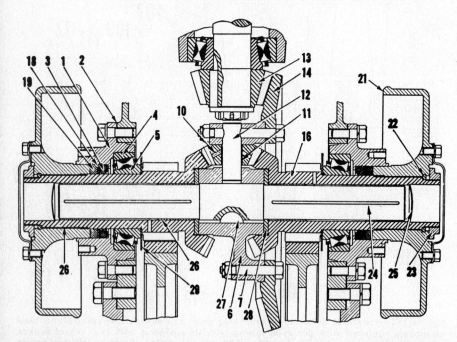

Fig. MM180—Sectional view of ZT series differential assembly. The ZA series which are not equipped with continuous type power take-off are similarly constructed. Refer to Fig. MM234 for view of the ZA series when equipped with continuous power take-off.

1. Bearing cage	11. Pinion bushing (after ZTU 565234 and ZTS 610388)
2. Shim	12. Pinion shaft (2)
3. Oil seal	13. Main drive bevel pinion
4. Bearing cup	14. Main drive bevel ring gear
5. Bearing cone	18. Washer
6. Cage (diff. case)	19. Felt seal
7. Cage bolt and nut	
10. Pinion (2)	

22. Snap ring
23. Brake drum retaining nut
24. Cross shaft
25. Expansion plug
26. Bushing
27. Cross shaft key
28. Thrust washer
29. Washer

MAIN DRIVE BEVEL GEARS
Model GTB and R, U, ZA and ZT Series

Main drive bevel pinion and ring gear are available only as matched pairs.

215. MESH AND BACKLASH ADJUSTMENT. Mesh position of model GTB and the U, ZA and ZT series main drive bevel pinion is controlled with shims (S—Fig. MM155), inserted between bevel pinion shaft bearing cage and transmission housing dividing wall. Mesh position of the R series main drive bevel pinion is controlled by shims (12—Fig. MM127) which are located between the pinion shaft rear bearing cup and the transmission housing. Main drive bevel gear backlash is controlled by removing shims from under one differential bearing cage, and inserting the same amount under the other cage.

Both bevel pinion and ring gear are marked as follows: One group of numbers indicates matched set number; number stamped as .008 BL indicates backlash value, and a number with a plus or minus sign indicates pinion position in relation to cone center distance. Refer to Fig. MM185.

If the renewed gears have a value within 2 of the plus or minus mark on old gears, reinstall same number of shims between bevel pinion bearing cage and transmission housing wall as were removed and used for the old gears.

If new gears have a backlash value greater than 2 from the plus or minus mark on old gears; then, add or remove shims from between pinion bearing cage or cup and transmission housing wall to offset the difference in cone center position. After this adjustment has been completed and the differential carrier bearings are adjusted as outlined in paragraph 205, 207 or 209, transfer shims from under one differential bearing cage or brake housing to the other bearing cage or brake housing to obtain the correct backlash as specified on the gears.

The bevel pinion mesh can be checked by using the following procedure. With backlash correctly adjusted, apply a coat of Prussian blue or red lead to gear teeth and rotate gears several revolutions. While rotating the gears, slightly brake the bevel ring gear.

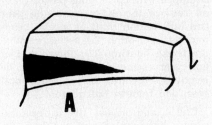

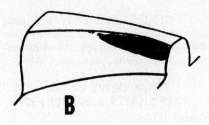

Fig. MM186—A. Heavy contact on heel of bevel ring gear tooth. To correct, move pinion away from ring gear. B. Heavy contact on toe of ring gear tooth. To correct, move pinion closer to ring gear.

If bluing or red lead is wiped from heel of tooth (A—Fig. MM186) move pinion away from ring gear by removing shims from between pinion bearing cage and transmission housing wall; then, transfer shims from differential left bearing cage to right side so as to re-establish correct backlash.

If bluing or red lead shows heavy toe contact (B—Fig. MM186) the pinion must be moved toward the ring gear. Add shims between pinion bearing cage or cup and transmission housing wall; then, transfer shims from differential right bearing cage to left bearing cage to re-establish correct backlash. With backlash properly adjusted, correct mesh is when ring gear indicates contact for ¾ to ⅞ of tooth length centered between toe and heel ends of gear.

216. RENEW BEVEL GEARS. The main drive bevel pinion and ring gear are available only as matched pairs.

The R series bevel pinion is integral with the transmission countershaft; for removal procedure, refer to paragraph 175. On other models, the bevel pinion is splined to the transmission constant mesh gear and shaft; for removal procedure, refer to paragraph 191.

Renewal of the bevel ring gear on all models requires R & R of differential as outlined in paragraph 206

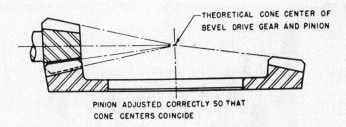

PINION ADJUSTED CORRECTLY SO THAT CONE CENTERS COINCIDE

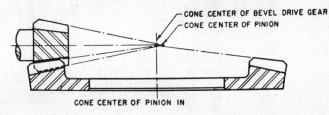

CONE CENTER OF PINION IN

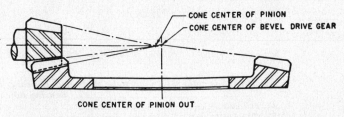

CONE CENTER OF PINION OUT

Fig. MM185—Series R main drive pinion and ring gears. The same numbers (A-5-852) on both gears indicate they are a matched set. The notation (0.008 BL) refers to the correct backlash adjustment of 0.008 for this set of gears. The (—4) indicates the cone center relative distance. Similar markings are used on other models.

Fig. MM187—Establishing the correct cone center distance as shown in top view for mesh adjustment of main drive bevel gears by positioning main drive bevel pinion shaft bearing cage with shims.

for the R series; paragraph 208 for model GTB and U series; and 210 for the ZA and ZT series. Never use other than heat treated bolts to replace defective ring gear to differential case bolts.

FINAL DRIVE GEARS
Model GTA

220. BULL PINION. The final drive bull pinion (3—Fig. MM112) is located on the transmission countershaft and renewal requires R & R of the countershaft as in paragraph 164.

221. BULL GEAR. The final drive bull gear (1—Fig. MM169) is bolted to the differential case halves and renewal requires R & R of differential as outlined in paragraph 200.

Model GTB and U Series

222. BULL PINION. To remove a bull pinion, first remove the transmission housing top cover, power take-off unit or transmission housing rear cover plate and the respective rear axle shaft and housing assembly. Remove the respective brake assembly from the U series and GTB models which are equipped with disc type brakes. Remove cap screws retaining the differential bearing cage to the transmission housing. Tilt lower end of bull gear (same side as pinion to be removed) toward the opposite bull gear, and remove bull pinion and bearing cage assembly. Check and adjust the differential carrier bearings as outlined in paragraph 207.

223. BULL GEARS. Either bull gear can be lifted from the transmission housing after removing the differential as outlined in paragraph 208.

ZA-ZT Series

224. BULL PINION. To remove a bull pinion, first remove the transmission housing top cover, power take-off unit or transmission housing rear cover plate and the respective rear axle shaft and housing assembly. Remove the respective brake assembly. On ZT series and ZA series not equipped with continuous power take-off remove the differential side gear and bull pinion shaft or sleeve bearing cage. On other ZA series, remove the brake housing. Tilt lower end of bull gear (same side as pinion to be removed) toward the opposite bull gear, and remove bull pinion.

Check and adjust the differential carrier bearings as outlined in paragraph 209.

225. BULL GEARS. Either bull gear can be lifted from the transmission housing after removing the differential as outlined in paragraph 210.

FINAL DRIVE UNITS, AXLE SHAFTS & HOUSINGS
Model GTA

230. BEARING ADJUSTMENT. Axle bearing play is controlled by shims (6—Fig. MM169) between bearing cap (7) and axle housing (5). Removing shims reduces bearing play. To adjust bearings, support rear of tractor under transmission and re-

move rear wheel. Remove bearing cap and vary number of shims between cap and housing to remove all bearing play but permitting shaft to turn without binding.

231. R & R ASSEMBLY. Support rear of tractor under transmission and remove rear wheel. Remove transmission cover and disconnect brake linkage from brake cross shaft on axle housing. Support differential assembly in a chain hoist and remove cap screws retaining housing to transmission and withdraw housing and shaft assembly. To reinstall, reverse removal procedure and make certain that bearing spacer (4—Fig. MM169) is in place.

232. R & R SHAFT OR BEARINGS. Remove assembly as outlined in paragraph 231. Remove bearing cap (7—Fig. MM169) and bump axle shaft (11) and outer bearing cup out through outer end of housing. Inner bearing cup can be driven or pulled from housing after removing snap ring (12). Bearing cones can be driven or pressed off shaft. Reassembly is reverse of disassembly. Refer to paragraph 230 for bearing adjustment.

Model GTB and U (Except UTC), ZA & ZT Series

233. BEARING ADJUSTMENT. Axle bearing play is controlled with shims (128—Fig. MM190) or (6—Fig. MM191) between bearing cap and axle housing. To adjust bearings, support rear of tractor under transmission and remove tire and wheel as-

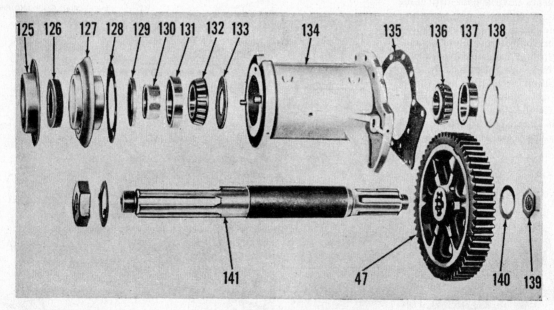

Fig. MM190—Model GTB rear axle shaft and housing, and related parts. Shims (128) control axle shaft bearing adjustment.

47. Bull gear	129. Oil seal	134. Housing	138. Snap ring
125. Oil collector ring	130. Spacer	135. Gasket	139. Bull gear retaining nut
126. Felt seal	131. Bearing cup	136. Bearing cone	140. Lock washer
127. Bearing retainer	132. Bearing cone	137. Bearing cup	141. Axle shaft
128. Shims			

sembly. On models equipped with rear wheel brakes it will be necessary to remove brake shoes and back plate assembly. Remove bearing cap and vary number of shims between cap and housing to provide zero end play to shaft and yet permit same to rotate without binding.

234. R & R ASSEMBLY. Support rear of tractor under transmission and remove tire and wheel assembly. Remove transmission top cover, and power take-off unit or rear cover plate from models so equipped. Straighten bull gear retaining nut lock and remove bull gear retaining nut. Remove axle housing to transmission housing retaining bolts and remove axle shaft and housing assembly.

235. SHAFT AND/OR BEARINGS RENEW. To renew either shaft and/or bearings, remove assembly as outlined in preceding paragraph 234. Remove bearing retainer and bump shaft on inner end. Inner bearing cup can be pulled or driven from housing after removing snap ring. Adjust bearings as outlined in paragraph 233.

236. SHAFT OIL SEAL RENEW. The axle shaft oil seal (129—Fig. MM 190) or (10—Fig. MM191) of treated leather can be renewed after removing rear tire and wheel assembly, and the shaft bearing retainer. Install seal in bearing retainer with lip of seal facing bull gear.

R Series

237. BEARING ADJUSTMENT. Axle bearing adjustment is controlled by shims (6—Fig. MM192) and the

5. Housing
6. Shim
7. Bearing cover
8. Collar (spacer)
9. Felt
10. Oil seal
11. Axle shaft
15. Retainer
16. Outer bearing cup
17. Outer bearing cone
18. Inner bearing cone
19. Inner bearing cup
20. Gasket
21. Axle shaft key

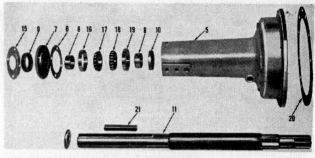

Fig. MM192—Exploded view of R series rear axle assembly.

adjustment procedure is similar to that which is outlined in paragraph 233.

238. R & R ASSEMBLY. Support rear of tractor under transmission and remove rear wheel. Disconnect brake cable and remove cap screws retaining housing to transmission and remove housing and shaft assembly. To reinstall, reverse removal procedure.

239. R & R SHAFT OR BEARINGS. Remove assembly as outlined in paragraph 238. Remove the brake friction plate and bearing cover (7—Fig. MM 192). Bump axle shaft, bearing cones and outer bearing cup out through outer end of housing. Inner bearing cup (19) can be pulled from the housing with a puller and bearing cones (17) and (18) pressed, pulled or driven off shaft. Reassembly is reverse of disassembly. Adjust bearings as outlined in paragraph 237.

Model UTC

250. AXLE BEARING ADJUSTMENT. Axle bearing adjustment is controlled by shims (6—Fig. MM195), and the adjustment procedure is simi-

lar to that which is outlined in paragraph 233.

251. R & R WHEEL AXLE SHAFT, BEARINGS, SPROCKET OR CHAIN. Support rear of tractor under transmission and remove rear wheel. Remove axle bearing cover and shims from housing. Remove upper corner cover from housing, remove hunting link from chain and remove chain. Wheel axle shaft can then be withdrawn from housing. Outer bearing cup can be pulled from cover and inner bearing cup pulled from housing. Bearing cones and sprocket can be pressed off shaft. Reassemble in reverse order and adjust bearings as outlined in paragraph 250.

252. ADJUST DRIVE SHAFT BEARINGS. Bearing play is controlled by position of nut (25—Fig. MM195) retaining drive shaft sprocket to shaft. To adjust bearings, remove upper corner cover and straighten lip of locking washer. Turning nut to the right reduces bearing play. Bearings should have no play but shaft should not bind. Bull gear retaining nut (23) on inner end of drive shaft must be tight when making this adjustment.

253. R & R DRIVE SHAFT SPROCKET. Remove rear wheel and upper corner cover. Remove hunting link from chain and remove chain. Remove nut (25—Fig. MM195) retaining sprocket to shaft and remove sprocket. Reassemble in reverse order and adjust bearings as in paragraph 252.

254. R & R DRIVE SHAFT OR BEARINGS. Remove assembly as outlined for U series in paragraph 234 and remove upper corner cover. Remove hunting link from chain and remove chain. Remove nut (25—Fig. MM195) retaining sprocket (27) to drive shaft (24) and pull sprocket from shaft. Bump shaft through outer bearing cone and out through inner end of housing. Inner bearing cone can be pressed off shaft and bearing cups pulled from housing. Reassemble in reverse order but do not adjust bearings until entire unit has been installed on the transmission and bull

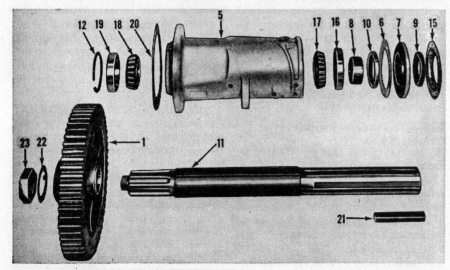

Fig. MM191—Exploded view of UTU, UTE and UTN rear axle assembly. UTS has similar construction with a shorter shaft (11) and housing (5). The ZA and ZT series are similar.

1. Bull gear
5. Housing
6. Shim
7. Bearing cover
8. Collar (spacer)
9. Felt
10. Oil seal
11. Axle shaft
12. Snap ring
15. Retainer
16. Outer bearing cup
17. Outer bearing cone
18. Inner bearing cone
19. Inner bearing cup
20. Gasket
21. Axle shaft key
22. Locking washer
23. Gear retaining nut

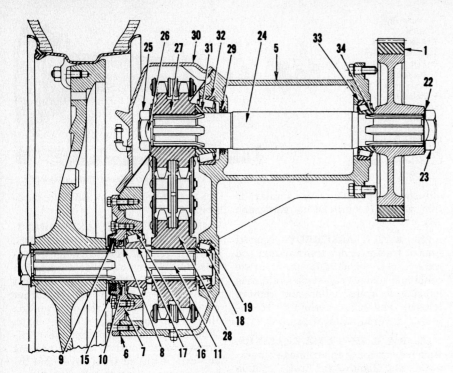

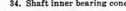

Fig. MM195—Sectional view of UTC rear axle and final drive assembly.

1. Bull gear	17. Axle outer bearing cone	28. Lower sprocket
5. Rear axle housing	18. Axle inner bearing cone	29. Oil seal
6. Shim	19. Axle inner bearing cup	30. Upper corner cover
7. Bearing cover	22. Locking washer	31. Drive shaft outer bearing cone
8. Collar (spacer)	23. Gear retaining nut	32. Drive shaft outer bearing cup
9. Felt	24. Drive shaft	33. Drive shaft inner bearing cup
10. Oil seal	25. Sprocket retaining nut	34. Shaft inner bearing cone
11. Wheel axle shaft	26. Locking washer	
15. Retainer	27. Upper sprocket	
16. Axle outer bearing cup		

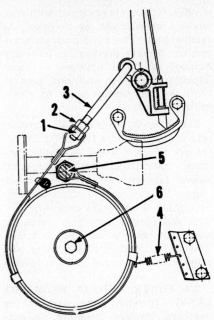

Fig. MM200—GTA external contracting brake operates on a drum fitted to extended countershaft.

1. Adjusting nut	4. Spring
2. Lock nut	5. Anchor
3. Link	6. Countershaft

gear retaining nut (23) tightened. Oil seal (29) is installed with sharp edge of seal towards transmission.

255. R & R ASSEMBLY (FINAL DRIVE). Follow same procedure as outlined for U series in paragraph 234.

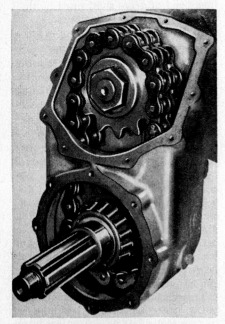

Fig. MM196—UTC rear axle housing with axle bearing cover and upper corner cover removed.

BRAKES

GTA Countershaft Brake

260. ADJUSTMENT. Adjust brake by positioning nut (1—Fig. MM200) on link (3). Tighten locknut (2) after adjustment is complete.

261. R & R BAND. Disconnect band from link, disconnect band spring (4), remove cotter pin from anchor (5) and slide band off drum and anchor.

262. R & R DRUM. Remove cap screw and washer retaining drum to transmission countershaft and pull drum off shaft.

GTA-GTB Double Anchor Type Bendix Brake

(See paragraph 279 for GTB disc brakes)

265. MINOR ADJUSTMENT. Support rear of tractor under transmission housing. Check and make certain that brake linkage is operating freely, and brake pedals are fully released. To adjust, turn eccentric (158—Fig. MM-203) in direction of drum rotation until shoes drag against drum, then back off just enough to permit drum to rotate freely. With a screw driver inserted through opening in back plate (161) rotate notched wheel until shoes are expanded against drum; then, ro-

tate notched wheel in opposite direction until drum is free to rotate.

266. MAJOR ADJUSTMENT. Loosen anchor bolt nuts (147). Rotate notched wheel until shoes are expanded tightly against drum. Tap ends of anchors with hammer to centralize shoes, then tighten anchor bolt nuts securely. Turn notched wheel in opposite direction to free drum. Rotate eccentric, (158) in the direction of drum rotation until shoes drag against drum; then, back off just enough to permit drum to rotate freely. With a screw driver inserted through opening in back plate, rotate notched wheel until shoes are expanded against drum; then, rotate notched wheel in an opposite direction until drum is free to rotate.

267. LINKAGE ADJUSTMENT. Loosen nuts on coupling (206—Fig. MM205) and slide coupling off serrations of brake camshaft. Adjust length of adjusting rods (209) on both sides so that extension shaft levers (208) are about 15 degrees below the horizontal when brake pedals are released and against their stops. Both levers should be adjusted to the same angle. Tighten brake shoes against the drum as in Shoe Adjustment.

Using a pipe wrench, turn camshaft in the direction to apply the brake until the cam is firmly seated against the shoes. Then, while holding the camshaft in this position and with the pedal in the brake fully released po-

Fig. MM202—Internal expanding type Bendix rear wheel brakes as used on early production GTB models and some GTA models.

Fig. MM205—Rear wheel brake, Bendix type, linkage installation as used on models GTA and GTB.

150. Camshaft	207. Extension shaft
154. Secondary shoe	208. Extension shaft
167. Primary shoe	lever
206. Coupling	209. Adjusting rod

sition, slide the coupling back onto the camshaft and tighten the nuts. Back off brake adjusting screw ten to twelve notches to free the wheel. If more than fourteen notches are required to free the wheel, adjust the shoes as in Major Adjustment, and repeat the above procedure.

268. R & R AND OVERHAUL. Brake shoe removal is self-evident after removing rear wheel, and wheel hub.

U-ZA-ZT Series Bendix Brake

270. ADJUSTMENT. Loosen anchor pin nut and anchor bracket cap screws (A) and (B) located on backing side of brake Fig. MM206. From drum side of brake remove small inspection port cover and working through port opening rotate the notched (star) wheel adjuster until shoes are tightly ex-

panded against drum. Now tap end of anchor and cap screws with hammer to permit shoes to centralize themselves in the drum. With drum still locked by shoe pressure tighten the anchor pin and cap screws securely. Back off the notched (star) wheel adjuster until drum just rotates freely. Twelve to 14 notches is usually sufficient to free the drum. Turn the eccentric adjustment located on backing plate side of brake in the direction opposite of road wheel normal rotation as far as it will go, then back it up slightly (not more than ⅛ turn) until drum rotates freely.

271. CABLE ADJUSTMENT. Disconnect cable from pedal. Expand shoes by means of notched wheel. With shoes expanded, adjust length of ca-

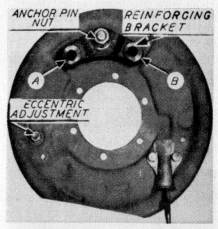

Fig. MM206—U, ZA & ZT Bendix brake, showing points for adjustment.

Fig. MM203—Rear wheel brakes, Bendix type, showing points of brake adjustment on models GTA and GTB. Port cover (161) covers adjusting screw notched wheel.

ble so that pin enters clevis and pedal while cable is pulled tightly against the expanded brake shoes and with the pedal in the brake fully released position. Reconnect cable and back-off notched wheel to free drum.

272. R & R SHOES. Remove drum as in paragraph 273. Remove shoe retracting springs and shoe retaining springs, cupped washers and pins. Reassemble in reverse order. Assemble light tension spring to primary shoe and heavy spring to secondary shoe. Primary shoe is the first shoe from the anchor pin in the direction of rotation. Adjust as in paragraph 270.

273. R & R DRUM. Remove drum cover and nut retaining drum to differential shaft. Drum can be pulled from shaft.

R Series Disc Brake

276. ADJUSTMENT (SINGLE DISC). Support rear of tractor under axle housing or transmission case. Make sure pedals are fully released. Loosen hexagon head cap screws (S—Fig. MM210) in the adjusting screws on the rear axle housing. Turn one ad-

justing screw in until brake begins to drag then back out just far enough to free the wheel. Do the same with the other adjusting screws, then back out each screw an additional ¼ turn and lock adjustments with the hexagon head cap screws.

277. ADJUSTMENT (DOUBLE DISC). Adjustment of the double disc type brakes is accomplished by loosening one lock nut and turning one adjusting nut. Procedure is similar to that described in paragraph 279.

278. R & R AND OVERHAUL. Procedure for removing and overhauling the brakes is evident after removing the axle shaft and housing assembly as outlined in paragraph 238.

Model GTB and U-ZA Series (Disc Type)

279. ADJUSTMENT. To adjust the disc type brakes, support rear portion of tractor and shorten the brake actuating rods by turning adjusting nut (N—Fig. MM213) until a slight drag is obtained while rotating the rear wheels; then, lengthen the rod ½ turn

Fig. MM213—Model GTB Lambert disc type brakes which are splined to outer ends of bull pinion shaft. Removing brake housing cover and outer brake plate (R) retaining bolts (Y) will permit removal of lined discs, and actuating plates.

N. Adjusting nut
115. Actuating rod clevis

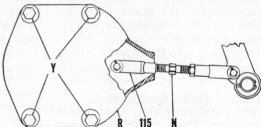

and tighten the jam nut. Both brakes should be free when pedal is depressed 1½ inches but should lock the wheels when pedal is depressed 2½ inches.

280. R & R AND OVERHAUL. The brake assembly can be removed from tractor after disconnecting the actuating linkage and removing the retaining cap screws. On models which are equipped with continuous, or live, power take-off, it is necessary to remove the PTO clutch and power release assembly before removing the left brake.

Procedure for overhauling the brakes is evident after an examination of the removed units. When installing the brake drum on U tractors which are equipped with continuous power take-off, install two ½ x 2½ inch cap screws in the lower holes of the brake drum and one ½ x 2¼ inch cap screw in the upper hole as shown in Fig. MM214; then install the brake assembly as shown in Fig. MM214A. Sectional views showing typical disc brake installations are shown in Figs. MM173, 233 and 234.

Refer to paragraphs 305 and 306 for information concerning the installation of the continuous power take-off clutch and power release mechanism.

Fig. MM210—Early production R series single disc brake adjusting screws are locked by hexagon head cap screws (S).

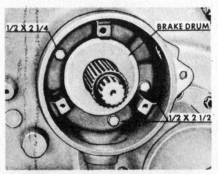

Fig. MM214—When installing the brake drum on U series tractors which are equipped with continuous type power take-off, install the different length cap screws as shown.

Fig. MM211 — Exploded view of early production R series single disc type brake.

1. Ring gasket
2. Stationary ring
3. Friction plate
4. Primary plate
5. Lever
6. Power plate
7. Roller insert (with nib)
8. Retainer
9. Roller
10. Retainer spring
11. Roller insert
12. Retainer pin
13. Plunger pin
14. Adjusting screw

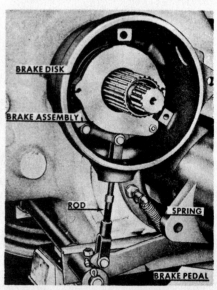

Fig. MM214A—Typical installation of double disc brake assembly as used on the U and ZA series tractors which are equipped with continuous type power take-off.

BELT PULLEY

Model GTA

285. Belt pulley is installed on right end of transmission powershaft. For service procedure, refer to Transmission, paragraph 165.

Model GTB and U Series

286. The belt pulley unit, Figs. MM 215 and 216, which is mounted on right side of transmission housing is driven by the integral transmission lower countershaft constant mesh gear and pulley bevel pinion.

Early production tractor models were equipped with a belt pulley unit which was constructed without any disengaging mechanism as shown in Fig. MM215. Later and current production belt pulley units are equipped with a positive drive clutch to engage or disengage the belt pulley unit, as shown in Figs. MM216 and 217.

287. **BEARING ADJUSTMENT.** Early production pulley shaft bearings can be adjusted without removing unit from tractor. Remove pulley or pulley shaft cover, and bearing cover (172—Fig. MM215). Straighten lip of lock washer (174) and rotate bearing adjusting nut (173) clockwise to reduce shaft end play. Bearings should be adjusted to provide zero end play to pulley shaft and yet permit shaft to rotate **without binding.** Lock adjustment by **bending lip of lock washer** into slot of bearing adjusting nut. The ball type bearings as used on late production units (Fig. MM216) are non-adjustable.

288. **GEAR MESH ADJUSTMENT.** Adjust belt pulley drive gear backlash to 0.006-0.008 by varying number of shims (S—Fig. MM215) or (20—Fig. MM216) located between pulley housing and transmission housing. To adjust position of pulley drive gear remove transmission top cover. Apply Prussian blue to gears, and check tooth contact. To correct heavy heel contact on pulley gear, remove shims (95—Fig. MM150) from between lower countershaft rear bearing cup and transmission housing; then, add shims (S—Fig. MM215) or (20—Fig. MM 216) between belt pulley housing and transmission case to re-establish correct backlash of 0.006-0.008. Removal of shims (95—Fig. MM150) requires removal of transmission Lower Countershaft as outlined in paragraph 190.

To correct a heavy toe contact on pulley gear, add shims (95—Fig. MM150) between lower countershaft rear bearing cup and transmission

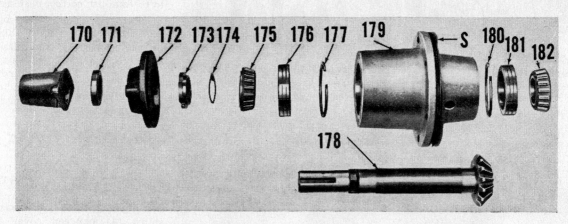

Fig. MM215—Belt pulley unit as used on early production U series and GTB models.

S. Shims	173. Bearing adjust-	176. Bearing cup	179. Housing
170. Shaft cover	ing nut	177. Snap ring	180. Snap ring
171. Oil seal	174. Lock washer	178. Pulley shaft &	181. Bearing cup
172. Bearing cover	175. Bearing cone	gear	182. Bearing cone

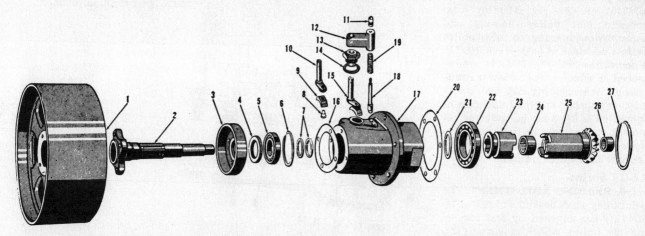

Fig. MM216—Belt pulley unit as used on late production U series and GTB models.

2. Drive shaft	8. Pin	16. Gasket	22. Inner ball bearing
3. Bearing retainer	9. Block	17. Housing	23. Sliding jaw
4. Oil seal	10. Shifting arm	18. Lock pin	24. Needle bearing
5. Ball bearing	12. Shift lever	19. Spring	25. Pulley drive pinion
6. Snap ring	13 & 14. Nut & gasket	20. Shims	26. Needle bearing
7. Snap ring	15. Shift arm	21. Snap ring	27. Snap ring

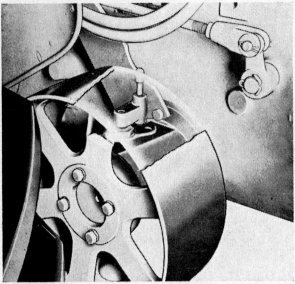

Fig. MM217—U series and model GTB belt pulley unit equipped with a hand-operated engaging mechanism. Early production tractor models were equipped with units which did not have this clutch.

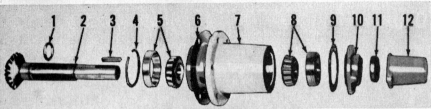

Fig. MM218—Exploded view of ZA series belt pulley unit. The ZT series is similar.

1. Snap ring
2. Pulley shaft
3. Key
4. Snap ring
5. Bearing
6. Shims
7. Housing
8. Bearing
9. Shims
10. Cover
11. Oil seal
12. Cover

Fig. MM220—Exploded view of R series belt pulley unit.

1. Shaft cover
2. Oil seal
3. Housing cover
4. Cover gasket
5. Outer bearing
6. Housing
7. Bearing retaining clip
8. Shim gasket
9. Snap ring
10. Inner bearing
11. Pulley key
12. Pulley shaft and gear

housing, and remove shims (S—Fig. MM215) or (20—Fig. MM216) from between belt pulley housing and transmission housing to re-establish correct backlash of 0.006-0.008. NOTE: When shims (95—Fig. MM150) are removed or added between lower countershaft rear bearing cup and transmission housing, an equal thickness of shims (86 & 87) must be added or removed, respectively, at the front bearing cup (88) to maintain lower countershaft bearing adjustment.

ZA-ZT Series

290. BEARING ADJUSTMENT. The belt pulley shaft bearings (5 & 8—Fig. MM218) are adjusted by first removing the pulley wheel or cover (12), removing cover (10) and adding or removing shims (9). Bearings should be adjusted to provide zero end play to pulley shaft and yet permit shaft to rotate without binding.

291. GEAR MESH ADJUSTMENT. Mesh position and backlash of the belt pulley drive bevel gears is controlled by shims (6—Fig. MM218) and (95—Fig. MM150). To adjust the gears, follow the procedure given in paragraph 288.

R Series

292. The R series pulley shaft is mounted in non-adjustable ball bearings.

293. GEAR MESH ADJUSTMENT. Adjust gear backlash to 0.006-0.008 by varying number of shims (8—Fig. MM 220) between pulley housing and transmission case. Apply bluing to gears and check tooth contact. To correct a heavy toe contact on the clutch shaft gear, add shims (4—Fig. MM118) between front of transmission case and clutch shaft transmission bearing outer race retaining ring; and add shims (8—Fig. MM220) between belt pulley housing and transmission case to re-establish correct backlash.

To correct a heavy toe contact on the pulley gear remove shims from between front of transmission case and clutch shaft transmission bearing outer race retaining ring; and remove shims from between belt pulley housing and transmission case to re-establish correct backlash.

POWER TAKE-OFF
Model GTA

300. BEARING ADJUSTMENT. Shims (14—Fig. MM222) between bearing cage (15) and housing and shims (4) between cover (7) and housing control bearing adjustment. Removing shims reduces bearing play. Remove an equal thickness of shims from both ends of housing to preserve original gear mesh adjustment.

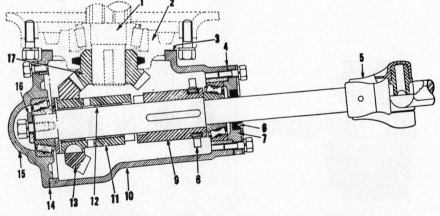

Fig. MM222—Sectional view of GTA power take-off unit.

1. Transmission powershaft
2. Powershaft bearing cage
3. Gear mesh shim
4. Bearing adjusting shim
5. Universal joint
6. Felt seal
7. Bearing cover
8. Shifter yoke
9. Clutch jaw
10. Housing
11. Hub and clutch jaw
12. Bushing
13. Bevel gear
14. Bearing adjusting shim
15. Bearing cage
16. Washer
17. Bevel pinion gear

301. R & R AND DISASSEMBLE. To remove the unit from the transmission housing, remove the cap screws retaining the power take-off housing to the transmission powershaft left bearing cage. Do not discard shims (3—Fig. MM222) from between PTO housing and bearing cage as they control backlash of PTO bevel gears.

The need and procedure for further disassembly will be evident after an examination of the parts and reference to Fig. MM222. If either or both bevel gears, or powershaft or PTO shaft, or PTO housing has been renewed, it will be necessary to check the gear mesh by bluing. Refer to Gear Mesh Adjustment, paragraph 302 for mesh adjustment procedure.

302. GEAR MESH ADJUSTMENT. Adjust gear backlash to 0.006-0.008 by varying number of shims (3) between PTO housing and powershaft bearing cage. Apply bluing to gears and check tooth contact. To correct a heavy toe contact on the PTO shaft bevel gear, remove shims (14) from between front bearing cage and housing and add shims (3) between PTO housing and powershaft bearing cage to re-establish correct backlash.

To correct a heavy toe contact on the powershaft bevel pinion gear, add shims (14) between front bearing cage and housing and remove shims (3) from between PTO housing and powershaft bearing cage to re-establish correct backlash. NOTE: When shims are removed or added at PTO shaft front bearing cage, an equal thickness must be added or removed, respectively, at the rear bearing cover to maintain PTO shaft bearing adjustment.

R Series

303. R & R AND DISASSEMBLY. Remove transmission cover and shifter forks and shafts as outlined in paragraphs 170 and 171. Remove the cap and oil seal assembly from the rear end of the PTO shaft. Remove cover plate (E — Fig. MM115) from left side of transmission case. Remove bearing cover shown in Fig. MM224. Remove castellated nut and washer from front end of shaft and push shaft rearward out of bearing.

As shaft is removed through the rear, gear front thrust washer (2—Fig. MM225), gear (3), gear rear thrust washer (4) and sliding jaw (5) can be withdrawn through top of transmission case. Bushings in gear and in differential case and oil seal in rear cap are renewable. Shifter fork (8) and shifter (10) can be removed from cover after removing pipe plugs, detent spring (6) and ball (7) and driving pin (9) out of shifter and fork.

Reassembly is reverse of disassembly. Install oil seal in rear cap with sharp edge of seal towards the differential. Gear rear thrust washer (4) (1½ inch diameter) should be installed with its inside bevel rearward. After installation, check to make certain that gear (3) has a slight amount of end play.

Model GTB and U-ZA-ZT Series

Model GTB and some U, ZA and ZT series tractors are equipped with the power take-off layout shown in Fig. MM230 and the system is known as a non-continuous type. On some late

Fig. MM224—Bearing cap removed from front end of R series power take-off shaft.

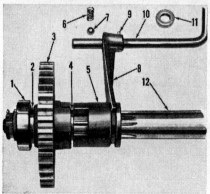

Fig. MM225—R series power take-off shaft, gear and shifter.

1. Bearing	7. Detent ball
2. Thrust washer	8. Shifter fork
3. Gear	9. Pin
4. Rear thrust washer	10. Shifter
5. Sliding jaw	11. Shifter seal
6. Detent ball spring	12. Shaft

Fig. MM230—Model GTB take-off unit, exploded view. Unit receives its power through connecting shaft (100) which is splined to rear end of transmission lower countershaft. Series U, ZA and ZT are similar, the differences of which are evident after an examination of the unit.

49. PTO shaft	189. Housing	197. Packing
50. PTO clutch jaw	190. Detent ball spring	198. Housing cap
100. Connecting shaft	191. Detent ball	199. Shim gasket
183. Shifter fork	192. Lever bracket	200. Bearing cone
184. Snap ring	193. Engaging lever	201. Bearing cup
185. Retaining washer	194. Engaging lever shaft	202. Collar for splined shaft
186. Felt seal	195. Shifter rail	203. Pilot bushing (in end of PTO
187. Gasket	196. Packing nut	connecting shaft)

production U and ZA series tractors, a disc type clutch is mounted on the left bull pinion sleeve and the clutch is used in conjunction with the shaft layout shown in Fig. MM230 to form a continuous type (live) power take-off.

Some early production U and ZT series tractors are equipped with the combination power take-off and power lift unit which is shown in Fig.

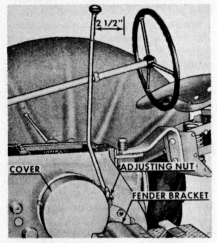

Fig. MM230A—U series continuous type power take-off clutch adjustment. The control lever should have a minimum of 2½ inches free travel. ZA series tractors are similar.

MM240 and discussed in paragraph 310.

305. CLUTCH ADJUSTMENT. To adjust the disc type power take-off clutch, refer to Fig. MM230A and proceed as follows: Turn the adjusting nut until the clutch control lever has a minimum of 2½ inches free travel.

306. CLUTCH OVERHAUL. The procedure for removing the power take-off clutch and power release mechanism is evident after an examination of the unit and reference to Figs. MM231, 233 and 234. Examine all parts and renew any which are questionable. When installing the power release mechanism on U series tractors, use two ½ x 1½ inch cap screws in the lower holes and one ½ x 6 inch cap screw in the upper hole as shown in Fig. MM231A. On ZA series tractors, the power release mechanism is retained by three ½ x 1½ inch cap screws. The remainder of the reassembly procedure is the reverse of the disassembly procedure. Adjust the clutch as outlined in the preceding paragraph (305).

307. BEARING ADJUSTMENT. Vary number of shims (199—Fig. MM 230) between housing cap (198) and housing (189) to provide zero end

play to PTO shaft, and yet permit same to rotate freely.

308. R & R AND DISASSEMBLE. Drain lubricant from transmission housing or raise rear of tractor far enough to prevent loss of lubricant from housing after PTO unit has been removed. Remove cap screws retaining PTO housing to rear of transmission housing and withdraw unit from transmission housing. To reinstall, reverse removal procedure. The need and procedure for further disassembly will be evident by an examination of the parts and reference to Fig. MM230.

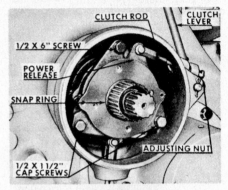

Fig. MM231A—U series power release mechanism installation. The ZA series is similar, except three equal length cap screws are used.

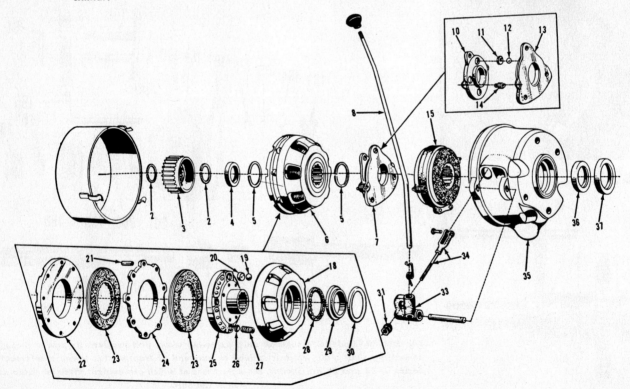

Fig. MM231—Exploded view of U series power release clutch unit which is mounted on the left bull pinion sleeve. The ZA series is similar except the clutch is of the single plate type.

2 & 5. Snap ring	10. Power release plate	18. Housing
3. Adapter gear	11. Ball insert	19. Ball
4. Oil seal	12. Ball	20. Insert
6. Clutch	13. Backing plate	21. Spacer
7. Power release	14. Spring	22. Cover plate
8. Release lever	15. Left brake	

23. Disc (lined)	31. Adjusting nut
24. Disc (unlined)	33. Fulcrum
25. Power plate	34. Release rod
26. Spring seat	35. Main housing
27. Spring	36. Inner oil seal
28, 29 & 30. Thrust bearing	37. Outer oil seal

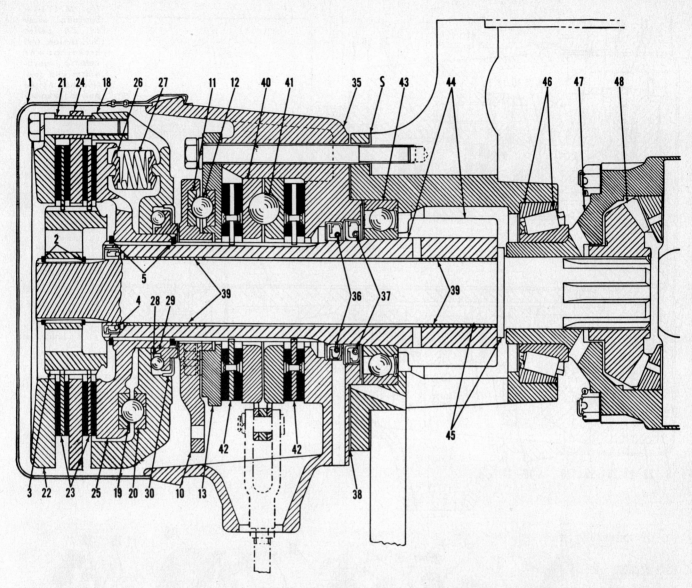

Fig. MM233—Sectional view of U series bull pinion, left brake, power release mechanism and continuous type power take-off clutch.

S. Shims
1. Cover
2. Snap ring
3. Adapter gear
4. Oil seal
5. Snap ring
10. Power release plate

11. Ball insert
12. Ball
13. Backing plate
18. Housing
19. Ball
20. Ball insert
21. Spacer

22. Cover plate
23. Lined disc
24. Disc (unlined)
25. Power plate
26. Spring seat
27. Spring
28, 29 & 30. Thrust bearing

35. Main housing
36. Inner oil seal
37. Outer oil seal
38. Gasket
39. Bushing
40. Actuating disc
41. Ball

42. Lined disc
43. Bearing
44. Bull pinion sleeve
45. Differential shaft (left)
46. Bearing cup & cone
47. Differential cage
48. Side gear

MECHANICAL POWER LIFT

U-ZT Series (Mechanical)

310. R & R AND DISASSEMBLE.
Disconnect the lifting link and the pedal spring and proceed as follows:

Drain lubricant from transmission housing or raise rear of tractor far enough to prevent loss of lubricant from housing after the unit has been removed. Remove cap screws retaining PTO and power lift housing to rear of transmission housing.

The procedure for disassembly and overhaul of the unit is evident after an examination of Fig. MM240.

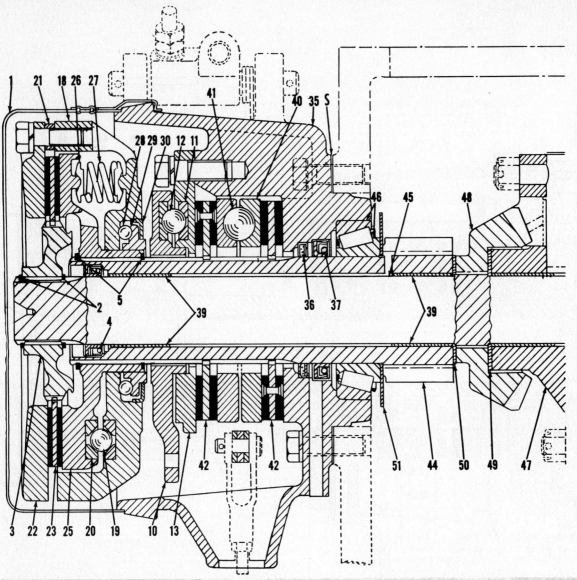

Fig. MM234—Sectional view of ZA series bull pinion, left brake, power release mechanism and continuous type power take-off clutch.

S. Shims
1. Cover
2. Snap ring
3. Adapter gear
4. Oil seal
5. Snap ring
10. Power release plate
11. Ball insert
12. Ball
13. Backing plate
18. Housing
19. Ball
20. Ball insert
21. Spacer
22. Cover plate
23. Lined disc
25. Power plate
26. Spring seat
27. Spring
28, 29 & 30. Thrust bearing
35. Main housing
36. Inner oil seal
37. Outer oil seal
39. Bushing
40. Actuating disc
41. Ball
42. Lined disc
44. Bull pinion sleeve
45. Differential shaft
46. Bearing cup & cone
47. Differential cage
48. Side gear
49. Thrust washer
50. Washer
51. Deflector

Fig. MM240—Exploded view of ZT and early U series combination power lift and power take-off unit.

1. Pedal crank key
2. Pedal
3. Side cover
4. Pedal crank
5. Clutch release disc
6. Pawl wheel
7. Pawl roller pin
8. Long pawl roller
9. Long pawl spring
10. Long pawl
11. Worm gear and clutch
12. Cross shaft
13. Housing
14. Cross shaft bearing
15. Leather washer
16. Cross shaft bearing cover
17. Lifting arm
18. Housing cap
19. Packing
20. Packing nut
21. Shaft guard
22. Splined shaft
23. Snap ring
24. Shaft rear bearing (double row ball)
25. Spacer
26. Worm gear
27. Shaft front bearing (single row ball)
28. Sliding clutch jaw
29. Pilot bushing
30. Connecting shaft
31. Worm gear key
32. Shifter rod
33. Detent ball spring
34. Detent ball
35. Felt retainer
36. Felt
37. Shifter fork
38. Pawl wheel key
39. Short retarder pawl
40. Retainer pawl pivot pin
41. Long retarder pawl
42. Retarder pawl spring (2)
43. Long pawl pivot pin
44. Pedal crank roller
45. Crank oil seal
46. Pedal spring
47. Clip for pedal spring

HYDRAULIC LIFT

First factory installations of hydraulic lift system were made on model R tractors which utilized a piston type pump and valves unit mounted on side of engine as shown in Figs. MM235, 236, 237 and 238. The available brief service information on this system is contained in paragraphs 311 and 312.

Later model R tractors and models GTB, series U and ZA are equipped with the MM Uni-Matic hydraulic system which is covered by the paragraphs beginning with 320.

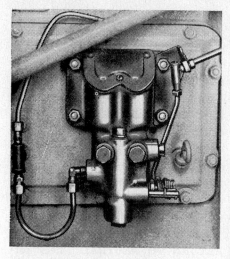

Fig. MM235—Early R series power lift hydraulic pump installation.

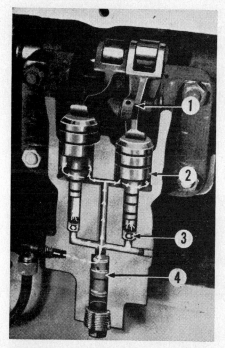

Fig. MM236—Sectional view through inlet system of early R series power lift hydraulic pump.

1. Rocker arm
2. Plunger
3. Check valve
4. Inlet valve

Fig. MM237—Sectional view through discharge system of early R series power lift hydraulic pump. "B" is one of two discharge valves.

Fig. MM238—Sectional view through relief valve of early R series power lift hydraulic pump, "V" is relief valve.

The maintenance of absolute cleanliness of all parts is of utmost importance in the operation and servicing of the hydraulic system. Of equal importance is the avoidance of nicks or burrs on any of the working parts.

R Series (Piston Type Pump)

311. REMOVE AND REINSTALL. To remove hydraulic pump unit from the engine, disconnect the control lever, the oil inlet line and oil outlet hose. Remove the nuts retaining the pump to the crankcase side cover and lift off the pump leaving the control bracket on the control rod.

312. OVERHAUL. Refer to Figs. MM235 to MM238. Remove the pump as outlined in paragraph 310. Normal overhaul of the pump consists of cleaning and renewing excessively worn parts. The procedure for disassembling the pump is evident after an examination of the unit.

Procedure for overhauling the early R series lift jack is evident after an examination of the unit and reference to Fig. MM239.

Uni-Matic Hydraulic System

PUMP
GTB-R-U-ZA Series

320. The positive displacement eccentric rotor type pump, Fig. MM245, is mounted on rear face of accessory housing (integral with timing gear case) and receives its drive from the accessory shaft.

To remove pump unit, first drain reservoir. Disconnect short hose from pump inlet tube to reservoir connection. Remove the pump retaining cap screws, and remove pump from tractor.

To disassemble pump unit, remove three cap screws retaining pump cover to pump body. All pump parts can now be removed. Install oil seal (18) with lip of seal facing pump unit. Service bushing (13) requires final sizing after installation to provide 0.003-0.005 diametral clearance.

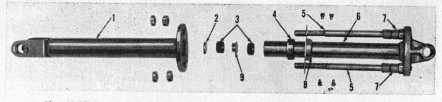

Fig. MM239—Exploded view of early R series power lift jack assembly.

1. Outer cylinder and plunger
2. Cup seal seat
3. Cup seal
4. Dust seal
5. Stud
6. Inner cylinder
7. Spacer
8. Steel cap
9. Spacer

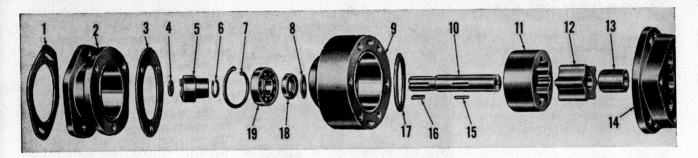

Fig. MM245—Eaton pump used with MM Uni-Matic hydraulic system. Items (11) and (12) are renewed as a unit.

1. Gasket
2. Pump adapter
3. Adapter gasket
4. Coupling washer
5. Shaft coupling
6. Snap ring
7. Bearing snap ring
8. Oil ring
9. Pump body
10. Pump shaft
11. Outer rotor
12. Inner rotor
13. Shaft bushing
14. Cover
15. Rotor key
16. Coupling key
17. Cover gasket
18. Oil seal
19. Shaft bearing

LIFTING JACK (RAM)
GTB-R-U-ZA Series

321. The lifting jack (ram) is of the double acting type. Refer to Fig. MM246.

With the lifting jack (ram) removed from tractor, proceed to disassemble the unit as follows: Remove ram head from rod end of ram, and bearing cap (29) from cylinder. With bearing cap removed, "O" ring seal and felt seal can be renewed. Withdraw piston from cylinder. Remove both relief valve assemblies and push rod (26).

The relief valves can be reseated by using a soft drift against the valve, and bumping the valve against the valve seat.

RESERVOIR AND CONTROL VALVE
GTB-R-U-ZA Series

322. The hydraulic unit reservoir contains the system filter, strainer, control linkage, and control valve.

To remove control valve, first drain the reservoir. Remove double oil line flange from reservoir and disconnect control lever from reservoir cross arm; then, remove control valve body. Control valve body contains a non-adjustable relief valve which is serviced only as a complete unit with the control valve body.

To remove reservoir unit, first drain reservoir. Remove fuel tank, and double oil line flange from reservoir. Disconnect control lever from reservoir cross arm. Remove bolts retaining reservoir bracket to tractor. Disassembly is self-evident after an examination of the unit and with reference to Fig. MM247.

Refill reservoir only when lifting jack (ram) is in the retracted position.

TROUBLE-SHOOTING
GTB-R-U-ZA Series

323. NOISY PUMP OR SYSTEM. Check oil level and all pump inlet connections.

324. SLOW RAM ACTION. Worn pump and/or relief valves are set too low. Relief valves are non-adjustable and should be serviced only as an assembly with the control valve.

325. CONTROL LEVER DOES NOT RETURN TO NEUTRAL. Check for binding linkage.

326. RAM WILL NOT STAY IN RAISED POSITION. Disassemble and clean ram unit. Reseat check valves and renew all ram gaskets and seals.

327. FOAMING OIL IN RESERVOIR. Check and renew all pump inlet seals and tighten all connections.

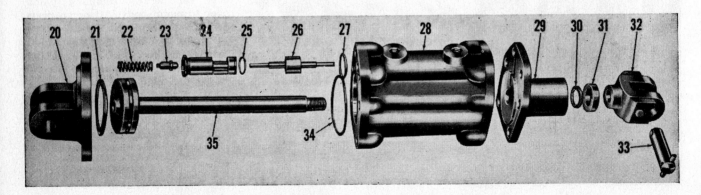

Fig. MM246—Lifting jack assembly used in Uni-Matic hydraulic system.

20. Cylinder head
21. Piston "O" ring
22. Relief spring
23. Relief valve lockout
24. Valve cage (2)
25. Cage "O" ring
26. Push rod & plunger
27. Cap gasket
28. Jack cylinder
29. Bearing cap
30. Rod "O" ring
31. Oil seal
32. Clevis
33. Clevis pin
34. Cap gasket
35. Piston & rod

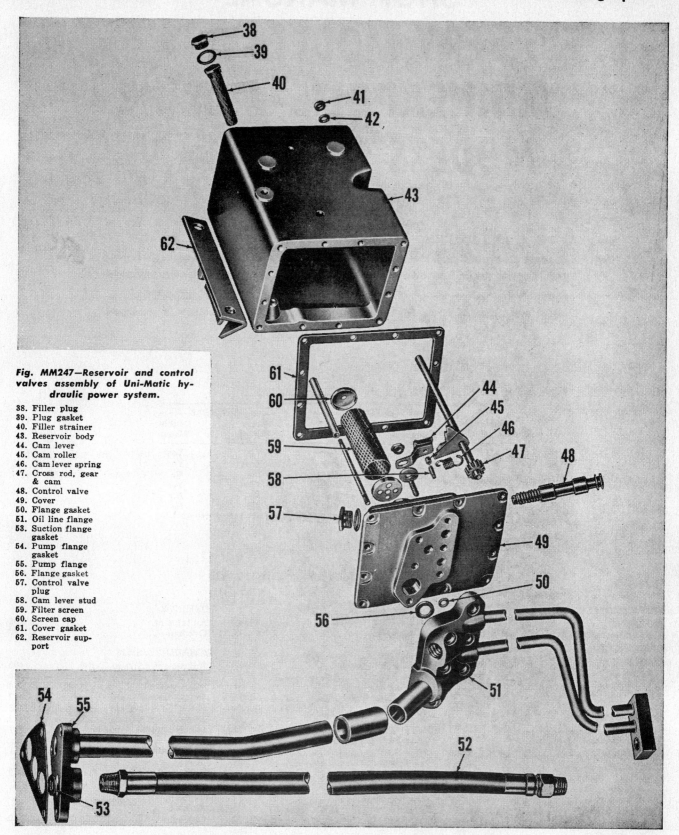

Fig. MM247—Reservoir and control valves assembly of Uni-Matic hydraulic power system.

38. Filler plug
39. Plug gasket
40. Filler strainer
43. Reservoir body
44. Cam lever
45. Cam roller
46. Cam lever spring
47. Cross rod, gear & cam
48. Control valve
49. Cover
50. Flange gasket
51. Oil line flange
53. Suction flange gasket
54. Pump flange gasket
55. Pump flange
56. Flange gasket
57. Control valve plug
58. Cam lever stud
59. Filter screen
60. Screen cap
61. Cover gasket
62. Reservoir support

SHOP MANUAL
B. F. AVERY MODELS A, R and V
MINNEAPOLIS-MOLINE
MODELS BF, BG and V

IDENTIFICATION

Models A, BF, BG and R tractor serial numbers are stamped on right frame rail. Engine serial number is stamped on plate on right side of crankcase.

Model V tractor serial number is stamped on top of frame rail adjacent to right hand side of flywheel bell housing. Engine serial number is stamped on plate on left side of crankcase.

BUILT IN THESE VERSIONS

Tractor Model	AXLE		TRICYCLE	
	Non-Adjustable	Adjustable	Single Wheel	Double Wheel
A	No	Yes	Yes	Yes
R	No	Yes	Yes	Yes
V	Yes	No	No	No
BF	No	Yes	Yes	Yes
BG	No	Yes	No	No
MM-V	No	Yes	No	No

INDEX   (By Starting Paragraph)

CONDENSED SERVICE DATA

TRACTOR MODEL	Avery A	MM BF BG	Avery R	Avery & MM V
GENERAL				
Engine Make	←————————Hercules————————→			
Engine Model	IXA 3 IXK 3 IXB 3	IXB 3SL	IXB 3SL	ZXB 3
Cylinders	4	4	4	4
Bore-Inches				
(IXA 3 & ZXB)	3			2 5/8
(IXK 3)	3 1/8			
(IXB 3 & IXB 3SL)	3 1/4	3 1/4	3 1/4	
Stroke-Inches	4	4	4	3
Displacement-Cubic Inches				
(IXA 3 & ZXB 3)	113			65
(IXK 3)	123			
(IXB 3 & IXB 3SL)	133	133	133	
Compression Ratio	6.5	6.5	6.5	6.5
Pistons Removed From	←————————Above————————→			
Main Brgs., Number of	3	3	3	3
Main Brgs., Adjustable	←————Yes only on IXA, IXK & ZXB————→			
Rod Bearings, Adjustable	←————Yes only on IXA, IXK & ZXB————→			
Cylinder Sleeves (IXB 3SL)		Dry	Dry	
Forward Speeds	3	4	4	3
Generator Make (latest)	D-R	D-R	D-R	D-R
Generator Model	1101851	1101856	1101856	1101856
Starter Make (latest)	D-R	D-R	D-R	D-R
Starter Model	1109602	1109609	1109609	1109604
TUNE-UP				
Firing Order	←————————1-2-4-3————————→			
Valve Tappet Gap Inlet	←————————.006H————————→			
Valve Tappet Gap—Exhaust	.008H	.008H	.008H	.006H
Inlet & Exh. Valve Face Angle	30	30	30	30
Inlet & Exh. Seat Angle	30	30	30	30
Ignition Distributor Make	←————Auto-Lite or Delco-Remy————→			
Model (Delco) Latest	1111714	1111736	1111736	1111715
Model (Auto-Lite) Latest	IAD4023A			IAD4010C
Breaker Gap Distributor	←————————.018-.024————————→			
Distributor Timing—Retarded	TC	TC	TC	TC
Flywheel Mark Indicating:				
Distributor Timing—Retarded	DC	DC	DC	DC
Spark Plug—Make	Ch.	Ch.	Ch.	Ch.
Spark Plug—Model	H10	J8	J8	H10
Carburetor Make	Til.	M-S	M-S	Til.
Carburetor Model (latest)	YC10A	TSX	TSX	YC6A
Carburetor Float Setting	1 5/64	1/4	1/4	1 5/64
Engine Low Idle RPM	450	550	550	550
Engine No Load RPM (Belt)	1700	1950	1950	1950
Engine No Load RPM (Drawbar)	1450	1950	1950	1950
Belt Pulley No Load RPM	1037	1225	1225	2140
PTO No Load RPM	550	559	559	540
SIZES-CAPACITIES-CLEARANCES				
(Clearances in Thousandths)				
Crankshaft Journal Diameter	1.9875	1.9875	1.9875	1.9875
Crankpin Diameter	1.7475	1.7475	1.7475	1.4975
Camshaft Journal Diameter	1.5955	1.5955	1.5955	1.2625
Piston Pin Diameter	0.749	0.749	0.749	0.6868
Valve Stem Diameter, Nominal	5/16	5/16	5/16	1/4
Compression Ring Width	1/8	1/8	1/8	1/8
Oil Ring Width	0.1875	0.1875	0.1875	0.1875
Main Bearings Run. Clearance	2-2½	2-2½	2-2½	2-2½
Rod Bearings Run. Clearance	1-1½	1-1½	1-1½	1-1½
Piston Skirt Clearance (Alum.)	2½-3	2½-3	2½-3	2-2½
Piston Skirt Clearance (Iron)	3-3½	3-3½	3-3½	2½-3
Crankshaft End Play	←————————2-4————————→			
Camshaft Bearing Clearance	←————————1½-2½————————→			
Cooling System—Gallons	2¾	2¾	2¾	1½
Crankcase Oil—Quarts	5	5	5	3
Transmission—Qts. (No BP or PTO)	8	9	9	2½
Transmission—Qts. (With BP & PTO)	10	11	11	3
Final Drive, Each—Qts.	←————————1½————————→			
Torque Ft. Lbs. Cylinder Head	45	45	45	35
Torque Ft. Lbs. Main Bearing Bolts	77	77	77	77
Torque Ft. Lbs. Rod Bearing Bolts	42	42	42	25

Minneapolis-Moline Model BF. Avery Models A and R were similarly constructed.

FRONT SYSTEM AND STEERING

AXLE AND KNUCKLES

Models A-BF-BG-R-V

1. Lemoine type integral spindles and knuckles are retained in the axle extensions or center members by steering arms which are secured to the spindles by clamp bolts or by set screws as shown in Figs. A1 and A3. On early production model V, the knuckle bushings are of the flanged type to take thrust; whereas on the other models, the thrust is taken by a separate thrust bearing.

2. On BF, BG and R, the front axle pivot pin bushings are of the same dimensions and carry the same parts number as the knuckle bushings. Axle and radius rod pivot bushings used on the Avery built model V are pre-sized. On this model, a renewable wear plate is located between the pivot block and the bell housing.

Fig. A1 — Adjustable type front axle with integral radius rod used on model V Avery tractors built by Minneapolis - Moline. In this installation the center steering arm (29) pivots in a bushing (6) in the axle. Center hole in arm receives the drag link (31) the opposite end of which attaches to the steering arm (30) mounted on the Ross cam and lever steering gear.

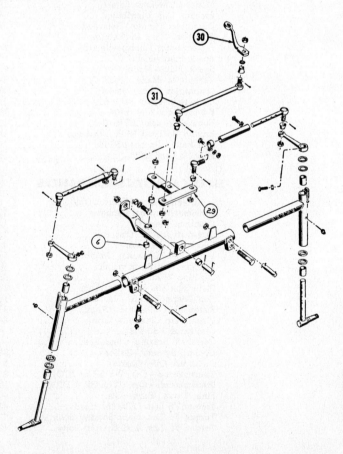

STEERING, TRICYCLE & AXLE TYPES
Models A-BF-R

On early production tricycle type tractors, the wheel carrying element is integral with the steering vertical spindle as shown in Fig. A2.

On later production tricycle type tractors, the fork (23—Fig. A4) or lower spindle assembly (51) is detachably bolted to the steering vertical spindle (29A).

Two adjustments are provided namely the upper spindle (worm wheel shaft) end play and the steering worm end play. Excessive backlash in the gear is corrected by repositioning the worm wheel on its splines or by renewal of the mating gears. Worm wheel shaft (vertical spindle) and wormshaft are carried in adjustable type roller bearings.

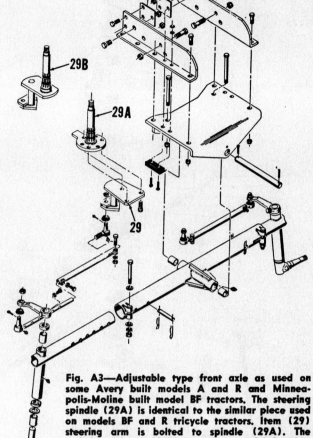

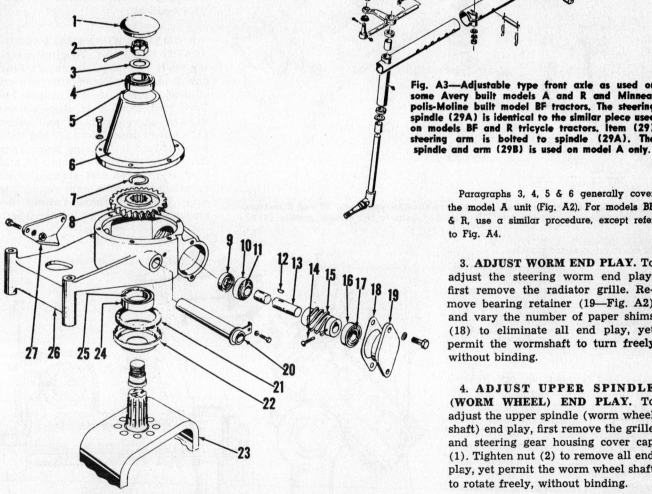

Fig. A3—Adjustable type front axle as used on some Avery built models A and R and Minneapolis-Moline built model BF tractors. The steering spindle (29A) is identical to the similar piece used on models BF and R tricycle tractors. Item (29) steering arm is bolted to spindle (29A). The spindle and arm (29B) is used on model A only.

Paragraphs 3, 4, 5 & 6 generally cover the model A unit (Fig. A2). For models BF & R, use a similar procedure, except refer to Fig. A4.

3. ADJUST WORM END PLAY. To adjust the steering worm end play, first remove the radiator grille. Remove bearing retainer (19—Fig. A2) and vary the number of paper shims (18) to eliminate all end play, yet permit the wormshaft to turn freely without binding.

4. ADJUST UPPER SPINDLE (WORM WHEEL) END PLAY. To adjust the upper spindle (worm wheel shaft) end play, first remove the grille and steering gear housing cover cap (1). Tighten nut (2) to remove all end play, yet permit the worm wheel shaft to rotate freely, without binding.

5. BACKLASH CORRECTION. To correct excessive backlash, it is necessary to either reposition the original worm wheel on its splines or to renew the worm wheel or wheel and worm. Procedure is to first remove the grille, radiator, steering housing

Fig. A2—Steering system details for axle and tricycle type model A tractors. Note that wheel fork (23) is integral with the steering verticle spindle.

1. Housing cover cap	10. Rear bearing cup	19. Bearing retainer
2. Spindle nut	11. Rear bearing cone	20. Starting crank tube
3. Upper bearing washer	12. Woodruff key	21. Felt
4. Upper bearing cone	13. Worm shaft	22. Housing bottom cover
5. Upper bearing cup	14. Worm rivet	23. Fork and spindle
6. Housing cover	15. Worm	24. Lower bearing cup
7. Worm gear snap ring	16. Front bearing cup	25. Lower bearing cone
8. Worm gear	17. Front bearing cone	26. Steering housing
9. Worm shaft oil seal	18. Shim	27. Front wheel stop

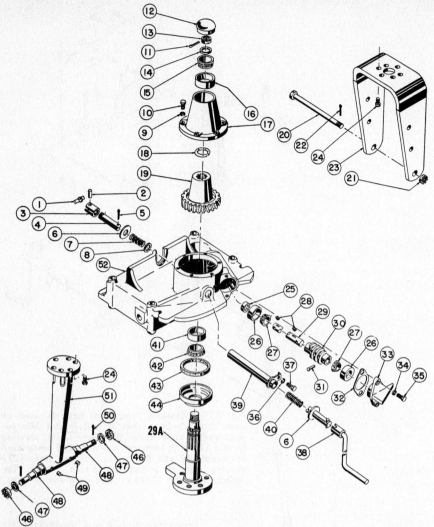

of the unit or by reference to Figs. A2 and A3. On models such as the BF, where the worm wheel shaft (upper spindle) is bolted to a front wheel carrying element, it is generally more convenient to unbolt the lower wheel carrying element from the upper spindle before removing the latter from the housing. Housing and gear unit can be removed from tractor by first removing the radiator, the starting crank and tube unit and the housing retaining cap screws.

Model V

On both Avery built and MM built model V tractors the steering is by a Ross cam and lever automobile type gear mounted back of the engine on the frame side rail. The gear is provided with an adjustment for control of the wormshaft (camshaft) end play and a second adjustment which controls backlash.

7. **ADJUST WORMSHAFT (CAMSHAFT) END PLAY.** To adjust steering shaft end play, disconnect drag link from Pitman arm and back-off adjusting screw (16—Fig. A5) to relieve load from lever stud. Loosen housing upper cover oil seal collar (11), unbolt upper cover (7) and slide same upward on steering shaft. Vary the number of shims (6) until all end play is removed and steering shaft turns freely or with only perceptible drag. Removing shims reduces the amount of end play in the wormshaft.

Fig. A4—Steering system details for axle and tricycle type model BF and R tractors. On axle models a steering arm (29—Fig. A3) bolts to the vertical spindle (29A).

1,2&3. Universal joint	31. Rivet
4. Starting crank shaft	32. Shims
12. Housing cover cap	33. Bearing retainer
13. Nut	38. Starting crank
15&16. Upper bearing	39. Starting crank tube
17. Housing cover	40. Spring
18. Snap ring	41&42. Upper bearing
23. Wheel fork	43. Felt
25. Oil seal	44. Bottom cover
26&27. Bearing	48. Spindle
28. Woodruff keys	49. Dowel pin
29. Wormshaft	51. Spindle assembly
30. Worm	52. Housing

cover cap (1) and nut (2). Remove housing cover (6) and snap ring (7). Remove worm wheel and carefully examine teeth of same for wear. If the consecutive teeth in ½ of the wheel appear unworn, reinstall the wheel in such a position that the unworn teeth will be presented to the worm. If all teeth are worn, install a new worm wheel.

6. **OVERHAUL.** Normal overhaul of the gear unit can be accomplished without removing the housing from the tractor by first removing the grille and radiator. The appropriate next steps are evident from an examination

Fig. A5—Ross cam and lever steering gear assembly used on model V tractors.

1. Retaining ring	6. Shims	10. Spring	14. Lever shaft
2. Bearing outer race	7. Upper cover	11. Collar	15. Housing cover
3. Lower bearing	8. Cork seal	12. Steering arm	16. Adjusting screw
4. Cam	9. Retainer	13. Oil seal	17. Lever shaft bushings
5. Upper bearing			

8. ADJUST BACKLASH. To adjust the gear unit backlash, first adjust the steering shaft (wormshaft) end play as outlined in paragraph 7, then proceed as follows: Place the steering wormshaft in the mid or straight ahead position (half way between full right and full left turn). Tighten adjusting screw (16) until all backlash is removed and a slight drag is felt when turning the s t e e r i n g shaft through this mid-position. If backlash is adjusted correctly there will be and should be some backlash in the gear when it is turned right or left from mid-position.

9. OVERHAUL. The lever shaft can be removed from the gear housing without removing the gear unit from the tractor. Wormshaft is removed upward through top of gear housing.

Inner and outer Pitman lever shaft bushings (17) should be renewed when the clearance between the lever shaft and bushings exceeds 0.004. These bushings should be pressed in position and reamed after installation to provide 0.001-0.0015 clearance for the lever shaft. Wear in the camshaft bearings (3) and (5) is rarely corrected by renewing only the cups and ball elements; usually it is necessary to renew the cam which is also the inner races.

Use Fig. A5 as a general guide during reassembly, and adjust the unit as outlined in paragraphs 7 and 8.

Model BG

10. ADJUSTMENT. Disconnect drag link from Pitman arm (16-Fig. A5A), back off adjusting screw (13) and

loosen clamp (7). Unbolt the gear housing upper cover (8), slide same upward on steering shaft and vary the thickness of shims (9) until all end play is removed and wormshaft turns freely or with only perceptible drag. Shims are available in thicknesses of 0.002, 0.003 and 0.010.

After the wormshaft end play is properly adjusted, turn steering wheel until the gear unit is in the mid or straight ahead position and tighten adjusting screw (13) until all backlash

is removed and a slight drag is felt when turning the s t e e r i n g shaft through this mid-position.

11. OVERHAUL. The procedure for disassembling the steering gear is evident after an examination of the unit. Bushings (14) for the lever shaft are renewable. Ream the bushings after installation, if necessary, to provide the I&T recommended clearance of 0.001-0.0015 for the lever shaft. After assembly, adjust the unit as outlined in the preceding paragraph.

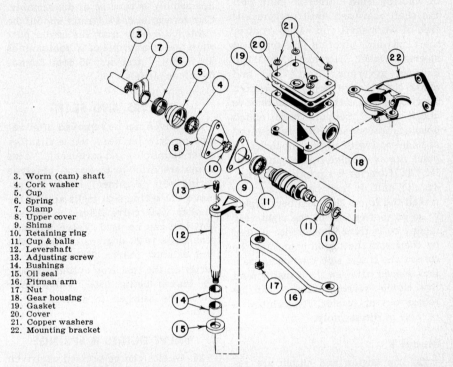

3. Worm (cam) shaft
4. Cork washer
5. Cup
6. Spring
7. Clamp
8. Upper cover
9. Shims
10. Retaining ring
11. Cup & balls
12. Levershaft
13. Adjusting screw
14. Bushings
15. Oil seal
16. Pitman arm
17. Nut
18. Gear housing
19. Gasket
20. Cover
21. Copper washers
22. Mounting bracket

Fig. A5A—Exploded view of Minneapolis-Moline model BG steering gear. Wormshaft end play is adjusted with shims (9). Backlash is adjusted with screw (13).

ENGINE AND COMPONENTS

Model A

20. Three different models of Hercules engines have been used. The original IXA-3 model (3-inch bore) was replaced by the IXK-3 model (3⅛-inch bore) which was later replaced by the IXB-3 model (3¼-inch bore). Except for the cylinder bore, the only major difference in these engine models is their bearing construction. The IXA-3 and IXK-3 connecting rod bearings are of the cast-in babbitt type while the main bearings have cast-in babbitt caps but removable, bronze-back inserts in the upper half. Both connecting rod and main bearings are provided with shims for adjustment. The IXB-3 main and connecting rod bearings are bronze-back, precision insert type.

The four bearing camshaft driven from the crankshaft by metal timing gears operates a conventional "L" head valve system through mushroom type tappets (cam followers). A helical gear pressed into the front end of the camshaft drives a battery ignition distributor mounted on the timing gear case cover. A governor drive gear mounted on the right side of the engine and driven by the camshaft gear, drives a centrifugal governor housed in the timing gear compartment. The governor shaft extends through the rear of the timing gear case where it drives the magneto or hydraulic pump unit on tractors so equipped. A gear type oil pump located in the oil pan and driven from a

helical gear on the center of the camshaft, supplies oil under pressure to the main and connecting rod bearings.

Models BF-BG-R

These models are equipped with the Hercules IXB-3SL engine. This engine is a duplicate of the IXB-3 (used in late model A tractors) except that it has dry cylinder sleeves as indicated by the suffix "SL".

Model V

21. The Hercules model ZXB-3 engine (2⅝-inch bore) is used in this series of tractors. This engine is similar to the IXA-3 and IXK-3 models and uses the same bearing construction; the only major difference being the engine size.

REMOVE AND REINSTALL

Models A-BF-BG-R

22. The engine and clutch are removed as an assembly. Remove hood and side plates, grille and radiator, muffler, fuel tank and hydraulic lines from hydraulic pump to unit. Disconnect engine front mount from timing gear cover. Disconnect steering shaft support from fuel tank support. Remove riveted pin from forward end of steering shaft universal joint, pull the shaft rearward until universal is free of wormshaft and swing front of shaft outward, pivoting on support at steering wheel. Disconnect electrical harness, governor throttle rod and choke control wire. Remove tube from air cleaner and carburetor and remove choke control support from clutch housing. Disconnect clutch release rod at pedal and with engine supported in hoist, remove engine rear mount bolts. NOTE: If tractor is equipped with hydraulic unit, it may be necessary to spread the frame side members slightly so as to free one of the right rear mount bolts from interference caused by the hydraulic piston connector. To spread the frame side members, use a jack placed between them just behind the clutch housing. Engine can be raised out of tractor. Reassembly is reverse of disassembly.

Model V

23. The engine and clutch are removed as an assembly. Remove hood and side plates, grille and radiator, starting motor, steering gear and steering gear shaft. Disconnect electrical harness and withdraw it rearward through hole in left side of bell housing. Remove propeller shaft cover. (To permit removal of cover after bolts have been removed, it is necessary to hold clutch in the disengaged position.) Disconnect clutch release rod at pedal, throttle rod at governor and choke control wire at carburetor. Disconnect radius rod at bell housing and front engine mount at frame cross member. Support engine in hoist and remove engine rear mounting bolts. Remove cotter pin retaining propeller shaft universal joint to clutch shaft and lift out engine. Reassembly is reverse of disassembly. Be sure that cotter pin hole in clutch shaft lines up with hole in propeller shaft universal joint and that starter rod and governor throttle rod are in proper position in rear engine mount spacer blocks.

CYLINDER HEAD

24. The cast iron cylinder head is retained to the block by cap screws on models A, BF, BG and R and by both cap screws and studs and nuts on the model V. To remove the cylinder head, remove the hood and muffler. Remove cylinder head cap screws and nuts from cylinder head studs and remove brackets for oil filter, coil, circuit breaker and air cleaner. Disconnect water outlet hose and remove head. Reassembly is reverse of disassembly. Cap screws and stud nuts should be tightened evenly from the center outward and to a torque of 35 foot pounds for model V tractors; 45 foot pounds for other models.

VALVES AND SEATS

25. Valves can be removed after removing cylinder head, valve chamber cover, manifolds and carburetor. Valve stems are fitted with round pin type spring seat (retainer) locks. To remove the spring seat locks any of the smaller K-D valve lifters or equivalent tool can be used. Valve face and seat angle is 30 degrees on both inlet and exhaust valves. Valves seat directly on the cast iron cylinder block; no inserts being used. Valve seats should be finished to a width of ⅛ inch.

VALVE GUIDES & SPRINGS

26. Guides can be pressed or driven out of the block through the valve chamber. Before removing old guides, measure the distance they protrude into valve chamber and install new guides to the same measurement. All guides of any one model should extend the same distance into the valve compartment. Check inside diameter of new guides after installation and re-size, if necessary, by reaming. Clearance between valve stem and guide should be 0.001-0.003 on all models. Intake and exhaust valve springs are interchangeable in any one model.

CAM FOLLOWERS (TAPPETS)

27. Valve tappets, which operate directly in bores in the cylinder block, are of the mushroom type fitted with an adjusting screw and locknut. Removal of valve tappets requires removal of camshaft. Clearance between tappet and cylinder block is 0.00075-0.001.

Pertinent data on valve system are listed below:

Inlet tappet gap, hot..........0.006

Exhaust tappet gap, hot
(A-BF-BG-R) 0.008
Exhaust tappet gap, hot (V)....0.006
Stem diameter (A-BF-BG-R)....0.310
Stem diameter (V)...........0.2475
Guide inside diameter
(A-BF-BG-R) 0.312
Guide inside diameter (V)......0.2495
Spring tension
(A-BF-BG-R) ..40-44 lbs. @ 1 3/16
Spring tension (V) 33-37 lbs. @ 59/64
Valve & seat angle..............30°

VALVE TIMING

28. Valves are correctly timed when the punch mark on the camshaft gear lines up with the punch mark on the crankshaft gear (Fig. A6). With intake valve tappet adjusted to 0.006 inch, intake valve opens 5 degrees or 1½ flywheel teeth past top dead center.

TIMING GEAR COVER

29. The timing gear cover can be removed without removing the engine. Remove hood and side plates, grille and radiator, fan assembly, crankshaft pulley and governor assembly. Remove cap screws retaining cover to engine (on "V" series be sure to remove cover retaining cap screw (1—Fig. A7) located inside cover behind governor assembly. This cap screw is safe-tied with a wire where it protrudes through the rear of the timing gear case). Remove the four cap screws retaining oil pan to timing gear cover, loosen balance of oil pan cap screws and carefully part timing gear cover from oil pan gasket. Pull timing gear cover and front oil seal forward and lift cover off the seal. Oil seal can be slid off front of crankshaft. When installing new crankshaft front oil seal (4—Fig. A8) place seal on shaft with feather edge toward crankshaft gear.

Fig. A6—Marks on gears for timing valves, all models.

TIMING GEARS

30. Camshaft gear removal requires removal of camshaft. Refer to paragraph 33 for removal procedure. With camshaft removed, press gear off the camshaft towards the rear. When installing a gear on the camshaft, be sure that front face of gear is seated against rear face of camshaft front shoulder.

31. The distributor drive gear (2—Fig. A8) on the front of the camshaft is not a replaceable item. The camshaft and distributor drive gear are furnished as a unit.

32. Crankshaft gear is a tight press fit on the crankshaft. To remove this gear it is necessary to either remove the frame front cross member or the engine.

Fig. A7—Front view of engine showing cover cap screw (1) behind governor, governor shaft rear bearing (2) on model V and screw (3) for internally adjusting end play of camshaft.

Due to the extremely tight fit of this gear it is almost impossible to pull it from the crankshaft with any of the commercial pullers. If a suitable arbor press is not available or if it is desired to remove the gear without removing the shaft from the engine, Hercules recommends splitting the gear after first drilling through with a ¼ inch drill midway between the edge of the keyway and the base of the teeth. A mild application of heat on the crankshaft gear of 450°F. or when gear turns a pale straw yellow will facilitate its reinstallation. Crankshaft gear backlash should be 0.000 to 0.002.

CAMSHAFT AND BEARINGS

33. To remove the camshaft, remove oil pan and oil pump, governor assembly and timing gear cover. With valve tappets held up by nails as shown in Fig. A9, withdraw camshaft from front of engine. On models A, BF and R, it is necessary to remove the steering housing (pedestal) or the engine to permit removal of the camshaft.

Reassembly is reverse of disassembly. Be sure bronze thrust washer is installed on camshaft between camshaft gear and cylinder block.

34. Camshaft bearings can be driven out and renewed. New bearings do not require final sizing if installed carefully. Clearance of camshaft in the bearings should be 0.0015 to 0.0025.

Oil leakage from camshaft rear bearing is prevented by the gasket installed between the cylinder block and flywheel housing. Camshaft end play

is controlled by an adjustable fibre tipped screw (3—Fig. A7) in timing gear cover. To obtain correct end play, turn screw in until it just contacts thrust button in shaft then back-out ⅛ turn.

34A. **PERTINENT DATA.** Pertinent data applying to camshaft and bearings are tabulated below:

Shaft Running Clearance 0.0015-0.0025
Preferred Running Clearance....0.002
Journal Diameter (A-BF-BG-R) 1.5955
Journal Diameter (V)..........1.2625
Number of Bearings................4

R & R OF ROD & PISTON UNITS

35. Connecting rod and piston assemblies are removable from above after removing cylinder head and oil pan. Connecting rods are numbered on the camshaft side. Aluminum pistons in engines which rotate clockwise should be installed with the split or "T" slot on the side opposite the camshaft.

PISTONS AND SLEEVES

36. Trunk type cast iron pistons with bronze bushed piston pin bosses are used in model V tractors equipped with the Hercules ZX engines and some of the IX series engines used in model A tractors. Split skirt aluminum pistons are also supplied for the engines in the model A tractor and are regular equipment for BF, BG & R tractors. Pistons for unsleeved engines are supplied in Standard, 0.020, 0.040 and 0.060 inch oversize. When checking iron or aluminum pistons for clearance, use a ½ inch wide feeler ribbon of 0.003 thickness. Pistons should have a slight drag (3 to 7 pounds) when pushed through the cylinder past feeler ribbon. On all clockwise-rotating engines the split or "T" slot in aluminum pistons should be installed on the side opposite the camshaft.

37. The Hercules IXB-3SL engines are equipped with dry type cylinder sleeves. Because these sleeves are installed with a tight press fit, their removal calls for the use of a sleeve puller and pusher. Sleeves should be coated with white lead mixed with oil before pressing into place. After sleeve

Fig. A9—If tappets are blocked up with nails cut to proper lengths, the camshaft can be removed without disturbing the cylinder head. Nails should be ¾ inch long for engine in model V tractor; 1 1/16 for engines in other tractor models.

Fig. A8—Timing gear train and view of oil pressure relief valve.

1. Governor gear timing marks
2. Distributor drive gear
3. Oil pressure relief valve
4. Front oil seal
5. Camshaft thrust pin

is installed, it should be honed to remove high spots and to provide the proper piston clearance. The IXB-3SL engines are factory installed in the BF, BG and R tractors and may be encountered as a replacement in model A tractors.

PISTON RINGS

38. Two compression and one oil ring are used on each piston. Recommended gap clearance is 0.015-0.020 inch. Piston ring side clearance should be 0.0015-0.0035 inch in aluminum pistons and 0.0015-0.0025 in cast iron pistons of model A, BF, BG and R engines, and 0.001-0.0025 in model V engines.

PISTON PINS AND BUSHINGS

39. Piston pins are locked in the connecting rod in all engine models. To remove pin, remove clamp screw and open split of connecting rod with an offset screwdriver, then push pin out of rod and piston. Standard, 0.003 and 0.005 oversize pins are supplied for the IXA & IXK engines; standard and 0.003 oversize for other models. Bronze bushings in cast iron pistons or pin bosses in aluminum pistons should be reamed or honed to provide the recommended clearance listed in paragraph 39A. Desired fit of pin in bushings of cast iron piston is a light finger push and in the bosses of the aluminum piston at room temperature, a hard push with palm of hand. When reinstalling pin, line up groove in pin with clamp screw hole in rod, install screw and tighten securely. Be sure screw is prevented from loosening by the installation of either a serrated type lockwasher or safety wire.

39A. **PERTINENT DATA.** Pertinent data applying to pistons, pins and rings are tabulated below:
Piston Ring Gap............0.015-0.020
Ring Side Clearance, Iron
   Pistons (A) 0.0015-0.0025
Ring Side Clearance, Iron
   Pistons (V) 0.001-0.0025
Ring Side Clearance, Alum.
   Pistons (BF-BG-R-V).0.0015-0.0035
Piston Skirt Clearance
   (Iron A-BF-BG-R) 0.003-0.0035
Piston Skirt Clearance
   (Alum. A-BF-BG-R) ..0.0025-0.003
Piston Skirt Clearance (2⅝
   bore below 1800 rpm)...0.002-0.0025
Piston Skirt Clearance (2⅝
   bore above 1800 rpm)...0.0025-0.003
Type of Piston Pin....Locked in rod
Piston Pin Diameter
   (A-BF-BG-R)...............0.749
Piston Pin Diameter (V).......0.6868
Oversize Pins Available.........Yes
Pin Clearance in Iron Piston....0.0005
Pin Clearance in Alum.
   Piston 0.0001-0.0002

CONNECTING ROD BEARINGS

40. Model A tractors with models IXA-3 and IXK-3 engines and engines in the model V tractors have babbitted connecting rod bearings provided with shims for adjustment. Connecting rods are supplied in standard and undersize, but require hand-fitting by bluing and scraping or reaming.

41. Model A. BF, BG & R tractors with IXB-3 and IXB-3SL engines are equipped with bronze-backed precision type insert bearings that require no hand fitting. No shims are provided for adjustment of these bearings; when worn, renew inserts. Refer to paragraph 41A for connecting rod bearing clearances.

41A. **PERTINENT DATA.** Pertinent data concerning the connecting rods and bearings are tabulated below:
Running Clearance 0.001-0.0015
Preferred Clearance 0.001
Repair if Clearance
   Greater Than 0.004
Crankpin Diameter
   (A-BF-BG-R) 1.747-1.748
Crankpin Length (A-BF-BG-R)..1⅛
Crankpin Diameter (V)....1.497-1.498
Crankpin Length (V).............1.0
Regrind if Out of Round
   More Than 0.002
Regrind if Worn More Than.....0.003

CRANKSHAFT AND BEARINGS

A three-main-bearing crankshaft with oil passages between main and connecting rod bearing journals is used in all engine models; the one in the IXB-3 and IXB-3SL models being induction hardened. Removal of the crankshaft requires removal of the engine.

Models V and Early A

42. Main bearings in the model A tractor (except in IXB-3 engine model) and model V tractor have babbitted bearing caps (lower halves) and bronze-backed inserts in the upper halves. The upper halves are removable from below. Shims are provided for bearing adjustment. New bearings should be checked by bluing and, if necessary, line-reamed or hand fitted to crankshaft journals. Refer to paragraph 43A.

Models BF-BG-R and Later A

43. Tractor models A, BF, BG, & R equipped with either the IXB-3 or IXB-3SL engines have bronze-backed, precision type, shimless, non-adjustable main bearing inserts which are renewable from below and require no hand-fitting. End play is controlled at crankshaft rear flange by flanged rear main bearing shell. NOTE: The cap screw on the right hand side of the

center main bearing has a thinner head than the other main bearing cap screws. Be sure to reinstall this cap screw in its correct location. Other cap screws, when installed at this point, do not allow clearance for oil pump housing. Refer to paragraph 43A for crankshaft bearing clearances.

43A. **PERTINENT DATA.** Pertinent data applying to the crankshaft and main bearings are tabulated below:
Main Journal Diameter,
   New 1.987-1.988
Regrind If Out of Round
   More Than 0.002
Regrind If Worn More Than.....0.003
Mains, Running Clearance,
   New 0.002-0.0025
Preferred Running Clearance....0.002
Crankshaft End Play......0.002-0.004
End Play Controlled by
   Rear Bearing ....Yes
Connecting Rod
   Crankpins..Refer to paragraph 41A

FLYWHEEL

44. Flywheel can be removed after removing clutch housing and clutch by removing retaining cap screws. Flywheel is positioned on crankshaft flange by two stepped dowels which are retained in holes of flywheel by Welch plugs. Flywheel ring gear is renewable and should be shrunk on flywheel with bevel of teeth towards the rear for easy engagement of starter pinion gear.

CRANKCASE OIL PAN

Models A-BF-BG-R

45. To remove pan, first remove the screws retaining the pan to the crankcase, timing gear cover and bell housing. Carefully (using a putty knife) separate oil pan from bell housing and remove oil pan. The gasket between bell housing and cylinder block and between bell housing and oil pan is one piece and if same has to be renewed, it will necessitate the removal of clutch, flywheel and bell housing. When reinstalling oil pan be sure the felt or felt and steel washers are in place on oil pump pick up tube.

Model V

46. Before oil pan can be removed from the model V tractor, it is necessary to first disconnect the drag link from Pitman arm (steering arm) and turn front wheels to the left as far as possible, then disconnect radius rod (reach) from the bell housing and remove the starting motor. Remainder of the procedure is the same as on the models A, BF and R as outlined in paragraph 45.

CRANKSHAFT OIL SEALS

47. Front oil seal (4—Fig. A8) is located in oil pan and timing gear cover. Refer to paragraph 29 for removal procedure.

48. Rear oil seal assembly is installed in bell housing (flywheel housing) and contacts a flange on front face of flywheel. Renewal of seal requires removal of clutch and flywheel. When installing seal in bell housing (Fig. A10) be sure seal is concentric with flywheel flange and flywheel flange is true and smooth.

OIL PUMP

49. Oil pump is located in oil pan and driven by helical gear from the center of the camshaft. To remove oil pump, remove oil pan and cap screws retaining oil pump to cylinder block. On model V tractors remove also the oil line connecting oil pump to engine oil passage. (On models A, BF, BG & R tractor engines, oil is discharged from pump directly to main oil passage through pump body and flange gasket.)

To disassemble pump, remove screws retaining cover to pump housing and remove cover and idler gear and shaft assembly. Drive riveted pin out of driving gear and remove gear and thrust washer. Oil pump body drive gear and shaft unit can be withdrawn from pump housing. To remove oil pump body drive gear and idler gear from their shafts, press gears farther onto shafts to expose snap ring in shaft groove. Remove snap rings and press gears from shafts. Reassembly is reverse of disassembly. Backlash between oil pump body gears is 0.008-0.010 inch and drive shaft end play 0.0015-0.003 inch. Gear cover plate is a lapped fit on the pump housing and no gasket is required. Cover retaining cap screws should be locked by cen-

Fig. A10—Installing crankshaft rear oil seal.

ter-punching cover into slots. NOTE: Oil pump from IXA3 or IXK3 engines cannot be used on IXB3 engine as body of pump will not clear main bearing cap screw.

PRESSURE RELIEF VALVE

50. Oil pressure relief valve (3—Fig. A8) is located externally on left side of engine just to the rear of the timing gear cover. Remove cover, loosen locknut and turn adjusting screw to adjust oil pressure. Oil pressure should be 15 pounds at 1000 rpm, with engine and oil completely warmed.

OIL FILTER

51. This unit is of the partial flow, replaceable element type. Cartridge type element may be renewed after first removing tractor hood. NOTE: Some model A tractors were equipped with the Michiana screw base type filter and removal of hood for renewal of cartridge is not necessary on these models.

CARBURETOR

60. Model A tractors are equipped with model YC2A, YC2B or YC10A Tillotson carburetor; model V tractors with Tillotson YC6A; models BF, BG & R with Marvel-Schebler TSX400. Adjustment procedures are conventional. Float setting is 1 5/64 inches for Tillotson, ¼ inch for Marvel-Schebler.

GOVERNOR

ADJUST

Models A and V

65. To completely adjust the governor, first disconnect the carburetor throttle rod (1—Fig. A11) at carburetor and governor throttle rod (7) at governor. Push carburetor throttle rod forward until resistance of governor is felt, then adjust it to ⅛-inch longer than required to enter hole in carburetor lever and reconnect to lever. Without tension on the manual control spring, reconnect the governor throttle rod. Screw the bumper screw (6) in until the spring just contacts the lever. Turn bumper screw in, if surging is present. Adjust governor throttle lever stop screw (5) to control maximum engine speed. Refer to Condensed Service Data for governed speeds.

Models BF-BG-R

66. Bend the governor-to-carburetor rod, if necessary, to make certain that governor weights are "in" when carburetor throttle butterfly is wide open. Back off the bumper spring screw and adjust the engine high idle,

no-load speed to 1950 rpm by moving the adjusting clamp which is located on the top of the frame rail, directly under the carburetor. Moving the clamp to the rear will increase the engine speed. Readjust the bumper spring screw to eliminate surging.

REMOVE AND REINSTALL

67. To remove governor, remove right side plate (panel). Disconnect governor throttle rod and carburetor throttle rod. Remove cap screws and governor cover. If engine is equipped with a magneto, turn engine backwards (with the fan belt) so that impulse coupling does not engage, until punch mark on camshaft gear is visible. Observe which mark on the governor gear indexes with the camshaft gear mark (1—Fig. A8). This mark may be a punch mark, a number 2 or 3, or a number 20 or 34. Withdraw governor and gear from timing gear cover.

68. When reinstalling mesh governor gear with camshaft gear being careful, on magneto equipped engines, to index the gear marks referred to in paragraph 67. If magneto was not disturbed while governor gear was removed, the governor gear will engage the magneto coupling in the correct position and retiming of the magneto will not be required.

OVERHAUL

69. In the V series tractors the rear end of governor shaft is supported in a ball bearing (2—Fig. A7). This bearing can be renewed without further disassembly of the engine.

Rear end of governor shaft in model A, BF, BG & R tractors is supported in a babbitt lined plain bearing which is pressed into the cylinder block. Renewal of this bearing requires removal

Fig. A11—Governor linkage on all model A Avery tractors and for Avery built model V tractors.

1. Carburetor throttle rod	4. Manual control lever
2. Governor lever	5. Stop screw
3. Manual control spring	6. Bumper screw
	7. Governor throttle rod

of governor and magneto or governor and hydraulic pump unit. Clearance between governor shaft and bearing should be 0.001-0.0015 inch.

The procedure for overhaul of the governor cover, the controls shafts mounted therein and the weight units is self-evident after an examination of the unit and reference to Figs. A12, A13, A14 and A15. However, the following repair notes should be observed.

70. IXB-3 ENGINES. On engines equipped with flyweight type governor, the rounded tips of the fork should be to the open end of the housing. If a new fork shaft is installed it will have to be drilled to take the taper pin. Before drilling hole for pin make sure that lever and fork are in the relative positions shown in Fig. A12.

71. ZX ENGINES. In these engines used in model V tractors, the procedure for repair of flyweight type governor shown in Fig. A13 is same as outlined in paragraph 70 except that the governor gear location on the shaft is determined by the snap ring at the ball bearing end of the shaft.

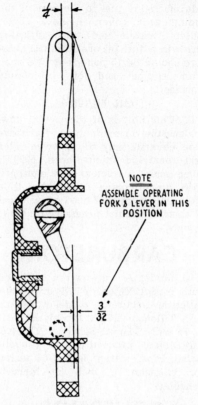

Fig. A14—On model V tractors equipped with laminated flyweight governor shown in Fig. A13, the relative position of fork and lever should be as shown.

The bushing in the governor cover should be installed with the oil groove in the **up** position. Relationship of fork shaft to lever should be as shown in Fig. A14.

72. BF AND R TRACTORS. When these tractors are equipped with Novi ball type governors shown in Fig. A15, repair procedure is conventional. If necessary to renew the fork lever shaft (10) establish the correct fork and lever relative positions from the original parts.

COOLING SYSTEM

On model A and V, the thermo-siphon system of coolant circulation is used. Pump circulation is used on models BF, BG and R.

FAN ASSEMBLY

80. Belt can be adjusted by positioning fan in slotted bracket or by moving generator on its adjusting strap.

On model A tractors to remove the fan unit it is necessary to remove hood and radiator.

On model V tractors remove generator adjusting strap and armature lead from the circuit breaker without disturbing hood or radiator. Push generator towards engine and remove fan belt; then swing generator away from engine. Remove fan assembly from bracket and withdraw over top of generator.

To disassemble fan Fig. A16, remove blades from hub and remove thrust nut assembly and washer from spindle. Neither the hub bushing nor the oil seal are supplied separately; if worn,

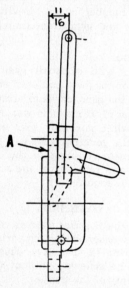

Fig. A12—On model A tractors with flyweight governors, the center of hole in governor arm should be 11/16 forward of housing face (A) when the fork (shown dotted) is flush with the face.

Fig. A13—Laminated type flyweights are used in the governors on some of the Hercules ZXB engines which power model V tractors.

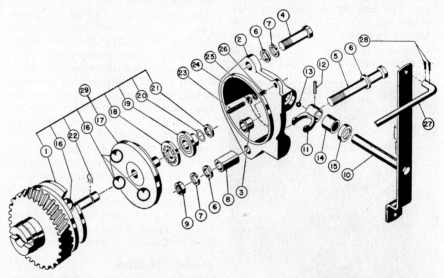

Fig. A15—Novi flyball type governor used in some Hercules IXB3 and IXB3SL engines which power models BF, BG and R tractors.

1. Shaft & gear assy.	14. Needle bearing	20. Ball stop washer
3. Bushing	15. Oil seal	21. Ball stop washer
8. Filler bushing	16. Ball 5/8 inch	23. Adjusting screw
10. Lever & shaft assy.	17. Upper race	26. Bumper spring
11. Fork	18. Thrust bearing	27. Carburetor throttle
13. Ball 3/16 inch		rod

renew hub which includes oil seal and bushing. Lubricate with engine oil through plug hole in side of hub.

On models BF, BG & R, fan blades are attached to the forward end of the coolant pump impeller shaft and hence no overhaul procedure is involved. Fan blades unit can be removed without removing the radiator.

COOLANT PUMP

81. Models BF, BG & R tractors are equipped with a permanently lubricated packless type pump shown in Fig. A17. To remove pump from engine without removing the radiator, it may be necessary in some installations to unscrew the one pump-to-cylinder-block stud from the cylinder block.

To disassemble the pump proceed as follows: Remove fan blades. Using a suitable jaw type puller remove fan hub from shaft. Support pump body suitably and press the shaft out of the impeller, and pump body in the direction towards the fan. Press the seal

unit out of the housing. Shaft and bearing are sold only as a unit. If seal contacting surface of impeller is scored or pitted, it should be refaced or a new one installed. Apply a coating of thin Permatex on seal unit then install same with graphite shoulder toward the impeller.

ELECTRICAL

IGNITION

89A. Model A tractor engines are equipped with either a Wico C1604 high tension magneto or a Delco-Remy 1111714 or an Auto-Lite IAD-4023A battery ignition distributor. Model BF, BG & R tractors are equipped with a Delco-Remy 1111736 battery ignition distributor. Model V tractors are equipped with a Delco-Remy 1111715 or an Auto-Lite IAD-4010A or IAD-4010C battery ignition distributor.

90. **TIMING WICO C1604 MAGNETO.** Breaker point opening is 0.014-

0.016 inch. Crank engine until Number 1 cylinder is on compression stroke, then crank slowly until mark "DC" on flywheel appears in center of timing hole in right side of bell housing. Turn magneto shaft backward until magneto rotor contact is under Number 1 cylinder contact of magneto distributor cap. Install magneto on engine. If magneto coupling does not align with slots in governor shaft, refer to paragraph 67 for timing governor gear. After magneto is installed, turn engine backwards past the "SPK" mark (if flywheel is so marked) on flywheel but not far enough back to engage impulse coupling, then slowly turn engine in direction of rotation until "SPK" mark on flywheel is in center of timing hole. Rotate magneto on its mountings until breaker points are just opening. When checking timing with a neon timing light, this "SPK" mark should appear in center of timing hole when engine is running faster than 500 rpm. To check impulse coupling trip point, turn engine in direction of rotation with switch off until impulse trips for Number 1 or Number 4 cylinder, at which time the "DC" mark on flywheel should be visible in center of timing hole.

91. **BATTERY DISTRIBUTOR TIMING.** Breaker point opening for Auto-Lite distributor is 0.020 inch; for Delco-Remy, 0.018 inch. With Number 1 cylinder on compression stroke, crank engine slowly until "DC" mark on flywheel is in center of timing hole in bell housing. (On the A, BF, BG & R tractors, timing hole is on right side of bell housing; on model V, left side.) Install distributor with rotor under Number 1 cylinder contact of distributor cap. With rotor held in this position, rotate distributor housing clockwise until breaker points are just opening and tighten lockscrew.

GENERATOR

92. Model A tractors have been equipped with Auto-Lite GAS-4169A, Auto-Lite GAS-4165B or Delco-Remy 1101851 generators, models BF, BG & R with Delco-Remy 1101856 generator and model V tractors with Delco-Remy 1101856 or Auto-Lite GAS-4169A generators.

STARTING MOTOR

93. Model A tractors have been equipped with Auto-Lite MZ4098 and Delco-Remy 1109602 starters, models BF, BG & R with Delco-Remy 1109609 starter and model V with Delco-Remy 1109604 or Auto-Lite MZ4130 starter.

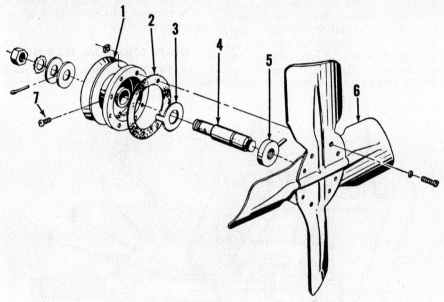

Fig. A16—Fan assembly for models A and V which are cooled by the thermo siphon system.

1. Hub assembly	3. Bronze washer	6. Blade assembly
2. Gasket	4. Spindle	7. Oil plug
	5. Thrust nut assembly	

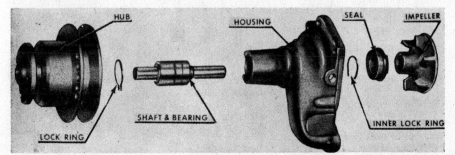

Fig. A17—Exploded view coolant pump used on models BF, BG and R.

CLUTCH

All late models are equipped with Rockford spring loaded single plate clutches. The 9-inch Rockford RM is used in models A, BF, BG & R and the 8-inch RM in the model V. Clutch fingers are adjustable, but should not be changed from the original adjustment, except when the clutch is being overhauled. Compensation for lining wear is obtained by restoring the pedal free travel as outlined in next paragraph. The clutch shaft, clutch shaft rear bearing and the clutch release bearing and the operating yoke are all carried in the clutch housing, which is bolted to the rear face of the flywheel housing. There are no inspection openings in the clutch housing.

NOTE: Some early model A tractors were equipped with a Long 9CF clutch.

CLUTCH PEDAL ADJUSTMENT

200. When the clutch is new or has just been relined, the clutch pedal should have approximately 1¾ inches free travel (1—Fig. A18), before the release bearing first contacts the release levers of the clutch unit. As the clutch wears the free travel will become less, but it should not be allowed to go lower than ¾ inch. Insufficient free travel may permit the release yoke to rub against the back face of the clutch and under conditions of zero free travel, the release bearing will rotate continuously and thus wear out prematurely, or the clutch may slip due to being partially disengaged. Too much free travel will prevent complete disengagement of the clutch. It is necessary, therefore, to have some pedal free travel although it need not be as much as 1¾ inches, except when the clutch is in new condition.

Free travel is adjusted by varying the length of the release rod (15) attached to the clutch pedal. This is accomplished by turning the clevis (16) at the pedal end of the rod after first removing the pedal from the tractor. Do not adjust the clutch unit release levers, except when the clutch is removed from the tractor during overhaul.

CLUTCH HOUSING
Models A-R

201. To R & R the clutch housing, remove the fuel tank and tank support. Remove the propeller shaft assembly by removing cotter pin from either joint, and sliding same on to propeller shaft splines far enough to disengage opposite end of joint. Remove propeller shaft and the pressed steel shaft cover over the propeller shaft. Disconnect clutch release rod from pedal. Remove clutch housing to flywheel housing bolts and withdraw the hous-

ing and clutch shaft and release bearing assemblies as a single unit. When reinstalling propeller shaft assembly be sure that it is assembled with the universal joint journal cap screws of each joint nearest the adjacent end of the propeller shaft. If cap screws are nearest the center of the shaft, the assembly cannot be collapsed (shortened) enough to permit installation to tractor.

Model V

202. Universal joints on this tractor are welded to the propeller shaft, thus it cannot be collapsed for removal and installation. To R & R the clutch housing, first detach the transmission—differential housing from the tractor main frame and move the rear portion of the tractor backward as per paragraph 220. Slide the propeller shaft and joints unit off the clutch shaft. Removal of the clutch housing from this point on is the same as for the model A as per paragraph 201.

Models BF-BG

202A. Disconnect choke control, governor control and hydraulic reservoir vent tube. Disconnect battery cable at starter, oil line at gage, temperature gage at engine and wiring harness at generator, coil, relay starter and ammeter. Remove hydraulic reservoir and support, instrument panel

and bolts attaching frame channels to engine. Unbolt torque tube from frame channels. Remove steering wheel and steering shaft support, disconnect brake rods, and remove clutch pedal, fuel tank and fuel tank support. Support both halves of tractor, roll rear half of tractor rearward approximately five inches or until front universal joint is free from clutch shaft. Remove the clutch housing retaining bolts, turn housing until notch in right side lines up with top edge of main frame channel and remove clutch housing and clutch shaft assembly.

When reassembling, reverse the removal procedure.

RELEASE BEARING

203. To renew the clutch release bearing, first remove the clutch housing as outlined in paragraph 201, 202 or 202A. Remove hairpin lock from clutch release fork shaft (7—Fig. A18), and then remove fork shaft from clutch housing. Disconnect clutch release rod (15) from the release fork or yoke (8) and withdraw the bearing and sleeve (11) unit from the housing. The bearing may be renewed by pressing it off the sleeve.

SHAFT AND REAR BEARING

204. To renew the clutch shaft and/or the clutch shaft rear bearing,

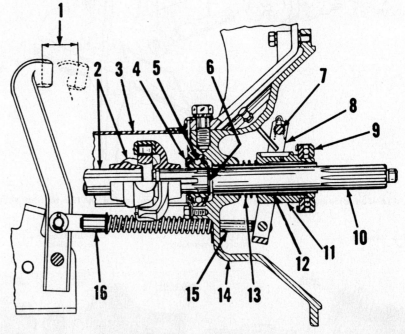

Fig A18—Section through clutch housing showing clutch shaft, releasing mechanism and propeller shaft.

1. Pedal free travel (¾" to 1¾")	6. Snap ring	12. Release sleeve guide
2. Propeller shaft	7. Release fork shaft	13. Release sleeve spring
3. Propeller shaft cover	8. Release yoke	14. Clutch housing
4. Bearing retainer	9. Release bearing	15. Clutch release rod
5. Clutch shaft rear bearing	10. Clutch shaft	16. Release rod clevis
	11. Release sleeve	

it is first necessary to remove the clutch housing as outlined in paragraph 201, 202 or 202A. The shaft and bearing assembly is removed from the clutch housing by removing the bearing retainer (4—Fig. A18) and bumping on the forward end of the shaft (10). Bearing (5) may be pressed off the shaft after removing the retaining snap ring (6).

R & R CLUTCH UNIT

205. R & R of the clutch assembly requires R & R of the clutch housing as outlined in paragraph 201, 202 or 202A. After the clutch housing and clutch shaft unit are removed, place a piece of 5/16 inch key stock approximately one inch long between each release lever and clutch backing plate (cover) to hold the pressure springs partially compressed. This procedure will facilitate both removal and reinstallation. When reinstalling unit to flywheel, use the original or a dummy clutch shaft to obtain and maintain alignment of the lined plate splines.

TRANSMISSION

Transmissions in models BF, BG and R are of the 4 speed type; in the models A and V they are of 3 speed type, basically similar in design to the BF and R. The transmission and differential assemblies are both contained in the same case to which are attached the final drive units. A wall in the case separates the differential from the transmission gear set. To overhaul the transmission it is necessary to remove the unit from the tractor and to remove the final drive units and differential from the transmission.

On model A tractors the transmission countershaft, which is the main drive bevel pinion, can be purchased separately from the bevel ring gear. On models BF, BG, R and V the bevel pinion and ring gear are available only as a matched set.

The combination belt pulley and power take-off which mounts in the rear of the transmission case may be directly removed without disturbing the differential unit.

R & R TRANSMISSION

220. Install a wheeled jack under transmission case and place support under main frame behind clutch housing. Remove rear wheels, fenders, seat, propeller shaft cover and on the models A, BF, BG and R also remove the instrument panel. (In the case of the model V where transmission case is being removed only to R & R the propeller shaft, the fenders, seat and rear wheels need not be removed.) Remove cotter pin which retains front universal joint to the transmission mainshaft, drawbar pin from cross member, and tail light bracket or the straps extending from brake upper cover to frame channels. Disconnect brake rods at pedals. Detach transmission case from the main frame and roll the case and final drive assemblies as a single unit away from the tractor.

OVERHAUL
Models A-V

221. **MODEL A SHIFTER UNIT.** Shifter rails and forks are located in the transmission side cover. The procedure for overhaul of this assembly is apparent after studying Fig. A19. Removal of the cover from model A tractors prior to 1947 requires removal of the main frame right side channel. Cover on model A tractors built in 1947 and later may be removed without disturbing main frame channels.

222. **MODEL V SHIFTER UNIT.** The shifter control assembly (34—Fig. A20) is located in transmission side cover and cannot be overhauled. When worn the complete assembly is renewed. (When removing cover, note that the top center cap screw is shorter than the others. Be sure to reinstall it in the same position to prevent interference with movement of shift lever.)

223. **MODEL A MAINSHAFT.** First step in removal of this shaft is to re-

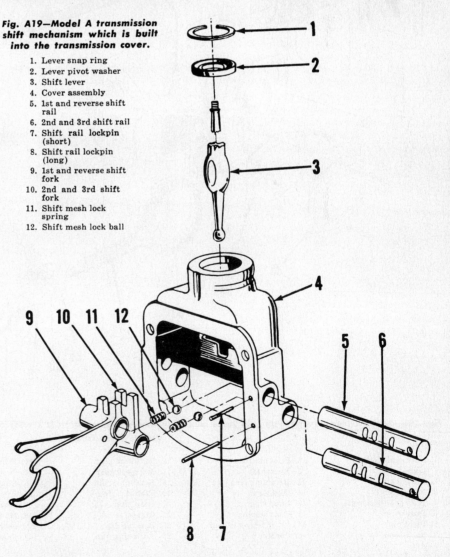

Fig. A19—Model A transmission shift mechanism which is built into the transmission cover.

1. Lever snap ring
2. Lever pivot washer
3. Shift lever
4. Cover assembly
5. 1st and reverse shift rail
6. 2nd and 3rd shift rail
7. Shift rail lockpin (short)
8. Shift rail lockpin (long)
9. 1st and reverse shift fork
10. 2nd and 3rd shift fork
11. Shift mesh lock spring
12. Shift mesh lock ball

move the transmission and final drives as a single unit from the tractor as per paragraph 220. Next remove the side cover (shifter rails) and the rear cover. Remove mainshaft bearing retainer (19—Fig. A21) at front of case, and push forward on mainshaft (14) from the differential chamber. Shaft and front bearing cone (17) and cup (16) will come out of case.

When reinstalling, adjust the tapered roller bearings by means of shims (18) between bearing retainer and case to provide end clearance of 0.002-0.005. Install oil seal (20) with lip toward inside of case.

224. MODEL V MAINSHAFT. With transmission removed from tractor, remove the control cover (35—Fig.

A20) and control assembly (34). Remove rear cover (37) and retaining ring (10) through differential chamber. (If difficulty is encountered in removing this ring, it may be necessary to remove final drive units and differential assembly.) Pry out front seal (21) and remove front bearing snap ring (20). Push forward on shaft to remove from case. Mainshaft is supported on non-adjustable bearings. Renew bushing (8) in rear of mainshaft if worn. Install seal (21) with lip toward inside of case.

225. BEVEL PINION (COUNTERSHAFT) SHAFT. To remove integral countershaft and bevel pinion, remove the transmission from the tractor as per paragraph 220. Detach both

of the final drive units from the transmission case. Remove the rear cover (or combination belt pulley and power take-off if used) and differential bearing carriers, and lift out the differential unit. Be careful not to mix the shims. Remove the transmission cover, cap (21—Fig. A21), or (22—Fig. A20) adjusting nut (22) or (23), and tap on forward end of shaft until free of front bearing then withdraw from rear of case.

If the bevel pinion shaft on model A tractors is damaged, it can be renewed separately. On model V, the bevel pinion cannot be renewed separately as it is available only with mating bevel ring gear as a matched set.

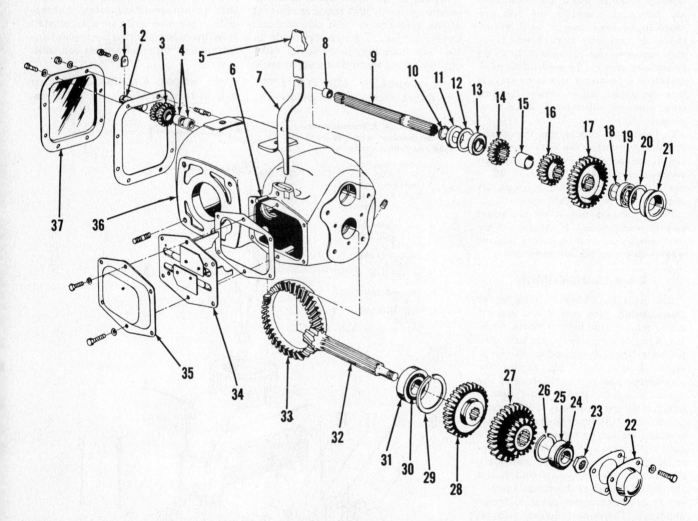

Fig. A20—Model V transmission with shift lever control assembly. Construction is similar on both Avery built and Minneapolis-Moline model V tractors.

1. Idler shaft lock plate	8. Pilot bushing	16. 2nd speed gear	24. Front bearing cone	30. Rear bearing cone
2. Idler shaft	9. **Mainshaft**	17. 3rd speed gear	25. Front bearing cup	31. Rear bearing cup
3. Idler gear	10. Retaining ring	18. Retaining ring	26. Snap ring	32. Countershaft and bevel pinion
4. Idler gear bushings	11. Oiling cup	19. Front bearing	27. 2nd & 3rd sliding gear	33. Bevel ring gear
5. Dust cover	12. Snap ring	20. Snap ring	28. 1st & reverse sliding gear	34. Control assembly
6. Pivot pin	13. Rear bearing	21. Oil seal	29. Snap ring	35. **Control cover**
7. Shift lever	14. 1st and reverse gear	22. Bearing cap		36. Transmission case
	15. Spacer	23. Adjusting nut		37. Rear cover

On model A, the pre-sized bushing (28—Fig. A21) in third speed gear is renewable. On this model install the third speed gear locating washer (27) with oil grooved side toward gear. When reinstalling countershaft, tighten adjusting nut (22—Fig. A21 or 23—Fig. A20) until a very slight drag can be felt when rotating shaft, equivalent to a one-pound pull on a 6-inch extension from the shaft. Lock the adjusting nut by driving a section of nut into groove in shaft. The fore and aft position of the pinion shaft is not adjustable.

226. REVERSE IDLER. The bevel pinion shaft must be removed before the reverse idler can be removed. After removing the lock plate (1) from differential chamber, the idler shaft and gear can be removed from case. Pre-sized bushings (4—Fig. A20) are replaceable. In the model A, the reverse idler gear is supported on two straight roller bearings.

Models BF-BG-R

227. SHIFTER RAILS & FORKS. Shifting mechanism in these four speed transmissions is similar to the model A except that it includes an additional shifter rail and fork as shown in Fig. A22. Shifter cover can be removed without disturbing frame side rail. Overhaul procedure is self-evident after referring to the actual unit and Fig. A22.

228. MAINSHAFT. First step in removing this shaft is to remove the transmission and final drives as a single unit from the tractor as outlined in paragraph 220. Remove side cover (shifter rails and forks) and rear cover from transmission. Remove mainshaft

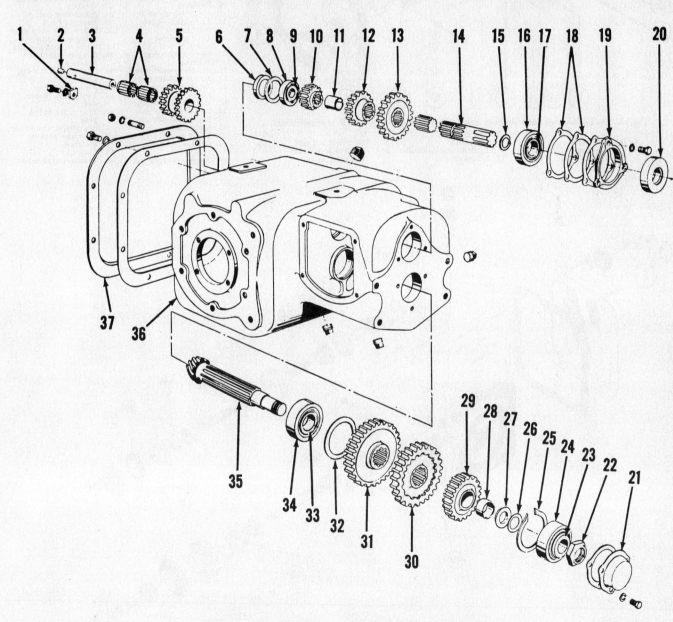

Fig. A21—Exploded view of model A transmission unit.

1. Idler shaft lock plate	10. 1st and reverse gear	18. Shims	26. Spring retaining washer
2. Idler shaft plug	11. Spacer	19. Bearing retainer	27. Locating washer
3. Idler shaft	12. 2nd speed gear	20. Oil seal	28. 3rd speed gear bushing
4. Idler shaft bearings	13. 3rd speed gear	21. Bearing cap	29. 3rd speed gear
5. Idler gear	14. Mainshaft	22. Adjusting nut	30. 2nd & 3rd sliding gear
6. Oiling cup	15. Snap ring	23. Front bearing cone	31. 1st & reverse sliding gear
7. Snap ring	16. Front bearing cup	24. Front bearing cup	32. Snap ring
8. Rear bearing cup	17. Front bearing cone	25. Snap ring	33. Rear bearing cone
9. Rear bearing cone			34. Rear bearing cup
			35. Countershaft and bevel pinion
			36. Transmission case
			37. Rear cover

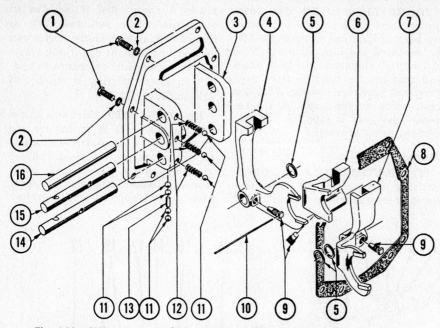

front bearing cap (30—Fig. A23) at front of case and push forward on mainshaft from differential chamber. Shaft and front bearing cone (19) will come out front opening in case and gears can be withdrawn through side cover opening. If rear bearing (19) requires renewal it will be advisable to remove the differential to give working space for removal of the snap ring (18).

Legend applies to Fig. A23.

3. Idler shaft lock	29. Gasket—bearing cap
4. Reverse idler shaft	30. Cap and oil seal
5. Reverse idler gear	32. Cap—front bearing
6. Bushing	33. Gasket
12. Lever—gear shift	34. Adjusting nut
16. Snap ring—pivot washer	35. Bearing cone
	36. Bearing & snap ring (ring not shown)
17. Oil cup—rear bearing	37. Shim—front bearing
18. Snap ring—rear bearing	38. Spacer—front bearing
19. Bearing—mainshaft	39. Bushing-pinion 4th gear
20. Mainshaft 1st gear	40. Pinion 4th gear
21. 1st & 3rd gear spacer	41. Pinion 2nd & rev. gear
22. Mainshaft 3rd gear	42. Pinion 1st & 3rd gear
23. 2nd & reverse gear	43. Bearing w/snap ring
24. Mainshaft 4th gear	44. Gear and pinion matched
25. Mainshaft	45. Lock nut
26. Shaft locating ring	49. Transmission case
27. Oil seal—bearing cap	
28. Shim—bearing cap	

Fig. A22—Shift cover and shifters used in models BF, BG and R transmissions.

4. 1st & 3rd fork	7. 2nd & 4th fork	14. 1st & 3rd rail
5. Stop washer	10. Lockwire	15. 2nd & 4th rail
6. Reverse fork	11. Lock & interlock balls	16. Reverse rail
	13. Interlock pin	

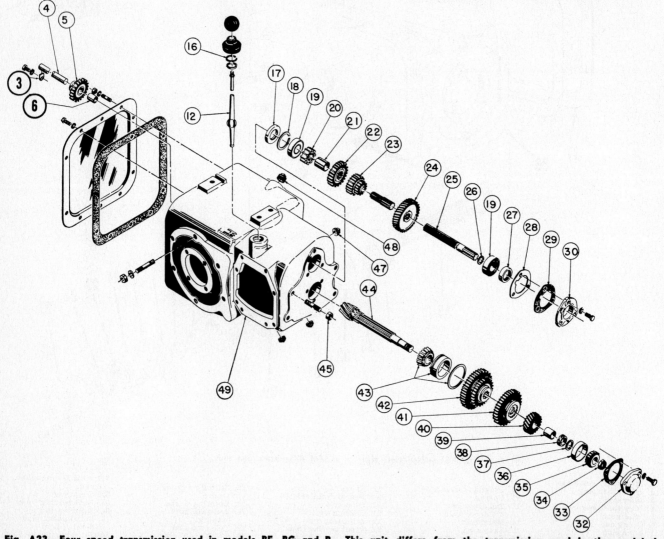

Fig. A23—Four speed transmission used in models BF, BG and R. This unit differs from the transmission used in the model A mainly that it has 4 speeds forward.

When shaft is reinstalled, adjust the bearings by varying the shims (28) which are furnished in the three thicknesses of 0.004, 0.007 and 0.010. Desired bearing adjustment is an end play of 0.002-0.005. Install oil seal (27) with lip facing toward inside of case.

229. BEVEL PINION (COUNTERSHAFT) SHAFT. This shaft cannot be purchased separately. It is sold only in combination with the bevel ring gear as a matched set. To remove this shaft from the transmission, it is necessary to first remove the transmission and final drives as a unit from the tractor as outlined in paragraph

220. Unbolt both of the final drive units from the transmission case. Remove the side cover and the rear cover or combination belt pulley and pto unit from rear of case. Remove the differential bearing carriers from transmission case and lift out the differential unit. Be careful not to mix the carrier shims. Remove front bearing cap (32) and bearing adjusting nut (34). Bump the shaft rearward until front bearing cone (35) is forced off shaft. Bump shaft rearward and out of case and withdraw gears through side cover opening.

The pre-sized bushing (39) for the

4th speed gear is renewable. The fore and aft or mesh position of the pinion shaft is not adjustable. When reinstalling shaft to case tighten the bearing adjusting nut (34) until a very slight rotational drag is obtained. If drag cannot be obtained remove a shim (37). Lock the adjusting nut by staking a section of it into the groove in shaft.

230. REVERSE IDLER. The bevel pinion shaft must be removed as per paragraph 229 before the reverse idler can be removed. Remove reverse idler lock plate (3) and bump shaft out of case. The pre-sized bushing (6) for the gear is renewable.

DIFFERENTIAL

Differential unit is of the two-pinion open case type mounted back of a dividing wall in the transmission case. The bevel ring gear is held to the one-piece differential case by rivets in the models A, BF, BG and R and by cap screws in the model V.

R & R AND OVERHAUL

231. To remove the differential assembly from the transmission case, first detach the final drive units from the transmission case as per paragraph 250 and remove the rear cover or combination belt pulley and power take-

off if used. Remove differential bearing carriers (6—Fig. A24) and lift differential unit from rear of transmission case.

232. To disassemble differential, remove pinion pin lockpin (5) by driving out of differential case (11) with a thin drift punch, then remove pinion pin (4), pinions (2) and side gears (13). When reassembling, be sure to lock the pinion pin lockpin in case by burring sides of hole with a punch.

The preferred method of removing the ring gear attaching rivets is by

drilling. When re-riveting, temporarily bolt the gear to the case to assist in getting a tight joint and to avoid distortion. After ring gear is attached, check trueness of unit at ring gear back face using a dial indicator with unit in its carriers or between centers of a lathe. Total run-out should not exceed 0.003. Where ring gear is attached to differential case by cap screws, use only heat treated or high nickel screws as replacements.

233. Reinstall differential in transmission case and adjust carrier bear-

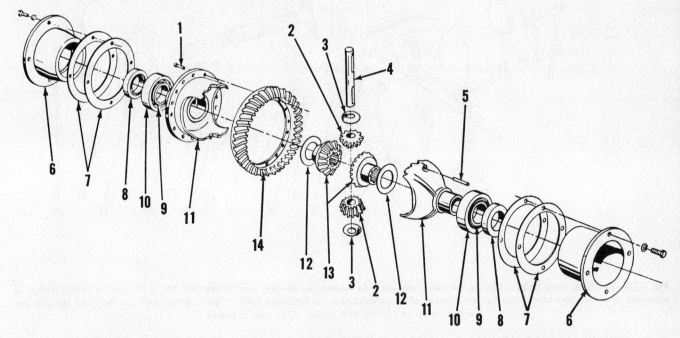

Fig. A24—Differential as used on models A, BF, BG, R and V. Pin (5) must be removed to disassemble the unit.

1. Ring gear rivet (cap screw-model V)
2. Differential pinion
3. Pinion thrust washer
4. Pinion pin
5. Pinion pin lockpin
6. Bearing carrier
7. Carrier shims
8. Bearing oil seal
9. Bearing cone
10. Bearing cup
11. Differential case
12. Side gear thrust washer
13. Differential side gear
14. Bevel ring gear

ings (9) by adding or removing shims (7) between carriers (6) and transmission case until a slight pre-load drag is obtained. **After** bearings are adjusted, adjust the backlash to 0.006-0.010 (measured at the teeth) by removing a shim or shims from one carrier and installing the same shim or shims to the other carrier. To reduce backlash remove shim from carrier nearest ring gear and install the same shim under carrier on opposite side of ring gear.

DRIVE BEVEL GEARS

On model A tractors, the main drive bevel pinion (which is also the transmission countershaft) and the bevel ring gear can be purchased as separate parts. On models BF, BG, R and V, the main drive bevel pinion and ring gears are furnished only in matched sets. On all models the tooth contact or mesh pattern of these gears is non-adjustable. Backlash of the gears is controlled by shims. Backlash should be checked and adjusted if necessary, whenever the differential is being overhauled and always when a new ring and pinion are installed.

ADJUST BACKLASH

240. Check backlash of main drive bevel pinion and ring gears AFTER differential carrier bearings have been correctly adjusted to a slight pre-load. Use a dial indicator, shim stock, or paper direct on teeth. Correct lash should be 0.006 to 0.010. If lash is more than 0.010, remove shim or shims (7)

from bearing carrier nearest to ring gear and add them to bearing carrier farthest from ring gear. If lash is less than 0.006, remove shims from farthest bearing carrier and add them to bearing carrier located nearest to ring gear side of differential.

RENEWAL OF BEVEL GEARS

241. **MODEL A.** To renew the bevel pinion only, follow the procedure outlined in paragraph 225. To renew the bevel ring gear, follow the procedure outlined in paragraphs 231, 232 and 233.

243. **MODELS BF-BG-R-V.** On these models to renew the bevel pinion and ring gear which are available only as a matched set, follow the procedure outlined in paragraphs 229, 231, 232 and 233.

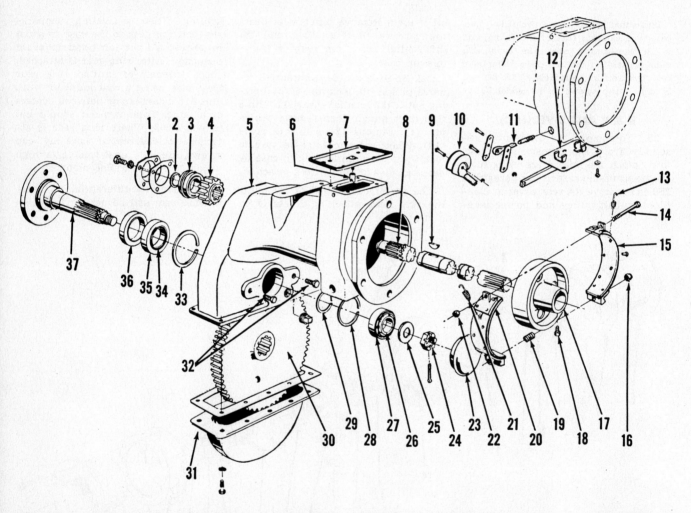

Fig. A25—Two final drive units similar to the above are used on models A, BF, BG and R tractors. The bull gear on these models is provided with two threaded holes for attachment of a puller-pusher to facilitate R&R of gear. Puller legs are installed through the housing holes into which the screws (32) are threaded.

1. Bearing cap	8. Main axle shaft	14. Brake adjusting bolt	22. Brake adjusting nut	30. Driven (bull) gear
2. Pinion snap ring	(bull pinion shaft)	15. Rear brake shoe	23. Bearing cap	31. Gear cover
3. Pinion bearing	9. Woodruff key	16. Fibre locknut	24. Adjusting nut	32. Puller cap screws
4. Final drive pinion	10. Brake locking cam	17. Brake drum	25. Washer	33. Outer bearing snap ring
(bull pinion)	11. Eyebolt	18. Set screw	26. Inner bearing cone	34. Outer bearing cone
5. Final drive housing	12. Brake anchor and	19. Lower brake spring	27. Inner bearing cup	35. Outer bearing cup
6. Brake guide	lower cover	20. Forward brake shoe	28. Bearing snap ring	36. Wheel axle oil seal
7. Brake upper cover	13. Rear shoe return spring	21. Shoe return spring	29. Driven gear snap ring	37. Wheel axle

FINAL DRIVE UNITS

Each tractor is provided with two final drive units consisting of a final drive spur (bull) pinion, a final drive spur (bull) gear and wheel axle shaft and brake assembly. The final drive units for the various models differ only in minor details as will be seen in Figs. A25, A26 and A27.

250. R & R OF UNIT. A final drive unit is removed from tractor by jacking up rear of transmission, disconnecting brake rod and removing fender and rear wheel. Remove final drive housing to transmission case stud nuts and unit can be lifted off the transmission case.

251. BULL PINION AND SHAFT. To remove final drive (bull) pinion (4—Fig. A25 and A26) or bull pinion shaft (8), first unbolt the final drive housing unit from the transmission case after removing rear wheel, fender and brake rod.

Remove upper cover (7) and loosen brake bands adjustment by backing off the brake adjusting bolt. Remove cap (1) and snap ring (2) and tap pinion shaft on outer end until free of bearing and pinion. Withdraw pinion shaft and brake drum as a unit.

When reinstalling, reverse the removal procedure and adjust brakes as

per paragraph 260. Pinion shaft bearing (3) is non-adjustable.

252. BULL GEAR & WHEEL AXLE SHAFT. To adjust the wheel axle shaft bearings, jack up rear end of the tractor, remove dust cap and turn adjusting nut (24—Fig. A25 or 70—Fig. A27) until all play is out of the bearings. Do not pre-load the bearings as this tends to distort the final drive housing.

253. MODELS A-BF-BG-R. To remove one of the final drive bull gears (30—Fig. A25) or wheel axle shaft (37), follow this procedure: Remove rear wheel, cover (31), cap (23), adjusting nut (24) and bearing cone (26). Lift

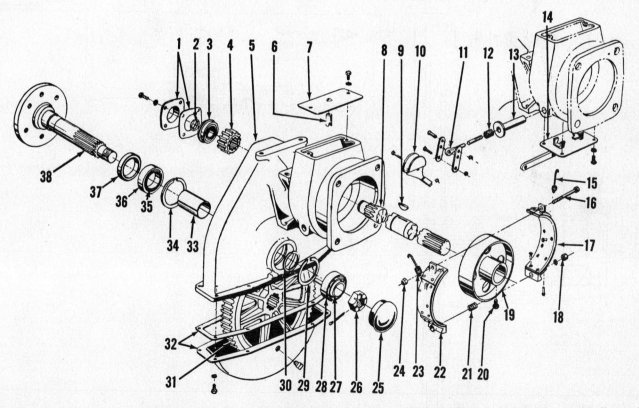

Fig. A26—Two final drive units similar to the above are used on model V tractors. When driving wheel shaft (38) out of bull gear be sure to buck up the gear with a heavy bar.

1. Bearing cap	9. Woodruff key	16. Brake adjusting bolt	24. Brake adjusting nut	31. Driven (bull) gear
2. Pinion snap ring	10. Brake locking cam	17. Rear brake shoe	25. Bearing cap	32. Gear cover
3. Pinion bearing	11. Brake shoe eyebolt	19. Brake drum	26. Adjusting nut	33. Driven gear spacer
4. Final drive (bull) pinion	12. Brake rod spring	20. Brake drum set screw	27. Inner bearing cone	34. Outer bearing snap ring
5. Final drive housing	13. Brake rod tube	21. Lower brake spring	28. Inner bearing cup	35. Outer bearing cone
6. Brake guide	14. Brake anchor and lower cover	22. Forward brake shoe	29. Inner bearing snap ring	36. Outer bearing cup
7. Brake upper cover	15. Rear brake shoe spring	23. Forward brake spring	30. Driven gear snap ring	37. Wheel axle oil seal
8. Bull pinion shaft				38. Wheel axle

snap ring (29) out of groove in shaft and cap screws (32) from housing. The tool necessary to push the wheel axle from the bull gear is made up of the following parts manufactured by OTC (any puller similar to this in design may be used); two short bolts No. 930L, push-puller No. O38, female adapter No. 923L.

Insert legs through holes in the inner side of housing and screw them into two threaded holes in bull gear hub. Place female adapter on threads of wheel axle and tighten. Install puller on the legs and adapter. Pres-

sure will have to be applied on the push-puller until the splines of the wheel axle shaft are completely free of bull gear. When reinstalling, use this tool to draw wheel axle into bull gear. Seal (36) should be installed with lip toward gear.

Bearings and oil seals for the wheel axle shaft can be renewed at this time. When adjusting bearings, tighten the adjusting nut (24) until all end play is out of bearings.

254. MODEL V. Removal of final drive (bull) gear or wheel axle shaft

from this model is accomplished in same manner as described in paragraph 253, except that there is no provision made for use of puller. When bumping the wheel axle shaft out of or into the bull gear splines, be sure to buck up the gear with a heavy bar so as to avoid distorting the final drive housing. A tool must be devised if wheel axle shaft has a heavy interference fit in splined hub of bull gear and it may be necessary to heat the gear slightly to aid removal and reinstallation.

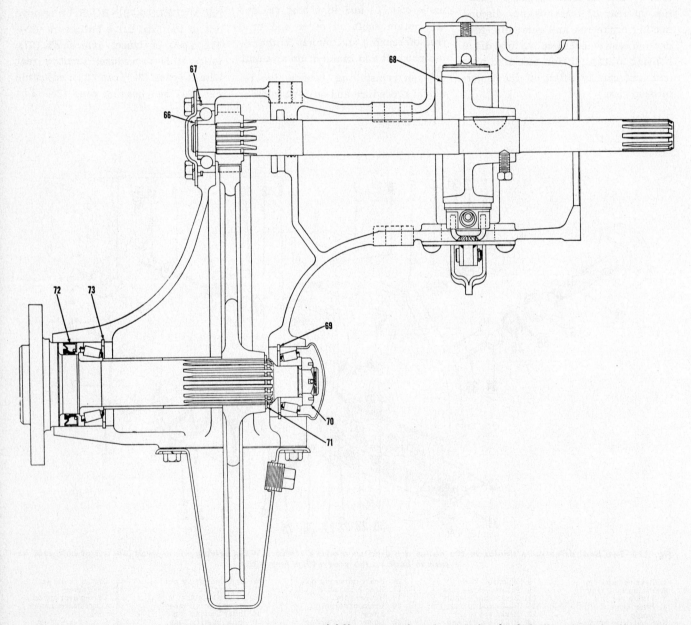

Fig. A27—Section through one final drive unit as used on model V tractors. There is no spring loaded oil seal on the pinion shaft where it passes through inner vertical wall of housing.

BRAKES

Brakes shown in Figs. A28 and A29 are external band type contracting on drums located in the final drive housings and mounted on the main axle (bull pinion) shafts. Brake eyebolts (11) are connected to brake pedals by rods and a brake pedal cross-shaft mounted in the frame. Individual brake locking cams (10) are provided on front of final drive housing on some models.

ADJUSTMENT

260. To adjust brakes, remove upper cover and tighten nut (2) on adjusting

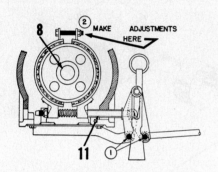

Fig. A28. Simplified view of brake element and linkage used on models A, BF, BG and R. A shoe centering guide (not shown) similar to (9) in Fig. A29 is used on these models.

bolt until rear wheel cannot be rotated by hand, then back nut off 2-2½ turns or until drag is removed. Bands are centered on drum by the adjustable brake guides (9) mounted on the top cover (7) as shown in Fig. A29. Test freedom of rotation of wheel after top cover is installed to make sure that guides (9) are not forcing

Fig. A29 — Section through one brake element used on model V tractors. This brake is similar to one shown in Fig. A28 except that cam linkage (10) is different than linkage (1) in Fig. A28.

2. Brake adjusting nut
6. Adjusting bolt
7. Top cover
8. Bull pinion shaft
9. Band centering guide
10. Actuating cam

top ends of bands against drums thus throwing bands eccentric to drum and causing drag. Guide should just contact the adjusting bolt when cover is installed.

Adjust the pedals by means of the brake connecting eyebolts (11) so that they both have the same amount of free travel.

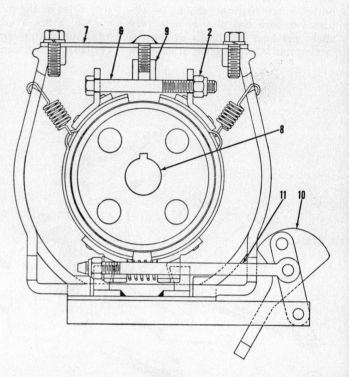

PTO & BELT PULLEY

A unit containing a pto shaft only, or a pto shaft and a belt pulley is optionally available on all models. In models A, BF, BG and R the pto external shaft is driven from the end of the transmission countershaft (input shaft) via a coupling shaft (22—Fig. A30) called the drive shaft. A spur gear (25) mounted on this shaft drives the combination spur and bevel gear (12) on the pto external shaft. The bevel toothed portion (not visible in Fig. A30) of gear (12) meshes with the bevel gear (46) on the inner end of the belt pulley shaft.

The belt pulley and pto unit on the model V employs a somewhat similar drive as shown in Fig. A32. In this model, however,

the drive shaft spur pinion (12) meshes with the spur gear (19) on the pto external shaft while the belt pulley shaft (29) is driven from a separate bevel pinion (13) on the drive shaft which meshes with the bevel gear (30) on the belt pulley shaft.

OVERHAUL
Models A-BF-BG-R

270. The procedure for removal of the unit from the rear face of the transmission housing is self-evident. To disassemble the removed unit, follow the procedure outlined in paragraphs 271, 272.

271. **DISASSEMBLY.** To remove the pto shaft, first remove the bearing cap

(5—Fig. A30) and shims and gaskets from the rear face of housing. Using a puller with jaws of same engaged over the front face of gear as shown in Fig. A31, press the pto shaft out of the gear. The front bearing cup (18—Fig. A30) and snap ring (20) will remain in the housing. If this cup is removed for any reason, be sure to mark and keep together the shim or shims (19) located between the cup and the housing. These shims are used to control the mesh position of the combination spur and bevel gear (12).

The belt pulley shaft can be removed after removing the pto shaft by first extracting the Welch plug (3) from the housing. Remove nut (47) and shims (48 and 49) from inner end of shaft. Bump pulley shaft out through opening in opposite side of housing and with it the oil seal (52) and outer bearing cone (54). Bearing cups can now be removed from the housing.

272. REASSEMBLY. During reassembly observe the following: Belt pulley shaft bearings should be adjusted to zero end play or to a very slight pre-load by means of the retaining nut (47). Function of the shim

washers (48 and 49) is to establish the tooth backlash of bevel gear (46). Reinstall the original shim washers in making the initial reassembly of the unit.

If pto shaft front bearing cup was removed, be sure to reinstall the same shim washer (19). Adjust the pto shaft bearings to free rotation with zero end play by varying the shims and gaskets (8). A gasket should be installed on both sides of the metallic shim washers which are available in two sizes 0.005 and 0.010 thick. Gaskets are also available in two sizes, 0.0075 and 0.010

thick. After bearings are correctly adjusted, observe mesh position of pto shaft bevel gear in relation to bevel gear on pulley shaft. The heel faces of both gears should be flush with each other within 0.006 when the backlash of mating teeth is within the limits of 0.004-0.007.

If backlash is less than 0.004, remove a shim (48 or 49) from the belt pulley shaft, or, add a shim if backlash is greater than 0.007. If heel faces are not within 0.006 of being flush with each other after correct backlash has been obtained, it will then be necessary to

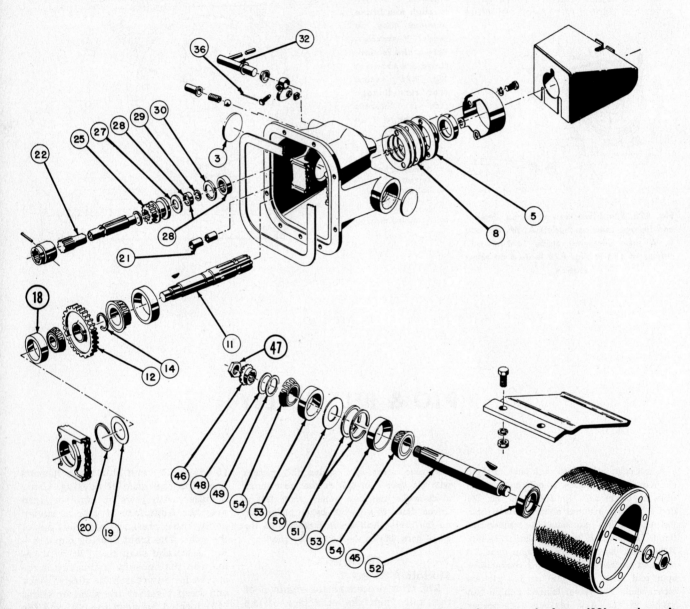

Fig. A30—Belt pulley and pto unit used on Models A, BF, BG and R tractors. Although only the spur teeth of gear (12) are shown, it has also a set of bevel teeth which drive the belt pulley bevel gear (46).

3. Welch plug	19. Inner bearing shim	32. Shift lever shaft	49. Shim
8. Shims and gaskets	20. Snap ring	36. Lockwire	50. Oil washer
11. Pto shaft	21. Bearing oil tube	45. Belt pulley shaft	51. Snap ring
12. Pto shaft gear	22. Pto drive shaft	46. Pulley bevel gear	52. Oil seal
14. Snap ring	25. Drive shaft gear	48. Shim	53. Bearing cup
	27. Inner race spacer		
	28. Roller bearing		
	29. Snap ring		
	30. Snap ring		

change the position to the pto gear by removing or adding shims (19). If this must be done, do so by removing the front bearing snap ring (20) to avoid the longer job of disassembling the pto shaft.

Model V

The procedure for removal of the unit from the rear face of the transmission housing is self-evident. When the unit housing is withdrawn from the transmission, the drive or input shaft assembly (7—Fig. A32) will come out with it.

273. DISASSEMBLY AND REASSEMBLY. Procedure for disassembly is practically self-evident by examining the unit and by referring to Fig. A32. The pto external shaft (18) can be removed after removing the shaft guard cap screws, snap rings (23) and gear (19). The drive shaft (7) is removed by extracting the large snap ring (9) and drive shaft special self-locking nut (14). The mesh position of the bevel gear (13) on this shaft is controlled by the shim washers (15, 16 and 17) which are available in 3 sizes of 0.003, 0.005 and 0.010 thickness. The position of belt pulley bevel gear (30) is not adjustable but the bearings for belt pulley shaft are adjustable by varying the shim washers (39 and 40). These shims are available in two sizes, 0.005 and 0.010 thickness.

Fig. A31—Removal of gear from front of pto shaft on models A, BF, BG and R usually requires a puller hooked up as shown.

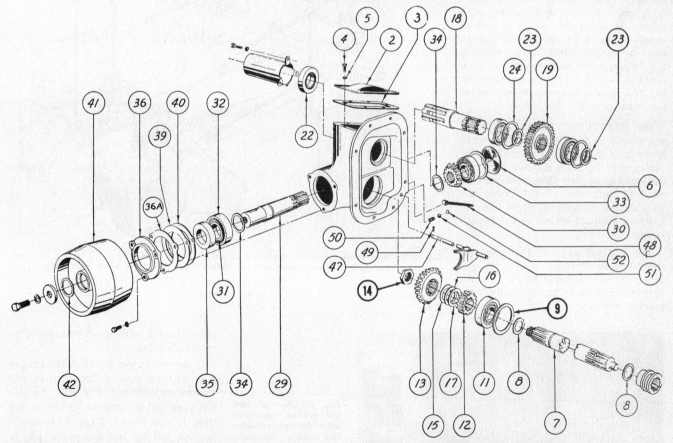

Fig. A32—Belt pulley and power take-off unit used on model V tractors. Mesh position of belt pulley driven gear (30) is not adjustable.

6. Welch plug	13. BP driving gear	29. BP shaft	36A. Gasket
7. PTO drive shaft	15. Shim	30. BP driven gear	39. Shim
8. Snap ring	16. Shim	33. Snap ring	40. Shim
11. Bearing	17. Shim	34. Snap ring	41. Pulley
12. PTO driving gear	18. PTO shaft	35. Oil seal	42. Snap ring
	19. PTO driven gear		
	22. Oil seal		
	23. Snap ring		
	24. Snap ring		

HYDRAULIC SYSTEM

The hydraulic system on all Avery built models and early production Minneapolis-Moline built models consists of a pump mounted on the back face of the timing gear case behind the governor gear, a combination work cylinder and valves unit of either the fixed or pivoted type, an implement shaft control and an implement shaft or lifting roll actuated by the work cylinders. BG and some BF models are equipped with the Minneapolis-Moline HKG hydraulic system, which includes a different pump mounted in the same location as on the Avery built tractors, a combination fluid reservoir and valves unit and a separately mounted work cylinder.

HKG SYSTEM

BG and some BF models are equipped with the same basic hydraulic system as used on Minneapolis-Moline late production tractors. In these installations the double acting work cylinder is not contained in the oil reservoir, but is mounted on a support bolted to the left frame rail as shown in Fig. A32A. In the HKG system, only the control valves are contained in the hydraulic system reservoir which is bolted to the clutch housing as shown. On the HKG system the pump is mounted on the engine as in the older system.

399. **SERVICING.** Length of control rod should be so adjusted so that when lever is in notch 9 the work cylinder piston will be fully extended on the out-stroke. At this time there should be 1/16 inch clearance between the stop on the implement shaft and the cylinder support bolted to the chassis frame.

The control stop on the quadrant should be so adjusted so that the system returns to neutral just before the cylinder piston is in the fully contracted position.

For overhaul information covering the work cylinder and the oil reservoir and valves unit, refer to the similar units on the Minneapolis-Moline tractors covered elsewhere in this manual.

AVERY SYSTEM

TEST AND ADJUST

To avoid haphazard removal and disassembly of system components, follow a logical test and adjustment procedure. Always make sure that implement shaft has free movement, and that the implement is installed and correctly adjusted. Make sure that

there is sufficient oil in the reservoir and correct any internal leaks before disassembling any of the sub assemblies of the system.

Older Type on Model A

400. To adjust power unit and control rod assembly, first check connections on pump and power unit for tightness, then check for any looseness or misalignment of the bearing plate (8—Fig. A32B), which will throw trip mechanism out of adjustment. To set the bearing plate in its proper position, first loosen the three bolts holding it to the frame. Back these off just enough to free the plate. Next loosen the locknuts on the angle support and screw the setscrews down until the

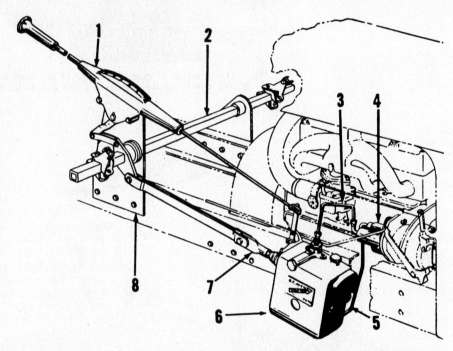

Fig. A32B—Hydraulic system as mounted on early Avery built model A tractors. The control assembly (1) and power unit (6) differs from the latter type installation.

1. Control assembly
2. Implement (rod) shaft
3. Hydraulic line
4. Hydraulic pump
5. Hydraulic line
6. Power unit
7. Piston connector
8. Bearing plate

Fig. A32A — BF and BG models equipped with Minneapolis-Moline HKG hydraulic system.

plate is solid with the frame. Retighten frame bolts.

If the cotter pin is not in the proper hole on the end of the control rod (Valve Adjustment) Fig. A33, the piston may fail to operate in one direction. If this should happen, shift the control rod by moving cotter pin to proper hole.

401. If the length of the piston rod is not properly adjusted, the control rod may not release in the lowered or raised position. To adjust, when it

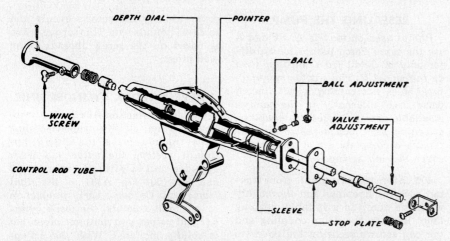

Fig. A33—Hydraulic unit control rod used on early production Avery built model A tractors. Refer to Fig. A35 for unit used on later production.

fails to release in the raised position, screw the piston connector (7—Fig. A32B) in. If it fails to release in the lowered position, screw the piston connector out.

402. The control rod is locked in one of three positions; neutral, raise, and lower, by a spring actuated ball engaging notches in a sleeve on the control rod. If the spring is too loose, the rod may be released ahead of time, or not locked at all. If the spring is too tight, the rod will not release and may bend the pointer levers. When properly adjusted, ball should enter the threaded hole of control housing approximately 5/16 inch. Proper spring tension is obtained when the control rod will "kick out" at the same depth setting. To check, examine stop plate on front of control housing to see that it is not binding the rod. Lower implement and set control for depth. Note position of pointer on dial. Raise and lower implement. If the pointer does not repeat to within ¼ inch of the dial reading, tighten the ball spring until it does. Lock jam nut on the screw to maintain proper spring tension on ball spring.

Models A (late)-BF-R-V

403. **PUMP.** Required for pump test are a gauge of 3000 pounds capacity and a gate valve as shown in Fig. A34. The pump has a rated capacity of 2.5 gallons per minute at 1200 pounds pressure at 2800 rpm of the pump shaft. To test pump on the tractor, remove the regulator pressure line and insert a ¼ inch steel or copper line with the valve and gauge installed as shown. Run the engine at governed speed (1800 rpm) and gradually reduce the valve opening until a pressure of 2000 pounds shows on the gauge. It should not be necessary to

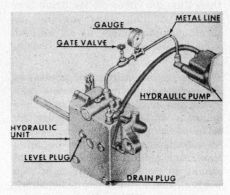

Fig. A34—Hookup for testing hydraulic pump while installed on tractor. Gauge is of 3000 psi capacity.

completely close the valve to obtain this pressure and there should be some flow during this test.

At 900 engine rpm the pump should show some flow when the gate valve is adjusted to produce a gauge pressure of 1600 pounds. If the pump will not produce the above pressures, it is not up to minimum standards and should be removed for repair. In most cases a renewal of the seals will correct the trouble and a repair kit containing a set of seals and a cover bearing spring is available. If the pump passes the above test the trouble is located elsewhere in the system.

404. **ADJUST NEUTRAL RETURN.** If the knob on the control rod (Fig. A35) is pushed forward and released when the implement is in the fully raised position, it should return the work cylinder unit to the neutral position. If unit does not return to the neutral position, loosen the screw at the front stop and move the stop rearward in small steps until the unit returns to neutral.

If the control shaft does not return the unit to neutral position after the implement is lowered, proceed as follows: Loosen wing screw (W) and set screw (S) and move control knob forward about ⅛ inch and tighten the knob set screw. Move depth control

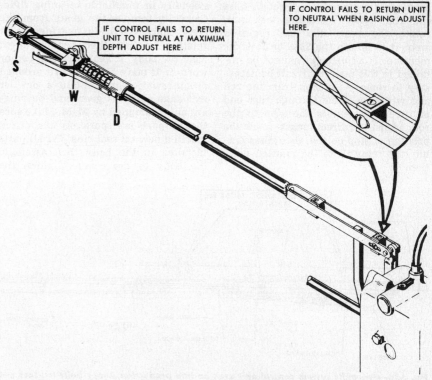

Fig. A35—Later version of control rod as used on late Avery built and early production Minneapolis-Moline built tractors.

(D) to the rear as far as possible then tighten the wing screw. If after once repeating this adjustment, the unit does not return to neutral, the control should be checked and reset as outlined in paragraph 405.

405. RESETTING THE CONTROL ROD UNIT. When the minor adjustment of the control rod outlined in paragraph 404 does not correct the failure of the unit to return to neutral, it should be given a major adjustment as follows:

405A. Remove the set screw from the control knob and withdraw the knob and rod unit. If the distance from the nearest face of the knob and the end of the rod is other than 7,5/16 inches as shown in Fig. A36, loosen the rod lock nut and turn the knob on the rod threads until this distance is obtained.

Measure the distance from the depth control rod pin to the farthest face of the rear control stop. If this distance is other than 28⅛ inches on models A, BF and R or 14⅛ inches on the model V, the rod must be reset. This usually can be done without completely disassembling the control by first determining the amount that the rod must be shortened or lengthened. Using a long screwdriver, loosen the set screw (O) and remove the pin and the front stop. Allow the depth control rod to move forward until hole in rod aligns with hole in control tube. Insert the previously removed pin through tube and rod. After loosening lock nut, rotate the rear stop the required amount to obtain the 28⅛ or 14⅛ dimension. If adjustment cannot be obtained in this manner it will be necessary to remove the stop from the rod and withdraw same through rear end of tube. Reassemble the stop to the rod, adjust to correct length, mark the position of stop on rod, then disassemble and reinstall to the marked position.

RESEALING THE PUMP

Pumps used on models A, BF and R are the same Pesco pumps which differ only in detail from the unit used on the model V. The tractor manufacturer does not catalog a full line of parts used internally in the pumps. Available are the necessary coupling, attaching parts and a repair kit containing a complete set of seals and a cover bearing spring.

406. After removing unit from tractor, cork the openings and thoroughly wash the pump in a suitable cleaning fluid. Remove the drive coupling and the cap screws securing the cover to the body. Loosen the cover by tapping it carefully with a plastic hammer then slide the cover off the drive gear shaft. Wash the cover assembly in cleaning fluid. Renew all of the seal rings, shims and the cover bearing spinrg.

If the cover bearings are grooved or otherwise worn, it will be necessary to obtain an exchange pump or a new pump as M-M does not catalog the cover bearings or gears. On model V tractors the shaft oil seal in the pump cover is a metallic cartridge type and should be renewed at this time. The shaft oil seal in the cover of the pumps for models A, BF and R is an "O" ring which should be renewed. Be sure that the small drain holes in the cover are not plugged.

Thoroughly wash the pump body assembly in a suitable cleaning fluid. Carefully remove the gears from the body. Mark the body bearings as to relative location then remove them from the body. If gears are chipped or worn or if body bearings are grooved or otherwise worn, obtain a new or exchange pump as gears and bearings are not catalogued by M-M. Make sure that all parts are spotlessly clean then install a new oil seal ring. Oil all parts installed in the body then assemble the body to the cover. Tighten the

cover-to-body cap screws evenly and to 20-25 pounds feet. This torque value is based on the screw threads being well oiled.

VALVE & WORK CYLINDER UNIT

On late production Avery built tractors and on all Minneapolis-Moline built tractors using the Avery hydraulic system, the valve and work cylinder unit is pivotally mounted at end cap (50—Fig. A39) on the right frame rail. On some early production Avery built tractors, the work cylinder and valves unit does not pivot, but is solidly mounted. With the exception of the release valves, the servicing and repair procedures are the same on both systems.

407. DISASSEMBLY & REPAIR. Procedure for removal of the unit from the tractor is self-evident. After the unit is off the tractor, the two hose openings should be corked and the exterior of the unit thoroughly washed in a suitable cleaning fluid.

408. FRONT CAP & PISTON. The front end cap, piston and cylinder sleeve units can be removed after disconnecting the selector valve lever and removing the cap screws which retain the end cap to the case. Install new retainers Fig. A41 and new cup seals to rod. If piston rod or cylinder sleeve show any scoring or pitting, install new ones. The self-locking nut on end of piston rod should be tightened to 30-35 pounds feet torque. Disassemble the end cap also and install new sealing parts and grease the piston rod before assembling it to the end cap.

409. REAR END CAP. Remove the plug, spring and ball from top of the rear end cap then remove the 4 cap-to-case retaining screws and the end cap unit Fig. A42. Disassemble the rear end cap and renew the large seal ring, medium seal ring and the back-up washer. The spring and ball in the upper part of the cap act as a detent for the selector valve cam. If spring is bent or has taken a set, install a new one. Renew the ball if it shows any perceptible wear. The selector valve and cam unit can be withdrawn from the housing at this time.

410. LATE MODEL RELEASE VALVES. One of the two release valves is located near the top of the case under the rear end cap as shown in Fig. A43. The other release valve is located in the same relative position in the opposite end of the case under the front end cap. Both valves are non-

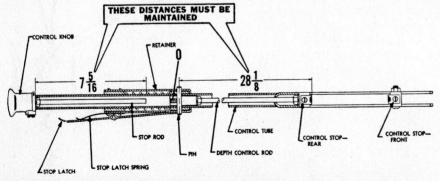

Fig. A36—Hydraulic system control unit used on late production Avery built tractors and early production MM built tractors. Automatic return of work cylinder to neutral position is dependent on maintaining the dimensions shown.

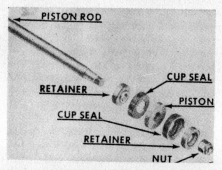

Fig. A41—All of the seals on the piston rod and in the end cap should be renewed at overhaul.

adjustable but the one under the rear end cap operates only when raising the implement and has a spring which permits the valve to unload at 120-125 psi. The other release valve located under the front end cap operates only when the implement is lowered and has a much "heavier" spring which unloads at 1100 psi. Both valves should be removed and inspected for bent or broken springs and condition of valve balls and seats. Care must be exercised when removing the valves to prevent damage to the bores in the case. Renew the small seal ring on

each valve seat and do the same to the balls if they show signs of not seating properly. Reseat a new ball by a few sharp blows, using a hammer and a brass drift. After reassembling the parts in the order shown, make certain that the small spring in each case is sealed straight in the retainer, the head of which should be flush or slightly within the case when fully tightened.

410A. EARLY TYPE RELEASE VALVES. On the older Avery built Avery tractors, the release valves require a different servicing procedure

Fig. A42—Removal of rear end cap sub-assembly from Avery hydraulic power unit.

1. Medium seal ring	3. Back-up washer
2. Large seal ring	4. Pipe plug
	5. End cap

Fig. A43—Assembly sequence of rear release valve. A similar valve having a much stiffer spring is mounted under the front end cap at opposite end of the power unit. Refer to Fig. A44 for early type release valves.

	23. Seal ring	
20. Spring	24. Seat	
21. Valve	25. Ball	26. Spring
		27. Retainer

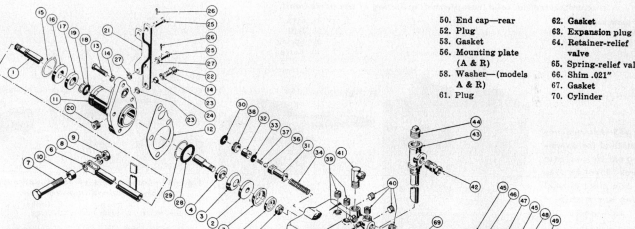

50. End cap—rear	62. Gasket
52. Plug	63. Expansion plug
53. Gasket	64. Retainer-relief
56. Mounting plate	valve
(A & R)	65. Spring-relief valve
58. Washer—(models	66. Shim .021"
A & R)	67. Gasket
61. Plug	70. Cylinder

1. Piston rod	28. Seal ring
2. Piston	29. Back-up washer
3. Cup seal	30. Seal ring
4. Retainer	31. Release valve
5. Self-locking nut	32. Valve seat
6. Piston rod extension	33. Seal ring
10. Bushing	34. Spring—front
11. End cap—front	release valve
15. Snap ring	35. Spring—rear
16. Washer	release valve
17. Oil seal	38. Retainer
18. Seal ring	45. Washer
19. Back-up washer	46. Spacer
20. Pipe plug	47. Washer
21. Selector valve lever	48. Cam-selector valve

Fig. A39—Exploded view of the hydraulic power unit (work cylinder & valves unit) used on late production Avery built and early production Minneapolis-Moline built Avery tractors.

than outlined in paragraph 410. With the unit off the tractor and both end caps removed, tip the assembly so that the pipe spacer, valve, light spring and ball will fall out. Using care to prevent damaging the bore, insert a drift or rod into the opening and push the remaining parts, Fig. A44, out through the front of the unit. Check the springs, balls and seats for wear and renew any that are worn or damaged. Remove the "O" ring seal from each seat and install new ones. Reseat a new ball by a few sharp blows, using a hammer and a brass drift.

410B. Procedure for reassembling is to first remove the two pipe plugs from the rear top side of the unit Fig. A45. Obtain a short piece of metal tubing, 9/16 inch outside diameter, ½ inch inside diameter. Select the valve seat with the larger hole, oil the inside wall of the tubing and place this seat into the tubing with the slotted end of the seat to the outside. Insert a small rod into the rear pipe plug hole and push the seat into the bore until it strikes

the rod. Hold the seat in place with a small punch then remove the tubing. Install the ball, light spring, valve and pipe spacer into the bore and reinstall the unit rear end cap.

410C. Assemble the plunger into the plunger housing. Using a small piece of 0.002 shim stock, place these parts into the piece of metal tubing as shown. Function of the shim stock is to prevent damaging the "O" ring seal when it passes the pipe plug hole. Install these parts into the bore from the front of the case and remove the shim stock and piece of tubing. Using the same procedure outlined in paragraph 410B, install the seat which has the small opening, then insert the ball, the large spring and the valve in that order. Install the front end cap to the unit.

411. SELECTOR VALVE AND CAM. The valve and cam unit can be lifted from the case after the rear end cap has been removed as outlined in paragraph 409.

With valve Fig. A46 removed, thoroughly and carefully clean the bore in the case and the valve. If valve is roughened or scored, it should be renewed. To remove the cam from the valve, first insert a ¼ inch drift or rod into the hole in the valve then remove the cotter pin. When removing the nut be careful as the releasing of the spring pressure may send the parts flying. The oil and dust cover seal located in the case at opposite end of the selector valve bore should be removed and a new one installed. Open end of seal should face to the inside.

412. RELIEF VALVE. The relief valve, Fig. A47 on all models, can be serviced without removing the valves and work cylinder unit from the tractor. To test the valve, remove the pipe plug from one of the end caps and install in its place a pressure gauge of 2000 pounds or higher capacity as shown in Fig. A48. Start the engine and operate the work cylinder a few times then run the piston to the opposite end of the unit. Hold the selector control so that it tries to force the piston even further in this direction and note the gauge reading. The reading should be 1400-1600 psi. If reading is less than 1400 add shims (4—Fig. A47) until this reading is obtained. If reading is higher than 1600, remove a shim or shims.

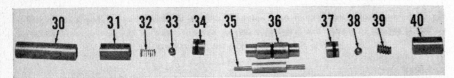

Fig. A44—Assembly sequence of early type release valves used in Avery built Avery tractors having the solid (non-pivoted) mounting of the power unit.

30. Pipe spacer
31. Valve
32. Spring
33. Ball
34. Seat
35. Plunger
36. Plunger housing
37. Seat
38. Ball
39. Spring
40. Valve

Fig. A45—Recommended method for assembling old style release valves involves the use of a piece of steel tubing and a strip of shim stock.

X. Rear pipe hole
41. Plunger housing
42. Metal tube
43. Shim stock (0.002)

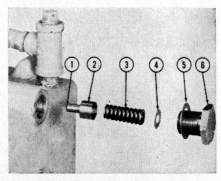

Fig. A47—Components of relief valve assembly contained in power unit.

1. Ball
2. Relief valve
3. Spring
4. Shim
5. Gasket
6. Plug

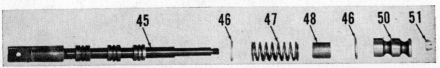

Fig. A46—Assembly sequence of selector valve and cam assembly. The cam need not be removed from valve unless the valve is to be renewed.

45. Selector valve
46. Washer
47. Spring
48. Spacer
50. Selector cam
51. Nut

Fig. A48—Using a pressure gauge to test hydraulic system relief valve without removing power unit from tractor.

MINNEAPOLIS-MOLINE

Minneapolis-Moline Models ■ GB ■ UB ■ ZB

Previously contained in I & T Shop Service Manual No. MM-6

SHOP MANUAL
MINNEAPOLIS - MOLINE

SERIES GB-UB-ZB

IDENTIFICATION
Tractor serial number is stamped on a plate which is riveted to side of transmission housing.

Engine serial number is stamped on a plate which is riveted to side of crankcase.

AXLE TYPE	TRICYCLE TYPE
Adjustable: UBE - ZBE	Double Wheel: UBU - ZBU
Non-Adjustable: GB - GBD - GBLP	Single Wheel: UBN - ZBN

INDEX (By Starting Paragraph)

CONDENSED SERVICE DATA

Model or Series	Model GB	Model GBLP	Model GBD	LP-Gas Series UB	Series UB	Diesel Series UB	LP-Gas Series ZB	Series ZB
GENERAL								
Engine Make	Own	Own	Own	Own	Own	Own	Own	Own
No. Cylinders	4	4	6	4	4	4	4	4
Bore—Inches	4⅝	4⅝	4¼	4¼	4¼	4¼	3⅝	3⅝
Stroke—Inches	6	6	5	5	5	5	5	5
Displacement—Cubic Inches	403.2	403.2	425.5	283.7	283.7	283.7	206	206
Compression Ratio (Except Tractor Fuel)	5.7:1	8.3:1	15:1	7.9:1	6.35:1	15:1	7.7:1	6.1:1
Compression Ratio (Tractor Fuel)	4.7:1	.....	.....	.....	4.4:1	.....	.....	4.7:1
Pistons Removed From?	Above	Above	Above	Above	Above	Above	*	*
Main & Rod Brgs. Adjustable?	No	No	No	No	No	No	No	No
Cylinders Sleeved?	No	No	No	No	No	No	No	No
Forward Speeds, Number of	5	5	5	5	5	5	5	5
Main Bearings, Number of	3	3	4	3	3	3	3	3
TUNE-UP								
Firing Order	1-3-4-2	1-3-4-2	1-5-3-6-2-4	1-3-4-2	1-3-4-2	1-3-4-2	1-3-4-2	1-3-4-2
Valve Tappet Gap—Inlet (Hot)	0.008	0.008	0.008	0.008	0.008	0.008	0.008	0.008
Valve Tappet Gap—Exhaust (Hot)	0.010	0.010	0.010	0.010	0.010	0.010	0.010	0.010
Valve Seat Angle (Degrees)	45	45	45	45	45	45	45	45
Ignition Distributor Make	D-R	D-R	.....	D-R	D-R	.....	D-R	D-R
Ignition Distributor Model	1111748	1111748	.....	1111748	1111748	.....	1111711	1111711
Breaker Contact Gap	0.020	0.020	.....	0.020	0.020	.....	0.020	0.020
Ignition Timing @ High Idle Speed								
Gasoline	4⅛"B	.....	.....	.....	3⅞"B	.....	.....	2⅛"B
Distillate	4⅛"B	.....	.....	.....	4⅛"B	.....	.....	2⅛"B
LP-Gas	.....	4⅜"B	.....	4⅛"B	.....	.....	1¾"B	.....
High Idle Engine Speed	1430	1430	***	1430	1430	1430	1650	1650
Flywheel Mark Indicating:								
Ignition Timing	None	None	.....	None	None	.....	None	None
Injection Timing	.....	.....	**	.....	.....	**	.....	.....
Spark Plug Electrode Gap	0.025	0.025	.....	0.025	0.025	.....	0.025	0.025
Carburetor Make (Except LP-Gas)	M-S	.....	.....	.....	M-S	.....	.....	M-S
Carburetor Make (LP-Gas)	.....	Ensign	.....	Ensign	.....	.....	Ensign	.....
Carburetor Model (Marvel-Schebler)	TSX625	.....	.....	.....	TSX67	.....	.....	TSX97
Carburetor Model (Ensign)	.....	Kgl	.....	Kgl	.....	.....	Kgl	.....
Carburetor Float Setting	¼ inch	.....	.....	.....	¼ inch	.....	.....	¼ inch
SIZES—CAPACITIES—CLEARANCES								
(Clearances in thousandths)								
Crankshaft Journal Dia. (Front)	2.9115	2.9115	2.9115	2.9115	2.9115	2.9115	Roller	Roller
Crankshaft Journal Dia. (Intermediate)	2.9115	2.9115	2.9115	2.9115	2.9115	2.9115	2.750	2.750
Crankshaft Journal Dia. (Rear)	2.9115	2.9115	2.9115	2.9115	2.9115	2.9115	3.000	3.000
Crankpin Dia.	2.7495	2.7495	2.9115	2.577	2.577	2.906	2.6245	2.6245
Camshaft Journal Dia. No. 1 (Front)	3.308	3.308	3.3385	3.308	3.308	3.308	1.24655	1.24655
Camshaft Journal Dia. No. 2	3.2755	3.2755	3.308	3.2755	3.2755	3.2755	1.24655	1.24655
Camshaft Journal Dia. No. 3	1.9965	1.9965	3.2755	1.9965	1.9965	1.9965	1.24655	1.24655
Camshaft Journal Dia. No. 4	.....	.....	1.9965	.....	.....	.....	.....	.....
Piston Pin Diameter	1.2497	1.2497	1.500	1.2497	1.2497	1.500	0.9995	0.9995
Valve Stem Diameter	7/16	7/16	7/16	7/16	7/16	7/16	11/32	11/32
Compression Ring Width	3/16	3/16	3/32	5/32	5/32	3/32	⅛	⅛
Oil Ring Width	¼	¼	3/16	¼	¼	3/16	3/16	3/16
Plain Main Brgs., Diam. Clearance	1.5-4	1.5-4	1.5-4	1.5-4	1.5-4	1.5-4	1.5-3.5	1.5-3.5
Rod Brgs., Diam. Clearance	1.5-4	1.5-4	1.5-4	1.5-4	1.5-4	1.5-4	1.5-4	1.5-4
Piston Skirt Clearance	4-5	4-5	6.5-7.5	4-5	4-5	6.5-7.5	2.5-4.5	2.5-4.5
Crankshaft End Play	2-6	2-6	2-6	2-6	2-6	2-6	3-4	3-4
Camshaft Brgs., Clearance Max.	8	8	8	8	8	8	7	7
Cooling System—Gallons	12	12	12	6	6	6	3¾	3¾
Crankcase Oil—Quarts	9	9	14	9	9	9	7	7
Trans. & Diff.—Quarts	52	52	52	52	52	52	28	28
Fuel Tank Capacity (Except LPG)—Gals.	29	.....	29	.....	21	21	.....	19
Gasoline Starting Tank—Gals.	¾	.....	.....	.....	1	.....	.....	⅞

*Pistons are removed with cylinder blocks.
**Refer to paragraph 121.
***1430 rpm for belt and pto work, 1650 for other work.

FRONT SYSTEM AND STEERING (TRICYCLE TYPE)

PEDESTAL (FRONT SUPPORT) & COMPONENTS

The support or pedestal unit of tricycle type models can be overhauled without removing the unit from the tractor.

Model ZBN

1. WHEEL BEARINGS AND AXLE. The two wheel axle shaft bearings can be renewed after removing two clamp bolts from lower end of fork. Each wheel bearing is individually adjusted by means of nut (25—Fig. MM250) so as to remove all end play and yet permit wheel to rotate freely.

2. FORK, EXTENSION SHAFT, BEARINGS AND SECTOR. To remove these parts, proceed as follows: Remove wheel and hub assembly, and hood, radiator and grille assembly. Remove starting crank extension shaft and upper bearing cover (18—Fig. MM250).

Remove wheel fork to extension shaft retaining cap screw (26), cap screw (34) and large washer (33) from upper end of extension shaft as shown in Fig. MM251. Remove cover plate (19—Fig. MM250) from support by placing large washer under the head of one of the radiator retaining cap screws and turning the screw into one of the threaded holes of the cover plate. Pry under the washer with a suitable bar until the cover plate, upper bearing and cage (30) are removed.

To remove the extension shaft from fork, place two pieces of "2x4" blocks on top of support and bridge these with two steel bars. Screw a long ⅝ inch threaded stud into extension shaft and place a washer and nut on the threads. Screw the nut down against the steel bars until the shaft extension is pulled out of the wheel fork.

3. With the shaft extension removed as per paragraph 2, the wheel fork can be driven or preferably pushed out of the sector as shown in Fig. MM252. The steel bars are placed under the deck of the support and push is obtained by a puller screw, nut and washer reacting against top of fork and undersides of steel bars. The wheel fork bearing and felt seal can be renewed at this time.

When reassembling the parts to front support, it will be necessary to center the cover plate (19—Fig. MM250) to insure correct alignment of upper bearing cone (32) before tightening the cover plate retaining screws as shown in Fig. MM253. All of the support bearings are adjusted by turning the upper cap screw (34—Fig. MM250). The bearings should be adjusted to a slight drag.

4. STEERING SECTOR AND WORM. To remove the steering gear sector which is keyed to the wheel fork, proceed as outlined in paragraphs 2 and 3. To remove the steering gear worm and shaft, proceed as follows: Drive pin out of steering worm shaft universal joint. Loosen socket head set screw which locks the worm adjusting plug (nut) and un-screw the plug. Rotating the worm, thread same and out of mesh with the sector.

Adjust worm shaft bearings with adjusting plug to remove all end play and yet permit worm shaft to rotate freely.

5. R & R PEDESTAL. To remove the pedestal assembly, first remove hood, radiator and grille. Support front assembly and engine separately and remove bolts retaining front assembly to engine. It will be necessary to slightly raise engine so that pedestal can clear crankshaft pulley.

Model UBN

6. WHEEL BEARINGS AND AXLE. To renew or adjust the wheel axle bearings, follow the procedure outlined in paragraph 1.

Fig. MM250—Exploded view of model ZBN front support (pedestal) and associated parts.

18. Bearing cover	27. Washer
19. Housing cover plate	28. Housing
20. Lower bearing cup	29. Fork extension shaft
21. Cone	30. Upper bearing cage
22. Retainer washer	31. Upper bearing cup
23. Felt oil seal	32. Cone
24. Wheel fork	33. Washer
25. Adjusting nuts	34. Cap screw
26. Cap screw	

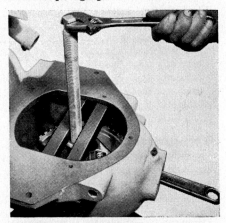

Fig. MM252—Pressing the wheel fork out of the steering sector on model ZBN.

Fig. MM251—Removing cap screw (34) and washer (33) from top of ZBN fork extension shaft.

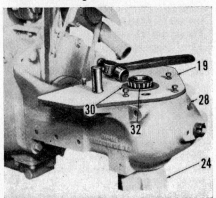

Fig. MM253—Model ZBN support housing cover plate is centered before tightening, by centering the upper bearing cone.

7. FORK, BEARINGS AND SECTOR. To remove these parts, proceed as follows: Raise and support front portion of tractor and remove wheel and hub assembly. Remove hood, radiator and grille assembly. Slide pedestal forward on pedestal supports, drive crankpin out of crank lower shaft and remove the sprocket housing cover, lower sprocket and chain. Drive the tapered pin out of the upper sprocket and shaft as in Fig. MM254 and remove the sprocket.

Remove cover from pedestal. Release pressure from spring by removing cotter pin from the crank extension shaft and withdraw crank extension shaft, spring and washer.

Remove nut and washer (9—Fig. MM255) from fork, and, using a piece of pipe slipped over threads of the wheel fork as shown in Fig. MM256, drive the fork and lower bearing cone unit down and out of sector. Bearing cage (14—Fig. MM255) can now be removed from the housing.

Reinstall parts by reversing the removal procedure and tighten nut (8) to obtain a slight amount of bearing drag.

8. STEERING SECTOR AND WORM. To remove the steering gear sector, which is keyed to the wheel fork, proceed as outlined in paragraph 7. To remove the steering worm and shaft, proceed as follows: Drive the pin out of the steering worm shaft universal joint, loosen the socket head set screw which locks the worm adjusting plug (nut) and unscrew the plug.

Steering worm can now be turned out of housing as shown in Fig. MM257.

Adjust the worm shaft bearings with adjusting plug (16) to remove all end play and yet permit same to rotate freely.

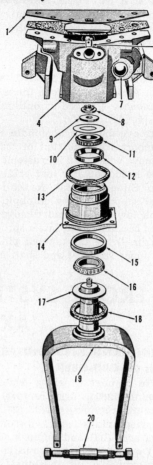

Fig. MM255—Exploded view of model UBN pedestal and associated parts. The taper roller bearings are carried in cage (14).

1. Housing cover	12 & 15. Bearing cups
4. Housing	13. Cork seal
7. Expansion plug	14. Bearing cage
8. Nut	17. Washer
9. Washer	18. Felt seal
10. Washer	19. Fork
11 & 16. Bearing cones	20. Axle

9. R & R SUPPORT ASSEMBLY. To remove the pedestal (front support) assembly, follow the general procedure given in paragraph 5.

Model ZBU

10. VERTICAL SPINDLE AND WHEEL AXLE. The wheel spindle (axle) and block assembly (11—Fig. MM258) can be removed as shown in

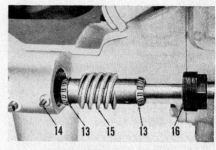

Fig. MM257—Removing steering gear worm on tricycle models. Adjusting nut (16) is locked by set screw (14).

13. Bearing cones   15. Steering worm

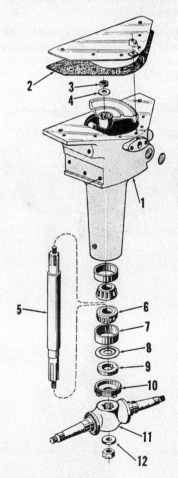

Fig. MM258—Exploded view of model UBU pedestal and related parts. Model ZBU is similarly constructed.

1. Pedestal	7. Cup
2. Gasket	8. Retainer
3. Nut	9. Felt seal
4. Washer	10. Adjusting nut
5. Spindle	11. Axle
6. Cone	12. Washer

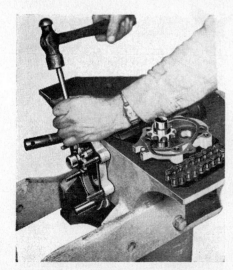

Fig. MM254—Removing crank sprocket assembly from models UBE, UBN and UBU pedestal.

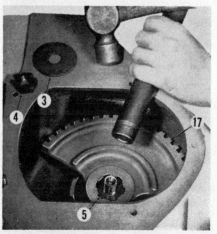

Fig. MM256—Using a piece of pipe to protect threads of vertical shaft when driving the shaft out of UBU pedestal. The same procedure can be used on model ZBU.

3. Washer   5. Shaft
4. Nut   17. Sector

Fig. MM259 by using a suitable puller, after removing the front wheel and hub assemblies, and the spindle block retaining nut.

10A. To remove axle & spindle (5—Fig. MM258), proceed as follows: Support front of tractor and remove hood, radiator and grille assembly. Remove pedestal cover, starting crank extension and front wheel and hub assemblies.

10B. Unscrew spindle shaft bearing adjusting nut (10) from lower side of pedestal after first removing the lock screw for same. Working through opening in top of pedestal, remove steering gear sector retaining nut. Using a piece of pipe as a drift, bump the vertical spindle down and out of the sector as shown in Fig. MM256. Vertical spindle bearing cups and cones can be renewed at this time.

Adjust vertical spindle bearings to a slight drag by turning adjusting nut (10—Fig. MM258) and then locking the adjustment with the socket head set screw.

11. STEERING SECTOR AND WORM. To remove the steering gear sector, proceed as outlined in paragraph 10A & 10B. Steering gear worm

& shaft overhaul and adjustment procedures are similar to the model which is outlined in paragraph 4.

12. R & R SUPPORT ASSEMBLY. To remove the pedestal (front support) unit, follow the procedure outlined in paragraph 5.

Model UBU

13. VERTICAL SPINDLE AND WHEEL AXLE. To remove the wheel axle assembly, proceed as outlined in paragraph 10.

To remove the vertical spindle, raise and support front portion of tractor and remove wheel and hub assemblies. Remove hood, radiator and grille assembly. Slide pedestal forward on pedestal supports, drive crankpin out of crank lower shaft and remove the sprocket housing cover, lower sprocket and chain. Drive the tapered pin out of the upper sprocket and shaft as in

Fig. MM254 and remove the sprocket.

Remove cover from pedestal. Release pressure from the crank extension shaft and withdraw crank extension shaft, spring and washer. For balance of disassembly, follow the procedure outlined in paragraph 10B.

Reassemble in reverse order and tighten adjusting nut (10 — Fig. MM258) to obtain a slight amount of bearing drag.

14. STEERING SECTOR AND WORM. To remove the steering sector, proceed as outlined in paragraph 13. The steering gear worm and shaft overhaul and adjustment procedures are similar to the model which is outlined in paragraph 4.

15. R & R SUPPORT ASSEMBLY. To remove the pedestal (front support) assembly, follow the general procedure given in paragraph 5.

FRONT SYSTEM AND STEERING (AXLE TYPE)

STEERING KNUCKLES AND ARMS
Models GB-GBD-GBLP

20. To remove steering knuckles (7—Fig. MM260), first remove the knuckle pin retaining screw (3). Remove snap rings (12), disconnect steering arm (23) and bump knuckle pin (2) out of axle and knuckle.

Ream knuckle pin bushings (10) after installation, if necessary, to provide 0.006-0.008 diametral clearance for the knuckle pin.

Models UBE-ZBE

22. The steering arm (14 — Fig. MM261) retains the knuckle to the spindle, and removal of the arm will release the knuckle from the axle spindle.

The old bushings can be pressed or driven out of knuckle by removing the one inch pipe plug in lower side of knuckle and using a drift.

The knuckle spindle bronze service bushings (11) require final sizing after

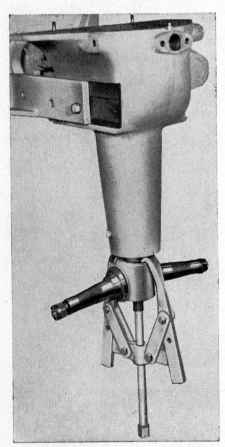

Fig. MM259—Removing horizontal axle from dual wheel tricycle type tractors.

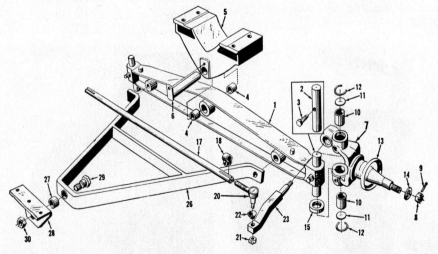

Fig. MM260—Exploded view of GB series front axle and associated parts. Pivot pins and knuckle pins are carried in bushings.

1. Front axle	8. Nut	22. Dust cover
2. Knuckle pin	9. Cotter pin	23. Steering arm
3. Screw	10. Bushings	26. Reach (radius rod)
4. Bushings	11. Plugs	27. Bushing
5. Pivot bracket	12. Snap rings	28. Support
6. Pivot pin	13. Dust shield	29. Pivot bolt
7. Knuckle	14. Washer	30. Nut
	15. Thrust bearing	
	17. Tie rod	
	18. Clamp	
	20. Tie rod end	
	21. Nut	

installation to provide a 0.006-0.008 clearance between spindle and bushing.

TIE RODS

Models GB-GBD-GBLP-UBE-ZBE

23. The GB series tractors are equipped with automotive type tie rod ends as shown in Fig. MM260. The procedure for renewing the tie rod ends is evident.

The UBE and ZBE tractors are equipped with renewable ball and socket type tie rod ends.

Recommended toe-in is approximately ¼ inch.

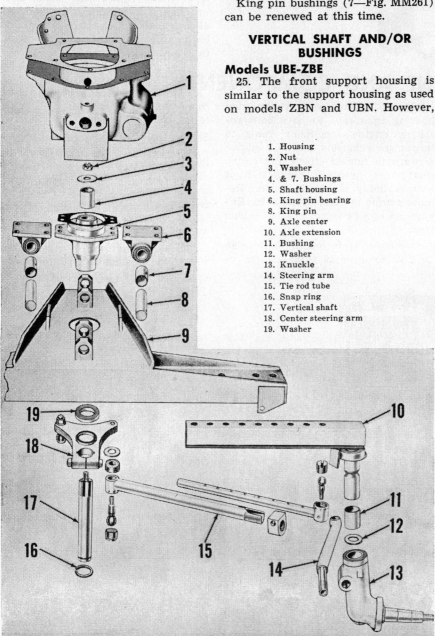

Fig. MM261—Exploded view of model ZBE pedestal and axle assembly. Model UBE is similarly constructed.

KING (PIVOT) PIN

Models GB-GBD-GBLP

24. The procedure for renewing the pivot pin (6—Fig. MM260) and/or bushings (4) is evident after an examination of the unit. Ream the bushings after installation to provide 0.003-0.005 diametral clearance for the pivot pin.

Models UBE-ZBE

24A. Axle main member king (pivot) pins can be removed after supporting front portion of tractor and removing center steering arm from vertical shaft. Remove king pin retaining cotter pins to release king pins and axle main member.

King pin bushings (7—Fig. MM261) can be renewed at this time.

VERTICAL SHAFT AND/OR BUSHINGS

Models UBE-ZBE

25. The front support housing is similar to the support housing as used on models ZBN and UBN. However,

1. Housing
2. Nut
3. Washer
4. & 7. Bushings
5. Shaft housing
6. King pin bearing
8. King pin
9. Axle center
10. Axle extension
11. Bushing
12. Washer
13. Knuckle
14. Steering arm
15. Tie rod tube
16. Snap ring
17. Vertical shaft
18. Center steering arm
19. Washer

the components which comprise the steering system (vertical shaft, center steering arm, vertical shaft housing) are different.

The procedure for renewing the vertical shaft (17—Fig. MM261) and/or bushings (4) is as follows: With the axle main member removed as outlined in paragraph 24A, remove the hood, radiator and grille assembly. On model UBE, move pedestal forward. On all models, remove pedestal cover and starting crank extension shaft. Remove the steering gear sector retaining nut and bump the vertical shaft down and out of sector and vertical shaft housing. The vertical shaft bushings can be renewed after removing the vertical shaft housing (5).

STEERING SECTOR AND WORM

Models UBE-ZBE

26. To remove the steering sector, proceed as outlined in paragraph 25. The steering gear worm and shaft overhaul and adjustment procedures are similar to the models which are outlined in paragraph 4.

REACH (RADIUS ROD)

Models GB-GBD-GBLP

28. Rear end of reach is supported on a bolt attached to a bracket at engine and transmission split line. Bushing in rear end of reach is renewable.

STEERING GEAR

Models GB-GBD-GBLP

29. ADJUSTMENT. Before adjusting the steering gear unit, disconnect drag link from steering gear arm to remove any load from gear and permit locating mid-position. Refer to Fig. MM262.

30. WORMSHAFT END PLAY. Loosen clamp bolt on clamp (15) and slide dust shield (26) away from steering gear housing. Remove cap screws from housing upper cover (16), and slide same away from gear housing. Wormshaft end play is controlled by adding or removing shims (17). Correct adjustment is when wormshaft has zero end play, yet rotates freely without binding.

31. STUD MESH. The stud mesh adjustment requires removal of the gear unit due to lack of clearance between gear unit and transmission housing when unit is installed.

The stud mesh (cross shaft end play) adjustment is always made with the steering gear on the high point and preferably with the drag link disconnected at the steering arm. To place gear on high point, turn steering wheel

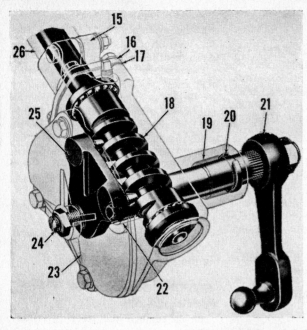

Fig. MM262—Models GB, GBD and GBLP steering gear assembly. Shims (17) control worm shaft bearing adjustment. Screw (24) controls stud mesh adjustment.

15. Dust shield clamp
16. Gear housing upper cover
17. Shims
18. Worm and shaft
19. Bushing (outer)
20. Oil seal
21. Steering arm
22. Bushing (inner)
23. Housing side cover
24. Adjusting screw
25. Cross shaft & lever
26. Dust shield

to mid-position of its rotation (half-way between full left and full right). Tighten adjusting screw (24) until a very slight drag is felt at the high point position when rotating the steering wheel. Gear should rotate freely at all positions off of the high point.

With mesh adjustment complete, re-install drag link to steering arm so that steering gear is in its mid-position of travel when the front wheels are straight ahead.

32. OVERHAUL. Remove gear unit from tractor. Procedure for disassembly is readily evident from an examination of Fig. MM262. The bronze service bushings (19 & 22) for the lever shaft require final sizing after installation to provide a 0.0005-0.0025 diametral clearance between shaft and bushing. Lip of oil seal (20) should face wormshaft.

ENGINE AND COMPONENTS

REMOVE AND REINSTALL

Series GB

33. Drain cooling system and disconnect upper and lower radiator hoses. Remove hood and radiator. Disconnect drag link and remove reach (radius) rod. Disconnect fuel lines, oil lines, control rods, wires and cables from engine and engine accessories. Disconnect the heat indicator sending unit.

Support engine and transmission housing separately. Remove bolts retaining engine and main frame to transmission housing, and pull engine forward to release clutch and clutch shaft from flywheel. Support front axle assembly and main frame. Remove engine to main frame bolts. Engine can now be removed from engine base.

Two bolts, ⅝ inch x 10 inches can be used to serve as guides when re-

connecting engine and frame assembly to transmission housing.

Series UB

34. Remove hood. Disconnect fuel lines, oil lines, control rods, wires and cables from engine and engine accessories. Disconnect the heat indicator sending unit and drive out pin retaining steering worm shaft to universal joint.

Block up front end of transmission and support engine on chain hoist. Re-

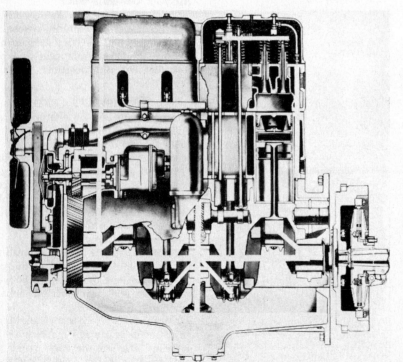

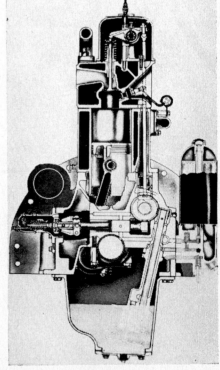

Fig. MM263—Typical sectional view of GB series non-Diesel engines. The engines are equipped with precision type rod and main bearings. Connecting rod and piston units are removed from above. The UB series non-Diesel engines are similarly constructed.

move cap screws retaining engine to transmission and separate tractor halves. Remove radiator hoses and, if engine is to be disassembled, drain crankcase. Remove frame bars from engine and pedestal; then, while steadying assembly, remove front wheels, pedestal and radiator as a unit.

Series ZB

35. Drain cooling system and disconnect upper and lower radiator hoses. Remove hood and radiator. Disconnect battery cable at starter, throttle rod at carburetor, steering shaft universal joint, carburetor fuel line, choke control at carburetor, generator wires at generator, ignition coil wire at coil, head light wires, and oil pressure gage line. Remove coolant temperature gage sending unit, and wiring harness clips from water manifold. Remove cap screws retaining throttle linkage and bracket from under hydraulic reservoir. Disconnect hydraulic pressure lines at reservoir. Disconnect water lines on LP-gas models.

Support the engine and transmission housing separately. Remove bolts retaining front support to engine. Slightly raise front portion of engine and

roll front support assembly away from engine. Remove bolts retaining engine to transmission housing and pull engine forward to release clutch shaft.

Two guide bolts ⅝ inch x 10 inches can be used as guides when reconnecting the engine to the transmission.

CYLINDER HEAD

Series GB-UB

36. Four cylinder engines are equipped with two heads, whereas six cylinder Diesels have three. To remove one cylinder head, first remove hood and drain cooling system. Remove upper radiator hose, water manifold, and air cleaner. On non-Diesels, disconnect throttle control rod and fuel line from carburetor, and remove exhaust and inlet manifold. On Diesels, disconnect nozzle lines and remove the manifold. On all models, remove cylinder head rocker cover, oil lines, and rocker arms and shafts assembly. Remove cylinder head retaining nuts and lift cylinder head from engine.

When reinstalling cylinder head, tighten water, and inlet and exhaust manifolds before tightening cylinder block and head hold down nuts.

On non-Diesels, tighten the head nuts to a torque of approximately 102 ft.-lbs. on camshaft side and 86 ft.-lbs. on exhaust manifold side. On Diesels, tighten ⅝ inch studs to approximately 102 ft.-lbs. on camshaft side

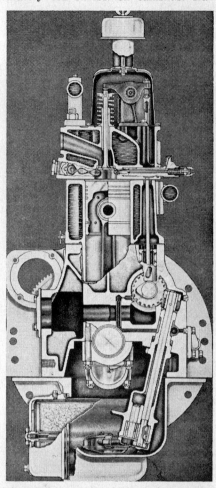

Fig. MM265—Sectional view of UB series four cylinder Diesel engine. Engines are equipped with American Bosch PSB injection pump and throttling type pintle nozzles. Except for the oil pan construction, an end sectional view of the six cylinder GB Diesel engine is similar.

Fig. MM266—Tighten cylinder head nuts on non-Diesel models of the GB and UB series in the sequence shown. Rocker arm oil connections are shown at (34).

Fig. MM264—Cut-away view of ZB series engine. The front main bearing is of the straight roller type, whereas the center and rear mains are of the slip-in precision type.

and 86 ft.-lbs. on exhaust manifold side. Tighten the nuts on 9/16 inch studs to a torque of 68-72 ft.-lbs. Torque values are for lubricated threads.

Series ZB

37. Cylinder head is located on right side of engine and can be removed for carbon removal and valve work. Drain cooling system, remove air cleaner and bracket and disconnect governor linkage and fuel line. Remove cap screw holding carburetor spacer to manifold and remove carburetor, spacer and air inlet pipe. On LP-Gas models, remove regulator. Remove retaining nuts and remove cylinder head. To install, reverse removal procedure. Tighten cylinder head retaining nuts in sequence shown in Fig. MM268 and to a torque of 45-50 ft.-lbs. for lubricated threads.

VALVES AND SEATS

All Models

38. Tappets should be set hot to 0.008 for the inlet and 0.010 for the exhaust. Inlet valves seat directly in cylinder head or cylinder block and are not interchangeable with exhaust valves which are equipped with seat inserts. Valves have a face and seat angle of 45 degrees and a desired seat width of 3/32 inch. Nominal stem diameter is 11/32 inch for the ZB series, 7/16 inch for the GB and UB series.

After refacing and reseating valves in Diesel models, check the valve head clearance as shown in Fig. MM269.

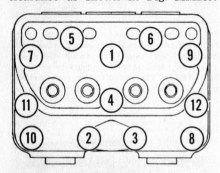

Fig. MM267—Diesel engine cylinder head nut tightening sequence. Refer to text for torque values.

Fig. MM268—Typical cylinder head nut tightening sequence on ZB series tractors.

Distance from gasket surface of cylinder head to head of closed valves should not vary more than 0.015. Variations in excess of this amount will cause different compression ratios in each cylinder and result in uneven engine operation. With intake valves closed, there should be a clearance of 0.015-0.025 between gasket surface of cylinder head and head of intake valves. If clearance is less than 0.015, valves may strike pistons.

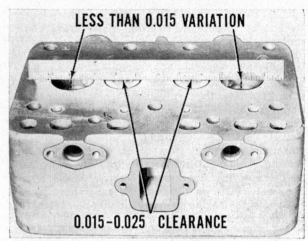

Fig. MM269—After refacing and reseating valves on Diesel models, it is important that proper clearances are maintained. Refer to text.

Fig. MM270—Exploded view of typical camshaft, rocker arms and related parts used on the UB series and four cylinder GB series engines.

A. Camshaft end play adjusting screw
1. Shaft support stud
2. Shaft support
3. Rocker arm shaft retaining screw
4. Rocker arm shaft spring
5. Rocker arm
6. Adjusting screw
7. Rocker arm shaft
8. Plug
9. Rocker arm oil line
10. Push rod
11. Valve spring keepers (split cone)
12. Valve spring seat
13. Valve spring
14. Valve guide
15. Valve
16. Cam follower
17. Exhaust valve seat insert
18. Camshaft
19. Camshaft gear
20. Retaining washer & cap screw

VALVE GUIDES AND SPRINGS

All Models

39. Inlet and exhaust valve guides are not interchangeable in all models. Ream guides after installation to provide a stem-to-guide clearance of 0.0015-0.0035. Inlet and exhaust valve springs are interchangeable and should test 53-59 lbs. @ 1 13/64 inches for the ZB series, 85-90 lbs. @ 2½ inches for the GB and UB series.

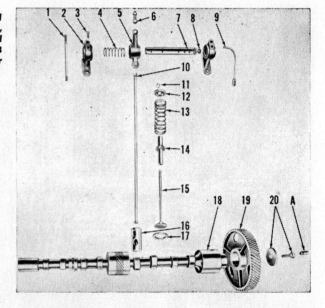

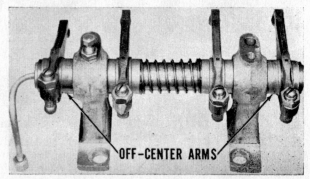

Fig. MM271—When assembling Diesel engine rocker arms, make certain that long part of end rocker arm bushings is toward the supports.

VALVE TAPPETS (CAM FOLLOWERS)

Series GB-UB

40. The barrel type tappets are supplied in standard size only and should have a clearance of 0.0005-0.002 in the case bores. Any tappet can be removed after removing either the camshaft or the cylinder block or blocks.

ROCKER ARMS

Series GB-UB

41. Rocker arms and shaft assembly can be removed after removing hood, valve cover and rocker arm shaft support retaining nuts. Desired clearance between rocker arm bushing and the 0.966-0.967 diameter shaft is 0.001-0.003. Bushings are not supplied for service; therefore, if clearance between bushing and shaft exceeds 0.008, it will be necessary to renew rocker arms and/or shaft.

On Diesel models, the end rocker arms for each pair of cylinders are offset on their bushings. When reassembling, make certain that long part of bushings (Fig. MM271) is toward the rocker arm shaft supports as shown.

Series ZB

42. Each cylinder is equipped with a separate pair of rocker arms and rocker arm shaft. To remove any pair, remove cylinder side cover, rotate crankshaft until both valves are closed and remove nut retaining rocker arm shaft to cylinder block.

New rocker arm bushings require final sizing after installation to provide a clearance of 0.001-0.0015 for the 0.810-0.811 diameter shaft. If clearance exceeds 0.008, renew shaft and/or bushings.

VALVE TIMING

All Models

43. Valves are properly timed when mark "1" on camshaft gear is in mesh with mark "1" on crankshaft gear as shown in Figs. MM273, MM274 or MM275.

TIMING GEAR COVER

Series GB-UB Non-Diesels

44. The timing gear cover is also the water pump body. Removal of this cover will expose only the camshaft gear. On models GB and GBLP, remove radiator. On the UB series, disconnect the radiator hoses, support engine and slide radiator, pedestal and front wheels assembly forward as a unit. Remove the fan and water pump cover. Bump Groov pin out of water pump impeller. Remove impeller which is left hand threaded by rotating same in clockwise direction. Loosen water pump outlet hose and pump inlet hose and remove the timing case cover retaining cap screws.

Camshaft end play is controlled by a thrust screw located in front face of timing gear cover. To adjust, turn screw in until same contacts the camshaft gear retaining cap screw; then, retract screw ½ turn.

Series GB-UB Diesels

45. To remove the timing gear cover, first drain cooling system and on model GBD, remove radiator. On UB Diesels, support engine and slide radiator, pedestal and front wheels assembly forward as a unit. On all Diesel models, remove water pump and the timing gear case cover retaining cap screws.

Camshaft end play is controlled by a thrust screw located in front face of timing gear cover. To adjust, turn screw in until same contacts the camshaft gear retaining cap screw; then, retract screw ½ turn.

TIMING GEARS

Series GB-UB Non-Diesels

46. Timing drive of three helical gears consists of the crankshaft gear, camshaft gear, water pump and ignition unit drive gear.

When reinstalling either the camshaft gear, crankshaft gear, and/or accessory shaft gear, mesh "1" mark on camshaft gear with an identical mark on crankshaft gear. Also mesh "O" mark on camshaft gear with an identical mark on accessory gear as shown in Fig. MM273.

Fig. MM274—Diesel engine timing gear train. Mesh "I" marks on camshaft and crankshaft gears.

Fig. MM273—Timing gear train for non-Diesel models of the GB and UB series. Mesh "I" marks on crankshaft and camshaft gears. Mesh "O" marks on camshaft and accessory gears. Allen screw (27) retains accessory drive shaft sleeve (28).

19. Camshaft gear	25. Crankshaft front oil seal
22. Water pump to cylinder manifold hose	26. Accessory shaft
	27. Allen screw
23. Lubrication tube to accessory shaft bushing	28. Accessory shaft sleeve
	30. Timing gear case

Fig. MM272—Exploded view of ZB series rocker arms for one cylinder.

1. Adjusting screw	4. Shaft
2. Locknut	5. Rocker arm
3. Bushing	6. Retaining spring

Fig. MM275—Series ZB timing gears with "I" marks in register.

47. CAMSHAFT GEAR. To remove camshaft gear, remove timing gear cover as outlined in paragraph 44. Remove cap screw and washer from end of camshaft. Using a suitable puller attached to the gear, remove camshaft gear. When reinstalling gear, it is advisable to remove one of the crankcase inspection plates and buck up the camshaft. Mesh gears as shown in Fig. MM273.

48. CRANKSHAFT GEAR. To remove crankshaft gear, it is first necessary to remove camshaft gear as previously outlined. Straighten cap screw locks which are located under camshaft gear; then, remove these cap screws and remaining cap screws retaining timing gear case to cylinder block. Disconnect oil line from gear case.

Remove four cap screws retaining oil pan to timing gear case and loosen

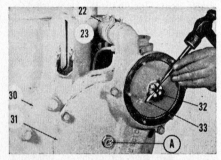

Fig. MM276—Bumping pin from impeller on series GB and UB non-Diesels. Impeller is left hand threaded to accessory shaft. Camshaft end play is adjusted with screw (A).

A. Camshaft end play adjusting screw
22. Water pump to manifold hose
23. Lubrication tube to accessory shaft bushing
30. Timing gear case
31. Water pump body & timing gear case cover
32. Water pump impeller
33. Groov pin

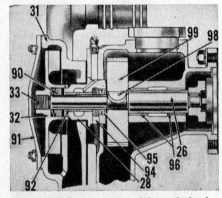

Fig. MM277—Accessory drive shaft installation on GB and UB series non-Diesels.

26. Accessory shaft
28. Shaft sleeve
31. Water pump body and timing gear case cover
32. Impeller
33. Groov pin
90. Water pump seal
91. Pump cover
92. Bushing (front)
94. Vent hole
95. Oil seal
96. Bushing (rear)
98. Woodruff key
99. Accessory drive shaft gear

balance of oil pan retaining cap screws. Carefully separate oil pan gasket from timing gear case and remove gear case. Using a suitable puller, remove crankshaft gear.

When reinstalling crankshaft gear, mesh same as shown in Fig. MM273.

49. ACCESSORY DRIVE SHAFT GEAR. To remove accessory shaft gear, proceed as follows: Remove camshaft gear as outlined in preceding paragraphs. Remove ignition unit, and cover plate or hydraulic lift pump at rear of accessory drive shaft. Bump accessory shaft rearward and out of gear and timing gear case. Remove accessory gear through camshaft gear opening located in front of gear case.

Accessory shaft bronze bushings and/or oil seal shown in Fig. MM277 can be renewed at this time. The front bushing and oil seal (95) are contained in a sleeve which is retained in position with an Allen screw, located at point (27—Fig. MM273). The other two bushings are pressed in the timing gear case and can be renewed without removing the case. Desired clearance between new bushings and shaft is 0.0015-0.003.

When reinstalling accessory shaft gear, mesh same as shown in Fig. MM273.

Series GB-UB Diesels

50. Timing gear train of four helical gears consists of the crankshaft gear (1—Fig. MM278), camshaft gear (3), adjustable gear (2) bolted to the camshaft gear and the water pump and injection pump drive gear (4).

51. WATER PUMP AND INJECTION PUMP DRIVE SHAFT AND GEAR. To renew the pump drive gear and shaft and/or bushings, remove the injection pump as outlined in paragraph 124 and the timing gear case

Fig. MM278—Timing gear train of GB and UB Diesels.

1. Crankshaft gear
2. Adjustable gear
3. Camshaft gear
4. Pump drive gear

cover as in paragraph 45. Remove floating coupling (6—Fig. MM279) and using two fairly long 3/8 inch-16 thread bolts as jack screws in holes (H), remove coupling gear (7). Remove the gear shaft Woodruff key and withdraw gear and shaft (4—Fig. MM280) from case. The adapter housing (9) and/or bushings (5) can be renewed at this time. Ream the bushings after installation, if necessary, to provide a recommended diametral clearance of 0.0015-0.003 for the gear shaft. When reinstalling the coupling gear (7), allow 0.005 clearance between front face of gear and housing.

52. CAMSHAFT GEAR AND/OR ADJUSTABLE GEAR. To remove the adjustable gear (2—Fig. MM278), remove the timing gear case cover as outlined in paragraph 45, unwire and remove the cap screws retaining the adjustable gear to the camshaft gear.

With the adjustable gear removed and the pump drive shaft and gear removed as in paragraph 51, remove cap screw and washer from end of camshaft and using a suitable puller, remove the camshaft gear.

When reinstalling gear, it is advisable to remove one of the crankcase

Fig. MM279—Rear view of pump adapter housing with the Diesel injection pump removed. Jack screws can be used in holes (H) to facilitate removal of gear (7).

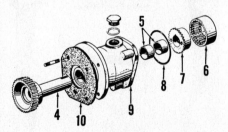

Fig. MM280—Diesel injection pump drive mechanism.

4. Pump drive gear
5. Bushings
6. Floating coupling
7. Coupling gear
8. "0" ring
9. Adapter housing

inspection plates and buck up the camshaft. Mesh gears as shown in Fig. MM278.

Before installing the timing gear case cover, check the injection pump timing as in paragraph 121.

53. CRANKSHAFT GEAR. To remove the crankshaft gear, first remove the camshaft gear as previously outlined. Straighten cap screw locks which are located under camshaft gear; then, remove these cap screws and remaining cap screws retaining timing gear case to cylinder block. Disconnect oil line from timing gear case.

Remove the cap screws retaining oil pan to timing gear case and loosen the remaining cap screws retaining oil pan to cylinder block. Carefully separate oil pan gasket from timing gear case and remove gear case. Using a suitable puller, remove crankshaft gear. When reinstalling gears, mesh same as shown in Fig. MM278.

Series ZB

54. Timing drive of four helical gears consists of the crankshaft, camshaft, hydraulic (Uni-Matic) pump drive and oil pump drive gears. The latter gear which also drives the ignition unit is located forward of the camshaft gear.

When reinstalling either the camshaft and/or crankshaft gear, mesh the mark "1" on the camshaft gear with an identical mark on the crankshaft gear. Marks can be viewed when the crankcase side cover is off.

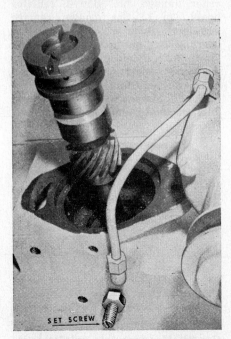

Fig. MM281—The ZB series oil pump and ignition unit drive shaft bushing is retained by a set screw as shown.

55. CAMSHAFT GEAR. Camshaft gear removal requires removal of camshaft as outlined in CAMSHAFT section.

56. CRANKSHAFT GEAR. Crankshaft gear removal requires removal of crankshaft as outlined in CRANKSHAFT section.

57. IGNITION UNIT & OIL PUMP DRIVE GEAR. To remove ignition unit and oil pump drive gear, it will be necessary to remove camshaft as outlined in CAMSHAFT section.

58. HYDRAULIC PUMP DRIVE. The hydraulic pump gear is a press fit to the hydraulic pump shaft and can be removed after removing the pump unit.

59. IGNITION UNIT & OIL PUMP DRIVEN GEAR & SHAFT. Shaft and gear assembly can be removed after removing the ignition unit, oil pump, pump gear and Woodruff keys; then, loosen thrust bushing retaining set screw (Fig. MM281) which is located on front face of crankcase and push shaft upward and out of crankcase. Shaft should have 0.001-0.0025 clearance in the shaft bushings.

Reassemble in reverse order, and with number one cylinder on compression stroke and flywheel mark "DC 1-4" aligned with pointer, mesh oil pump and ignition unit drive shaft gear so that the ignition unit drive coupling slot is at right angles to the crankshaft center line.

CAMSHAFT
Series GB-UB Non-Diesels

60. To remove camshaft, first remove timing gear cover (water pump body), as outlined in paragraph 44. Remove rocker arms and shafts assembly, push rods, governor, oil pan and oil pump. Block up and support cam followers; then, withdraw camshaft with camshaft gear through front of timing gear case.

Camshaft journals ride directly in three machined bores in the crankcase. Shaft journal sizes are: Front, 3.3075-3.3085; center, 3.275-3.276; rear,

1.996-1.997. Recommended clearance of camshaft journals in their bores is 0.0025-0.005. The maximum permissible clearance is 0.008 and when it exceeds this amount, it will be necessary to renew camshaft and/or crankcase or make-up and install bushings.

Series GB-UB Diesels

61. To remove the camshaft, first remove the water pump and injection pump drive gear and shaft as outlined in paragraph 51. Remove the rocker arms and shaft assemblies, push rods, oil pan and oil pump. Block up the cam followers and withdraw camshaft from front of engine.

All of the camshaft journals ride directly in the machined bores in crankcase of series UB Diesels. The rear two journals of the GB Diesel camshaft ride directly in the machined crankcase bores, whereas the front two journals ride in bronze bushings. The GBD construction differs from the GTBD which had all four journals riding directly in the crankcase. Recommended camshaft journal running clearance is 0.003-0.005. The maximum permissible clearance is 0.008 and when it exceeds this amount, it will be necessary to renew camshaft and/or crankcase or, make-up and install bushings. Note: Factory replacement bushings are available for field installation in the front two camshaft bearing bores of the GB Diesel.

Camshaft journal sizes for the UB Diesel are as follows:

Front 3.3075-3.3085
Center 3.275-3.276
Rear 1.996-1.997

Camshaft journal sizes for the GB Diesel are as follows:

No. 1 (Front) 3.338-3.339
No. 2 .... 3.3075-3.3085
No. 3 .... 3.275-3.276
No. 4 (Rear) 1.996-1.997

When reinstalling camshaft and gear assembly, mesh gears as shown in Fig. MM278. After the timing gear case cover is installed, adjust cam-

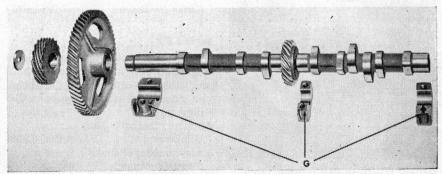

Fig. MM282—The ZB series camshaft, gears and bearing caps. Bearing caps must be installed with groove (G) up.

shaft end play by turning the adjusting screw (located in case cover) **in** until screw contacts cap screw in end of camshaft; then retract the screw ½ turn.

Series ZB

62. To remove the camshaft, first remove engine crankcase side cover, valve covers, rocker arms and shafts, and camshaft bearing caps. See Fig. MM282.

Camshaft journals ride directly in three machined bores which are fitted with caps in the crankcase. Shaft journal sizes for all three journals are 1.2465-1.2470. Recommended clearance of camshaft journals in their bores is 0.0025-0.004. The maximum permissible clearance is 0.007 and when **it** exceeds this amount, it will be necessary to renew the camshaft and/or the crankcase.

Mesh "1" mark on camshaft gear with an identical mark on the crankshaft gear as shown in Fig. MM275. Reinstall camshaft journal bearing caps with the oil grooves UP as shown in Fig. MM282. Adjust camshaft end play by locating front bearing cap (provided with elongated holes) to crankcase to obtain a clearance of 0.003. Clearance is between bearing cap rear face and hub face of camshaft gear as shown in Fig. MM283.

81A. Tappet gap (hot) is 0.008 for the intake; 0.010 for the exhaust.

ROD AND PISTON UNITS
Series GB-UB

63. Piston and connecting rod assemblies are removed from above after removing cylinder head and oil pan.

Piston and connecting rod assemblies are installed with the rod correlation marks facing the camshaft. Tighten the connecting rod bolts to 64-68 ft.-lbs. torque for lubricated threads.

Fig. MM283—Measuring distance between camshaft gear and camshaft front bearing on ZB series.

Series ZB

64. Piston and connecting rod assemblies are removed from above after removing the cylinder head, cylinder block and crankcase side cover as shown in Fig. MM284.

Tighten the connecting rod cap screws to 48-52 ft.-lbs. torque for lubricated threads.

PISTONS AND RINGS
Series GB-UB

65. Pistons and rings for non-Diesel engines are available in standard size and oversizes of 0.030, 0.063 and 0.094. Pistons and rings for Diesel engines are available in standard size and oversize of 0.030. Check pistons, cylinders and rings against the values which follows: Notice that the GB LP-Gas tractor has a larger bore than the former model GTC which had a bore of 4.251-4.252.

Standard Cylinder Bore Diameter
  GB-GBLP 4.625-4.627
  GBD-UB Diesel 4.251-4.252
  UB Series Non-Diesel ...4.251-4.252
Recommended Piston Skirt Clearance
  Diesels 0.0065-0.0075
  Non-Diesels 0.004-0.005
Maximum Cylinder Wear..0.008
Maximum Top Ring Side Clearance
  Diesels 0.0065
  Non-Diesels 0.005
Maximum Second Ring Side Clearance
  Diesels 0.0055
  Non-Diesels 0.005
Maximum Third Ring Side Clearance
  Diesels 0.0045
  Non-Diesels 0.005
Maximum Fourth Ring Side Clearance
  Diesels 0.0035
  Non-Diesels 0.005
Maximum Fifth Ring Side Clearance
  Diesels 0.035
Compression Ring End Gap
  GB-GBLP 0.025-0.030
  UB Series Non-Diesel ..0.020-0.030
  GBD-UB Diesel 0.015-0.020
Oil Ring End Gap
  GB-GBLP 0.018-0.025
  UB Series Non-Diesel ..0.020-0.030
  GBD-UB Diesel 0.015-0.020

Series ZB

66. Pistons and rings are available in standard size and oversizes of 0.020 and 0.040. Check the pistons, cylinders and rings against the values which follow:
Standard Cylinder Bore
  Diameter 3.6255-3.6265
Recommended Piston
  Skirt Clearance 0.0025-0.0045
Maximum Cylinder
  Wear 0.008

Maximum Ring Side
  Clearance 0.005
Recommended Ring
  End Gap 0.015-0.022

Install oil ring with beveled edge up. Install compression rings with word "TOP" facing up.

CYLINDER BLOCKS
Series GB-UB

67. Four cylinder engines are of the twin-block design whereas the six cylinder GBD has three blocks. In either case, however, the general removal procedure given in the following paragraph can be used.

68. To remove cylinder block or blocks, remove hood, rocker arms and shafts assembly, push rods and cylinder head and block retaining nuts. Remove manifold and on Diesel models, remove injection pump. Disconnect and slide water pump hose away from block and lift block or blocks off of crankcase. Cylinder blocks can be removed before or after removing connecting rod and piston assemblies.

Cylinder block or blocks can be installed to crankcase while rod and piston assemblies are attached to crankshaft by lowering block over pistons, or by first attaching block to crankcase and then installing rod and piston assemblies from above.

Series ZB

69. To remove cylinder blocks, remove hood, valve cover, and rocker arms and shaft units. Disconnect governor linkage, fuel line & radiator hoses. On LP-Gas models, remove regulator. Remove connecting rod bearing caps and cylinder block hold down nuts. Remove blocks, cylinder head and connecting rod and piston assemblies as a unit.

If only one block is to be removed, also remove cylinder head, manifolds

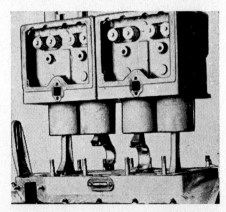

Fig. MM284—Lifting both cylinder blocks along with piston and connecting rod units from ZB series crankcase.

and water manifold; then remove cylinder block from crankcase. When reinstalling cylinder blocks, assemble connecting rod and piston assembly to crankcase. Do not tighten cylinder block hold down nuts until head and manifolds have been tightened.

PISTON PINS

Series GB-UB

70. Piston pins are of the full floating type which are retained in the piston pin bosses by snap rings. The 1.2497-1.2500 diameter piston pins for non-Diesels or 1.500 diameter pins for Diesels are available in standard size, and oversizes of 0.005 and 0.010.

Install piston pin bushing in rod so that oil hole in bushing registers with oil hole in top end of connecting rod.

Fit pins to a palm push fit in both rod and piston.

Series ZB

71. The 0.9994-0.9996 diameter floating type piston pins are retained in piston pin bosses by snap rings and are available in standard, as well as 0.005 oversize.

Install piston pin bushing in rod so that oil hole in bushing registers with oil hole in top end of connecting rod.

Pin should be fitted to a finger push fit (0.0003 clearance) in both rod and piston.

ROD BEARINGS

All Models

72. Connecting rod bearings are of the shimless, non-adjustable, slip-in, precision type, renewable after removing oil pan or side cover. When installing new bearing shells, be sure that bearing shell projection engages milled slot in rod and cap, and rod and cap correlation marks face toward camshaft side of engine. Bearings are available in 0.0025, 0.005, 0.020 and 0.040 undersize, as well as standard.

Check the bearings and crankshaft against the values listed below: Notice that the GBD crankpins are larger than the 2.7495-2.750 diameter crankpins of the former GTB Diesel.

Crankpin diameter
GB-GBLP 2.7495-2.7500
GBD 2.9115-2.912
UB Series Non-Diesels. 2.5770-2.5775
UB Diesels 2.906
ZB Series 2.6245-2.6250
Running clearance 0.0015-0.004
Side clearance 0.002-0.006
Bolt torque (ft.-lbs.)
ZB Series 48-52
Other Models 64-68

Bolt torque is for well lubricated threads.

73. NOTE: *New engines, using precision insert main and/or rod bearings, which have a letter "K" suffixed to model number have 0.0025 undersize crankpins; letter "F", 0.0025 undersize main bearing journals; letters "KF", 0.0025 undersize crankpins and main journals.*

CRANKSHAFT & BEARINGS

Series GB-UB

74. MAIN BEARINGS. Crankshaft main bearings are slip-in, precision shell type, which may be renewed from below. Rear and intermediate bearing caps are marked "FRONT", and should be installed with marking toward front of engine. Bearings are available in 0.0025, 0.005, 0.020 and 0.040 undersize as well as standard.

75. CRANKSHAFT. Crankshaft end play is controlled by rear main bearing. Recommended end play is 0.002-0.006.

To remove crankshaft, it is necessary to remove engine, oil pan, timing gear cover, timing gear case, oil pump, connecting rod bearing caps and flywheel.

Check crankshaft, crankpins and journals for wear, scoring and out-of-round condition against values listed below. Refer also to paragraph 73.

Crankpin diameter—See paragraph 72

Main journal diameter 2.911-2.912

Main bearing oil
clearance 0.0015-0.004

Main bearing bolt torque. (ft.-lbs.)
Lubricated threads

Front (Non-Diesels) 88-96

Front (Diesels) 155-165

Others (Non-Diesels) 60-64

Others (Diesels) 76-84

Series ZB

76. MAIN BEARINGS. The crankshaft center and rear journals are supported in two shimless, non-adjustable, slip-in, precision type main bearings; whereas, the front journal is supported in a roller type bearing.

Crankshaft end play 0.003-0.004 is controlled by the rear main bearing.

The center and rear main bearings can be renewed after removing the crankcase side cover, and are available in 0.0025, 0.005, 0.020, and 0.040 undersize as well as standard.

To renew the front main bearing, it will be necessary to remove the crankshaft, and using a suitable puller, remove bearing from shaft.

77. CRANKSHAFT. To remove crankshaft, it is necessary to remove the engine, crankcase side cover, starting crank jaw, fan pulley, flywheel, and camshaft. Working through crankcase side cover opening, disconnect oil line at rear bearing, and remove connecting rod bearing caps, and center main bearing cap. Remove rear main bearing cage retaining cap screws. Rotate crankshaft, until number 2 & 3 crank throws are facing crankcase opening, and pull crankshaft rearward until center journal is past center bearing bore; then, rotate shaft until number 1 & 4 crank throws are facing crankcase opening, and withdraw crankshaft and rear bearing housing. The front bearing can be renewed after removing the bearing lock. To remove rear bearing housing from crankshaft, remove crankshaft rear oil seal retainer and main bearing cap.

Check the crankshaft journals for wear, scoring and out-of-round condition against the values listed below. Refer also to paragraph 73.

Crankpin diameter 2.6245-2.6250
Journal diameter
Front ....Roller
Center 2.7495-2.7500
Rear 2.9995-3.000
Running clearance 0.0015-0.0035
End play 0.003-0.004
Bearing cap bolt torque for
lubricated threads 44-48

CRANKSHAFT OIL SEALS
Series GB-UB

78. FRONT SEAL. The felt type seal is contained in a bell-shaped metal retainer (25—Fig. MM286)

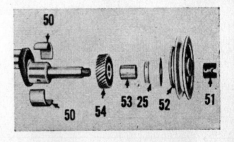

Fig. MM286—Crankshaft and associated parts for series GB and UB. Four cylinder engines have three main bearings, whereas, six cylinder engines have four.

25. Front oil seal
50. Front main bearing
51. Crank jaw
52. Pulley
53. Spacer
54. Crankshaft gear

which is pressed into timing gear case. Procedure for renewing the seal is evident after removing the radiator on GB series, radiator and pedestal as a unit on UB series.

79. REAR SEAL. The rear bearing crankshaft oil seal cork is of a two-piece type. The lower half (59—Fig. MM287) is contained in a retainer, and the upper half in a groove which is machined in the crankcase.

Lower half of cork seal can be renewed from below after removing oil pan and seal retainer. Allow ends of oil seal to extend slightly above edge of retainer. Renew corks (57) before reinstalling the retainer. When reinstalling the retainer, insert a sufficient number of gaskets between mating surfaces of crankcase and seal retainer so that retainer will protrude 0.005 beyond gasket surface of crankcase when retainer is bolted in position.

Oil seal upper half can be pulled out, and a new seal inserted from below after removing oil pan, retainer for lower seal and loosening main bearing caps.

Series ZB

80. FRONT SEAL. Crankshaft front oil seal is pressed into front of crank-

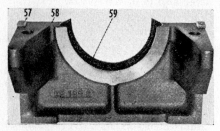

Fig. MM287—Crankshaft rear oil seal and retainer assembly as used on series GB and UB.

(57) Cork seal, (58) Seal retainer, (59) Crankshaft rear oil seal

Fig. MM288—Inside view of UB Diesel oil pan. The oil filter element and can have been removed.

case and renewal requires removal of radiator, pedestal, crank jaw and pulley.

81. REAR SEAL. The crankshaft rear oil seal can be renewed after detaching engine from transmission housing and removing flywheel. Install seal with lip of same facing the timing gears.

FLYWHEEL

All Models

82. The flywheel can be removed after separating engine from transmission as outlined in the clutch section. To install a new flywheel ring gear, heat same to approximately 500 deg. F. and install gear on flywheel with beveled edge of teeth facing front of engine.

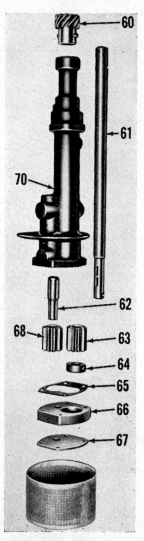

Fig. MM289—Typical oil pump used on GB and UB series tractors. On some models, the construction of the oil pump is different in details which are evident.

60. Spiral drive gear
61. Drive shaft
62. Idler gear shaft
63. Pump drive gear
64. Thrust collar
65. Shim gasket
66. Spacer plate
67. Cover
68. Idler gear
70. Pump body

CRANKCASE AND OIL PAN

Series GB—Non-Diesel UB

83. The oil pan is removable from below after removing cap screws retaining oil pan to crankcase, timing gear case and transmission case. On models so equipped, it is necessary to remove the reach from the transmission case and front axle to permit oil pan removal.

Series UB Diesels

84. To remove the oil pan, first remove the oil filter element and filter can from oil pan. Working through opening in side of oil pan, remove the two cap screws (CS—Fig. MM288) retaining oil pan to crankcase. Remove the remaining cap screws retaining oil pan to crankcase and timing gear case and remove pan.

When reassembling, make certain that gasket (G) is in good condition and that oil line (L) fits down into hole of oil pan.

CRANKCASE SIDE COVER

Series ZB

85. The one-piece crankcase is main supporting member between front pedestal and transmission case. There is no removable oil pan; the case being provided with a large removable cover on the left side.

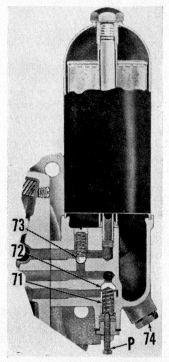

Fig. MM290—Oil filter and pressure regulator used on non-Diesel series GB and UB. The GB Diesels are similar except two filter elements are used.

(P) Relief valve adjusting screw, (71) relief valve spring, (72) valve, (73) differential valve ball, (74) drain plug

Removal of side cover provides accessibility to connecting rods, camshaft and center and rear main bearings. Be sure gasket is in good condition especially around oil passages.

OIL PUMP AND RELIEF VALVE

Series GB-UB

86. The gear type pump, shown in Fig. MM289, can be removed after removing oil pan. To disassemble pump, remove pump screen and cover plate (67). Bump pin from spiral drive gear (60) and remove gear. Withdraw drive shaft (61) and gear unit from pump body. Bump pin out of thrust collar, and remove collar. Gear (63) can now be removed from drive shaft, and idler gear (68) from idler gear shaft (62).

End clearance between pump body gears and plate (66) should be 0.002-0.006 and is controlled with shim gaskets (65). The recommended diametral clearance between gears and pump body is 0.001-0.004. Check pump drive shaft and its mating surface for wear.

The piston type relief valve (72—Figs. MM290 and 291) is adjusted by

means of an adjusting screw (P) to maintain a pressure of 25 psi at rated engine speed.

Series ZB

87. The oil pump is located externally at front of engine on underside of crankcase and is driven by the oil pump drive shaft which is driven by a gear at front end of camshaft. The pump can be removed from the engine as shown in Fig. MM292. The drive gear can be removed as shown in Fig. MM293.

The lower bushing (15 — Fig. MM294) in the crankcase, is renewable from below after removing the oil pump and oil pump drive shaft. To

remove oil pump drive shaft refer to Timing Gears, paragraph 59. Oil pump gear end clearance should be not less than 0.0015 or more than 0.004 and can be adjusted by varying number of shims shown in Fig. MM292. The recommended diametral clearance between the gears and pump body is 0.001-0.0025.

Oil pressure regulator is built into pump. It can be adjusted by loosening lock nut (1—Fig. MM295) and turning adjusting screw (2) to obtain a pressure of 35 psi at 1200-1500 rpm.

CARBURETOR (EXCEPT LP-GAS)

All Models

88. Idling mixture adjustment is controlled by the needle valve nearest to the carburetor flange. Turning adjustment in to the right (clockwise) richens the mixture. Approximate setting is two turns open. Power mixture adjustment is controlled by the other needle valve. Turning adjustment in to the right (clockwise) leans the mixture. Approximate setting is two turns open. Float setting is 1/4 inch.

Calibration data for the TSX625 is as follows:

Repair kit 286-1086
Gasket set 16-594
Inlet needle and seat 233-543

TSX67
Repair kit 286-922
Gasket set 16-594
Inlet needle and seat......233-543

TSX97
Repair kit 286-921
Gasket set 16-654
Inlet needle and seat......233-543

Fig. MM293—Removing ZB series oil pump drive gear (5) from drive shaft (4).

Fig. MM291—Recommended oil pressure of 25 psi on the UB Diesels is obtained by turning adjusting screw (P).

Fig. MM294—ZB series engine sectional view, showing the oil pump drive shaft installation. Shaft bushings are shown at (15).

Fig. MM292—Underside of crankcase on ZB series, showing the oil pump removed.

Fig. MM295—ZB series oil pressure adjustment is made by loosening nut (1) and turning screw (2).

LP-GAS SYSTEM

Minneapolis-Moline model GBLP and series UB and ZB tractors are available with factory installed LP-Gas systems using Ensign equipment. These systems are designed to operate with the fuel supply tank not more than 80% filled.

It is important when starting LP-Gas tractors to open the vapor valve on the supply tank SLOWLY; if opened too fast, the fuel supply to the regulator will be shut off. Too rapid opening of vapor or liquid valves may cause freezing.

SYSTEM ADJUSTMENTS
Model GBLP & Series UB

The GBLP tractor is equipped with a No. 7595 Kgl carburetor, a No. 8059 model R regulator and a No. 8628 pre-set gas economizer.

The UB series tractors are equipped with a No. 7593 Kgl carburetor, a No. 8059 model R regulator and a No. 8628 pre-set gas economizer.

All of these models have three points of mixture adjustment plus a throttle stop screw. Refer to Fig. MM296.

89. THROTTLE STOP SCREW. Stop screw on carburetor throttle should be adjusted to provide an engine low idle speed of approximately 525 rpm.

90. STARTING ADJUSTMENT. Initial adjustment for the starting screw is one full turn open.

Immediately after engine is started and with throttle open and choke closed, rotate the starting screw until the highest engine speed is obtained.

91. IDLE MIXTURE ADJUSTMENT. With the choke open, engine warm and the throttle stop screw set, rotate the idle adjusting screw until the best idle is obtained.

92. LOAD ADJUSTMENT. The Kgl carburetor used on model GBLP and series UB is equipped with a pre-set gas economizer shown exploded in Fig. MM297. This economizer provides automatic control of the partial or light load mixture. The richer mixture needed for maximum power is adjusted by varying the depth to which the entire economizer body is screwed into the fuel passage of the carburetor. The economizer body thus

becomes the load screw. High manifold vacuum overcomes the diaphragm spring and moves the restricting plunger into the fuel passage; thus, leaning the mixture and providing economizer action. When the manifold vacuum falls below 4-6 inches Hg., the spring retracts the plunger causing a richer maximum power mixture.

93. ADJUSTMENT WITHOUT LOAD. With the idle mixture adjusted as outlined in paragraph 91, disconnect the vacuum line (Fig. MM296) from economizer body and plug the line. With the engine running at the recommended high idle speed of 1430 rpm, loosen the locknut (5—Fig. MM297) on economizer body and turn the entire economizer unit until maximum engine rpm is obtained. Note this position; then, rotate the entire economizer unit counter-clockwise until rpm begins to fall and note this position. Set the unit at the midpoint of these two positions and tighten the locknut (5). Reconnect vacuum line.

94. ANALYZER METHOD. Disconnect vacuum line from economizer and plug the line. With the throttle wide open, load the engine to obtain an engine speed of from one half to maximum loaded speed of 1300 rpm. One method of loading the engine is to disconnect or short out two or more spark plug wires. Turn the entire economizer unit to give a reading of 12.8 on the analyzer gasoline scale or 14.3 on an analyzer with a LPG scale. Reconnect vacuum line.

Series ZB

The ZB series tractors are equipped with a No. 7593 Kgl carburetor, a No. 2090 model W regulator and a No. 7078 gas economizer.

These models have three points of mixture adjustment plus a throttle stop screw. Refer to Fig. MM298.

95. THROTTLE STOP SCREW. Stop screw on carburetor throttle should be adjusted to provide an engine low idle speed of approximately 500 rpm.

96. STARTING ADJUSTMENT. Initial adjustment for the starting screw is one full turn open.

Immediately after engine is started and with throttle open and choke closed, rotate the starting screw until the highest engine speed is obtained.

97. IDLE MIXTURE ADJUSTMENT. With the choke open, engine warm and the throttle stop screw set, rotate the idle adjusting screw until the best idle is obtained.

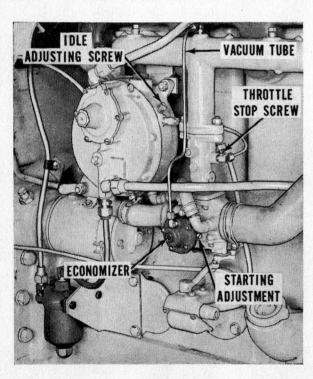

Fig. MM296—Typical LP-gas equipment installation on series UB. Model GBLP is similar. The units have a pre-set economizer.

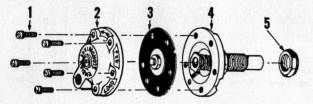

Fig. MM297—Pre-set Ensign gas economizer used on models shown in Fig. MM296.

98. LOAD ADJUSTMENT. The Kgl carburetor used on the ZB series is equipped with the economizer shown in Fig. MM299. This economizer provides adjustable control of the partial or light load mixture by means of adjusting screw (A). The richer mixture needed for maximum power is adjusted by varying the depth to which the entire economizer body is screwed into the fuel passage of the carburetor. High manifold vacuum overcomes the diaphragm spring and moves the restricting plunger into the fuel passage thus leaning the mixture and providing economizer action. When the manifold vacuum falls below 4-6 inches Hg., the spring retracts the plunger causing a richer maximum power mixture.

99. ADJUSTMENT WITHOUT LOAD. With the idle mixture adjusted as outlined in paragraph 97, disconnect the vacuum line (Fig. MM298) from economizer body and plug the line. Completely back out the partial load adjusting screw (A) and with engine running at the recommended high idle speed of 1650 rpm, loosen the locknut (5—Fig. MM299) on economizer body and turn the entire economizer unit until maximum engine rpm is obtained. Note this position; then, rotate the entire economizer unit counter-clockwise until rpm begins to fall and note this position. Set the unit at the midpoint of these two posi-

tions, tighten locknut (5) and reconnect the vacuum line.

Turn the partial load mixture adjusting screw (A) in a clockwise direction until the engine rpm just begins to fall; then lock the adjustment.

100. ANALYZER AND VACUUM GAGE METHOD. Disconnect the vacuum line from the economizer and plug the line. Completely back out the partial load adjusting screw (A—Fig. MM299) and with the throttle wide open, load the engine to obtain an engine speed of from one half to maximum loaded speed of 1500 rpm. One method of loading the engine is to disconnect or short out two or more spark plug wires. Turn the entire economizer unit to give a reading of 12.8 on the analyzer gasoline scale or 14.3 on an analyzer with a LPG scale. Reconnect vacuum line to economizer.

101. To adjust the part throttle (partial load) mixture screw, reduce both the opening of the throttle valve and the load until a manifold vacuum of 10-13 inches Hg. is obtained at the same rpm as used in paragraph 100. Turn the economizer adjusting screw (A) in a clockwise direction until the analyzer reads 13.8-14.5 on the gasoline scale or 14.9-15.5 on the LPG scale.

LP-GAS FILTER

102. Filters used on these systems should be able to stand high pressure without leakage. Unit should be drained periodically at the blow off cock (L—Fig. MM300). When major engine work is being performed, it is advisable to remove the lower part of the filter, thoroughly clean the interior and renew the felt cartridge if it is not in good condition.

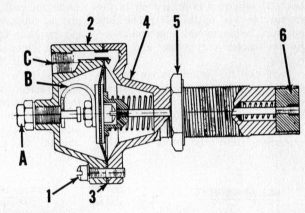

Fig. MM299—Sectional view of Ensign gas economizer used on series ZB.

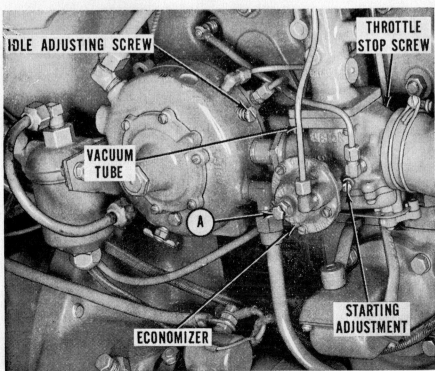

Fig. MM298—Side view of ZB series LP-gas tractors. Mixture adjustment for partial load is made with screw (A).

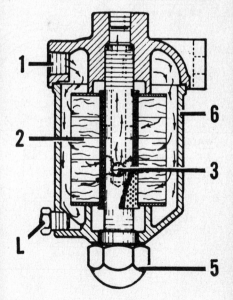

Fig. MM300—Sectional view of LP-gas filter used on MM tractors.

L. Drain plug	3. Outlet passage
1. Fuel inlet	5. Stud nut
2. Filter cartridge	6. Filter bowl

LP GAS REGULATOR
Series ZB (Ensign Model W)

103. **HOW IT OPERATES.** Fuel from the supply tank enters the regulating unit inlet (A—Fig. MM301) at a tank pressure of 25 to 80 psi and is reduced from tank pressure to about 4 psi at the high pressure reducing valve (C) after passing through the strainer (B). Flow through high pressure reducing valve is controlled by the adjacent spring and diaphragm. When the liquid fuel enters the vaporizing chamber (D) via the valve (C), it expands rapidly and is converted from a liquid to a gas by heat from the water jacket (E) which is connected to the coolant system of the engine. The vaporized gas then passes at a pressure slightly below atmospheric via the low-pressure reducing valve (F) into the low pressure chamber (G) where it is drawn off to the carburetor via outlet (H). The low pressure reducing valve is controlled by the larger diaphragm and small spring.

Fuel for the idling range of the engine is supplied from a separate outlet (J) which is connected by tubing to a separate idle fuel connection on the carburetor. Adjustment of the carburetor idle mixture is controlled

by the idle fuel screw (K) and the calibrated orifice (L) in the regulator. The balance line (M) is connected to the air inlet horn of the carburetor so as to reduce the flow of fuel and thus prevent over-richening of the mixture which would otherwise result when the air cleaner or air inlet system becomes restricted.

Model GBLP & Series UB
(Ensign Model R)

104. **HOW IT OPERATES.** Liquid LP-Gas from the supply tank enters the model R regulator at (1—Fig. MM302) and is reduced from tank pressure to about 4 psi at high pressure reducing valve (3) after passing through the strainer. Flow through high pressure valve is controlled by diaphragm (4), lever (5) and spring (6). When the liquid fuel enters the vaporizer coil (7) it expands rapidly and is converted from a liquid to a gas by heat from the engine coolant system water which surrounds the vaporizing coil. The vaporized gas then passes (at a pressure slightly below atmospheric) via the main valve (8) to the carburetor via the outlet (9). Control of the outlet pressure is obtained by operation of the large diaphragm (10), pin (11) and spring (12).

Fuel for the idling range of the engine is supplied by a separate outlet (15) via tube (16) from vapor reserve chamber (17) which is supplied by port (19). Outlet (15) is connected by tubing to a separate connection on the carburetor. Adjustment of the carburetor idle mixture is controlled by the idle fuel screw (20). A tube connects the atmospheric vent (21) to a pitot tube in the carburetor air horn so as to reduce the flow of fuel vapor and thus prevent over-richening of the mixture which would otherwise result when the air cleaner or air inlet system becomes restricted.

TROUBLE-SHOOTING

These procedures apply to all model W Ensign regulators and to model R regulators factory installed on Minneapolis-Moline tractors.

105. **SYMPTOM.** Engine will not idle with Idle Mixture Adjustment Screw in any position.

CAUSE AND CORRECTION. A leaking valve or gasket is the cause of the trouble. Look for leaking low pressure valve caused by deposits on valve or seat. To correct the trouble, wash the valve and seat in gasoline or other petroleum solvent.

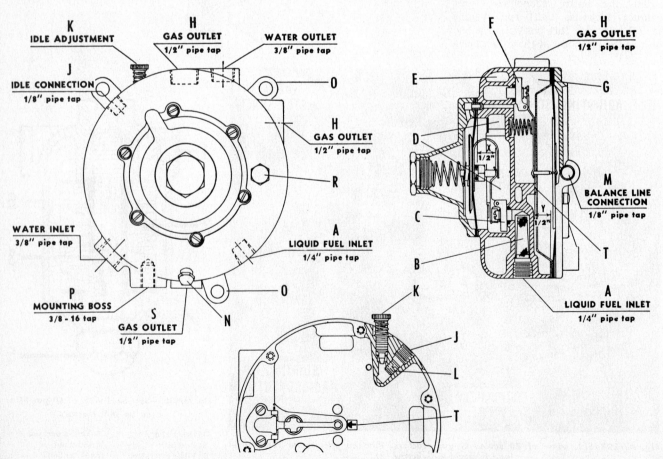

Fig. MM301—Ensign model W regulating unit used on series ZB.

If foregoing remedy does not correct the trouble, check for leak at high pressure valve by connecting a low reading (0 to 20 psi) pressure gauge at point (22) on model R regulator or at point (R) on the model W regulator. If the pressure increases **after** a warm engine is stopped, it proves a leak in the high pressure valve. Normal pressure is 3½-5 psi on model W, 4-5 psi on model R.

106. **SYMPTOM.** Cold regulator shows moisture and frost after standing.

CAUSE AND CORRECTION. Trouble is due either to leaking valves as per paragraph 105 or the valve levers are not properly set. For information on setting of valve lever refer to paragraph 107.

REGULATOR OVERHAUL

If an approved station is not available the model R regulator and the model W can be overhauled as follows:

107. Remove the unit from the engine and completely disassemble, using Figs. MM303 and MM304 as references. Thoroughly wash all parts and blow out all passages with compressed air. Inspect each part carefully and discard any that are worn.

Before reassembling the unit, note dimension (X—Figs. MM301 and 302) which is measured from the face on the high pressure side of the casting to the inside of the groove in the valve lever when valve is held firmly shut. If dimension (X) which can be measured with Ensign gauge No. 8276 or with a depth rule is more or less than ½ inch, bend the lever until this setting is obtained. A boss or post (T—Fig. MM305) is machined and marked with an arrow to assist in setting the lever. Be sure to center the lever on the arrow before tightening the screws holding the valve block. The top of the lever should be flush with the top of the boss or post (T).

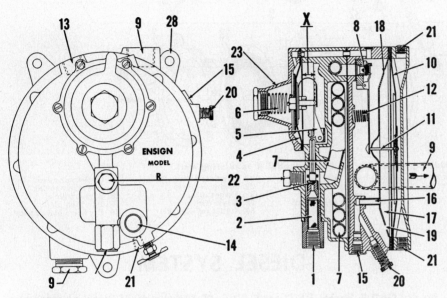

Fig. MM302—Ensign model R regulating unit used on models GBLP and series UB.

1. Fuel inlet
2. Filter screen
3. High pressure valve
4. Inlet pressure diaphragm
5. Inlet diaphragm lever
6. Inlet diaphragm spring
7. Fuel vaporizer coil
8. Main low pressure valve
9. Outlet to carburetor
10. Outlet pressure diaphragm
11. Push pin
12. Outlet diaphragm spring
13. Water inlet
14. Water outlet
15. Idling fuel outlet
16. Vapor reserve chamber
17. Push pin
18. Partition plate
19. Orifice
20. Idle fuel adjustment
21. Atmospheric vent
23. Regulator cover

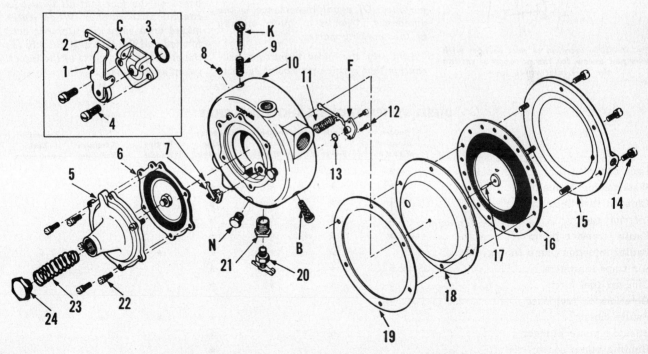

Fig. MM303—Exploded view of Ensign model W regulating unit.

B. Fuel inlet strainer
C. Valve seat
F. Outlet valve assy.
K. Idle adjusting screw
1. Inlet diaphragm lever
2. Pivot pin
3. "O" ring
5. Regulator cover
6. Inlet pressure diaphragm
7. Inlet valve assembly
8. Bleed screw
9. Idle screw spring
10. Regulator body
11. Outlet diaphragm spring
13. "O" ring
15. Back cover plate
16. Outlet pressure diaphragm
17. Push pin
18. Partition plate
19. Partition plate gasket
20. Drain cock
21. Reducing bushing
23. Inlet diaphragm spring
24. Spring retainer

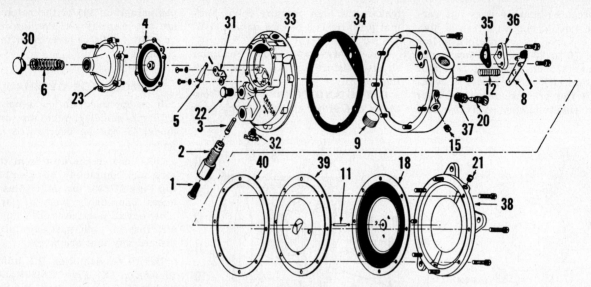

Fig. MM304—Exploded view of Ensign model R regulating unit.

1. Fuel inlet strainer	6. Inlet diaphragm spring	15. Bleed screw	23. Regulator cover	36. Outlet valve seat
2. Fuel inlet valve	8. Outlet valve lever	18. Outlet pressure	30. Spring retainer	37. Idle screw spring
3. Needle valve	9. Plug (⅜)	diaphragm	31. Pivot support	38. Support plate
4. Inlet pressure diaphragm	11. Push pin	20. Idle fuel adjustment	32. Drain cock	39. Partition plate
5. Inlet diaphragm lever	12. Outlet valve	21. Pipe plug (⅛)	35. Outlet valve gasket	40. Partition plate gasket

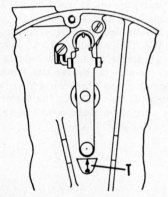

Fig. MM305—Location of post or boss with stamped arrow for the purpose of setting the fuel inlet valve lever.

DIESEL SYSTEM

Model GBD & Series UB Diesel

The Diesel fuel system consists of three basic units; the fuel filters, injection pump and injection nozzles. When servicing any unit associated with the fuel system, the maintenance of absolute cleanliness is of utmost importance. Of equal importance is the avoidance of nicks or burrs on any of the working parts.

Probably the most important precaution that service personnel can im-part to owners of Diesel powered tractors, is to urge them to use an approved fuel that is absolutely clean and free from foreign material. Extra precaution should be taken to make certain that no water enters the fuel storage tanks. This last precaution is based on the fact that all Diesel fuels contain some sulphur. When water is mixed with sulphur, sulphuric acid is formed and the acid will quickly erode the closely fitting parts of the injection pump and nozzles.

DIESEL SYSTEM TROUBLE SHOOTING CHART

	Sudden Stopping of Engine	Lack of Power	Engine Hard to Start	Irregular Engine Operation	Engine Knocks	Excessive Smoking	Excessive Fuel Consumption
Lack of fuel	★	★	★	★			
Water or dirt in fuel	★	★	★	★			
Clogged fuel lines	★	★	★	★			
Inferior fuel	★	★	★	★			
Faulty transfer pump	★	★	★	★			
Faulty injection pump timing		★	★	★	★	★	★
Air traps in system	★	★	★	★			
Clogged fuel filters	★	★	★	★			
Deteriorated fuel lines	★						★
Faulty nozzle				★	★	★	★
Sticking pump plunger		★		★			
Binding pump control rod				★			
Weak or broken governor springs				★			
Fuel delivery valve not seating properly				★			
Improperly set smoke stop		★					

108. QUICK CHECKS-UNITS ON TRACTOR. If the Diesel engine does not start or does not run properly, and the Diesel fuel system is suspected as the source of trouble, refer to the Diesel System Trouble Shooting chart and locate points which require further checking. Many of the chart items are self-explanatory; however, if the difficulty points to the fuel filters, injection nozzles and/or injection pump, refer to the appropriate paragraphs which follow:

FUEL FILTERS & BLEEDING
Models GBD & Series UB Diesel

109. The fuel filtering system consists of a screen type primary filter and two stages of renewable element type filters.

110. CIRCUIT DESCRIPTION AND MAINTENANCE. With the fuel shut off at valve (V—Figs. MM 306 & 307) open petcock (P) and drain off any accumulation of water and dirt. This should be done daily before tractor is operated.

Fuel from the fuel tank flows by force of gravity to the primary filter (PF) which contains a fine mesh screen that filters water from the fuel. After each 60 hours of operation, the filter bowl should be removed and the screen thoroughly cleaned with Diesel fuel. From the primary filter, the fuel flows through the renewable element type secondary filter (SF). It is recommended that this secondary filter element be renewed after each 90 days

of operation. After flowing through the secondary filter, the fuel passes through the positive displacement, gear type transfer pump (TP) to the renewable element type final filter and on to the injection pump. The filtering system is equipped with a pressure relief valve (PRV) located at the inlet side of the final fuel filter. If the final filtering element becomes clogged, the valve will release, the fuel will be by-passed back to the transfer pump and the engine will die from lack of fuel. The final filtering element should be renewed only when it becomes clogged.

111. BLEEDING. It is necessary to bleed the fuel system whenever the fuel flow is interrupted or air has been allowed to enter the system. To do so, refer to Figs. MM306 or MM307 and proceed as follows:

Open the shut-off valve (V) and remove bleed plug (1) at top of primary filter. Reinstall the plug when the fuel flows free of air. Remove bleed plug (2) from top of secondary filter. Reinstall plug (2) when the fuel flows free of air. Remove bleed plug (3) from the final filter, turn the engine over with the starting motor until the fuel flows free of air and install the bleed plug. Loosen the cap nut (4) on the check valve at front of injection pump, motor the engine until air is removed and tighten the nut. At this time, the engine will start, but if it does not run evenly, loosen the high pressure line fittings (5) at each nozzle to bleed out any air.

INJECTION NOZZLES
Model GBD & Series UB Diesel

WARNING: Fuel leaves the injection nozzles with sufficient force to penetrate the skin. When testing, keep your person clear of the nozzle spray.

112. TESTING AND LOCATING FAULTY NOZZLE. If the engine does not run properly, or not at all, and the quick checks outlined in paragraph 108 point to a faulty injection nozzle, locate the faulty nozzle as follows:

If one engine cylinder is misfiring, it is reasonable to suspect a faulty nozzle. Generally, a faulty nozzle can be located by loosening the high pressure line fitting on each nozzle holder in turn, thereby allowing fuel to escape at the union rather than enter the cylinder. As in checking spark plugs in a spark ignition engine, the faulty nozzle is the one which, when its line is loosened, least affects the running of the engine.

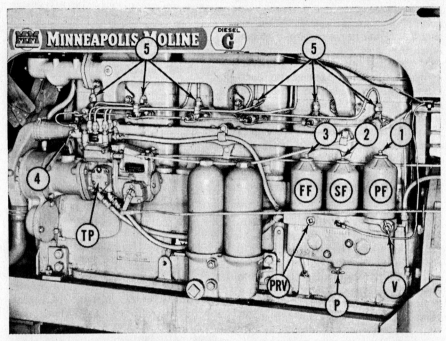

Fig. MM306—Left side view of the six cylinder GB Diesel tractor engine. The engines are equipped with an American Bosch PSB injection pump and throttling type pintle nozzles. The gear type fuel transfer pump is shown at (TP).

Fig. MM307—Left side view of the four cylinder UB Diesel tractor engine. The American Bosch injection equipment is similar to the GB Diesel.

113. Remove the suspected nozzle from the engine as outlined in paragraph 118. If a suitable nozzle tester is available, check the nozzle as in paragraph 114, 115, 116 and 117. If a nozzle tester is not available, reconnect the fuel line and with the nozzle tip directed where it will do no harm, crank the engine with the starting motor and observe the nozzle spray pattern as shown in Fig. MM308.

If the spray pattern is ragged, as shown in the left hand view, the nozzle valve is not seating properly and same should be reconditioned as outlined in paragraph 119. If cleaning and/or nozzle and tip renewal does not restore the unit and a nozzle tester is not available for further checking, send the complete nozzle and holder assembly to an official Diesel service station for overhaul.

114. NOZZLE TESTER. A complete job of testing and adjusting the nozzle requires the use of a special tester such as the American Bosch Nozzle Tester TSE7722D which is available through any of the Bosch authorized service agencies. The nozzle should be tested for leakage, spray pattern and opening pressure.

Operate the tester lever until oil flows and attach the nozzle and holder assembly.

Note: Only clean, approved testing oil should be used in the tester tank.

Close the tester valve and apply a few quick strokes to the lever. If undue pressure is required to operate the lever, the nozzle valve is plugged and same should be serviced as in paragraph 119.

115. *Leakage.* The nozzle valve should not leak at a pressure less than 1700 psi. To check for leakage, actuate the tester handle slowly and as the gage needle approaches 1700 psi, observe the nozzle tip for drops of fuel. If drops of fuel collect at pressures less than 1700 psi, the nozzle valve is not seating properly and same should be serviced as in paragraph 119.

116. *Spray Pattern.* Operate the tester handle at approximately 100 strokes per minute and observe the spray pattern as shown in Fig. MM308. If the nozzle has a ragged spray pattern as shown in the left view, the nozzle valve should be serviced as in paragraph 119.

117. *Opening Pressure.* While operating the tester handle observe the gage pressure at which the spray occurs. The gage pressure should be 1800 psi. If the pressure is not as specified, remove the nozzle protecting cap, exposing the pressure adjusting screw and locknut. Loosen the locknut and turn the adjusting screw as shown in Fig. MM309 either way as required to obtain an opening pressure of 1800 psi. Note: If a new pressure spring has been installed in the nozzle holder, adjust the opening pressure to 1900 psi. Tighten the locknut and install the protecting cap when adjustment is complete.

118. **REMOVE AND REINSTALL.** Before loosening any lines, wash the nozzle holder and connections with clean Diesel fuel or kerosene. After disconnecting the high pressure and leak-off lines, cover open ends of connections with caps to prevent the entrance of dirt or other foreign material. Remove the nozzle holder stud nuts and carefully withdraw the noz-

zle from cylinder head, being careful not to strike the tip end of the nozzle against any hard surface.

Remove "O" ring (Fig. MM310) and thoroughly clean the nozzle recess in the cylinder head. It is important that the seating surface of recess be free of even the smallest particle of carbon which could cause the nozzle to be cocked and result in blowby of hot gases. No hard or sharp tools should be used for cleaning. A piece of wood dowel or brass stock properly shaped is very effective. Do not reuse the copper ring gasket (1—Fig. MM311), always install a new one. If the "O" ring (Fig. MM310) is in good shape, reinstall it and insert the nozzle. Tighten the nozzle holder stud nuts to a torque of 14-16 Ft.-Lbs.

119. **MINOR OVERHAUL OF NOZZLE VALVE AND BODY.** Hard or sharp tools, emery cloth, crocus cloth, grinding compounds or abrasives of any kind should NEVER be used in the cleaning of nozzles. A nozzle cleaning and maintenance kit is available through any American Bosch Service Agency under the number of TSE7779.

Wipe all dirt and loose carbon from the nozzle and holder assembly with a clean, lint free cloth. Carefully clamp the nozzle holder assembly in a soft jawed vise and remove the nozzle holder nut and spray nozzle. Reinstall the holder nut to protect the lapped end of the holder body. Normally, the nozzle valve (V—Fig. MM312) can be easily withdrawn from the nozzle body. If the valve cannot be easily withdrawn, soak the assembly in fuel oil, acetone, carbon tetra-

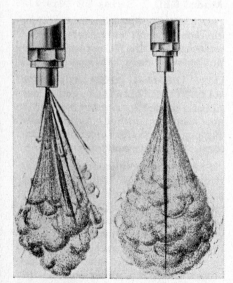

Fig. MM308—Typical spray patterns of a throttling type pintle nozzle. Left: Poor spray pattern. Right: Ideal spray pattern.

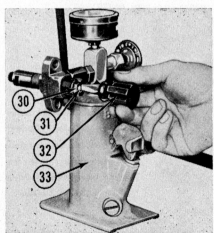

Fig. MM309—Adjusting the nozzle opening pressure, using a suitable nozzle tester.
30. Nut   32. Screw driver
31. Adjusting screw   33. Nozzle tester

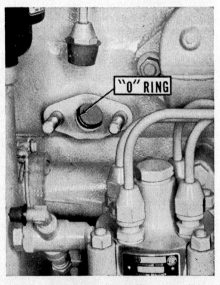

Fig. MM310—Before installing the injection nozzles, make certain that the "O" ring is in good condition.

chloride or similar carbon solvent to facilitate removal. Be careful not to permit the valve or body to come in contact with any hard surface.

Clean the nozzle valve with mutton tallow used on a soft, lint free cloth or pad. The valve may be held by its stem in a revolving chuck during this cleaning operation. A piece of soft wood, well soaked in oil will be helpful in removing carbon deposits from the valve.

The inside of the nozzle body (tip) can be cleaned by forming a piece of soft wood to a point which will correspond to the angle of the nozzle valve seat. The wood should be well soaked in oil. The orifice of the tip can be cleaned with a wood splinter. The outer surfaces of the nozzle body should be cleaned with a brass wire brush and a soft, lint free cloth soaked in a suitable carbon solvent.

Thoroughly wash the nozzle valve and body in clean Diesel fuel and clean the pintle and its seat as follows: Hold the valve at the stem end only and using light oil as a lubricant, rotate the valve back and forth in the body. Some time may be required in removing the particles of dirt from the pintle valve; however, abrasive materials should never be used in the cleaning process.

Test the fit of the nozzle valve in the nozzle body as follows: Hold the body at a 45 degree angle and start the valve in the body. The valve should slide slowly into the body under its own weight. Note: Dirt particles too small to be seen by the naked eye, will restrict the valve action. If the valve sticks, and it is known to be clean, free-up the valve by working the valve in the body with mutton tallow.

Before reassembling, thoroughly rinse all parts in clean Diesel fuel and make certain that all carbon is removed from the nozzle holder nut. Install nozzle body and holder nut, making certain that the valve stem is located in the hole of the holder body. It is essential that the nozzle be perfectly centered in the holder nut. A centering sleeve is supplied in American Bosch kit TSE7779 for this purpose. Slide the sleeve over the nozzle with the tapered end centering in the holder nut as shown in Fig. MM313. Tighten the holder nut, making certain that the sleeve is free

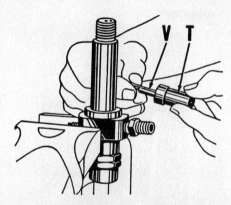

Fig. MM312—Removing injection nozzle valve (V) from tip (T). If the valve is difficult to remove, soak the assembly in a suitable carbon solvent.

Fig. MM313—Using Bosch sleeve to center the nozzle tip while tightening the cap nut.

Fig. MM314—In the absence of Bosch centering sleeve (Fig. MM313), 0.003 shim stock can be used to center the nozzle tip while tightening the cap nut.

while tightening. In the absence of the centering sleeve, a piece of 0.003 shim stock can be placed around the nozzle while tightening the holder nut as shown in Fig. MM314.

Test the nozzle for spray pattern and leakage as in paragraphs 115 and 116. If the nozzle does not leak under 1700 psi, and if the spray pattern is symmetrical as shown in the right hand view of Fig. MM308, the nozzle is ready for use. If the nozzle will not pass the leakage and spray pattern tests, renew the nozzle valve and seat, which are available only in a matched set; or send the nozzle and holder assembly to an official Diesel service station for a complete overhaul which includes reseating the nozzle valve pintle and seat.

120. OVERHAUL OF NOZZLE HOLDER. Refer to Fig. MM315. Remove cap nut (1) and gasket. Loosen jam nut (2) and adjusting screw (3). Remove the spring retaining nut (4) and withdraw the spindle (5) and spring (6). Thoroughly wash all parts in clean Diesel fuel and examine the end of the spindle which contacts the nozzle valve stem for any irregularities. If the contact surface is pitted or rough, renew the spindle. Examine

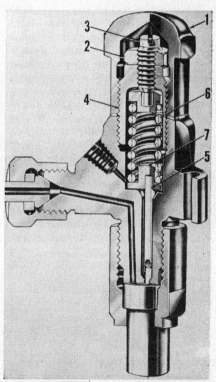

Fig. MM315—Injection nozzle sectional view. This particular nozzle is not used on Minneapolis-Moline tractors, however, the internal construction is similar.

2. Jam nut
3. Adjusting screw
4. Spring retainer cap nut
5. Spindle
6. Spring
7. Lower spring seat

Fig. MM311—Sectional view showing a typical installation of an American Bosch injection nozzle. Whenever the nozzle has been removed, always renew the copper gasket (1).

spring seat (7) for tightness to spindle and for cracks or worn spots. Renew the spring seat and spindle unit if the condition of either is questionable. Renew any questionable parts.

Reassemble the nozzle holder and leave the adjusting screw locknut loose until after the nozzle opening pressure has been adjusted as outlined in paragraph 117.

INJECTION PUMP
Model GBD & Series UB Diesel

Minneapolis-Moline Diesel tractors are equipped with American Bosch single plunger model PSB injection pumps. See Fig. MM316.

The subsequent paragraphs will outline ONLY the injection pump service work which can be accomplished without the use of special, costly pump testing equipment. If additional service work is required, the pump should be turned over to an official Diesel service station for overhaul. Inexperienced service personnel should never attempt to overhaul a Diesel injection pump.

121. TIMING TO ENGINE. Injection should occur 27 degrees B.T.C. To check and retime the pump to the engine after the pump is installed as outlined in paragraph 124, proceed as follows:

Remove the rocker arm cover from the front cylinder head and crank engine until the intake valve of number one cylinder is closing. Remove the inspection plate from flywheel housing and continue cranking until the timing mark on flywheel is exactly in line with the pointer in the flywheel housing as shown in Fig. MM317. On engines which do not have degree markings, use the "INJ" mark. On engines which have degree marks as well as the "INJ" mark, use 27 degrees B.T.C. Remove the inspection plug from top of pump adapter housing and observe the pump coupling timing marks. If pump timing is correct, the line mark on the drive gear

hub will be exactly in register with the pointer extending from front face of the pump. Refer to Fig. MM318.

If the timing marks are not exactly in register, and it is certain that the pump has been properly installed (refer to paragraph 124) remove the timing gear case cover as outlined in paragraph 45. Unwire and loosen the four cap screws retaining the pump drive gear (2—Fig. MM319) to the camshaft gear and turn the pump drive gear in the elongated cap screw holes until the coupling timing marks shown in Fig. MM318 are exactly in register. Tighten and wire the four pump drive gear retaining cap screws and install the timing gear case cover.

122. TRANSFER PUMP. The Diesel injection pumps are equipped with a positive displacement, gear type transfer pump which is gear driven from the injection pump camshaft. Refer to Fig. MM320.

If the pump is not operating properly, the complete pump can be re-

newed as a unit; or, the transfer pump can be disassembled and cleaned and checked for improved performance. Quite often, a thorough cleaning job will restore the pump to its original operating efficiency.

123. HYDRAULIC HEAD. The hydraulic head assembly (Fig. MM321) can be renewed without the use of special testing equipment. The head assembly contains all of the precision components which are essential to accurate pumping, distributing, metering and delivery of the fuel. To renew the hydraulic head assembly, first wash the complete injection pump and injection lines with clean fuel oil. Remove the injection lines and disconnect the inlet and outlet lines from the hydraulic head. Remove the timing window cover (20—Fig. MM322) and crank engine until the line mark on the apex of one of the teeth on the pump plunger drive gear is in register with the pointer stamped on the lower face of the timing window hole as shown in Fig. MM323. Remove the two screws and carefully withdraw the control assembly being careful not

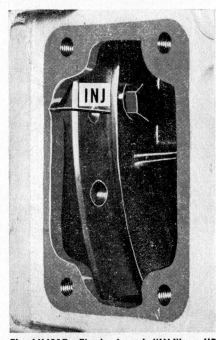

Fig. MM317—Flywheel mark "INJ" on UB Diesel tractors. The flywheel mark on the GB Diesel is similar. Use degree marks on engines so equipped.

Fig. MM316—Typical American Bosch PSB injection pump. The unit contains a flyweight type governor.

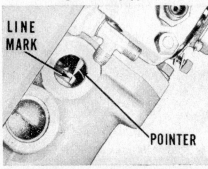

Fig. MM318—Pump drive coupling timing marks on Diesel tractors.

Fig. MM319—Timing gear train of GBD and UB Diesel tractors.

1. Crankshaft gear
2. Adjustable gear
3. Camshaft gear
4. Pump drive gear

Fig. MM320—Cut-away view of the positive displacement, gear type fuel transfer pump used on the American Bosch PSB injection pump.

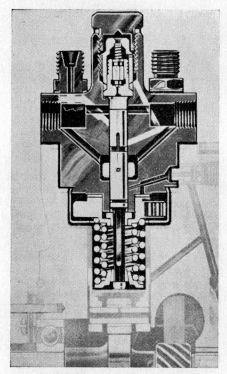

Fig. MM321—Sectional view of Bosch model PSB injection pump hydraulic head. The complete head assembly can be renewed as a unit.

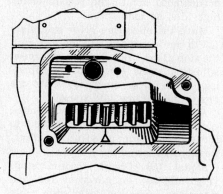

Fig. MM323—Side view of Bosch model PSB injection pump with timing window cover removed. Notice that the line on one of the gear teeth is in register with pointer on the housing.

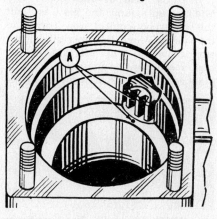

Fig. MM324—When installing a hydraulic head on a model PSB injection pump, make certain that open tooth on quill shaft gear is in register with punch mark in housing as shown at (A).

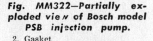

Fig. MM322—Partially exploded view of Bosch model PSB injection pump.

2. Gasket
4. Delivery valve spring
5. Gasket
6. Hydraulic head
7. Governor cover
8. Oil filter
9. "O" ring
10. Gasket
11. Filter screen
12. Snap ring
13. Gear
14. Seal
15. Transfer pump
16. Sleeve pin
17. Snap ring
18 & 19. Control unit
20. Timing window cover
21, 22, 23 & 25. "O" ring

to lose plunger sleeve pin (16—Fig. MM322). Remove governor cover (7) and unscrew and remove lube oil filter (8). Remove the hydraulic head retaining stud nuts and carefully withdraw the hydraulic head assembly from the pump housing. Do not use force when attempting to withdraw the hydraulic head. If difficulty is encountered, check to make certain that the plunger drive gear is properly positioned as shown in Fig. MM323.

When installing a new hydraulic head assembly, make certain that the line marked plunger drive gear tooth is in register with the pointer stamped on the lower face of the timing window as shown in Fig. MM323 and that open tooth on quill shaft gear is in register with punch mark in pump housing as shown at (A) in Fig. MM324. When installing the control sleeve assembly, the plunger sleeve pin (16—Fig. MM322) must be lined up with the slot in the control block. The remainder of the reassembly procedure is evident.

124. **REMOVE AND REINSTALL INJECTION PUMP.** Before attempting to remove the injection pump, thoroughly wash the pump and connections with clean Diesel fuel. Disconnect the injection lines from injection pump and the inlet and outlet lines from the transfer pump. Disconnect the remaining lines and control rods. Cover all fuel line connections with composition caps to eliminate the entrance of dirt. Remove the rocker arm cover from the front cylinder head and crank engine until the intake valve of number one cylinder is closing. Remove the inspection plate from flywheel housing and continue cranking until the timing mark (Refer to paragraph 121) on flywheel is exactly in line with the pointer in the flywheel housing as shown in Fig. MM317. Remove the pump mounting cap screws and withdraw the pump.

125. To install the injection pump, first make certain that the flywheel mark "INJ" is in the proper position as previously outlined. Remove the timing window cover (20 — Fig. MM322) from side of injection pump and turn the pump hub until the line mark on the apex of one of the pump plunger drive gear teeth is approximately in the center of the timing window. Then, continue turning the hub until the line mark on the hub is as nearly in register with the pointer as possible. See Fig. MM326. Make

Fig. MM326—Coupling timing marks in the proper position for installing the injection pump. Notice that line mark is to left of pointer.

certain that the marked tooth is still visible in the timing window.

Mount pump to engine by meshing the pump drive coupling gear with the floating coupling inside the adapter housing. Turn top of pump toward engine until the cap screws can be installed and observe the coupling timing marks which should be aligned as shown in Fig. MM327.

If the marks are in register as shown, the pump is installed properly and no additional timing will be required.

If the marks are less than one drive coupling tooth of being aligned, the pump is installed properly, but the final timing adjustment should be made as outlined in paragraph 121.

If, however, the marks are more than one coupling tooth of being aligned, remove and reinstall pump until the proper register is obtained.

126. GOVERNOR. Model PSB injection pumps are equipped with a mechanical flyweight type governor. For the purposes of this manual, the governor will be considered as an integral part of the injection pump.

127. ADJUSTMENT. Recommended governed speeds are as follows:
No load engine speed
UB .... 1430 rpm
GB, belt and pulley
 work .... 1430 rpm
GB, other work .... 1650 rpm

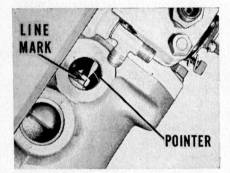

Fig. MM327—Pump drive coupling timing marks on Diesel tractors.

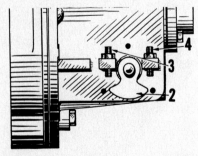

Fig. MM328—High and low speed adjustment screws on Bosch model PSB injection pump.

2. Adjusting screw stop plate
3. Low speed adjusting screw
4. High speed adjusting screw

Recommended low idle
engine speed .... 600 rpm

To adjust the governor, first start engine and run until engine is at normal operating temperature, then proceed as follows:

Disconnect governor rod from governor arm and remove adjusting screw cover from side of injection pump. Move the operating lever stop plate (2—Fig. MM328) to the high speed position and with the stop plate contacting the high speed adjusting screw (4), turn the adjusting screw up or down to obtain the recommended high idle, no load speed.

Move the operating lever stop plate (2) to the low speed position and with the stop plate contacting the low speed adjusting screw (3), turn the adjusting screw up or down to obtain the recommended low idle speed.

After obtaining the recommended speeds, connect the governor rod to the governor arm and adjust the throttle stops as follows:

Model UB Diesel. Loosen stops (Fig. MM329) on governor rod and move the operating lever stop plate (2—Fig. MM328) to the low speed position and with the stop plate contacting the low speed adjusting screw (3), adjust one of the stops (Fig. MM329) up against the plate to limit the governor control rod travel to that point. Move the operating lever stop plate (2—Fig. MM328) to the high speed position and with the stop plate contacting the high speed adjust-

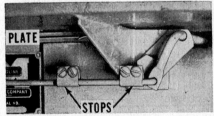

Fig. MM329—Model UB Diesel governor control rod stops.

Fig. MM330—Model GB Diesel governor control rod stops.

ing screw (4), adjust the other stop (Fig. MM329) up against the plate to limit the governor control rod travel to that point.

Model GB Diesel. Move the speed control lever rearward and against the rear stop bolt (Fig. MM330). Adjust the length of the control rod by means of clevis (6—Fig. MM331) until the operating lever stop plate just touches the low speed adjusting screw (3). Tighten jam nut (7). Move the operating lever stop plate to the high speed position and with the stop plate contacting the high speed adjusting screw (4), adjust the front bolt (Fig. MM330) up against the speed control lever to limit the lever movement at that point. Some GB diesels have a stop for the injection pump control arm. With stop in front position, a no load speed of 1430 rpm is obtained. With stop in rear position, a no load speed of 1650 rpm is obtained.

ENERGY CELLS
Model GBD & Series UB Diesel

128. R&R AND CLEAN. The necessity for cleaning the energy cells is usually indicated by excessive exhaust smoking, or when fuel economy drops. To remove the energy cells, unscrew the retainer plug and remove the cap holder. Grasp the energy cell cap (3—Fig. MM332) with a pair of pliers and withdraw cap from cylinder head. Using a 15/16 inch NEF-2 puller screwed into energy cell (4), pull cell from head as shown in Fig. MM333.

Fig. MM331—Model GB Diesel governor control rod clevis adjustment.

Fig. MM332—Exploded view of Diesel engine energy cell.

1. Plug
2. Holder
3. Cell cap
4. Energy cell

Clean all parts in a suitable carbon solvent and renew any which are cracked or damaged. Clean the small orifice in the cell chamber with a brass brush or a piece of hard wood. Check seating surface of cell body in cylinder head and mating surfaces of energy cell and cell cap. If the surfaces are rough, they can be cleaned by lapping with a mixture of jeweler's rouge and Diesel fuel.

When reinstalling the energy cell, make certain that it fits squarely into cylinder head. Tighten the retainer plug securely.

Fig. MM333—Using special threaded puller to remove energy cell from Diesel engines.

ELECTRIC MANIFOLD HEATER
Model GBD & Series UB Diesel

129. The heater unit is equipped with a Champion J-14 single electrode spark plug. The other electrode is attached to a cap screw in the housing. Bend only the electrode attached to the cap screw to obtain an electrode gap 3/32 inch.

NON-DIESEL GOVERNOR

ADJUSTMENT
All Models

130. Make certain that all governor linkage is free from binding at all points. Binding linkage can sometimes be corrected by shifting carburetor position on its studs.

To adjust governor, first adjust carburetor idle speed and mixture; then, with throttle hand control in full speed position, adjust screw (X—Fig. MM334) on governor, to obtain the recommended speeds which are listed later. Turning adjusting screw clockwise decreases engine speed; turning it counter-clockwise increases engine speed.

Engine Loaded rpm
GB-UB Non-Diesels 1300
ZB Series 1500
Engine No Load rpm
GB-UB Non-Diesels 1430
ZB Series 1650

Belt Pulley Loaded rpm
GB-UB Non-Diesels 741
ZB Series 786
Belt Pulley No Load rpm
GB-UB Non-Diesels 815
ZB Series 865

R & R AND OVERHAUL
Series GB-UB

131. To remove governor, unscrew the governor to crankcase retaining cap screws and withdraw governor unit.

Before disassembling, mark governor housing (115—Fig. MM335) and cover (113) so that cover can be reinstalled in the correct position. Remove cover retaining screws and cover. Remove bearing retaining plate (102), and separate plate from governor housing. Remove plug from housing and bump pin (111) out of control

lever arm and shaft (112), and remove control lever shaft as shown in Fig. MM336. Bump pin (109—Fig. MM335) out of speed control lever (75) and shaft (108) and remove shaft and speed adjusting arm (114). Ball (105) will roll out of governor shaft (119). Remove weight pins (93) and withdraw thrust thimble (104) from governor shaft. From governor, remove snap ring (118) and ball bearing (103). To remove weights (101), remove weight shafts (100).

Control arm shaft bushings (110) require final sizing after installation to provide a 0.0015-0.002 diametral clearance. Spring adjusting sleeve (117) should be a close fit in housing but should not bind. Check speed adjusting lever shaft (108) and mating surface in housing for wear. Diametral clearance in excess of 0.007 will require renewal of housing and/or lever

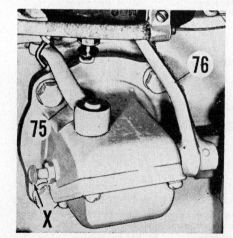

Fig. MM334—Typical Minneapolis-Moline governor unit installation, showing the speed adjusting screw (X).

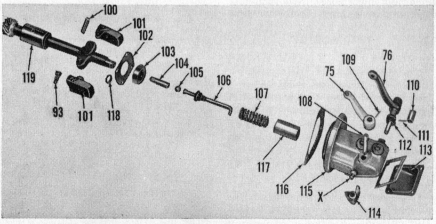

Fig. MM335—Exploded view of governor used on series GB and UB.

X. Speed control adjusting screw	104. Thrust thimble	112. Control arm
75. Speed control hand lever	105. Thimble ball	113. Cover
76. Governor control lever	106. Spindle	114. Speed adjusting arm
93. Weight pin	107. Spring	115. Housing
100. Weight shaft	108. Speed adjusting lever shaft	116. Housing gasket
101. Weight	109. Speed adjusting lever pin	117. Spring adjusting sleeve
102. Bearing retainer plate	110. Control arm shaft bushing	118. Bearing snap ring
103. Housing bearing	111. Control arm pin	119. Rotor shaft

shaft. Taper pin holes can be reamed with a No. 0 taper pin reamer for a tight fit of pins.

Series ZB

132. Remove governor from engine. Mark governor housing and cover so that cover can be reinstalled in the correct position. Remove retaining screws and cover (113—Fig. MM337). Drive pin (109) out of speed adjusting

lever (75) and remove shaft (108) and arm at lower end of shaft through housing. Drive taper pin out of control arm shaft and control arm (112) from inside of housing. Unhook spindle (106) from control arm and withdraw control arm lever (76) and shaft from housing. Drive grooved pin out of flyball rotor and remove pinion gear, shaft, and thrust washer. Remove rotor assembly. Remove hexagon head threaded pins (93) from gov-

ernor weights (101) and withdraw thrust thimble (104) from rotor.

Governor weights can be removed by removing cotter pins and weight shafts (100). Bushings for control arm shaft should be renewed when governor is overhauled. Spring adjusting sleeve (117) should be a close fit in housing, but should not bind. End play in governor shaft should be held to a minimum by thrust washers. To reassemble, reverse disassembly procedure.

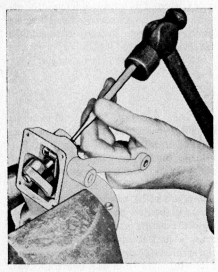

Fig. MM336—Bumping pin out of governor control arm and shaft on series GB and UB.

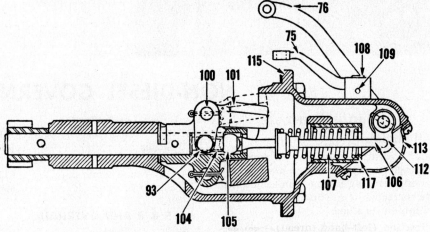

Fig. MM337—Sectional view of ZB series governor unit.

75. Speed control hand lever	105. Thimble ball	109. Speed adjusting lever pin
76. Control lever	106. Spindle	112. Control arm
93. Weight pin	107. Spring	113. Cover
100. Weight shaft	108. Speed adjusting lever shaft	115. Housing
101. Weight		117. Spring adjusting sleeve
104. Thrust thimble		

COOLING SYSTEM

RADIATOR
All Models

133. The radiator assembly which on some models has detachable upper and lower tank units can be removed after removing hood and disconnecting upper and lower hoses; then, removing the radiator retaining cap screws.

THERMOSTAT
All Models

134. On models GB, GBD and UB Diesels, the thermostat is located in a flanged elbow bolted to front of outlet manifold on top of engine. On other models, the thermostat is located in an elbow attached to the radiator top tank.

FAN ASSEMBLY
All Models

135. Procedure for removal and/or overhaul of the fan assembly is evident after an examination of the unit and reference to Figs. MM338 & 339. The taper roller fan shaft bearings as used on some models should be adjusted to remove all end play, yet permit shaft to rotate freely.

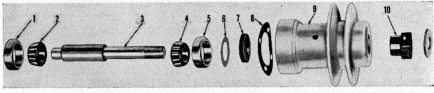

Fig. MM338—Exploded view of UB series fan hub. Gaskets (8) control bearing adjustment.

1. Front bearing cup	4. Rear bearing cone	8. Fan gasket
2. Front bearing cone	5. Rear bearing cup	9. Fan hub
3. Fan spindle	6. Retaining washer	10. Spindle collar
	7. Felt seal	

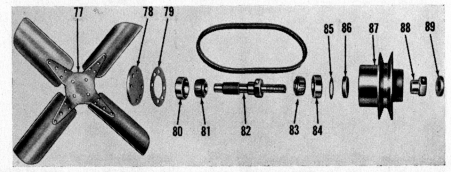

Fig. MM339—Exploded view of GB series fan shaft assembly. The ZB series fan shaft is similarly constructed.

77. Fan blades	81. Fan end bearing cone	86. Fan hub felt
78. Bearing retainer	82. Fan spindle	87. Fan hub
79. Shim	83. Rear bearing cup	88. Collar (nut)
80. Fan end bearing cup	84. Rear bearing cone	89. Clamp washer
	85. Retainer washer for felt	

26. Accessory shaft
27. Allen screw
28. Accessory shaft sleeve
30. Gear case
31. Water pump body & timing
     gear case cover
32. Water pump impeller
90. Pump seal
91. Pump cover
92. Bushing (front)
95. Oil seal
96. Bushing (rear)
97. Accessory shaft drive gear
120. Cover gasket
121. Water outlet manifold
122. Water pump inlet elbow

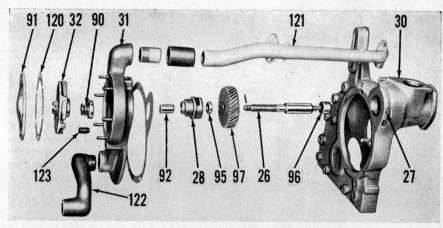

Fig. MM340—Water pump, accessory drive shaft and timing gear case as used on non-Diesel GB and UB series.

WATER PUMP
Series GB-UB Non-Diesels

The water pump body is integral with timing gear case cover.

136. PUMP SEAL. To renew water pump seal (90—Fig. MM340), proceed as follows: Remove fan belt and pump cover (91). Bump Groov pin out of impeller and shaft and remove impeller by rotating same in clockwise direction (left-hand thread). Seal assembly is retained in impeller and can be renewed at this time without further pump disassembly. Check condition of seal contacting thrust surface which is the outer face of bushing and sleeve assembly (28) and reface or renew if same is scored.

137. PUMP BODY, ACCESSORY SHAFT AND/OR BUSHINGS. To renew pump body (timing gear case cover), accessory shaft and/or bushings, proceed as follows: Remove timing gear cover as outlined in paragraph 44. Loosen Allen screw (27) (located left side of timing gear case) Fig. MM340, and remove sleeve (28) which contains bushing (92) and oil seal (95). Remove ignition unit, and power lift pump; then, bump accessory shaft rearward and out of gear and timing gear case. Bushings (96) which should have a 0.0015-0.003 diametral clearance between shaft and bushings can be renewed at this time.

When reinstalling accessory shaft gear, mesh same as shown in Fig. MM273.

Series GB-UB Diesels

138. R&R AND OVERHAUL. To remove the water pump, drain cooling system and remove hood, grille and radiator. Remove nuts retaining pump to timing gear case and remove pump from tractor.

Fig. MM341—Exploded view of Diesel engine water pump. Pump must be removed to renew seal (2).

1. Impeller
3. Drive shaft
4. Oil seal
5. Collar
6. Roll pin
7. Bushing

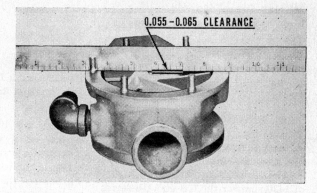

Fig. MM342—Checking clearance between front of Diesel engine water pump body and impeller.

Remove cover from pump body and drive roll pin (6-Fig. MM341) out of collar and drive shaft. Withdraw impeller, shaft and seal assembly. If seal seating surface in pump body is scored, pitted or rough and cannot be refaced, renew the pump body. If running clearance between pump shaft and bushing (7) is excessive, or if shaft is scored, renew shaft and/or bushing. Ream the bushing after installation, if necessary to provide a suggested running clearance of 0.0015 minimum.

After collar (5) and roll pin (6) are installed, lay a straight edge across front of pump body and check the clearance between straight edge and impeller. Desired clearance is 0.055-0.065 as shown in Fig. MM342. If clearance is not as specified, it will be necessary to move impeller on the pump shaft.

Before assembling cover to pump, mount pump on engine with gasket and "O" ring in place and check end play of impeller shaft with a straight edge and feelers or with a dial indi-

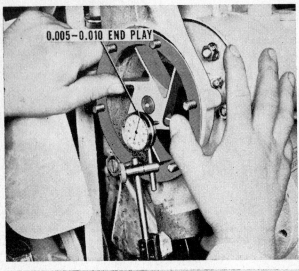

cator as shown in Fig. MM343. Desired end play is 0.005-0.010 which can be obtained by varying the number of gaskets between pump body and engine.

Fig. MM343—On Diesel engine water pumps, the gaskets between pump body and engine should be varied to give the pump shaft an end play of 0.005-0.010.

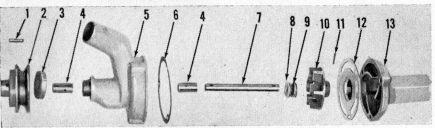

Fig. MM344—Exploded view of ZB series water pump.

1. Pulley pin	5. Pump body	10. Impeller
2. Pulley	6. Gasket	11. Impeller pin
3. Felt seal assembly	7. Pump shaft	12. Baffle plate
4. Bushing	8. Thrust washer	13. Water manifold
	9. Shaft seal	

Series ZB

139. RESEAL AND OVERHAUL. Remove fan belt. Remove bolts and nuts retaining water pump to water manifold and remove water pump. Water pump and water manifold can be removed as a unit by removing four cap screws retaining manifold to cylinder block.

140. If pump and manifold have been removed as a unit, remove bolts and nuts retaining pump to manifold and remove pump. Drive pin (1—Fig. MM344) from pulley (2) and shaft (7) and remove pulley. Pull impeller (10) and shaft from pump body (5). Thrust washer (8) and seal assembly (9) can be renewed at this time without further disassembly. Thrust surface contacted by thrust washer must be smooth and true.

If thrust surface is scored, it should be refaced or renewed. When installing bushings (4), register oil holes in bushings with grease reservoir in pump body.

IGNITION AND ELECTRICAL SYSTEM

All Non-Diesel Models

140. DISTRIBUTOR APPLICATIONS. The GB and UB series tractors are equipped with Delco-Remy 1111748 distributor and the ZB series is equipped with a Delco-Remy 1111711.

141. IGNITION TIMING. To time the ignition, it is strongly recommended that a neon timing light be used and time the ignition with the engine running at the high idle no load speed of 1430 rpm for the GB and UB series, 1650 rpm for the ZB series. Timing procedure is as follows: Adjust breaker contact gap to 0.018-0.020. Remove front rocker cover and inspection cover from flywheel housing.

Crank engine until the "DC 1-4" mark on flywheel is approximately in register with the pointer when both valves of number one cylinder are closed. Using white paint or chalk, mark a running timing index on flywheel rim. The timing index should be before (ahead) of the "DC 1-4" mark by the number of inches listed in the following table.

Timing Index
(Inches Before DC)

GB Gasoline & Distillate	4⅛
GB LP-Gas	4⅜
UB Gasoline	3⅞
UB LP-Gas & Distillate	4⅛
ZB Gasoline & Distillate	2⅛
ZB LP-Gas	1¾

After the timing index has been placed on flywheel rim, rotate flywheel to a point where the "DC 1-4" mark is approximately ⅝ inch past the pointer; then insert the distributor. Turn distributor housing until breaker contacts just start to open when rotor is in the number one cylinder firing position. Tighten the distributor clamp bolt and start engine.

With engine running at the high idle no load speed of 1430 rpm for the GB and UB series or 1650 rpm for the ZB series, use a neon timing light focused on flywheel rim and observe if the affixed running timing index registers with pointer at inspection port. If not in register, loosen the distributor clamp bolt and turn distributor slightly until registration is obtained.

NOTE: Final setting may have to be varied slightly from listed timing to take care of variations in fuel, compression ratio, altitude and mechanical condition of engine. On the GB and UB series, if the timing is checked at rated loaded rpm, the spark will occur ⅜-½ inch (measured on flywheel rim) later.

142. GENERATOR, REGULATOR & STARTING MOTOR. All models are equipped with Delco-Remy electrical units. Applications are as follows:

Series GB
Generator with regulator...1100314
Starting motor (non-Diesel).1108983
Starting motor (Diesel).....1109801
Series UB
Generator with regulator...1100954
Starting motor (non-Diesel).1107605
Starting motor (Diesel).....1109236
Series ZB
Generator with regulator...1100954
Starting motor 1108109

Test specifications for the 1100314 generator are as follows:
Cold output, 20.0 amperes @ 14.0 volts @ 2300 rpm.
Field draw, 1.58-1.67 amperes @ 12 volts.

Test specifications for the 1109801 starting motor are as follows:

Brush spring tension, 24-28 ounces. No load test, 75 amperes max. @ 11.25 volts @ 6000 rpm.

Lock test, 29 foot-pounds @ 615 amperes @ 5.85 volts.

CLUTCH

ADJUSTMENT

(Over-Center Type)

Series GB

143. With clutch compartment cover removed and transmission gear shift lever in neutral position, rotate engine

Fig. MM345 — Adjusting the over-center type clutch used on GB series tractors. Pull lockpin (P) out as far as possible; then rotate adjusting yoke to the right (Up, when viewed through clutch compartment opening).

Fig. MM346—Clutch linkage adjustment for spring loaded type clutches used on UB and ZB series tractors.

crankshaft until lockpin (P), shown in Fig. MM345, is accessible; then pull pin out as far as it will go. Place transmission gear shift lever in any gear; then, disengage clutch, and rotate adjusting yoke to the right (**UP**, when viewed through clutch compartment opening) to tighten clutch. Clutch should be tightened to a point where no slippage will occur under full load, yet not so tight that difficulty is encountered when engaging the clutch. Be sure lock pin is firmly seated in one of the holes in the floating plate after completing the adjustment.

ADJUSTMENT

(Spring Loaded Type)

Series UB-ZB

144. Adjustment to compensate for lining wear is accomplished by adjusting the clutch pedal linkage, NOT by adjusting the position of the clutch release levers. The clutch linkage is properly adjusted when the clutch pedal has a free travel of 1¼-1¾ inches. If specified free travel cannot be obtained, renewal or relining of lined plate is indicated.

To adjust the linkage, vary the length of the release rod (X—Fig. MM346) by means of clevis (Y) at front end of rod.

R & R AND OVERHAUL
Series GB (Over-Center Type)

145. To remove clutch unit, it is first necessary to perform a tractor split (detach engine from transmission) as outlined in paragraph 148. Disconnect actuating (clutch hand lever and shifter fork) rod. Remove nut and washer retaining clutch unit to clutch shaft, and using a puller attached as shown in Fig. MM348, pull clutch assembly forward until same is free from clutch shaft Woodruff key. Rotate clutch assembly on clutch shaft until sliding sleeve keyway is in line with the Woodruff key; then, remove clutch unit from shaft.

The clutch brake disc (33—Fig. MM355) can be renewed at this time. The shifter yoke can be removed from sliding sleeve by removing bolts which join the two halves. Adjust diametral clearance of shifter yoke on sliding sleeve, by varying the number of shims (11—Fig. MM347) between yoke mating surfaces, to zero running clearance without permitting the yoke to bind when same is rotated.

To disassemble clutch unit, pull out adjusting lock pin and retract adjusting yoke and sleeve assembly, lift off floating plate and driving plate and remove release springs. Adjusting yoke, finger levers, lever links and sliding sleeve can be disassembled by removing snap rings and pins.

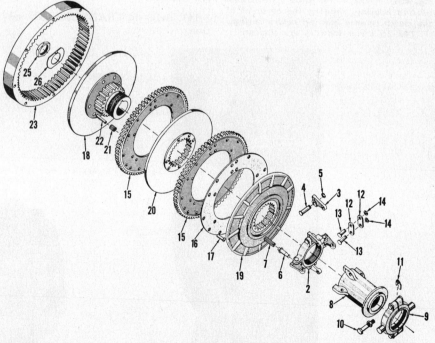

Fig. MM347—Exploded view of the double disc, over-center type clutch used on the GB series tractors.

2. Adjusting yoke	8. Sliding sleeve	14. Snap rings	20. Center plate
3. Fingers	9. Shifter ring	15. Driving plate	21. Release spring
4. Pins	10. Bolt	16. Lining	22. Release spring pin
5. Snap rings	11. Shim	17. Rivets	23. Ring gear
6. Lock pin	12. Lever link	18. Back plate	25. Lock nut
7. Spring	13. Link pin	19. Floating plate	26. Lock washer

Fig. MM348—Using a suitable puller to remove clutch unit from clutch shaft on GB series tractors.

Fig. MM349—Front view of UB series transmission housing, showing the removal of the clutch release bearing return springs. The ZB series tractors are similar.

Check all of the unlined plates for grooving, warpage, heat checks and for wear in splines. Check links and pins for wear. Renew any parts which are damaged beyond repair.

Series UB-ZB (Spring Loaded Type)

146. To remove the clutch, it is first necessary to detach engine from transmission as outlined in paragraph 148.

The clutch release bearing and collar can be removed after disconnecting the return springs as shown in Fig. MM349.

Unscrew the cap screws retaining the clutch cover assembly to flywheel and remove cover assembly and lined plate. Note: Three 5/16 inch cap screws 1¼ inches long can be installed through the cover plate as shown in Fig. MM350 to unload the pressure springs prior to unbolting the assembly from flywheel. If this procedure is not used, the cover retaining cap screws must be unscrewed evenly to avoid damaging the cover plate.

The procedure for disassembling and/or overhauling the removed clutch units is given in Appendix 1, beginning on page 46.

CLUTCH SHAFT

All Models

147. Refer to TRANSMISSION section.

TRACTOR SPLIT

All Models

A general procedure for splitting the tractor is given in the following paragraphs. Minor differences in construction are obvious after an examination of the unit.

148. Remove hood and disconnect fuel lines, oil lines, control rods, wires and cables. Disconnect drag link or steering shaft. Block up engine and transmission separately, using a traveling chain hoist or some other device for one section so that it can be moved independently from the other section. Remove bolts retaining engine and main frame to transmission housing, and move transmission and rear axle unit away from engine and engine frame unit, as shown in Fig. MM353.

Fig. MM350—Before removing spring loaded type clutches from flywheel, it is advisable to install three 5/16 inch cap screws as shown, to unload the pressure springs.

Fig. MM353—Splitting Minneapolis-Moline tractors. Notice long pilot studs in transmission housing to facilitate reconnecting the units.

TRANSMISSION AND CONNECTIONS

All Models

149. TRANSMISSION COVER. Cover can be removed after removing the instrument panel, battery and battery shelf. Remove cap screws retaining cover to transmission case and lift off cover. Reinstallation is reverse of removal.

150. SHIFTER RAILS AND FORKS. Rails and forks can be removed after removing transmission cover, and four cap screws retaining shifter rail bearings (69 & 70—Fig. MM354) to transmission housing. Complete disassembly of rails and forks is self-evident after an examination and reference to Fig. MM354.

151. SLIDING GEAR (CLUTCH) SHAFT. The sliding gear (clutch) shaft (63—Figs. MM355 & 356) can be removed after "splitting" tractor as outlined in paragraph 148, and removing transmission cover, transmission shifter rails and forks, and clutch shifter fork.

On models equipped with over-center type clutches, remove brake plate (32—Fig. MM355) and disc (33) from clutch shaft. Remove clutch shaft ball bearing cover from front of transmission case; then, using a soft drift as in Fig. MM357, bump clutch shaft forward and out of transmission housing. Remove sliding gear shaft gears out through top cover opening. Pocket bearing (52—Figs. MM355 & 356), can be renewed at this time from pocket in main drive bevel pinion shaft. Constant mesh gear (36) can be removed at this time after removing snap ring (82). To remove clutch shaft bearing (62) remove snap ring and press bearing off toward front end of shaft.

Reassembly is reverse of disassembly. Install constant mesh pinion (36) with long part of hub toward front of transmission. Install oil seal (80) with lip of same facing the rear.

152. UPPER COUNTERSHAFT. The upper countershaft (57—Fig. MM358) can be removed after removing clutch and sliding gear shaft and power take-off unit.

Working through clutch compartment, remove front bearing retainer (61); then, working through the power take-off unit opening in rear of transmission case, bump upper countershaft forward and out of transmission housing. Gears, spacer, and countershaft rear bearing can be removed through top of housing.

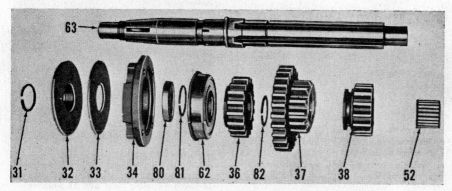

Fig. MM354—Exploded view of shifter rails and forks. Slight differences in some models is evident after an examination of the unit.

66. Gear shifter separating bracket
68. Detent ball
69. Rail bearing (rear)
70. Rail bearing (front)
71. 2nd & reverse fork
73. 1st, 3rd, 4th & 5th fork
74. 2nd & reverse rail
75. 3rd & 4th rail
76. 1st & 5th rail
77. Shifter ball spring
78. Spring seat
79. Shifter cap

Fig. MM355—GB series clutch and transmission sliding gear shaft.

31. Snap ring
32. Thrust brake plate
33. Asbestos brake disc
34. Bearing cover
36. Constant mesh gear
37. 1st & 4th sliding gear
38. 3rd & 5th sliding gear
52. Clutch shaft pocket bearing
62. Bearing (ball)
63. Sliding gear shaft
80. Oil seal
81. Snap ring
82. Snap ring

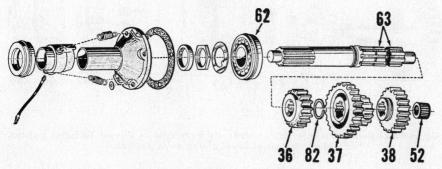

Fig. MM356—UB series clutch and transmission sliding gear shaft. The ZB series is similarly constructed. See legend for Fig. MM355.

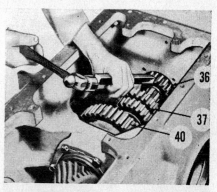

Fig. MM357 — After removing the clutch shaft front bearing retainer, use a soft drift to bump clutch and sliding gear shaft forward and out of housing.

36. Constant mesh gear
37. 1st & 4th sliding gear
40. Main drive bevel pinion shaft and gear

Reinstall the upper countershaft by reversing the removal procedure and on ZB series tractors, vary the number of shims (83—Fig. MM358) to provide a slight amount of pre-load for the taper roller bearings.

153. LOWER COUNTERSHAFT. The lower countershaft, Fig. MM359, can be removed after "splitting" tractor and removing transmission cover, shifter rails and forks, clutch shaft, power take-off unit, upper countershaft, and belt pulley unit.

Working through transmission top cover opening, remove belt pulley drive gear positioning snap ring (91—Fig. MM360) from its groove and slide same rearward. Working through clutch compartment, remove cap screws from front bearing carrier (85—Fig. MM359). Insert a split spacer, approximately 5¼ inches long, between sliding gear and belt pulley drive gear as shown in Fig. MM361 to prevent damaging the gear teeth or bearing cone when bumping shaft forward. Working through differential compartment, bump lower countershaft forward and out of transmission housing. Remove gears, snap ring and rear bearing cone out through transmission top cover opening.

Shims (95—Fig. MM359) located between rear bearing cup (94) and bearing cup bore in transmission housing control mesh position of belt pulley drive gear (90). Always reinstall the same shims that were removed.

Adjust lower countershaft bearings by varying number shims (86 & 87), interposed between transmission compartment forward wall and front bearing carrier (85) to provide a slight bearing pre-load of 0.001-0.003. If the lower countershaft and/or belt pulley drive gear are renewed, adjust belt pulley drive gear backlash to 0.006-0.008 as outlined in BELT PULLEY section.

154. MAIN DRIVE BEVEL PINION AND SHAFT. Main drive bevel pinion, constant mesh gear and shaft, and bearing cage assembly (Fig. MM362 or 363) can be removed after "splitting" tractor, and removing other transmission shafts and gears as outlined in preceding paragraphs.

Fig. MM358—Upper countershaft used on GB and UB series tractors. The ZB series is similar except shaft is carried in taper roller bearings and spacer (55) is not used.

53. Ball bearing (rear)
54. Constant mesh gear
55. Spacer
56. Double gear
58. Spacer
59. Constant mesh gear
60. Ball bearing (front)
61. Bearing retainer
83. Gasket (GB & UB)
83. Shims (ZB)

Fig. MM359—Transmission lower countershaft. Belt pulley drive gear (90) mesh position is controlled with shims (95) inserted between bearing cup (94) and bearing cup bore. Shims (86 & 87) control bearing adjustment.

51. Lower countershaft
85. Bearing retainer
86 & 87. Shims & gasket
88. Bearing cup
89. Bearing cone
90. Constant mesh gear
91. Snap ring
92. 2nd & reverse gear
93. Bearing cone
94. Bearing cup
95. Shim

Fig. MM361—A spacer is installed between belt pulley drive gear and sliding gear when bumping transmission lower countershaft forward and out of housing.

Fig. MM360—Removing belt pulley drive gear positioning snap ring prior to removal of lower countershaft.

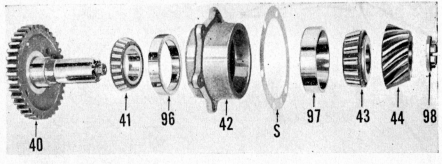

Fig. MM362—Main drive bevel pinion shaft and gear used on UB and ZB series tractors. Shims (S) control bevel pinion mesh position.

40. Gear
41. Bearing cone
42. Bearing cage
43. Bearing cone
44. Main drive bevel pinion
96. Bearing cup
97. Bearing cup
98. Nut

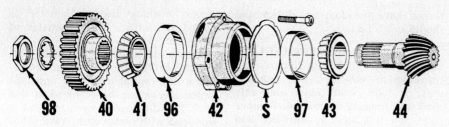

Fig. MM363—Main drive bevel pinion shaft and gear used on GB series tractors. Refer to legend for Fig. MM362.

Remove safety wire and cap screws retaining bearing cage (42) to transmission housing wall. A half-moon box wrench is best suited for this operation. The complete assembly (shaft, gears and bearing) can be withdrawn forward and out of transmission housing. Do not discard shims (S) located between bearing cage and transmission housing.

Pinion and ring gears are available only as matched pairs, and can be identified as such by etched numbers on both pinion and gear.

When reassembling, tighten retaining nut (98) to slightly pre-load the bearings. Install assembly so that the bearing cage oil reservoir is facing up. For bevel pinion gear mesh adjustment, refer to MAIN DRIVE BEVEL GEARS section.

DIFFERENTIAL AND FINAL DRIVE

DIFFERENTIAL

Series GB-UB

155. BEARING ADJUSTMENT. Differential carrier bearing adjustment is controlled with shims (S—Fig. MM364) inserted between bearing cages and transmission housing. The same shims also control bevel ring gear and pinion backlash which should be set to the value as etched on individual sets of matched gears.

To adjust differential carrier bearings, first remove transmission top cover. Remove left brake assembly. Remove cap screws retaining left bearing cage to transmission housing and slide cage out far enough to permit removal of required thickness of shims to provide zero end play and yet permit differential unit to rotate without binding. Reinstall bearing cage and check bearing adjustment and backlash. If bearing adjustment is O.K. but backlash is .002 greater or less than value stamped on ring gear it will be necessary to adjust backlash by transferring shims from one side to the other until correct backlash is obtained.

156. R & R AND OVERHAUL. To remove differential unit, first remove transmission housing top cover, power take-off unit or transmission housing rear cover plate and rear axle shaft and housing assemblies. Remove both brake assemblies. Remove cap screws retaining differential bearing cages to transmission housing. Tilt lower end of left bull gear to the right and remove left differential bearing cage and bull pinion shaft (or sleeve) and left differential shaft on models which are equipped with continuous type power take-off. With the left bull gear in an upright position, tilt lower end of right bull gear to the left and remove right differential cage and bull pinion shaft.

Do not discard shims located between bearing cages and transmission housing. With bearing cages removed, the differential unit can be lifted out through top opening of transmission housing.

Mark both halves of differential case. Remove bolts and nuts joining both halves of differential case. Pinions (121—Fig. MM364 or 365), pinion spider (105), side gears (120) and side gear thrust washers (119) can then be removed. New pinion shaft diameter is 0.996-0.997. Service bushings for pinions are to be sized after installation to an inside diameter of 1.000-1.001.

When reassembling differential unit, install side gear thrust washers (119) with bevel edge facing inward. Install oil seal (118) with lip of same facing the differential.

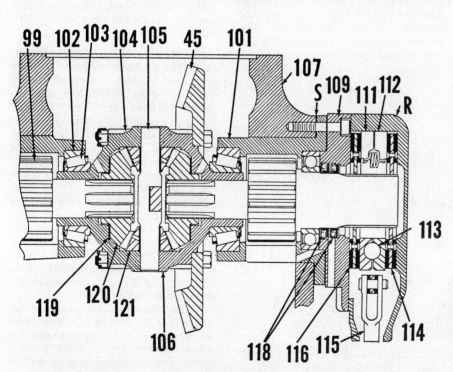

Fig. MM364—Sectional view of the UB series transmission case showing the installation of the differential. The general construction of the GB series is similar as shown in Fig. MM365. Notice in Fig. 365 that the GB series is fitted with a ring gear overload block (M).

R. Brake housing cover & outer brake plate	103. Bearing cone	113. Actuating disc ball
S. Shims	104. Differential case	114. Brake disc
45. Main drive bevel ring gear	105. Spider	115. Brake actuating rod
99. Bull pinion	106. Differential case	116. Brake disc
101. Bearing cage	107. Transmission housing	118. Oil seal (2 used)
102. Bearing cup	109. Brake plate (inner)	119. Thrust washer
	111 & 112. Brake actuating disc	120. Differential side gear

Paragraphs 157-159

Reinstall differential unit by reversing removal procedure. Reinstall differential bearing cages with same thickness of shims as was removed.

Check and adjust differential carrier bearings, as in paragraph 155 and mesh and backlash of main drive bevel gears as outlined in paragraph 159.

After differential is installed and before installing the transmission case top cover on the GB series, adjust the overload block as follows: Loosen jam nuts on screws (N—Fig. MM365) and turn the screws either way as required to obtain a clearance of 0.002 between block (M) and ring gear. Check the clearance at top and bottom of overload block to make certain that block is parallel to ring gear.

Series ZB

157. BEARING ADJUSTMENT. Differential bearing adjustment is controlled by shims (S—Fig. MM366) which are located between the brake housing and the transmission case. These shims, also control bevel ring gear and pinion backlash to the value as etched on the gear.

To make a bearing adjustment, remove transmission cover. Remove the left brake discs and cap screws retaining brake housing to transmission housing and slide housing out far enough to permit removal of required thickness of shims. Retighten housing and check bearing play. Bearings

should have no play, but differential should not bind.

158. R & R AND OVERHAUL. To remove differential unit, first remove transmission cover, power take-off unit, or rear cover plate, rear axle shaft and housing assemblies. Remove right and left hand brake discs and housings.

Tilt the bottom of the left bull gear to the right and remove the left bull pinion and differential side gear. Straighten up the left bull gear and tilt the bottom of the right bull gear to the left and remove the right differential side gear and bull pinion. Shims (S—Fig. MM366) control differential bearing end play and main drive bevel ring gear backlash.

Place a piece of wood (approximately 2½ inches wide) between back face of bevel ring gear and transmission housing. Working through the right hand opening in transmission housing, bump differential shaft out of the differential case. Lift the differential and bevel ring gear assembly out through transmission top cover opening.

To disassemble the differential unit, remove the two long bolts retaining differential bevel pinion shafts to differential case. Bump one pinion shaft through the cage, forcing the other pinion shaft out; then bump the first pinion shaft out. Differential pinion

bronze bushing inside diameter is 1.000-1.001, with a shaft diameter of 0.996-0.997.

Differential shaft bushings (10—Fig. MM366) which are pressed in the integral differential side gear and bull pinion sleeve can be renewed at this time. The differential case, on models equipped with continuous power take-off, contains bushings which should be renewed if they are worn.

Install oil seals (11 and 12) with lip of seal facing differential unit.

Reverse removal procedure. Reinstall brake housings with same thickness of shims between each brake housing and transmission as was removed. If bearing play exists, remove an equal thickness of shims from between each brake housing and transmission until all bearing play is eliminated, but being sure that sufficient backlash exists between teeth of the bevel gears.

If main drive pinion and ring gear, which are available only as matched pairs, were renewed; they must be checked and adjusted for correct mesh and backlash. For adjusting procedure, refer to paragraph 159.

MAIN DRIVE BEVEL GEARS
All Models

Main drive bevel pinion and ring gear are available only as matched pairs.

159. MESH AND BACKLASH ADJUSTMENT. Mesh position of main drive bevel pinion is controlled with shims (S—Figs. MM362 and 363), inserted between bevel pinion shaft bearing cage and transmission housing dividing wall. Main drive bevel gear backlash is controlled by removing shims from under one bearing cage and inserting the same amount under the other cage.

Both bevel pinion and ring gear are marked as follows: One group of numbers indicates matched set number; number stamped as .008 BL indicates backlash value, and a number with a plus or minus sign indicates pinion position in relation to cone center distance. Refer to Fig. MM367.

If the renewed gears have a value within 2 of the plus or minus mark on old gears, reinstall same number of shims between bevel pinion bearing cage and transmission housing wall as were removed and used for the old gears.

If new gears have a backlash value greater than 2 from the plus or minus mark on old gears; then, add or remove shims from between pinion bearing cage and transmission housing wall to offset the difference in cone

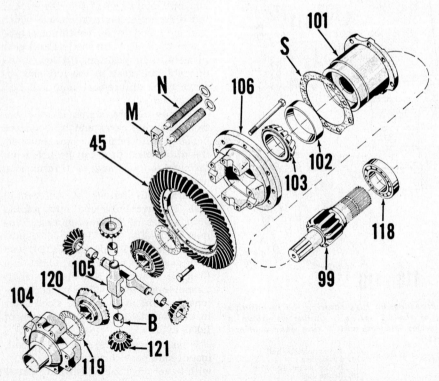

Fig MM365—Exploded view of GB series differential and associated parts. Refer to text for method of adjusting overload block (M). Refer to legend for Fig. MM364.

center position. After this adjustment has been completed and the differential carrier bearings are adjusted as outlined in paragraph 155 or 157, transfer shims from under one brake housing to the other brake housing to obtain the correct backlash as specified on the gears.

The bevel pinion mesh can be checked by using the following procedure. With backlash correctly adjusted, apply a coat of Prussian blue or red lead to gear teeth and rotate gears several revolutions. While rotating the gears, slightly brake the bevel ring gear.

If bluing or red lead is wiped from heel of tooth, move pinion away from ring gear by adding shims; then, transfer shims from differential right bearing cage to left so as to re-establish

the correct backlash. If bluing or red lead shows heavy toe contact, move pinion toward ring gear by removing shims; then, transfer shims from differential left bearing cage to right side to re-establish correct backlash.

With backlash properly adjusted, correct mesh is when ring gear indicates contact for ¾ to ⅞ of tooth length centered between toe and heel ends of gear.

160. RENEW BEVEL GEARS. The main drive bevel pinion and ring gear are available only as matched pairs.

On the UB and ZB series, the bevel pinion is splined to the transmission constant mesh gear shaft; for removal procedure, refer to paragraph 154. The GB bevel pinion is integral with the shaft and the removal procedure is covered in paragraph 154.

Renewal of the bevel ring gear on all models requires R & R of differential as outlined in paragraph 156 for the GB and UB series, 158 for the ZB series.

Fig. MM367—Minneapolis-Moline bevel pinion and ring gears. The same numbers, such as (A-5-852) on both gears indicate they are a matched set. The notation (0.008BL) refers to the correct backlash adjustment of 0.008 for this set of gears. The (-4) indicates the cone center relative distance.

1. Pinion shaft
2. Bevel pinion
3. Bearing cup
4. Brake housing
5. Brake linings
6. Power plate
7. Ball
8. Housing cover
9. Expansion plug
10. Bushing
11. Seal
14. Pinion bushings
15. Bushing
16. Bearing cup
17. Brake disc
18. Washer
19. Bull pinion sleeve
20. Bevel ring gear
21. Differential case
22. Cross shaft
23. Thrust washer

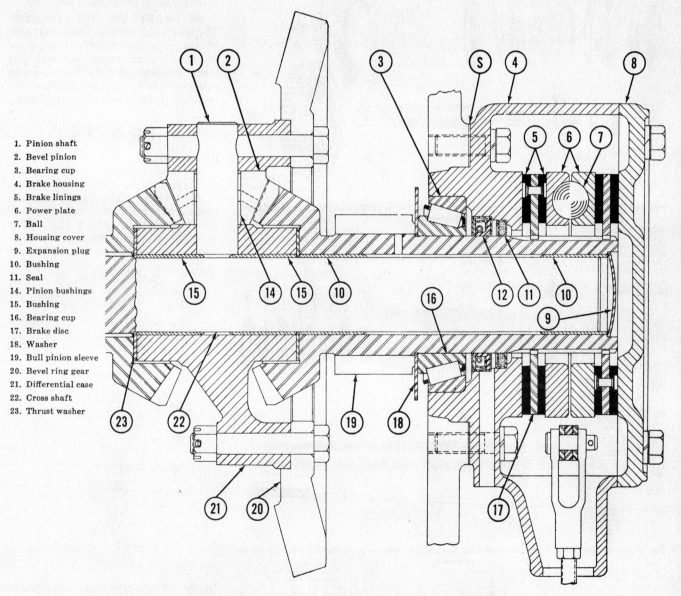

Fig. MM366—ZB series differential installation on models with continuous power take-off. Models without continuous pto are similar except differential case is keyed to cross shaft.

FINAL DRIVE GEARS
All Models

161. BULL PINION. To remove a bull pinion, first remove the transmission top cover, power take-off unit or transmission housing rear cover plate and the respective rear axle shaft and housing assembly. Remove the respective brake discs and brake housing. On the GB and UB series, remove cap screws retaining the differential bearing cage to the transmission housing. On all models, tilt lower end of bull gear (same side as pinion to be removed) toward the opposite bull gear and remove bull pinion shaft (or bull pinion sleeve). On the GB and UB series, the bull pinion and bearing cage are removed as an assembly.

When reassembling, check and adjust the differential carrier bearings as outlined in paragraph 155 or 157.

162. BULL GEARS. Either bull gear can be lifted from the transmission housing after removing the differential as outlined in paragraph 156 or 158.

AXLE SHAFTS AND HOUSINGS
All Models

163. BEARING ADJUSTMENT. Axle bearing play is controlled with shims (128—Fig. MM368) or (6—Fig. MM369) between bearing cap and axle housing. To adjust bearings, support rear of tractor under transmission and remove tire and wheel assembly. Remove bearing cap and vary number of shims between cap and housing to provide zero end play to shaft and yet permit same to rotate without binding.

164. R & R ASSEMBLY. Support rear of tractor under transmission and remove tire and wheel assembly. Remove transmission top cover, and power take-off unit or rear cover plate from models so equipped. Straighten bull gear retaining nut lock and remove bull gear retaining nut. Remove axle housing to transmission housing retaining bolts and remove axle shaft and housing assembly.

165. SHAFT AND/OR BEARINGS RENEW. To renew either shaft and/or bearings, remove assembly as outlined in preceding paragraph 164. Remove bearing retainer and bump shaft on inner end. Inner bearing cup can be pulled or driven from housing after removing snap ring. Adjust bearings as outlined in paragraph 163.

166. SHAFT OIL SEAL RENEW. The axle shaft oil seal (129—Fig. MM 368) or (10—Fig. MM369) can be renewed after removing rear tire and wheel assembly, and the shaft bearing retainer. Install seal in bearing retainer with lip of seal facing bull gear.

BRAKES
All Models

167. ADJUSTMENT. To adjust the disc type brakes, support rear portion of tractor and shorten the brake actuating rods by turning adjusting nut (N—Fig. MM370) until a slight drag is obtained while rotating the rear wheels; then, lengthen the rod ½ turn

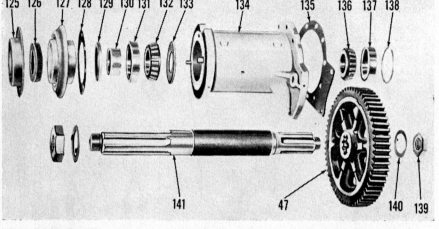

Fig. MM368—GB series rear axle shaft and housing. Shims (128) control axle shaft bearing adjustment.

47. Bull gear	130. Spacer	136. Bearing cone
125. Oil collector ring	131. Bearing cup	137. Bearing cup
126. Felt seal	132. Bearing cone	138. Snap ring
127. Bearing retainer	134. Housing	139. Bull gear retaining nut
128. Shims	135. Gasket	140. Lock washer
129. Oil seal		141. Axle shaft

Fig. MM369—Typical rear axle shaft and housing assembly used on UB and ZB series tractors.

1. Bull gear	10. Oil seal	18. Inner bearing cone
5. Housing	11. Axle shaft	19. Inner bearing cup
6. Shim	12. Snap ring	20. Gasket
7. Bearing cover	15. Retainer	21. Axle shaft key
8. Collar (spacer)	16. Outer bearing cup	22. Locking washer
9. Felt	17. Outer bearing cone	23. Gear retaining nut

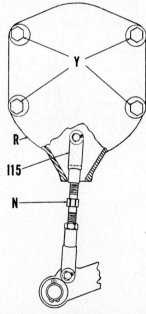

Fig. MM370—Disc type brakes are adjusted by varying the length of the brake actuating rod by turning nut (N).

and tighten the jam nut. Both brakes should be free when pedal is depressed 1½ inches but should lock the wheels when pedal is depressed 2½ inches.

168. R & R AND OVERHAUL. The brake assembly can be removed from tractor after disconnecting the actuating linkage and removing the retaining cap screws. On models which are equipped with continuous, or live, power take-off, it is necessary to remove the PTO clutch and power release mechanism before removing the left brake.

Procedure for overhauling the brakes is evident after an examination of the removed units. When installing the brake drum, make certain that the retaining cap screws are installed in their original position. Install the brake assembly as shown in Fig. MM 371. Sectional views showing typical disc brake installations are shown in Figs. MM364, 366 & 378.

Refer to paragraph 171 for information concerning the installation of the continuous power take-off clutch and power release mechanism.

BELT PULLEY

All Models

169. The belt pulley unit (Fig. MM372, 373 or 374) is mounted on side of transmission case and is driven by a bevel gear on the transmission lower countershaft. The procedure for removing, disassembling and overhauling the pulley unit is evident after an examination of the unit and reference to the accompanying illustrations.

The unit used on GB and UB series tractors is equipped with non-adjustable ball type bearings (5 & 22—Fig. MM372). When assembling the ZB series unit shown in Fig. MM373, vary the number of shims (9) to provide zero end play to pulley shaft and yet permit shaft to rotate without binding. On ZB tractors with the clutched unit shown in Fig. MM374, adjust the bearings by tightening nut (12).

When installing the belt pulley unit, vary the number of shims between pulley shaft housing and the transmis-

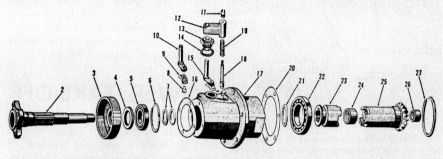

Fig. MM372—Belt pulley unit used on GB and UB series tractors. Backlash of the pulley driving bevel gears is controlled by shims (20).

2. Drive shaft	8. Pin	16. Gasket	22. Inner ball bearing
3. Bearing retainer	9. Block	17. Housing	23. Sliding jaw
4. Oil seal	10. Shifting arm	18. Lock pin	24. Needle bearing
5. Ball bearing	12. Shift lever	19. Spring	25. Pulley drive pinion
6. Snap ring	13 & 14. Nut & gasket	20. Shims	26. Needle bearing
7. Snap ring	15. Shift arm	21. Snap ring	27. Snap ring

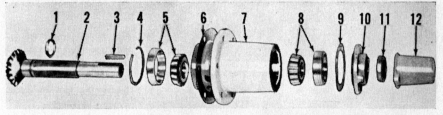

Fig. MM373—ZB series continuous running belt pulley unit. Pulley shaft bearings are adjusted with shims (9). Bevel gear backlash is controlled by shims (6).

1. Snap ring	4. Snap ring	7. Housing	10. Cover
2. Pulley shaft	5. Bearing	8. Bearing	11. Oil seal
3. Key	6. Shims	9. Shims	12. Cover

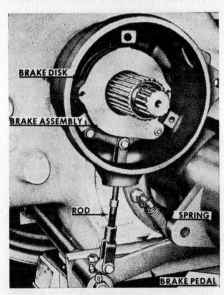

Fig. MM371—Typical installation of double disc brake assembly on left side of tractors which are equipped with continuous type power take-off.

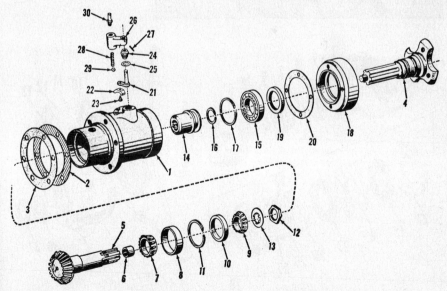

Fig. MM374—ZB series clutched belt pulley unit. The taper roller bearings are adjusted with nut (12). Shims (2) control bevel gear backlash.

1. Pulley housing		23. Pin
2. Shims	9. Bearing cone	16. Snap ring	24. Nut
3. Gasket	10. Bearing cup	17. Snap ring	25. Gasket
4. Drive shaft	11. Snap ring	18. Retainer	26. Shift lever
5. Pinion	12. Nut	19. Oil seal	27. Pin
6. Needle bearing	13. Washer	20. Gasket	28. Spring
7. Bearing cone	14. Sliding jaw	21. Shifting arm	29. Ball
8. Bearing cup	15. Ball bearing	22. Bronze block	30. Stud

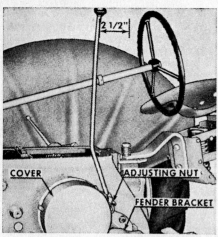

Fig. MM375—The continuous type power take-off clutch is properly adjusted when the control lever has a free travel of 2½ inches.

sion case to provide a backlash of 0.006-0.008 for the pulley driving bevel gears. Measure the tooth backlash by using a piece of 0.007 thick paper on gear teeth. Bolt pulley unit to transmission case, rotate pulley several times, remove the pulley unit and observe the piece of paper. If the surface of the 0.007 thick paper shows a heavy impression but is not punctured, it indicates that actual backlash of approximately 0.006 exists.

POWER TAKE-OFF

Some tractors are equipped with the power output shaft layout shown in Fig. MM379 and the system is known as a non-continuous type. On

Fig. MM376—The UB series pto clutch outboard bearing cage can be removed after removing screws (S). The GB series is similar.

other tractors, a disc type clutch is mounted on the left bull pinion and the clutch is used in conjunction with the shaft layout shown in Fig. MM379 to form a continuous (live) power take-off.

CLUTCH
All Models

170. **ADJUSTMENT.** To adjust the disc type power take-off clutch, turn the adjusting nut (Fig. MM375) either way as required to give the clutch control handle a free travel of 2½ inches minimum.

171. **OVERHAUL.** Except for detailed differences, overhaul of the GB, UB and ZB power take-off clutches are the same.

Remove left rear wheel, fender and fender bracket. Remove cover from unit, on GB and UB series, remove screws (S—Fig. MM376) and withdraw the bearing cage. The outboard bearing bronze bushing (B) can be renewed at this time. On all models, remove outer snap ring (2—Fig. MM 377) and withdraw adapter (3). Remove inner snap ring (2), outer snap ring (5) and withdraw the clutch assembly.

Note: On the GB series, the outer snap ring (5) is not used, but it is necessary to remove a large nut from bull pinion sleeve before clutch can be withdrawn. This nut contains an oil seal and an "O" ring which should be renewed if there is any evidence of oil leakage. When reinstalling this sleeve nut, wrap a thin sheet of shim stock around the differential shaft to protect the seal lip.

The clutch can be disassembled after removing the cover plate cap screws. Inspect all internal parts and renew or recondition any which are questionable. Linings should be renewed if they are warped or worn. Machined surfaces of cover plate, intermediate discs and power plate should be smooth and not scored or grooved. Springs, spring seats, balls and ball inserts must be in good condition and not heat discolored. When reassembling the clutch, make certain that all parts are in position and properly aligned.

To remove the power release mechanism, remove inner snap ring (5), remove the three retaining cap screws and disconnect the linkage. Disassemble the unit and renew any questionable parts.

Reassemble the clutch and power release mechanism by reversing the disassembly procedure and adjust the unit as outlined in paragraph 170.

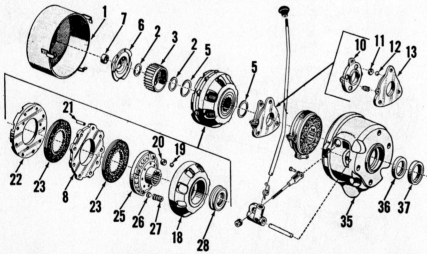

Fig. MM377—Exploded view of the UB series pto clutch and power release mechanism. Except for detailed differences, the GB and ZB units are similar. The GB unit has three lined clutch discs whereas the ZB has one.

1. Cover	8. Intermediate disc	19. Ball	26. Spring seat
2. Snap ring	10. Power release plate	20. Ball insert	27. Spring
3. Adapter gear	11. Ball insert	21. Spacer	28. Thrust bearing
5. Snap ring	12. Ball	22. Cover plate	35. Main housing
6. Bearing cage	13. Backing plate	23. Lined disc	36. Inner oil seal
(UB & GB)	18. Housing	25. Power plate	37. Outer oil seal
7. Bearing (UB & GB)			

OUTPUT SHAFT

All Models

172. BEARING ADJUSTMENT. Vary number of shims (16—Fig. MM379) between housing cap (15) and housing to provide zero end play to PTO shaft, and yet permit same to rotate freely.

173. R & R AND DISASSEMBLE. Drain lubricant from transmission housing or raise rear of tractor far enough to prevent loss of lubricant from housing after PTO unit has been removed. Remove cap screws retaining PTO housing to rear of transmission housing and withdraw unit from transmission housing. The need and procedure for further disassembly will be evident by an examination of the parts and reference to Fig. MM379. To reinstall, reverse removal procedure.

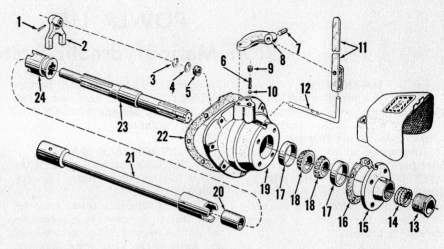

Fig. MM379—Exploded view of pto output shaft. Bearings are adjusted with shims (16).

1. Pin	7. Pin	13. Packing nut	19. Housing
2. Shifter fork	8. Bracket	14. Packing	20. Bushing
3. Snap ring	9. Pipe plug	15. Housing cap	21. Connecting shaft
4. Washer	10. Ball	16. Shims	22. Gasket
5. Seal	11. Lever	17. Bearing cup	23. Splined output shaft
6. Spring	12. Shifter rod	18. Bearing cone	24. Sliding jaw

Fig. MM378—Sectional view of ZB series bull pinion, left brake, power release mechanism and continuous type power take-off clutch.

S. Shims
1. Cover
2. Snap ring
3. Adapter gear
4. Oil seal

5. Snap ring
10. Power release plate
11. Ball insert
12. Ball

13. Backing plate
18. Housing
19. Ball
20. Ball insert
21. Spacer

22. Cover plate
23. Lined disc
25. Power plate
26. Spring seat
27. Spring

28, 29 & 30. Thrust bearing
35. Main housing
36. Oil seal
37. Oil seal

39. Bushing
40. Actuating disc
41. Ball
42. Lined disc
44. Bull pinion sleeve

45. Differential shaft
46. Bearing cup & cone
47. Differential case

48. Side gear
49. Thrust washer
50. Washer
51. Deflector

POWER LIFT
(Uni-Matic Hydraulic System)

LUBRICATION

174. It is recommended that the complete hydraulic system be drained at least once a year. Before refilling the system, remove and thoroughly clean the filter screen which is located in the filler plug opening.

Fill the reservoir with MM hydraulic oil, operate the hydraulic jack several times and refill the reservoir. Capacity of the system is approximately 1¾ gallons.

PUMP

175. The hydraulic pump (Fig. MM380) is of the positive displacement, eccentric rotor type. The pump is engine driven and supplies continuous power to the hydraulic system.

To remove pump unit, first drain reservoir. Disconnect short hose from pump inlet tube to reservoir connection. Remove the pump retaining cap screws, and remove pump from tractor.

To disassemble pump unit, remove three cap screws retaining pump cover to pump body. All pump parts can now be removed. Install oil seal (18) with lip of seal facing pump unit. Service bushing (13) requires final sizing after installation to provide 0.003-0.005 diametral clearance.

LIFTING JACK (RAM)

176. The lifting jack (ram) is of the double acting type. Refer to Fig. MM381.

With the lifting jack (ram) removed from tractor, proceed to disassemble the unit as follows: Remove ram head and bearing cap (29) from cylinder. With bearing cap removed, "O" ring seal and felt seal can be renewed. Withdraw piston from cylinder and renew piston ring if damaged. Remove both relief valve assemblies and push rod (26).

Renew the valve cage "O" rings (25) if they are damaged. Remove the ball retainer keys (Fig. MM382) and renew the balls if they are damaged. Examine bores and seats of valve cages. If they are damaged, renew the cages or recondition them as follows: Using a valve seat reamer (MM Part No. 10T1667), ream the cage bores from both ends to free-up the push rod, carefully ream the seat and thoroughly clean out the metal shavings. Refer to Fig. MM383. If the jack is equipped with steel valves, discard them and install the new type nylon valves.

Reassemble and reinstall jack by reversing the removal and disassembly procedure. After unit is installed and if jack is used on a lifting roll, place the control lever in the number nine position, allowing jack to fully extend. Adjust control linkage at clevis (Fig. MM384) until jack extends 8 inches when measured at piston rod.

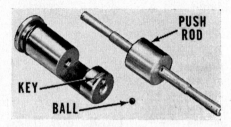

Fig. MM382—Hydraulic jack valve cage and push rod. The ball is retained in the cage by a key.

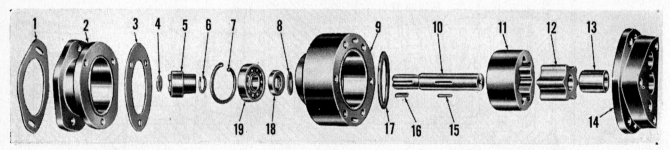

Fig. MM380—Eaton pump used with MM Uni-Matic hydraulic system. Items (11) and (12) are renewed as a unit.

1. Gasket	5. Shaft coupling	9. Pump body	12. Inner rotor	16. Coupling key
2. Pump adapter	6. Snap ring	10. Pump shaft	13. Shaft bushing	17. Cover gasket
3. Adapter gasket	7. Bearing snap ring	11. Outer rotor	14. Cover	18. Oil seal
4. Coupling washer	8. Oil ring		15. Rotor key	19. Shaft bearing

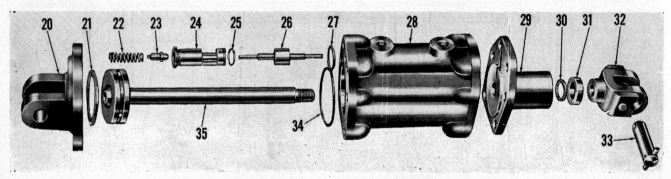

Fig. MM381—Lifting jack assembly used in Uni-Matic hydraulic system.

20. Cylinder head	24. Valve cage (2)	28. Jack cylinder	32. Clevis
21. Piston "O" ring	25. Cage "O" ring	29. Bearing cap	33. Clevis pin
22. Relief spring	26. Push rod & plunger	30. Rod "O" ring	34. Cap gasket
23. Relief valve lockout	27. Cap gasket	31. Oil seal	35. Piston & rod

RESERVOIR AND CONTROL VALVE

177. The hydraulic unit reservoir contains the system filter, strainer, control linkage, and control valve. The procedure for removing the reservoir unit is evident after an examination of the tractor.

Remove the reservoir cover and inspect the filter, gear, cam and control valve assemblies. Do not attempt to service the control valve assembly. If its operation is questionable, renew the complete unit. Thoroughly clean the reservoir screen and all internal parts.

When reassembling, renew all gaskets and seals.

DEPTH CONTROL VALVE

178. On some models, a depth control valve is used to control the working stroke of the jack. The length of the stroke is adjusted by a knurled thumb screw located at the end of the valve. When the screw is turned all the way in, the valve does not function as a stop and the jack is free to travel a full stroke. The procedure for removing and overhauling the valve is evident after an examination of the unit and reference to Fig. MM385.

TROUBLE-SHOOTING

179. NOISY PUMP OR SYSTEM. Check oil level and all pump inlet connections.

180. SLOW RAM ACTION. Worn pump and/or relief valves are set too low. Relief valves are non-adjustable and should be serviced only as an assembly with the control valve.

181. CONTROL LEVER DOES NOT RETURN TO NEUTRAL. Check for binding linkage.

182. RAM WILL NOT STAY IN RAISED POSITION. Disassemble and clean ram unit. Reseat check valves and renew all ram gaskets and seals.

183. FOAMING OIL IN RESERVOIR. Check and renew all pump inlet seals and tighten all connections.

Fig. MM383—Reaming the hydraulic jack valve cages.

Fig. MM384—Adjusting the hydraulic jack control linkage.

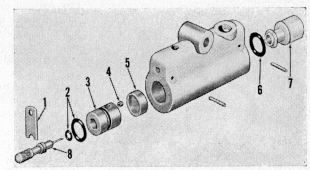

Fig. MM385—Exploded view of the depth control valve used on some models.

1. Lock clip
2. "O" rings
3. Adjusting screw cage
4. Ball seat
5. Piston
6. "O" ring
7. Piston seat
8. Adjusting screw

38. Filler plug
39. Plug gasket
40. Filler strainer
43. Reservoir body
44. Cam lever
45. Cam roller
46. Cam lever spring
47. Cross rod, gear & cam
48. Control valve
49. Cover
50. Flange gasket
56. Flange gasket
57. Control valve plug
58. Cam lever stud
59. Filter screen
60. Screen cap
61. Cover gasket
62. Reservoir support

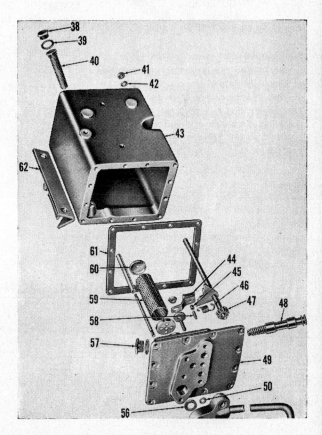

Fig. MM386—Reservoir and control valves assembly of Uni-Matic hydraulic power system.

APPENDIX I

Pertaining to spring loaded type clutches used on UB and ZB series tractors.

OVERHAUL. To disassemble the clutch cover unit, compress the pressure springs by placing the assembly in an arbor press or by using unloading cap screws as shown in Fig. MM 390 until the release lever pins can be removed as shown in Fig. MM391.

Fig. MM390—UB series clutch cover assembly. Three cap screws can be installed as shown to unload the clutch prior to removing the assembly from the flywheel. The screws can also be used when disassembling the clutch or when adjusting the position of the release levers. The same procedure can be used on the ZB series.

Remove the assembly from the arbor press or, if unloading cap screws were used, remove them and disassemble the remaining parts.

Inspect all parts and renew any which are damaged or show wear. Friction surface of pressure plate must be smooth, flat and free from grooves and cracks. Cover plate must not be bent, distorted or excessively worn at drive lug windows. Inspect release lever tips or contact screws, pivot pins and pin holes. Renew pressure springs if they are distorted, rusted, heat discolored or if they do not meet the test specifications listed in the accompanying table.

After the unit is assembled, install and tighten the three cover to pressure plate cap screws (shown in Fig. MM390) until the dimension (A—Fig. MM392 or 393) from underside of cover plate to friction face of pres-

Fig. MM391—Removing release lever pins from UB series clutch.

sure plate agrees with the dimension shown in column (A) in the accompanying table. This dimension (A) must be the same all the way around the pressure plate.

With the cap screws (Fig. MM390) still in place (to retain the A setting) turn the release lever adjusting screws (S—Fig. MM 392 or 393) until the distance (B) between friction face of pressure plate and release bearing contacting surface of each release lever is identical within 0.005 and within 0.015 either way of the dimension listed in column (B) in the accompanying table for the particular clutch being serviced.

After the release levers are adjusted, install cover assembly and lined plate to flywheel and remove the three cover to pressure plate cap screws.

ROCKFORD SPRING LOADED CLUTCH DATA

Tractor Series	Minn.-Moline Assembly Part No.	Rockford Clutch Model	(A) Cover Setting Inches	(B) Lever Height Inches	PRESSURE SPRINGS		
					No. Used	Pounds Test @	Height Inches
ZB	10A3743	11RM	1.088	2.650	9	180-190 @	1 13/16
UB Non-Diesel	10A6582*	12RM	1.020	2.614	12	200-210 @	1 13/16
UB Diesel	10A6583**	12RM	1.020	2.614	12	200-210 @	1 13/16

*Replaces 10A5188
**Replaces 10A5497

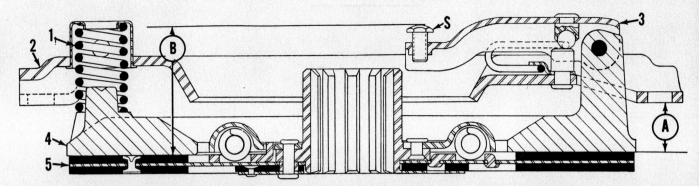

Fig. MM392—Sectional view of the UB Diesel clutch assembly. Notice that the driven (lined) plate is equipped with dampener springs. The UB non-Diesel clutch is similar except the driven plate is of the solid hub type.

A. Position of pressure plate in relation to cover plate which must be maintained when adjusting the release lever height (B). See Table.

S. Adjusting screw   1. Pressure spring   2. Cover plate   3. Release lever   4. Pressure plate   5. Driven (lined) plate

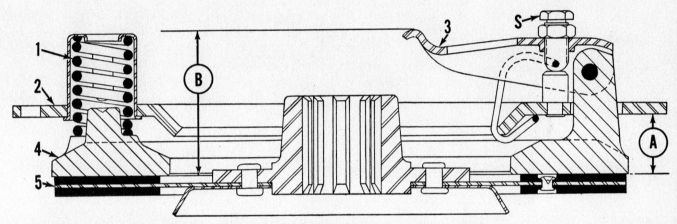

Fig. MM393—Sectional view of ZB clutch. The unit is equipped with a solid hub type driven plate. See legend for Fig. MM392.

NOTES

NOTES

MINNEAPOLIS-MOLINE

Minneapolis-Moline Models

■ 335 ■ 445 ■ Jet Star ■ Jet Star Two ■ Jet Star Three

■ 4 Star ■ 4 Star Super ■ U-302

Previously contained in I & T Shop Service Manual No. MM-14

SHOP MANUAL
MINNEAPOLIS-MOLINE

335 - 445 - JET STAR - JET STAR TWO - JET STAR THREE
4 STAR - 4 STAR SUPER - U302

IDENTIFICATION

Tractor serial number is stamped on a plate which is riveted to the side of transmission housing.

Engine serial number is stamped on a plate which is riveted to the side of crankcase.

INDEX (By Starting Paragraph)

CONDENSED SERVICE DATA

Series	335	445 Non-Diesel	445 Diesel	Series Jet Star 4 Star Non-Diesel	Series Jet Star 4 Star Diesel	U-302 Non-Diesel
GENERAL						
Engine Make	Own	Own	Own	Own	Own	Own
Engine Model	165A	206H	D206-4	206L-4	D206-4	220-4A
Number of Cylinders	4	4	4	4	4	4
Bore—Inches	3⅝	3⅝	3⅝	3⅝	3⅝	3¾
Stroke—Inches	4	5	5	5	5	5
Displacement—Cubic Inches	165	206	206	206	206	220.9
Compression Ratio (Gasoline)	7.35:1	7.3:1	....	7.3:1	....	7.6
Compression Ratio (LP-Gas)	8.23:1	9.1:1	....	9.1:1	....	8.55:1
Compression Ratio (Diesel)	....	....	15.9:1	....	15.9:1	....
Pistons Removed From	Above	Above	Above	Above	Above	Above
Cylinders Sleeved?	No	No	No	No	No	No
Forward Speeds, Number of	5 or 10	5 or 10	5 or 10	5 or 10	5 or 10	10
Main Bearings, Number of	3	3	3	3	3	3
TUNE-UP						
Firing Order	1-3-4-2	1-3-4-2	1-3-4-2	1-3-4-2	1-3-4-2	1-3-4-2
Compression Pres. @ Cranking Speed						
Gasoline	145-165	150-170	....	150-170	....	150-170
LP-Gas	160-180	175-210	....	175-210	....	170-190
Diesel	....	....	475-495	....	475-495	....
Valve Tappet Gap—Inlet (Hot)	0.010	0.010	0.010	0.010	0.010	0.010
Valve Tappet Gap—Exhaust (Hot)	0.018	0.018	0.018	0.018	0.018	0.018
Valve Seat Angle (Degrees)	45	45	45	45	45	45
Ignition Distributor Make	D-R	D-R	....	D-R	....	D-R
Ignition Distributor Model	1111711	1111711	....	1111898	....	1112642
Breaker Contact Gap	0.022	0.022	....	0.022	....	0.013-0.019
Ignition Timing @ High Idle Speed						
Gasoline	24° B	25° B	....	28° B	....	15°B @ 1200
LP-Gas	25° B	28° B	....	28° B	....	16°B @ 1200
High Idle Engine Speed	1650	1700	1925	1900	1925	2100
Spark Plug Electrode Gap	—See Paragraph 54—					
Injection Pump Make	....	....	Am. Bosch	....	See Text	....
Injection Timing	....	....	27° B	....	See Text	....
Nozzle Opening Pressure	....	....	1800 psi.	....	1800 psi.	....
Carburetor Make (Except LP-Gas)	M-S	M-S	....	M-S	....	M-S
Carburetor Make (LP-Gas)	Ensign	Ensign	....	Ensign	....	Century
Carburetor Model (Marvel-Schebler)	TSX	TSX	....	TSX	....	TSX
Carburetor Float Setting	¼-inch	¼-inch	....	¼-inch	....	¼-inch
SIZES—CAPACITIES—CLEARANCES (Clearances in thousandths)						
Crankshaft Journal Diameter (Front)	2.750	2.750	2.750	2.750	2.750	2.750
Crankshaft Journal Diameter (Center)	2.750	2.750	2.750	2.750	2.750	2.750
Crankshaft Journal Diameter (Rear)	3.000	3.000	3.000	3.000	3.000	3.000
Crankpin Diameter	2.625	2.625	2.625	2.625	2.625	2.625
Camshaft Journal Diameter	1.247	1.247	1.247	1.247	1.247	1.247
Piston Pin Diameter	0.99945	0.99945	1.250	0.99945	1.250	0.9995
Valve Stem Diameter	0.341	0.341	0.341	0.341	0.341	0.341
Main Bearing Dia. Clearance (Front)	1.5-3.6	1.5-4	1.5-4	1.5-4	1.5-4	1.5-4
Main Bearing Dia. Clearance (Center)	1.5-3.6	1.5-4	1.5-4	1.5-4	1.5-4	1.5-4
Main Bearing Dia. Clearance (Rear)	1.5-3.5	1.5-3.5	1.5-3.5	1.5-3.5	1.5-3.5	1.5-3.5
Rod Bearings Dia. Clearance	1.1-2.7	1.1-3.1	1.5-3	1.1-3.1	1.5-3	1.5-3
Piston Skirt Clearance (Iron)	2.5-4.5	2.5-4.5	....	....	....	....
Piston Skirt Clearance (Aluminum)	3.0-5.0	....	4.5-6	2.5-4	4.5-6	3-5
Crankshaft End Play	2.0-6.0	3.0-4.0	3.0-4.0	3.0-4.0	3.0-4.0	2-6
Camshaft Bearings Clearance, Max.	7.0	7.0	7.0	7.0	7.0	7.0
Cooling System—Gallons	2.75	3.37	3.87	3.87	3.87	3
Crankcase Oil—Quarts (With Filter)	8	8	8	8	8	6
Transmission and Differential—Quarts (With Ampli-Torc)	32	40	40	40	40	40
(No Ampli-Torc)	24	32	32	32	32	....

FRONT SYSTEM

Minneapolis-Moline 335 and 445 Utility tractors are available with an adjustable type front axle wherein tread widths are adjustable in increments of four inches. The 335 and 445 Industrial tractors are available with a heavy duty non-adjustable type front axle. Universal type tractors are available with three interchangeable front ends: The fork mounted single wheel tricycle, type N; the dual wheel tricycle, type U; and the adjustable axle, type E.

Jet Star tractors are utility type with adjustable front axle. Later models are also available with 2,000 pound, non-adjustable utility axle.

Four Star, 4 Star Super and U-302 tractors are agricultural type and are available with Type "E" adjustable axle, and Type "N" single wheel or Type "U" dual wheel tricycle.

STEERING KNUCKLES
Adjustable Axle Models

2. Refer to Fig. MM602 for agricultural Type "E" front system used on most models. Spindles (64) can be withdrawn after removing knuckle arm (53); and wheel, hub and bearings if spindle is to be renewed. The 1.248-1.249 diameter steering spindle (64) should have 0.002-0.006 clearance in bushings (65). Bushings will not require final sizing if carefully installed.

The adjustable, Utility type front axle used on Series 335 and 445 tractors is shown in Fig. MM602A. Dimensions and overhaul procedures are similar to Type "E" axle shown in Fig. MM602.

Heavy Duty (Non-Adjustable) Axle

2A. The Industrial Type front axle and associated parts used on 445 and Jet Star tractors is shown in Fig. MM-

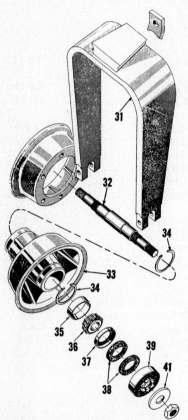

Fig. MM600—Type "N" front axle and associated parts.

31. Wheel fork	36. Bearing cone
32. Front axle	37. Seal retainer
33. Wheel hub	38. Felt seals
34. Snap ring	39. Dust shield
35. Bearing cup	41. Washer

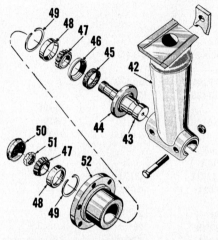

Fig. MM601—Type "U" front axle and associated parts. Wheel spindles are retained in the pedestal by clamp bolts.

42. Pedestal	48. Bearing cup
43. Spindle	49. Snap ring
44. Dust shield	50. Hub cap
45. Felt seal	51. Nut
46. Seal retainer	52. Wheel hub
47. Bearing cone	

WHEEL FORK OR PEDESTAL
All Models So Equipped

1. Exploded views of the tricycle type front end components are shown in Fig. MM600 and MM601. The procedure for removing and overhauling either type "N" or "U" is conventional. Front wheel bearings should be adjusted to remove all free play without binding.

Fig. MM602 — Type "E" front axle, pivot brackets, extensions and associated parts. Tie rods should be adjusted an equal amount to provide a front wheel toe-in of ¼-inch.

53. Steering knuckle arm
54. Tie rod
55. Pivot bracket (clevis)
56. Tie rod tube
57. Center steering arm
58. Radius rod pivot bracket
59. Rear pivot bushing
60. Front pivot bushing
61. Axle center member
62. Axle extension
63. Thrust bearing
64. Knuckle and spindle
65. Knuckle bushings
66. Dust shield
67. Felt seal
68. Seal retainer
69. Bearing cone
70. Bearing cup
71. Snap ring
72. Hub
73. Nut
74. Hub cap

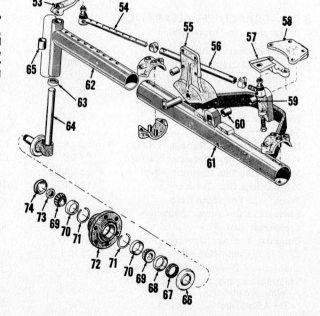

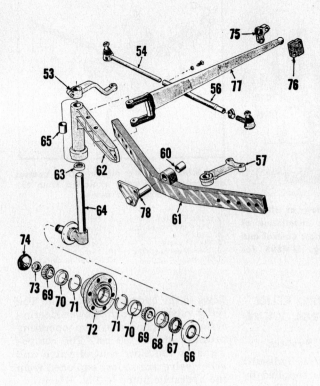

Fig. MM602A — Model 445 Utility front axle components and associated linkage. Model 335 Utility tractors are similar.

53. Steering knuckle arm
54. Tie rod
56. Tie rod tube
57. Center steering arm
60. Front pivot bushing
61. Axle center member
62. Axle extension
63. Thrust bearing
64. Knuckle and spindle
65. Knuckle bushings
66. Dust shield
67. Felt seal
68. Seal retainer
69. Bearing cone
70. Bearing cup
71. Snap ring
72. Hub
73. Nut
74. Hub cap
75. Socket
76. Socket plate
77. Radius rod
78. Axle pivot pin and bracket

603. The steering knuckle (15) pivots on a king pin (2) which is retained in front axle by a set screw (1). To remove the steering knuckle, proceed as follows: Remove retaining set screw (1). Remove snap ring (17) and expansion plug (18) from steering knuckle above and below king pin bore; then drive king pin out with a heavy hammer and drift. The 1.372-1.737 diameter king pin (2) should have 0.003-0.007 clearance in presized bushings (19).

TIE RODS AND TOE-IN

All Models, Axle Type

3. Tie rod ends can be disassembled and component parts renewed. When reassembling, adjust the tie rod length to provide a toe-in of ¼-inch. It is recommended that tie rod ends be lubricated with chassis lubricant once each week.

AXLE PIVOT PINS AND BUSHINGS

All Models, Axle Type

4. Axle main (center) member is fitted with a renewable bushing (or bushings) at pivot pin locations. Bushings are pre-sized and will not require reaming if carefully installed. On Type "E" axle shown in Fig. MM-602, the 1.248-1.249 diameter pivot pins should have a clearance of 0.002-0.006 in the bushings. On models 335 Utility and 445 Utility, the 1.242-1.246 diameter pivot pin should have a clearance of 0.005-0.012 in the bushing. Bushings do not require final sizing if carefully installed. On 445 and Jet Star Industrial, the 1.492-1.496 diameter pivot pin should have a clearance of 0.0055-0.0125 in the bushing. On model 335 Industrial, the 1.248-1.249 diameter pivot pin should have a clearance of 0.004-0.006 in the bushing.

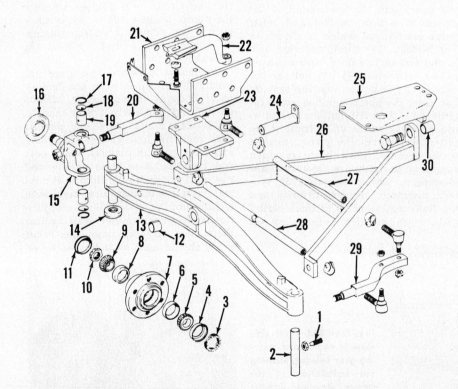

Fig. MM603 — Industrial Type front axle and associated parts used on Models 445 and Jet Star.

1. Set screw
2. King pin
3. Felt seal
4. Seal retainer
5. Bearing cone
6. Bearing cup
7. Hub
8. Bearing cup
9. Bearing cone
10. Nut
11. Hub cap
12. Pivot bushing
13. Axle assembly
14. Thrust bearing
15. Steering knuckle
16. Dust shield
17. Snap ring
18. Expansion plug
19. Spindle bushing
20. Knuckle arm
21. Support
22. Steering arm
23. Axle clevis
24. Pivot pin
25. Reach support
26. Reach
27. Drag link
28. Tie rod
29. Knuckle arm
30. Reach bushing

STEERING SYSTEM
(Except Hydrostatic)

Series 335 and 445 tractors are available with a conventional manual steering system, or a power steering system (Fig. MM603A) where the working fluid is supplied by the tractor hydraulic system. 4 Star Series is available with power steering only. Early Jet Star tractors were available with manual steering only; Jet Star Two with manual steering or linkage type power steering. Jet Star Three is available with manual steering or with hydrostatic power steering covered in a separate section beginning with paragraph 17. Model U-302 is available with hydrostatic power steering only; refer to paragraph 17.

Note: When working on the power steering system, the maintenance of absolute cleanliness of all parts is of utmost importance. Of equal importance is the avoidance of nicks or burrs on any of the working parts.

LUBRICATION AND BLEEDING

Linkage Type Power System

6. The regular tractor hydraulic system fluid reservoir is the source of fluid supply to the power steering system. Only Automatic Transmission Fluid, Type A, should be used in the hydraulic system and the reservoir fluid level should be maintained 1-1¼ inches below top of filler opening.

It is recommended that the system working fluid and the filter cartridge be changed every 1000 hours of operation as outlined in paragraph 100. Whenever the oil lines have been disconnected or the fluid drained, reconnect the lines, fill the reservoir and cycle the power steering and the hydraulic lift system several times to bleed air from the system; then, refill the reservoir to 1-1¼ inches below top of filler opening.

TROUBLE SHOOTING

Linkage Type Power System

7. The table on page 8 lists troubles which may be encountered in the operation of the power steering system. The procedure for correcting most of the troubles is evident; for those not readily remedied, refer to the appropriate subsequent paragraphs.

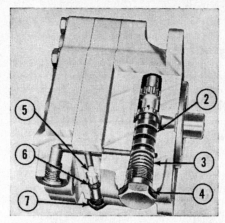

Fig. MM604—Cut-away view of the hydraulic pump, showing the installation of the power steering system flow control and relief valve. Refer to Fig. MM605 for legend.

OPERATING PRESSURE, RELIEF VALVE, FLOW CONTROL VALVE

Linkage Type Power System

8. Working fluid for the hydraulic power steering system is supplied by the same pump which powers the hydraulic system. Interposed between the pump and the remainder of the system is a flow control and relief valve mechanism which is shown in Fig. MM604. The small metering hole in the end of the flow control piston passes approximately 2½ gallons per minute to the power steering system; but, since the pump supplies considerably more than 2½ gallons per minute, pressure builds up in front of the piston and moves the piston, against spring pressure, until the ports which supply oil to the hydraulic system are uncovered. The power steering system, therefore, receives priority and the fluid requirements of the steering system are satisfied before any oil

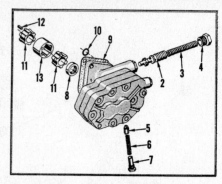

Fig. MM605—Power steering flow control and relief valve units exploded from the hydraulic pump.

2. Flow control piston	8. Oil seal
3. Flow control spring	9. Gasket
4. Plug	10. "O" ring
5. Relief valve	11. Coupling
6. Relief valve spring	12. Key
7. Plug	13. Coupling collar

flows to the hydraulic lift system. The relief valve (5) for the power steering system maintains a system operating pressure of 650-750 psi. The components of the flow control valve and relief valve are shown exploded from the hydraulic pump in Fig. MM605.

9. A pressure test of the power steering circuit will disclose whether the pump, relief valve or some other unit in the system is malfunctioning. To make such a test, proceed as follows:

Connect a pressure test gage (at least 2000 psi capacity) in the damper valve body as shown in Fig. MM606 on 335, 445 and early 4 Star models. On Jet Star 2 and late 4 Star, disconnect pressure line at steering valve and tee a gage in between valve port and pressure line. Start engine and run until the hydraulic fluid is at normal operating temperature; then, with engine running at fast idle speed, turn the front wheels either way against their stop. At this time, the relief valve should open as indicated by an

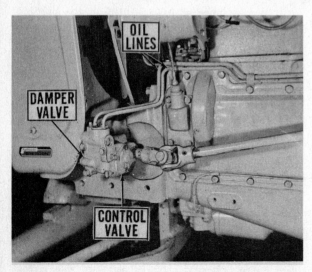

Fig. MM603A—Left side view of engine and steering gear housing, showing the installation of the power steering damper valve and control valve used on 335, 445 and early 4 Star models.

Fig. MM606—Using a pressure gage connected to the damper valve body to check the power steering system relief valve cracking pressure on 335, 445 and early 4 Star models. On Jet Star 2 and late 4 Star, tee into steering pressure line. Pressure should be 650-750 psi.

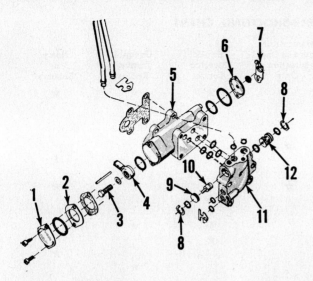

Fig. MM607 — Exploded view of the power steering system damper valve and control valve used on 335, 445 and early 4 Star models. The control valve spool and body are available as matched units only. Refer to Fig. MM-607A for valve used on Jet Star 2 and late 4 Star.

1. Front cover plate
2. Lever end plate
3. Locking bolt
4. Actuating lever
5. Control valve assy.
6. Rear cover plate
7. Seal retainer
8. Snap ring
9. Damper plug
10. Damper plunger
11. Damper valve body
12. Damper by-pass

audible buzzing sound and the pressure gage should read 650-750 psi. If the gage reading is between 650 and 750 psi, the hydraulic pump and relief valve are O.K. and any trouble is located elsewhere in the system.

If the gage reading is more than 750 psi, the relief valve may be stuck in the closed position. If the gage reading is less than 650 psi, remove the relief valve spring and renew same if it does not test 31.5-38.5 lbs. when compressed to a height of 1¾ inches. If the gage reading is still less than 650 psi, and there are no external fluid leaks or internal cylinder or valve leaks as indicated by an increase of oil in the steering gear housing, a faulty hydraulic pump is indicated.

The flow control valve spring should test 39.6-48.4 lbs. when compressed to a height of 1 57/64 inches.

PUMP

Linkage Type Power System

9A. The hydraulic pump supplies fluid to both the power steering system and hydraulic system. Refer to paragraph 137.

DAMPER VALVE

Series 335-445—Early 4 Star

10. **R&R AND OVERHAUL.** The damper valve restricts the return flow from the power steering valve to maintain approximately equal pressure in both power steering cylinders during any turning action, thus eliminating any tendency of "shimmy" in the steering system.

The damper valve plunger (10—Fig. MM607) must slide freely in the body passage to provide proper steering control. If a sticking or binding plunger is found, first clean the plunger and body bore and remove any small nicks or scoring. If plunger

is not then free, renew the plunger and/or body as required.

To remove the damper valve, disconnect the oil lines and unbolt and remove the valve body from the control valve housing. Remove snap rings (8) from each end of damper valve housing and tap by-pass valve (12) forward, forcing plug (9) and plunger (10) out front of housing.

When reassembling, renew all seals, dip parts in clean hydraulic fluid and reinstall. Make sure small orifice and pin in by-pass valve (12) is toward inside of body, and that pin end of plunger (10) is facing plug (9).

When installing the assembled damper valve, tighten the retaining cap screws in a criss-cross manner to a torque of 15 ft.-lbs.

CONTROL VALVE

Series 335-445—Early 4 Star

11. **R&R AND OVERHAUL.** To remove the control valve, disconnect the oil lines, unbolt and remove the damper valve housing, then unbolt and remove the control valve from the steering worm shaft housing. Remove covers (1 and 6—Fig. MM607) from ends of valve housing. Remove cap screw (3), unscrew valve spool from actuating lever (4) and withdraw the spool from housing. Thoroughly clean and examine all parts. If the valve spool or spool bore are damaged, it will be necessary to renew the complete valve unit; "O" ring seals, however, are available separately.

When reassembling, renew all seals, dip all parts in clean hydraulic fluid and reverse the disassembly procedure. Leave cap screw (3) loose, and covers (1 and 6) off, for valve centering adjustment after unit is installed. Install the assembled control valve unit and tighten the retaining

screws securely. Install the damper valve and tighten the retaining screws to a torque of 15 ft.-lbs.

After the lines are connected, and the hydraulic fluid installed, connect a suitable hydraulic pressure gage to the damper valve as shown in Fig. MM606, start engine and run at fast idle speed. Insert a large screw driver in the slot at the rear end of the control valve spool and turn the spool into the actuating lever while observing the gage reading. When a definite increase in gage pressure is noted, back the spool out of the actuating lever while counting the turns, until the pressure drops, then increases to the same level. Half way between these points, in the area of lowest gage pressure, should be the valve center position.

Temporarily lock the valve to the actuating lever by tightening cap screw (3) and, while turning the steering wheel to the right and left, check that approximately equal steering effort is required for a right or left turn. If more steering effort is required for a right turn, loosen the locking cap screw and rotate the valve spool slightly counter-clockwise and recheck. If more effort is required for a left turn, rotate the valve spool clockwise. When the valve center position has been established, tighten locking cap screw (3) and install end covers (1 and 6).

After centering the control valve spool, turn the steering wheel in each direction and check to be sure the spool moves 0.040 in each direction. If the spool travels more or less than 0.040, the separator clearance must be adjusted as in paragraph 15.

Jet Star Two—Late 4 Star

12. **R&R AND OVERHAUL.** To remove the power steering control valve, disconnect the oil lines and unbolt and remove the control valve from the steering worm shaft housing. Be careful not to lose actuating lever (6—Fig. MM607A) when the two parts are separated.

Remove the two cap screws retaining end cap (11) to housing (5) and remove the end cap. Remove snap ring (1) and plate (2) from rear of housing. While holding clevis rod (3) from turning, loosen and remove nut (10), washers (7 and 9) and spring (8) from end of clevis rod. Withdraw clevis rod (3) from rear end of housing and push control valve spool (4) from body bore. Control valve spool and body (5) are matched, and can only be renewed as an assembly.

POWER STEERING SYSTEM TROUBLE-SHOOTING CHART

	Hard Steering	Loss of Power Assistance	Power Assistance in One Direction Only	Erratic Steering Control	Unequal Turning Radius	Noisy or "Shimmy"
Linkage damaged, worn or mis-aligned..	★			★	★	★
Control spool not centered............	★			★		
Insufficient fluid in reservoir...........	★	★				
Low pump pressure...................	★	★				
Sticking control valve spool...........	★	★	★	★		
Faulty relief valve...................	★	★				★
Faulty flow control valve.............	★	★				
Damaged or restricted oil lines........	★	★	★			★
Wrong fluid in system...............		★		★		
Faulty cylinder	★	★		★		
Improperly adjusted tie rods...........				★	★	
Air in system......................				★		
Sticking damper valve plunger.........	★					★
Cylinder piston installed wrong........					★	
Binding worm shaft..................	★					

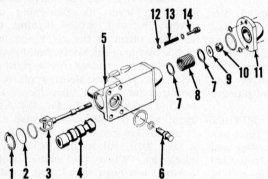

12 13 14

5

10 11

7

8

7 9

1 2 3 4 6

Fig. MM607A — Exploded view of power steering control valve used on Jet Star Two and late 4 Star.

1. Snap ring
2. End plate
3. Clevis rod
4. Valve spool
5. Valve housing
6. Actuating lever
7. Centering washer
8. Centering spring
9. Retaining washer
10. Nut
11. End cap
12. Check valve ball
13. Valve spring
14. Check valve plug

Working with a small wire from inside the housing, push check valve ball (12), spring (13) and plug (14) from the valve body. Thoroughly clean and examine all parts.

When reassembling, renew all seals, dip the parts in clean hydraulic fluid and reinstall by reversing the disassembly procedure. Tighten nut (10) until washer (9) is bottomed on its shoulder on the clevis rod. When re-installing valve, make sure fork on end of actuating lever (6) engages pin in clevis rod (3) and that opposite end of lever engages groove in the actuating sleeve on steering shaft.

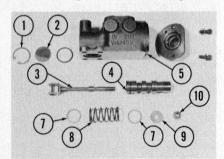

Fig. MM607B — Disassembled view of Jet Star Two and late 4 Star power steering control valve. Refer to Fig. MM607A for legend.

STEERING CYLINDER

Linkage Type Power System

13. To remove the steering cylinder, remove hood and side panels, then on tricycle models, unscrew the pedestal stop pin. On axle models, disconnect the center steering arm from the vertical steering shaft. Then remove the retaining snap rings (10—Fig. MM608) and withdraw the end plugs and tubes (7 and 8). Turn the vertical steering shaft (26) or (8—Fig. MM612) to left until piston teeth are disengaged from the sector teeth and withdraw the piston (4—Fig. MM608) and sleeves (2).

Examine all parts and renew any which are damaged or worn. Inner inside diameter of the right hand sleeve must be chamfered as shown in Fig. MM609 to permit installation of the piston and seals without damaging the seals. If the sleeve is not already chamfered, use a fine cut file and chamfer about $\frac{1}{16}$-inch of the inner inside edge of the sleeve; then smooth the chamfer with crocus cloth.

Install the piston "O" rings and back-up washers and if the back-up washers are tapered, be sure the high side is toward the "O" ring.

Install the chamfered sleeve with gasket in right side of cylinder and install snap ring to prevent sleeve from coming out when piston is installed. Lubricate the piston rings with No. 130-AA lubricant and install the left sleeve over piston. Insert piston and sleeve into cylinder so that piston teeth align with the sector teeth; then push piston and sleeve into cylinder until outer end of piston is 1¼ inches from outer end of cylinder as shown in Fig. MM610. Turn steering wheel toward right until piston teeth engage sector teeth, then continue turning steering wheel toward right to pull piston into cylinder.

Note: Very little effort is required to pull piston into cylinder. If undue effort is required, check for improper alignment of the gear teeth.

Install snap ring at left end of cylinder, turn the front wheels straight ahead and on axle type tractors, install center steering arm; on tricycle models, tighten the stop screw. Turn steering wheel all the way to the right and measure the distance from end of piston to end of right sleeve. Then turn the steering wheel all the way to the left and measure the distance from end of piston to end of left sleeve. If the measured distances differ more than ½-inch, the piston is not meshed properly with the sector. In which case, remove piston and reinstall same as previously outlined. With the piston properly installed, remove the snap rings, install cylinder end plugs and reinstall the snap rings.

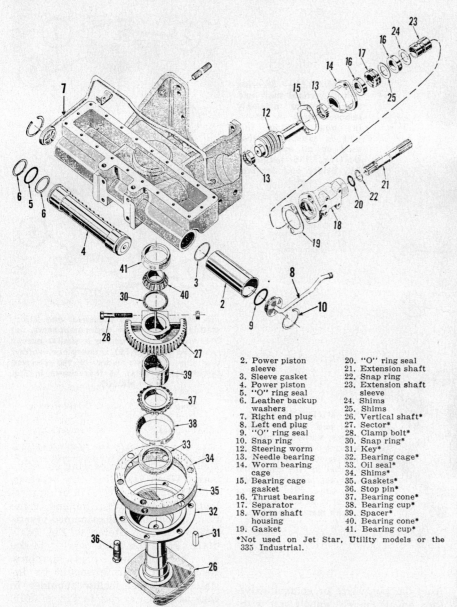

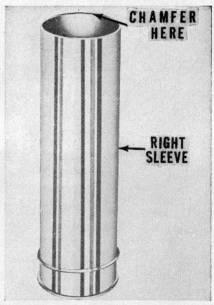

Fig. MM609 — To prevent damaging the power piston seals during installation, the inside diameter of the right hand sleeve should be chamfered approximately 1/16-inch as shown.

2.	Power piston sleeve	20.	"O" ring seal
3.	Sleeve gasket	21.	Extension shaft
4.	Power piston	22.	Snap ring
5.	"O" ring seal	23.	Extension shaft sleeve
6.	Leather backup washers	24.	Shims
7.	Right end plug	25.	Shims
8.	Left end plug	26.	Vertical shaft*
9.	"O" ring seal	27.	Sector*
10.	Snap ring	28.	Clamp bolt*
12.	Steering worm	30.	Snap ring*
13.	Needle bearing	31.	Key*
14.	Worm bearing cage	32.	Bearing cage*
15.	Bearing cage gasket	33.	Oil seal*
16.	Thrust bearing	34.	Shims*
17.	Separator	35.	Gaskets*
18.	Worm shaft housing	36.	Stop pin*
19.	Gasket	37.	Bearing cone*
		38.	Bearing cup*
		39.	Spacer*
		40.	Bearing cone*
		41.	Bearing cup*

*Not used on Jet Star, Utility models or the 335 Industrial.

Fig. MM608—Steering gear housing, gear unit, power piston and associated parts used on all except early Jet Star series, the Utility models and the 335 Industrial. Early Jet Star series, Utility models and the 335 Industrial are similar except for the sector and shaft arrangement which is shown in Fig. MM612.

Fig. MM610—Power steering piston extending 1¼ inches from left side of steering gear housing.

STEERING SECTOR AND SHAFT
All Models

14. To remove the steering sector and/or shaft, first drain the gear housing by removing the center bolt from left side of bearing cage, support front of tractor and on tricycle models, remove the fork or pedestal and wheels assembly. On axle type tractors, remove the axle, wheels and tie rods assembly. Refer to Fig. MM608. Place assembly marks on sector shaft, bearing cage and steering gear housing so they can be reinstalled in the same position, then unbolt and withdraw the bearing cage, sector and shaft as-

sembly from the gear housing. To disassemble the unit used on all models equipped with linkage type power steering, refer to Figs. MM611 and MM608 and proceed as follows:

Using a suitable knife edge type puller, remove bearing cone (40). Remove snap ring (30), loosen clamp bolt (28) and remove sector gear (27), key (31) and spacer (39). Press the sector shaft out of the bearing cage. The need and procedure for further disassembly is evident.

When reassembling, install seal (33) in bearing cage with lip of seal facing upward. Upper bearing cone (40)

should be packed with a good grade of wheel bearing grease prior to installation.

To disassemble the unit used on manual steering models, refer to Figs. MM612 and 613 and proceed as follows: Remove snap rings (1) and lift off the center steering arm (6), sector (3) and key (2). Then withdraw the vertical shaft from the bearing cage. The 1.249-1.250 diameter vertical shaft (8) should have a clearance of 0.001-0.005 in bushings (5). Bushings (5) are pre-sized and will not require reaming if carefully installed. Lip of oil seal (7) should face upward.

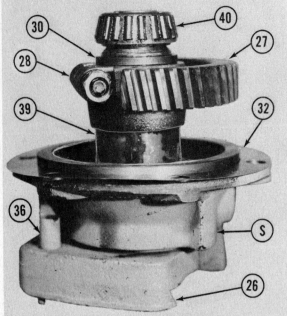

Fig. MM611 — Steering sector, vertical shaft and bearing cage assembly removed from the steering gear housing. This unit is typical of that used on all except 335 Utility, 335 Industrial, 445 Utility and Jet Star models.

26. Vertical shaft
27. Sector
28. Clamp bolt
32. Bearing cage
39. Spacer
40. Bearing cone

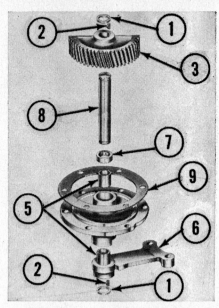

Fig. MM613 — 335 Industrial and Utility steering sector, shaft and components. Jet Star with manual steering is similar except shaft (8) and arm (6) is one piece, welded assembly. The remainder of the steering system is the same as that shown in Fig. MM608.

1. Snap rings	6. Center steering
2. Keys	arm
3. Sector	7. Oil seal
5. Bushings	8. Vertical shaft

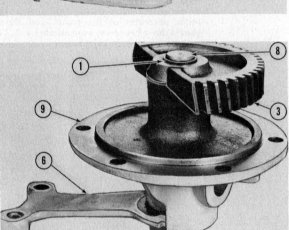

Fig. MM612—335 Industrial and Utility steering sector, vertical shaft and bearing cage assembly. The vertical shaft (8) is carried in two renewable bushings located in bearing cage (9). Jet Star sector is similar on models with manual steering.

On all models, install the assembled unit by reversing the removal procedure and be sure to align the previously affixed assembly marks. On models with tapered roller bearings, vary the number of shims (34—Fig. MM608) to provide a slight rotational drag.

After assembly is complete on models with power steering, check to make certain that the front wheels are against their stop when turned to both extreme positions. If not, it will be necessary to remesh the sector with the power piston teeth.

STEERING WORM
All Models

15. To remove the steering worm, use a suitable drift punch and remove the roll pins retaining the front and rear universal joints to the front steering shaft. Bump the front universal joint rearward and off the steering worm extension shaft. On models with power steering, disconnect the oil lines

from damper valve or control valve; then on all models, unbolt and withdraw the worm assembly from gear housing. On models with power steering, separate the damper valve and/or control valve unit from the steering worm, then on all models, separate the worm housing (18—Figs. MM608 and MM614) from bearing cage (14). Drive out the roll pin retaining sleeve (23) to the worm shaft and withdraw the worm from the bearing cage. Remove shim (24), rear bearing (16), shim (25), separator (17) and front bearing (16). Remove snap ring (22) at rear of worm housing and withdraw extension shaft (21). Note: On models with manual steering, item (17) is a spacer.

Thoroughly clean all parts and renew any which are damaged or worn. Needle bearing (13) can be pressed from the bearing cage if renewal is required. To remove the front needle bearing located in steering gear housing, cut through the bearing cage with

a chisel and pry the bearing out of its bore. When installing the bearings, use MM tool No. 10T 5178 or equivalent and press only on the end of the bearing which has the stamped identification letters. Refer to Fig. MM-614A. Press the front bearing in the gear housing until it just bottoms. Rear needle bearing should be installed 1/64-inch below shoulder in cage as shown at (x) in Fig. MM615.

On models with power steering, turn the screws (S—Fig. MM616) either way as required to obtain a clearance of 0.041 between the separator halves when checked around the entire circumference of the separator. Then, when installing the worm shaft in the bearing cage, vary the number of shims (25—Fig. MM614) between separator and rear thrust bearing so the clearance is 0.040 when sleeve (23) is secured to the worm shaft with the roll pin. The 0.040 clearance can be checked with a narrow feeler blade inserted through opening in side of bearing cage as shown in Fig. MM617. Shims are available in thicknesses of 0.002 and 0.006.

On all models vary the number of shims (24—Fig. MM614) located between rear thrust bearing and worm housing to remove all worm shaft end play when worm housing and bearing cage are bolted together with the two.

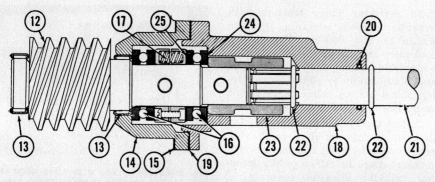

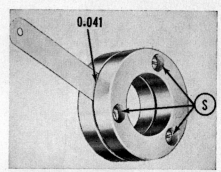

Fig. MM616—On models with power steering, turn screws (S) to obtain 0.041 clearance between the separator halves.

Fig. MM614—Sectional view of the steering worm shaft and associated parts used on all power steering equipped models. Models with manual steering are similar except a spacer is used instead of separator (17).

12. Steering worm	16. Thrust bearing	21. Extension shaft
13. Needle bearing	17. Separator	22. Snap ring
14. Worm bearing cage	18. Worm shaft housing	23. Extension shaft sleeve
15. Bearing cage gasket	19. Gasket	24. Shims
	20. "O" ring	25. Shims

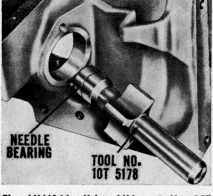

Fig. MM614A—Using MM tool No. 10T 5178 to install the steering worm shaft front needle bearing in steering gear housing. Press only on end of bearing which has the stamped identification numbers.

screws. IMPORTANT: Always use new gaskets between worm housing, bearing cage and gear housing.

STEERING LINKAGE

Linkage Type Power System

16. Any binding or lost motion in the steering linkage will result in hard steering. With the engine running and the front wheels on a clean, dry concrete floor, it should not require more

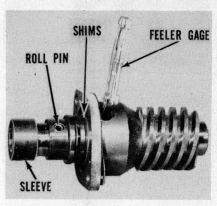

Fig. MM617—Using feeler gage to check clearance between separator halves when sleeve is pinned to the worm shaft. Clearance at this time should be 0.040.

than 10 lbs. pull on rim of steering wheel to actuate the power steering system.

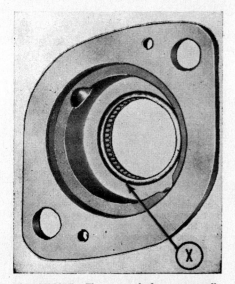

Fig. MM615—The wormshaft rear needle bearing should be installed 1/64-inch below shoulder in bearing cage as shown.

HYDROSTATIC STEERING SYSTEM

Some Jet Star Three and all U302 tractors are equipped with Ross Hydrapower hydrostatic steering, in which no mechanical linkage exists between steering control and front spindle.

The steering wheel is attached to a gerotor manual pump which operates the power control valve, steers the tractor when engine is not running; and meters the steering fluid when power steering pump is operating.

The system consists of a power pump, manual pump, steering valve, steering cylinder, and associated parts. Model U302 uses a separate, belt driven power pump; Jet Star Three divides the flow from tractor hydraulic pump and uses part of the flow to actuate the steering.

OPERATION

17. The gerotor manual pump is completely reversible and applies actuating pressure to either end of the self-centering spool in control valve. Fluid from the power steering pump is directed by the control valve through the manual pump to one end of the power steering cylinder. The fluid from opposite end of power steering cylinder returns through the valve, to power steering reservoir. A recirculating check valve connects the power steering pump pressure and return lines within the valve housing. The recirculating valve is seated by pump pressure when power pump is

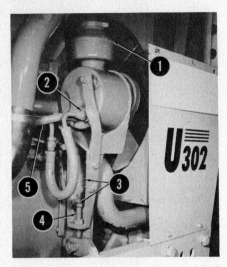

Fig. MM618 — Power steering pump used on U302 tractors.

1. Reservoir
2. Pressure line
3. Clamp bolts
4. Adjusting bolt
5. Return line

operating; but unseats to allow fluid to circulate between manual pump and steering cylinder when power pump is not operating, to permit manual control of the system.

LUBRICATION AND BLEEDING

17A. MM Hydraulic fluid, or equivalent, is used as the operating fluid. On U302, system capacity is approximately 2 quarts and fluid is contained in power steering pump reservoir; on Jet Star Three, the steering system uses fluid from the tractor hydraulic reservoir, with a total system capacity of 2½ gallons on models equipped with Tel-O-Flo system; or 3 gallons on models equipped with Type E system.

The power steering system is self-bleeding. If any part of the system has been disassembled and units are dry, fill the reservoir and cycle system several times to bleed air from the cylinders and lines, then refill reservoir to full mark. If manual pump is in satisfactory condition and was properly lubricated, spinning the steering wheel rapidly in either direction should unseat control valve and allow system to prime.

OPERATING PRESSURE AND RELIEF VALVE

17B. The system relief pressure on U302 should be 800-900 psi and is controlled by a fixed-setting flow control and relief valve located in power steering pump.

On Jet Star Three tractors with hydrostatic power steering, pressure should be 950-1050 psi. Pressure is controlled by a relief valve located in a manifold on rear of hydraulic pump and is adjustable by adding or removing shims behind relief valve spring as outlined in paragraph 18C.

To test the system on either tractor, proceed as follows: Remove the left rear hood side panel and tee a 0-2000 pressure gage in either of the steering cylinder lines at coupling, as shown in Fig. MM618A. With power steering system at operating temperature, run tractor at approximately 1000 rpm and turn steering wheel against stop in the direction to pressurize the line containing the gage. Note the gage pressure.

If the noted pressure is low, connect a gage directly to power supply line and check pump pressure independently of the steering control valve. On U302, disconnect pressure line (2—Fig. MM618) from power steering pump and connect gage to pump fitting; on Jet Star Three, disconnect pump pressure tube (2—Fig. MM620) from steering control valve and connect gage to end of tube. Start and run engine ONLY long enough to note the pressure.

If reading is now normal, overhaul the recirculating check valve in control valve housing as outlined in paragraph 18H. If reading was still low; on U302, renew the power steering pump flow control and relief valve as outlined in paragraph 18A; or, on Jet Star Three, adjust valve as outlined in paragraph 18C.

TROUBLE SHOOTING

17C. **LEAKAGE.** Leakage at steering cylinder seals will cause overflowing of steering sector reservoir. Internal leakage anywhere else in the system may be ignored unless leakage is sufficient to cause slow or erratic steering action.

Leakage at recirculating check valve ball will not affect manual operation, but can cause partial loss of power assist.

Internal leakage in manual pump will not materially affect power steering, but may not allow tractor to be steered manually.

17D. **CONTROL VALVE.** If unusual initial effort is required to start the tractor turning, and noticeable reverse effort is required to stop the turn; a partially sticking control valve is indicated. Valve assembly should

Fig. MM618A — Tee a pressure gage in cylinder line coupling to check system pressure. Relief pressure should be 800-900 psi. on U302; or 950-1050 psi. on Jet Star. Refer to text.

be removed and overhauled as outlined in paragraph 18H. Because considerable pressure can be exerted by the manual pump, the control valve will rarely stick completely, or freeze.

17E. **SHIMMY.** If the front wheels shimmy, the trouble is probably caused by a broken or weak control valve centering spring or bent centering spring washers. Another possible cause is worn, broken or damaged steering sector (or linkage on axle models).

17F. **HARD STEERING.** Hard steering may be caused by a malfunctioning system relief valve, flow divider or flow control valve, power steering pump; a leaking recirculating valve; or by binding of the spindles or linkage. When checking the operating pressure as outlined in paragraph 17B, note also the pressure required to turn the wheels (while cylinder is moving). If steering linkage or spindles are binding, this trouble should

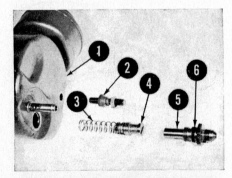

Fig. MM618B — Rear face of power steering pump showing component parts which may be removed without disassembly. Reservoir can be removed after removing pressure fitting (5) and mounting stud (2).

1. Reservoir
2. Mounting stud
3. Flow control spring
4. Flow control & pressure relief valve
5. Pressure fitting
6. "O" ring

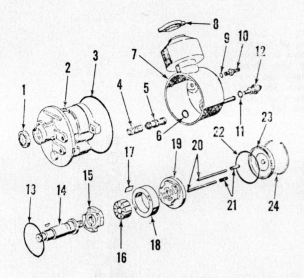

1. Oil seal
2. Housing & bushing assy.
3. "O" ring
4. Flow control spring
5. Flow control & pressure relief valve
7. Reservoir
8. Filler cap
9. "O" ring
10. Mounting stud
11. "O" ring
12. Pressure fitting
13. "O" ring
14. Drive shaft
15. Thrust plate
16. Rotor
17. Vane
18. Cam ring
19. Pressure plate
20. Dowel
21. Compression spring
22. "O" ring
23. End plug
24. Snap ring

Fig. MM618F — Pump body with pumping units removed. Bushing (1) is serviced only as an assembly with body. Seal (2) is renewable. "O" rings (3, 4 & 5) should be renewed whenever pump is disassembled.

Fig. MM618C — Exploded view of balanced vane type power steering pump used on U302 tractors.

be corrected before any of the hydraulic units are overhauled, and the system re-tested.

POWER STEERING PUMP

Model U302

18. **REMOVE AND REINSTALL.** To remove the power steering pump, disconnect pressure line (2—Fig. MM618) and return line (5), and allow reservoir to drain. Remove the pump mounting bolts (3) and withdraw pump and mounting bracket as a unit.

Install by reversing the removal procedure. Turn the belt tension adjusting screw (4), if necessary, to provide approximately ¼-inch deflec-

tion of drive belt, before completely tightening mounting bolts (3).

18A. **RELIEF VALVE.** The combined flow control and pressure relief valve (4—Fig. MM618B) can be renewed without removing the power steering pump. To renew the valve, disconnect pressure line (2—Fig. MM-618); remove pressure line fitting (6—Fig. MM618B) and withdraw the valve (4). Relief pressure is pre-set, and no attempt should be made to disassemble or overhaul the valve.

18B. **PUMP OVERHAUL.** To disassemble the removed power steering pump, refer to Fig. MM618C. Remove the mounting bracket, mounting stud (10) and pressure line fitting (12). Withdraw the flow control and relief valve (5) and valve spring (4); then tap reservoir (7) from pump body, using a rubber mallet or other suitable means.

Secure pump body in a vise and turn retaining snap ring (3—Fig. MM618D) if necessary, until one end is located over the small hole in hous-

ing at snap ring groove. Insert a small punch into hole as shown at (4), unseat and remove snap ring (3) and end plug (2) from pump body.

NOTE: Two compression springs (21—Fig. MM618C) fit over dowel pins (20) and apply pressure against end plug. Do not lose the springs when end plug is removed.

Remove the pulley retaining nut and drive pulley; then push the drive shaft (14—Fig. MM618E), cam ring (18), rotor (16), end plates (15 and 19) and associated parts from pump body.

The pumping elements (rotor, vanes and cam ring) are hydraulically balanced, with two pressure areas 180° apart, therefore no side thrust is created on shaft or shaft bushing by hydraulic pressure. The shaft bushing (1—Fig. MM618F) is not available for service.

Examine rotor (16—Fig. MM618C) for wear in vane slots, and cam ring (18) for ridging or scoring in vane contact area. Examine vane area of thrust plate (15) and pressure plate

Fig. MM618D — Pumping elements are retained in body by snap ring (3) and end plug (2). "O" ring (5) seals the formed steel reservoir.

1. Body
2. End plug
3. Snap ring
4. Punch
5. "O" ring

Fig. MM618E — Partially exploded view of drive shaft and pumping elements. Refer to Fig. MM618C for parts identification.

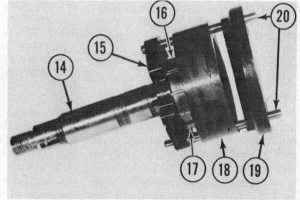

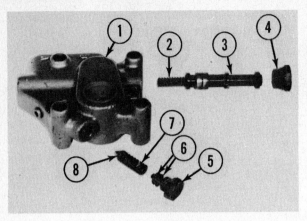

Fig. MM618G — Disassembled view of tractor hydraulic pump manifold used on Jet Star Three with hydrostatic power steering. Power steering relief pressure is adjusted by shims (6).

1. Manifold
2. Flow control spring
3. Flow control valve
4. Valve plug
5. Valve plug
6. Pressure adjusting shims
7. Relief valve spring
8. Relief valve

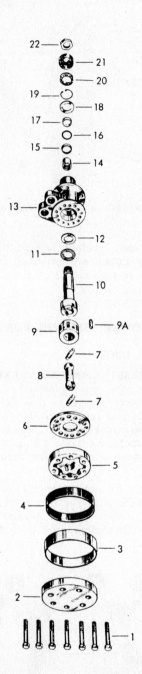

(19) for wear. Renew all "O" rings whenever pump is disassembled, and seal (1) if its condition is questionable.

Assemble the pump by reversing the disassembly procedure, using Fig. MM618C as a guide. Adjust belt tension as outlined in paragraph 18, after pump is reinstalled.

Jet Star Three

18C. PRESSURE RELIEF AND FLOW CONTROL VALVES. The power steering pressure relief and flow control valves are contained in a manifold mounted on the tractor main hydraulic pump. Refer to Fig. MM618G. The flow control valve (3) supplies 2.5-3.5 gpm to the power steering system from the 13.5 gpm main hydraulic system pump. Maximum steering system pressure is controlled at 950-1050 psi by the power steering pressure relief valve (8).

To adjust the steering system pressure, first test pressure as outlined in paragraph 17B. If pressure is not as specified, remove the plug (5) from lower side of manifold, and add or remove shims (6), until the specified pressure is obtained.

18D. PUMP. Removal, installation and overhaul procedures of the tractor hydraulic pump are given in paragraphs 136 through 138. Refer to these paragraphs for the required information.

MANUAL PUMP

18E. REMOVE AND REINSTALL. To remove the manual pump, first remove both hood rear side panels and disconnect manual pump hoses from control valve. Tag the hoses as they are disconnected, for convenience in reinstallation. Disconnect hand throttle linkage at rear end and un-

bolt lower throttle lever bracket from steering support. Remove the four cap screws securing steering shaft support housing to instrument panel and lift off steering wheel, throttle lever, steering support housing and manual pump as a unit.

Remove the steering wheel and the four cap screws retaining manual pump to support housing, and withdraw the pump and hoses. Install by reversing the removal procedure.

NOTE: Front hose on hand pump should be attached to upper elbow on steering control valve; rear hose to lower valve elbow. Refer to Fig. MM620.

18F. OVERHAUL. To disassemble the removed pump, place unit in soft-jawed vice with end plate uppermost. Remove the end plate retaining cap screws and lift off the end plate. Refer to Figs. MM619 through MM619C.

NOTE: Lapped surfaces of end plate (2), pumping element (5), spacer (6), commutator (9) and pump body (13) must be protected from scratching, burring or any other damage as sealing of these parts depends only on their finish and flatness.

Remove seal retainer (3), seal (4), pumping element (5) and spacer (6) from body (13). Remove commutator (9) and drive link (8), with link pins (7) and commutator pin (9A), from body. Smooth any burrs or nicks which may be present on input shaft (10), wrap spline with masking tape, then remove input shaft from body. Remove bearing race (12) and thrust bearing (11) from input shaft. Remove snap ring (19), washer (18), spacer (17), back-up washer (16) and seal (15). Do not remove needle bearing (14) unless renewal is required. If it should be necessary to renew bearing, press same out pumping element end of body.

Fig. MM619 — Exploded view of manual steering pump used on U302 and some Jet Star Three tractors.

1. Cap screw	11. Thrust bearing
2. End plate	12. Bearing race
3. Seal retainer	13. Body
4. Seal	14. Needle bearing
5. Pumping element	15. Seal
6. Spacer plate	16. Back-up washer
7. Link pin	17. Spacer
8. Drive link	18. Washer
9. Commutator	19. Retainer
9A. Commutator pin	20. Felt seal
10. Coupling (input) shaft	21. Water seal
	22. Nut

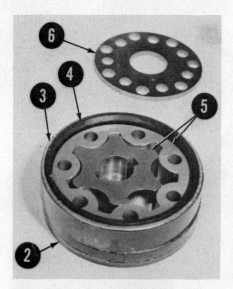

Fig. MM619A — Pump rotor, seal and spacer plate partially disassembled. Refer also to Fig. MM619.

Clean all parts in a suitable solvent and if necessary, remove paint from outer edges of body, spacer and end plate by passing these parts lightly over crocus cloth placed on a perfectly flat surface. Do not attempt to dress out any scratches or other defects since these sealing surfaces are lapped to within 0.00002 of being flat. However, in cases of emergency, a spacer that is damaged on one side only may be used if the smooth side is positioned next to the pumping element and the damaged side is lapped flat.

Inspect commutator and housing for scoring and undue wear. Bear in mind that burnish marks may show, or discolorations from oil residue may be present, on commutator after unit has been in service for some time. These can be ignored providing they do not interfere with free rotation of commutator in body.

Check fit of commutator pin in the commutator. Pin should be a snug fit

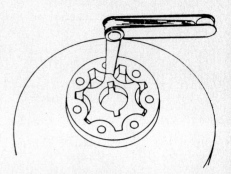

Fig. MM619D — Position pumping element as shown to check tooth clearance. Refer to text.

and if bent, or worn until diameter at contacting points is less than 0.2485, renew pin.

Measure inside diameter of input shaft bore in body and outside diameter of input shaft bearing surface. If body bore is 0.006, or more, larger than shaft diameter, renew shaft and/or body and commutator. Note: Body and commutator are not available separately.

Check thrust bearing and race for excessive grooving, flat spots or any other damage and renew bearing assembly if necessary.

Place pumping element on a flat surface and in the position shown in Fig. MM619D. Use a feeler gage and check clearance between ends of rotor teeth and high points of stator. If clearance exceeds 0.003, renew pumping element. Use a micrometer and measure width (thickness) of rotor and stator. If stator is 0.002 or more wider (thicker) than the rotor, renew the pumping element. Pumping element rotor and stator are available only as a matched set.

Check end plate for wear, scoring and flatness. Do not confuse the polish pattern on end plate with wear. This pattern, which results from rotor rotation, is normal. Renew end plate if worn or scored and if surface is not within 0.00002 of being flat.

When reassembling, use all new seals and back-up washers. All parts, except those noted below, are installed dry. Reassemble as follows: If needle bearing (14) was removed, lubricate with MM hydraulic fluid, install from pumping element end of body and press bearing into bore until inside end measures $3\frac{13}{16}$-$3\frac{7}{8}$ inches from pumping element end of body as shown in Fig. MM619E. Lubricate thrust bearing assembly with hydraulic fluid and install assembly on input shaft with race on top side. In-

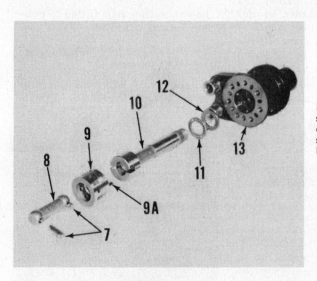

Fig. MM619B — Steering shaft, commutator and drive link exploded from steering housing. Refer to Fig. MM619 for parts identification.

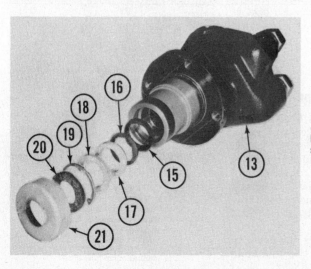

Fig. MM619C — Upper end of manual pump body, showing exploded shaft seal. Refer to Fig. MM619.

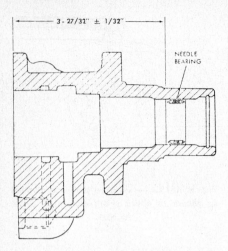

Fig. MM619E — When renewing needle bearing in body, install to dimension shown.

Fig. MM619F — Special care should be used when installing SAE Straight Tubing fittings with "O" ring seals (J. I. C. fittings). The "O" ring (4) will be cut and fitting will leak, if fitting is turned with jam nut (2) tight. If fitting must be repositioned, back off the locknut, and make sure "O" ring is free. Tighten jam nut only after fitting is properly positioned.

1. Fitting
2. Jam nut
3. Washer
4. "O" ring

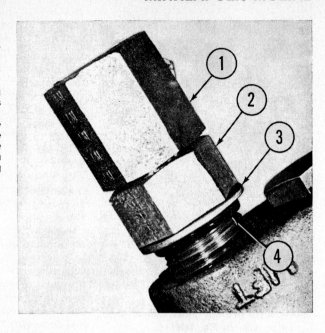

stall input shaft and bearing assembly in body and check for free rotation. Install a link pin in one end of the drive link, then install drive link in input shaft by engaging the flats on link pin with slots in input shaft. Use a small amount of grease to hold commutator pin in commutator, then install commutator and pin in body while engaging pin in one of the long slots of the input shaft. Commutator is correctly installed when edge of commutator is slightly below sealing surface of body. Clamp body in a soft jawed vise with input shaft pointing downward. Again make sure surfaces of spacer, pumping element, body and end plate are perfectly clean, dry and undamaged. Place spacer on body and align screw holes with those of body. Put link pin in exposed end of drive link, then install pumping element rotor while engaging flats of link pin with slots in rotor. Position pumping element stator over rotor and align screw holes of stator with those of spacer and body. Lubricate pumping element seal lightly with hydraulic fluid and install seal in seal retainer, then install seal and retainer over pumping element stator. Install end cap, align screw holes of end cap with those in pumping element, spacer and body, then install cap screws. Tighten cap screws evenly and to a torque of 18-22 ft.-lbs.

NOTE: If input shaft does not turn evenly after cap screws are tightened, loosen and tighten them again. However, bear in mind that the unit was assembled dry and some drag is normal. If stickiness or binding cannot be eliminated, disassemble unit and check for foreign material, nicks or burrs which could be causing interference.

Lubricate input shaft seal with hydraulic fluid and with input shaft splines taped to protect seal, install seal, back-up washer, spacer, washer and snap ring. The felt washer and water seal may be installed at this time but there will be less chance of loss or damage if installation is postponed until the time the steering wheel is installed.

After unit is assembled, turn unit on side with hose ports upward. Pour unit full of oil and work pump slowly until interior (pumping element) is thoroughly coated. Either plug ports or drain excess oil.

Reinstall unit by reversing the removal procedure and bleed steering system as outlined in paragraph 17A.

CAUTION: The fittings used are SAE Straight Tubing Fittings with "O" ring seal (J. I. C. fittings). Refer to Fig. MM619F. To prevent leakage, carefully position the fitting with jam nut (2) loose; then tighten jam nut to secure the fitting. DO NOT attempt to reposition any fitting with jam nut tight, or "O" ring (4) will be cut and leakage will result. Do not allow fitting to turn while tightening connections.

STEERING CONTROL VALVE

18G. REMOVE AND REINSTALL. To remove the steering control valve, first remove left rear hood side panel. Disconnect the cylinder pressure hoses (5—Fig. MM620) at front end of hoses, and the other hoses and tubes at the valve. Remove the three retaining bolts and nuts and lift off the valve assembly.

Reinstall by reversing the removal procedure. Connect the two tubes and

four hoses as follows: Refer to Fig. MM620.

Upper, outside port fitting to power pump pressure tube (2).

Lower, outside port fitting to power pump return tube (3).

Lower end cap port fitting to manual pump rear hose (4).

Lower, inside port hose (5) to left cylinder pressure tube.

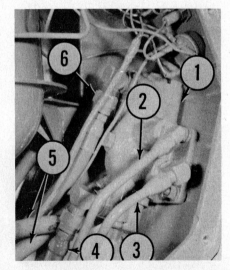

Fig. MM620 — Connect the steering control valve as shown.

1. Valve assembly
2. Power pump pressure tube
3. Power pump return tube
4. Manual pump rear hose
5. Steering cylinder hoses:
   Upper hose/right cylinder
   Lower hose/left cylinder
6. Manual pump rear hose

Upper, inside port hose (5) to right cylinder pressure tube.

Upper, end cap port fitting to manual pump front hose (6).

Bleed the system as outlined in paragraph 17A.

18H. **OVERHAUL.** To overhaul the steering control valve, remove the valve spool end caps and withdraw the spool (4—Fig. MM620A) with centering spring (3) and centering washers (2).

Remove the recirculating valve plug (9) and the loose valve ball (6). Examine ball seat in valve housing for damage or dirt particles which might prevent check ball from seating. The roll pin (7) in valve plug should extend a distance (A) of 15/16-inch from seating surface of plug. The roll pin may be repositioned or renewed.

Examine valve spool (4) and valve body for scoring or scratches; if damaged, renew the valve assembly, as spool and body are matched and not available separately. The valve spool contains internal drillings which must be open and clean. To renew centering spring (3) or centering washers (2), unscrew the valve end, using two punches inserted in holes in valve spool and valve end screw.

Assemble by reversing the disassembly procedure, using new "O" rings and seals. Tighten end cap retaining screws to a torque of 25 ft.-lbs.

Install the valve and connect hydraulic lines as outlined in paragraph 18G.

CAUTION: The fittings are SAE Straight Tubing Thread fittings with "O" ring seal (J. I. C. fittings). Refer to Fig. MM619F. To prevent leakage, carefully position the fitting with jam nut (2) loose; then tighten jam nut to secure the fitting. DO NOT attempt to reposition any fitting with jam nut tight, or "O" ring (4) will be cut and leakage

will result. Do not allow fitting to turn while tightening connections.

STEERING CYLINDERS

A rack and sector type steering unit is used. The design is similar to that used on models with manual steering or the earlier power steering models. Some of the parts are interchangeable, but overhaul procedures differ because of design changes.

19. **R&R AND OVERHAUL.** To remove the steering piston or cylinder sleeves on U302, first prepare the tractor as follows:

Drain cooling system and remove hood, grille and lower grille support. Remove hood left rear side panel and disconnect power steering cylinder tubes at couplings on left side of clutch housing. Disconnect the radiator hoses.

Suitably support the tractor beneath clutch housing. Remove the six cap screws (A—Fig. MM621) which secure front support to each side rail, and move the radiator and front support forward until piston cover (C) is exposed as shown. One cap screw (B) on each side, can be reinstalled for safety.

On axle models, disconnect center steering arm (7—Fig. MM621A) from vertical shaft (6). On tricycle models, remove the wheel fork or pedestal. Drain steering gear housing by removing the square-head drain plug from lower face of housing. Remove left piston cover (C—Fig. MM621) and piston guide (D).

Remove one cap screw from each side of bearing cage (5—Fig. MM-621A) and loosely install two 5/8-11 x 2½ inch bolts (4) in holes from which cap screws were removed. Remove the other four securing cap screws from bearing cage (5) and allow vertical shaft to drop down on the longer bolts as shown; then withdraw the piston from left side of housing.

Fig. MM621 — On U302 tractors, move front end forward to clear side rails, for service on steering cylinders. Refer to text.

    A. Securing cap screws
    B. Reinstall for safety
    C. Piston cover
    D. Piston guide

The cylinder sleeve can be removed using a pair of pliers after piston cover is off; before or after removing the piston. Refer to Fig. MM621B. If sleeve is damaged, however, piston seals should be renewed, which requires removal of piston.

The piston seal (2—Fig. MM621A) consists of an "O" ring and two leather backup rings. After piston seals are renewed, reinsert and cen-

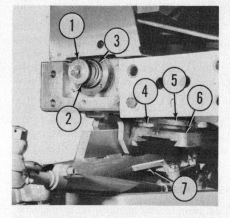

Fig. MM621A — To remove the power steering cylinder, remove one bolt on each side which secures bearing cage (5) to support housing; and install longer, 2½-inch bolts (4). Disconnect center steering arm (7), pedestal or wheel fork. Remove remainder of bearing cage securing bolts and allow vertical shaft (6) and bearing cage to drop down as shown.

    1. Piston
    2. Piston rings
    3. Sleeve sealing ring
    4. 5/8 - 11 x 2½ bolts
    5. Bearing cage
    6. Vertical shaft
    7. Center steering arm

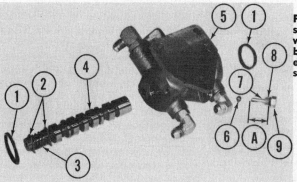

Fig. MM620A — Disassembled view of steering valve. Recirculating valve ball (6) seats when power pump is operating, unseats for manual operation.

    1. Seal
    2. Centering washer
    3. Centering spring
    4. Valve spool
    5. Valve housing
    6. Recirculating valve ball
    7. Roll pin
    8. "O" ring
    9. Plug

Fig. MM621B — The sleeve can be withdrawn as shown, after piston cover has been removed. Refer to text.

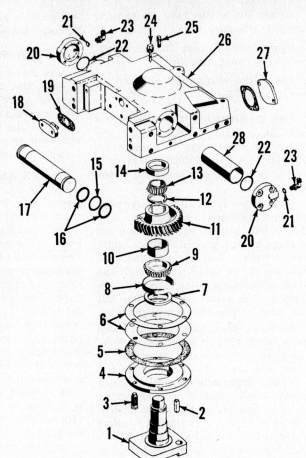

Fig. MM622 — Exploded view of front support, steering piston, vertical shaft and associated parts used on models with hydrostatic steering.

1. Vertical shaft
2. Key
3. Steering stop
4. Bearing cage
5. Gasket
6. Adjusting shims
7. Oil seal
8. Bearing cup
9. Cone & roller
10. Spacer
11. Sector gear
12. Snap ring
13. Cone & roller
14. Bearing cup
15. Piston "O" ring
16. Backup rings
17. Steering piston
18. Piston guide
19. Gasket
20. Piston cover
21. "O" ring
22. "O" ring
23. Fitting
24. Filler plug
25. Breather
26. Support housing
27. Cover
28. Cylinder sleeve

ter the piston in housing; then reinstall bearing cage with vertical shaft in straight-ahead position.

NOTE: If only the left piston cover is removed, make sure sleeve is fully seated and install piston so that end measures 3⅛ inches from outer end of sleeve.

After vertical shaft is installed, turn vertical shaft in each direction and check to be sure that stop pin is contacted when turned fully right or left, and that piston does not extend beyond end of seated sleeve on left turn.

Complete the assembly by reversing the disassembly procedure. Fill steering sector to level of filler plug with SAE 80 Multipurpose gear oil. Fill and bleed steering system as outlined in paragraph 17A.

NOTE: The steering cylinder on models without side rails can be overhauled in the same manner, except front end will not need to be moved forward.

STEERING SECTOR

19A. Refer to Fig. MM622. To remove the vertical shaft, sector gear, and bearings, suitably support front of tractor and remove front pedestal, wheel fork, or axle and pivot brackets.

Drain steering compartment by removing the square head drain plug on lower face of housing. Turn vertical shaft to a straight-ahead position, remove bearing flange retaining cap screws and withdraw vertical shaft assembly.

Upper bearing cup (14) fits a counterbore in housing and should be renewed if upper cone (13) is renewed.

To disassemble the vertical shaft, remove upper bearing cone (13) using a suitable knife edge puller. Remove snap ring (12), loosen the clamp bolt and remove sector gear (11), key (2) and spacer (10). Press sector shaft out of bearing cage and renew seal (7) before reassembling.

Reassemble by reversing the disassembly procedure. Make sure bearing cones and cups are fully seated and install a sufficient quantity of 0.006 shims (6) to provide a slight drag when shaft is rotated, with no shaft end play.

After vertical shaft is installed, turn shaft in each direction and check to see that stop (3) is contacted when turned to each extreme position. If not, re-mesh sector gear and steering piston until contact is made with stop, when turned in either direction.

Fill gear housing to level of filler plug with SAE 80, Multi-purpose gear oil. Check to be sure breather (25) is open and clean.

ENGINE AND COMPONENTS

Series 335 tractors are equipped with a gasoline or LP-Gas engine having a bore of 3⅝ inches, a stroke of 4 inches and a piston displacement of 165 cubic inches. Series 445, Jet Star, 4-Star and 4-Star Super tractors are equipped with a gasoline, LP-Gas or diesel engine having a bore of 3⅝ inches, a stroke of 5 inches and a displacement of 206 cubic inches. U-302 is equipped with a gasoline or LP-Gas engine having a bore of 3¾ inches, a stroke of 5 inches and a displacement of 220 cubic inches.

The engine consists of two cylinder blocks and two cylinder heads which are mounted in line on a one piece crankcase. The cast crankcase is fitted with a side cover providing access to the crankshaft, camshaft, timing gears, connecting rods and engine bearings.

This same basic engine design is used on the gasoline, LP-Gas, and diesel versions of all series tractors. A number of engine parts are interchangeable and service procedures remain the same except where evident or noted.

R&R ENGINE AND CLUTCH

All Models

20. To remove the engine and clutch as an assembly, first drain cooling system and if engine is to be disassembled, drain the oil. On models with power steering, drain hydraulic system and disconnect the power steering oil lines. Remove the hood top (service) panel pivot pins and lift off the service panel. Remove the side panel tie braces and tool box. On series 335 and 445, disconnect the headlight wires and remove the headlights. Note: On 4-Star series, headlights are mounted in grille and removal is unnecessary. A kit is available for grille mounting of headlights on 335 and 445 series tractors which, if used, makes removal unnecessary. Unbolt and remove side panels from tractor. Disconnect the upper and lower radiator hoses and remove fan belt. Support tractor under transmission housing, then unbolt and remove the steering gear housing, radiator and axle assembly from engine.

Remove the two bolts retaining front of fuel tank to the exhaust manifold and cylinder head adapter plate. Disconnect the heat indicator sending unit from the rear cylinder head. Remove fuel line and disconnect wires from generator, regulator and starting motor. Disconnect the starter rod, remove the oil pressure gage line and disconnect the tachourmeter cable.

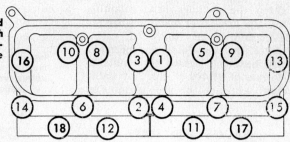

Fig. MM624—Cylinder head nut tightening sequence. With engine at operating temperature, desired tightening torque is 95-100 ft.-lbs.

On gasoline and LP-Gas models, disconnect throttle rod at forward end, choke wire at carburetor end and switch wire from coil.

On diesel models, remove bleed back line from tractor, disconnect stop cable and housing and forward throttle control rod from injection pump.

On all models, swing engine in a hoist, then unbolt and remove engine from tractor.

CYLINDER HEADS

All Models

Engine is equipped with two cylinder heads, each covering a pair of cylinders. A small pipe located between the heads connects the cylinder head water jackets. Both heads must be removed and reinstalled at the same time.

Cylinder heads are widely interchangeable and compression ratio can be varied over a wide range just by changing heads. Make certain that identical cylinder heads are used in both locations when engine is assembled.

21. To remove the cylinder heads, first drain cooling system, raise the hood top (service) panel and remove the side panel tie braces and tool box. Remove the valve cover, disconnect the rocker arms oil tube and remove the rocker arms assembly and push rods.

On gasoline and LP Gas models, remove muffler and disconnect the air cleaner hose, choke wire and throttle rod at carburetor. Shut-off the fuel and remove the fuel line. Remove the support bolt connecting rear end of exhaust manifold to fuel tank and remove the exhaust manifold outlet elbow. Unbolt and remove the exhaust and inlet manifold and carburetor assembly. Disconnect the radiator upper hose and remove the engine water outlet pipe. Unbolt the coil and water pump bracket from the cylinder head adapter plate and remove the support bolt retaining rear end of adapter plate to fuel tank.

On diesel models, remove muffler, disconnect air cleaner hose and unbolt and remove manifold. Disconnect and remove injector and bleed back lines, being sure to cap all exposed fittings. Disconnect upper radiator hose and remove engine water outlet pipe. Disconnect water pump brace and fuel tank support bolt from cylinder head adapter plate.

On all models disconnect the heat indicator sending unit from the rear cylinder head. Remove the cylinder head retaining stud nuts but do not remove the two ⅜-16 cap screws retaining the adapter plate to top of heads. Refer to Fig. MM623. Lift off the adapter plate and both cylinder heads as a unit, then remove the adapter plate and separate the heads.

When reassembling, be sure to renew the "O" rings on the small water tube located between the heads. Install the adapter plate but do not completely tighten the two ⅜-16 cap screws until after the cylinder head retaining nuts are tightened. Install the cylinder head gasket with copper side up, then install the cylinder heads and adapter plate unit but do not

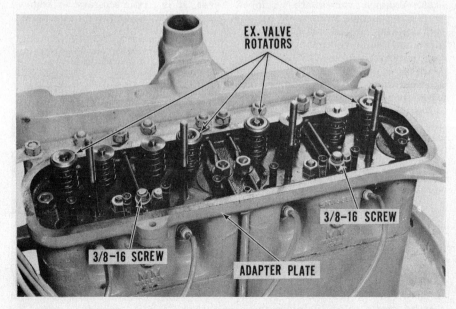

Fig. MM623—Cylinder heads and adapter plate installation, typical of all except LP-Gas engines. Adapter plate and both cylinder heads must be removed as a unit. LP-Gas engines are similar except the exhaust valve rotators are not used.

tighten the cylinder head retaining stud nuts until after manifolds are installed and securely tightened.

After the manifolds are permanently installed, tighten head nuts to a torque of 95-100 ft.-lbs. Nut tightening sequence is shown in Fig. MM624.

VALVES AND SEATS

All Models

22. Intake and exhaust valves are not interchangeable. Intake valves seat directly in cylinder head; whereas, the cylinder head is fitted with renewable seat inserts for the exhaust valves. Valves have a face and seat angle of 45 degrees and a seat width of $\frac{3}{32}$-inch. Seats can be narrowed, using 15 and 70 degree stones. Valves have a stem diameter of 0.3405-0.3415. Tappet gap should be set Hot to 0.010 for the intake, 0.018 for the exhaust.

The renewable exhaust valve seat inserts can be removed from cylinder head by using a suitable puller. Chill new inserts in dry ice to facilitate installation. Inserts are available in standard size only.

VALVE GUIDES AND SPRINGS

All Models

23. Intake and exhaust valve guides are interchangeable and can be pressed from cylinder head if renewal is required. Ream new guides after installation to an inside diameter of 0.343-0.344. The 0.3405-0.3415 diameter valve stems have a clearance of 0.0015-0.0035 in the guides.

Intake and exhaust valve springs are interchangeable. Springs have a free length of $1\frac{29}{32}$ inches and should test 51-56 lbs. when compressed to a height of 1 13/64 inches. Renew any spring which is rusted, discolored or does not meet the pressure test specifications.

VALVE TAPPETS
(Cam Followers)

All Models

24. The barrel type tappets are available in standard size' only and should have a clearance of 0.001-0.003 in the case bores. Tappets can be easily withdrawn from the case bores after removing the camshaft as outlined in paragraph 29.

VALVE TAPPET LEVERS
(Rocker Arms)

All Models

25. Desired clearance of the 0.747-0.748 diameter rocker arm shaft in the rocker arm bushings is 0.002-0.003.

Fig. MM625 — Exploded view of engine camshaft, valves, rocker arms and associated parts.

1. Camshaft
2. Camshaft timing gear
3. Oil pump drive gear
4. Washer
5. Cap screw
6. Rocker arm
7. Rocker arm
8. Tappet adjusting screw
9. Rocker arm shaft
10. Rubber plug
12. Spring, 1 9/16" long
13. Spring, 2 9/16" long
14. Rocker arm bracket
15. Bracket stud
16. Rocker arms oil tube
17. Oil supply pipe
18. Nut
19. Seal
20. Intake valve
21. Exhaust valve
22. Valve spring
23. Intake valve spring seat
24. "Rotocap" (Except LP-Gas)
25. Spring seat locks
26. Exhaust valve seat insert
27. Valve guide
28. Push rod
29. Valve tappet

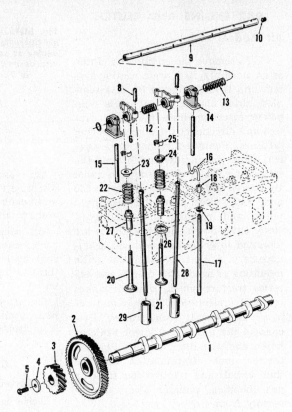

Inside diameter (new) of the rocker arm bushings is 0.750. Bushings are not supplied separately for service; therefore, if clearance between bushing and shaft exceeds 0.008, it will be necessary to renew the rocker arms and/or shaft.

VALVE ROTATORS
All Models

26. Exhaust valves are equipped with positive type rotators on all except LP-Gas engines. If LP-Gas engines are found equipped with rotators, remove them and install the regular spring seats. Normal servicing of the rotators consists of renewing the units. It is important, however, to observe the valve action after engine is started. The valve rotator action can be considered satisfactory if the valve rotates a slight amount each time the valve opens. Valve spring test specifications are listed in paragraph 23.

VALVE TIMING
All Models

27. Valves are properly timed when timing gears are meshed so that chisel mark on camshaft gear is in register with chisel mark on crankshaft throw as shown in Fig. MM626. The quickest way to check valve timing is to remove the crankcase side cover and observe the timing marks.

TIMING GEARS
All Models

28. Timing drive of three helical gears consists of the crankshaft gear, camshaft gear and the oil pump drive gear. The latter gear which also drives the ignition unit via the oil pump drive shaft is located forward of the camshaft gear. To remove the oil pump drive gear and/or camshaft gear, it is first necessary to remove the camshaft as outlined in paragraph

Fig. MM626—Engine timing marks. Notice that chisel mark on camshaft gear registers with similar mark on crankshaft throw.

29. To remove the crankshaft gear, it is necessary to remove the crankshaft as outlined in paragraph 36.

When installing the camshaft and/or crankshaft, mesh the gears so that chisel mark on camshaft gear is in register with chisel mark on crankshaft throw as shown in Fig. MM626.

CAMSHAFT
All Models

29. To remove the camshaft, first remove the valve cover, rocker arms assembly and push rods. Disconnect the steering shaft front universal joint and slide the joint off of the steering worm extension shaft. On diesel models shut off fuel, remove fuel, bleed back and injector lines. Disconnect stop cable and throttle linkage from injection pump and unbolt and remove pump. Disconnect the tachourmeter cable, then unbolt and remove the crankcase side cover. Crank engine until the chisel mark on camshaft gear is in register with the chisel mark on crankshaft throw as shown in Fig. MM626. Refer also to Fig. MM627. Remove the camshaft rear bearing cap and mark the front and center caps so they can be reinstalled in the same position. Remove the small machine screws retaining the oil tubes to the front and center main bearing caps, then unbolt and remove the camshaft front and center

bearing cap and oil tube assemblies. Carefully withdraw the camshaft and cam followers from the crankcase and keep the cam followers in their original order.

The 1.2465-1.2470 diameter camshaft bearing journals should have a recommended clearance of 0.0025-0.004 in the bearings. The maximum permissible clearance is 0.007 and when it exceeds this amount, it will be necessary to renew the camshaft and/or crankcase and bearing caps.

Install the cam followers in their original order and use heavy grease to hold them up when installing the camshaft; then mesh the camshaft gear with the crankshaft gear so that chisel mark on camshaft gear is in register with chisel mark on crankshaft throw as shown in Fig. MM626. Install the shaft rear bearing cap with the oil trough up. Front and center caps must be installed in their original position and can be installed one way only as oil lines must enter bottom of caps. After bearing caps are securely tightened, pry the camshaft rearward as far as possible without forcing and measure the camshaft end clearance between front of camshaft gear and rear face of front bearing cap. Recommended end clearance is 0.003-0.005. If clearance is less than 0.003, remove the camshaft and camshaft gear; then remove the necessary amount of metal from rear surface of

gear hub and press gear further on shaft. If end clearance is more than 0.005, remove the camshaft and oil pump drive gear; then remove the necessary amount of metal from the camshaft shoulder against which the oil pump drive gear seats and press the oil pump drive gear further on shaft. Time and bleed the injection pump as outlined in paragraph 49N or paragraph 50.

ROD AND PISTON UNITS
All Models

30. Connecting rod and piston units are removed from above after removing the cylinder heads, crankcase cover and connecting rod bearing caps.

Cylinder numbers on connecting rods and caps must be in register when reassembling. Tighten the connecting rod bolts to a torque of 70-75 ft.-lbs.

PISTONS AND RINGS
All Non-Diesel Models

31. Pistons and rings are available in standard size and oversizes of 0.020 and 0.040. Pistons are fitted with three $\frac{3}{32}$-inch wide compression rings and one $\frac{3}{16}$-inch wide oil control ring. Piston ring end gap should be 0.010-0.020 for compression rings, 0.010-0.018 for the oil control rings. Ring side clearance in cast iron piston grooves is 0.0025-0.0035 for the compression rings, 0.0015-0.0020 for the oil control rings. Ring side clearance in aluminum piston grooves is 0.0025-0.004 for the top compression ring, 0.002-0.0035 for other compression rings and 0.0015-0.003 for the oil control ring. Recommended piston skirt clearance is 0.0025-0.0045 for iron pistons, 0.003-0.005 for aluminum pistons in series 335, 445 or U302, or 0.0025-0.004 for aluminum pistons in Jet Star or 4 Star series. Standard size cylinder bore is 3.7518-3.7522 for U302; or 3.6255-3.6265 for other models.

Diesel Models

31A. Pistons (aluminum) and rings are available in standard size and oversizes of 0.020 and 0.040. Pistons are fitted with one ⅛-inch wide top compression ring, two 3/32-inch wide compression rings and one 3/16-inch wide oil control ring. Piston ring end gaps should be 0.010-0.020 for the compression rings and 0.010-0.018 for the oil control ring. Ring side clearance is 0.002-0.0035 for the compression rings and 0.0015-0.003 for the oil control ring. Recommended piston skirt clearance is 0.0045-0.006. Standard size cylinder bore is 3.6255-3.6265.

Fig. MM627—Engine side cover removed, showing the installation of the camshaft and crankshaft. Notice that the oil tubes are retained to the main bearing caps by two small machine screws.

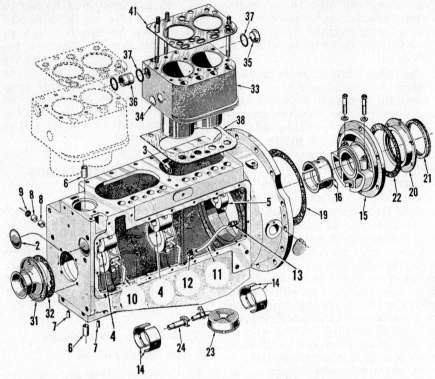

Fig. MM628—Engine crankcase, cylinder blocks and bearings. Oil pump drive shaft is carried in bushings (6) and governor fork shaft in bushings (8). Crankshaft front oil seal is located in cover (31).

2. Expansion plug	11. Oil tube, rear bearing	31. Cover
3. Plug, slotted	12. Oil tube connectors	32. Gasket
4. Camshaft bearing cap, front and center	14. & 16. Main bearing inserts	33. Cylinder block
	15. Main bearing housing	34. Expansion plug
5. Camshaft rear bearing cap	19. Gasket	35. Plug
6. Oil pump shaft bushings	20. Rear oil seal retainer	36. Water tube
7. Dowel pin	21. Crankshaft rear oil seal	37. "O" ring seal
8. Governor shaft bushings	22. Gasket	38. Cylinder block gasket
9. Governor shaft oil seal	23. Oil strainer	41. Head gasket
10. Oil tubes, front and center bearings	24. Connector	

CYLINDER BLOCKS

All Models

32. To remove the cylinder blocks, first remove the cylinder heads as outlined in paragraph 21 and the camshaft as outlined in paragraph 29. Disconnect the radiator lower hose and fan belt and unbolt the water pump from crankcase. Move the water pump, air cleaner and fan assembly forward until the water inlet pipe clears the front cylinder block. Remove the rocker arm oil supply pipe from upper left side of crankcase. Reinstall the cylinder head adapter plate on cylinder block studs and reinstall at least four of the retaining stud nuts. This procedure permits lifting off both of the cylinder blocks at the same time without damaging the small water pipe located between the blocks. Unbolt and lift both cylinder blocks, rods and pistons from crankcase. Refer to Fig. MM629. Refer to paragraph 31 or 31A for cylinder bore size and recommended piston skirt clearance.

When reinstalling the cylinder

blocks, tighten the retaining bolts finger tight then install the connecting rod bearing caps and crank the engine several revolutions to align the cylinder blocks. Alignment can be checked by using a straight edge along the machined right side of blocks. Tighten the block hold down bolts securely and install the remaining parts.

PISTON PINS

All Non-Diesel Models

33. The full floating type piston pins are retained in the piston bosses by snap rings and are available in standard size and oversize of 0.005. The 0.9993-0.9996 diameter piston pin has a clearance of 0.0001-0.0007 in the piston bosses and 0.0004-0.0009 in the connecting rod bushing.

Diesel Models

33A. The full floating type piston pins are retained in the piston bosses by snap rings and are available in

standard size and oversize of 0.005. The 1.2497-1.2500 diameter piston pin has a diametral clearance of 0.0004-0.001 in the connecting rod bushing and a thumb push fit in the piston.

ROD BEARINGS

All Models

34. Connecting rod bearings are of the shimless, non-adjustable, slip-in, precision type which can be renewed after removing the injection pump (diesel models), crankcase side cover and the connecting rod bearing caps. When installing new bearing shells be sure that the bearing shell projections engage the milled slot in rod and cap and that cylinder numbers on rod and cap are in register. Bearing inserts are available in standard size as well as undersizes of 0.0025, 0.005, 0.020 and 0.040. On gasoline and LP-Gas models connecting rod bearings have a diametral clearance of 0.0011-0.0031 for the 445, Jet Star and 4-Star series; 0.0011-0.0027 for the 335 series; and 0.0015-0.003 for U302. All diesel model connecting rod bearings have a diametral clearance of 0.0015-0.003. Connecting rod side play is 0.006-0.013 for gasoline and LP-Gas models and 0.010-0.020 for diesel models. Crankshaft crankpin diameter is 2.6245-2.6250 for all models. Tighten the connecting rod bolts to a torque of 70-75 ft.-lbs.

NOTE: New engines which have a letter "K" suffixed to model number have 0.0025 undersize crankpins; letter "F", 0.0025 undersize main bearing journals; letters "KF", 0.0025 undersize crankpins and main journals.

CRANKSHAFT AND MAIN BEARINGS

All Models

35. Main bearing inserts are of the slip-in, precision type and are available in standard size as well as undersizes of 0.0025, 0.005, 0.020 and 0.040.

To remove the main bearings, first remove the injection pump (diesel models) and crankcase side cover. Crank engine until the chisel mark on camshaft gear is in register with the chisel mark on crankshaft throw as shown in Fig. MM626 and proceed as follows: Mark the camshaft front and center bearing caps so they can be reinstalled in the same position, remove the small machine screws retaining the oil tubes to the front and center main bearing caps, then unbolt and remove the camshaft front and center bearing cap and oil tube assemblies. (Refer to Fig. MM627.) Unbolt and remove the bearing caps and main bearing inserts.

Standard size crankshaft main journal diameter is 2.7495-2.7500 for the front and center bearings, 2.9995-3.0000 for the rear bearing. On the 445, Jet Star and 4-Star series, the bearing diametral clearance is 0.0015-0.004 for the front and center bearings, 0.0015-0.0035 for the rear bearing. On the 335 series the bearing diametral clearance is 0.0015-0.0036 for the front and center bearings, 0.0015-0.0035 for the rear bearing. Normal crankshaft end play of 0.003-0.004 for the 445, Jet Star and 4-Star series or 0.002-0.006 for 335 or U302 is controlled by the flanged rear bearing shells.

NOTE: New engines which have a letter "K" suffixed to model number have 0.0025 undersize crankpins; letter "F", 0.0025 undersize main bearing journals; letters "KF", 0.0025 undersize crankpins and main journals.

When installing the main bearing caps, observe the following: Nos. 1 and 2 bearing caps are marked top. Number one bearing cap has one punch mark and number two bearing cap has two punch marks. Crankcase is similarly punch marked at main bearing locations. Rear bearing cap is not marked right or left, but tab on upper insert must face crankcase opening. Tighten the main bearing bolts to a torque of 60-65 ft.-lbs. for gasoline and LP-Gas engines. On diesel models, tighten the front and intermediate main bearing bolts to a torque of 90-100 ft.-lbs. and the rear bolts to a torque of 60-65 ft.-lbs.

36. To remove the crankshaft, first remove the engine from tractor as outlined in paragraph 20 and proceed as follows: Remove the fan drive pulley, pulley key and oil seal housing from front of crankcase. Withdraw the governor weight unit from forward end of crankshaft. Remove the clutch, flywheel and flywheel hub. Remove the rear oil seal retainer (20—Fig. MM630) and the cap screws retaining the rear main bearing housing (15) to the crankcase. Remove the crankcase side cover and the front and center main bearing caps as previously outlined in paragraph 35. Refer to paragraph 41 and remove the oil pump and oil pump drive shaft. Bump the crankshaft rearward, remove one of the flywheel dowel pins, then remove the rear main bearing housing from crankshaft. Withdraw crankshaft from engine.

CRANKSHAFT OIL SEALS
All Models

37. **FRONT SEAL.** Crankshaft front oil seal and cover unit (31—Fig. MM-628) is retained to front of crankcase

by four screws. The procedure for renewing the seal and cover unit is evident after splitting the steering gear housing from the engine, as follows:

Drain cooling system and on models with power steering, drain hydraulic system and disconnect the power steering oil lines. Remove the hood top (service) panel pivot pins and lift off the service panel. Remove the side panel tie braces and tool box. Disconnect the head light wires and remove head lights; then, unbolt and remove side panels from tractor. Disconnect the upper and lower radiator hoses and remove fan belt. Support tractor under transmission housing, then unbolt and remove the steering gear housing, radiator and axle assembly from engine.

38. **REAR SEAL.** The crankshaft rear oil seal (21—Fig. MM628) can be renewed after removing the flywheel as in paragraph 39 or 39A, and the oil seal retainer (20). Refer also to Fig. MM628A and to Fig. MM630.

FLYWHEEL
All Models Except U302

39. The flywheel can be removed after splitting the engine from clutch housing as outlined in paragraph 63 and removing the clutch. To facilitate installation of the flywheel ring gear, heat same evenly to approximately 500 deg. F. Tighten the flywheel bolts to a torque of 70-75 ft.-lbs.

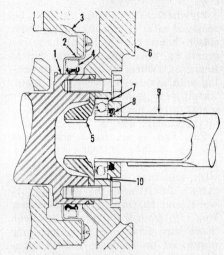

Fig. MM628A—Cross sectional view of engine flywheel, clutch pilot bearing, seal and pto driving hub used on U302 tractors.

1. Crankshaft
2. Crankshaft seal retainer
3. Main bearing housing
4. Rear oil seal
5. PTO driving hub
6. Flywheel
7. Pilot bearing
8. Oil seal
9. Clutch shaft
10. Tolerance ring

Model U302

39A. On model U302, the pto driving hub is mounted between flywheel and crankshaft flange as shown in cross-sectional view, Fig. MM628A. Flywheel and driving hub are retained to crankshaft flange by the same four cap screws.

Fig. MM629—Left side view of engine with cylinder blocks, rod and piston units and camshaft removed.

Flywheel and driving hub can be removed after separating engine from clutch housing as outlined in paragraph 63, then removing the clutch. Remove flywheel ring gear by spreading with a chisel between gear teeth. Install new gear from front of flywheel after heating gear evenly to approximately 500° F.

The ball type clutch shaft pilot bearing (7—Fig. MM628A) is a slip fit in flywheel bore when installed with tolerance ring (Part No. 10A-21205). Install seal (8) with lip forward, and bearing (7) and tolerance ring (10) from front face of flywheel. Make sure drive hub (5) is properly positioned on crankshaft dowels before installing flywheel. Tighten flywheel cap screws to a torque of 80 ft.-lbs.

OIL PUMP AND RELIEF VALVE
All Models

40. The oil pump is located externally at front of engine on underside of crankcase and the pump drive shaft is driven by a gear at front end of camshaft. To remove the oil pump, drain the engine crankcase and remove the pump retaining stud nuts. Withdraw the pump, drive gear and the drive gear Woodruff keys. Recommended diametral clearance between gears and pump body is 0.003-0.005. Desired body gear end play of 0.002-0.004 is controlled by the compressible gaskets between pump body and crankcase. Normally, four of these gaskets will provide the desired end clearance. End clearance, however, can be checked by using Plastigage under gears and bolting pump body to crankcase. Be sure to renew the by-pass valve ball and spring as well as the relief valve and spring if they are damaged or worn.

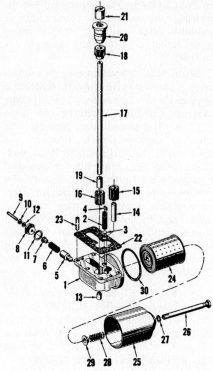

Fig. MM631—Exploded view of engine oil pump. Oil pump is driven by a gear located on forward end of camshaft. On non-diesels, the ignition distributor is driven by coupling (21).

1. Pump body	16. Drive gear
2. By-pass spring	17. Drive shaft
3. Steel ball	18. Drive shaft pinion
4. By-pass spring retainer	19. Drive shaft bushing
5. Check valve	20. Grooved bushing
6. Check valve spring	21. Coupling
7. Check valve spring retainer	22. Pump body gasket
8. Check valve cover	23. Stud
9. Adjusting screw	24. Filter cartridge
10. Jam nut	25. Filter case
11. Copper gasket	26. Center tube
12. Lead gasket	27. Copper gasket
13. Plug	28. Spring
14. Idler gear shaft	29. Spring retainer
15. Idler gear	30. Gasket

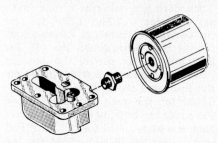

Fig. MM631A—Oil pump base and adapter used on late tractors with throw-away filter. Other parts are identical to those shown in Fig. MM631.

Oil pressure should be 25-30 psi with engine at operating temperature and running at high idle speed. Oil pressure can be adjusted by turning the screw (9—Fig. MM631) in or out as required.

41. **OIL PUMP DRIVE SHAFT.** To remove the oil pump drive shaft, first remove oil pump, oil pump drive gear and drive gear Woodruff keys as outlined in paragraph 40. On non-diesel models and diesel engines with Roosa Master pump, crank engine until number one piston is coming up on compression stroke and continue cranking until the flywheel mark "DC1-4" is in register with the index at flywheel housing timing port as shown in Fig. MM632; then remove the ignition distributor or injection pump and pump adapter. Mark the position of the distributor drive slot in upper end of drive shaft as shown in Fig. MM633 so that the shaft can be installed in its original position. On diesel models with PSB pump, remove pump drive shaft cover from crankcase. On all models, loosen the jam nut (Fig. MM634) and back out the set screw. Turn the pump drive shaft as required to disengage the gears and withdraw the shaft from top of crankcase. Examine the oil pump driveshaft bushings in crankcase and renew them if bushing to shaft clearance is excessive. New bushings should be reamed to provide the drive shaft with a recommended running clearance of 0.001-0.0025.

Install the drive shaft in its original position, tighten its retaining set screw and jam nut securely; then, install the oil pump. On non-diesel models, install ignition distributor and check the ignition timing as outlined in paragraph 56. On diesel models with Roosa-Master pump, install drive adapter as outlined in paragraph 50B and injection pump as outlined in paragraph 50A.

Fig. MM630 — Rear view of engine with flywheel removed. It is necessary to remove one of the flywheel dowel pins before the main bearing housing can be removed from the crankshaft.

15. Rear main bearing housing
20. Crankshaft rear oil seal retainer
21. Rear oil seal

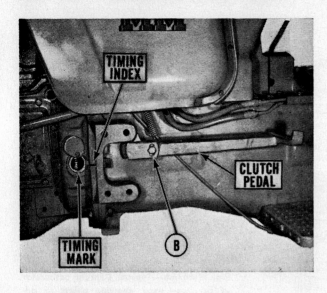

Fig. MM632 — Flywheel mark "DC1-4" in register with the timing index on flywheel housing.

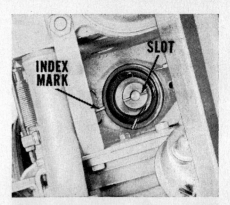

Fig. MM633 — Before removing the oil pump drive shaft on non-diesel engines or diesel models with Roosa-Master pump, index mark the distributor drive slot with respect to the crankcase so the oil pump drive shaft can be reinstalled in the same position.

CARBURETOR

(Except LP-Gas)

All Models

42. All gasoline models use Marvel-Schebler TSX carburetors. Recommended float setting is ¼-inch when measured from nearest face of float to gasket on carburetor body.

Suggested initial adjustment of both the high speed and low speed mixture adjustment needles is 1¾-2 turns open from the closed position. Readjust high speed mixture needle for satisfactory performance under load after engine is warm; then readjust low speed mixture needle for smooth, slow speed operation.

Model TSX633
Repair kit 286-1105
Gasket set 16-654
Inlet needle & seat..........233-543
Idle jet 49-101-L
Nozzle 47-449
Power jet 49-364

Model TSX650
Repair kit 286-1133
Gasket set 16-677

Inlet needle & seat..........233-536
Idle jet 49-165
Nozzle 47-393

Model TSX713
Repair kit 286-1167
Gasket set 16-654
Inlet needle & seat..........233-543
Idle jet 49-101-L
Nozzle 47-449
Power jet 49-364

Model TSX714
Repair kit 286-1164
Gasket set 16-677
Inlet needle & seat..........233-536
Idle jet 49-165
Nozzle 47-393

Model TSX878
Repair kit 286-1440
Gasket set 16-654
Inlet needle & seat..........233-608
Idle jet 49-101-L
Power jet 49-224
Nozzle 47-A12
Main adjusting needle kit.....43-730

Fig. MM634—The engine oil pump drive shaft is retained by a set screw located in forward face of crankcase.

TROUBLE SHOOTING
All Models Except U302

44. To locate trouble in the LP-Gas fuel system, connect a low reading pressure gage to the regulator as shown in Fig. MM635. Open the liquid withdrawal valve and crank engine; at this time, the gage should read 3½-5 psi. If gage reading is O.K., any trouble is due either to a plugged fuel line between regulator and carburetor or a faulty carburetor. If there is no pressure reading, close the liquid withdrawal valve; be sure also that the vapor withdrawal valve is closed. Then disconnect the outlet fuel line from the regulator, open the liquid withdrawal valve and observe the open connection. If liquid fuel appears, close the withdrawal valve immediately.

NOTE: Liquid fuel will appear as a fine white mist. CAUTION—Keep clear of open connections. Severe freezing and serious flesh damage can result if the mist contacts the skin.

LP-GAS SYSTEM

All models are available with a factory installed liquid withdrawal type LP-Gas system. Model U302 uses a Century converter and carburetor; all other models use Ensign equipment. Fuel tank should never be filled more than 80% full. The remaining 20% allows for expansion of the fuel due to a possible rise in temperature.

CAUTION: LP-Gas expands readily with any decided increase in temperature. If tractor must be taken into a warm shop to be worked on during extremely cold weather, make certain that fuel tank is as near empty as possible. LP-Gas tractors should never be serviced or stored in an unventilated space.

Fig. MM635 — When trouble shooting on the Ensign system, connect a low reading pressure gage to the regulator as shown. Refer to text.

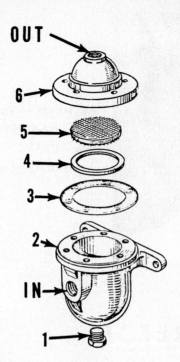

Fig. MM635A — Exploded view of LP-Gas system filter used on tractors with Century system.

1. Drain plug
2. Filter bowl
3. Gasket
4. Retaining ring
5. Filter element
6. Cover

Fig. MM636A—Typical Century carburetor of the type used, showing points of adjustment.

1. Primer button
2. Idle speed screw
3. Power adjusting screw
4. Drag link

This condition is due to a broken low pressure diaphragm in the regulator. If no liquid fuel appears and the tank is not empty, close the valve, clean the fuel filter and lines between tank and regulator and recheck.

If engine does not idle properly with the idle adjusting screw in any position, the cause is usually due to leaking valves and/or gaskets. This trouble can usually be traced to the low pressure valve since any impurities in the fuel are deposited on the low pressure valve seat after the fuel has vaporized. If the idle gas mixture is too lean when the idle adjusting screw is opened 3 or 4 turns, the trouble is due to restricted idle line or leakage in the idle line connections. Poor idling as well as poor engine performance under load can be caused by a restricted or plugged balance line.

With the pressure gage connected to the regulator as shown in Fig. MM-635, start and warm the engine up; then turn the engine off and observe the pressure gage. If the pressure rises after a warm engine is stopped, the high pressure valve is leaking. If the regulating unit is cold and shows moisture and frost after standing, there is an indication that either the high or low presure valves are leaking or the valve levers are not properly set.

Model U302

44A. Operating pressures on the Century system cannot be checked without partial disassembly. The pressures are fixed, and should be approximately correct if system is in operating condition.

If engine will not start and appears to not be getting fuel, close both withdrawal valves and remove drain plug (1—Fig. MM635A) from fuel

filter. Slowly and momentarily open the liquid withdrawal valve. Fuel should emerge from drain plug opening as a white mist and purge the filter trap of any foreign material.

CAUTION: The escaping fuel can cause severe freezing and damage to unprotected skin. Keep clear of escaping LP-Gas fuel.

If no fuel emerges, the trouble is in withdrawal valve or lines, or tank is empty. Repeat the test using the vapor withdrawal valve. Repair or renew the parts found to be malfunctioning.

If fuel emerges with drain plug removed, disassemble the filter and clean or renew filter element (5).

Fig. MM636 — Ensign carburetor installation showing the location of the adjusting screws. Recommended engine low idle speed is 400-450 rpm.

If filter is clean and lines open, tractor should fire when turned with starter while intermittently depressing primer button (1—Fig. MM636A) on convertor.

If convertor becomes noticeably cool to the touch, or frosts over, after standing with engine stopped and liquid withdrawal valve open, convertor valves are leaking and convertor should be overhauled as outlined in paragraph 48A.

SYSTEM ADJUSTMENTS
All Models Except U302

45. If the engine fails to start or does not run properly, refer to Figs MM636 or 637 and completely close the starting adjustment screw, load adjustment screw and idle adjustment screw; then, open the starting adjustment screw ½-¾ turn, open the load adjustment screw four turns and open

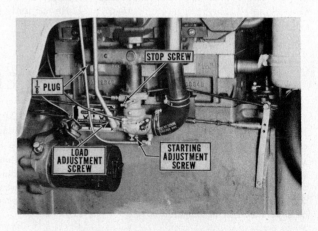

the idle adjustment screw 1½ turns. Completely close the choke and open the throttle about ½-way. Open the fuel tank withdrawal valve SLOWLY. Note: If the tank valve is opened too fast, a safety valve in the tank will shut off the fuel supply to the regulator. In which case, close the withdrawal valve to re-set the safety valve, then after a short time, open the withdrawal valve slowly.

Turn on the ignition and start the engine. Turn the starting adjustment screw either way as required to obtain maximum engine speed; then turn the screw out (enrich the mixture) until the engine speed drops slightly and tighten the lock nut. When engine is running smoothly, open the choke and close the throttle at the same time.

Note: Never run the engine with choke button in an intermediate position. Either the button must be all the way out for starting the engine, or all the way in for operating the engine.

Now, place the throttle in the wide open position and temporarily adjust the load screw by turning the screw either way as required to obtain the highest engine rpm.

Open the fuel tank liquid withdrawal valve and at the same time, close the vapor withdrawal valve. When engine reaches normal operating temperature, close the throttle and turn the idle adjusting screw on regulator to obtain the best idle. Then, turn the throttle stop screw either way as required to obtain an engine slow idle speed of 400-450 rpm.

Either one of the following two procedures can be used to make the final load screw adjustment.

ANALYZER AND VACUUM GAGE METHOD. Install analyzer and vacuum gage on tractor. Note: On some models, a ⅛-inch hole is provided in the intake manifold for connecting the vacuum gage. On others, it will be necessary to drill and tap the hole. Load the engine until the vacuum gage shows a manifold vacuum of 6-7 inches of mercury, then turn the load adjusting screw either way as required until the analyzer reads 14.3 on the LP-Gas scale or 12.8 on the gasoline scale.

Close the throttle and turn the idle adjusting screw (located on regulator) to obtain the best idle. At which time, the analyzer should read 13.5-14.2 on the LP-Gas scale or 12-12.8 on the gasoline scale. Readjust the throttle stop screw to obtain a slow idle speed of 400-450 rpm.

ADJUSTMENT WITHOUT ANALYZER. In lieu of an analyzer or loading device, disconnect or short out three spark plugs and open the throttle. Turn the load adjustment in until the engine speed drops due to leanness; then turn the screw out ½-turn and tighten the lock nut.

Close the throttle and turn the idle adjusting screw (located on regulator) to obtain the best idle. Readjust the throttle stop screw to obtain a slow idle speed of 400-450 rpm.

Model U302

45A. Preliminary adjustments are: six full turns open for power adjusting screw (3—Fig. MM636A); and the idle drag link (4) to the longest position possible to obtain a smooth idle.

The carburetor is not equipped with a choke valve. Depressing the primer button (1) manually opens the convertor low-pressure valve and allows fuel to enter the carburetor mixing chamber a 5-9 psi pressure. A hiss should be heard as the primer button is depressed.

Final adjustments must be made with engine at operating temperature and liquid withdrawal valve open to assure adequate fuel supply. Fuel for part-throttle operation is controlled by the metering valve and balanced to the throttle valve by adjusting the length of drag link (4).

To adjust the idle mixture after engine is at operating temperature, loosen the locknuts on drag link (4) and turn the knurled center section to the point of smoothest idle. Adjust idle speed stop screw (2) to provide a slow idle speed of 600 rpm, then recheck drag link adjustment. Leave drag link as long as possible to still produce a smooth idle.

Turn the power adjusting screw (3) to produce a reading of 12.5-13.5 on gasoline scale of exhaust analyzer, with throttle wide open and engine under full load. If an exhaust gas analyzer is not used, adjust the power mixture to the leanest point at which engine will accelerate from slow idle to fast idle without hesitating or faltering, when hand throttle is quickly opened. Power mixture can be adjusted for best performance under full dynamometer load; or highest speed with three spark plug wires disconnected, if these methods are normally used.

Recheck idle settings after power mixture has been adjusted, and correct as necessary.

OVERHAUL NOTES
All Models Except U302

46. REGULATOR. Refer to Figs. MM638 and 639. Disassembly sequence is as follows: Carefully remove spring retainer (24), spring (23) and regulator cover (5). Remove the high pressure diaphragm by pulling up on side toward the word "ENSIGN" and the

Fig. MM637 — Ensign regulator installation showing the location of the idle adjusting screw.

IDLE ADJUSTING SCREW

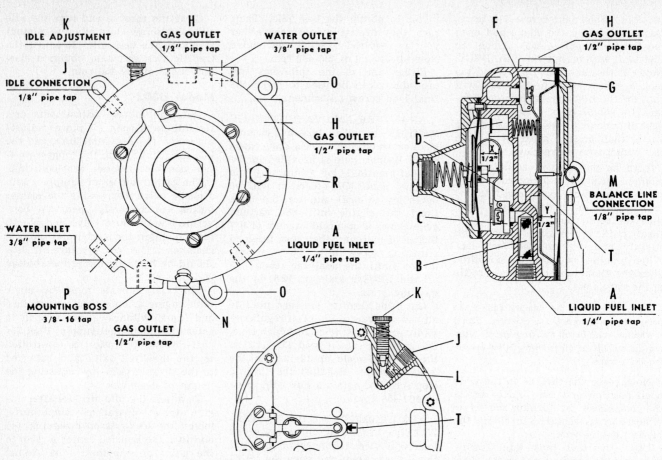

Fig. MM638—Ensign model W LP-Gas regulator unit. An exploded view of this unit is shown in Fig. MM639.

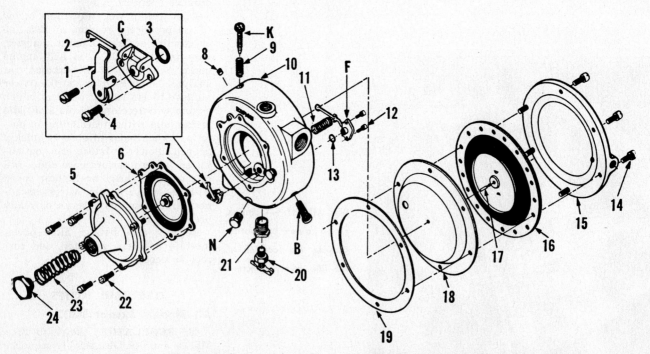

Fig. MM639—Exploded view of the Ensign model W LP-Gas regulating unit.

B. Fuel inlet strainer
C. Valve seat
F. Low pressure valve assy.
K. Idle adjusting screw
1. Inlet diaphragm lever
2. Pivot pin

3. "O" ring
5. Regulator cover
6. High pressure diaphragm
7. High pressure valve assy.
8. Bleed screw
9. Idle screw spring

10. Regulator body
11. Outlet diaphragm spring
13. "O" ring
15. Back cover plate
16. Low pressure diaphragm
17. Push pin

18. Partition plate
19. Partition plate gasket
20. Drain cock
21. Reducing bushing
23. Inlet diaphragm spring
24. Spring retainer

small orifice. Note: The diaphragm assembly is tied in with the high pressure valve lever and must not be forced out. Unscrew and remove the high pressure valve. Mark the position of the back cover plate with respect to the regulator body and remove the back plate (15), low pressure diaphragm (16) and partition plate (18). Using one of the regulator mounting bolts, thread same into the inlet strainer and withdraw the strainer (B). Unscrew and remove the low pressure valve assembly (F) and "O" ring (13). Remove the idle adjusting screw (K) and spring (9).

Thoroughly clean all parts in a suitable solvent and renew any that are damaged or worn. Be sure to renew all gaskets and seals.

Install the low pressure valve assembly and spring and install the retaining screws loosely. Tighten the screws after centering the end of the valve lever with the arrow on post (T—Fig. MM638). Top of lever must be flush with the top of the post. If not, bend the lever as required, being careful not to damage the valve seat while bending. Reinstall the inlet strainer, partition plate and low pressure diaphragm, making certain that the diaphragm push pin is properly located on the valve lever. Align the previously affixed index marks and install the back cover plate. Install new "O" ring (13—Fig. MM639), then install the high pressure valve assembly. When valve is held firmly shut, bend valve lever as required until dimension (X) which is measured from machined face of body to inside of groove in valve lever is ½-inch as shown in Fig. MM638. Dimension (X) can be measured with a depth rule or Ensign gage No. 8276. Being careful not to bend the valve lever, install the high pressure diaphragm so that curved strap under diaphragm is under valve lever. Install the regulator cover, diaphragm spring and spring retainer.

47. **CARBURETOR.** Refer to Fig. MM639A for exploded view of carburetor. Venturi (12) can be removed after removing throttle valve (11), throttle shaft (17) and locking screw (21). To remove choke assembly, first remove valve cover (6) and choke valve (8). The valve (8) is actuated by cam on choke shaft (9), and closes main fuel passage for starting only. Choke is not intended to be operated in intermediate position. Check the economizer valve (3) for scoring or

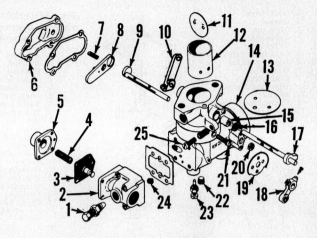

Fig. MM639A—Exploded view of Ensign LP-Gas carburetor of the type used on most models.

1. Load adjustment screw
2. Inlet body
3. Economizer diaphragm
4. Economizer spring
5. Economizer cover
6. Valve cover
7. Choke shaft spring
8. Valve lever
9. Choke shaft & cam
10. Throttle lever
11. Throttle valve
12. Venturi
13. Choke valve
14. Carburetor body
15. Throttle bushing
16. Packing
17. Throttle shaft
18. Choke lever
19. Support
20. Packing
21. Venturi lock screw
22. Body plug
23. Starting adjusting screw
24. Bleed screw
25. Idle stop screw

sticking and diaphragm for cracks or deterioration. Renew parts as required.

Initial settings are as follows: Load adjustment screw (1), 4 turns open; starting adjustment (23), 1¼ turns open. Adjust as outlined in paragraph 45, after engine is warm.

48. **FUEL FILTER.** It is recommended that filter element be cleaned every 500 hours of operation. When cleaning the unit, make sure that fuel tank withdrawal valves are closed, then unscrew the filter stud nut slowly to relieve any built-up pressure. Element can be washed in cleaning solvent.

Model U302

48A. **CONVERTER.** Refer to Fig. MM639B and Fig. MM639C for exploded view of the Century Model H converter. Back plate (1—Fig. MM639B) and gasket (2) seals the heat exchanger passages for both the coolant liquid and the fuel; it is imperative that gasket surfaces of plate (1) and body (3) be perfectly flat to prevent coolant leaks into fuel system. Disassemble primary and secondary regulator as follows: Remove the screws retaining primer cover (17) and lift off cover and primer plunger (19) as a unit. Remove secondary regulator cover (15) and diaphragm assembly. Remove the two screws which retain valve lever shaft (7) and lift out low pressure valve lever (8) as an assembly. Remove inlet cover (1—Fig. MM639C) and lever (5); then remove high pressure cover (12) and lift out spring (11) and diaphragm assembly.

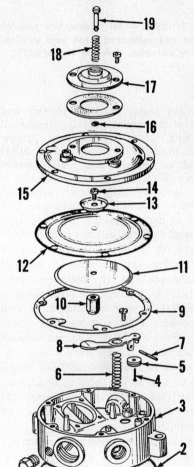

Fig. MM639B — Exploded view of Century converter body, low pressure diaphragm and associated parts. Refer to Fig. MM-639C for high pressure valve and associated parts.

1. Back cover	11. Diaphragm plate
2. Gasket	12. Diaphragm
3. Converter body	13. Diaphragm plate
4. Valve pin	14. Button screw
5. Valve seat	15. Cover
6. Valve spring	16. "O" ring
7. Pivot pin	17. Primer base
8. Valve lever	18. Primer spring
9. Gasket	19. Primer plunger
10. Button	

1. Inlet cover
2. Gasket
3. Pivot pin
4. Valve seat
5. Valve lever
6. Diaphragm link
7. Damper spring
8. Gasket
9. Diaphragm
10. Diaphragm plate
11. Spring
12. High pressure cover
13. Converter body

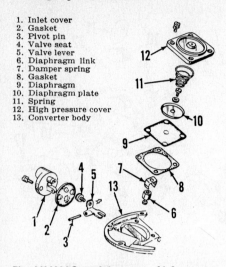

Fig. MM639C — Inlet cover, high pressure valve and associated parts used on Century converter. Refer to Fig. MM639B.

Fig. MM639D—Exploded view of Century carburetor and associated parts.

1. Air horn
2. Bearing
3. Packing
4. Valve lever
5. Idle speed screw
6. Drag link
7. Valve lever
8. Thrust washer
9. Metering valve body
10. Metering valve
11. Spring
12. Valve plug
13. Gasket
14. Carburetor body
15. Throttle valve
16. Throttle shaft
17. Retainer
18. Spray bar
19. Power adjusting screw
20. Jam nut

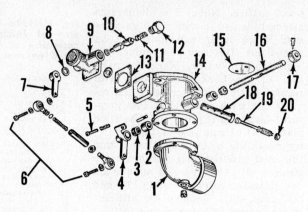

Wash metal parts in solvent and dry with compressed air. Renew all gaskets when reassembling. Renew high pressure diaphragm (9) if hardened or cracked and high pressure valve (4) if sealing surface of seat is damaged. If high pressure diaphragm must be disassembled, make sure that legs of damper spring (7) align with flats of link (6) and are parallel with edges of diaphragm. The damper spring legs apply pressure to sides of diaphragm slot in heat exchanger body (13) and correct positioning is essential. Proper installation is also important. Four aligning pins (Century Part No. M-501) should be used to position the parts during assembly. Proceed as follows: Install the aligning pins in screw holes in diaphragm cover (12). Install a new gasket (8) over aligning pins; then install the assembled diaphragm, making sure legs of damper spring (7) properly enter slot in heat exchanger body. Position spring (11), small end down as shown, then install cover (12) over aligning pins making sure spring is properly located. Insert a screwdriver or similar tool through opening for inlet cover (1) and hold up on diaphragm link (6); carefully push down on diaphragm cover (12), compressing spring (11). Remove aligning pins one at a time and immediately install and tighten cover screw before removing the next aligning pin. Release the pressure on diaphragm link (6) only after all screws are tightened.

Examine low pressure valve seat (5—Fig. MM639B) and renew if damaged; then reinstall low pressure lever assembly. Lay a straight edge across gasket surface of heat exchanger body (3) and measure distance from straight edge to nearest point of valve lever (8). Adjust, if necessary, to $\frac{5}{16}$-inch by bending the lever. Renew low pressure diaphragm (12) if its condition is questionable; then reinstall gasket (9), diaphragm assembly and cover (15), leaving the cover retaining screws loose. Using a pair of needle-nosed pliers and working through opening for primer cover (17), grasp head of diaphragm screw (14) and pull diaphragm plate (13) firmly into contact with cover (15); then tighten cover retaining screws evenly. Complete the assembly by reversing the disassembly procedure.

48B. CARBURETOR. Refer to Fig. MM639D. Carburetor is simply constructed and overhaul procedures are self-evident. Use a thread sealant when installing reducer bushing in metering valve housing (9), and do not overtighten. Overtightening may distort the housing and cause valve to bind. If metering valve (10) does not move freely, remove lever (7) and plug (12) and push metering valve from housing. Clean the valve and housing bore with an oil base solvent. Coat valve with Lubriplate and reinsert in housing bore. If valve is not now free, chuck lever end of valve in a slow-speed drill and reseat the valve, using tallow or penetrating oil as a lubricant. DO NOT use a lapping compound, or allow valve and housing to become excessively warm. If condition is questionable, renew the parts.

DIESEL SYSTEM

The diesel fuel system consists of three basic components; the fuel filters, injection pump and injector nozzles. When servicing any unit associated with the fuel system, the maintenance of absolute cleanliness is of utmost importance. Of equal importance is the avoidance of nicks or burrs on any of the working parts.

Probably the most important precaution that service personnel can impart to owners of diesel powered tractors, is to urge them to use an approved fuel that is absolutely clean and free from foreign material. Extra precaution should be taken to make certain that no water enters the fuel storage tanks. This last precaution is based on the fact

that all diesel fuels contain some sulphur. When water is mixed with sulphur, sulphuric acid is formed and the acid will quickly erode the closely fitting parts of the injection pump and nozzles.

QUICK CHECKS
All Diesel Models

49. If the engine does not run properly and the fuel system is suspected as the source of trouble, refer to the accompanying trouble-shooting chart and locate points which require further checking. Many of the chart items are self-explanatory; however, if the difficulty points to the fuel

DIESEL SYSTEM TROUBLE-SHOOTING CHART

	Sudden Stopping of Engine	Lack of Power	Engine Hard to Start	Irregular Engine Operation	Engine Knocks	Excessive Smoking	Excessive Fuel Consumption
Lack of fuel	★	★	★	★			
Water or dirt in fuel	★	★	★	★			
Clogged fuel lines	★	★	★	★			
Inferior fuel	★	★	★	★			
Faulty transfer pump	★	★	★	★			
Faulty injection pump timing		★	★	★	★	★	★
Air traps in system	★	★	★	★			
Clogged fuel filters	★	★	★	★			
Deteriorated fuel lines	★						★
Faulty nozzle			★		★	★	★
Sticking pump plunger			★	★			
Binding pump control rod				★			
Weak or broken governor springs				★			
Fuel delivery valve not seating properly				★			
Improperly set smoke stop		★		★		★	

filters, injection nozzles and/or injection pump, refer to the appropriate sections in the following paragraphs:

FUEL FILTERS AND BLEEDING
All Diesel Models

49A. The fuel filtering system consists of a screen type primary filter and two stages of renewable element type filters.

49B. CIRCUIT DESCRIPTION AND MAINTENANCE. With the fuel shut off at valve, open petcock and drain off any accumulation of water and dirt. This should be done daily before tractor is operated.

Fuel from the fuel tank flows by force of gravity to the filter housing which contains a fine mesh screen strainer that filters water from the fuel. After each 60 hours of operation, the housing plug should be removed and the screen thoroughly cleaned with diesel fuel. From the filter housing, the fuel flows through the renewable element type secondary filter. It is recommended that this secondary filter element be renewed after each 90 days of operation. After flowing through the secondary filter, the fuel passes through the positive displacement, gear type transfer pump to the renewable element type final filter and on to the injection pump. The final filtering element should be renewed only when it becomes clogged.

49C. BLEEDING. It is necessary to bleed the fuel system whenever the fuel flow is interrupted or air has been allowed to enter the system. To do so, proceed as follows:

Be sure the tank is filled with fuel and the shut-off valve open. Open the drain cock at the bottom of the filter base until a full flow of clean fuel emerges. Close the drain cock and remove bleed plug at top of secondary filter until the air is exhausted and a flow of clean fuel appears, then reinstall the plug. Remove the bleed plug at the top of the final filter and turn the engine over with the starter until a full flow of air-free fuel is being pumped through the plug opening. Install and tighten plug while the fuel is flowing from the bleed port.

Loosen the high pressure lines at the injectors, open the throttle and turn the engine over with the starter until the air is exhausted from the pump plunger and lines. Retighten the connections and start the engine.

INJECTION NOZZLES
All Diesel Models

WARNING: Fuel leaves the injection nozzles with sufficient force to penetrate the skin. When testing, keep your person clear of the nozzle spray.

49D. TESTING AND LOCATING FAULTY NOZZLE. If the engine does not run properly and the quick checks, outlined in paragraph 49, point to a faulty injection nozzle, locate the faulty nozzle as follows:

If one engine cylinder is misfiring, it is reasonable to suspect a faulty nozzle. Generally, a faulty nozzle can be located by loosening the high pressure line fitting on each nozzle holder in turn, thereby allowing fuel to escape at the union rather than enter

the cylinder. As in checking spark plugs in a spark ignition engine, the faulty nozzle is the one which, when its line is loosened, least affects the running of the engine.

Remove the suspected nozzle from the engine as outlined in paragraph 49J. If a suitable nozzle tester is available, check the nozzle as in paragraphs 49E, 49F, 49G and 49H. If a nozzle tester is not available, reconnect the fuel line and with the nozzle tip directed where it will do no harm, crank the engine with the starting motor and observe the nozzle spray pattern.

If the spray pattern is ragged, the nozzle valve is not seating properly and should be reconditioned as outlined in paragraph 49K. If cleaning and/or nozzle and tip renewal does not restore the unit and a nozzle tester is not available for further checking, send the complete nozzle and holder assembly to an official diesel service station for overhaul.

49E. NOZZLE TESTER. A complete job of testing and adjusting the nozzle requires the use of a special tester. The nozzle should be tested for leakage, spray pattern and opening pressure.

Operate the tester lever until oil flows and attach the nozzle and holder assembly.

Note: Only clean, approved testing oil should be used in the tester tank.

Close the tester valve and apply a few quick strokes to the lever. If undue pressure is required to operate the lever, the nozzle valve is plugged and should be serviced as in paragraph 49K.

49F. LEAKAGE. The nozzle valve should not leak at a pressure less than 1700 psi. To check for leakage, actuate the tester handle slowly and as the gage needles approaches 1700 psi, observe the nozzle tip for drops. If drops of fuel collect at pressures less than 1700 psi, the nozzle valve is not seating properly and should be serviced as in paragraph 49K.

49G. SPRAY PATTERN. Operate the tester handle at approximately 100 strokes per minute and observe the spray pattern. If the nozzle has a ragged spray pattern, the nozzle valve should be serviced as in paragraph 49K.

49H. OPENING PRESSURE. While operating the tester handle observe the gage pressure at which the spray occurs. The gage pressure should be 1800 psi. If the pressure is not as specified, remove the nozzle protecting cap, exposing the pressure adjusting screw and locknut. Loosen the locknut and turn the adjusting screw either way as required to obtain an opening pressure of 1800 psi. Note: If a new pressure spring has been installed in the nozzle holder, adjust the opening pressure to 1900 psi. Tighten the locknut and install the protecting cap when adjustment is complete.

49J. REMOVE AND REINSTALL. Before loosening any lines, wash the nozzle holder and connections with clean diesel fuel or kerosene. After disconnecting the high pressure and leak-off lines, cover open ends of connections with caps to prevent the entrance of dirt or other foreign material. Remove the nozzle holder stud nuts and carefully withdraw the nozzle from cylinder head, being careful not to strike the tip end of the nozzle against any hard surface.

Remove "O" ring and thoroughly clean the nozzle recess in the cylinder head. It is important that the seating surface of recess be free of even the smallest particle of carbon which could cause the nozzle to be cocked and result in blowby of hot gases. No hard or sharp tools should be used for cleaning. A piece of wood dowel or brass stock properly shaped is very effective. Do not reuse the copper ring gasket, always install a new one. If the "O" ring is in good shape, reinstall it and insert the nozzle. Tighten the nozzle holder stud nuts to a torque of 14-16 ft.-lbs.

49K. MINOR OVERHAUL OF NOZZLE VALVE AND BODY. Unless complete and proper equipment is available do not attempt to overhaul injector nozzles. Hard or sharp tools, emery cloth, crocus cloth, grinding compounds or abrasives of any kind should NEVER be used in the cleaning of nozzles.

Wipe all dirt and loose carbon from the nozzle and holder assembly with a clean, lint-free cloth. Carefully clamp the nozzle holder assembly in a nozzle holder or soft jawed vise and remove the nozzle holder nut and spray nozzle. Reinstall the holder nut to protect the lapped end of the holder body. Normally, the nozzle valve can be easily withdrawn from the nozzle body. If the valve cannot be easily withdrawn, soak the assembly in fuel oil, acetone, carbon tetrachloride or similar carbon solvent to facilitate removal. Be careful not to permit the valve or body to come in contact with any hard surface.

Clean the nozzle valve with mutton tallow used on a soft, lint-free cloth or pad. The valve may be held by its stem in a revolving chuck during this cleaning operation. A piece of soft wood, well soaked in oil will be helpful in removing carbon deposits from the valve.

The inside of the nozzle body (tip) can be cleaned by forming a piece of soft wood to a point which will correspond to the angle of the nozzle valve seat. The wood should be well soaked in oil. The orifice of the tip can be cleaned with a wood splinter. The outer surfaces of the nozzle body should be cleaned with a brass wire brush and a soft, lint-free cloth soaked in a suitable carbon solvent.

Thoroughly wash the nozzle valve and body in clean diesel fuel and clean the pintle and its seat as follows: Hold the valve at the stem end only and using light oil as a lubricant, rotate the valve back and forth in the body. Some time may be required in removing the particles of dirt from the pintle valve; however, abrasive materials should never be used in the cleaning process.

Test the fit of the nozzle valve in the nozzle body as follows: Hold the body at a 45 degree angle and start the valve in the body. The valve should slide slowly into the body under its own weight. Note: Dirt particles too small to be seen by the naked eye, will restrict the valve ac-

tion. If the valve sticks, and it is known to be clean, free-up the valve by working the valve in the body with mutton tallow.

Before reassembling, thoroughly rinse all parts in clean diesel fuel and make certain that all carbon is removed from the nozzle holder nut. Install nozzle body and holder nut, making certain that the valve stem is located in the hole of the holder body. It is essential that the nozzle be perfectly centered in the holder nut. A centering cleeve is supplied in American Bosch kit TSE 7779 for this purpose. Slide the sleeve over the nozzle with the tapered end centering in the holder nut. Tighten the holder nut, making certain that the sleeve is free while tightening. In the absence of the centering sleeve, a piece of 0.003 shim stock can be placed around the nozzle while tightening the holder nut.

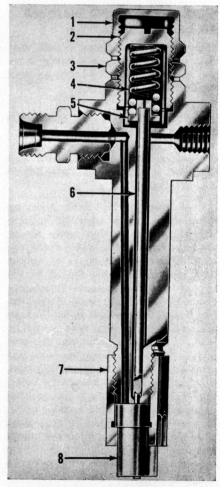

Fig. MM640—Cross sectional view of typical Bosch injector of the type used in MM diesel tractors.

1. Cap nut
2. Adjusting screw
3. Jam nut
4. Pressure spring
5. Spring seat
6. Spindle
7. Holder nut
8. Nozzle assembly

Test the nozzle for spray pattern and leakage as in paragraphs 49F and 49G. If the nozzle will not pass the leakage and spray pattern tests, renew the nozzle valve and seat, which are available only in a matched set; or send the nozzle and holder assembly to an official diesel service station for a complete overhaul which includes the nozzle valve pintle and seat.

49L. OVERHAUL OF NOZZLE HOLDER. Refer to Fig. MM640. Remove cap nut (1) and gasket. Loosen jam nut (3) and adjusting screw (2). Remove the adjusting screw and withdraw the spindle (6) and spring (4). Thoroughly wash all parts in clean diesel fuel and examine the end of the spindle which contacts the nozzle valve stem for any irregularities. If the contact surface is pitted or rough, renew the spindle. Examine the spring seat (5) for tightness to spindle and for cracks or worn spots. Renew the spring seat and spindle unit if condition of either is questionable. Renew any other questionable parts.

Reassemble the nozzle holder and leave the adjusting screw locknut loose until after the nozzle opening pressure has been adjusted as outlined in paragraph 49H.

INJECTION PUMPS

Models With Bosch Pump

Early tractors are equipped with an American Bosch single plunger model PSB pump. The following paragraphs will outline ONLY the injection pump service work which can be accomplished without the use of special, costly pump testing equipment. If additional service work is required, the pump should be turned over to an official diesel service station for overhaul. Refer to paragraph 50 for service data on models equipped with Roosa-Master pump.

49N. TIMING TO ENGINE. Injection should occur 27 degrees before top center. To check and retime pump to the engine after the pump is installed as outlined in paragraph 49R proceed as follows:

Remove the rocker arm cover from the cylinder head and crank the engine until the intake valve of number one cylinder is closing. Open timing window on left side of flywheel housing and continue cranking until engine is at 27 degrees

BTDC for No. 1 piston. Note: Flywheel has timing marks every 2½ degrees. Also DC1, 10, 20 and 30 are marked to indicate TDC and BTDC positions for No. 1 piston. 27 degree position is slightly more than one mark past the indicated 30 degree mark. Remove the inspection plug from side of engine side cover and observe the pump coupling timing marks. If the pump timing is correct, the line mark on the drive gear hub will be exactly in register with the pointer extending from front face of the pump.

If the timing marks are not exactly in register, and it is certain that the pump has been properly installed remove the pump drive gear front cover, unwire and loosen the four cap screws retaining the adjustable gear and turn the adjustable gear in the elongated cap screw holes until the coupling timing marks are exactly in register. Tighten and wire the gear retaining cap screws and install the timing gear case cover.

49P. TRANSFER PUMP. The diesel injection pumps are equipped with a positive displacement, gear type transfer pump which is gear driven from the injection pump camshaft.

If the pump is not operating properly, the complete pump can be renewed as a unit; or the transfer pump can be disassembled, cleaned and checked for improved performance. Quite often, a thorough cleaning, will restore the pump to its original operating efficiency.

49Q. HYDRAULIC HEAD. The hydraulic head assembly can be renewed without the use of special testing equipment. The head assembly contains all of the precision components which are essential to accurate pumping, distributing, metering and delivery of the fuel. To renew the hydraulic head assembly, first wash the complete injection pump and injection lines with clean fuel oil. Remove the injection lines and disconnect the inlet and outlet lines from the hydraulic head. Remove the timing window cover and crank engine until the line mark on the apex of one of the teeth on the pump plunger drive gear is in register with the pointer stamped on the lower face of the timing window hole. Remove the two screws and carefully withdraw the control assembly, being careful not to lose the plunger sleeve pin. Remove governor cover and unscrew and

remove the lube oil filter. Remove the hydraulic head retaining stud nuts and carefully withdraw the hydraulic head assembly from the pump housing. Do not use force when attempting to withdraw the hydraulic head. If difficulty is encountered, check to make certain that the plunger drive gear is properly positioned.

When installing a new hydraulic head assembly, make certain that the line marked plunger drive gear tooth is in register with the pointer stamped on the lower face of the timing window and that open tooth on quill shaft gear is in register with punch mark in pump housing. When installing the control sleeve assembly, the plunger sleeve pin must be lined up with the slot in the control block. The remainder of the reassembly procedure is evident.

49R. REMOVE AND REINSTALL INJECTION PUMP. Before attempting to remove the injection pump, thoroughly wash the pump and connections with clean diesel fuel. Disconnect the injection lines from injection pump and the inlet and outlet lines from the transfer pump. Disconnect the remaining lines and control rods. Cover all fuel line connections with composition caps to eliminate the entrance of dirt. Remove the rocker arm cover from the front cylinder head and crank engine until the intake valve of number one cylinder is closing. Remove the inspection plate from flywheel housing and continue cranking until the 27 degree BTDC timing position (Refer to paragraph 49N) on flywheel is exactly in line with the pointer in the flywheel housing. Remove the pump mounting cap screws and withdraw the pump.

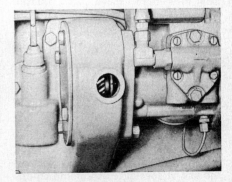

Fig. MM641—When timing PSB diesel injection pump the scribed line on pump flange should align with timing pointer as shown.

To install the injection pump, first make certain that the flywheel timing mark is in the proper position as previously outlined. Remove the timing window cover from side of injection pump and turn the pump hub until the line mark on the apex of one of the pump plunger drive gear teeth is approximately in the center of the timing window. Then, continue turning the hub until the line mark on the hub is as nearly in register with the pointer as possible. See Fig. MM 641. Make certain that the marked tooth is still visible in the timing window.

Mount pump to engine by meshing the pump drive coupling gear with the floating coupling inside the adaptor housing. Turn top of pump toward engine until the cap screws can be installed and observe the coupling timing marks which should be aligned.

If the marks are in register as shown, the pump is installed properly and no additional timing will be required.

If the marks are less than one drive coupling tooth of being aligned, the pump is still installed properly, but the final timing adjustment should be made as outlined in paragraph 49N.

If, however, the marks are more than one coupling tooth of being aligned, remove and reinstall pump until the proper register is obtained.

49S. GOVERNOR. Model PSB injection pumps are equipped with a mechanical flyweight type governor. For the purposes of this manual, the governor will be considered as an integral part of the injection pump.

49T. ADJUSTMENT. Recommended governed speeds are as follows:
No load engine speed.......1925 rpm
Full load engine speed......1750 rpm
Low idle engine speed...... 600 rpm

Models With Roosa-Master Pump

Late tractors are equipped with a Roosa-Master Model DBG injection pump. The following paragraphs will outline ONLY removal, installation, timing and similar service work which can be accomplished without the use of special, costly pump equipment. If additional pump work is required, the pump should be turned over to an authorized Roosa-Master service station for overhaul.

50. TIMING TO ENGINE. The Roosa-Master injection pump is timed at end of injection. The pump timing marks (See Fig. MM642) should align when No. 1 piston is on compression stroke and the specified flywheel timing mark is aligned with timing pointer:

Fuel	Timing
No. 1	11° BTDC
No. 2	9° BTDC

If pump timing marks do not align, loosen the stud nuts retaining injection pump to adapter, and rotate injection pump body slightly until timing marks are aligned.

If pump cannot be timed as outlined, the engine oil pump drive gear is out of time and must be removed and re-timed as outlined in paragraph 50B.

50A. REMOVE AND REINSTALL. The injection pump is driven by a slot in upper end of oil pump drive shaft and is mounted vertically at top front of crankcase housing. Before removing the pump, clean pump, lines and crankcase area thoroughly with a suitable solvent.

Shut off the fuel and remove timing window from pump housing as shown in Fig. MM643. With pump window removed, turn crankshaft until pump timing marks are aligned as shown in Fig. MM642. Disconnect fuel lines and cap the fittings to prevent dirt entry; disconnect linkage, remove the two retaining stud nuts and lift the pump straight up off of mounting adapter.

Reinstall by reversing the disassembly procedure. Make sure injection pump is properly timed as outlined in paragraph 50. Bleed the system as outlined in paragraph 49C.

50B. R&R PUMP DRIVE ADAPTER. The injection pump drive adapter is retained to engine block by two stud nuts. Drive adapter must be removed for service on oil pump drive shaft as outlined in paragraph 41. When reinstalling, tighten the retaining stud nuts to a torque of 35 ft.-lbs.

Fig. MM642—Pump port is open for injection to number one cylinder when timing mark on governor case is aligned with timing mark on cam ring as shown.

Fig. MM643 — Injection pump with timing window (1) removal for timing or installation of pump. Refer to text.

Fig. MM644 — Exploded view of diesel engine energy cell.

1. Plug
2. Holder
3. Cell cap
4. Energy cell

ENERGY CELLS

All Diesel Models

50C. R&R AND CLEAN. The necessity for cleaning the energy cells is usually indicated by excessive exhaust smoking, or when fuel economy drops. To remove the energy cells, unscrew the retainer plug and remove the cap holder. Grasp the energy cell cap (3—Fig. MM644) with a pair of pliers and withdraw cap from cylinder head. Using puller supplied with tractor or a $\frac{15}{16}$-inch NEF-2 puller screwed into energy cell (4), pull cell from head.

Clean all parts in a suitable carbon solvent and renew any which are cracked or damaged. Clean the small orifice in the cell chamber with a brass brush or a piece of hard wood. Check seating surface of cell body in cylinder and mating surfaces of energy cell and cell cap. If the surfaces are rough, they can be cleaned by lapping with a mixture of jeweler's rouge and diesel fuel.

When reinstalling the energy cell, make certain that it fits squarely into cylinder head. Tighten the retainer plug securely.

NON-DIESEL GOVERNOR

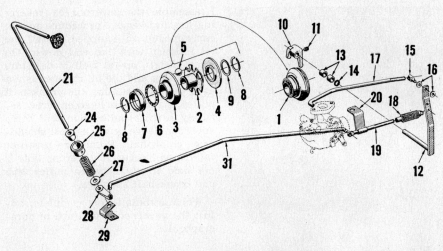

Fig. MM651 — Typical exploded view of governor and associated linkage. Weight unit (1) is mounted on engine crankshaft.

ADJUSTMENT
Non-Diesel Models

51. Before attempting to adjust the governed speed, first free up all linkage to remove any binding or lost motion. Start engine and run until normal operating temperature is reached; then stop engine and disconnect the spring and plunger unit (18 — Fig. MM650) and control rod (17) from the fork shaft lever (12). With lever (12) in the wide open position (fully rearward) and the carburetor throttle butterfly in the wide open position (lever against stop) adjust the length of the control rod (17), with the pin (15) at forward end of rod, until the control rod is ½-hole long; then, reconnect the rod and install the cotter pin.

1. Weight unit	12. Fork shaft	20. Adjusting rod guide
2. Ball driver	13. Shaft bushings	21. Throttle control
3. Ball race, rear	14. Oil seal	lever
4. Ball race, front	15. Lever shaft pin	24. Friction cone
5. Ball	16. Washer	25. Friction cone
6. Thrust bearing	17. Governor to	bushing
7. Fork base	carburetor rod	26. Tension spring
8. Snap ring	18. Spring and plunger	27. Washer
9. Thrust washer	assembly	28. Lever arm
10. Control fork	19. Adjusting rod	29. Hand lever
11. Set screw		support

Move the throttle lever forward to the slow idle position and connect the governor spring to the governor lever; then turn the plunger (P) in or out as required until the plunger just contacts the edge of the lever and tighten the plunger lock nut.

Start engine, bring to operating temperature and adjust the throttle stop screw to obtain the recommended slow idle speed of 600 rpm for U302; or 400-450 rpm for other models. Move the throttle lever to the full speed position and turn the nuts (N) either way as required to obtain a high idle, no load speed of 1700 rpm for the 445 series, 1650 rpm for the 335 series, 1900 rpm for the Jet Star and 4 Star series or 2100 rpm for

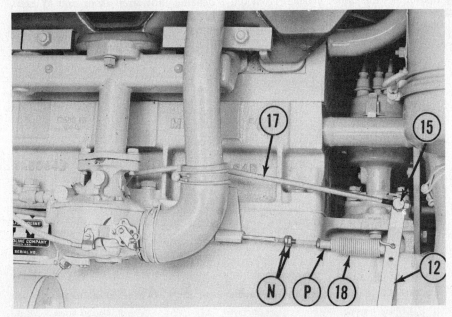

Fig. MM650 — Side view of 445 series gasoline engine, showing governor linkage and adjustments. Adjustments on tractor fuel and LP-Gas engines are similar. Other models are similar.

Fig. MM652—Governor weight unit installation on front end of crankshaft.

Fig. MM653—Governor fork shaft can be removed after removing set screw (11) retaining fork to shaft.

U302. If governor surges, it will be necessary to remove same and check for binding, damaged or worn parts.

R&R AND OVERHAUL
Non-Diesel Models

51A. To remove the governor, drain cooling system and on models with power steering, drain the hydraulic system and disconnect the power steering oil lines. Remove the hood top (service) panel pivot pins and lift off the service panel. Remove the side panel tie braces and tool box. Disconnect the head light wires and remove the head lights; then, unbolt and remove side panels from tractor. Disconnect the radiator upper and lower hoses and remove fan belt. Support tractor under transmission housing, then unbolt and remove the steering gear housing, radiator and axle assembly from engine.

Remove the crankshaft pulley, pulley key and the crankshaft front oil seal retainer. Disconnect the throttle control rod and spring from the governor arm and withdraw the governor weight unit (Fig. MM652). Remove snap rings (8—Fig. MM651), disassemble the weight unit and renew any damaged or worn parts.

Governor fork shaft is carried in two bushings which can be renewed after removing the Allen head set screw (11 — Fig. MM653) retaining fork to shaft and withdrawing the shaft. Old bushings can be pressed out with the new ones. It may be necessary to ream the bushings slightly to insure a free fit for the shaft.

Reassemble the governor by reversing the disassembly procedure and on early models so equipped, install the oil retainer with cup end down. On later models, an oil well is cast into the housing and the oil retainer is not used. When installing the crankshaft pulley, tighten the retainer screw securely so that pulley hub will force governor sleeve driver against shoulder on crankshaft. Premature governor failure will occur if governor unit is not held firmly between pulley hub and crankshaft shoulder.

When installation is complete, adjust the governor as outlined in paragraph 51.

COOLING SYSTEM

RADIATOR
All Models

52. On 445, Jet Star and 4-Star the radiator lower tank is integral with the steering gear housing. On the 335 series, the radiator lower tank is integral with the core unit. Removal of the radiator can be accomplished after removing the hood side panels.

WATER PUMP AND FAN
All Models

53. **R&R AND OVERHAUL.** To remove the water pump, raise the hood top (service) panel and remove the fan belt. Remove the air cleaner and disconnect the upper bracket from the pump cover. Drain cooling system and disconnect the lower hose. Unbolt

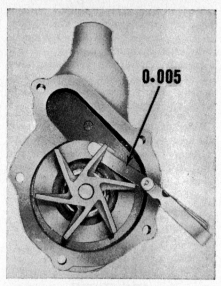

Fig. MM655 — Checking the clearance between the water pump impeller and housing cavity. Desired clearance is 0.005.

pump from crankcase and withdraw the pump and fan assembly from right side of tractor.

To disassemble the pump, remove the fan blades and pull the fan hub from pump shaft. Refer to Fig. MM654. Remove the pump back cover plate and withdraw the pump shaft retaining lock spring (4). Press the pump shaft rearward and out of pump housing, then pull the impeller from the pump shaft and remove the seal assembly. Inspect all parts and renew any which are damaged or worn.

When reassembling, install seal in pump housing by pressing on the seal flange. Install the pump shaft and bearing unit from front end of housing and install the shaft retaining lock spring. Press the impeller on the shaft

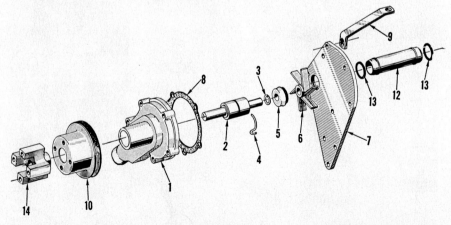

Fig. MM654—Exploded view of water pump. Pump shaft and bearings are an integral unit.

1. Pump housing	6. Impeller	9. Support brace
2. Shaft and bearings	7. Water pump	10. Pulley
3. Slinger ring	cover	12. Water tube
4. Lock spring	8. Gasket	13. "O" ring
5. Seal		14. Fan hub

until there is a clearance of 0.005 between the impeller and the housing cavity as shown in Fig. MM655. Press the fan hub on shaft until there is a distance of 2¾ inches between rear of

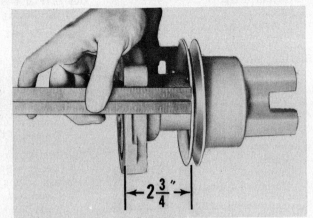

Fig. MM656 — Fan hub should be pressed on the pump shaft until the distance from rear of pulley to rear face of pump housing is 2¾ inches.

pulley and the machined rear face of the pump housing as shown in Fig. MM656. Using a new gasket, install the back cover, then install the assembled pump on tractor.

IGNITION AND ELECTRICAL SYSTEM

Non-Diesel Models

54. SPARK PLUGS. Plug electrode gap is 0.022-0.025 for gasoline engines, 0.025-0.027 for tractor fuel engines, 0.020-0.022 for LP-Gas engines on series 335 and 445 and 0.014-0.016 for series Jet Star and 4-Star. Recommended plug tightening torque is 34 ft.-lbs. Firing order is 1-3-4-2.

55. DISTRIBUTOR. Delco-Remy distributor No. 1111711 is used on 335 and 445 Series. Jet Star and 4-Star Series use Delco-Remy distributor No. 1111898. Specification data are as follows:

D-R 1111711

Breaker contact gap.......0.022
Breaker arm spring
   pressure ....17-21 oz.
Cam angle ....25°-34°

Advance data is in distributor degrees and distributor rpm:

Start advance ...... 0-2 @ 275
Intermediate advance 4-6 @ 400
Maximum advance..11.5-13.5 @ 625

D-R 1111898

Breaker contact gap 0.022
Breaker arm spring
   pressure ....17-21 oz.
Cam angle ....31°-37°

Advance data is in distributor degrees and distributor rpm:

Start advance .... 0-2 @ 275

Intermediate advance . 5-7 @ 400
Maximum advance ...12-14 @ 1000
D-R 1112642
Breaker contact gap......0.022
Breaker arm spring
   pressure ....17-21 oz.
Cam angle ....31°-34°
Advance data is in distributor degrees and distributor rpm:
Start advance .... 0-2 @ 275
Intermediate advance.. 5-7 @ 400
Intermediate advance.. 8-10 @ 650
Maximum advance ...12-14 @ 1000

56. INSTALLATION AND TIMING. To install and time the distributor, first adjust the breaker contact gap to 0.022, crank engine until number one piston is coming up on compression stroke; then, continue cranking until the specified fully advanced timing mark on flywheel is in register with the index at timing port. The fully advanced timing mark is as follows:

335 Gasoline ....24° or 2¹⁵⁄₁₆ inches
335 LP-Gas ....25° or 3¹⁄₁₆ inches
445 Gasoline ....25° or 3¹⁄₁₆ inches
445 LP-Gas ....28° or 3⁷⁄₁₆ inches
Jet Star ....28° or 3⁷⁄₁₆ inches
4-Star Series .....28° or 3⁷⁄₁₆ inches

Note: On **U302** models, install distributor when "DC-1" mark on flywheel is aligned with timing pointer **without** rotating breaker cam; then, set timing with timing light with engine running at 1200 rpm. Set gasoline models to 15° before "DC-1" mark

and LP-Gas models to 16° before "DC-1" mark.

With the crankshaft in this position, turn the distributor shaft until the rotor arm is in the number one firing position, mount distributor on engine and tighten the clamp screws finger tight. Rotate the breaker cam in the normal direction as far as it will go and while holding the cam in this fully advanced position, turn the distributor body in the opposite direction until the breaker contacts just start to open; then, tighten the distributor clamp securely.

Recheck the advanced timing, using a timing light with engine running at high idle no-load speed.

With the engine running at the slow idle speed of 400-450 rpm, the retarded timing mark should register with the index at timing port. Retarded timing mark is as follows:

335 Gasoline ......1° before "DC-1"
335 LP-Gas ....   "DC-1"
445 Gasoline .....   "DC-1"
445 LP-Gas ....3° before "DC-1"
Jet Star ....3° before "DC-1"
4-Star Series .....3° before "DC-1"

Note: If the fully advanced timing is O.K., but the retarded timing is not, a malfunctioning distributor advance governor is indicated.

57. ELECTRICAL UNITS. Delco-Remy electrical units are used on all models. Parts numbers, unit applications, and test data are as follows:

Generator-1100039—Series 335
  Brush spring tension .....28 oz.
Field Draw
    Volts 6.0
    Amperes 1.85-2.03
  Output (Cold)
    Max. Amperes 35.0
    Volts 8.0
    Max. rpm 2650
Generator-1100314 — Series 445, Jet Star and 4-Star
  Brush spring tension .....28 oz.
  Field Draw
    Volts 12.0
    Amperes 1.58-1.67
  Output (Cold)
    Max. Amperes 20.0
    Volts 14.0
    Max. rpm 2300
Generator-1100430
  Brush spring tension .....28 oz.
  Field Draw
    Volts 12.0
    Amperes 1.5-1.62
  Output (Cold)
    Max. Amperes 25
    Volts 14.0
    Approx. rpm 2710

Regulator-1118790—Series 335
  Cut-out Relay
    Air gap 0.020
    Point gap 0.020
    Closing voltage
      (Range) 5.9-7.0
      Adjust to 6.4

  Voltage Regulator
    Air gap 0.075
    Voltage range 6.8-7.4
    Adjust to 7.1
    Ground polarity ....Positive

Regulator-1118791 — Series 445, Jet
Star and 4-Star
  Cut-out Relay
    Air gap 0.020
    Point gap 0.020
    Closing voltage
      (Range) 11.8-14.0
      Adjust to 12.8

  Voltage Regulator
    Air gap 0.075
    Voltage range 14.0-15.0
    Adjust to 14.4
    Ground polarity ....Positive

Regulator-1119270
  Cut-out Relay
    Air gap 0.020
    Point gap 0.020
    Closing voltage (range) .11.8-13.5

  Voltage Regulator
    Air gap 0.075
    Voltage range
      (@ 85° F.) 14.2-15.2

  Current Regulator
    Air gap 0.075
    Current range
      (Amp. @ 85° F.)......24.5-29

Starting Motor-1107332—U302
  Brush spring tension ..(min.) 35 oz.

No load test
  Volts 10.6
  Amperes 49-76*
  RPM (min.) 6200
    *Includes solenoid

Resistance test
  Volts 4.3
  Amperes (min.) 270
    Max. 310

Starting Motor-1108059—Series 335
  Brush spring tension ..(min.) 24 oz.
No load test
  Volts 5.0
  Amperes 60
  RPM 6000

Lock test
  Volts 3.0
  Amperes 600
  Torque Ft.-Lbs. 15

Starting Motor-1108162 — Series 445,
Jet Star & 4-Star, Non-Diesel
  Brush spring tension ..(min.) 24 oz.

No load test
  Volts 11.3
  Amperes 70
  RPM 6000

Lock test
  Volts 6.7
  Amperes 530
  Torque, Ft.-Lbs. 16

Starting Motor-1113078 — Series 445,
Jet Star & 4-Star, Non-Diesel
  Brush spring tension ....48 oz.

No load test
  Volts 11.5
  Amperes 50
  RPM 6000

Lock test
  Volts 3.3
  Amperes 500
  Torque, Ft.-Lbs. 22

Starting Motor-1113058 — Series 445,
Jet Star & 4-Star Diesel
  Brush spring tension ....48 oz.
No load test
  Volts 11.5
  Amperes 50
  RPM 6000
Lock test
  Volts 3.3
  Amperes 500
  Torque, Ft.-Lbs. 22

ENGINE CLUTCH

ADJUSTMENT

All Models

58. Adjustment to compensate for lining wear is accomplished by adjusting the clutch pedal linkage, NOT by adjusting the position of the clutch release levers. The clutch linkage is properly adjusted when the clutch pedal has a free travel of 1½ inches. If the specified free travel cannot be obtained, relining or renewal of lined plate is indicated.

To adjust the linkage on series 335 and 445 loosen the bolt (B—Fig. MM657), move the pedal either way as required to obtain 1½ inches free travel and tighten the bolt.

Correct linkage adjustment on U302, Jet Star and 4-Star models is obtained by means of the adjusting clevis on the link rod as shown in Fig. MM658.

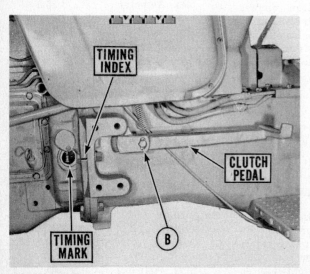

Fig. MM657 — Clutch pedal free travel for 335 and 445 series is adjusted by loosening bolt (B) and moving the pedal as required.

Fig. MM658 — On U302, Jet Star and 4 Star series adjust clutch by means of yoke (A) until pedal free play is 1½-inches as shown.

Fig. MM658A — Using dial indicator to check eccentricity of pilot bushing bore.

R&R AND OVERHAUL
All Models

59. **REMOVE AND REINSTALL.** To remove the clutch, it is first necessary to detach (split) engine from transmission housing as outlined in paragraph 63.

The clutch release bearing and sleeve can now be removed after disconnecting the return spring.

If clutch cover is marked with a white spot (indicating heavy side) be sure to note its location with respect to flywheel so it can be reinstalled in the same position. Use three cap screws in the tapped holes provided in the clutch pressure plate to unload the pressure springs; then unbolt and remove clutch assembly from flywheel. If clutch is not unloaded prior to removal, be sure to unscrew the clutch retaining cap screws evenly to avoid damaging the cover plate.

59A. **IMPORTANT:** Before installing the clutch (on all models except U302) use a suitable chisel and remove the clutch shaft pilot bushing from the flywheel hub; then mount a dial indicator as shown in Fig. MM658A and check the eccentricity of the pilot bushing bore in hub. If eccentricity does not exceed 0.007, install a new pilot bushing (10A12499). If eccentricity exceeds 0.007, remove the hub, turn it 180 degrees, reinstall same, tighten the hub bolts to a torque of 70-75 ft.-lbs. and recheck the eccentricity. If eccentricity is now less than 0.008, install a new bushing (10A12499). If eccentricity is more than 0.007, eccentric bushing (10A-12619) should be installed. Be sure to install the bushing so as to obtain the least amount of eccentricity. In other words, thicker wall of bushing should be toward side of hub which has the most eccentricity.

NOTE: To avoid upsetting the bushing, be sure to install same, using a piloted type driver.

On model U302, renew clutch shaft pilot bearing and seal, if necessary, as outlined in paragraph 39A.

60. **OVERHAUL.** On 335 Industrial and all models of the 445, Jet Star, 4-Star and U302, the pressure springs should test 145-155 lbs. when compressed to a height of $1\frac{7}{16}$ inches. On the 335E, 335U, 335N and the 335 Utility, pressure springs should test 125-135 lbs. when compressed to a height of $1\frac{7}{16}$ inches. Pressure spring free length for all models is approximately $2\frac{5}{32}$ inches. A sectional view of the clutch, showing the release lever setting dimensions, is shown in Figs. MM659 and MM659A.

To adjust the release levers, bolt cover assembly to a spare flywheel or surface plate and use a new lined plate or key stock of specified thickness shown in Fig. MM659 or MM659A in place of the lined plate. Turn the release lever adjusting screws until distance from release bearing contacting surface of each lever to friction face of pressure plate is as shown. If lever height is measured from friction face of flywheel the distance will be $2\frac{1}{16}$ inches.

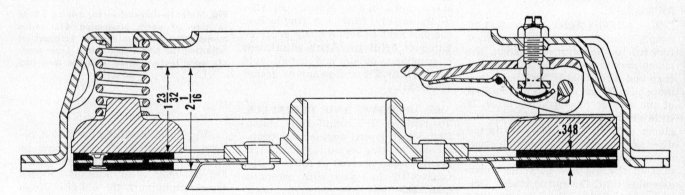

Fig. MM659—Sectional view of clutch used on 335 Industrial, 445, Jet Star and 4-Star series tractors, showing the dimensions for adjusting the clutch release levers.

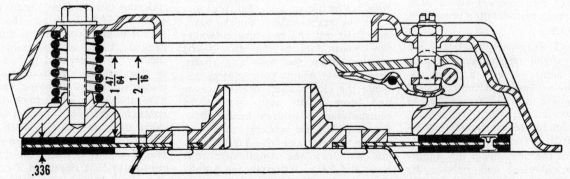

Fig. MM659A—Sectional view of 335E, 335N, 335U and 335 Utility engine clutch, showing the dimensions for adjusting the clutch release levers.

ENGINE CLUTCH SHAFT

All Models With Ampli-Torc

61. To remove the clutch shaft, first remove the Ampli-Torc clutch assembly as outlined in paragraph 65. Then, press the engine clutch shaft out of the Ampli-Torc clutch hub.

All Models Without Ampli-Torc

62. To remove the clutch shaft, first detach (split) engine from transmission housing as outlined in paragraph 63. Remove the engine clutch release bearing. Drift out the roll pins retaining the release fork to the cross shafts and withdraw the fork and shafts. Remove cover and withdraw the clutch shaft.

TRACTOR SPLIT

All Models

63. To detach (split) engine from transmission housing, first drain cooling system and on models with power steering, drain the hydraulic system and disconnect the power steering oil lines. Remove the hood top (service) panel pivot pins and lift off the service panel. Remove the side panel tie braces (and tool box on 335 and 445 series). Disconnect the head light wires and remove the head lights; then, unbolt and remove side panels from tractor. Remove the two bolts retaining front of fuel tank to the exhaust manifold and cylinder head adapter plate. Disconnect the throttle rod at forward end, choke wire at carburetor on non-diesel models, or throttle stop cable and forward throttle control rod on diesel models. Disconnect heat indicator sending unit from the rear cylinder head. Remove fuel line and disconnect wires from generator, regulator, starting motor and coil. Disconnect the starter rod, remove the oil pressure gage line and disconnect the tachourmeter cable. Securely support both halves of tractor, then unbolt and separate the tractor halves.

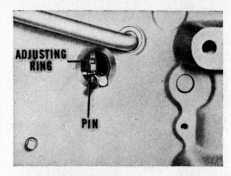

Fig. MM660—Ampli-Torc clutch is adjusted through opening in side of transmission housing. Refer to text for early 445 models not equipped with the adjusting hole.

AMPLI-TORC

CLUTCH

All Models

64. **ADJUSTMENT.** When the Ampli-Torc control lever is pushed forward to the engaged position, the clutch should engage with a distinct snap and a reasonably hard push (not more than 35 lbs.) should be required at the end of the engaging lever. If little effort is required to engage the clutch, pull the lever rearward to the disengaged position, remove the small cover plate from right side of transmission housing and turn the clutch assembly until the spring loaded lock pin (Fig. MM660) is visible through the cover opening. Depress the lock pin, turn the notched adjusting ring clockwise until the pin engages the next notch and recheck the adjustment. Repeat the adjusting procedure, if necessary.

Note: On very early models of the 445 series, the transmission housing was not equipped with a clutch adjusting hole. To adjust the clutch on these models, it will be necessary to either remove the planetary opening cover from top of transmission housing or drill a hole.

To drill the hole, drain the Ampli-Torc compartment and remove the fuel tank, steering shaft and support assembly and planetary cover. Drill the 1½-inch hole, using the dimensions shown in Fig. MM661. Be sure to thoroughly flush the Ampli-Torc compartment to remove any accumulation of drillings. After adjustment is complete, obtain and install hole cover (11A9225) and neoprene gasket (10A9834).

65. **REMOVE AND REINSTALL.** To remove the Ampli-Torc clutch, first detach (split) engine from transmission housing as outlined in paragraph 63 and proceed as follows: Disconnect the fuel gage wire, speedometer cable and fuse wire at instrument panel, then unbolt and remove the fuel tank. Unbolt and remove the steering wheel, shaft and support assembly. Remove the planetary cover from top of transmission housing. Remove the engine clutch release bearing. Drift out the roll pins retaining the release fork to the cross shafts and withdraw the fork and shafts. Engage the Ampli-Torc clutch, remove the clutch shaft opening cover and save shims and gasket for reinstallation. Withdraw washer (21—Fig. MM662) and bearing (20). Drift out the two roll pins (47—Fig. MM663) and withdraw the Ampli-Torc shift lever and forks. Withdraw the Ampli-Torc clutch assembly from the planet carrier.

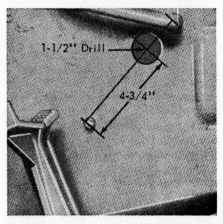

Fig. MM661—Dimensions for drilling a hole in side of early production 445 series transmission housings for the purposes of adjusting the Ampli-Torc clutch. Later models were factory fitted with the adjusting hole.

65A. When installing the clutch, reverse the removal procedure and be sure the bronze thrust washer (26—Fig. MM662) is in position between the clutch hub and the sun gear. Note: Some early 445 models were fitted with a bronze washer instead of bearing (20). When such tractors are encountered, discard the washer and install the needle type thrust bearing, part No. 10A8381. Be sure that washer (21) is in good condition and properly located in hub of clutch shaft opening cover. Renew seal if its condition is questionable. When installing the clutch shaft opening cover, use a suitable sleeve or shim stock to avoid damaging the seal lip when installing same over the clutch shaft splines. Tighten the cover cap screws securely, mount a dial indicator in a manner similar to that shown in Fig. MM664 and check the clutch shaft end play by moving the planetary unit back

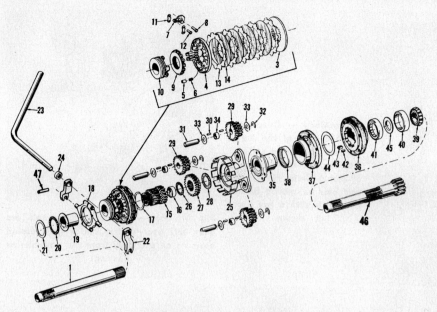

Fig. MM662—Exploded view of the Ampli-Torc clutch, planetary gear set, over-running clutch and associated parts.

1. Clutch shaft	14. Driven plate	26. Thrust washer	37. Bearing cage
3. Back plate	15. Clutch hub	27. Sun gear	38. Needle bearing
4. Floating plate	16. Hub bushing	28. Washer	39. Bearing cone
5. Lock pin	17. Snap ring	29. Planetary gear	40. Bearing cup
6. Pin spring	18. Shifting ring	30. Needle rollers	41. Roller bearing
7. Lever	19. Spacer	31. Planetary gear	42. Roller
8. Lever pin	20. Bearing	shaft	43. Spring
9. Adjusting ring	21. Thrust washer	32. Snap ring	44. Washer
10. Sliding sleeve	22. Forks	33. Washer	45. Washer
11. Lever link	23. Engaging lever	34. Spacer	46. Transmission
12. Lever pin	24. Oil seal	35. Hub	sliding gear
13. Driving plate	25. Planet carrier	36. Cam cage	(upper) shaft
			47. Roll pins

and forth with a pry bar. If the shaft end play is not between the limits of 0.008-0.015, remove clutch shaft opening cover and add or remove shims as required. A gasket should be installed on each side of the shim pack. Adjust the Ampli-Torc clutch as outlined in paragraph 64.

66. OVERHAUL. With the Ampli-Torc clutch removed as outlined in paragraph 65, remove pins (8—Fig. MM662) and lift off sliding sleeve (10). Depress the spring loaded pin (5), completely unscrew the notched adjusting ring (9) and disassemble floating plate (4), driving plates (13), driven plates (14) and back plate (3) from the clutch hub (15). Thoroughly clean all parts and renew any which are damaged or worn. Be sure that friction faces of back plate (3) and floating plate (4) are not scored or excessively heat checked. The five driving plates (13) and the four driven plates (14) must not be warped or worn. Renew pins (8 and 12) if they are grooved. Renew levers (7) and links (11) if they are worn or if pin holes are enlarged. When reassembling, be sure that the driven discs are installed between the driving discs.

PLANET GEARS, SUN GEARS AND OVER-RUNNING CLUTCH
All Models

67. REMOVE AND REINSTALL. To remove the Ampli-Torc gear set and over-running clutch, first remove the Ampli-Torc clutch as outlined in

paragraph 65, remove the transmission top cover and proceed as follows: Turn the planet carrier (25—Fig. MM-665) until the cut-out groove in carrier is aligned with one of the cap screws retaining bearing cage (37) to transmission case wall and remove the cap screw. Continue this procedure and remove all of the bearing cage retaining screws. Withdraw the planet carrier, bearing cage and cam cage as an assembly from the transmission case as shown in Fig. MM666, but be careful not to separate the bearing cage from the cam cage or the over-running clutch parts will drop into bottom of case. Note: Removal of the assembly will be simplified by prying on the rear face of the cam cage with a bar inserted through the transmission top cover opening.

67A. When reinstalling the unit, be sure the oil hole in cam cage and bearing cage are up and tighten the bearing cage retaining screws securely. Install the Ampli-Torc clutch as outlined in paragraph 65A and adjust the unit as in paragraph 64.

68. OVERHAUL. With the Ampli-Torc gear set and over-running clutch removed as outlined in paragraph 67, lift off the cam cage (36—Fig. MM-662) and catch the rollers (42) and springs (43) which may fly out. Lift off bearing cage (37), then unbolt and remove hub (35) from the planet carrier. Remove snap rings (32), withdraw shafts (31) and lift out the planet gears (29), but be careful not to lose washers (33), needle bearings (30) or spacers (34) as the planetary gears are removed. Remove the sun

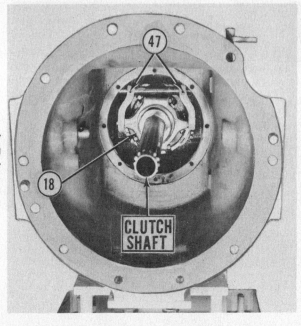

Fig. MM663—Front view of transmission housing with the clutch shaft opening cover removed.

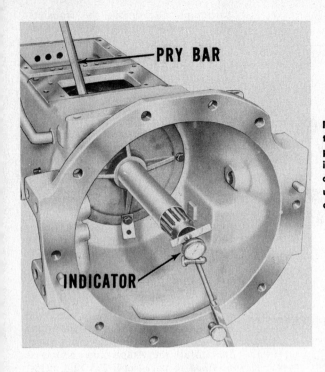

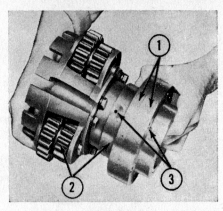

Fig. MM664 — Checking the end play of the Ampli-Torc unit, using a dial indicator at forward end of clutch shaft. Planetary unit can be moved back and forth with a pry bar as shown.

Fig. MM666 — Removing the Ampli-Torc gear set, over-running clutch and related parts as an assembly from the transmission housing.

gear (27) and thrust washer (28). Inspect rollers, springs and ramps of over-running clutch and renew any damaged parts. Renew hub (35) if it is worn at bearing areas. Bushing (16) in clutch hub is available as a separate replacement part or, a new hub is factory fitted with a bushing. Inspect planet gears (29), needle bearings (30), spacer washers (33) and renew any questionable parts.

When reassembling, use heavy grease to facilitate installation of the planet gears, needle bearings and spacers. Planet gears must be installed so that centerline of oil groove in each gear will converge on centerline of carrier as shown in Fig. MM666A. Tighten the hub retaining cap screws securely and install bearing cage (37—Fig. MM 662). Assemble the springs and rollers in the cam cage as shown in Fig. MM 667, then assemble cam cage to carrier hub. Install the assembled planetary unit as outlined in paragraph 67A.

Fig. MM666A—Install planetary gears so that center line of oil groove (G) in each gear will converge on center line of carrier.

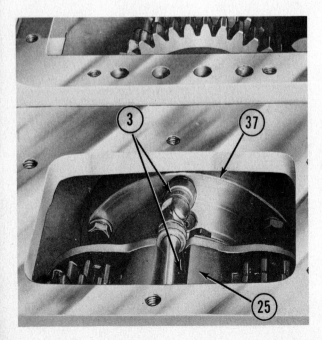

Fig. MM665—Using ½-inch drive extension, universal and socket to remove the cap screws retaining the Ampli-Torc bearing cage to the transmission case wall.

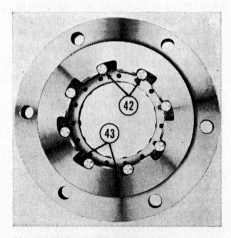

Fig. MM667—Rollers and springs of over-running clutch properly installed in the Ampli-Torc cam cage.

REVERSE SHUTTLE UNIT

A reverse shuttle unit enabling the operator to reverse the direction of travel in any transmission gear, is optionally available for installation in all tractor models not equipped with the "Ampli-Torc" planetary under-drive attachment. The reverse shuttle unit is equipped with a planetary reversing unit and a sliding gear shift, which reverses the direction of rotation of the main transmission, as well as the differential and final drive.

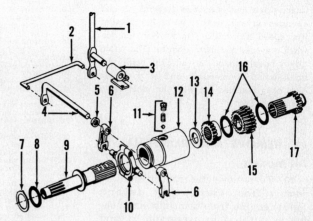

Fig. MM668 — Exploded view of Reverse Shuttle shaft and associated parts.

1. Control lever
2. Link
3. Bracket
4. Shifter shaft
5. Oil seal
6. Shifter fork
7. Tab washer
8. Thrust bearing
9. Input shaft
10. Shifting ring
11. Detent assembly
12. Sliding coupling
13. Thrust washer
14. Forward gear
15. Reverse gear
16. Thrust washers
17. Spur gear

R&R AND OVERHAUL

69. To remove the reverse shuttle unit, first split the tractor between the engine and transmission case as outlined in paragraph 63 and proceed as follows: Disconnect clutch release bearing lubrication line and remove release bearing. Drift out the roll pins retaining clutch release fork to cross shafts and remove shafts and fork; then, unbolt and remove input shaft cover. Disconnect link rod (2—Fig. MM668) from fork shaft (4) and rotate shaft to release fork levers (6) from shifting ring (10), and withdraw clutch shaft (9) and sliding jaw (12) forward out of transmission as a unit. Forward gear (14), reverse gear (15), spur gear (17) and the thrust washers may now be withdrawn from the transmission case. If sliding jaw (12) is to be removed from clutch shaft, first remove detent ball, spring and plug (11) from sliding jaw then separate the units. When reassembling, make sure the hole for the detent ball assembly is centered over the detent grooves machined in clutch shaft splines.

Unbolt and remove gear cage from front of transmission case. The four shuttle unit pinions rotate on needle bearings and their shafts are retained in the cage by set screws.

Tractors equipped with the reverse shuttle unit require a different sliding gear shaft front bearing cup (11—Fig. MM674) and reverse shifter rail (25—Fig. MM672), than is used where the reverse shuttle unit is not installed.

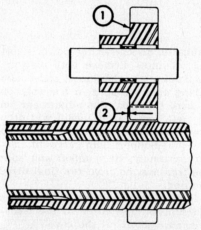

Fig. MM668A—When installing gear cage and spur gear, make sure forward edge of spur gear teeth (2) are 0.020-0.035 forward of narrow pinion (1) in gear cage.

To assemble the unit, reverse the disassembly procedure, tighten the gear cage retaining cap screws to a torque of 25-30 ft.-lbs., and check the end play of the main transmission upper shaft. If the shaft end play exceeds 0.004, adjust as outlined in paragraph 72D. Reinstall spur gear (17—Fig. MM668) and check to make

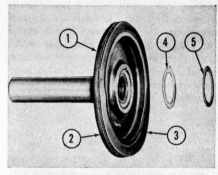

Fig. MM668B—Input shaft cover and associated parts used on tractors equipped with reverse shuttle unit.

1. Cover
2. Gasket
3. Shim pack
4. Tab washer
5. Thrust washer

sure that front edge of spur gear teeth is 0.020-0.035 forward of the teeth of the narrow pinions as shown in Fig. MM668A. Shims (3—Fig. MM668B) are available in thicknesses of 0.006 and 0.010 to obtain the recommended clutch shaft end float of 0.008-0.012. After the remainder of the unit is installed, measure the end float with a dial indicator, then add or remove shims to obtain the recommended clearance.

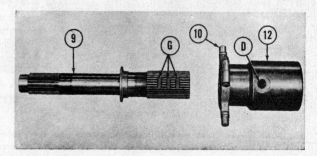

Fig. MM669A – Disassembled view of input shaft and sliding coupling showing detent grooves (G) and detent plug hole (D).

TRANSMISSION

All models are equipped with a sliding gear type transmission which provides five forward speeds and one reverse. On models with Ampli-Torc drive, a planetary type under drive unit is located forward of, and operates in conjunction with, the regular five speed transmission to provide ten forward speeds and two reverse. The main drive bevel pinion is integral with the transmission countershaft and is available only as a matched set with the main drive bevel ring gear.

REMOVE AND REINSTALL

All Models

70. To remove the transmission assembly from tractor, first detach (split) engine from transmission housing as outlined in paragraph 63, and proceed as follows: Disconnect and unclip tubing and wiring from transmission housing. Loosen the adjustment on the left brake so the pedal will drop down and clear the pedal stop plate and pin. Support the transmission and final drive housing separately, then unbolt and separate the housings.

OVERHAUL

All Models

71. **SHIFTER SHAFTS AND FORKS.** To remove the transmission shifter shafts and forks, first drain the hydraulic system, transmission and final drive housings and on models so

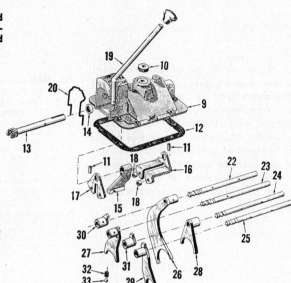

Fig. MM672 — Exploded view of typical transmission shifter shafts and shifter mechanism.

9. Transmission top cover
10. Pipe plug
11. Stop for quadrant plates
12. Gasket
13. Shifting rod
14. Felt seal
15. Shifting rod bracket (used on early models)
16. Shifting rod bracket (used on later models)
17. Quadrant plate
18. Spacers
19. Shifting lever
20. Lever spring
22. Shifting shaft (1st & 5th)
23. Shifting shaft (2nd & 3rd)
24. Shifting shaft (4th)
25. Shifting shaft (reverse)
26. Shifting fork (1st & 5th)
27. Shifting fork (2nd & 3rd)
28. Shifting fork (4th)
29. Shifting fork (reverse)
30. Shifting lug (1st & 5th)
31. Shifting lug (4th)
32. Detent spring
33. Detent ball

equipped, disconnect the power steering oil lines. Remove both platform assemblies, and disconnect and unclip tubing and wiring from transmission housing. Loosen the adjustment on the left brake so the pedal will drop down and clear the pedal stop plate and pin. Support both halves of tractor separately, then unbolt and split the transmission from the final drive housing.

Remove the cap screws retaining the transmission top cover to the transmission and lift off the cover.

On all models except U302, remove the detent springs (32—Fig. MM672) and balls (33) from vertical bores in transmission housing. Slide the shifter shafts forward until the detent ball grooves at front of each shaft are inside the shaft bores in transmission housing. Drift out the roll pins retaining the shifter forks and lugs to the shifter shafts, pull the shifter shafts rearward out of the transmission case and lift out the forks and lugs.

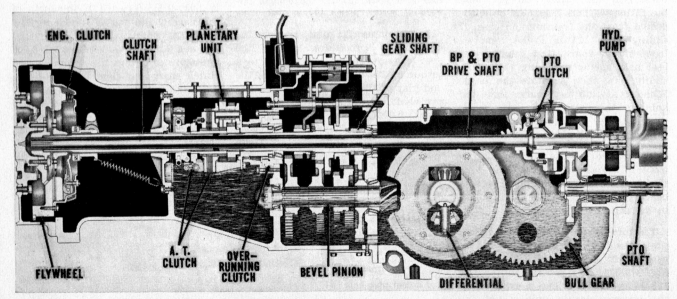

Fig. MM670—Sectional view of transmission and final drive housing, showing internal components. Main drive bevel pinion and ring gear are available as matched units. The B.P. and P.T.O. drive shaft is splined to and driven by a hub in the engine flywheel.

Fig. MM673 — Installation view of transmission shifter shafts, lugs and forks. Lugs and forks are retained to shafts by Roll pins. Refer to Fig. MM-672 for legend.

(15). Refer also to Fig. MM675. Using a long drift punch against the rear bearing inner race as shown in Fig. MM676, bump the bearing rearward. Turn the shaft and again bump the bearing cone rearward. Continue this procedure until the bearing cup and cone are removed. Move the sliding gear shaft assembly toward right side of transmission case as far as possible, remove the reverse idler gear shaft retaining set screw and push the reverse idler gear shaft forward and out of the transmission case. Lift out the reverse idler gear.

Note: It is not absolutely necessary to remove the reverse idler gear to permit removal of the sliding gear shaft, however considerable time will be saved by doing so.

72A. Using a pair of right angle Tru-Arc snap ring pliers, disengage the snap ring (29—Fig. MM674) from the groove in front of the bevel pinion (counter-shaft) third speed gear (27). Move the snap ring and the third speed gear forward on the bevel pinion shaft as far as possible, then lift the sliding gear (upper) shaft and gears out through top opening in transmission housing.

72B. Place the removed unit in a suitable press and remove the front bearing cone. On models with Ampli-Torc drive, be careful not to damage the thrust washer (45—Fig. MM662) when pressing off the bearing cone. Remove shaft from press and withdraw the second and reverse sliding

When reassembling, use Fig. MM-673 as guide for proper location of parts and when installing the fork and lug retaining roll pins, slide the shifter shafts forward in the transmission housing bores to provide support for the shafts when the pins are bumped in place.

On Model U302, detent balls and springs are located below shifter shafts in bores (D—Fig. MM673A) at rear end of shifter shafts. Three ⅝-inch steel interlock balls (I) are located between the shafts in a horizontal bore at front end. The interlock balls prevent two adjacent shafts from being shifted from neutral position at the same time. Interlock balls are removed or installed by removing plug (P). The model U302 shifting mechanism is shown exploded in Fig. MM673B.

72. SLIDING GEAR (UPPER) SHAFT. To remove the sliding gear shaft (Fig. MM670), first remove the transmission assembly from tractor as outlined in paragraph 70, then remove

the transmission case top covers and the shifter shafts and forks. On models with Ampli-Torc drive, remove the Ampli-Torc clutch as outlined in paragraph 65 and the planetary gear unit and over-running clutch as in paragraph 67. On models with reverse shuttle, remove unit as in paragraph 69. On models without Ampli-Torc drive, unbolt and remove the sliding gear shaft front bearing retainer (12—Fig. MM674).

On all models, remove lock clip (16) then unscrew and remove the sliding gear shaft bearing adjustment nut

Fig. MM673B — Exploded view of transmission top cover and shifter mechanism used on Model U302.

1. Shift lever
2. Dust cover
3. Spring retainer
4. Spring
5. Spring retainer
6. Top cover
7. Neutral safety switch
8. Guide plate
9. Long shifting yoke
10. Short shifting yoke
11. Shifting fork (reverse)
12. Shifting fork (3rd)
13. Shifting fork (2nd & 4th)
14. Shifting fork (1st & 5th)
15. Detent assembly
16. Shifting shaft
17. Interlock ball
18. Shifting shaft
19. Shifting shaft
20. Shifting shaft

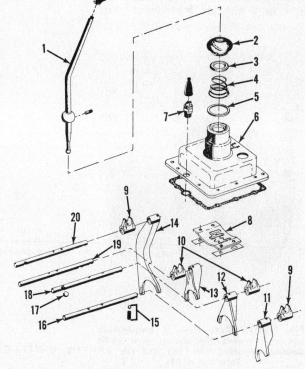

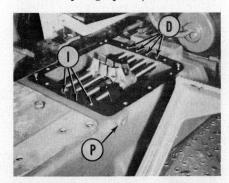

Fig. MM673A—U302 transmission with top cover removed, showing (D) shift detent bores; (I) interlock ball location; and (P) port plug for interlock bore.

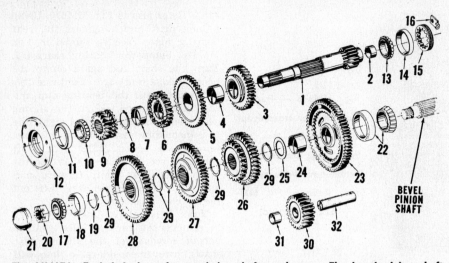

Fig. MM674—Exploded view of transmission shafts and gears. The bevel pinion shaft is available only as a matched set with the main drive bevel ring gear. Bearing retainer (12) is not used in models with Ampli-Torc drive. Items (1, 3, 4 and 5) are available as an assembled unit only.

1. Sliding gear shaft	9. Gear, 2nd & reverse	18. Bearing cup
2. Bushing	10. Bearing cone	19. Snap ring
3. Gear, 4th speed	11. Bearing cup	20. Pinion shaft nut
4. Bushing	12. Bearing retainer	21. Cover
5. Gear, 5th speed	13. Bearing cone	22. Bearing cup and
6. Gear, 3rd speed	14. Bearing cup	cone
7. Bushing	15. Adjusting nut	23. Gear, 1st speed
8. Snap ring	16. Lock clip	with bushing
	17. Bearing cone	24. Bushing

25. Washer	
26. Gear, 4th & 5th speed	
27. Gear, 3rd speed	
28. Gear, 2nd speed	
29. Snap ring	
30. Gear, reverse	
31. Bushing	
32. Shaft	

and must be line-bored or honed after installation to provide a bushing to shaft clearance of 0.0025-0.004. Unless precision sizing equipment is available, field installation of the bushing is not recommended.

Note: Although it is possible to remove the fourth and fifth speed gears (3 and 5) from the sliding gear shaft, it would be pointless to do so. If the shaft, fourth speed gear and/or fifth speed gear are damaged or excessively worn, it will be necessary to renew all parts which are available as a factory assembled unit only.

If the sliding gear shaft and gears unit are in otherwise good condition, install the third speed gear and its retaining snap ring (8). With the third speed gear contacting the snap ring, use a feeler gage and check the clearance between the shoulder on the third speed gear and the shoulder on the fifth speed gear. Desired clearance is 0.005-0.012 as shown in Fig.

gear (9—Fig. MM674). Remove snap ring (8) and withdraw the third speed gear (6).

Inside diameter of the third speed gear bushing (7) is 2.113-2.114. Diameter of sliding gear shaft at third speed gear location is 2.1100-2.1105. If bushing is worn or if inner teeth of gear are damaged or worn, install a new gear which contains a factory installed bushing reamed to size. The third speed gear bushing (7) is available as a separate replacement part

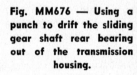

Fig. MM676 — Using a punch to drift the sliding gear shaft rear bearing out of the transmission housing.

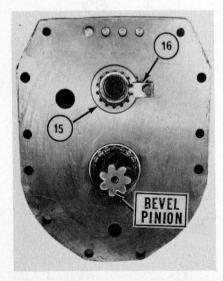

Fig. MM675—Rear view of transmission housing showing the sliding gear shaft bearing adjusting nut (15) and the nut lock clip (16).

1. Sliding gear shaft
3. Gear, 4th speed
5. Gear, 5th speed
6. Gear, 3rd speed
8. Snap ring

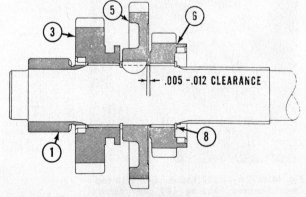

.005 -.012 CLEARANCE

Fig. MM677—Cutaway view of sliding gear shaft showing the point for checking the clearance between the 3rd and 5th speed gears.

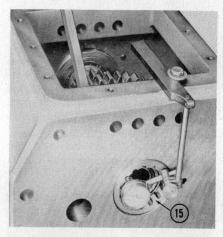

Fig. MM678 — Installing the assembled sliding gear shaft in the transmission housing.

Fig. MM679—Checking the sliding gear shaft end play which should be 0.001-0.004. Indicator button must be contacting the sliding gear shaft and not the adjusting nut.

MM677. If clearance exceeds 0.012, measure the thickness of the third speed gear (6) and fifth speed gear (5) where they contact the shaft (1). If the thickness of the third speed gear (6) is not 0.919-0.922, renew the gear. If the width of the fifth speed gear is not 0.935-0.940, renew the upper shaft and gear assembly.

When reassembling, install the third speed gear and its retaining snap ring. Install the second and reverse speed sliding gear with the shortest teeth toward the third speed gear. Using a suitable press, install the sliding gear shaft front bearing cone, then on models with Ampli-Torc drive, press the thrust washer (45—Fig. MM662) on the shaft with shoulder on washer toward the bearing cone. Use extreme care not to damage or warp the washer during installation.

72C. Install the assembled sliding gear shaft unit in the transmission housing as shown in Fig. MM678, then move the shaft unit toward right side of the housing. Slide the third speed gear and snap ring back into position on the bevel pinion (countershaft). Install the reverse idler gear and shaft and tighten the shaft retaining set screw until end of screw is flush with the lock nut; then tighten the nut securely.

72D. Move the sliding gear shaft over into position and install the rear bearing cone and cup. Install the bearing adjustment nut and turn the nut in until rear face of nut stands out about $\frac{3}{16}$-inch from rear face of transmission housing. On models without Ampli-Torc drive, install the sliding gear shaft front bearing retainer and tighten the screws securely. On mod-

Fig. MM680—Left brake installation on 335 and 445 series tractors. Jet Star and 4-Star models are similar. Speedometer drive gear (G) can be removed after loosening the chuck screw (CS).

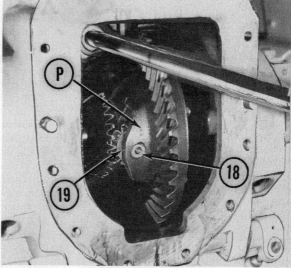

Fig. MM681—Front view of final drive housing showing the differential installation. Punch marks (P) identify spider gear shaft (18) which must be removed before the differential cross shaft or differential can be removed. Spider gear shaft (18) is retained in the differential cage by Roll pin (19).

els with Ampli-Torc drive, install the planetary gear unit as outlined in paragraph 67A.

Tighten the sliding gear shaft bearing adjusting nut to remove all shaft end play. Tap each end of the shaft

lightly with a soft driver to be sure bearings are seated and re-tighten the adjusting nut if necessary, to remove all shaft end play. Then, back off the adjusting nut enough to provide a shaft end play of 0.001-0.004 and install the adjusting nut lock clip and cap screw as shown in Fig. MM675.

Note: End play can be checked by mounting a dial indicator as shown in Fig. MM679, but be sure the indicator button is contacting the sliding gear shaft and not the adjusting nut.

On models with Ampli-Torc drive, install the clutch as outlined in paragraph 65A. Install the remaining parts by reversing the removal procedure.

73. REVERSE IDLER. The reverse idler gear (30—Fig. MM674) and shaft (32) can be removed by following the procedure outlined in paragraph 72.

The 1.2420-1.2425 diameter reverse idler gear shaft should have a clearance of 0.0015-0.003 in the reverse idler gear bushing. The bushing and/or shaft are available as separate replacement parts; or, a new idler gear is factory fitted with a bushing. When installing the idler gear and shaft, tighten the retaining set screw until end of screw is flush with the lock nut; then tighten the nut securely. Reinstall the sliding gear (upper) shaft as outlined in paragraph 72D.

74. BEVEL PINION (COUNTER-SHAFT). To remove the bevel pinion shaft (Fig. MM670), first remove the sliding gear (upper) shaft as outlined in paragraphs 72 and 72A and proceed as follows:

Remove cover (21 — Fig. MM674), cotter pin and nut (20) from forward end of shaft; then, working through top opening in transmission housing, use a pair of right angle Tru-Arc snap ring pliers and disengage snap ring (29) from groove in front of the first speed gear (23). Bump the bevel pinion shaft rearward until shaft is out of the front bearing cone (17). Disengage the remaining snap rings from the bevel pinion shaft, withdraw the shaft rearward and remove gears from above. Rear bearing cone can be removed from shaft and cups can be removed from transmission case at this time.

Inside diameter of the first speed gear bushing (24) is 2.0035-2.0040. Diameter of bevel pinion shaft at first speed gear location is 1.995-2.000. If bushing is worn or if inner teeth of gear are damaged or worn, install a new gear which contains a factory

installed bushing reamed to size. The first speed gear bushing is available as a separate replacement part and must be line-bored or honed after installation to provide a bushing to shaft clearance of 0.0035-0.0045. Unless precision sizing equipment is available, field installation of the bushing is not recommended.

The bevel pinion shaft is available only as a matched set with the main drive bevel ring gear. Therefore, if the bevel pinion shaft must be renewed, it will be necessary to remove the differential as outlined in paragraph 75 or 76A, and install the new mating bevel ring gear.

Install the bevel pinion shaft and gears by reversing the removal procedure and tighten the bearing adjusting nut (20) to remove all shaft end play. Tap each end of the shaft lightly with a soft hammer to be sure the bearings are seated, then retighten the nut to pre-load the bearings. Desired pre-load is 10-20-inch pounds of rolling torque when checked at bevel pinion (rear) end of shaft.

Install the reverse idler gear and sliding gear (upper) shaft as outlined in paragraphs 72C and 72D.

DIFFERENTIAL AND MAIN DRIVE BEVEL GEARS

DIFFERENTIAL
All Models Except U302

75. REMOVE AND REINSTALL. To remove the differential, first drain the hydraulic system, transmission and final drive housings and on models so equipped, disconnect the power steering oil lines. Remove both platform assemblies and disconnect and unclip tubing and wiring from transmission housing. Loosen the adjustment on the left brake so the pedal will drop down and clear the pedal stop plate and pin. Support both halves of tractor separately, then unbolt and split the transmission from the final drive housing.

Remove both brake covers, loosen the chuck screw (CS—Fig. MM680) and pry the speedometer drive gear (G) from the bull pinion sleeve. Remove the brake outer lined discs, both of the brake adjusting bolts and withdraw the actuating plate assemblies and the inner lined discs. Remove the

three nuts retaining each of the inner brake plates to the final drive housing and remove the plates, but do not mix or lose the shims located between the brake plates and the housing. Use a double nut arrangement and remove the front stud located in the right brake compartment. Turn the differential assembly until the punch marks (P—Fig. MM681) on differential cage adjacent to one of the spider gear shafts is visible through front opening in final drive housing as shown. Using a long drift punch through hole from which stud was removed, bump the roll pin (19) inward until the pin is just centered in the spider gear shaft (18); then, using a pair of pliers, withdraw the spider gear shaft from the differential cage. CAUTION: Do not bump the roll pin in too far or the pin will be imbedded in the differential cage metal and it will be extremely difficult to remove the spider gear shaft.

Bump the differential cross shaft out through right side of the final drive housing and withdraw the differential assembly through front opening in housing as shown in Fig. MM682. Withdraw the combination bull pinion and differential side gears as shown in Fig. MM683.

75A. When reassembling, install the combination bull pinion and differential side gears, then position the differential assembly in the final drive housing and slide the cross shaft into position so that hole in cross shaft registers with the spider gear shaft bore in differential cage. Remove the roll pin from the spider gear shaft, then reinstall the spider gear shaft so that tip engages hole in the differential cross shaft. Lock the spider gear shaft in position by driving the roll pin into differential cage and spider gear shaft until end of roll pin is just less than flush with the differential cage. Using sealer on the threads, reinstall the stud in the right hand brake compartment, then reinstall the inner brake plates but be sure that the original shims are installed between each of the brake plates and the final drive housing. If differential carrier bearing play exists, remove an equal thickness of shims from each side of the final drive housing until all bearing play is eliminated, but still permitting differential to rotate freely without binding.

NOTE: When adjustment is correct, removal of one 0.005 shim will prevent one bull pinion sleeve from being rotated by hand while the other is held from turning.

Using a new gasket, reconnect the final drive housing to the transmission housing and tighten the retaining bolts securely. Disconnect the lift links from the rockshaft arms and remove tractor seat; then remove the hydraulic lift unit and top cover from the final drive housing.

Observe the main drive bevel pinion and ring gear where the matched set numbers and backlash are stamped. If the backlash between the bevel gears is not as specified, it will be necessary to transfer shims from under one brake plate to the other until the specified backlash value is obtained.

When the differential carrier bearings and bevel gear backlash are properly adjusted, remove the inner brake plates but be careful not to mix or lose any of the shims. Install new seals in the brake plates; then, using a tin sleeve or shim stock to avoid damaging the seal lips, reinstall the brake plates. Using Permatex as a sealer, install a new expansion plug in the right bull pinion shaft sleeve. Using a new "O" ring, install the speedometer drive gear in the left bull pinion shaft sleeve and tighten the chuck screw. Install the brake lined discs, actuating discs and covers.

Fig. MM682 — Removing the differential through front opening in final drive housing. Bevel ring gear is available only in a matched set with the bevel pinion shaft.

Fig. MM683—With differential removed from the final drive housing, the combination bull pinion shaft and differential side gear units can be removed as shown.

Note: The single grooved cover spacer should be installed on rear cover bolt.

Install the remaining parts by reversing the removal procedure and adjust the brakes as outlined in paragraph 82.

76. **OVERHAUL.** With the differential removed from tractor as outlined in paragraph 75, lift out the spider gear which is already released by the removal of the spider gear shaft. Using a punch, bump the other roll pin inward until the pin is just centered in the spider gear shaft (17—Fig. MM684 or 684A); then, using a pair of pliers, withdraw the spider gear shaft from the differential cage and remove the spider gear. The 0.996 — 0.997 diameter spider gear shafts should have a clearance of 0.003-0.005 in bushing (16). New spider gears contain factory installed bushings; or, bushings are available separately for field installation. On 445, Jet Star, 4-Star and U302, the 2.117-2.118 diameter differential cross shaft should have a clearance of 0.002-0.004 in the sleeve bushings (12). New sleeves contain factory installed bushings; or, bushings are available separately for field installation. On the 335 series, the 1.739-1.740 diameter differential cross shaft should have a clearance of 0.002-0.004 in the bull pinion sleeves. Renew any other damaged parts and reassemble. Note: The tipped spider gear shaft (18) is installed during reinstallation of the differential assembly and should be installed in the differential cage bore which has adjacent punch marks. Refer to Fig. MM681.

Install differential as outlined in paragraph 75A.

Model U302

76A. **REMOVE AND REINSTALL.** To remove the differential, first drain the hydraulic system and transmission. Remove the hydraulic reservoir, seat, and final drive housing top cover. Remove the pto clutch and clutch shaft as outlined in paragraph 87. Disconnect brake linkage and remove both brake assemblies.

Remove the retaining snap ring and plug (3—Fig. MM683A) from each bull pinion sleeve (2). Remove both inner brake plates (1), being careful not to lose or mix the adjusting shim packs. Move right bull pinion sleeve out as far as possible as shown in Fig. MM683B, and unseat the wrap-around snap ring (R). Support the differen-

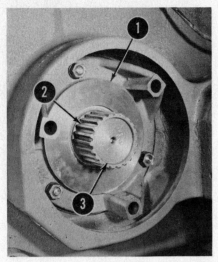

Fig. MM683A — Bull pinion sleeve with brake removed, showing details of construction.

1. Inner brake plate
2. Bull pinion sleeve
3. End plug

tial assembly from above or by blocking up beneath bevel ring gear; bump the differential cross shaft out left side of tractor, and lift differential assembly and bull pinion sleeves out top opening.

Before attempting to reinstall the differential assembly, fully insert cross shaft through differential cage as shown in Fig. MM683C and mark the cross shaft and cage hub as shown at (A), to assist in spline alignment when reassembling. Note that left bull pinion sleeve is of larger inside diameter than right sleeve. Place bull pinion sleeves and thrust washers in position in housing, then position differential assembly, supporting the assembly from above or by blocking up beneath bevel ring gear. In-

Fig. MM683B—To remove the differential cross shaft on U302, snap ring (R) must first be unseated. Refer to text.

sert small end of cross shaft in left bull pinion sleeve and, as end appears through differential cage hub, place the wrap-around snap ring over end of cross shaft. Align the marks (A—Fig. MM683C) as shaft is inserted, and feed the snap ring into groove (G—Fig. MM683D) when shaft is in place.

If carrier bearing preload or bevel gear backlash are not to be adjusted, renew outer and inner oil seals (9 & 10—Fig. MM683E) and "O" ring (7), and reinstall inner brake plates (8), using the removed shim packs and a protector sleeve to prevent damage to oil seal lips. Install the retaining stud nuts and tighten to a torque of 52-58 ft.-lbs. Complete the assembly by reversing disassembly procedure.

NOTE: If parts are renewed which will alter bearing adjustment or backlash, final drive housing must be separated from transmission to properly adjust the bearings. When separating the housings, note the number and color of flange gaskets located between the housings. The gaskets determine cone point position of main drive bevel pinion. Refer to paragraph 77A. Three different thickness shims are used, as follows:

Red 0.002
Green 0.003
Blue 0.005

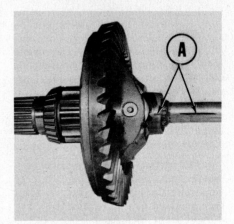

Fig. MM683C—Before installing differential on U302, fully insert cross shaft and place alignment marks (A) on shaft and cage hub.

If adjustment is required, omit the seals (9 & 10) and "O" ring (7) on both sides, and make a trial installation using the removed shim packs. Add shims (6) to right brake plate; or remove shims from left brake plate, until there is no end play but differential assembly rolls freely.

NOTE: A preload on the carier bearings will cause wear and scoring of pinion sleeve thrust washers (14), and must be avoided.

Reconnect transmission and final drive housings, using shim gaskets of the same number and color of those removed. Tighten flange cap screws

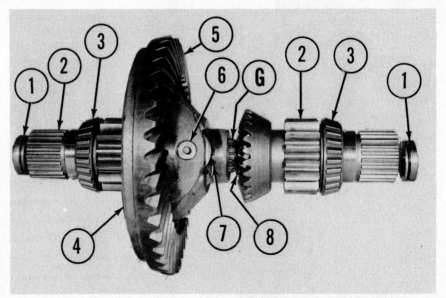

Fig. MM683D—Partially assembled view of U302 differential and associated parts.

1. End plug
2. Bull pinion sleeve
3. Carrier bearing cone
4. Differential cage
5. Main drive bevel gear
6. Spider gear shaft
7. Spider gear
8. Snap ring
G. Snap ring groove (in cross shaft)

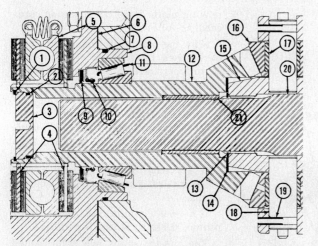

Fig. MM683E—Cross sectional view of left bull pinion sleeve and associated parts used on U302 tractor. Note the two oil seals (9 & 10) and cross shaft retaining snap ring (13). Right side is similar except for snap ring (13) and size of sleeve bushing (21).

1. Snap ring
2. "O" ring
3. End plug
4. Brake discs
5. Actuating assy.
6. Shim pack
7. "O" ring
8. Inner brake plate
9. Outer seal
10. Inner seal
11. Carrier bearing
12. Bull pinion sleeve
13. Snap ring
14. Thrust washer
15. Differential cage
16. Spider gear
17. Gear bushing
18. Spider gear shaft
19. Roll pin
20. Cross shaft
21. Bushing

MAIN DRIVE BEVEL GEARS

All Models Except U302

77. The main drive bevel pinion and ring gear are available in matched sets only. To renew the bevel pinion, follow the procedure outlined in paragraph 74. To remove the bevel ring gear, first remove the differential as outlined in paragraph 75; then unbolt and remove the bevel ring gear from the differential cage.

Install the new bevel ring gear and tighten the retaining bolts securely. Install the differential and adjust the bevel gear backlash as outlined in paragraph 75A.

Model U302

77A. The main drive bevel pinion and ring gear are available in matched sets only. To renew the bevel pinion, follow the procedure outlined in paragraph 74. To renew the bevel

to a torque of 162-178 ft.-lbs. then adjust bevel gear backlash to 0.005-0.007 by transferring shims (6) from right brake plate to left side, without altering the combined thickness of the two shim packs.

NOTE: If bevel ring gear and pinion, final drive housing, or transmission housing are renewed, refer to paragraph 77A for mesh position adjustment.

76B. **OVERHAUL.** With differential removed from tractor as outlined in paragraph 76A, bump the roll pins (19—Fig. MM683E) in until they are centered in spider gear shafts (19) and clear the walls of differential cage (15); then pull the spider gear shafts using suitable pliers. The 0.996-0.997 diameter spider gear shafts should have a clearance of 0.003-0.005 in bushings (17). New spider gears (16) are equipped with bushings, or bushings are available separately for field installation. Before reinstalling spider gears, drive the roll pins from spider gear shafts; align the holes in shaft and differential cage, and install roll pins flush with outer wall of cage as shown.

The differential cross shaft (20) should have a clearance of 0.002-0.004 in sleeve bushings. Nominal shaft diameter is 1¾-inches for right bushing and 2⅛-inches for left bushing. New bull pinion sleeves are equipped with bushings; or bushings are available separately for service installation.

If main drive bevel gears are renewed, refer to paragraph 77A. Install the assembled differential assembly as outlined in paragraph 76A.

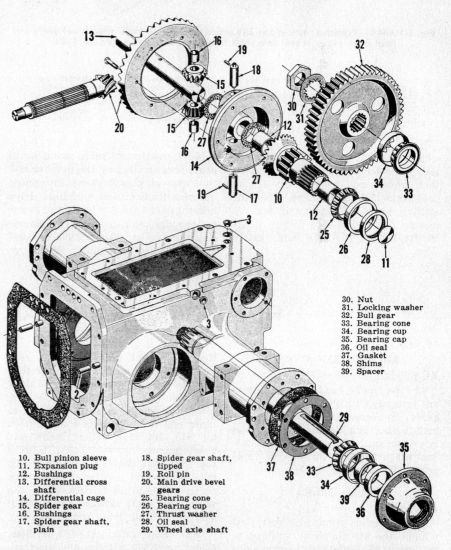

30. Nut
31. Locking washer
32. Bull gear
33. Bearing cone
34. Bearing cup
35. Bearing cap
36. Oil seal
37. Gasket
38. Shims
39. Spacer

10. Bull pinion sleeve
11. Expansion plug
12. Bushings
13. Differential cross shaft
14. Differential cage
15. Spider gear
16. Bushings
17. Spider gear shaft, plain
18. Spider gear shaft, tipped
19. Roll pin
20. Main drive bevel gears
25. Bearing cone
26. Bearing cup
27. Thrust washer
28. Oil seal
29. Wheel axle shaft

Fig. MM684—Exploded view of the 445, Jet Star and 4-Star series differential, main drive bevel gears and final drive gears. Wheel axle shaft bearings are adjusted with shims (38).

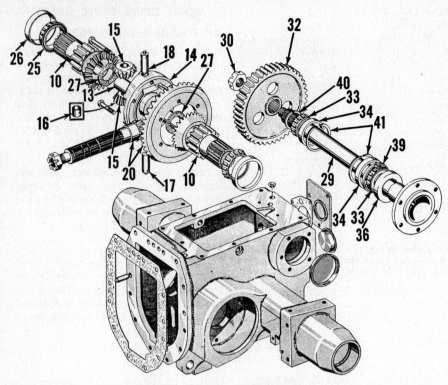

Fig. MM684A—Exploded view of the 335 series differential, main drive bevel gears and final drive gears. Wheel axle shaft bearings are adjusted with nut (30).

10. Bull pinion sleeve	17. Spider gear shaft, plain	25. Bearing cone	33. Bearing cone
13. Differential cross shaft	18. Spider gear shaft, tipped	26. Bearing cup	34. Bearing cup
14. Differential cage		27. Thrust washers	36. Oil seal
15. Spider gear	20. Main drive bevel gears	29. Wheel axle shaft	39. Spacer
16. Bushings		30. Nut	40. Snap ring
		32. Bull gear	41. Snap ring

newing main drive bevel pinion, proceed as follows:

Note the mounting dimension number etched on old and new pinions. If numbers are the same, install a shim pack of identical thickness as that removed.

If a +0.001 pinion is used to replace a 0.000 pinion, add 0.001 in plastic shims to the previously installed shim pack.

If a —0.001 pinion is used to replace a 0.000 pinion, remove 0.001 of shims.

If a +0.001 pinion replaces a —0.001 pinion, 0.002 in shims is required.

The plastic shims are color coded as follows:

Red 0.002
Green 0.003
Blue 0.005

If either of the main housings are renewed; or if bevel gear teeth showed an abnormal wear pattern when removed, the correct shim pack must be determined by trial assembly using Prussian blue. Assemble the housings using approximately 0.010 thickness of shims, making sure some backlash exists. Tighten the flange bolts to the recommended torque of 162-178 ft.-lbs. Coat gear teeth with Prussian blue and rotate the gear set with no load, in the normal direction of rotation. If tooth contact is even from tip to base of teeth, shim pack thickness is correct.

If heavy contact is noted at tips of teeth, add shims; at base of teeth, remove shims.

Adjust backlash and complete the assembly as outlined in paragraph 76A, after mesh position has been properly adjusted.

ring gear, first remove the differential as outlined in paragraph 76A, then unbolt and remove bevel ring gear from differential cage. When installing bevel ring gear, tighten retaining cap screws to a torque of 52-58 fts.-lbs. and secure with safety wire.

Mesh position of main drive bevel gears is controlled by the number and thickness of plastic shims interposed between transmission and final drive housing. 0.009-0.020 thickness of shims is normally used. A mounting dimension number of —0.001, 0.000 or 0.001 is etched on end of pinion. When re-

FINAL DRIVE AND REAR AXLE

BULL PINION GEARS
All Models

78. The final drive bull pinion gears are integral with the differential side gears. To remove, overhaul and reinstall the combination differential side gear and bull pinion sleeves, follow the procedure outlined in paragraphs 75 and 75A; or 76A.

BULL GEARS
All Models

79. To remove either bull gear, first remove the pto clutch as outlined in paragraph 87. Unlock and remove nut and driven gear from inner end of

the pto output shaft. Support rear of tractor and remove respective fender and wheel and tire unit. Unlock and remove the large nut (30—Fig. MM684 or 684A) retaining bull gear to inner end of wheel axle shaft and on the 445, Jet Star, 4-Star series and U302 unbolt the axle outer bearing cap (35) from the final drive housing, but be careful not to damage the shims (38). On all models, bump the wheel axle shaft outward and lift bull gear from final drive housing.

When reassembling the 445, Jet Star, 4-Star or U302, tighten the gear retaining nut securely and lock the nut

in place by bending over a portion of washer (31). On the 335 series, install the remaining parts by reversing the removal procedure and adjust the axle shaft bearings as outlined in paragraph 80A.

WHEEL AXLE SHAFT AND BEARINGS
All Models

80. To remove either wheel axle shaft, first remove the respective bull gear as outlined in paragraph 79, then withdraw the axle shaft from the

housing. The procedure for renewing the bearing cups and cones and seal is evident at this time.

When reassembling the 445, Jet Star, 4-Star or U302, tighten the bull gear retaining nut securely and lock the nut in place by bending over a portion of washer (31—Fig. MM684). Install the bearing cap (35) and tighten the retaining cap screws securely to seat the bearings; then, back off the cap screws to relieve any pre-load on the bearings and using a torque wrench attached to outer end of axle shaft, check the rolling torque required to keep the axle shaft in motion. Then tighten the cap screws and make a second rolling torque check. If the wheel axle shaft bearings are properly adjusted, the rolling torque reading made with the bearing cap retaining screws tightened will be 30-130 inch pounds greater than the torque reading taken with the screws

loose. If bearing pre-load is not as specified, vary the number of shims (38) located between bearing cap (35) and final drive housing. Refer also to Fig. MM685.

80A. When reassembling 335 series, tighten the bull gear retaining nut (30 —Fig. MM684A) securely to firmly seat all parts; then, back-off the nut to relieve any pre-load on the bearings and using a torque wrench attached to outer end of axle shaft, check the rolling torque required to keep the axle shaft in motion. Then tighten the nut to pre-load the bearings and make a second rolling torque check. If the wheel axle shaft bearings are properly adjusted, the rolling torque reading made with the nut tightened will be 30-130 inch pounds greater than the torque reading taken with the nut loose.

WHEEL AXLE SHAFT OIL SEAL

Series 445-Jet Star-4 Star-U302

81. The procedure for removing the oil seal (36—Fig. MM684) is evident after removing the axle shaft bearing cap (35). Removal of the bearing cap can be accomplished after removing the wheel and tire unit and the wheel hub.

Series 335

81A. The procedure for removing the oil seal (36—Fig. MM684A) is evident after removing the axle shaft as outlined in paragraph 80.

BRAKES

All Models

82. **ADJUSTMENT.** The disc type brakes are adjusted properly when both brakes are equalized and pedal pads have 1½ to 2 inches of free travel. To adjust the brakes, loosen lock nut (27—Fig. MM686) and turn the adjusting bolt (26) on each brake either way as required to obtain the desired free travel.

83. **R&R AND OVERHAUL.** To remove the brake lined discs, first remove both platform assemblies and both brake covers. Loosen the chuck screw (CS—Fig. MM687) and pry the speedometer drive gear (G) from the bull pinion sleeve. Remove the brake outer lined discs, remove both of the brake adjusting bolts and withdraw

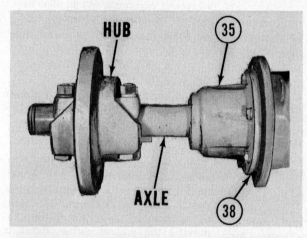

Fig. MM685—Series 445, Jet Star and 4-Star wheel axle shaft bearings are adjusted by varying the number of shims (38) located between final drive housing and bearing cap (35).

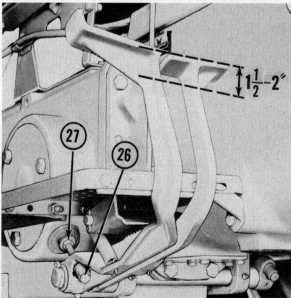

Fig. MM686—Turn the brake adjusting bolt (26) on each side of tractor until brake pedals have a free travel of 1½-2 inches.

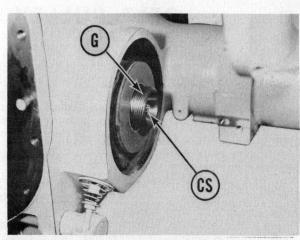

Fig. MM687—Left brake installation on 335 and 445 series tractors. Speedometer drive gear (G) can be removed after loosening the chuck screw (CS). 4 Star Series is similar. Speedometer drive gear is omitted in Jet Star.

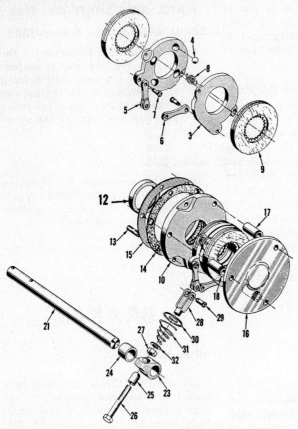

Fig. MM688 — Exploded view of brakes and actuating linkage. Brake linings are of the bonded type.

3. Actuating disc
4. Ball
5. Yoke link
6. Plain link
7. Shoulder bolt
8. Spring
9. Lined disc
10. Inner brake plate
12. Seal
13. Stud
14. Gasket
15. Shims
16. Brake cover
17. Spacer, single groove
18. Spacer, double groove
21. Pedal shaft
23. Lever
24. Spacer
25. Ball joint
26. Adjusting bolt
27. Jam nut
28. Clevis
29. Clevis pin
30. Dust shield
31. Spring
32. Washer

pounds is required to keep the pulley shaft in motion.

84B. When installing the pulley unit, vary the number of shim gaskets (6 and 7) to provide a backlash of 0.005-0.007 between the driving bevel gears. Backlash can be measured by using Plasti-gage betewen the gear teeth.

POWER TAKE-OFF

The power take-off system is driven by a hub located in the engine flywheel and is in continuous operation as long as the engine is running and the pto clutch is engaged.

The occasion for overhauling the complete power take-off system will be infrequent. The subsequent paragraphs will therefore be outlined on the basis of local repairs.

DRIVING HUB
All Models

85. The pto clutch shaft is driven at the forward end by a hub located in the engine flywheel as shown in Fig. MM690.

On all models except U302, the procedure for removing the hub is evident after detaching (splitting) the engine from the transmission housing as outlined in paragraph 63 and removing the engine clutch. Refer to paragraph 59A.

On model U302 the pto driving hub is mounted ahead of the flywheel, and renewal requires removal of flywheel as outlined in paragraph 39A.

the actuating plate assemblies and the inner lined discs. Disconnect the springs (8—Fig. MM688) and separate the actuating discs. Thoroughly inspect all parts and renew any which are damaged or worn.

If oil is leaking around the bull pinion shaft sleeve, remove the inner brake plate and renew the seal (12). Be careful, however, not to damage or lose the shims located between the inner brake plate and the final drive

housing. When installing the inner brake plates, use a tin sleeve or shim stock to avoid damaging the seal lips. If oil is leaking around the expansion plug in the right bull pinion shaft sleeve, use Permatex as a sealer and install a new plug. When reassembling, use a new "O" ring on the speedometer drive gear. Note: The single grooved cover spacer (17) should be installed on rear cover bolts. Adjust the brakes as outlined in paragraph 82.

BELT PULLEY

All Models

The belt pulley unit is driven by a bevel gear which is mounted on the power take-off clutch shaft. The unit will be in continuous operation as long as the engine is running and the pto clutch is engaged. To renew the driving bevel pinion (32—Fig. MM698), it is necessary to remove and disassemble the pto clutch as outlined in paragraphs 87 and 89.

84. R&R AND OVERHAUL. Remove pulley (10—Fig. MM689) from hub (11), then unbolt and remove the driven unit from the final drive housing, being careful not to damage or lose shim gaskets (6 and 7)).

84A. Remove the lock nut retaining the pulley hub to the pulley shaft and remove the hub (11). Place the assembly in a press and press the pulley shaft from the pulley housing. The need and procedure for further disassembly is evident.

When reassembling, press the bearing cups (9) tightly against snap rings in housing. Press bearing cone (8) tightly against shoulder on pulley shaft, then install pulley shaft and outer bearing cone and use the pulley hub to bump the bearing cone in place. Install the oil seal, pulley hub and lock nut. Tighten the lock nut (2) until a rolling torque of 15 inch-

PTO CLUTCH AND CLUTCH SHAFT
All Models

86. ADJUST CLUTCH. When the belt pulley and pto control lever is pushed forward to the engaged position, the clutch should engage with a distinct snap and a 65-75 pound push should be required at the end of the engaging lever. If little effort is required to engage the clutch, pull the lever rearward to the disengaged position, drain the hydraulic system and remove the hydraulic lift unit, seat and cover from top of final drive housing. Turn the clutch assembly until the spring loaded lock pin (Fig. MM691) is visible through the cover

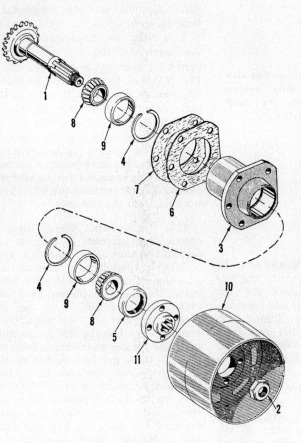

Fig. MM689 — Exploded view of belt pulley attachment. Shim gaskets (6 & 7) control the driving bevel gear backlash of 0.005-0.007.

1. Pulley shaft
2. Nut
3. Housing
4. Snap ring
5. Oil seal
6. & 7. Shim gaskets
8. Bearing cone
9. Bearing cup
10. Pulley
11. Hub

Fig. MM691A—PTO brake assembly used on U302 tractors. Spring adjustment (A) controls applied pressure of brake band (4). Adjusting nuts (5) adjust band-to-drum clearance.

1. Actuating arm
2. Frame
3. Clutch drum
4. Brake band
5. Adjusting nuts
6. Spring adjustment
A. Installed length (1⅝-in.)

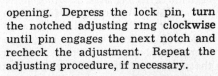

opening. Depress the lock pin, turn the notched adjusting ring clockwise until pin engages the next notch and recheck the adjustment. Repeat the adjusting procedure, if necessary.

On model U302, the pto clutch drum is equipped with a brake, shown partially disassembled in Fig. MM691A. The steel brake band (4) should be completely free of drum when clutch is engaged, yet apply sufficient tension to stop the output shaft when clutch is released. Adjust the brake as follows:

Turn adjusting nut (6) until compressed length of spring is 1⅝-inches when measured at (A) with clutch engaged. Release the pto clutch and back off the band adjusting nuts (5) until band (4) is completely free of drum. With clutch released and band (4) free of drum measure rolling torque of pto output shaft; then tighten adjusting nuts (5) until an ADDITIONAL torque of 22-26 ft.-lbs. is required to rotate output shaft. Band (4) must be free of drum with pto clutch ENGAGED after adjustment is completed.

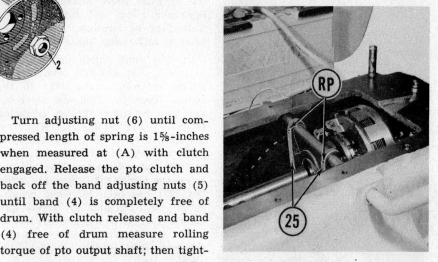

Fig. MM692 — After drifting out the Roll pins (RP), the BP and PTO engaging lever, forks (25) and yoke can be removed.

Fig. MM690—Rear view of engine flywheel showing the installation of the pto driving hub.

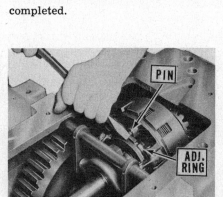

Fig. MM691 — Adjusting the pto clutch. Final drive housing cover must be removed as shown to make the adjustment.

Fig. MM692A—On model U302, the pin must be driven from brake actuating arm (A) as well as clutch forks, before actuating lever can be removed.

Fig. MM693 — Top view of final drive housing showing the pto clutch installation.

Fig. MM694 — Before removing the pto clutch shaft, the clutch must be moved forward as shown and the long key (22) removed.

Fig. MM695—Be sure thrust washer (34) is in position on clutch shaft before installing the clutch cage and pinion gear.

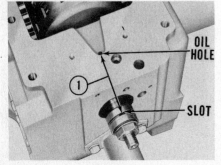

Fig. MM696 — When installing the pto clutch shaft, be sure slot in bearing spacer is in register with oil hole in final drive housing.

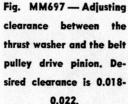

Fig. MM697 — Adjusting clearance between the thrust washer and the belt pulley drive pinion. Desired clearance is 0.018-0.022.

87. **REMOVE AND REINSTALL.** To remove the pto clutch, drain the hydraulic system, disconnect the lift links from the rockshaft arms and remove the tractor seat. Unbolt and remove the hydraulic lift unit from top of final drive housing and the hydraulic pump and drive coupling from rear of housing. Remove the final drive housing top cover.

Using a small punch, drive out the pins (RP—Fig. MM692) retaining the clutch throwout forks (25) to the control lever. On U302, also drive out the pin retaining brake actuating lever (A—Fig. MM692A). Withdraw the control lever, forks and throwout yoke. Bend lockwasher (21—Fig. MM693) away from nut (20) and unscrew the nut as far as possible. After nut (20) has been loosened, remove cotter pin (P) and set screw (3). NOTE: The hardened and drilled set screw may break if excess leverage or shock load is applied. Move the

clutch assembly forward and continue unscrewing the lock nut until the nut is free from the threads; then, turn the clutch shaft 180 degrees, move the clutch forward and remove key (22—Fig. MM694). Using a suitable puller attached to rear of shaft, remove the clutch shaft and lift out the clutch and clutch cage. If a puller is not available, the shaft can be bumped rearward by using a punch and hammer against set screw seating surface on shaft. The shaft can also be bumped rearward after splitting the final drive housing from the transmission.

87A. To reinstall the clutch and clutch shaft, proceed as follows: Insert the clutch shaft through rear opening in final drive housing and install the thrust washer (34—Fig. MM-695). Position the pinion gear and clutch cage assembly over the pto driven gear and slide the clutch shaft forward. Position the clutch assembly part way on the clutch shaft, then install the lock nut and washer on the shaft so they are between the sliding sleeve and adjusting ring. Also, be sure the lip on lock washer is toward the adjusting ring. Slide the shaft forward and turn the bearings until slot in bearing spacer is up and in register with oil hole in final drive housing as shown in Fig. MM696. Turn the shaft until the splined forward end engages the flywheel hub, then bump the shaft into position. Recheck the position of the spacer washer slot by sighting through the oil hole.

Insert key (22 — Fig. MM694) in clutch shaft and slide clutch assembly rearward into the clutch cage while threading the lock nut rearward on

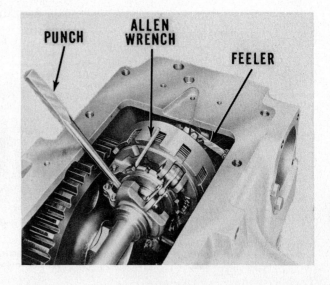

the clutch shaft. Turn the clutch shaft 180 degrees and install the Allen head set screw (3—Fig. MM693). The fore and aft position of the clutch on the clutch shaft is adjusted by the lock nut and the Allen head set screw. Insert a feeler gage as shown in Fig. Fig. MM694). Using a suitable puller MM697 or Fig. MM697A, and check the clearance between the thrust washer and the bevel pinion which should be 0.018-0.022. If clearance is excessive, loosen the Allen head set screw and tighten the lock nut. If insufficient clearance exists, loosen the lock nut and tighten the set screw. Make the final adjustment by tightening lock nut (20) to avoid applying excessive pressure to the drilled set screw (3). When the specified clearance is obtained, lock the adjustments by bending lock washer over against flat of nut and installing cotter pin in the Allen head set screw. Install the clutch throwout forks and shaft. Adjust the clutch (and pto brake, if so equipped) as outlined in paragraph 86 and install the belt pulley unit as in paragraph 84B.

88. OVERHAUL CLUTCH SHAFT.

With the clutch shaft removed as outlined in paragraph 87, remove the adjusting nut (29—Fig. MM698), press the bearings from the shaft and renew any damaged parts.

When reassembling, press the inner bearing cone tightly against shoulder on shaft and install the remaining parts. Tighten the adjusting nut until bearings are slightly pre-loaded; then back-off the nut to just remove the pre-load. Bearing cups should clamp the spacer tight enough to prevent free movement of the spacer.

Install clutch and clutch shaft as outlined in paragraph 87A.

89. OVERHAUL CLUTCH AND CLUTCH CAGE.

With the clutch removed as outlined in paragraph 87,

Fig. MM697A—On U302 with pto brake, clutch position adjustment must be made through belt pulley mounting hole as shown.

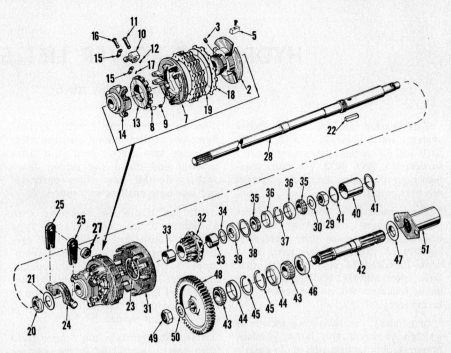

Fig. MM698—Exploded view of 445 series pto clutch, clutch shaft and associated parts. Other models are similar.

2. Back plate	16. Pin	28. Clutch shaft	40. Sleeve
3. Set screw	17. Roll pin	29. Stop nut	41. Gasket
5. Key	18. Driving plate	30. Washer	42. Pto shaft
7. Floating plate	19. Driven plate	31. Clutch cage	43. Bearing cone
8. Adjusting pin	20. Lock nut	32. Pinion	44. Bearing cup
9. Pin spring	21. Lock nut washer	33. Pinion bushings	45. Snap ring
10. Lever	22. Key	34. Thrust washer	46. Oil seal
11. Pin	23. Snap ring	35. Bearing cone	47. Dust shield
12. Roll pin	24. Throwout yoke	36. Bearing cup	48. Driven gear
13. Adjusting ring	25. Throwout fork	37. Spacer	49. Nut
14. Sliding sleeve	27. Oil seal	38. Snap ring	50. Washer
15. Link		39. Retainer	51. Guard

remove pins (16—Fig. MM698) and lift off sliding sleeve (14). Depress the spring loaded pin (8), completely unscrew the notched adjusting ring (13) and disassemble the floating plate (7), driving plates (18) and driven plates (19) from the back plate (2). Thoroughly clean all parts and renew any which are damaged or worn. Be sure that friction faces of back plate (2) and floating plate (7) are not scored or excessively heat checked. The five driving plates (18) and the four driven plates (19) must not be warped or worn. Renew pins (11 and 16) if they are grooved. Renew levers (10) and links (15) if they are worn or if pin holes are enlarged.

Pinion gear (32) can be removed from the clutch cage by removing snap ring (23). Pinion bushings (33) should have an inside diameter of 1.3055-1.3065. Bushings are available separately for field installation or, a new pinion gear contains factory installed bushings reamed to size. Diameter of clutch shaft where bushings ride is 1.3030-1.3035.

When reassembling, install the clutch and clutch shaft as outlined in paragraph 87A.

PTO OUTPUT SHAFT
All Models

90. R&R AND OVERHAUL. To remove the pto output shaft, first remove the pto clutch and clutch shaft as outlined in paragraph 87. Remove nut (49 — Fig. MM698), flat washer (50) and driven gear (48); then bump the pto shaft rearward and out of the final drive housing. If bearing cups (44) are damaged, drift them out of the final drive housing. When installing new bearing cups, press them tightly against their retaining snap rings. Rear bearing cone must be pressed tightly against the pto shaft shoulder.

When reassembling, be sure that hub end of pto driven gear (48) is toward rear of tractor; then tighten the gear retaining nut to pre-load the bearings. Desired pre-load is when 3-6 inch pounds of rolling torque are required to keep the pto shaft in motion when checked at rear end of shaft. Pto shaft oil seal should be installed $\frac{3}{16}$-inch past rear face of final drive housing. Install dust seal flush with rear of housing.

Install the pto clutch and clutch shaft as outlined in paragraph 87A.

HYDRAULIC POWER LIFT SYSTEM

(Early 3-Point Hitch)

This section applies to 445 series systems built prior to Ser. No. SNB 5218 and 335 series systems built prior to Ser. No. SNA 1872. For later tractors equipped with Tel-O-Flo system see paragraph 118.

There have been several improvement packages installed in the hydraulic systems since they were first introduced. Some of the parts have been installed to replace those that failed prematurely; while others have been incorporated to improve performance.

In general, the following section is written to cover the latest version; however, this section will apply equally well to earlier versions which may or may not have detailed differences in construction.

Note: The maintenance of absolute cleanliness of all parts is of utmost importance in the operation and servicing of the hydraulic system. Of equal importance is the avoidance of nicks or burrs on any of the working parts.

LUBRICATION AND BLEEDING

100. It is recommended that the hydraulic system working fluid (Automatic Transmission Fluid, Type A) and the system filter cartridge be changed every 1000 hours of operation, as follows:

With the three point hitch in the lowered position, loosen the lock nut, back out the drain plug set screw and remove the fluid reservoir drain plug. Crank engine several revolutions to remove oil from the pump and lines. Cycle the power steering system several times to remove oil from steering system. Install drain plug, remove cover from control valve housing and refill the reservoir with clean Diesel fuel, distillate or kerosene. Operate engine for not more than two minutes and cycle the hydraulic and power steering system several times to flush the entire hydraulic system. With the three point hitch in the lowered position, remove the reservoir drain plug, crank engine several revolutions to remove flushing oil from the pump and lines and cycle the power steering system several times to remove

flushing oil from the steering system. Remove the filter cover, pull the filter cartridge and screen from the filter housing and clean the screen thoroughly. Install new filter cartridge and use new gaskets as needed.

Fill the hydraulic reservoir with Automatic Transmission Fluid, Type A, start engine and cycle the lift system and power steering system several times to fill the system components. Then, refill the fluid reservoir so that fluid level is 1-1¼ inches below top of filler opening and install the control valve housing cover.

Note: To maintain the proper fluid level when operating large remote cylinders, it may be necessary to add more oil. Always have the cylinders contracted when adding oil.

SYSTEM CHECKS AND ADJUSTMENTS

101. Before removing a suspected faulty unit from tractor, it is advisable to attach a pressure gage to the system and make a few simple checks and adjustments. Quite often system malfunctions will be corrected without disassembly and/or overhaul. Proceed as follows:

102. Remove filler cover from top of control lever housing and check the hydraulic oil level to make certain it

is just below the control rod. Reinstall cover. Remove the right hand pipe plug from top of valve housing and connect a suitable pressure gage as shown in Fig. MM700. It is desirable to use a dual gage set-up as shown since accurate adjustments depend on both high and low pressure readings. Start engine, run same until hydraulic fluid is at normal operating temperature and proceed as follows:

Make certain the lifting rods and linkages are free and do not bind. Do not have any implements mounted on the three-point hitch.

103. **NEUTRAL POSITION (335 AND 445).** Back out the draft plunger adjusting screw (S—Fig. MM701) until the screw does not contact the plunger (P) and with the engine running at 800 rpm, pull the three-point lift control lever (outer lever on multiple lever systems) back until the lift arms raise about half-way. Then move the lever forward until the lift arms JUST start to lower. Slide the socket-head screw and detent assembly (D—Fig. MM702) in the desired direction until about ⅛-inch of the socket-head is visible at the rear of the control lever with the lift arms just starting to lower. Tighten the lock nut to hold the position of the socket-head screw and detent, then recheck the adjustment.

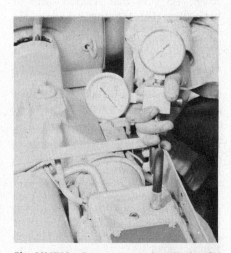

Fig. MM700—Pressure gage installation for checking the operation of the hydraulic system. A low reading gage is required for some checks whereas a high reading gage is required for others.

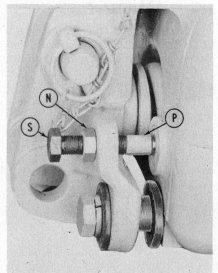

Fig. MM701—Rear view of hydraulic reservoir, showing the draft control plunger (P), lock nut (N) and adjusting screw (S).

After establishing the correct location of the detent, it is recommended that its position be marked with respect to the quadrant. This will enable the tractor operator to reposition the detent in case it should become loose and slip during operation.

104. MASTER SPOOL SYNCHRONIZATION (335 AND 445.) Move stop (A—Fig. MM703) to position the three-point hitch control lever at middle of quadrant as shown. (Distance from front of quadrant to lever will be approximately 5 inches). Remove the lock nut (N—Fig. MM701) from the draft plunger adjusting screw, then reinstall the screw without the lock nut. With engine running at full governed speed, turn the adjusting screw IN until the lift arms just start to raise; at which time the gage pressure should not exceed 200 psi.

If the pressure exceeds 200 psi just before the lift arms start to raise, re-move the oil filler cover and wear plate (445 only) from top of control lever housing as shown in Fig. MM704, loosen the lock nut (B), back-off the adjusting nut (C) from fork (E) ¼-turn and unscrew the draft plunger adjusting screw to lower the lift. Now, slowly turn the draft plunger adjusting screw in until the lift starts to raise. If the gage reading still exceeds 200 psi, back-off the control rod adjusting nut another ¼-turn and repeat the check with the draft plunger screw. Continue to back-off the adjusting nut ¼-turn at a time until the lift will raise without causing a pressure exceeding 200 psi and secure the adjustment with the lock nut (B).

Note: To avoid reducing the lift sensitivity, do not back-off the control rod adjusting nut any more than necessary to eliminate excessive pressure.

If the pressure is less than 200 psi as the lift arms just start to raise, turn the adjusting nut (C) toward the fork (E) until the pressure reading slightly exceeds 200 psi before lift arm actuation; then, back the nut away from the fork just enough to bring the pressure reading down to 200 psi.

105. SENSITIVITY CHECK (335 AND 445.) With the engine operating at full governed rpm and the 3-point lift control lever in the mid-range position as shown in Fig. MM703, slowly turn the draft plunger adjusting screw (S—Fig. MM701) in until the lift starts to raise. As soon as the lift starts to raise, back out the adjusting screw until the lifting action stops and the lift arms are stationary. At this point, carefully note the position of the adjusting screw; then, continue to back out the adjusting screw slowly until the lift JUST starts to lower. If it requires more than 1½ turns of the adjusting screw (0.080 draft plunger travel) to start lowering the lift from a stationary position, the unit is not properly adjusted for sensitivity. In which case, readjust the unit as outlined in paragraph 104 and recheck. If the condition is not corrected, check the following:

a. Draft plunger sticking due to paint or other foreign material.

b. Internal control linkage binding.

c. Internal overload spring lacks proper tension.

d. Selector valve spool is sticking.

e. Improper spring installed on selector valve or spring is out of position.

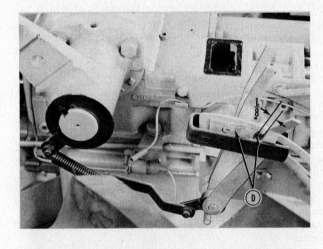

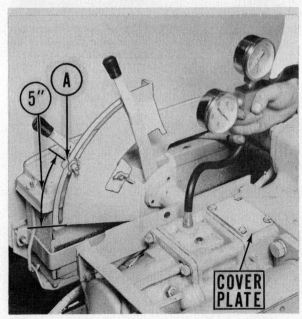

Fig. MM702—View showing the proper position of detent assembly (D). Notice that ⅛-inch of the socket head screw is visible at rear of control lever.

Fig. MM703—Three point control lever positioned at mid-range of quadrant. Stop (A) positions the lever.

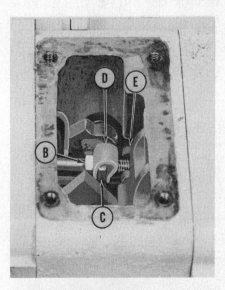

Fig. MM704—Cover plate removed from top of control lever housing to expose the control rod adjusting nut (C), lock nut (B) and fork (E).

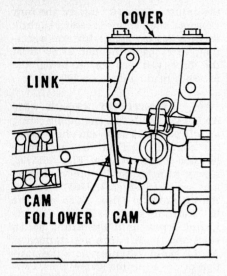

Fig. MM705—Sectional view of 445 controls, showing the proper installation of the cover and wear plate.

106. DRAFT PLUNGER ADJUSTING SCREW (335 AND 445). Remove the draft plunger adjusting screw (S—Fig. MM701) from the reservoir hinge bracket, install lock nut (N) then re-install screw (S) in the hinge bracket. Install the wear plate (445 only) and cover to top of control lever housing, making certain that the wear plate is between the cam and cam follower and the link is to the rear. Refer to Fig. MM705.

Place the three-point hitch control lever in the neutral position, turn the draft plunger adjusting screw in until it is finger tight and tighten the lock nut (N—Fig. MM701).

106A. CENTERING (KICKOUT) DEVICE (335 ONLY). With the filler cover removed as shown in Fig. MM-705A, loosen the lock nut and turn the adjusting nut (AN) either way as re-

quired so the three-point control lever will return to neutral when the lift arms are all the way up.

107. CENTERING (KICKOUT) DEVICE (445 ONLY). The externally located centering device must be adjusted so that the three-point lift control lever will return to neutral position when the lift arms are approximately all the way up. Proceed as follows:

With engine running at full governed rpm, move the control lever all the way back and check to be sure the centering device returns the control lever to neutral when the lift arms are approximately at the end of their upward travel. If adjustment is not as specified, relocate the spring (F—Fig. MM706) in the proper hole in adjusting bar (9).

Note: It is essential that this centering device be properly adjusted or the hydraulic oil may overheat due to excessive operation of the pressure relief valve.

108. RELIEF VALVE PRESSURE (335 AND 445). To check the relief valve operating pressure, start engine and run same until the hydraulic fluid is at normal operating temperature. Then with engine running at 1550 rpm, hold one of the hydraulic control levers rearward momentarily and note the pressure gage reading as the relief valve opens which can be detected by an audible buzzing or hissing sound. Normal relief valve opening pressure is 1200-1300 psi. Pressures exceeding 1300 psi indicate that the relief valve spring tension is too great or the relief valve is sticking. In either case, it will be necessary to remove one or more of the pressure spring adjusting washers as outlined in paragraph 117 and/or free-up the

relief valve. Each 0.025 thick washer represents approximately 40 psi.

If the pressure is less than 1200 psi and the relief valve opens, the relief valve spring tension is insufficient and spring must be renewed and/or adjusting shims must be added as in paragraph 117. If the pressure is less than 1200 psi and the relief valve does not open, the hydraulic pump output is inadequate and pump must be renewed.

109. QUADRANT STOP BOLT (445 only). A stop bolt (H—Fig. MM707) must be installed in the lower section of the quadrant at the end of the sensitivity range and the purpose of this bolt must be explained to the tractor operator. It must also be explained to the operator that if the desired operating depth cannot be attained with the lever against the stop bolt, the upper lift link can be repositioned to the upper hole in the hinge plate as shown in Fig. MM708.

To determine the point at which to place the stop bolt, first make sure the pressure gage is installed in the

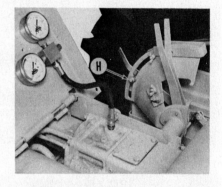

Fig. MM707—445 series quadrant stop bolt (H) must be positioned at the end of the sensivity range.

Fig. MM705A—Location of adjusting nut for the 335 three-point control lever centering device.

Fig. MM706—445 series three point control lever centering device. Adjustment is made by repositioning spring (F) in adjusting bar (9).

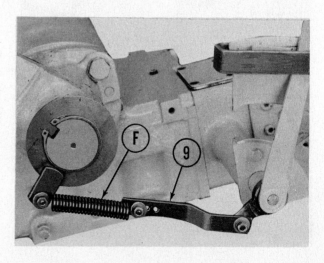

Control Lever Position	Auxiliary Port opened	Adjusting Screw location
Center lever forward	Upper front	Upper left
Center lever back	Upper rear	Bottom left
Inner lever forward	Lower rear	Upper right
Inner lever back	Lower front	Bottom right

right-hand port as shown in Fig. MM-707. Remove both limit bolts (J—Fig. MM708) and washers (K) from the hinge plate. Note the position of the shim washers and limit washers on each bolt, as these must be reinstalled in their exact original position.

Pull the hinge plate out far enough so the main spring (L) can be removed. After removing the main spring, reinstall the right-hand limit bolt (J), shim washer, and limit washer in the exact order they were before they were removed. Tighten the limit bolt.

Move the top link (M) to the upper hole (N) in the hinge plate, and place a wedge between the top link and hinge plate. Using the top link, apply pressure against the hinge plate so the hinge plate will be held tightly against the limit washer (K).

Move the 3-point lift control lever all the way down to the bottom of the quadrant. With the engine running at full-governed speed, VERY slowly move the control lever back until the lift arms JUST start to raise. Hold the lever at the point on the quadrant where the lift arms just started to raise and note the pressure registered on the gage after the lift arms reach the top of their stroke. With the hinge plate held tightly against the limit washers, the pressure registered should be the relief valve pressure of 1200-1300 psi. If the pressure registered is less than the relief valve pressure, move the control lever up (back) JUST enough so the gage registers maximum relief valve pressure. At the point where the lift arms just start

raising and the maximum relief valve pressure is obtained, install the lock bolt (H—Fig. MM707) on the quadrant. This point is the end of the sensitivity control by the lift.

Reinstall the main spring and the limit bolt assemblies.

110. **DROP RETARDER ADJUSTMENT (335 AND 445).** Check the adjustment of the drop retarder by observing the rate at which an implement can be lowered. The desired rate of drop can be obtained by inserting a screwdriver through opening in top of control valve housing and turning the notched wheel of the drop retarder adjusting screw.

Note: Adjustments related to the 3-point lift are now complete.

111. **AUXILIARY VALVES.** Proper spool co-ordination between master and auxiliary valves requires adjustment of the four small screws shown in Fig. MM709. The accompanying chart shows the relationship between the control levers, the auxiliary ports and the adjusting screws.

From the chart, it will be noted that proper remote cylinder extension and contraction depends on the correct setting of separate adjusting screws—one screw adjusts for extension and the other for contraction.

TWO-WAY CYLINDERS. With two-way cylinders and pressure gage connected to the system (Fig. MM709), start engine and run same at a speed of 800 rpm. While observing the pressure gage, slowly move the control lever to extend and retract the cylinders. If pressure exceeds 50 psi before cylinder actuation (extension or retraction) occurs, back out the related adjusting screw or screws (see chart) ¼-turn and recheck the cylinder actuation. If pressure still exceeds 50 psi, continue to back out the adjusting screws ¼-turn at a time until excessive pressure is eliminated on both the extension and retraction cycles.

Cylinder actuation should start when control lever is moved approximately one inch. If more than one inch of movement is required to actuate the cylinders, the screw or screws are backed out too far.

Now increase the engine speed to 1550 rpm and actuate the cylinders; at which time, the pressure should not exceed 100 psi.

ONE - WAY CYLINDERS. Check and adjust the extension cycle for one-way cylinders in a manner similar to that for checking two-way cylinders as outlined in the preceding para-

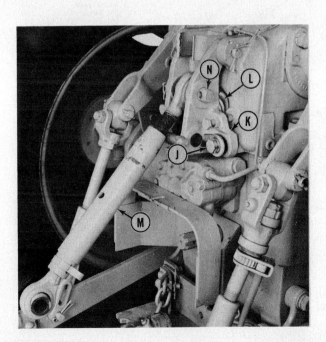

Fig. MM708—445 series hinge plate installation.

J. Limit bolts
K. Washers
L. Main spring
M. Top link
N. Upper hole

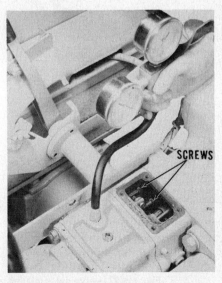

Fig. MM709—Cover plate removed from top of control lever housing to expose the auxiliary control valve adjusting screws.

Fig. MM710—Pipe plug location for connecting a pressure gage to check the reverse flow valve.

graph. When the control lever is against the long leg of the quadrant stop to contract a one-way cylinder, the pressure build-up should not exceed 200 psi. If gage pressure exceeds 200 psi, back out the related screw until excessive pressure is eliminated.

112. PRESSURE CHECK — REVERSE FLOW VALVE. Connect the pressure gage to pipe plug opening (1—Fig. MM710) which is located between the rear auxiliary ports. With engine running at 1550 rpm, hold one of the control levers back momentari-

ly and note the maximum pressure build-up. To avoid a sudden pressure surge, pull the lever back slowly. If pressure exceeds 1500 psi, the reverse flow valve is sticking and must be cleaned.

CAUTION: If the valve is sticking, release the control lever before the pressure build-up becomes excessive.

113. After completing all of the previous checks, refill the reservoir to the proper level as outlined in paragraph 100.

PUMP
All Models

114. Paragraphs 8 and 9 outline the procedures for overhaul of power steering flow control and relief valves. Complete pump rebuilding is not generally satisfactory on early pumps with fixed wear plates; however, pump may be disassembled and resealed, as outlined in paragraph 137.

ROCKSHAFT
All Models So Equipped

115. REMOVE AND REINSTALL. To remove the rockshaft, first remove the right fender. Then disconnect the 3-point hitch rods, remove snap rings and withdraw the lifting arms from rock (cross) shaft. Gently tap the

rockshaft out right side of housing. Then on 445 series unbolt and remove hubs (8—Fig. MM711) from reservoir. On 335 series, renew rockshaft bushings in reservoir if they are worn.

When reassembling, install rockshaft from right side of reservoir and push it through left side until the internal lifting arm key (42) can be installed. Then push the shaft toward right and into position. Install the remaining parts.

ROCKSHAFT CYLINDER
All Models So Equipped

116. R&R AND OVERHAUL. To remove the rockshaft operating cylinder, first drain the hydraulic fluid, remove the seat assembly and disconnect the 3-point hitch lift rods. Disconnect the power steering oil lines, unbolt and lift the complete hydraulic unit from tractor. Note: To avoid damaging the ferrule which extends into bottom of reservoir, keep the reservoir housing parallel to differential case when lifting. Place the removed unit on a work bench and with the lift arms in the raised position, remove the four cap screws retaining the cylinder to the reservoir. Using caution to prevent distorting the cylinder tube, push the cylinder away from the filter housing and gently pry

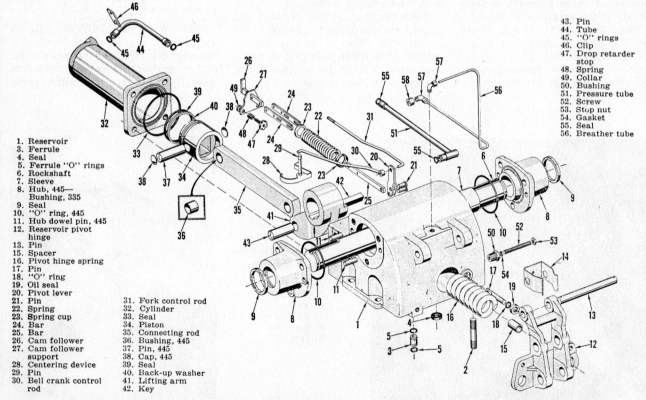

1. Reservoir
3. Ferrule
4. Seal
5. Ferrule "O" rings
6. Rockshaft
7. Sleeve
8. Hub, 445—Bushing, 335
9. Seal
10. "O" ring, 445
11. Hub dowel pin, 445
12. Reservoir pivot hinge
13. Pin
15. Spacer
16. Pivot hinge spring
17. Pin
18. "O" ring
19. Oil seal
20. Pivot lever
21. Pin
22. Spring
23. Spring cup
24. Bar
25. Bar
26. Cam follower
27. Cam follower support
28. Centering device
29. Pin
30. Bell crank control rod
31. Fork control rod
32. Cylinder
33. Seal
34. Piston
35. Connecting rod
36. Bushing, 445
37. Pin, 445
38. Cap, 445
39. Seal
40. Back-up washer
41. Lifting arm
42. Key
43. Pin
44. Tube
45. "O" rings
46. Clip
47. Drop retarder stop
48. Spring
49. Collar
50. Bushing
51. Pressure tube
52. Screw
53. Stop nut
54. Gasket
55. Seal
56. Breather tube

Fig. MM711—Typical exploded view of 445 series reservoir, rockshaft, rockshaft operating cylinder and associated parts used on all models with 3-point hitch. The 335 series is similarly constructed and differs only in details.

the tube out of cylinder head. Then slide cylinder from piston, Fig. MM713. The need and procedure for further disassembly is evident.

Thoroughly clean all parts in a suitable solvent and renew any which are damaged or worn. Connecting rod bushings on 445 series are available as separate replacement parts. Renew all seals and back up washers and re-assemble. Tighten the cylinder retaining cap screws to a torque 100 ft.-lbs.

CONTROL VALVES AND LINKAGE

All Models

117. **R&R AND OVERHAUL.** To remove the valves, first drain the hydraulic system, remove the seat assembly and disconnect the 3 - point hitch lift rods. Disconnect the power steering oil lines, unbolt and lift the complete hydraulic unit from tractor.

Note: To avoid damaging the ferrule which extends into bottom of reservoir, keep the reservoir housing parallel to differential case when lift-

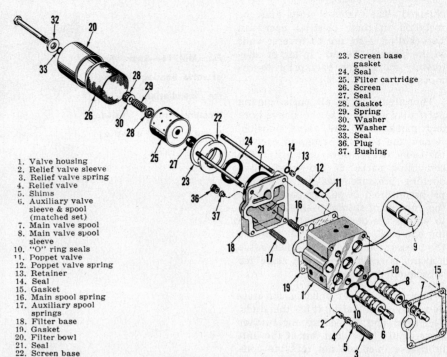

23. Screen base gasket
24. Seal
25. Filter cartridge
26. Screen
27. Seal
28. Gasket
29. Spring
30. Washer
32. Washer
33. Seal
36. Plug
37. Bushing

1. Valve housing
2. Relief valve sleeve
3. Relief valve spring
4. Relief valve
5. Shims
6. Auxiliary valve sleeve & spool (matched set)
7. Main valve spool
8. Main valve spool sleeve
10. "O" ring seals
11. Poppet valve
12. Poppet valve spring
13. Retainer
14. Seal
15. Gasket
16. Main spool spring
17. Auxiliary spool springs
18. Filter base
19. Gasket
20. Filter bowl
21. Seal
22. Screen base

Fig. MM715—Exploded view of typical late model hydraulic system filter and valves. Item (9) is used on models without auxiliary valves. The filter construction is considerably different on early models.

Fig. MM713—445 series hydraulic lift unit with rockshaft cylinder removed. Piston is fitted with one "O" ring and two back-up washers. 335 is similar except piston pin is not used.

ing. Place the removed unit on a work bench and with the lift arms in the raised position, remove the four cap screws retaining the cylinder to the reservoir. Using caution to prevent distorting the cylinder tube, push the cylinder away from the filter housing and gently pry the tube out of cylinder head. Note: It is not necessary to remove cylinder from piston.

Remove the four filter housing retaining stud nuts and remove the housing while carefully pulling the pressure tube out of the valve housing. Carefully note the location of the valve spool springs, as shown in Fig. MM714 for early models, then set the springs aside. Using care to prevent valve spools from falling out, slide the valve housing from the studs and withdraw the main valve spool (7—Fig. MM715), relief valve spring (3), shims (5) and relief valve (4) but be careful not to lose any of the adjusting shims. Extract poppet spring retainer (13), spring (12) and poppet valve (11). If retainer (13) does not extend beyond the housing enough to grasp it with a pair of pliers, it can be pushed out by inserting a stiff wire through pipe plug opening in side of valve housing. Valve spool sleeves can now be removed from the housing, but when doing so, observe the following CAUTION: Spools and sleeves are matched units, select - fitted to within 0.0004 and must not be inter-

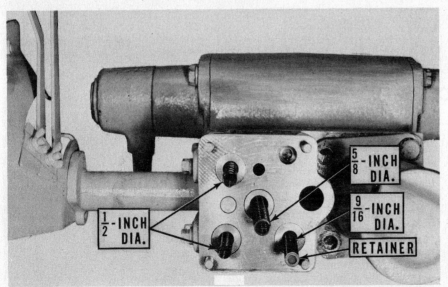

Fig. MM714—Front view of early production 445 hydraulic unit with filter housing removed. Note the proper location of the valve spool springs. On later models only two sizes of springs are used.

changed. The matched units must be installed in their original positions. Use caution, also, not to reverse ends of the sleeves. Be sure to tag or adequately mark each part prior to removal.

Thoroughly clean all parts, paying particular attention to the sleeve bore and passages in the valve housing. Renew the four "O" rings in each of the spool sleeves bores and install the remaining parts. If the relief valve opening pressure was not 1200-1300 psi as outlined in paragraph 108 vary the number of shims (5—Fig. MM715) to obtain the desired pressure. Adding one 0.025 thick shim will increase the pressure about 40 psi. When valve housing is assembled, set it aside for subsequent installation.

The control lever housing can now be removed by sliding it off the studs. The need and procedure for further disassembly is evident, but if the unit is disassembled, do not mix the control valve spools.

When reassembling, first remove the draft plunger adjusting screw from the reservoir hinge bracket, then, when installing the control lever housing on the studs, use a length of stiff wire to guide the draft plunger through rear opening in reservoir. Install the assembled valve housing on the studs and position the spool springs as shown in Fig. MM714. Install the filter housing making certain that the spool springs are properly seated on the projecting nipples in the filter housing. Tighten the filter housing retaining stud nuts to a torque of 30 ft.-lbs.

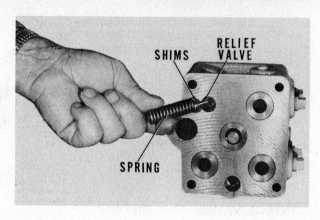

Fig. MM716—Rear view of valve housing showing the installation of the pressure relief valve, spring and adjusting shims.

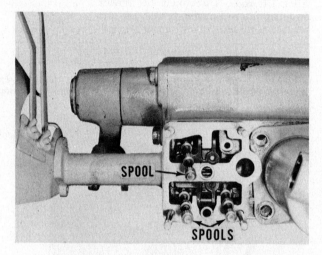

Fig. MM717—Front view of hydraulic unit showing the installation of the control lever housing. Valve spools are not interchangeable.

HYDRAULIC POWER LIFT

(TEL-O-FLO SYSTEM)

Series 335 tractors after serial number SNA1872, series 445 tractors after serial number SN5218 and all Jet Star, 4-Star and U302 tractors with three-point hitch, are equipped with the Tel-O-Flo hydraulic system covered in this section.

The Tel-O-Flo system, while similar in appearance to earlier systems, differs considerably in operation and method of adjustment. The Tel-O-Flo system can easily be distinguished from earlier systems by the presence of "Rate" and "Cycle" levers on the filler opening cover. (See Fig. MM718.)

OPERATION

118. The Tel-O-Flo system control valve consists of a master valve and three directional valves which control the three-point hitch and two remote cylinders. Proper hydraulic action depends on accurate synchronization of the master control valve with the directional valve being used. Before a raising action can be accomplished with the three-point hitch or single acting remote applications (or any action with double acting remote cylinders), the master control valve

Fig. MM718—To add or check the hydraulic fluid, remove valve cover (1), containing the rate and cycle levers (2).

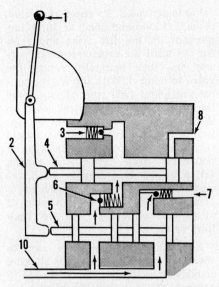

Fig. MM719—Schematic view of "Tel-O-Flo" hydraulic control valve showing oil flow through master control valve and three-point hitch directional valve.

1. Control lever
2. Activating lever
3. Relief valve
4. Directional valve
5. Master control valve
6. Check valve
7. Regulating valve
8. Ram passage
10. From pump

must be moved to block the system by-pass opening. At the same time the directional valve must move to open the proper passage to hydraulic system pressure.

Refer to Fig. MM719 for a schematic view of the three-point lift system operation. Hydraulic fluid under pump pressure enters the control valve at (10) and through the master control valve (5) at two points. The passage at the left is connected to the center area of the directional valve (4) by the check valve (6), and around the directional valve to the relief valve (3). This path is never closed, but is always open to pump pressure. The passage on the right leads through the master valve to the regulating valve (7). Oil passing through regulating valve (7) goes through the system filter back to the sump.

When the control lever (1) is moved to the raising position, linkage lever (2) and the two valves (4 and 5)

are moved to the right. The land on master valve spool (5) closes passage (7) leading to the sump. At the same time, the directional valve (4) opens passage (8) leading to the lift cylinder, oil from the pump passes through check valve (6), directional valve (4) and through opened passage (8) to the ram cylinder, and a raising action takes place. A mechanical linkage (not pictured) returns the control lever and valves to a neutral position at the completion of the lifting action.

When the control lever is moved to the lowering position the master valve (5) remains stationary allowing oil from the pump to bypass, and the directional valve moves to the left opening passage (8) to the sump through the area at the end of the valve spool. The hydraulic fluid trapped in the ram cylinder is then exhausted back to the sump.

Automatic draft action is controlled by a combination of hydraulic and spring pressure as shown in Fig. MM720. Metered oil is fed through line (14) to draft linkage cylinder (15) from the bypass line in front of regulating valve (7). A pressure of 25-50 psi is maintained in the system by valve (7). The draft linkage cylinder (15) is connected to the draft actuating cap (12) by the hollow linkage tube (11) which contains ports (P) at either end. When the control lever (1) is in the neutral position, port (P) at the front end of the tube is uncovered and the metered oil escapes. When the control lever is moved to the automatic draft position, tube (11) is moved forward by draft link (10) and the front port is closed by the lip of the draft linkage cylinder (15), directional valve (4) is moved into the lowering position and the three point lift lowers into operating position. When the implement enters the ground to the selected depth, the implement draft, acting through the upper link against spring pressure, moves the actuating cap (12) forward to close the rear port in the linkage tube allowing pressure to

build up in draft linkage cylinder (15). Piston (16) moves forward under hydraulic pressure to automatically actuate linkage lever (2) and the control valves. The selected implement operating draft is maintained by the automatic metering of the oil in the draft linkage cylinder at the linkage tube rear port.

LUBRICATION AND BLEEDING

119. To check the hydraulic fluid, remove the cover (1—Fig. MM718) containing the rate and cycle levers (2). Fluid level is correct when filled to within 1-1¼ inches of the top of reservoir. When draining and refilling the system, start the engine and cycle all operating levers several times to bleed air from the cylinders, then refill to the proper level with all cylinders retracted.

SYSTEM CHECKS AND ADJUSTMENTS

120. Unless the system is inoperative or defect is obvious, the following checks may pinpoint the trouble, eliminating unnecessary tear-down and overhaul.

Before an attempt is made to check the system, remove the filler cover and check the fluid level as outlined in paragraph 119, start the engine and warm the hydraulic fluid to operating temperature.

121. **PIVOT PLATE SPRINGS.** Spring (6—Fig. MM721) on each side of pivot plate (2) should have 0-1⁄₁₆-inch pre-load. To check the adjustment, loosen the two bolts (8 and 9) and turn the springs to rid the assembly of any accumulated dirt or

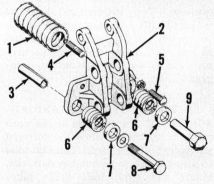

Fig. MM721—Exploded view of draft actuating pivot plate and springs used with "Tel-O-Flo" system.

1. Draft spring
2. Pivot plate
3. Spacer
4. Stud
5. Adjusting bolt
6. Tension springs
7. Spacer washer
8. Retaining bolt
9. Retaining bolt

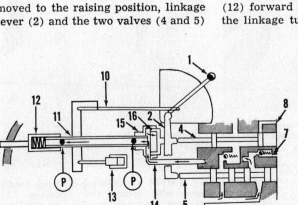

Fig. MM720 — Schematic view of automatic draft control mechanism used on "Tel-O-Flo" system.

10. Draft link
11. Linkage tube
12. Actuating cap
13. Dash pot
14. Supply tube
15. Draft linkage cylinder
16. Linkage piston
P. Activating ports

rust. Continue to turn the spring as the bolt is retightened. The pre-load is correct when the spring can barely be turned with the bolt tight. Four different thicknesses of shim washer (7) are available to adjust the pre-load.

122. DRAFT CONTROL BUTTON ADJUSTMENT. The adjustment of the draft control button determines the length of the secondary lift range on the control lever quadrant. (See Fig. MM722). The adjustment is correct if the length of the secondary lift range is approximately 2 inches on the quadrant as shown.

To make the adjustment, loosen the locknut on the adjusting bolt (A—Fig. MM723) and turn the bolt out until, with the engine running at 1000 rpm, the lift arms will not raise while the control lever is slowly moved through the entire secondary lift range. Now turn the bolt in, until the lift arms will just raise and the total length of the secondary lift range is approximately ⅛-inch; then, turn the adjusting bolt in 3¾ turns and tighten the locknut.

If the proper adjustment cannot be obtained, it will be necessary to disassemble and check the draft linkage as outlined in paragraph 132.

123. VALVE SYNCHRONIZATION CHECK. To check the synchronization of the master valve with the three-point lift directional valve, remove plug (1—Fig. MM725) from the top of the control valve housing and install a 300 psi pressure gage. Make sure the lift arms are all the way down before removing the plug.

With the engine running at full governed speed, and with no load on the lift arms, slowly move the three-point lift control lever to the raising position. The momentary pressure while the lift arms are raising should be 25-200 psi. If the pressure is not as indicated, disassemble and synchronize the valves as outlined in paragraph 134.

124. DASH POT CHECK AND ADJUSTMENT. The purpose of the dash pot is to restrict or slow the forward movement of the draft linkage tube to allow quick implement penetration before the first draft cycle takes place. To check the dash pot, move the three point lift control lever down the quadrant into the secondary lift range and the rate and cycle levers into the fast position as shown in Fig. MM724. Position the depth stop (S)

on the quadrant at the secondary lift position as shown. With the engine running at full governed speed, move the control lever to the raise position and allow the lift arms to raise and neutralize the valve. Now move the control lever quickly down the quadrant to the depth stop and check the time required for the lift arms to lower and again start to raise. If the dash pot is correctly adjusted, the lift arms should start to raise 1 to 1½ seconds after the lowering action starts.

To adjust the dash pot needle valve remove the pipe plug in the top of the lift housing and, using a ¼-inch hex head socket and extension (A—Fig. MM724), adjust the needle valve through the plug opening. Note: Use care to avoid applying undue pressure to valve. Needle valve or seat may be damaged if pressure is applied when needle is bottomed.

If the dash pot action is still too fast when needle is bottomed, remove the lift and overhaul the dash pot assembly as outlined in paragraph 132.

125. BACK FLOW VALVE CHECK. The purpose of the back flow valve is to prevent the lift arms from momentarily dropping when the control

valve is activated. To check the valve, place a 120-pound load or light implement on the lift arms and raise the lift until the arms are about halfway up, then manually return the valve to neutral. With the engine running at about 1000 rpm, slowly move the three-point lift control lever to the raising position and note the action of the lift arms. The load should rise to the transport position with no noticeable drop before the raising action begins. If a drop is noted, remove the filter base as outlined in paragraph 131 and, with a pair of pliers remove and service the back flow valve.

A pressure gage may be used to check the back flow valve for sticking or binding as follows: Remove plug (6—Fig. MM727) in side of control valve housing and install a 0-2000 psi pressure gage. With the engine running at full governed speed and the lift arms in a lowered position, move the three-point lift control lever to the raising position and note the pressure gage reading. If the pressure while the

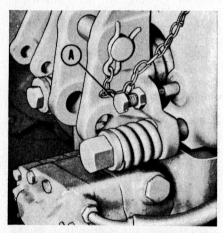

Fig. MM723—To adjust the draft control button, turn adjusting bolt (A) until the length of secondary lift range is approximately two inches.

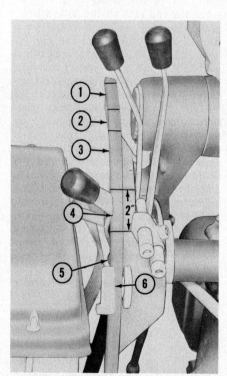

Fig. MM722—Draft control quadrant showing the general location of the different control ranges.

1. Lifting range
2. Neutral
3. Lowering and float range
4. Secondary lift range
5. Automatic draft control range
C Control lever stop

Fig. MM724 — Adjusting dash-pot needle valve with socket and extension (A) through plug hole provided in housing.

Fig. MM725—To adjust system relief valve pressure remove valve cover, install gage in system pressure port (1), loosen lock nut (N) and turn pressure adjusting screw in or out as required.

arms are raising is more than 250 psi greater than the pressure registered in checking the valve synchronization as outlined in paragraph 123, the back flow valve is sticking or binding and should be removed and serviced.

126. REGULATOR VALVE PRESSURE TEST. The regulator valve supplies the necessary hydraulic pressure to activate the automatic draft control linkage. To check the pressure, remove plug (2—Fig. MM725) in the top of the control valve housing and install a 0-300 psi pressure gage. With the hydraulic fluid at operating temperature and the engine running at 1000 rpm, the minimum pressure reading should be at least 25 psi with all of the control valves in the neutral position. At full governed speed (and the control valves in the neutral position) the pressure should not exceed 50 psi. If the pressures are not as indicated, service or renew the valve or spring after removing the filter base as outlined in paragraph 131.

127. RELIEF VALVE PRESSURE. The recommended relief valve pressure is 1400-1500 psi. To check the pressure, remove plug (1—Fig. MM-725) and install a 0-2000 psi pressure gage. With the engine running at full governed speed and the hydraulic fluid at operating temperature, move one of the auxiliary valve levers back to the raising position and hold it just long enough for the relief valve to act, and observe the gage reading. To adjust the pressure, remove the filler plate, loosen the lock nut (N—Fig. MM725) and turn the adjusting screw in or out until the correct pressure is

obtained. To remove the relief valve assembly it is first necessary to remove the control valve housing as outlined in paragraph 131.

128. RATE AND CYCLE CONTROL. A cam at the lower end of the rate lever (4—Fig. MM726) restricts the movement of the three-point directional control valve to the lowering position, thus controlling the speed of implement drop. The cycle lever (5) has the same effect after completion of the first draft cycle, thus smoothing the draft response to enable the operator to control the bobbing of the implement.

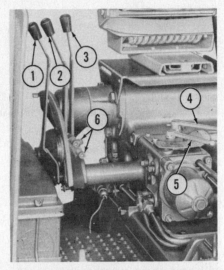

Fig. MM726—Operators platform showing hydraulic system controls.

1. Three-point lift control lever
2. & 3. Auxiliary valve control levers
4. Rate control lever
5. Cycle control lever
6. Auxiliary valve stop screws

To check the action of the rate lever, move the lever to the left ("Transport Lock") position and with the engine running at 1000 rpm and a weight or implement on the lower links, move the three-point lift control lever to the raised position. After the system has returned to neutral in the transport position, move the three-point lift control lever to the lowering position. The lift arms should remain in the transport position. The speed of implement drop should progressively increase as the rate lever is moved toward the right (fast position), until a free drop is obtained at the extreme fast setting.

To check the action of the cycle lever, move the rate lever (4) to the fast (right) position and the cycle lever (5) to the extreme left (slow) position. With the engine running at

1000 rpm, move the three-point lift control lever to the raised position. After the system has returned to neutral in the transport position, move the lift control lever to the automatic draft range. The lift arms should lower freely. After the arms have lowered, move the lift control lever to the secondary lift position and allow the lift arms to rise almost to the transport position, then return the control lever to the automatic draft range. The lift arms should remain stationary or fall very slowly. As the cycle lever (5) is moved toward the right, the speed of drop should progressively increase until a free drop is obtained at the extreme right (fast) position. The lowering speed of the cycle lever setting will never exceed the speed selected by the rate lever setting.

No adjustments are provided for the rate and cycle levers. If the correct action is not obtained, remove the filler plate and examine the eccentric shafts and the draft control linkage for wear or damage.

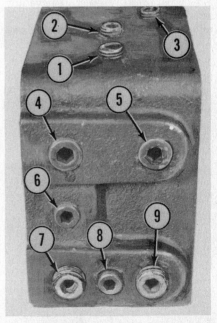

Fig. MM727—Control valve body showing port location and use.

1. System pressure port.
2. Regulating valve pressure port (System by-pass port).
3. Three-point lift synchronizing port.
4. Jack tapping for single or double acting remote cylinders (center lever).
5. Jack tapping for double acting remote cylinder (center-lever).
6. Back flow valve pressure port.
7. Jack tapping for double acting remote cylinder (inner lever).
8. Valve body plug.
9. Jack tapping for single or double acting remote cylinder (inner lever)

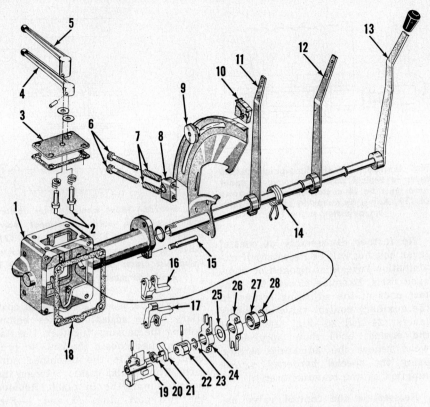

Fig. MM730—Exploded view of control valve lever housing and associated parts.

1. Lever housing	11. Inner auxiliary lever	18. Gasket
2. Rate & cycle cams	12. Center auxiliary lever	19. Draft control lever
3. Valve cover	13. Three-point control lever	20. Spring
4. Cycle lever	14. Centering spring	21. Cycle pawl
5. Rate lever	15. Spring anchor	22. Detent cam
6. Stop screws	16. Spool control fork	23. Snap ring
7. Springs	17. Spool control fork	24. Activating lever
8. Stop block		25. Washer
9. Stop nut		26. Activating lever
10. Adjustable stop		27. Spacer
		28. Thrust shim

the unit is removed for adjustment only, keep valve body (15—Fig. MM-729) and control lever housing (1—Fig. MM730) together.

If overhaul or inspection is indicated, withdraw valve body (15—Fig. MM729) from control lever housing by pulling straight out. The two auxiliary directional valves will be withdrawn from valve body as the two units are separated. Withdraw the master control valve and the three-point lift directional valves from valve body. The three directional valves and their sleeves are interchangeable and are available only as a matched set consisting of valve and sleeve. The master control valve (18—Fig. MM-729) and sleeve (27) are available individually. Keep the valve spools identified so that they can be reinstalled in their original sleeves, and keep the matched sets together if the sleeves are removed from valve body. Withdraw the relief valve (24), regulating valve (14) and back pressure valve (11) from valve body, together with their springs and retainer. Clean all parts in a suitable solvent and renew any which are scored, worn or damaged.

132. To remove the draft control linkage from the control lever housing, first remove the bolt (B—Fig. MM732) connecting the link rod (L) to the draft linkage tube. Withdraw linkage tube (T), with the dash pot piston (P) attached. Disconnect the draft pressure tube at connecting nut (N) and remove the tube. Using a socket and extension, remove the cap screw at the closed end of the dashpot cylinder (C), then the other two cap screws retaining the linkage cylinder, and lift off the cylinder. Remove the pressure tube adapter (A) from the linkage cylinder and make

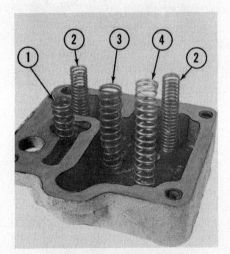

Fig. MM731—Filter base showing correct installation of valve springs.

1. Regulating valve spring.
2. Auxiliary valve springs.
3. Master valve spring.
4. Three-point lift valve spring.

Fig. MM729) with filter attached. Do not lose the five springs (Fig. MM731) between filter base and valve housing. Withdraw the control lever housing (1—Fig. MM730) and valve housing (15—Fig. MM729) from lift housing studs (S). The removed unit will contain the draft control mechanism. If

Fig. MM732—To remove draft control linkage from lever housing, first remove bolt (B) and slide the linkage tube (T) and dashpot piston (P) from housing. Disconnect nut (N) and remove fluid supply tube and unbolt and remove linkage cylinder. One attaching cap screw is located inside dashpot cylinder (C).

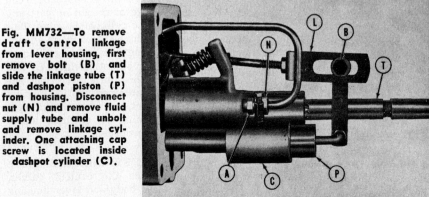

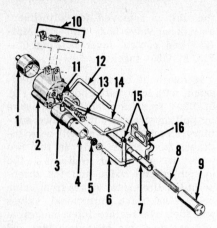

Fig. MM733 — Exploded view of draft linkage.

1. Draft piston
2. Linkage cylinder
3. Dashpot cylinder
4. Dashpot piston
5. Piston seal
6. Dashpot link
7. Linkage tube
8. Spring
9. Actuating cap
10. Detent assembly
11. Adjusting screw
12. Link rod
13. Adapter
14. Pressure tube
15. Tube clamp
16. Adjusting bar

sure it is of the restricter type, containing a ⅛-inch metering hole. If it is not, renew the adapter with one of the proper restriction.

Dashpot cylinder (3—Fig. MM733) and piston (4) are only available in a matched set. Examine draft control piston (1) and cylinder (2) for scoring, sticking or excessive wear.

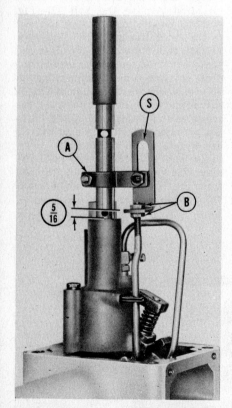

Fig. MM734—Adjust length of link rod by adjusting nuts (B) until upper edge of tube port is 5/16-inch from edge of cylinder as shown. Tube must be free to fall in slot (S) of its own weight.

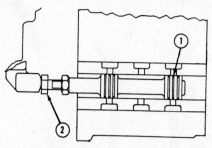

Fig. MM735 — With three-point control lever in neutral position, groove of spool land must be in center of port as shown at (1). Adjust by removing spool and turning adjusting screw (2).

No further disassembly of control lever housing will be necessary if examination reveals no broken or damaged parts. Examine closely the contact ends of the adjusting screws in the auxiliary control valve activating levers (24 and 26—Fig. MM730). If the contact ends show appreciable wear renew the adjusting screws, using the special hardened screws supplied by the manufacturer.

Reassemble the control valve assembly by reversing the disassembly procedure. Leave the locknuts on the adjusting yokes of the auxiliary directional valve spools loose during assembly for adjustment as outlined in paragraph 133.

133. CONTROL VALVE ADJUST-MENT. After the control valve assembly has been removed for adjustment or reassembled after overhaul, stand the unit on a bench with the linkage tube in a vertical position as shown in Fig. MM734. Grasp the tube and move it upward to the upper end of slot (S), then release the tube. The assembly should fall slowly to the bottom of the slot of its own weight. If it does not, realign the dashpot linkage with the two locknuts (A), or control rod linkage at (B) until a free drop is obtained. With the linkage tube in the bottom of the slot as shown, measure the distance between the upper edge of the lower port and the edge of the cylinder housing. This distance should be 5/16-inch as shown. If the adjustment is incorrect, loosen one of the rod adjusting nuts (B) and tighten the other until the proper adjustment is obtained. After making the adjustment, recheck the linkage tube for binding as outlined above and correct as needed.

134. VALVE SYNCHRONIZATION. To synchronize the control valves, bolt the valve body and lever housing together with two bolts. If not pre-

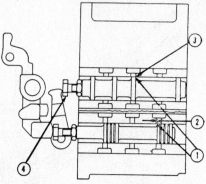

Fig. MM736—Move control lever toward raising position until directional valve opens port 2/5 to 1/2 width of port (2). Valves are synchronized if land of master valve just closes port (3). Adjustment is made on master spool at (4).

viously done, loosen locknuts on auxiliary valve adjusting yokes before bolting the housings together. Use flat washers underneath the nuts to prevent damage to the machined surfaces. The regular gasket between the housings must be in place. Remove the two port plugs (2 and 3—Fig. MM737). With the three-point lift directional valve lever in the neutral position and the spool held back against the lever, the middle annular groove should be centered in port (3) as shown at (1—Fig. MM735). If it is not, withdraw the directional valve from the front of the valve body,

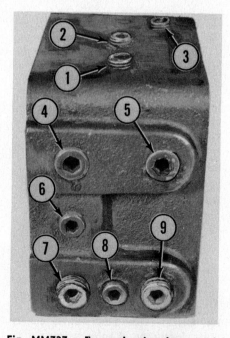

Fig. MM737 — To synchronize the control valves, master valve must be viewed through port (2), three-point directional valve through port (3) and the two auxiliary directional valves through ports (4 and 7).

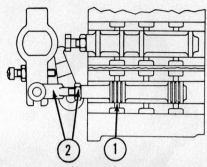

Fig. MM738—With auxiliary control levers in neutral position, middle groove of directional valve must center in port as shown at (1). Adjust by turning valve on adjusting yoke (2).

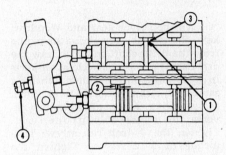

Fig. MM739 — When auxiliary valve is moved either direction until port is opened 2/5 to 1/2 port width (2), land (1) of master valve must just close port (3).

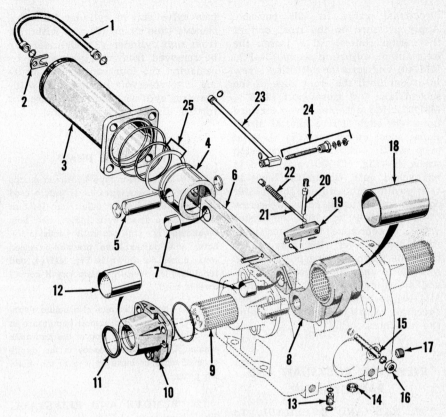

Fig. MM741 — Exploded view of system housing showing ram cylinder, rockshaft and associated parts.

1. Pressure tube	9. Rockshaft	14. Seal	21. Valve centering
2. Tube clip	10. Rockshaft	15. Activating	pin
3. Ram cylinder	housing	plunger	22. Spring
4. Ram piston	11. Oil seal	16. Oil seal	23. Pressure tube
5. Piston pin	12. Rockshaft	17. Drain plug	24. Retaining screw
6. Connecting rod	bushing	18. Spacer	25. Piston seal
7. Rod bushings	13. Pump pressure	19. Rocker arm	
8. Ram arm	tube	20. Pivot pin	

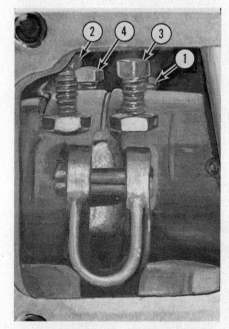

Fig. MM740—Master valve spool is synchronized with auxiliary valves by means of the four adjusting screws in actuating levers as shown.

1. Center lever (rearward)
2. Inner lever (forward)
3. Center lever (forward)
4. Inner lever (rearward)

loosen the locknut and turn the adjusting screw (2) in or out as needed to properly align the valve. After the three-point lift directional valve has been properly centered in the neutral position, move the control lever slowly toward the raising position while applying pressure on the front end of the valve until the rear edge of the front land opens the port 2/5-1/2 of the port width as shown at (2—Fig. MM736). At this time the front edge of the second land on the master control valve should just close port (2—Fig. MM737) as shown at (3—Fig. MM736). If the adjustment of the master control valve is incorrect, remove the valve, loosen the lock nut and turn the adjusting screw (4) in or out as required. Recheck both adjustments a second time after the lock nuts have been tightened.

To synchronize the two auxiliary valve spools with the master control valve, proceed as follows: Remove the plugs in ports (4 and 9—Fig. MM737) for viewing the adjustment of the two directional valves. Leave port (2) un-

plugged for checking the setting of the master control valve. With the auxiliary valve control levers in the neutral position, check and center the middle groove of the spool lands visible through ports (4 and 9). See Fig. MM738. Note: If the adjusting yoke lock nuts were loosened when the valve was removed or assembled, adjustment can be made by turning the valve spool through the open front end of valve body. Most valve spools are equipped with a screw driver slot in the end for valve adjustment. Valves not so equipped can usually be turned with eraser end of a pencil or other friction tool. After the directional spools are properly centered, loosen the two bolts securing valve body to lever housing, separate the two units slightly and tighten the adjusting yoke lock nuts; then, tighten the securing bolts and recheck adjustment. After the directional spools are properly centered, move the center lever rearward until the front edge of rear land opens port (4—Fig. MM737) 2/5-1/2 of port width. Clamp the control lever to quadrant with directional valve in this position. Apply pressure on the front end of the master control valve, loosen the lock nut on adjusting screw (3—Fig. MM740) and turn the adjusting screw in or out until the front edge of the second land just closes port (2—Fig. MM737). Move center lever forward until rear edge of rear land of directional spool opens port (4) ⅖-½ of port width. (Auxiliary lever stop screw (6—Fig. MM730) may need to be backed out). Clamp the lever in this position and adjust the master control valve, using adjusting screw (1—Fig. MM740) to adjust the master valve. Synchronize the inner auxiliary valve lever (lower spool) in the same manner, using port (9—Fig. MM737) to view the directional valve, and adjusting screws (2 and 4—Fig. MM740) to adjust master valve. Recheck all adjustments after tightening the lock nuts.

RESERVOIR, ROCKSHAFT AND RAM CYLINDER

135. R&R AND OVERHAUL. To remove the system reservoir, drain the system by removing drain plug (17—Fig. MM741), remove seat and disconnect the three-point hitch lift rods. Disconnect power steering return line from reservoir. Attach a hoist to reservoir and remove by lifting it straight up to avoid damage to the pressure tube (13) and "O" rings. Unbolt and remove filter housing to

Fig. MM742—Before removing gears or gear housing on Webster hydraulic pump, mark the gears as shown at (A) and measure gear to housing clearance. Refer to text.

free valve end of cylinder tube (1), remove tube clamp (2) and withdraw from ram cylinder (3). Cylinder can be removed from ram piston (4) by removing the four cap screws securing it to reservoir housing and withdrawing cylinder. The procedure for further disassembly is evident.

HYDRAULIC PUMP

The Webster, gear type hydraulic pumps are of two different types. Early pumps used on 335, 445 and some 4-Star and Jet Star tractors have fixed wear plates, and field rebuilding is not generally satisfactory. Later type pumps have pressure-balanced wear plates as shown in Fig. MM744, and rebuilding is generally satisfactory if normal care is used.

NOTE: The maintenance of absolute cleanliness of all parts is of utmost importance in the operation and servicing of the hydraulic system. Of equal importance is the avoidance of nicks or burrs on any of the working parts.

136. REMOVE AND REINSTALL. The gear-type hydraulic pump is mounted on rear of final drive housing and driven by pto clutch shaft. Removal procedures are evident and consist of disconnecting the hydraulic lines and unbolting and withdrawing pump.

137. RESEAL (EARLY PUMPS). To disassemble the unit, unbolt and remove the pump cover and lift out the idler gear and shaft. Remove snap ring retaining driver gear to shaft and

Fig. MM743—Examine pressure areas of gear housing bore as shown by arrow. Refer to text.

remove the driver gear and Woodruff key. Remove the remaining snap ring from the drive shaft and withdraw the drive shaft. Thoroughly clean all parts in a suitable solvent, then lubricate same with clean hydraulic fluid. When reassembling, renew all seals and reverse the disassembly procedure. Tighten the $\frac{5}{16}$-inch cap screws to a torque of 9-12 ft.-lbs. Tighten the ¼-inch cap screws to a torque of 6-8 ft.-lbs.

138. OVERHAUL (LATE PUMPS). Before disassembling the pump, scribe correlation marks on all housings for alignment during reassembly. Remove the retaining cap screws and lift off the manifold plate and pump rear end plate. Before removing the gears or gear plate, mark the gears as shown at (A—Fig. MM742) and check gear to housing clearance with

Fig. MM744 — Partially disassembled view of end housing and wear plate, showing component parts.

1. End housing
2. Outer seal
3. Inner seal
4. Backup ring
5. "O" ring
6. Needle bearings
7. Wear plate
P. Pressure ports
R. Relief grooves

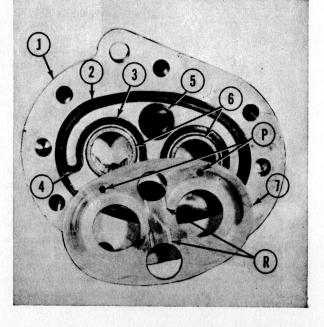

a feeler gage as shown. If clearance exceeds 0.005, renew the pump. Examine bores of gear housing as shown in Fig. MM743. If badly scored or heat-discolored, renew the pump.

On most pumps the drive shaft is retained in front housing by a snap ring; remove gears and their shafts. Do not attempt to disassemble the shafts and gears. Examine ends and sides of gear teeth for scoring and shaft areas for scoring or wear.

Examine wear plates for wear or deep scoring in gear travel area. Slight marking is normal, and is more

pronounced on pressure side. The rear wear plate contains relief slots (R—Fig. MM744).

If gear shafts are worn at bearing area and gears are renewed, the shaft needle bearings should also be renewed. Heating end plates to 200° will facilitate removal of blind bearings. Pump end plates are not available separately, if damaged, the pump must be renewed.

Always renew all seals when pump is reassembled. Make sure pressure ports (P) in wear plates open into area enclosed by inner pressure seal

(3). Bearing areas of end plates are ported to inlet side of pump to prevent pressure build-up, and return any hydraulic fluid leaking past bearings. Lubricate the parts thoroughly with MM hydraulic fluid or equivalent, when assembling; and tighten the retaining cap screws alternately and evenly to a torque of 190-210 inch-pounds.

If pump binds after assembly, disassemble and determine the cause before installing the pump. Be sure hydraulic reservoir is filled and lines connected, before starting the motor.

REMOTE HYDRAULIC SYSTEMS
(TYPE E)

Some late tractors are equipped with a remote hydraulic system (Type E), consisting of a pump, reservoir, valve and breakaway couplings which may be connected to double acting remote cylinders.

SYSTEM OPERATING PRESSURE

139. OPERATION. The control valve spools are equipped with a detent which automatically releases when system pressure reaches a predetermined setting. In addition, a main relief valve is provided, which comes into operation if detent relief pressure is overridden or improperly adjusted; or malfunctions.

Normal operating pressure is therefore controlled by individual setting of the detent release pressure, and the main relief valve normally operates in a safety capacity only.

140. ADJUSTMENT. To check the adjustment, first make sure hydraulic reservoir is filled to proper level with MM hydraulic fluid or equivalent, and that tractor and hydraulic system are at operating temperature. For best test results, connect a 0-3000 psi pressure gage in series with the remote cylinder being used. Operate tractor at rated speed, move control lever in direction to pressurize the line containing the gage, and carefully note pressure reg-

istered at the moment valve returns to neutral. The pressure should be 1475-1550 psi. Also note pressure required to actuate the remote cylinder.

This pressure should be negligible, however, if remote cylinder is of the type containing check valves (MM Lifting Jack 11A80B, etc.) and cylinder is malfunctioning, pressures might approach release pressure setting and cause operating problems similar to a low pressure setting. If actuating pressure approaches release pressure, overhaul cylinder as outlined in paragraph 146, or use another cylinder for the adjustment.

Before adjusting the detent release pressure, momentarily hold control lever in open position to override the detent release, and note the maximum relief pressure.

This pressure should be 1750-1850 psi. If it is not, remove control valve and overhaul the main relief valve as outlined in paragraph 143, before proceeding with the adjustment.

To adjust the detent release pressure, refer to Fig. MM746. Working from behind and below the reservoir, remove the valve spool venting cap (1) on spool to be adjusted; and using an Allen wrench, turn nylock set screw (3) clockwise to increase the pressure, or counter-clockwise to decrease pressure. Check the "O" ring

(2) to make sure it is good condition before installing venting cap (1). If the pressure cannot be satisfactorily adjusted, overhaul the valve as outlined in paragraph 144.

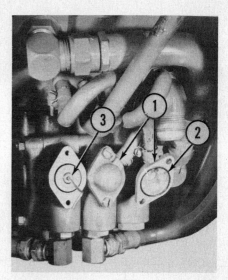

Fig. MM746 — To adjust detent release pressure on Type E system, remove venting cap (1) and turn nylock adjusting screw (3) using an Allen wrench.

1. Venting cap
2. "O" ring
3. Adjusting screw

CONTROL VALVE

141. REMOVE AND REINSTALL. To remove the control valve, first drain the hydraulic system reservoir, disconnect pump pressure and return lines and remove the seat assembly; then unbolt and remove the reservoir and valve assembly from tractor. Remove reservoir front cover retaining bolts, disconnect control levers, and lift off the front cover. Carefully mark the position of control valve on mounting plate to assist in alignment of control levers during assembly. Mark and disconnect hoses from control valve, remove the mounting stud nuts; and lift off the valve.

Reinstall by reversing the removal procedure. Align control valve with previously marked position on mount-

ing plate; or check to be sure control lever links can be installed without binding, before tightening mounting stud nuts.

The fittings contain sealing "O" rings as shown in Fig. MM747. Install and connect fittings as outlined in paragraph 142 to prevent subsequent leakage.

142. FITTINGS. The hydraulic fittings have SAE straight tubing threads with "O" ring seals (J. I. C. fittings) as shown in Fig. MM747. DO NOT attempt to install pipe fittings in valve ports.

The "O" ring (4) is compressed in its groove to form a leak proof seal, by tightening jam nut (2). DO NOT attempt to alter the position of fitting without first loosening jam nut (2)

and making sure "O" ring (4) is free in groove. If "O" ring is cut by improper installation or maintenance, leakage will result.

143. MAIN RELIEF VALVE. The main relief valve can be removed for service or adjustment after control valve has been removed as outlined

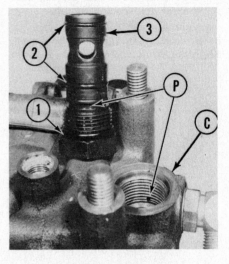

Fig. MM749—When removing main relief valve cartridge from inlet cover, examine sensing ports (P) to see that they are open. Refer to text.

1. "O" ring
2. "O" rings
3. Cartridge
C. Inlet cover
P. Sensing ports

Fig. MM747 — Special care must be taken when installing J. I. C. fittings, to be sure "O" ring (4) is not cut causing the fitting to leak. Refer to text.

1. Fitting
2. Jam nut
3. Washer
4. "O" ring

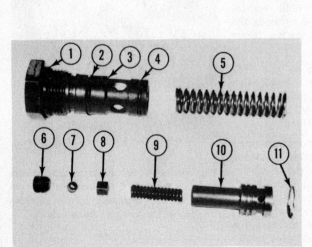

Fig. MM748 — Disassembled view of the main relief valve used in Wooster control valve of Type "E" system.

1. "O" ring
2. "O" ring
3. Cartridge
4. "O" ring
5. Spring
6. Sensing valve seat
7. Valve ball
8. Block
9. Spring
10. Piston
11. Snap ring

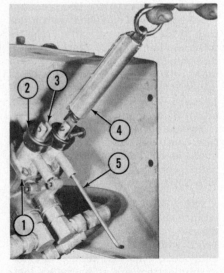

Fig. MM750—Adjust detent release pressure to 18-21 lbs. by turning Allen wrench (5).

1. Detent housing
2. Boot
3. Control valve spool
4. Spring scale
5. Allen wrench

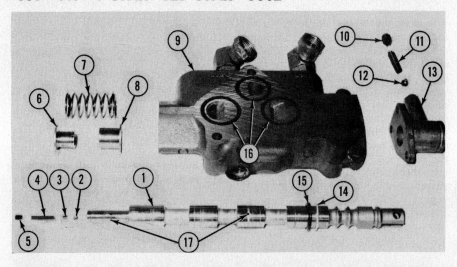

Fig. MM751—Disassembled view of control valve body section showing component parts. Release piston (6) and sleeve (8), move apart by hydraulic pressure entering through valve (2) and internal passages in valve spool, to override detent ball (12) and return spool to neutral.

1. Valve spool	7. Centering spring	13. Detent housing
2. Release valve	8. Centering sleeve	14. Backup ring
3. Block	9. Valve body	15. Sealing ring
4. Spring	10. Detent adjusting	16. Tetra (quad ring)
5. Detent release	screw	seals
adjusting screw	11. Detent spring	17. Passage ports
6. Release piston	12. Detent ball	

in paragraph 141. The valve (See Fig. MM748) is located in mounting side of inlet cover.

To service the main relief valve, unscrew cartridge (3—Fig. MM749) from cover (C). Check to see that sensing ports (P) in cartridge and cover are open, and that "O" rings (1 & 2) are in satisfactory condition.

Clamp hex head of cartridge (3—Fig. MM748) in a vise, lightly press down on piston (10) and remove snap ring (11); then withdraw piston (10) and spring (5). Piston must slide freely in cartridge bore.

Using an Allen wrench, remove the threaded pilot valve seat (6), while COUNTING THE TURNS seat is threaded into piston. Remove seat (6), valve ball (7), block (8) and spring (9). Check the block (8) and internal threads in piston (10), to make sure that sharp corners of block are not hanging up in threads in piston, causing erratic action of the valve. If interference is noted, chamfer corners of block or renew the cartridge, using one with fewer threads.

Assemble by reversing the disassembly procedure. If parts have been renewed in valve piston, install pilot valve seat (6) in piston until end of seat protrudes approximately 1/16-

inch from valve. If parts are not renewed, install seat THE SAME NUMBER OF TURNS used in removing valve; then turn seat in slightly to raise pressure (or out slightly to lower pressure) if other defects were not found while valve was disassembled.

144. CONTROL VALVE. The control valve spool and associated parts can be removed for service without disassembling the valve body housings. Proceed as follows:

Remove the spool boot (2—Fig. MM750) and venting cap (1—Fig. MM746). Remove detent adjusting screw (10—Fig. MM751), spring (11) and detent ball (12); then unbolt and remove detent housing (13). Depress centering piston (6) and remove the retaining snap ring, then withdraw centering piston, centering spring (7) and centering sleeve (8). Withdraw spool (1) from valve housing. Remove nylock set screw (5) and withdraw detent release valve spring (4), block (3) and valve (2) from end of spool. Check to be sure that drillings (17) in valve are open, that valve and body are not scored, and that valve does not bind. Valve and body are available only as a matched assembly.

Assemble by reversing the disassembly procedure. To renew the tetra (quad ring) seals (16), remove the valve body retaining stud nuts and separate the sections as shown in Fig. MM752.

Adjust detent ball pressure as outlined in paragraph 145, install valve as in paragraph 141, then adjust detent release pressure as in paragraph 140.

145. DETENT ADJUSTMENT. To adjust the detent spring pressure, refer to Fig. MM750. With valve mounted and before installing control levers and front cover, push valve spool downward from neutral (center) detent. Attach a spring scale (4) as shown, and measure the pull required to move valve back to neutral position. Adjust the pull to 18-21 lbs. by tightening or loosening detent adjusting screws with Allen wrench (5).

Fig. MM752 — Partially disassembled view of valve body sections, which are held together with three studs and sealed with tetra seals. Body sections are available separately.

LIFTING JACK
(REMOTE CYLINDER)

146. The lifting jack (ram) is of the double acting type. Refer to Fig. MM753.

With the lifting jack (ram) removed from tractor, proceed to disassemble the unit as follows: Remove ram head and bearing cap (29) from cylinder. With bearing cap removed, "O" ring seal and felt seal can be renewed. Withdraw piston from cylinder and renew piston ring if damaged. Remove both relief valve assemblies and push rod (26).

Renew the valve cage "O" rings (25) if they are damaged. Remove the ball retainer keys (Fig. MM754) and renew the balls if they are damaged. Examine bores and seats of valve cages. If they are damaged, renew the cages or recondition them as follows: Using a valve seat reamer (MM part No. 10T-1667), ream the cage bores from both ends to free up the push rod, carefully ream the seat and thoroughly clean out the metal shavings.

Reassemble and reinstall jack by reversing the removal and disassembly procedure.

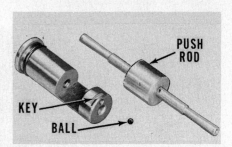

Fig. MM754—Hydraulic jack valve cage and push rod. The ball is retained in the cage by a key.

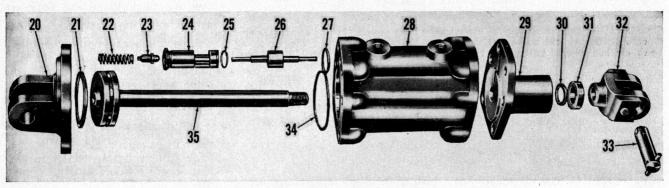

Fig. MM753 — Exploded view of a typical M-M lifting jack assembly.

20. Cylinder head	24. Valve cage (2)	28. Jack cylinder	32. Clevis
21. Piston "O" ring	25. Cage "O" ring (2)	29. Bearing cup	33. Clevis pin
22. Valve spring (2)	26. Push rod plunger	30. Rod "O" ring	34. Cap gasket
23. Relief & lockout valve (2)	27. Cap gasket	31. Oil seal	35. Piston and rod

MINNEAPOLIS-MOLINE

Minneapolis-Moline Models

■ UB Special ■ UTS Special ■ 5 Star ■ M5 ■ M504 ■ M602

■ M604 ■ M670 ■ M670 Super

Previously contained in I & T Shop Service Manual No. MM-16

SHOP MANUAL

MINNEAPOLIS-MOLINE

SERIES

UB Special — UTS Special — 5 Star
M5 - M504 - M602 - M604 - M670 - M670 Super

IDENTIFICATION

Tractor serial number is stamped on a plate which is riveted to side of transmission housing.

Engine serial number is stamped on a plate which is riveted to side of crankcase.

INDEX (By Starting Paragraph)

INDEX (Con't)

CONDENSED SERVICE DATA

	UB Special UTS Special	5 Star	M5 M504 M602 M604	M670 M670 Super
GENERAL				
Engine Make	Own	Own	Own	Own
Number of Cylinders	4	4	4	4
Bore—Inches (Non-Diesel)	4¼	4¼	4⅝	4⅝
Bore—Inches (Diesel)	4¼	4⅝	4⅝	4⅝
Stroke—Inches	5	5	5	5
Displacement—Cu. In. (Non-Diesel)	283.7	283.7	336	336
Displacement—Cu. In. (Diesel)	283.7	336	336	336
Cylinders Sleeved	No	No	No	No
Forward Speeds, Number of	5	5-10	10	10
Main Bearings, Number of	3	3	3	3
TUNE-UP				
Firing Order	1-3-4-2	1-3-4-2	1-3-4-2	1-3-4-2
Valve Tappet Gap—Inlet (Hot)	0.010	0.010	0.010	0.010
Valve Tappet Gap—Exhaust (Hot)				
Diesel	0.018	0.018	0.018	See Para. 39
Non-Diesel	0.020	0.020	0.020	0.022
Compression @ Cranking Speed (PSI)				
Gasoline	140-160	150-160	136-160	140-170
LPG	170-195	170-200	160-190	210-240
Diesel	440-460	440-460	440-460	440-460

NOTE: Average compression when equipped with standard, sea level—4000 ft. head. Refer to paragraph 38.

CONDENSED SERVICE DATA (Con't)

TUNE-UP (Cont'd)	UB Special UTS Special	5 Star	M5 M504 M602 M604	M670 M670 Super
Ignition Distributor Make	D-R	D-R	A-L or D-R	D-R
Ignition Distributor Model	1112565	1112565	IBT-4001G or 1112629	1112660 or 1112661
Breaker Contact Gap	0.022	0.022	See par. 117	0.022
Ignition Timing @ High Idle Speed				
Gasoline	3⅞" B	3⅛" B	3⅛" B	11° B@1200
Distillate	4⅛" B	....	....	....
LP-Gas	4⅛" B	2⅞" B	2⅞" B	10° B@1200
Injection Timing (APE pump)	27° B	29° B	40° B	....
Injection Timing (PSB pump)	27° B	29° B	30° B	....
Injection Timing (Roosa-Master)	....	....	9° B, 10° B	9° B
Timing Mark Location	Flywheel	Flywheel	Flywheel	Flywheel
Spark Plug Electrode Gap:				
Tractor Fuel	0.025-0.030	....	....	
LP-Gas	0.022-0.025	0.022-0.025	0.014-0.016	0.015
Gasoline	0.022-0.025	0.022-0.025	0.022-0.025	0.025
Carburetor Make (Except LP-Gas)	M-S	M-S	M-S	M-S
Carburetor Make (LP-Gas)	Ensign	Ensign	Ensign	Ensign
Carburetor Flood Setting	¼"	¼"	¼"	¼"
Engine Low Idle RPM (Non-Diesel)	450	450	475	600
Engine Low Idle RPM (Diesel)	600	600	600	600
Engine High Idle RPM (Non-Diesel)	1430	1650	1650	See. Para. 105
Engine High Idle RPM (Diesel)	1430	1550	1650	1750
Engine Loaded RPM (Non-Diesel)	1300	1500	1500	1600
Engine Loaded RPM (Diesel)	1300	1400	1500	1600
PTO Rated RPM	585@1300	553@1400	540@1366	540@1366*

*Standard single speed pto. Optional dual speed pto, 540 rpm—1000 rpm @ 1460.

SIZES—CAPACITIES—CLEARANCES (Clearances in Thousandths)

	UB Special UTS Special	5 Star	M5 M504 M602 M604	M670 M670 Super
Crankshaft Journal Diameter	2.9110-2.9120	2.9110-2.9120	2.9110-2.9120	2.9110-2.9120
Crankpin Diameter (Non-Diesel)	2.5770-2.5775	2.5770-2.5775	2.9110-2.9120	2.9110-2.9120
Crankpin Diameter (Diesel)	2.9115-2.9120	2.9115-2.9120	2.9115-2.9120	2.9115-2.9120
Camshaft Journal Diameter:				
No. 1 (Front)	3.3075-3.3085	3.3075-3.3085	3.3075-3.3085	3.3075-3.3085
No. 2	3.275-3.276	3.275-3.276	3.275-3.276	3.2750-3.2760
No. 3	1.996-1.997	1.996-1.997	1.996-1.997	1.9960-1.9970
Piston Pin Diameter (Non-Diesel)	1.2497-1.2500	1.2497-1.2500	1.2497-1.2500	1.2497-1.2500
Piston Pin Diameter (Diesel)	1.4997-1.5000	1.4997-1.5000	1.4997-1.5000	1.4997-1.5000
Valve Stem Diameter	0.4335-0.4345	0.4335-0.4345	0.4335-0.4345	0.4335-0.4345
Main Bearings, Diameter Clearance	1.4-4.4	1.4-4.4	1.4-4.4	1.4-4.4
Rod Bearing, Diameter Clearance (Non-Diesel)	1.5-2.4	0.9-3.0	0.9-3.0	0.9-3.0
Rod Bearings, Diameter Clearance (Diesel)	2.4-3.9	0.9-3.0	0.9-3.0	0.9-3.0
Piston Skirt Clearance (Non-Diesel)	4-5	4.5-5	4.5-5	7-9
Piston Skirt Clearance (Diesel)	6.5-7.5	7-9	7-9	7-9
Crankshaft End Play	4-8	6-10	6-10	4-10
Camshaft Bearings, Clearance:				
No. 1 (Front)	3-5	3-5	3-5	3-5
No. 2	5-7	5-7	5-7	5-7
No. 3	2-4	2-4	2-4	2-4
Cooling System—Gallons	6	5.5	5.5	5.5
Crankcase Oil—Gallons	2.5	2.25	2.25	2.25
Transmission and Differential—Gals	16	** 11	14	14

** 14 gallons with Ampli-Torc.

FRONT SYSTEMS

Minneapolis-Moline UTS Special tractors are available only with a heavy-duty type front axle.

All other models are optionally equipped with a fork mounted single wheel tricycle (Type N); dual wheel tricycle (Type U); adjustable axle (Type E); or heavy duty, non-adjustable front unit.

Models M504 and M604 are equipped with a front drive axle covered in a separate section beginning with paragraph 5.

WHEEL FORK OR PEDESTAL

All Tricycle Models

1. An exploded view of the tricycle type front end components is shown in Figs. MM750 and MM751. The procedure for removing and overhauling the components is conventional. Front wheel bearings should be adjusted to remove all free play without binding.

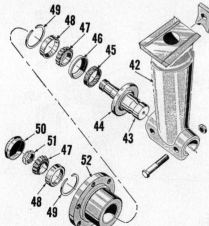

Fig. MM750 — Type "N" front axle and associated parts.

31. Wheel fork	36. Bearing cone
32. Front axle	37. Seal retainer
33. Wheel hub	38. Felt seals
34. Snap ring	39. Dust shield
35. Bearing cup	41. Washer

Fig. MM751 — Type "U" front axle and associated parts.

43. Spindle	48. Bearing cup
44. Dust shield	49. Snap ring
45. Felt seal	50. Hub cap
46. Seal retainer	51. Nut
47. Bearing cone	52. Wheel hub

Fig. MM752—Exploded view of "E" front axle and associated parts used on UB Special. Pivot pins and knuckle pins are carried in bushings.

1. Front axle	10. Pivot pin	18. Steering arm	27. Hub cap
2. Axle extension	11. Vertical shaft	19. Ball stud	28. Bearing cup
3. Steering knuckle	12. Right steering arm	21. Seal	30. Bearing cup
4. Dust shield	13. Left steering arm	22. Seal retainer	31. Bearing cone
5. Bushing	14. Tie rod	23. Safety stop	32. Bearing cone
6. Thrust bearing	15. Tie rod tube	24. Bolt	33. Felt ring
7. Front support	16. Clamp	25. Spring	34. Felt retainer
8. Rear support	17. Adjusting plug	26. Hub	35. Washer
9. Bushing			36. Nut

STEERING KNUCKLES

All Axle Type Models Except 4-Wheel Drive

2. The procedure for removing the steering knuckles is evident after an examination of the unit and reference to Figs. MM752, MM753, MM754 and MM755.

On Model UBE Special, the 1.870-1.871 diameter steering knuckle post has a recommended clearance of 0.006-0.008 in the steering knuckle bushings (5—Fig. MM752). If steering knuckle post is excessively worn, axle extension (2) must be renewed.

On all models with heavy duty, non-adjustable axle, the 1.373-1.374 diameter knuckle pin should have a recommended clearance of 0.001-0.005 in the steering knuckle bushings. If steering knuckle pin is excessively worn, it must be renewed.

On all models, except M670 Super tractors, using the "Type E" adjustable front end shown in Fig. MM754, the 1.373-1.374 steering spindles have recommended 0.002-0.006 clearance in the spindle bushings. On the M670 Super tractors equipped with the adjustable front axle shown in Fig. MM755, the steering knuckle shaft diameter is 1.500 and should have a recommended clearance of 0.002-0.006 in the steering knuckle bushings.

Bushings will not require final sizing if carefully installed with a suitable piloted arbor.

TIE-RODS, DRAG LINK AND TOE-IN

All Axle Type Models Except 4-Wheel Drive

3. On Model UB Special, tie-rod ends can be disassembled and component parts renewed. On other models, automotive type tie-rod and drag link ends are used. When reassembling, adjust the tie-rod length to provide toe-in of ¼-inch.

AXLE PIVOT PINS AND BUSHINGS

All Axle Type Models Except 4-Wheel Drive

4. Axle main (center) member is fitted with a renewable bushing (or bushings) for the pivot pin. Bushings are pre-sized and will not require reaming if carefully installed. On Type E adjustable axle types, the 1.247-1.248 diameter pivot pins should have a clearance of 0.003-0.007 in the bushing.

On heavy duty, non-adjustable axle models, renew bushings and/or pivot pin if clearance exceeds 0.031 (1/32-inch).

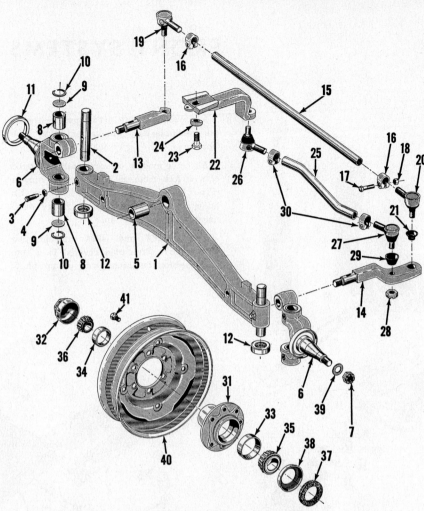

Fig. MM753—Exploded view of "UTS Special" front axle and associated parts.

1. Front axle	12. Bearing	21. Dust cover	30. Clamp
2. Knuckle pin	13. Right steering arm	22. Steering arm	31. Hub
3. Lock screw	14. Left steering arm	24. Washer (tapered)	32. Hub cap
5. Bushing	15. Tie rod	25. Drag link	33. Bearing cup
6. Steering knuckle	16. Clamp	26. Socket (right hand thread)	34. Bearing cup
8. Bushing	19. Socket (left hand thread)	27. Socket (left hand thread)	35. Bearing cone
9. Expansion plug	20. Socket (right hand thread)	29. Dust cover	36. Bearing cone
10. Snap ring			37. Felt seal
11. Dust shield			38. Seal retainer

Fig. MM754—Adjustable axle used on 5-Star tractor. Other models are similar.

53. Steering arm
54. Tie rod
55. Front support
56. Tie rod tube
57. Steering arm
58. Rear support
59. Pivot bushing
60. Pivot bushing
61. Axle center member
62. Axle extension
63. Thrust bearing
64. Spindle
65. Spindle bushing
66. Dust seal
67. Felt seal
68. Seal retainer
69. Bearing cone
70. Bearing cup
71. Snap ring
72. Front hub
73. Spindle nut
74. Hub cap

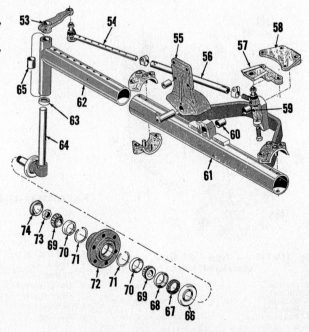

Fig. MM755—Adjustable axle used on M670 Super tractors.

1. Axle center member
2. Bushing
3. Bushing
5. Rear support
6. Washer
7. Snap ring
9. Front support
10. Pivot pin
11. Axle extension
13. Bushing
14. Extension clamp
15. Steering knuckle
17. Dust shield
18. Thrust bearing
19. Steering arm
20. Center steering arm
21. Cap screw
22. Washer
23. Tie rod
24. Tie rod end
26. Tube
27. Clamp
29. Hub
30. Snap ring
31. Bearing cup
32. Bearing cone
33. Bearing cup
34. Bearing cone
35. Felt seal
36. Felt retainer
37. Nut
38. Cap

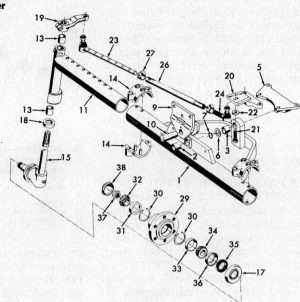

FRONT DRIVE AXLE

Some tractor models are optionally equipped with a front drive axle which converts the tractor into a 4-wheel drive unit.

A chain drive transfer case (Elwood Unit) is used on model M504. All M604 models are equipped with a gear drive (American Coleman) transfer case.

This section covers all service and adjustment of front drive axle, wheel and pivot bearings, front drive shaft and transfer case, but does not include service on transmission driving unit, steering gear or power steering system.

Early (Elwood) Type

Elwood type front drive axles can be identified by the chain drive transfer case without disconnect, and the exposed drive flange hub as shown in Fig. MM756. Front wheel caster and camber are fixed and not adjustable.

5. **ADJUSTMENTS.** Toe-in should be 1/16-1/8 inch, and is adjusted by shortening or lengthening the tie-rod.

Wheel bearings are adjusted to a slight rotational drag with no end

play, by tightening or loosening the spindle adjusting nuts. To check and/or adjust wheel bearings, proceed as follows:

Support axle housing so that front tire is clear of ground and unbolt and remove front wheel drive flange (F—Fig. MM756). Bend down locking tabs and remove outer adjusting nut using a suitable punch and hammer; then remove tab washer and adjust the bearings. Reassemble by reversing the disassembly procedure.

The tapered roller type pivot bearings are adjusted by means of shims located between upper and lower pivot bearing trunnions (T) and steering support housing (S). Because of possible drag or binding, any adjustment is approximate only, without removal of drive axle and joint assembly (9—Fig. MM757) and steering support seal (15). Proceed as follows:

Support the tractor and remove front wheel and drive flange (1). Remove screws retaining steering spindle (3) to steering support (7) and remove spindle, drive hub and spindle bearings as a unit. Withdraw axle shaft and joint assembly (9). Disconnect tie-rod from steering support and unbolt seal assembly (15). On left unit, disconnect drag link or steering cylinder connecting rod. Attach a pull scale to tie rod pivot boss (P) and measure the turning effort with force applied parallel to front axle housing. Pivot bearing adjustment is correct when a steady pull of 12-15 lbs. is required to turn the support.

Transfer case drive chain tension should be adjusted to remove all slack without applying tension to chain and sprockets. To check the adjustment, disconnect front drive shaft from rear yoke (1—Fig. MM760) and remove cap screws from eccentric housings (2 and 15). Using suitable spanner wrenches, turn the eccentric housings an equal amount until backlash at rear yoke (1) is reduced to a minimum. Reinstall retaining cap screws and front drive shaft.

6. **OVERHAUL.** Overhaul of the front drive axle can logically be divided into three operations; overhaul of drive hub and spindle unit, overhaul of main drive bevel gears and differential and overhaul of transfer case. All operations can be performed without removing front drive axle housing from tractor, refer to the appropriate following paragraphs.

Fig. MM756 — Early (Elwood) type front drive unit installed on M504 tractor.

F. Drive flange
L. Level plug
S. Steering support
T. Trunnions

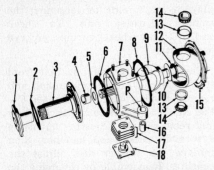

Fig. MM757 — Exploded view of steering support housing, drive axle and associated parts used on early (Elwood) front drive unit.

1. Drive flange	11. Oil seal
2. Gasket	12. Axle housing
3. Spindle	13. Bearing cup
4. Bushing	14. Bearing cone
5. Thrust washer	15. Seal assy.
6. Gasket	16. Bushing
7. Steering support	17. Shim pack
8. Gasket	18. Trunnion
9. Shaft & U-joint	P. Tie rod pivot
10. Washer	boss

7. DRIVE HUB AND SPINDLE. To disassemble either front drive hub and spindle unit, first suitably support the tractor and remove front wheel and tire unit and drive flange (1—Fig. MM757). If drive hub, spindle or spindle bearings are to be serviced, remove adjusting nuts (19—Fig. MM758), lockwasher (20), washer (21), the wheel spindle bearings and hub (24).

Spindle (3—Fig. MM757) may be removed without disturbing drive hub or spindle bearings if their condition is satisfactory. Withdraw axle shaft and joint assembly (9) after spindle has been removed. Component parts of axle shaft and joint are not serviced separately; therefore, disassembly of the joint is not recommended. Bushing (4) in spindle (3) is available for service and can be renewed at this time.

Unbolt spindle support seal (15), tie-rod and upper pivot bearing trunnion (18), being careful not to lose or damage shim pack (17). Tilt upper end of steering support (7) outward until clear of upper bearing cone (14), then remove steering support, lower trunion and lower pivot bearing cone from axle housing. Upper bearing cone (14) can now be lifted out, and cups (13) can be removed from axle housing (12) if renewal is indicated.

Inspect all parts and renew if condition is questionable. Pivot bearing shims (17) are available in thicknesses of 0.002, 0.005, 0.010 and 0.032, and total shim requirements should be approximately equally divided between upper and lower trunnions.

Assemble by reversing the disassembly procedure. Install steering support using a sufficient quantity of shims (17) until a turning effort of 12-15 lbs. is required to turn support before installing drive axle or support seal (15). Turning effort should be measured at tie-rod pivot boss (P) parallel to axle. After unit is reassembled, remove upper plug from axle housing pivot ball (12) and fill joint with approximately 4 lbs. of chassis lubricant.

8. MAIN DRIVE BEVEL GEARS & DIFFERENTIAL. To remove the differential carrier unit, first drain front drive housing, suitably support front of tractor and remove both front wheels. Remove both front wheel drive flanges (1—Fig. MM757) and remove the tie-rod. Unbolt both spindles (3) from steering supports (7)

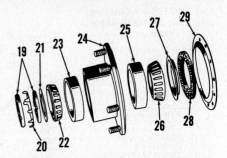

Fig. MM758 — Exploded view of drive hub, spindle bearings and associated parts used on early (Elwood) front drive unit.

19. Adjusting nuts	25. Bearing cup
20. Tab washer	26. Bearing cone
21. Washer	27. Retainer
22. Bearing cone	28. Seal
23. Bearing cup	29. Retainer
24. Drive hub	

and remove spindles and assembled wheel hubs. Withdraw axle shafts (9). Remove front drive shaft and universal joint assembly.

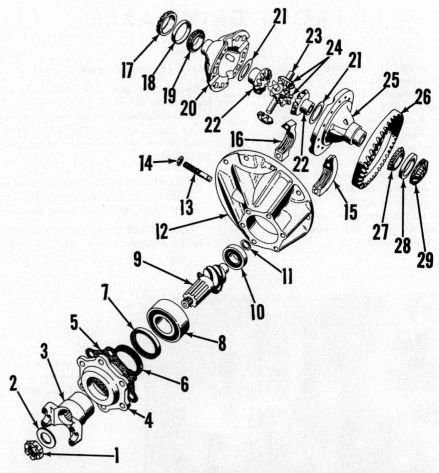

Fig. MM759—Exploded view of main drive bevel gears, differential, differential carrier and associated parts used on early (Elwood) front drive unit.

1. Nut	11. Snap ring	20. Case half
2. Washer	12. Carrier	21. Thrust washer
3. Drive yoke	13. Thrust screw	22. Axle gear
4. Retainer	14. Locknut	23. Spider
5. Gasket	15. Cap	24. Spider pinions
6. Packing	16. Cap	25. Case half
7. Oil seal	17. Adjuster	26. Bevel ring gear
8. Pinion bearing	18. Bearing cup	27. Bearing cone
9. Drive pinion	19. Bearing cone	28. Bearing cup
10. Pilot bearing		29. Adjuster

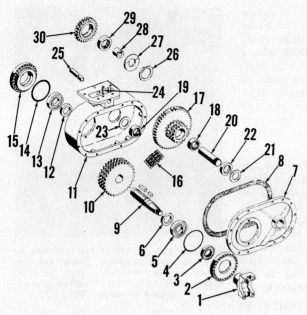

Refer to Fig. MM760 for an exploded view of transfer case. Idler gear shaft (25) is retained in housing by roll pin (24). Drive chain tension is controlled by eccentric housings (2 and 15). To adjust, rotate housings an equal amount to provide minimum backlash of output shaft without chain tension.

To check or adjust the thickness of mounting shim pack, remove transfer case cover (7), sprockets and drive chain, and install case housing (11) with only idler gear (30) in place. Vary the thickness of mounting shims to provide minimum backlash without bottoming or binding of gear teeth.

Assemble and install by reversing the removal procedure. Transfer case is lubricated by the transmission lubricant.

Late (Coleman) Type

American Coleman type drive axles can be identified by the front drive disconnect lever, stub housings bolted to ends of differential center housing, and the outboard type wheel universal joints shown in Fig. MM761.

Front wheel caster and camber are fixed and not adjustable.

10. ADJUSTMENT. Toe-in should be 1/16-1/8 inch, and is adjusted by shortening or lengthening the tie-rod.

Wheel bearings are adjusted to a slight rotational drag with no end play, by adding or removing shims behind the drive hub retaining clamp

Remove stud nuts securing carrier unit (12—Fig. MM759) to axle housing, carefully balance unit on a rolling floor jack and roll the assembly out from underneath the tractor.

Cut safety wires and remove bearing caps (15 and 16), bearing adjusters (17 and 29), bearing cups (18 and 28) and the differential unit. Differential carrier bearing cones (19 and 27) can be renewed at this time if renewal is indicated.

Remove the cap screws retaining pinion bearing retainer (4) and bump the drive pinion (9), bearings and associated parts from carrier housing. Pilot bearing (10) is retained to pinion shaft by snap ring (11). To disassemble the pinion, clamp drive shaft yoke (3) in a vise and remove shaft nut (1) and washer (2), then withdraw the yoke and retainer (4). Remove bearing (8) using a suitable puller.

Ring gear and pinion are available only as a matched set. Cone point (mesh position) of bevel gears is fixed and not adjustable.

Separate the differential case halves and examine axle gears, spider pinions, spider and thrust washers, renewing any parts which are worn, scored or otherwise damaged. Spider and spider pinions are serviced only as a matched set.

Assemble and install drive pinion and associated parts by reversing the disassembly procedure; then, before reinstalling the differential unit, loosen lock nut (14) and back out thrust screw (13) several turns. Install the assembled differential unit, bearing cups (18 and 28) and ad-

justers (17 and 29), then install carrier caps (15 and 16) in their original positions, making sure adjuster threads do not bind as cap screws are tightened.

Turn the adjusters (17 and 29) until all carrier bearing end play is removed, making sure some backlash exists between bevel gears and that clearance exists between bevel gear (26) and thrust screw (13). After ALL end play is eliminated with minimum preload, adjust backlash to 0.008-0.011 when measured with a dial indicator. With backlash correctly adjusted, turn thrust screw (13) into housing until it contacts rear face of ring gear, back screw out 1/4-1/2 turn and secure with locknut (14).

Assemble by reversing the disassembly procedure. Fill differential housing to level of lower plug (L—Fig. MM756), with SAE 90 EP, multipurpose gear lubricant.

9. TRANSFER CASE. The chain drive transfer case is mounted underneath the transmission housing and driven through idler gear (30—Fig. MM760) from bevel pinion shaft fourth gear.

To remove the unit, drain transmission and transfer case and remove front drive shaft; then remove attaching cap screws and lower the transfer case assembly from tractor. Remove and save the mounting shim gaskets as transfer case is removed. The shim pack controls the backlash between transfer case idler gear (30) and mating transmission gear. Shims are available in thicknesses of 0.002, 0.005 and 0.010.

Fig. MM761 — Coleman type front drive wheel with cover removed, showing components of outboard universal joint.

1. Drive axle
2. Power yoke
3. Compensating ring
4. Drive hub
5. Plug

Fig. MM762 — The full floating drive axle (1) can be withdrawn after detaching flange from power yoke (2).

plate. To check and/or adjust wheel bearings, proceed as follows:

Support the axle housing and remove wheel cover and wheel. Remove the safety wire, drive axle flange bolts and drive axle as shown in Fig. MM762. Move power yoke (2) out of the way, bend tabs on lock plates (7—Fig. MM762B) and remove retaining cap screws and clamp plate (8); then add or remove shims (10) as required. Shims are available in thicknesses of 0.002, 0.005 and 0.010. Reassemble by reversing the disassembly procedure.

The tapered roller type pivot bearings are adjusted by a tapered wedge (15—Fig. MM762C) and adjusting screw (18.) Adjustment is correct when a steady pull of approximately 12 lbs. is required at steering arm, to move the steering spindle (11—Fig. MM 763). Make the adjustment as follows:

Remove wheel cover, wheel and driving axle as outlined for wheel bearing adjustment; then disconnect drag link from steering arm. Loosen

locknut on spindle adjusting screw and turn adjusting screw clockwise into spindle to tighten pivot bearings. Adjustment may be checked with a spring scale as shown in Fig. MM-767A. NOTE: If adjustment must be loosened instead of tightened, drive hub and spindle must be partially disassembled as outlined in paragraph 12, and inspection of pivot bearings is advised.

11. **OVERHAUL.** Overhaul of the front drive axle is logically divided into three operations; overhaul of drive hub and spindle unit, overhaul of main drive bevel gears and differential, and overhaul of transfer case. All operations can be performed without removing front drive axle housing from tractor. Refer to the appropriate following paragraphs:

12. **DRIVE HUB & SPINDLE.** To disassemble either front drive hub and spindle unit, suitably support axle housing and remove wheel cover and wheel. Remove lock wire retaining axle flange cap screws, remove the cap screws and carefully withdraw drive axle (1—Fig. MM762) to keep from damaging axle inner oil seal. Remove the two pipe plugs (5—Fig. MM761) which retain drive pins (6—Fig. MM762A). Thread a ⅜-inch NC cap screw (C) into end of drive pin (6) and remove pins by pulling straight out. NOTE: Slotted inner ends of drive pins fit over dowels (A), which prevent pins from rotating during operation or removal.

Lift out power yoke (2) and compensating ring (3). Compensating ring contains oilite bushings which are renewable.

Bend down tabs on lock plates (7—Fig. MM762B), and remove the cap screws, lock plates, clamp plate (8) and adjusting shims (10). Remove drive hub (4) carefully, to avoid dropping outer wheel bearing cone as hub is removed.

Fig. MM762B — Wheel hub (4) can be removed after removing power yoke as shown in Fig. MM762A, then removing clamp plate (8). Wheel bearings are adjusted by shims (10).

4. Drive hub	9. Seal
7. Lock plates	10. Adjusting shims
8. Clamp plate	

To remove clamp ring (12—Fig. MM763), inner wheel bearing (13) or steering spindle (11), back out the spindle bearing adjusting screw (18—Fig. MM762C) several turns. Using a pin punch or similar tool and a hammer, drive the adjusting wedge (15—Fig. MM764) against point of adjusting screw. If clamp ring binds, two knockout holes are provided in spindle flange, for removal of inner wheel bearing cone (13). Refer to Fig. MM765. Using a pin punch and working through the knockout holes, clamp ring and bearing cone can be removed at same time. IMPORTANT:

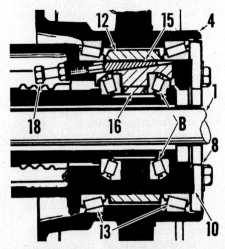

Fig. MM762C — Cross sectional view of wheel hub and associated parts, showing method of adjusting spindle bearings. Refer to text for details.

B. Pivot bearings	13. Wheel bearings
4. Drive hub	15. Adjusting wedge
8. Clamp plate	16. Bearing cap
10. Shims	18. Adjusting screw
12. Clamp ring	

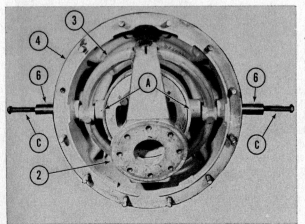

Fig. MM762A — Power yoke and compensating ring can be removed as a unit after removing wheel cover, wheel, drive axle and the two plugs (5—Fig. MM761). Drive pins (6) are internally threaded for pulling. Roll pins (A) fit slots in inner end of drive pins to prevent rotation in drive hub (4). The ⅜-inch NC cap screws (C) are used for pulling only.

Fig. MM763 — Before clamp ring or inner wheel bearing can be removed, adjusting wedge (15) must be loosened; refer to text.

11. Steering spindle   14. Seal
12. Clamp ring   15. Adjusting wedge
13. Wheel bearing

Before attempting to remove clamp ring and bearing cone in this manner, first completely remove the spindle bearing adjusting screw (18 —Fig. MM762C) and BE SURE that adjusting wedge (15) is loose and pushed to end of slot in pivot bearing cap (16—Fig. MM765). If adjusting wedge is dragged outward with clamp ring or bearing cone, outer end of slot may be covered before wedging action locks the assembly, making removal extremely difficult.

If clamp ring can be easily removed, lift out adjusting wedge (15) before drifting off inner wheel bearing cone.

To remove wheel spindle after inner wheel bearing cone has been removed, first remove boot retainers

(21—Fig. MM766) if so equipped, and double back the boot (19). Insert a slim punch in knockout hole (R—Fig. MM764) and tap lower pivot bearing cup out of housing stub (17). Lift off pivot bearing cap (16—Fig. MM-765) and upper pivot bearing cone; then remove spindle, lower bearing cone and lower bearing cup as a unit.

Clean all parts in a suitable solvent and renew any which are damaged or worn. Seals (9—Fig. MM762B and 14—Fig. MM763) are available only in a kit which contains both seals for one wheel.

When assembling the spindle, place lower pivot bearing cup over cone and position spindle over housing stub (17—Fig. MM766A). Place a solid wooden support beneath spindle as shown in Fig. MM767, and lower full weight of tractor on support, making sure lower pivot bearing cup is properly aligned with bore in housing stub; then, use a heavy hammer and drift (D), to seat lower bearing cup into stub bore.

If pivot bearings show considerable wear, but are to be re-used, completely remove adjusting screw (18—Fig. MM765). Install pivot bearing cap (16) and adjusting wedge (15); then install clamp ring, omitting inner wheel bearing cone. Move clamp ring toward inner side of spindle until approximately 1½ inches of bearing cap (16) extends beyond outer edge of clamp ring. Using a long pin punch and working through adjusting screw hole, tap adjusting wedge (15) outward in slot until wedge is tight; then measure the dis-

Fig. MM765 — To check for pivot bearing wear, reinstall clamp ring and tighten adjusting screw until adjusting wedge (15) is tight; then measure distance (M) from outer end of wedge to end of slot. If distance (M) is less than 1⅜ inches, pivot bearings must either be renewed or shimmed beneath lower bearing cone.

M. 1⅜ inches min.   15. Adjusting wedge
P. Knockout holes   16. Bearing cap
11. Steering spindle   18. Adjusting screw
14. Seal

tance (M) between outer end of adjusting wedge and extreme outer end of slot. The distance (M) should be at least 1⅜ inches. If distance is less than specified, remove the spindle and renew the bearings; or place 0.012 of shims beneath lower pivot bearing cone inner race, for each ⅛ inch distance (M) must be increased.

Complete the assembly by reversing the disassembly procedure. Before installing drive hub, tighten pivot bearing adjusting screw until a steady pull of 12 lbs. is required to maintain turning motion when tested with a spring scale as shown in Fig. MM767A.

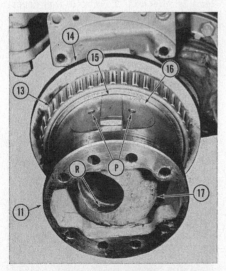

Fig. MM764—Steering spindle with clamp ring removed showing details of construction. Drillings (P & R) are knockout holes for removal of spindle bearings.

11. Steering spindle   15. Adjusting wedge
13. Wheel bearing   16. Bearing cap
14. Seal   17. Housing stub

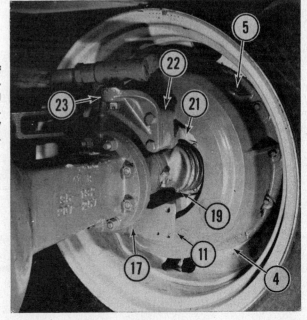

Fig. MM766 —View of Coleman drive axle showing attachment of ball stud and steering arm. Spindle boot (19) may not be used on all models.

4. Drive hub
5. Plug
11. Steering spindle
17. Housing stub
19. Spindle boot
21. Boot clamp
22. Steering arm
23. Ball stud bracket

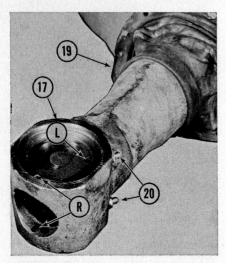

Fig. MM767—Weight of tractor should be used to assist in spindle pivot bearing installation. Refer to text.

D. Drift
11 Steering spind'e
17. Housing stub

Fig. MM766A—Stripped axle housing stub showing details of construction. Grease fittings (20) open to pivot bearing lube passages in upper and lower pivot bearing areas.

L. Lube passage
R. Knockout holes
17. Housing stub
19. Spindle boot
20. Lube fittings

13. MAIN DRIVE BEVEL GEARS & DIFFERENTIAL. To remove the differential carrier unit, first drain front drive housing and disconnect tie-rod at one end. Remove front drive shaft and universal joint assembly. Remove both front wheel covers and unbolt and remove both drive axle shafts. NOTE: As wheel covers are removed, reinstall two stud nuts on either wheel, to support wheel discs.

Remove stud nuts securing carrier unit to axle housing, carefully balance unit on a rolling floor jack and roll the assembly out from underneath the tractor.

Cut safety wires and remove bearing caps (5 and 7—Fig. MM768A), bearing adjusters (10 and 23), bearing cups (11 and 22), and the differential unit. Differential carrier bearing cones (12 and 21) can be renewed at this time if renewal is indicated.

Unbolt and remove seal retainer (37), bearing carrier (30), pinion (25) and associated parts, being sure to lay aside and save shim pack (28) as pinion assembly is removed. The shim pack controls mesh position (cone point) of main drive bevel gears.

To disassemble pinion shaft unit, remove castellated nut, flat washer and yoke (38), then press pinion shaft and front bearing cone (26) forward out of bearing carrier (30) and rear bearing cone (34). Withdraw spacer

(32) from pinion and remove front bearing cone (26) with a suitable puller. DO NOT unstake and remove pilot bearing (24) unless renewal of pinion or bearing is indicated. NOTE: If pilot bearing or pinion must be renewed, stake the installed pilot bearing in at least 4 places.

When disassembling the differential unit, match-mark the differential case halves, remove case retaining cap screws; then separate case and remove spider, pinions, axle gears and thrust washers. If bevel ring gear is to be renewed, drill and press out the rivets to prevent damage to the salvaged part.

Clean all parts and inspect for wear, scoring, chipped teeth or other damage, and renew as necessary. Ring gear and pinion are available only as a matched set; all other parts are available individually.

The thickness of spacer (32) controls the pre-load of pinion shaft carrier bearings, which should be adjusted to provide a rolling torque of 15-35 inch-lbs. Oil seal (35), felt seal (36) and retainer (37) should be omitted from the assembly when pre-load is checked. To avoid the necessity of completely assembling pinion and carrier unit when checking and adjusting pre-load, proceed as follows:

Fig. MM767A — Using a spring scale to check pivot bearing adjustment. Refer to text.

S. Spring scale
22. Steering arm

Fig. MM768—Front drive differential and carrier unit removed from axle housing. Refer to Fig. MM768A for legend.

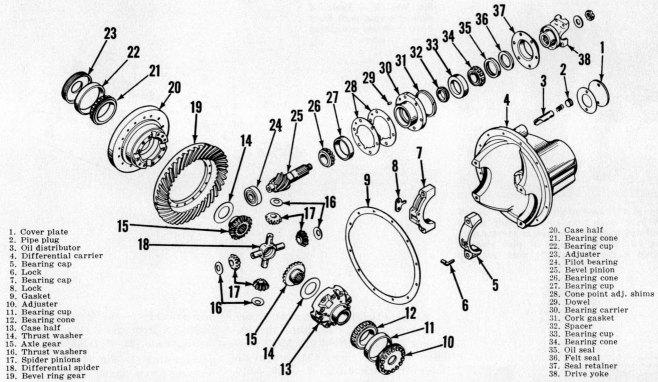

1. Cover plate
2. Pipe plug
3. Oil distributor
4. Differential carrier
5. Bearing cap
6. Lock
7. Bearing cap
8. Lock
9. Gasket
10. Adjuster
11. Bearing cup
12. Bearing cone
13. Case half
14. Thrust washer
15. Axle gear
16. Thrust washers
17. Spider pinions
18. Differential spider
19. Bevel ring gear

20. Case half
21. Bearing cone
22. Bearing cup
23. Adjuster
24. Pilot bearing
25. Bevel pinion
26. Bearing cone
27. Bearing cup
28. Cone point adj. shims
29. Dowel
30. Bearing carrier
31. Cork gasket
32. Spacer
33. Bearing cup
34. Bearing cone
35. Oil seal
36. Felt seal
37. Seal retainer
38. Drive yoke

Fig. MM768A—Exploded view of the Eaton Single Speed differential, drive gears and carrier unit used in the Coleman front drive axle.

Install front bearing cone (26) on pinion and bearing cups (27 and 33) in carrier. Install the removed spacer (32) and rear bearing cone (34); then secure a pipe spacer of proper size to apply pressure to inner race of rear bearing cone, and of sufficient length to extend beyond end of pinion shaft. Place the unit in a suitable press and apply approximately 15 tons pressure while checking rolling torque of carrier. Spacers are available in thicknesses of 0.513 to 0.543 in increments of 0.003. After the proper bearing spacer has been selected, install the seals, pinion shaft yoke and retaining nut and washer. Tighten shaft nut to a torque of 325-450 ft.-lbs.

Cone point (mesh position) of main drive bevel gears is controlled by thickness of shim pack (28). If used bevel gears are reinstalled, both cone point and backlash should remain as nearly as possible, unchanged from previous settings. If new bevel gears are installed, the tooth contact pattern must be checked and the gears adjusted to provide the proper tooth contact. Proceed as follows:

Reassemble by reversing the disassembly procedure, using the removed shim pack (28) as a starting point. With clearance between the gears, tighten the adjusters (10 and 23) until carrier bearing end play is removed; then slightly preload the bearings by tightening either adjuster two notches. Measure the backlash of bevel gears and adjust to 0.010-0.012 by loosening one adjuster and tightening the other an equal amount. Paint 10 or 12 teeth of bevel ring gear with red lead or prussian blue and turn pinion in direction of normal rotation; then check tooth contact pattern as indicated by the paint. The point of heaviest tooth contact should be on approximate center of teeth and in the same position on pressure and coast side of teeth. A general in-dication of required adjustment can be obtained from pressure side of bevel ring gear teeth, using the following guide.

Heavy Contact Pattern — **Corrective Action**

Heel (Outer) Ends .... Decrease Backlash

Toe (Inner) Ends .... Increase Backlash

High (Tips) Contact ...... Remove Shims

Low (Root) Contact .... Add Shims

Fig. MM769 — Inside view of front drive axle housing, showing location of axle inner oil seal (S).

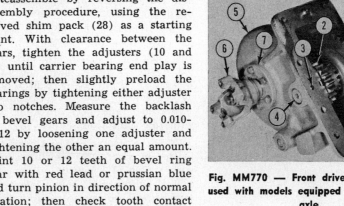

Fig. MM770 — Front drive transfer case used with models equipped with Coleman axle.

1. Input gear
2. Pinion gear
3. Roll pin
4. Input shaft
5. Housing
6. Drive yoke
7. Bearing cap

Fig. MM770A—Partially disassembled view of front drive transfer case. Shift detent ball and spring are located in internal drilling (D) which is closed by pipe plug located in the approximate area indicated by (P).

7. Bearing cap
13. Output gear
14. Shifter fork
15. Roll pin
16. Output shaft
17. Bellcrank

Fig. MM772 — Exploded view of output shaft, front drive shaft and associated parts.

6. Yoke
7. Bearing cap
13. Output gear
16. Output shaft
18. Oil seal
19. Shims
20. Bearing cup
21. Bearing cone
22. Bearing cone
23. Bearing cup
24. Joint kit
25. Snap ring
26. Drive shaft
27. Dust cap
28. Steel washer
29. Cork washer
30. Shaft sleeve

Fig. MM771 — Input gear is splined to pinion gear and retained by snap ring (9). Bearings (12) consist of loose rollers contained in a cage.

1. Input gear
2. Pinion gear
9. Snap ring
10. Snap ring
11. Outer collar
12. Bearing

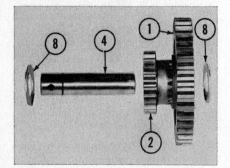

Fig. MM771A — Input shaft thrust washers (8) have formed tabs to prevent rotation in housing.

1. Input gear
2. Pinion gear
4. Input shaft
8. Thrust washers

After adjustment is completed, backlash should be within the extreme limits of 0.006-0.016. Mesh position adjusting shims (28) are available in thicknesses of 0.005, 0.010, 0.020 and 0.030.

Before reinstalling the differential carrier assembly, check the axle oil seals (S—Fig. MM769) and renew if their condition is questionable. Assemble the tractor by reversing the disassembly procedure. Fill differential housing to level of filler plug with 19 pints of SAE 90 EP transmission oil.

14. TRANSFER CASE. The gear-type transfer case can be detached from transmission housing after draining the unit and disconnecting shift link and front drive shaft. Lay aside and save the plastic mounting shim pack as case housing is removed. The shim pack controls the clearance between input gear (1—Fig. MM770) and mating gear in transmission housing.

To disassemble the removed transfer case, drive out the roll pin (3) and push input shaft (4) either way out of input cluster gear and case. Drive the roll pin (15—Fig. MM770A) out of shifter fork (14), disconnect shifter bellcrank (17) or cable, and withdraw the shifter shaft.

NOTE: A detent ball and spring is located in a bore (D) which is closed with a plug (P), located on opposite side of shifter shaft bore. Detent assembly will be released as shaft is withdrawn.

Shifter Fork (14) can be lifted out after removal of shifter shaft. Remove the screws retaining output shaft bearing cap (7) and use a slide ham-

mer or other means to remove shaft assembly from gear (13) and rear bearing cone (22—Fig. MM772).

Input gear (1—Fig. MM771) can be removed from pinion gear (2) after expanding and removing snap ring (9). The two gear bearings (12) consist of a cage and loose rollers which are only available as an assembly. The bearings, outer collars (11) and center spacer can be withdrawn after removing either of the retaining snap rings (10).

When assembling the transfer case, vary the thickness of shim pack (19—Fig. MM772) to apply a slight preload to shaft bearings (21 and 22). Shims (19) are available in thicknesses of 0.002, 0.003 and 0.010.

Install shifter fork (14—Fig. MM-770A), remove plug (P); and install and depress detent spring and ball in its bore using a punch or similar tool, before inserting shifter shaft. Complete the assembly by reversing the disassembly procedure.

Use the removed mounting-shim pack, or install a shim pack of correct thickness to provide a minimum gear backlash without binding, when installing transfer case assembly. The plastic mounting shims are color coded as follows:

Red 0.002
Green 0.003
Brown 0.010

Adjust shifter linkage after installation, so that shifter shaft moves fully into detent notch in both the engaged and disengaged positions.

If front drive shaft is disassembled, reassemble so that universal joints are in register as shown at (P—Fig. MM772).

STEERING SYSTEM
(Except Hydrostatic)

Series UB Special and UTS Special tractors are equipped with a manual steering system; or an optional power steering system, where the working fluid is supplied by the tractor hydraulic system.

Power steering is supplied as standard equipment on all other models.

Note: When working on the power steering system, the maintenance of absolute cleanliness of all parts is of utmost importance. Of equal importance is the avoidance of nicks and burrs on any of the working parts.

FILLING AND BLEEDING

All Models (Power System)

15. The regular tractor hydraulic system reservoir is the source of fluid supply to the power steering system. Only genuine MM hydraulic oil should be used in the system. Fill the reservoir only when the lifting jack is contracted. After filling, operate jack and power steering several times; recheck oil level and add oil if necessary. Reservoir should be filled to the level of the filler plug on UB Special and UTS Special, to within 1-1¼ inches of top of filler opening on models with "Tel-O-Flo" system, or to the "Full" mark on the dipstick on models with Type "E" hydraulic system.

It is recommended that hydraulic oil be changed at least once each year.

Whenever the oil lines have been disconnected or the fluid drained, reconnect the lines, fill the reservoir and cycle the power steering and the hydraulic lift system several times to bleed air from the system; then, refill the reservoir to the proper level.

TROUBLE-SHOOTING

All Models (Power System)

16. Some of the troubles which may be encountered in the operation of the power steering system and their possible causes are listed below. The procedure for correcting most of the troubles is evident; for those not readily remedied, refer to the appropriate subsequent paragraphs.
1. Hard Steering
   a. Linkage damaged, worn or misaligned
   b. Insufficient fluid in reservoir
   c. Low pump pressure
   d. Sticking control valve spool
   e. Faulty flow control valve
   f. Faulty cylinder

2. Loss of Power Assistance
   a. Insufficient fluid in reservoir
   b. Low pump pressure
   c. Faulty flow control valve
   d. Faulty cylinder
   e. Sticking control valve spool
3. Power Assistance in One Direction Only
   a. Control valve spool not centered
   b. Damaged or restricted oil lines
   c. Faulty cylinder
4. Erratic Steering Control
   a. Linkage damaged or worn
   b. Sticking control valve spool
   c. Incorrect fluid in system
   d. Air in system
5. Unequal Turning Radius
   a. Linkage damaged or worn
   b. Improperly adjusted tie-rods
   c. Cylinder piston installed wrong
6. Noisy Operation or "Shimmy".
   a. Linkage damaged, worn or misaligned
   b. Faulty relief valve
   c. Damaged or restricted oil lines
   d. Air in system

OPERATING PRESSURE, RELIEF VALVE, FLOW CONTROL VALVE

All Models (Power System)

17. Working fluid for the hydraulic power steering system is supplied by the same pump which powers the hydraulic lift system. Placed between the pump and the remainder of the system is a flow control and relief valve mechanism which is mounted on the rear face of the hydraulic pump. The small metering hole in the end of the flow control piston passes a predetermined amount of fluid to the power steering system; but, since the pump supplies considerably more fluid than is required by the steering system, pressure builds up in front of the piston and moves the piston, against spring pressure, until the ports which supply oil to the hydraulic system are uncovered. The power steering system, therefore, receives priority and the fluid requirements of the power steering system are satisfied before any oil flows to the hydraulic lift system.

18. **SYSTEM PRESSURE TEST.** A pressure test of the power steering circuit will disclose whether the pump,

relief valve or some other unit in the system is malfunctioning. To make such a test, proceed as follows:

On UB Special and UTS Special, connect a pressure test gage (at least 2000 psi capacity) in the damper valve body as shown in Fig. MM773. Start engine and run until the hydraulic fluid is at normal operating temperature; then, with engine running at fast idle speed, turn the front wheels either way against their stop. At this time, the relief valve should open as indicated by an audible buzzing sound and the pressure gage should read 600-650 psi. If the gage reading is between 600 and 650 psi, the hydraulic pump and relief valve are O.K. and any trouble is located elsewhere in the system.

If the gage reading is more than 650 psi, the relief valve may be stuck in the closed position. If the gage reading is less than 600 psi, check and/or adjust the relief valve pressure as outlined in paragraph 19. If the gage reading is still less than 600 psi, and there are no external fluid leads or internal cylinder or valve leaks as indicated by an increase of oil in the steering gear housing, a faulty hydraulic pump is indicated.

On 5 Star tractors, proceed as outlined for UB and UTS Special, except power steering relief pressure should be 800-900 psi.

On all other models, tee a pressure gage into pressure line leading to power steering control valve. Start and run engine until hydraulic fluid is at normal operating temperature; then, with engine running at fast idle

Fig. MM773—Using a pressure gage connected to the damper valve body to check the power steering system relief valve cracking pressure. Pressure should be 600-650 psi.

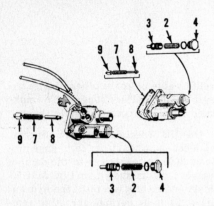

Fig. MM774—Power steering flow control and relief valves and associated parts used on UB Special and UTS Special. Upper view showing unit used on Webster pump; lower view, Eaton pump.

2. Spring
3. Flow control valve
4. Plug
7. Spring
8. Relief valve
9. Spring seat

speed, turn front wheels either way against their stop. Hold steering wheel against stop only long enough to observe gage pressure, which should be 900-1000 psi on early M5, or 950-1050 on other models.

Refer to Fig. MM774 through MM-777 for exploded views of flow control and relief valve located on hydraulic system pump.

19. **OVERHAUL.** Power steering flow control and relief valves can, in all cases, be removed for inspection or adjustment of relief pressure without removing hydraulic pump from tractor. On UB Special and UTS Special, flow control and relief valve housing must be removed from pump for service on relief valve.

On UB Special and UTS Special, check relief valve (8—Fig. MM774) for binding or sticking in spring seat (9). On these models, a renewable relief valve seat is located in flow control valve housing. When installing a new seat, make sure front face

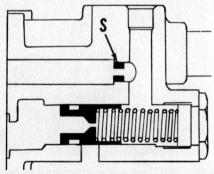

Fig. MM775—When installing new relief valve seat in flow control valve housing used on UB Special, UTS Special, make sure edge of seat is flush with shoulder of bore as shown.

of seat is flush with shoulder in bore as shown in Fig. MM775, and that seat is not cocked in bore. On all other models, housing must be renewed if seat is damaged. On all models, shims are available for adjusting opening pressure.

Refer to the appropriate exploded view when removing or installing flow control valve and spring. The spring is installed at plug-end of valve in all models except those which use flow control valve housings of the type shown in Fig. MM777.

On all models, make sure valve slides freely in bore, and that valve and bore are free of deep scratches or scoring, and that spring is not distorted.

PUMP

All Models (Power System)

20. The hydraulic pump supplies fluid to both the power steering system and the hydraulic system.

Refer to paragraphs 190 through 194 for overhaul data on hydraulic pumps.

CONTROL VALVE

Series UB Special-UTS Special-5 Star

21. **DAMPER VALVE.** The damper valve restricts the return flow from the power steering control valve to maintain approximately equal pressure in both power steering cylinders during any turning action, thus eliminating any tendency of "shimmy" in the steering system.

The damper valve plunger (10—Fig. MM778) must slide freely in the body passage to provide proper steering control. If a sticking or binding plunger is found, first clean the plunger and body bore and remove any small nicks or scoring. If plunger is not then free, renew plunger and/or body as required.

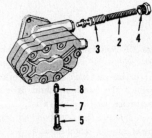

Fig. MM776—Power steering pump used on 5 Star and some M5 tractors, showing power steering flow control and relief valves exploded.

2. Spring
3. Flow control valve
4. Plug
5. Plug
7. Spring
8. Relief valve

To remove the damper valve, disconnect the oil lines and unbolt and remove damper body from control valve housing. Remove snap rings (8) from each end of plunger body bore and tap by-pass valve (12) forward, forcing plunger (10) and plug (9) out front of housing.

When reassembling, renew all seals, dip parts in clean hydraulic fluid and reinstall. Make sure by-pass valve (12) is installed with small orifice and pin to inside of housing and that plunger (10) is installed with pin toward plug (9).

22. **R&R AND OVERHAUL.** To remove the control valve, disconnect the oil lines, unbolt and remove the damper valve housing; then unbolt and remove the control valve from the steering worm shaft housing. Remove covers (1 and 6—Fig. MM778) from ends of valve housing. Remove cap screw (3), unscrew valve spool from actuating lever (4) and withdraw the spool from control valve housing. Thoroughly clean and examine all parts. If the valve spool or spool bore are damaged, it will be necessary to renew the complete valve unit. "O" ring seals, however, are available separately.

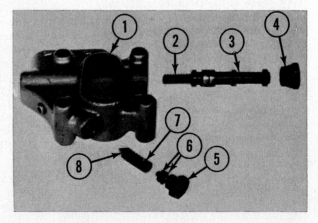

Fig. MM777 — Flow control valve housing of the type used on most late models, showing power steering flow control and relief valves.

1. Housing
2. Spring
3. Flow control valve
4. Plug
5. Plug
6. Adjusting shims
7. Spring
8. Relief valve

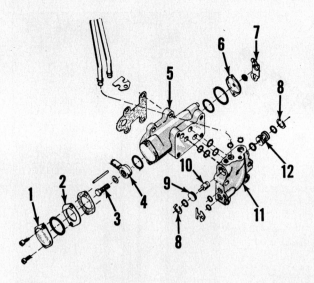

Fig. MM778 — Exploded view of power steering control valve assembly used on UB Special, UTS Special and 5-Star tractors.

1. Valve end cover
2. Lever end plate
3. Retaining bolt
4. Valve lever
5. Valve body
6. End cover
7. Seal retainer
8. Snap ring
9. Plunger plug
10. Damper valve plunger
11. Damper valve body
12. By-pass valve

When reassembling, renew all seals, dip all parts in clean hydraulic fluid and reverse the disassembly procedure. Leave cap screw (3) loose and covers (1 and 6) off for valve centering adjustment after completion of assembly. Install the assembled control valve and tighten the retaining cap screws securely. Install the damper valve assembly and tighten the retaining screws to a torque of 15 ft.-lbs.

After the lines are connected and the hydraulic system reservoir filled, connect a pressure gage to the damper valve as shown in Fig. MM773, start engine and run at fast idle speed. Insert a large screw driver in the slot at the rear end of the control valve spool and turn the spool into the actuating lever while observing the gage reading. When a definite increase in gage pressure is noted, record the pressure and back the spool out of the actuating lever while counting the turns, until the pressure drops. Then, continue backing out the spool until the pressure increases to the previously recorded value. Halfway between these points, in the level of lowest gage pressure, should be the valve center position. Tempo-

rarily lock the valve to the actuating lever by tightening cap screw (3) and, while turning the steering wheel to the right and left, determine that approximately equal steering effort is required for a right or left turn. If more steering effort is required for a right hand turn, rotate the valve spool slightly counter-clockwise and recheck. If more effort is required for a left hand turn, rotate valve spool clockwise. When the valve center position has been established, tighten locking cap screw (3) and reinstall end covers (1 and 6).

After centering the control valve spool, turn the steering wheel in each direction and check to be sure the spool moves 0.040 in each direction. If the spool travels more or less than 0.040, the separator clearance must be adjusted as outlined in paragraph 26.

Series M5-M504-M602-M604-M670

23. R&R AND OVERHAUL. To remove the power steering control valve, disconnect the oil lines and unbolt and remove the control valve from the steering worm shaft housing. Be careful not to lose actuating lever (6—Fig. MM779) when the two parts are separated.

Remove the two cap screws retaining end cap (11) to housing (5) and remove the end cap. Remove snap ring (1) and plate (2) from rear of housing. While holding clevis rod (3) from turning, loosen and remove nut (10), washers (7 and 9) and spring (8) from end of clevis rod. Withdraw clevis rod (3) from rear end of housing and push control valve spool (4) from body bore. Control valve spool and body (5) are matched, and can only be renewed as an assembly. Working with a small wire from inside the housing, push check valve ball (12), spring (13) and plug (14) from the valve body. Thoroughly clean and examine all parts.

When reassembling, renew all seals, dip the parts in clean hydraulic fluid and reinstall by reversing the disassembly procedure. Tighten nut (10 until washer (9) is bottomed on its shoulder on the clevis rod. When reinstalling valve, make sure fork on end of actuating lever (6) engages pin in clevis rod (3) and that opposite end of lever engages groove in the actuating sleeve on steering shaft.

STEERING CYLINDERS

All Models Except M670 Super

24. To remove the steering piston and cylinder sleeves, remove hood and side panels, then unscrew the pedestal stop pin (36—Fig. MM781). On axle models, disconnect the center steering arm from the vertical steering shaft. Remove snap rings (10) from support housing and withdraw end plug and tube assemblies (7 and 8). With the steering wheel, turn vertical steering shaft (26) to the left until sector (27) is disengaged from teeth on piston (4). Withdraw piston, and sleeves (2) from support housing.

Examine all parts and renew any which are damaged or worn. To facilitate assembly, the inner end of the right sleeve should be chamfered on the inside as shown in Fig. MM782,

Fig. MM779 — Exploded view of power steering control valve used on M5, M504, M602, M604 and M670.

1. Snap ring
2. End plate
3. Clevis rod
4. Valve spool
5. Valve housing
6. Actuating lever
7. Centering washer
8. Centering spring
9. Retaining washer
10. Nut
11. End cap
12. Check valve ball
13. Valve spring
14. Check valve plug

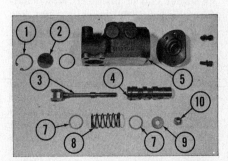

Fig. MM780 — Disassembled view of late power steering control valve. Refer to Fig. MM779 for legend.

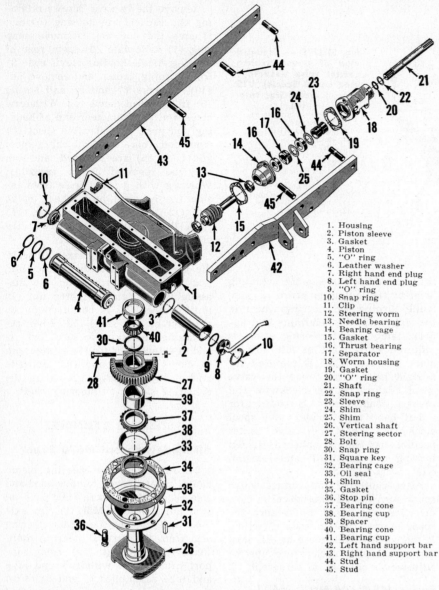

1. Housing
2. Piston sleeve
3. Gasket
4. Piston
5. "O" ring
6. Leather washer
7. Right hand end plug
8. Left hand end plug
9. "O" ring
10. Snap ring
11. Clip
12. Steering worm
13. Needle bearing
14. Bearing cage
15. Gasket
16. Thrust bearing
17. Separator
18. Worm housing
19. Gasket
20. "O" ring
21. Shaft
22. Snap ring
23. Sleeve
24. Shim
25. Shim
26. Vertical shaft
27. Steering sector
28. Bolt
30. Snap ring
31. Square key
32. Bearing cage
33. Oil seal
34. Shim
35. Gasket
36. Stop pin
37. Bearing cone
38. Bearing cup
39. Spacer
40. Bearing cone
41. Bearing cup
42. Left hand support bar
43. Right hand support bar
44. Stud
45. Stud

Fig. MM781 — Steering gear housing, gear unit and associated parts used on all tractors except M670 Super. On models with manual steering item (17) is a spacer.

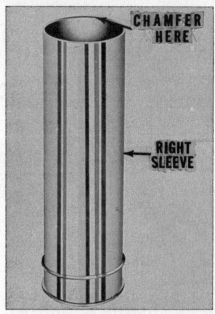

Fig. MM782 — To prevent damaging the power piston seals during installation, the inside diameter of the right hand sleeve should be chamfered approximately 1/16-inch as shown.

Fig. MM783 — Power steering piston extending 1¼ inches from left side of steering gear housing.

to prevent damage to piston seals during installation. If the sleeve is not already chamfered, use a fine cut file and remove about $\frac{1}{16}$-inch of the inner edge then smooth with crocus cloth.

Install "O" rings and back-up rings on either end of piston. Install chamfered sleeve with gasket in right side of housing with snap ring (10) in place to keep sleeve from working out. Thoroughly lubricate the piston and rings and install the left sleeve over the piston. Align piston teeth in their proper operating position at the rear of the housing and insert piston and left sleeve into the housing and right sleeve until 1¼ inches of the left end of piston extends from housing as shown in Fig. MM783. Turn steering wheel to the right until sector teeth engage the teeth of the

piston, then continue turning until sector is centered in a straight ahead position. Note: Very little effort should be required to turn steering wheel. If undue resistance is encountered after sector tooth engagement, check for improper alignment of the gear teeth.

Install snap ring in left end of housing, install center steering arm (axle models) or tighten stop screw (tricycle models). Turn steering wheel all the way to the right and measure the distance from the end of piston to outer edge of sleeve. Turn the steering wheel to the left and recheck. If the measured distances differ more than ½-inch, the piston is not properly meshed with the sector and should be realigned in the manner previously described.

With the piston properly installed, remove the snap rings and reinstall end plate assemblies and the retaining snap rings.

STEERING GEAR UNIT

All Models Except M670 Super

25. **SECTOR AND SHAFT.** To remove the steering sector and/or shaft, first drain the gear housing by removing center bolt from the left side of the bearing cage. Support front of tractor and on tricycle models, remove the fork (or pedestal) and wheels assembly. On axle type tractors, remove the axle, wheels and tie-rods assembly. Unbolt bearing cage from steering housing and withdraw shaft, sector and bearing cage as an assembly. Note the position of the two stop lugs

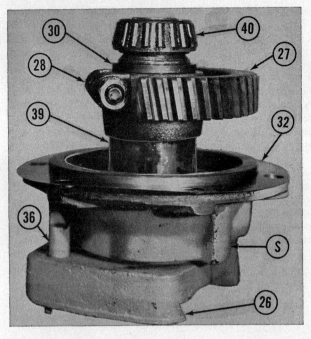

Fig. MM784 — Steering
sector, vertical shaft and
bearing cage assembly re-
moved from steering gear
housing.

26. Vertical shaft
27. Sector
28. Clamp bolt
30. Snap ring
32. Bearing cage
39. Spacer
40. Bearing cone
S. Stop

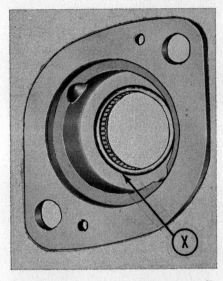

Fig. MM786 — The wormshaft rear needle
bearing should be installed 1/64-inch below shoulder in bearing cage as shown.

(S—Fig. MM784) on right side of bearing cage, and stop pin in vertical shaft, for proper location in reassembly.

To disassemble the vertical shaft assembly, remove bearing cone (40—Fig. MM781), using a suitable knife edge type puller. Remove snap ring (30), loosen clamp bolt (28) and remove sector gear (27), key (31) and spacer (39). Press the sector shaft out of the bearing cage. Shaft seal (33), bearing cones (37 and 40), or any of the other parts in the vertical shaft assembly can be renewed at this time. Install seal (33) with lip facing to the inside of the bearing cage.

Assemble the unit by reversing the disassembly procedure. Make certain stop pin (36) is installed between limit stops (S—Fig. MM784) and that

stops (S) are to the right when the assembly is installed. Vary the number of shims (34—Fig. MM781) to provide a slight rotational drag for the tapered roller bearings.

26. STEERING WORM. To remove the steering worm, use a suitable drift punch and remove the roll pins retaining the front and rear universal joints to the front steering shaft. Bump the front universal joint rearward and off the steering worm extension shaft. On models with power steering, disconnect the oil lines leading to the power steering valve. Unbolt and withdraw the worm assembly (with valve attached on power steering models). On power steering models, unbolt and remove the control valve, and on all models, separate the extension shaft housing (18—Fig. MM-785) from bearing cage (14). Drive

out the roll pin retaining sleeve (23) to worm shaft and withdraw steering worm from the bearing cage. Remove shim (24), rear bearing (16), shim (25), separator (17) and front bearing (16). Remove snap ring (22) at rear of extension housing and withdraw extension shaft (21).

Thoroughly clean all parts and renew any which are damaged or worn. Rear needle bearing (13) can be pressed from the bearing cage if renewal is required. To remove the front needle bearing located in steering gear housing, cut through the bearing cage with a chisel and pry the bearing out of its bore. When installing the bearings, use MM tool No. 10T 5178, or other suitable arbor and press only on the end of bearing which has the stamped identification letters. Press the front bearing in the gear housing until it just bottoms. Rear bearing should be installed 1/64-inch below shoulder in cage as shown at (X) in Fig. MM786.

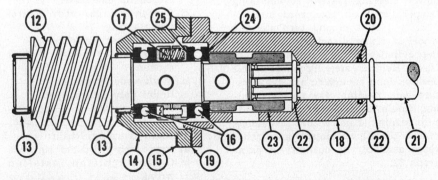

Fig. MM785 — Sectional view of the steering worm shaft and associated parts in the
power steering system.

12. Steering worm
13. Needle bearing
14. Worm bearing cage
15. Bearing cage gasket
16. Thrust bearing
17. Separator
18. Worm shaft housing
19. Gasket
20. "O" ring
21. Extension shaft
22. Snap ring
23. Extension shaft sleeve
24. Shims
25. Shims

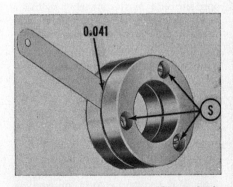

Fig. MM787 — Turn screws (S) to obtain
0.041 clearance between the separator
halves. Refer to paragraph 26.

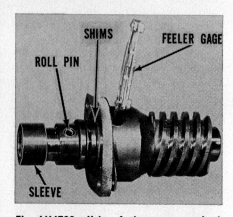

Fig. MM788—Using feeler gage to check clearance between separator halves when sleeve is pinned to the worm shaft. Clearance at this time should be 0.040.

On models with power steering, turn the screws (S—Fig. MM787) either way to obtain a clearance of 0.041 between the spring loaded separator halves when checked around the entire circumference of the separator. When installing the worm shaft in the bearing cage, vary the number of shims (25—Fig. MM785) between separator and rear thrust bearing to remove all shaft end play, except that provided in the spring loaded separator, when coupling is pinned to shaft. Separator clearance on the assembled unit should be 0.040, when measured through the opening in the bearing cage as shown in Fig. MM788. Shims are available in thicknesses of

0.002 and 0.006. Note: If assembled separator clearance is less than the specified 0.040, shaft movement will be insufficient to actuate the power steering control valve.

On all models, vary number of shims (24—Fig. MM785) located between rear thrust bearing and extension shaft housing to just remove any worm shaft free end play. Note: A shim pack which is too thick or too thin will show up as shaft free end play. If end play exists after the shaft is assembled, re-measure the separator gap as previously described to determine whether to add or remove shims.

HYDROSTATIC STEERING SYSTEM

Model M670 Super tractors are equipped with Saginaw hydrostatic steering which has no mechanical linkage between the steering control and the steering cylinder.

OPERATION

27. The pressurized oil for the power steering system is furnished by a belt driven pump which is mounted on right side of engine. The oil is pumped to the Hydramotor unit and if system is in neutral position, the oil flows through the control valve and returns to the reservoir. However, when the steering wheel is turned, the control valve is shifted and the oil is directed to the metering unit of the Hydramotor. This unit displaces a given amount of oil which is directed back through the control valve and delivered to one end of the steering cylinder. The return oil from opposite end of the steering cylinder flows through the control valve and back to the reservoir.

A check ball which is seated by pump pressure when the supply pump is operating, unseats to allow oil to recirculate between the Hydramotor and steering cylinder to provide manual steering when the supply pump is not operating.

LUBRICATION AND BLEEDING

28. MM Hydraulic fluid, or equivalent, is used as the operating fluid. The reservoir is a part of the supply

pump and the system capacity is approximately 2 quarts.

The power steering system is self-bleeding. If any part of the system has been disassembled and units are dry, fill the reservoir and cycle the system through full range of travel several times. Then, refill reservoir to the full mark.

OPERATING PRESSURE AND RELIEF VALVE

29. The system relief pressure is controlled by a fixed-setting flow control and relief valve located in the power steering pump. To check the operating pressure, tee a 0-2000 psi pressure gage in the pump pressure line on right side of tractor. With power steering system at operating temperature, run tractor at approximately 1000 rpm and turn steering wheel in either direction until steering cylinder is at extreme end of travel. Hold the steering wheel in this position long enough to observe pressure gage reading. The normal reading should be 900-1000 psi. If pressure reading is not within this range, renew the flow control and relief valve assembly as outlined in paragraph 32.

TROUBLE-SHOOTING

30. Some of the troubles which may be encountered in the operation of the hydrostatic steering system and

their possible causes are listed as follows:

1. Hard Steering
   a. Low pump pressure
   b. Insufficient fluid in reservoir
   c. Faulty pump flow control and relief valve
   d. Hydramotor control valve damaged or sticking
   e. Faulty steering cylinder
2. Power Assistance in One Direction Only
   a. Hydramotor control valve sticking
   b. Damaged or restricted oil lines
   c. Faulty steering cylinder
3. Erratic Steering Control
   a. Vanes sticking in Hydramotor rotor
   b. Hydramotor metering unit scored or excessively worn
   c. Broken Hydramotor control valve spring
4. Loss of Power Assistance
   a. Hydramotor torsion shaft broken
   b. Faulty supply pump
   c. Relief valve stuck open
   d. Manual control ball not seating
5. Unequal Turning Radius
   a. Improperly adjusted tie rods
   b. Cylinder piston installed wrong
6. Noisy Operation
   a. Insufficient fluid in reservoir
   b. Air in system
   c. Faulty relief valve
   d. Damaged or restricted oil lines

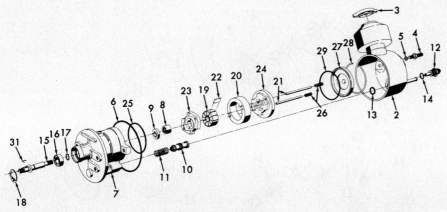

Fig. MM789—Exploded view of the Saginaw power steering pump assembly used on M670 Super tractors.

2. Reservoir	10. Flow control &	16. Bearing	24. Pressure plate
3. Filler cap	pressure relief	17. Snap ring	25. "O" ring
4. Mounting stud	valve	18. Snap ring	26. Pressure spring
5. "O" ring	11. Spring	19. Rotor	27. End plate
6. "O" ring	12. Pressure fitting	20. Pump ring	28. Snap ring
7. Pump housing	13. "O" ring	21. Dowel pin	29. "O" ring
8. Needle bearing	14. "O" ring	22. Vane (10 used)	31. Woodruff key
9. Oil seal	15. Drive shaft	23. Thrust plate	

POWER STEERING PUMP

31. REMOVE AND REINSTALL. To remove the power steering pump, disconnect the pressure line and return line and allow reservoir to drain. Remove the pump mounting bolts and withdraw pump and mounting bracket as a unit.

Install by reversing the removal procedure. Turn the belt tension adjusting screw to provide approximately ¼-inch belt deflection when 10 pounds pressure is applied to belt at mid-point between pulleys. Tighten mounting bolts, then fill and bleed system as outlined in paragraph 28.

32. RELIEF VALVE. The combined flow control and pressure relief valve (10—Fig. MM789) can be renewed without removing the power steering

pump. To renew the valve, disconnect the pressure line, remove pressure line fitting (12) and withdraw the valve. Relief pressure is pre-set, and no attempt should be made to disassemble or overhaul the valve.

33. PUMP OVERHAUL. To disassemble the removed power steering pump, refer to Fig. MM789. Remove the mounting bracket, mounting stud (4) and pressure line fitting (12). Withdraw the flow control and relief valve (10) and valve spring (11), then remove the reservoir (2).

Secure pump body in a vise and turn retaining snap ring (3—Fig. MM790) if necessary, until one end is located over the small hole in housing at snap ring groove. Insert a small punch (4) into hole as shown, unseat and remove snap ring (3) and end plate (2).

NOTE: The two pressure springs (26—Fig. MM789) fit over dowel pins (21) and are compressed to apply pressure to the pressure plate. Do not lose the springs when end plate (27) is removed.

Remove the pressure plate (24), cam ring (20), rotor (19) with vanes (22) and thrust plate (23). Note the direction of rotation arrow on cam ring for aid in correct reassembly.

Remove the pulley retaining nut and drive pulley, then after first removing snap ring (18), withdraw the drive shaft (15) with bearing (16). Needle bearing (8) and oil seal (9) can now be removed from pump housing (7).

Examine rotor (19) for wear in vane slots and cam ring (20) for ridging or scoring in vane contact area.

Examine vane area of thrust plate (23) and pressure plate (24) for wear. Check the vanes (22) for nicks and wear.

Reassemble the pump by reversing the disassembly procedure using Fig. MM789 as a guide. Renew all "O" rings and oil seal (9), and any worn or otherwise damaged parts. Reinstall pump as outlined in paragraph 31.

HYDRAMOTOR

34. REMOVE AND REINSTALL. To remove the power steering Hydramotor, use a suitable puller to remove the steering wheel. Do not hammer on the attached puller as the Hydramotor will be damaged. Remove the throttle lever, then unbolt and remove the steering motor cover. Identify and disconnect the pressure and return lines and the steering cylinder lines from Hydramotor. Unbolt and remove the Hydramotor unit.

Reinstall unit by reversing the removal procedure, then fill and bleed system as outlined in paragraph 28.

35. OVERHAUL. To disassemble the removed Hydramotor, refer to Fig. MM792 and remove cover retaining ring (17). To remove the retaining ring, insert a ⅛-inch punch into hole provided in cover (16) and drive punch inward to unseat end of ring from groove. With the punch under the ring, use screwdrivers to pry ring from cover. See Fig. MM793.

Place the housing assembly in a vise so that steering shaft is pointing downward. Usually, spring (13—Fig. MM792) will push housing assembly from the cover. If binding condition exists, it may be necessary to bump cover loose by tapping around edge of cover with a soft faced mallet.

Fig. MM790 — Pumping elements are retained in body by snap ring (3) and end plate (2). "O" ring (5) seals the formed steel reservoir.

1. Body
2. End plate
3. Snap ring
4. Punch
5. "O" ring

Fig. MM791 — View showing the power steering pump on model M670 Super tractor. The pump mounting bolts are shown at (1) and belt tension adjusting screw at (2).

Remove the pressure plate spring, then lift off pressure plate (9). Remove dowel pins (24), then using suitable snap ring pliers and screwdriver, remove snap ring (7) from torsion shaft (29). Discard snap ring (7) as a new snap ring must be used when reassembling. Pull pump ring and rotor assembly (6) off torsion shaft (29). Tap end of shaft (28) with soft faced mallet until bearing support (2) can be removed, then carefully withdraw actuator assembly from housing (22). NOTE: It is recommended that the actuator assembly not be disassembled as it is a factory balanced unit.

Housing (22) and actuator assembly, which includes spring (23), spool (25), actuator (26), shaft (28) and torsion shaft (29) are not serviced separately. If these parts are serviceable, needle bearing (21) and seals (19 and 20) can be renewed as necessary. Install new needle bearing (21) by pressing on lettered side of bearing cage only until bearing cage is flush with counter bore.

Needle bearing (1 and 8) in bearing support (2) and pressure plate (9) may be renewed if support and/or plate are otherwise serviceable. Install new bearings by pressing on lettered side of bearing cage only. Remove plugs (12) and withdraw springs (11) and check balls (10). Inspect the ball seats and balls for excessive wear. Renew parts as necessary.

Rotor, ring, vanes and vane springs are serviced as a complete assembly (6) only; however, the unit may be disassembled for cleaning and inspection. Reassemble by placing rotor in ring on flat surface. Insert vanes (rounded side out) in rotor slots aligned with large diameter of ring, turn rotor ¼-turn and insert remaining vanes. Hook the vane springs behind each vane with screwdriver as shown in Fig. MM794; be sure that vane springs are in proper place on both sides of rotor.

To reassemble Hydramotor unit, place housing, with needle bearing, seals and snap ring installed, in a vise with flat (bottom) side up. Check to be sure that pin in actuator is engaged in valve spool; if spool can be pulled away from actuator as shown in Fig. MM795, push spool back into actuator and engage pin into hole in spool. Carefully insert actuator assembly into bore of housing. Install bearing support (2—Fig. MM792), with bearing (1), "O" rings and Teflon rotor

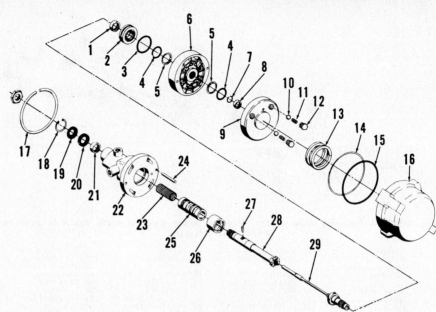

Fig. MM792—Exploded view of the power steering Hydramotor used on M670 Super tractors.

1. Needle bearing	8. Needle bearing
2. Bearing support	9. Pressure plate
3. "O" ring	10. Ball
4. "O" ring	11. Spring
5. Rotor seal	12. Plug
6. Rotor and ring assembly	13. Pressure plate spring
7. Snap ring	14. Back-up ring
15. "O" ring	23. Valve spool spring
16. Cover	24. Dowel pin
17. Retaining ring	25. Valve spool
18. Snap ring	26. Actuator
19. Dust seal	27. Pin
20. Oil seal	28. Shaft
21. Needle bearing	29. Torsion shaft
22. Housing	

seal, over end of shaft and carefully push the assembly in flush with housing. Place the pump ring and rotor assembly on shaft and housing with chamfered outer edge of pump ring away from housing. Install a **new** rotor retaining snap ring (7) and insert the dowel pins through pump ring and into housing. Stick the "O" ring and Teflon rotor seal into pressure plate with heavy grease, then install pressure plate on shaft, pump ring and rotor assembly and the dowel pins. Place pressure plate spring (13) on pressure plate. Install new "O" ring (15) and back-up ring (14) in groove in cover, then install cover over the assembled steering unit. To

install the cover retaining ring, it is recommended that the unit be placed in an arbor press and the housing be pushed into cover by a sleeve. CAUTION: DO NOT push against end of shaft (28). Place retaining ring over housing before placing unit in press. Carefully apply pressure on housing with sleeve until flange on housing is below retaining ring groove in cover. Note that lug on housing must enter slot in cover. If housing binds in cover, **do not** apply heavy pressure; remove unit from press and bump cover loose with mallet. When housing has been pushed sufficiently into cover, install retaining ring in groove with end gap near hole in cover.

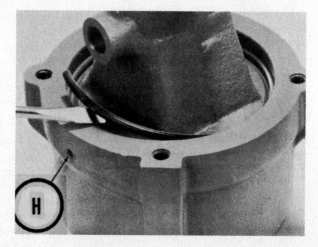

Fig. MM793—Drive a ⅛-inch punch into hole (H) to unseat retaining ring, then pry ring out with screwdriver.

Fig. MM794—All vane springs must be engaged behind the rotor vanes. Springs can be pried into position with screwdriver as shown.

STEERING CYLINDER AND SECTOR GEAR

36. R&R AND OVERHAUL. To remove the steering piston or cylinder sleeves, first drain cooling system, then remove hood, grille, lower grille support and front side panels. Suitably support the tractor and remove the front axle assembly. Drain the steering gear housing. Unbolt and remove the radiator and radiator braces. Disconnect the steering cylinder lines from the piston end covers and remove breather from top of housing. Remove cap screws securing steering gear housing to side rails and slide housing forward and out of rails. Place the housing on a bench with the vertical shaft flange facing upward.

Turn the vertical shaft to the straight-ahead position. Mark the vertical shaft in relation to the bearing housing and the bearing housing to the steering gear housing so the sector gear and piston can be properly indexed when reassembling. Remove the piston end covers and measure the distance from end of piston to end of

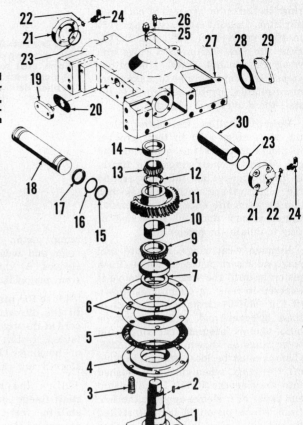

Fig. MM796 — Exploded view of the steering gear housing, steering cylinder, vertical shaft and associated parts used on model M670 Super.

1. Vertical shaft
2. Key
3. Stop pin
4. Bearing cage
5. Gasket
6. Adjusting shims
7. Oil seal
8. Bearing cup
9. Bearing cone
10. Spacer
11. Sector gear
12. Snap ring
13. Bearing cone
14. Bearing cup
15. Teflon seal ring
16. "O" ring
17. Teflon wear ring
18. Piston
19. Piston guide
20. Gasket
21. Piston end cover
22. "O" ring
23. "O" ring
24. Elbow fitting
25. Filler plug
26. Breather
27. Steering gear housing
28. Gasket
29. Cover
30. Sleeve

each sleeve. Record these dimensions for aid in reassembly. Note: The distance from right hand end of piston to sleeve end is greater than that on the left side.

Unbolt and remove the piston guide (19—Fig. MM796) from front of steering gear housing. Remove the four hex head cap screws and two 12-point cap screws from sector gear bearing cage (4). Note that the two 12-point cap screws were in the area traveled by the stop pin (3). Withdraw the vertical shaft and sector gear assembly from steering gear housing. Piston (18) and cylinder sleeves (30) can now be removed. Discard all "O" rings, seal rings and wear rings.

To disassemble the vertical shaft assembly, remove bearing cone (13) using a suitable knife edge puller. Remove snap ring (12), loosen clamp bolt and remove sector gear (11), key (2) and spacer (10). Press vertical shaft (1) out of bearing cage (4) and renew seal (7) before reassembling. Bearing cups (8 and 14) should be renewed if bearing cones (9 and 13) are renewed.

Reassemble the vertical shaft, bearings and sector gear by reversing the disassembly procedure but do not install in steering housing at this time.

Install cylinder sleeves (30) in housing (27). Coat new "O" rings (16) with Lubriplate and install the "O"

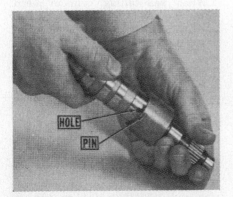

Fig. MM795—Pin in actuator sleeve must be engaged in hole in end of spool before actuator assembly is installed.

Fig. MM797—Install piston with seal ring (2) into sleeve until wear ring groove (1) is positioned as shown.

rings in the outer grooves at each end of piston. Install Teflon seal rings (15) in same grooves on "O" rings. NOTE: Heat the new Teflon seal rings and wear rings in hot water (110-120 degrees) for a few minutes to make them more pliable. Stretch seal rings to install them over end of piston.

Fig. MM798—View showing a strap-type hose clamp used to hold seal ring and wear ring (1) in position during piston installation.

Before installing the piston, place the wear rings (17) in their grooves in piston to check the wear ring end gap. With the wear rings held firmly in their grooves all the way around the piston, there must be a ⅛-inch gap between the ends. If not, remove the necessary material from end of ring to obtain the proper gap.

Remove wear rings, lubricate seal ring and insert piston in sleeve. Push piston in until the wear ring groove is exposed in housing opening as shown in Fig. MM797. Install wear rings in their grooves and place strap-type hose clamps around seal rings and wear rings as shown in Fig. MM798. Clamps must be loose enough to slide off the rings when piston is pushed into the sleeves. NOTE: Install piston end cover over sleeve opposite the side from which piston is being installed to prevent sleeve from being pushed out. Using a wooden hammer handle,

bump piston into sleeves until seal rings and wear rings fully enter the sleeves. At this point, remove clamp from piston inside of housing.

Move the piston into the sleeves until the dimensions measured and recorded during piston removal are obtained. Install piston guide on front of housing. Use new "O" rings on sleeves and reinstall end covers.

Align the marks on the vertical shaft flange and bearing cage and install the vertical shaft and sector gear assembly. Use a new gasket (5—Fig. MM796) and sufficient quantity of

0.006 shims (6) to provide zero end play of vertical shaft.

Rotate the vertical shaft to see that stop pin (3) contacts the stops in both directions. If the stop pin fails to contact a stop in one direction, sector gear and piston teeth are not correctly meshed.

Reinstall the steering gear unit on tractor and refill with SAE 80 Multipurpose gear oil. The balance of reassembly in the reverse of disassembly procedure. Fill and bleed power steering system as outlined in paragraph 28.

ENGINE AND COMPONENTS

The engines used in all models covered, conform to the same general design, consisting of a one-piece cast crankcase, with cylinder blocks and heads cast in pairs. The basic design is used in gasoline, LP-Gas and diesel engines, and many of the engine parts are interchangeable.

Series UB Special, UTS Special and 5-Star gasoline and LP-Gas engines, and UB Special and UTS Special diesel engines have four cylinders with a bore of 4¼ inches, a stroke of 5 inches and a piston displacement of 283.7 cubic inches. The engines used in 5-Star diesel and all M5, M504, M602, M604, M670 and M670 Super tractors have a bore of 4⅝ inches, a stroke of 5 inches and a piston displacement of 336 cubic inches.

REMOVE AND REINSTALL

All Models

37. To remove the engine assembly, remove hood and disconnect fuel lines and throttle linkage. Drain radiator and, if engine is to be disassembled,

drain oil pan. Disconnect wiring harness, heat indicator sending unit and drive out pin retaining steering worm shaft to universal joint. On series UB Special, UTS Special and M670 Super remove hydraulic pressure and return lines. On other models remove power steering oil lines.

On all models block up front end of transmission and support engine in chain hoist. Remove cap screws retaining engine to transmission and separate tractor halves. Remove frame bars from engine and pedestal, disconnect radiator hoses; then, while steadying assembly, remove front wheels, pedestal and radiator as a unit.

CYLINDER HEAD

All Models

38. To remove one cylinder head, first remove hood and drain cooling system. Remove upper radiator hose, water manifold and air cleaner. On

non-diesels, disconnect throttle control rod and fuel line from carburetor, and remove exhaust and inlet manifold. On diesels, disconnect nozzle lines and remove the manifold. On all models, remove cylinder head rocker cover, oil lines, and rocker arms and shaft assembly. Remove cylinder head retaining nuts and lift cylinder head from engine.

When reinstalling cylinder head, tighten inlet and exhaust manifold nuts finger tight to align mounting faces, then tighten cylinder head stud nuts.

On UB Special and UTS Special non-diesel engines, tighten the head nuts to a torque of 100-105 ft.-lbs. on camshaft side and 85-90 ft.-lbs. on exhaust manifold side using tightening sequence shown in Fig. MM800.

On 5-Star, M5 and M504 non-diesel engines, tighten the head nuts to a torque of 125-130 ft.-lbs. on camshaft side and 105-110 ft.-lbs. on exhaust manifold side using the sequence shown in Fig. MM800.

Fig. MM800—Tighten cylinder head nuts on non-diesel models in the sequence shown. Rocker arm oil connection is shown at (34).

On M602 and M604 non-diesel models, tighten all cylinder head stud nuts to a torque of 170-175 ft.-lbs. using the sequence shown in Fig. MM800.

On M670 and M670 Super non-diesel engines, tighten all cylinder head stud nuts to a torque of 170-175 ft.-lbs. using the tightening sequence shown in Fig. MM801.

On UB Special and UTS Special diesel engines, tighten the ⅝-inch stud nuts to 100-105 ft.-lbs. on camshaft side and 85-90 ft.lbs. on exhaust manifold side and the $\frac{9}{16}$-inch stud nuts to a torque of 68-72 ft.-lbs.

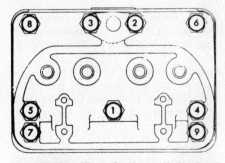

Fig. MM801—View showing cylinder head nut tightening sequence for M670 and M670 Super non-diesel tractors.

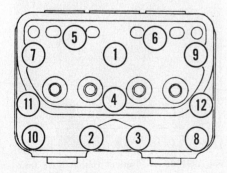

Fig. MM802—Diesel engine cylinder head nut tightening sequence. Refer to text for torque values.

Fig. MM803—With No. 1 piston at T.D.C. (compression), adjust four valves as indicated. Refer to text for correct tappet gap.

using the tightening sequence shown in Fig. MM802.

On 5 Star, M5 and M504 diesel engines tighten the ⅝-inch stud nuts to a torque of 125-130 ft.-lbs. on the camshaft side and 105-110 ft.-lbs. on exhaust manifold side and the $\frac{9}{16}$-inch stud nuts to a torque of 85-90 ft.-lbs. using sequence shown in Fig. MM802.

On M602, M604, M670 and M670 Super diesel models, tighten all $\frac{9}{16}$ inch stud nuts to a torque of 130-135 ft.-lbs.; and all ⅝ inch stud nuts to a torque of 170-175 ft.-lbs., using the sequence shown in Fig. MM802.

On all models, adjust valve tappet gap (cold) as outlined in paragraph 39. Retighten cylinder head stud nuts using the indicated tightening sequence and torque, after engine is at operating temperature. Then, readjust valve tappet gap (hot) as outlined in paragraph 39.

NOTE: Cylinder heads are widely interchangeable and compression ratio can be varied on spark ignition engines by installing heads of a different configuration. Cylinder heads are identified by the part number cast into the head. Make certain that identical cylinder heads are used when engine is assembled.

VALVES AND SEATS

All Models

39. Cylinder head is fitted with renewable seat inserts for the exhaust valves, while intake valves seat directly in the cylinder head. Intake and exhaust valves are not interchangeable. Valves have a face and seat angle of 45 degrees and a desired seat width of 3/32-inch. Valve stem diameter is 0.4335-0.4345.

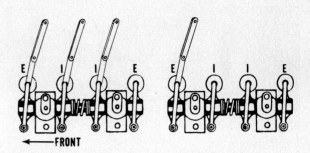

To adjust valve tappet gap, crank engine until No. 1 piston is at T. D. C. of compression stroke. At this time, adjust tappet gap of the four valves indicated in Fig. MM803. Crank engine one revolution to position No. 4 piston at T.D.C. of compression stroke and adjust the tappet gap of the remaining four valves indicated in Fig. MM804.

Adjust intake valve tappet gap to 0.012, cold, for all models. Cold tappet gap adjustment for exhaust valves is 0.028 for M670 and M670 Super non-diesels and 0.022 for all other non-diesel models; or 0.017 for M670 Super diesel and 0.020 for all other diesel models.

After engine has run for at least 15 minutes and has reached operating temperature, check and readjust tappet gap as required using the procedure outlined above. Adjust intake valve tappet gap to 0.010, hot, for all models. Adjust exhaust valve tappet gap to 0.022, hot, for M670 and M670 Super non-diesels and 0.020, hot, for all other non-diesel models; or 0.015, hot, for M670 Super diesel and 0.018, hot, for all other diesel models.

VALVE GUIDES AND SPRINGS

All Models

40. Inlet and exhaust valve guides are interchangeable in all except diesel models. Ream guides after installation to provide a stem-to-guide clearance of 0.002-0.004. Inlet and exhaust valve springs are interchangeable in all except gasoline models. On gasoline models, the intake valve springs should test 85-90 lbs. at 2½ inches and the exhaust valve springs should test 100-110 lbs. at 2¼ inches.

Fig. MM804—With No. 4 piston at T.D.C. (compression), adjust four valves as indicated. Refer to text for correct tappet gap.

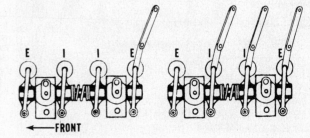

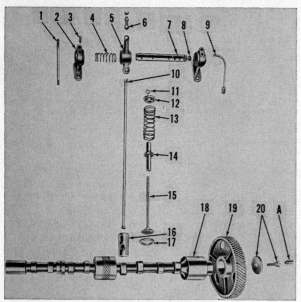

Fig. MM805 — Exploded view of typical camshaft, rocker arms and related parts.

A. Camshaft end play adjusting screw
1. Shaft support stud
2. Shaft support
3. Rocker arm shaft retaining screw
4. Rocker arm shaft spring
5. Rocker arm
6. Adjusting screw
7. Rocker arm shaft
8. Plug
9. Rocker arm oil line
10. Push rod
11. Valve spring keepers
12. Valve spring seat
13. Valve spring
14. Valve guide
15. Valve
16. Cam followers (tappet)
17. Exhaust valve seat insert
18. Camshaft
19. Camshaft gear
20. Retaining washer and cap screw

Fig. MM807—Diesel engine timing gear train. Mesh "I" marks on camshaft and crankshaft gears. The timing marks on non-diesel engines are similar.

On all other models, the intake and exhaust valve springs should test 85-90 lbs. at 2½ inches.

On gasoline models, exhaust valves are equipped with positive type valve rotators ("Rotocaps"). Normal servicing of the valve rotators consists of renewing the units. Rotator action can be considered satisfactory if the valve rotates a slight amount each time the valve opens.

VALVE TAPPETS (CAM FOLLOWERS)
All Models

41. The barrel type tappets (16—Fig. MM805) are supplied in standard size only and should have a clearance of 0.0018-0.0033 in the case bores. Any tappet can be removed after removing either the camshaft or the cylinder block.

ROCKER ARMS
All Models

42. Rocker arms and shaft assembly can be removed after removing hood, valve cover and rocker arm shaft support retaining nuts. Desired clearance between rocker arm bushing and the

0.9645-0.9670 diameter shaft is 0.001-0.0045. Bushings are not supplied separately for service; therefore, if clearance between bushing and shaft exceeds 0.008, it will be necessary to renew rocker arms and/or shaft.

On diesel models, the end rocker arms for each pair of cylinders are offset on their bushings. When reassembling, make certain that long part of bushings (Fig. MM806) is toward rocker arm shaft supports as shown.

VALVE TIMING
All Models

43. Valves are properly timed when mark "1" on camshaft gear is in mesh with mark "1" on crankshaft gear as shown in Fig. MM807.

TIMING GEAR COVER
All Models

44. To remove the timing gear cover, first drain cooling system, disconnect radiator hoses and disconnect power steering lines, if so equipped. Support engine, remove the retaining bolts and slide radiator, pedestal and front wheels assembly forward as a unit.

Remove the fan assembly, water pump and the timing gear cover retaining cap screws.

Camshaft end play is controlled by a thrust screw located in front face of timing gear cover. To adjust, turn screw in until same contacts the camshaft gear retaining cap screw; then, retract screw one-half turn and lock in place with the lock nut.

TIMING GEARS
All Models

45. Valves are correctly timed when "1" mark on crankshaft and camshaft timing gears are meshed as shown in Fig. MM807.

The timing gear train consists of the camshaft gear, crankshaft gear; and water pump and distributor or injection pump drive gear. On diesel models equipped with Bosch injection pump, an adjustable gear (2—Fig. MM808) is bolted to front face of camshaft gear. On non-diesel

OFF-CENTER ARMS

Fig. MM806 — When assembling diesel engine rocker arms, make certain that long part of end rocker arm bushings is toward supports.

Fig. MM808 — Typical timing gear train used on diesel engines equipped with Bosch pump.

1. Crankshaft gear
2. Adjustable gear
3. Camshaft gear
4. Pump drive gear

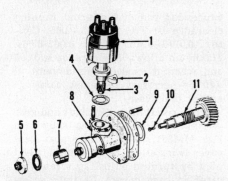

Fig. MM809 — Exploded view of distributor drive gear and housing used on some models. Other tractors are similar but do not contain drive (5 and 10) for tachometer.

1. Distributor	6. Oil seal
2. Clamp	7. Bushing
3. Distributor gear	8. Housing
4. Gasket	9. Thrust washer
5. Tachometer	10. Tachometer drive
adapter	11. Drive gear

models or diesel models equipped with Roosa-Master fuel system, the adjustable gear is not used, and distributor drive gear (11—Fig. MM809) or injection pump drive gear (1—Fig. MM812) meshes with the camshaft gear. Gears are available in standard size only, if backlash is excessive renew the worn gear or gears.

To remove the timing gears, proceed as outlined in the appropriate following paragraphs.

46. CAMSHAFT GEAR. To remove the camshaft gear, first remove timing gear cover as outlined in paragraph 44. On diesel models equipped with Bosch injection pump, remove injection pump drive shaft and gear as outlined in paragraph 50 and adjustable gear as outlined in paragraph 49.

Remove cap screw and washer from front of camshaft, then remove the gear using a suitable puller.

When installing the gear, heat gear to approximately 300°F. and use a longer cap screw if necessary, to draw gear against camshaft shoulder. Make sure timing marks are aligned as shown in Fig. MM807, when gear is installed.

47. CRANKSHAFT GEAR. To remove the crankshaft gear, first remove camshaft gear as outlined in paragraph 46. If not already off, remove distributor or injection pump and drive housing unit. On UB Special, UTS Special and M670 Super, remove the hydraulic pump. On M670 Super remove power steering pump and alternator.

Remove crankshaft pulley and all cap screws retaining timing gear

housing to engine block. Remove the four cap screws securing oil pan to to timing gear housing and loosen the remaining oil pan cap screws; then carefully separate oil pan gasket from timing gear housing. Remove timing gear housing.

Remove the crankshaft gear using a suitable puller. Assemble by reversing the disassembly procedure, making sure timing marks are aligned as shown in Fig. MM807 when gears are installed.

48. DISTRIBUTOR DRIVE GEAR & HOUSING. Refer to Fig. MM809 for an exploded view of distributor drive gear and housing. The water pump is driven by a slot in front face of drive gear (11). If only the gear, drive housing and associated parts are to be overhauled, the unit can be removed from the rear without major disassembly of the tractor; proceed as follows:

Remove the distributor and, where interference exists, disconnect tachometer drive cable. Remove the retaining cap screws and withdraw housing and gear from timing gear housing. To reinstall, align water pump drive tang with slot in front face of gear (11) and insert gear in timing gear housing. Fit thrust washer (9) over shaft of gear and install housing (8).

Complete the assembly by reversing the disassembly procedure. With No. 1 piston on firing stroke, rotor should point toward engine block and slightly to rear when distributor is installed. Time engine as outlined in paragraph 115.

Bushings (7) in housing can be renewed when housing is disassembled. Desired clearance between new bushings and shaft is 0.0007-0.0019.

49. ADJUSTABLE GEAR. The adjustable gear (2—Fig. MM808) can be removed after removing timing gear cover as outlined in paragraph 44; the safety wire and timing adjustment screws (T). Slotted holes in gear permit adjustment of injection timing.

When installing gear, check injection pump timing as outlined in paragraph 87 or 90.

50. INJECTION PUMP DRIVE (BOSCH). On models equipped with APE pump, the double drive gear (4—Fig. MM808) can be withdrawn from front after removing timing gear cover as outlined in paragraph 44.

On models equipped with PSB pump, remove timing gear cover as outlined in paragraph 44 and injection pump as outlined in paragraph 91.

Fig. MM810—Rear view of Bosch PSB injection pump adapter housing with the injection pump removed. Jack screws can be used in holes (H) to facilitate removal of gear (7).

Remove floating coupling (6—Fig. MM810) and, using two fairly long ⅜-inch NC bolts as jack screws, remove coupling gear (7). Remove the Woodruff key and withdraw gear and shaft (4—Fig. MM811) forward out of housing. Adapter housing (9) or bushings (5) can be renewed at this time. Ream bushings after installation to provide the recommended 0.0007-0.0019 diametral clearance for shaft.

Assemble by reversing the disassembly procedure. Install and time injection pump as outlined in paragraph 91.

51. INJECTION PUMP DRIVE (ROOSA-MASTER). Refer to Fig. MM812. The injection pump drive gear (1) meshes with the camshaft gear, and the entire drive unit can be removed from rear without removing timing gear cover.

To remove the unit, first remove injection pump, adapter (8) and gear (7) as outlined in paragraph 95, being careful not to lose thrust plunger (5) and spring (6) which are inserted in bore of injection pump adapter shaft.

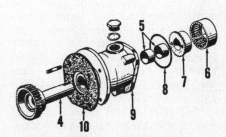

Fig. MM811 — Bosch PSB injection pump drive mechanism.

4. Pump drive gear	7. Coupling gear
5. Bushings	8. "O" ring
6. Floating coupling	9. Adaptor housing

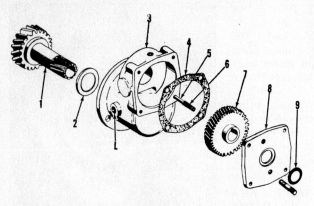

Fig. MM812 — Exploded view of injection pump drive gears, adapter housing and associated parts used on models equipped with Roosa-Master injection pump.

L. Lube passage
1. Drive gear
2. Thrust washer
3. Adapter housing
4. Gasket
5. Thrust button
6. Spring
7. Pump gear
8. Mounting plate
9. "O" ring

Disconnect the lubricant lines, remove retaining cap screws and lift off housing (3) and gear (1). The gear can be withdrawn from housing bore at this time.

Gears, bushings and housing are pressure lubricated. If shaft bushings must be renewed, make certain that lube hole in bushing aligns with passage hole (L) in housing when bushing is installed. Ream the bushings after installation to provide the recommended 0.0007-0.0019 shaft diametral clearance. Also check to be sure the cup plug in bore of gear shaft (1) is in place and to the rear of the two holes in bearing area of shaft.

To install the injection pump drive unit, align the water pump drive tang with drive slot in front face of gear (1), and install gear and thrust washer (2); then install housing (3) by reversing the removal procedure. Install and time injection pump as outlined in paragraph 95.

CAMSHAFT
All Non-Diesel Models

52. To remove the camshaft, first remove timing gear cover as outlined in paragraph 44. Remove rocker arms and shaft assembly, push rods, governor, oil pan and oil pump. Block up cam followers and withdraw camshaft with camshaft gear through front of timing gear case.

On all models except M670 and M670 Super, camshaft journals ride directly in the machined bores in the crankcase. On models M670 and M670 Super, the front camshaft journal rides in a renewable bushing while the intermediate and rear journals ride directly in the crankcase bores.

Shaft journal sizes for all non-diesel models are: Front, 3.3075-3.3085; Center, 3.275-3.276; Rear, 1.996-1.997. Recommended clearance for camshaft journals is: Front, 0.003-0.005; Center, 0.005-0.007; Rear, 0.002-0.004. Maximum allowable clearance is 0.008 and

when it exceeds this amount, it will be necessary to renew the camshaft and/or crankcase.

When reinstalling camshaft and gear assembly, mesh gears as shown in Fig. MM807. After the timing gear case cover is installed, adjust camshaft end play by turning adjusting screw (located in case cover) IN until screw contacts cap screw in end of camshaft; then retract the screw one-half turn and lock in place with the locking nut.

All Diesel Models

53. To remove the camshaft, first remove water pump and injection pump drive gear and shaft as outlined in paragraph 50 or 51. Remove rocker arms and shaft assemblies, push rods, oil pan and oil pump. Block up cam followers and withdraw camshaft from front of engine.

On all models except M670 and M670 Super, camshaft journals ride directly in machined bores in crankcase. On models M670 and M670 Super, the front camshaft journal rides in a renewable bushing while the intermediate and rear journals ride directly in the crankcase bores.

Camshaft journal sizes for all diesel models are: Front, 3.3075-3.3085; Center, 3.275-3.276; Rear, 1.996-1.997. Rec-

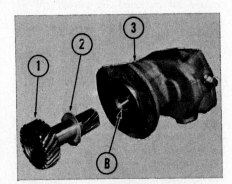

Fig. MM813—Roosa-Master injection pump adapter housing with shaft removed. Bushings (B) may be renewed, refer to text for oil passage alignment. Refer to Fig. MM812 for legend.

ommended camshaft journal running clearance is: Front, 0.003-0.005; Center, 0.005-0.007; Rear, 0.002-0.004. Maximum allowable clearance is 0.008 and when it exceeds this amount, it will be necessary to renew camshaft and/or crankcase.

When reinstalling camshaft and gear assembly, mesh gears as shown in Fig. MM807. After timing gear case cover is installed, adjust camshaft end play by turning adjusting screw (located in case cover) IN until screw contacts cap screw in end of camshaft; then retract the screw one-half turn and lock in place with the locking nut.

ROD AND PISTON UNITS
All Models

54. To remove piston and connecting rod units, first remove cylinder heads as outlined in paragraph 38. Drain the oil and remove oil pan and connecting rod caps; remove water manifold and lift off each cylinder block and the two rod and piston units as an assembly. Withdraw pistons from below after cylinder block has been removed from crankcase.

Piston and connecting rod assemblies are installed with the rod correlation marks facing the camshaft. Tighten the connecting rod bolts to 70-75 ft.-lbs. torque on models M670 and M670 Super and to 80-85 ft.-lbs. torque for all other models.

Connecting rods used in some non-diesel engines are offset at the piston pin end. The long portion of the offset must face the center of each block. Mark new rods and caps on the camshaft side, corresponding to the cylinder number.

PISTONS AND RINGS
All Models

55. Pistons and rings for UB Special, UTS Special and 5 Star non-diesel engines are available in standard size and oversizes of 0.030, 0.063 and 0.094. Pistons and rings for all other engines are available in standard size and oversizes of 0.020, 0.040 and 0.060. Check pistons, cylinders and rings against the values which follow:

UB SPECIAL-UTS SPECIAL
Standard Cylinder Bore Diameter
  Diesel .... 4.251 -4.252
  Non-Diesel .... 4.251 -4.252
Recommended Piston Skirt Clearance
  Diesel 0.0065-0.0075
  Non-Diesel 0.004-0.005
Maximum Cylinder Wear 0.008
Top Ring Side Clearance
  Diesel 0.0045-0.0065
  Non-Diesel 0.0035-0.005

Second Ring Side Clearance
Diesel 0.0035-0.0055
Non-Diesel 0.0035-0.005
Third Ring Side Clearance
Diesel 0.0025-0.0045
Non-Diesel 0.0035-0.005
Fourth Ring Side Clearance
Diesel 0.0020-0.0035
Non-Diesel 0.0035-0.005
Fifth Ring Side Clearance
Diesel 0.0020-0.0035
Compression Ring End Gap
Diesel 0.015-0.020
Non-Diesel 0.020-0.030
Oil Ring End Gap
Diesel 0.015-0.020
Non-Diesel 0.020-0.030

5-STAR
Standard Cylinder Bore Diameter
Diesel 4.626-4.627
Non-Diesel 4.251-4.252
Recommended Piston Skirt Clearance
Diesel 0.007-0.009
Non-Diesel 0.0045-0.005
Maximum Cylinder Wear 0.008
Top Ring Side Clearance
Diesel 0.0045-0.006
Non-Diesel 0.0015-0.003
Second Ring Side Clearance
Diesel 0.0025-0.004
Non-Diesel 0.001-0.0025
Third Ring Side Clearance ....
Diesel 0.0025-0.004
Non-Diesel 0.001-0.0025
Fourth Ring Side Clearance
Diesel 0.002-0.0035
Non-Diesel 0.001-0.0025
Fifth Ring Side Clearance
Diesel 0.002-0.0035
Compression Ring End Gap
Diesel 0.013-0.023
Non-Diesel 0.020-0.030
Oil Ring End Gap
Diesel 0.013-0.023
Non-Diesel 0.020-0.030

M5-M504-M602-M604
Standard Cylinder Bore Diameter
Diesel 4.626-4.627
Non-Diesel 4.626-4.627
Recommended Piston Skirt Clearance
Diesel 0.007-0.009
Non-Diesel 0.0045-0.005
Maximum Cylinder Wear 0.008
Top Ring Side Clearance
Diesel 0.0045-0.006
Non-Diesel 0.0035-0.0055
Second Ring Side Clearance
Diesel 0.0025-0.004
Non-Diesel 0.0035-0.0055
Third Ring Side Clearance
Diesel 0.0025-0.004
Non-Diesel 0.0025-0.0055
Fourth Ring Side Clearance
Diesel 0.002-0.0035
Non-Diesel 0.0025-0.0035
Fifth Ring Side Clearance
Diesel 0.002-0.0035

Compression Ring End Gap
Diesel 0.013-0.023
Non-Diesel 0.013-0.025
Oil Ring End Gap
Diesel 0.013-0.023
Non-Diesel 0.013-0.025

M670-M670 SUPER
Standard Cylinder Bore
Diameter 4.626-4.627
Recommended Piston Skirt
Clearance 0.007-0.009
Maximum Cylinder Wear,
Bottom of Cylinder 0.003
Top of Cylinder 0.013
Piston Ring Side Clearance,
Top Ring 0.0025-0.004
Second Ring 0.0025-0.004
Third Ring 0.002-0.0035
Fourth Ring 0.0015-0.003
Piston Ring End Gap,
All Rings 0.016-0.031

CYLINDER BLOCK

All Models

56. To remove any cylinder block, remove hood, rocker arms and shaft assembly, push rods and cylinder head and block retaining nuts. Remove inlet water manifold. Drain the oil and remove oil pan. Remove connecting rod bearing caps and lift off the block and two rod and piston units as an assembly. Withdraw pistons from below after block has been removed from crankcase.

On models M670 and M670 Super, cylinder blocks should be renewed or rebored if wear exceeds 0.003 at bottom of cylinder or 0.013 at top of cylinder. On all other models, cylinder blocks should be renewed or rebored if wear or taper exceeds 0.008. Reboring should be done from bottom of block to duplicate factory alignment. Rebore to standard oversizes listed in paragraph 55, or check parts stock for available oversize. Install cylinder heads as outlined in paragraph 38 and adjust valves as outlined in paragraph 39.

PISTON PINS

All Models

57. Piston pins are of the full floating type which are retained in the piston pin bosses by snap rings. The 1.2497-1.2500 diameter piston pins for non-diesels or 1.4997-1.5000 diameter pins for diesels are available in standard size and oversizes of 0.005 and 0.010.

Install piston pin bushing in rod so that oil hole in bushing registers with oil hole in top end of connecting rod.

Fit pins to a palm push fit in both rod and piston.

ROD BEARINGS

All Models

58. Connecting rod bearings are of precision type, renewable from below after removing the oil pan. When installing new bearing shells, be sure that bearing shell projection engages milled slot in rod and cap, and rod and cap correlation marks face toward camshaft side of engine. On models UB Special, UTS Special and model 5-Star non-diesel, bearings are available in 0.0025, 0.005, 0.020 and 0.040 undersizes as well as standard. On all other models, bearings are available in standard as well as undersizes of 0.0025, 0.005, 0.010, 0.020, 0.030 and 0.040.

Standard crankpin diameter is 2.5770-2.5775 on UB Special, UTS Special and 5 Star non-diesel; and 2.911-2.912 on all other models. Recommended connecting rod bearing diametral clearance is 0.0015-0.0024 for UB Special, non-diesel; 0.0024-0.0039 for UB Special, UTS Special, diesel; and 0.0014-0.004 for all other models. Connecting rod side clearance should be 0.008-0.013. Tighten connecting rod cap nuts to a torque of 70-75 ft.-lbs. for models M670 and M670 Super and 80-85 ft.-lbs. for all other models.

CRANKSHAFT AND BEARINGS

All Models

59. **MAIN BEARINGS.** Crankshaft main bearings are precision, babbitt lined type on UB Special, UTS Special and 5-Star non-diesels and precision, tri-metal type on all other models, which may be renewed from below. Rear and intermediate bearing caps are marked "FRONT" and should be installed with markings toward front of engine. Bearings are available in 0.0025, 0.005, 0.010, 0.020, 0.030 and 0.040 undersizes as well as standard.

60. **CRANKSHAFT.** Crankshaft end play is controlled by rear main bearing flange. Recommended end play is 0.004-0.008 for UB Special and UTS Special; 0.004-0.010 for other models.

To remove crankshaft, it is necessary to remove engine, oil pan, timing gear cover, timing gear case, oil pump, connecting rod bearing caps and flywheel.

Check crankshaft, crankpins and main bearing journals for wear, scoring and out-of-round condition against values listed below. Refer also to paragraph 58.
Crankpin diameter..See paragraph 58
Main journal diameter..2.9110-2.9120
Main bearing oil
clearance 0.0014-0.0044

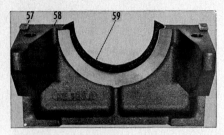

Fig. MM814—Crankshaft rear oil seal and
retainer assembly.

57. Cork seal   59. Crankshaft rear
58. Seal retainer   oil seal

Main bearing bolt torque (ft.-lbs.)
with lubricated threads

UB Special-UTS Special
  Front (non-diesels) 135-145
  Front (diesels) 195-205
  Center &
  Rear (non-diesels) 100-105
  Center & Rear (diesels) ..100-105

M670 Super
  Front 280-285
  Center & Rear 170-175

All Other Models
  Front, Center & Rear 100-105

CRANKSHAFT OIL SEALS
All Models

61. FRONT SEAL. The felt type
seal is contained in a metal retainer
which is pressed into timing gear case.
Procedure for renewing the seal is
evident after sliding the radiator,
pedestal and wheels assembly forward.

62. REAR SEAL. The crankshaft
rear oil seal cork is a two-piece type.
The lower half (59—Fig. MM814) is
contained in a retainer, and the upper
half in a groove which is machined
in the crankcase.

Lower half of cork seal can be renewed from below after removing oil

Fig. MM815—Flywheel can be installed in
any one of six positions. Timing marks
will be correct if crankshaft is turned until
No. 1 piston is at top dead center (DC1)
and flywheel installed with timing marks
(TM) at 9-O'Clock position as shown.

pan and seal retainer. Allow ends of
oil seal to extend slightly above edge
of retainer. Renew side corks (57) before reinstalling the retainer. When
reinstalling the retainer, insert a sufficient number of gaskets between mating surfaces of crankcase and seal retainer so that retainer will protrude
0.005 beyond gasket surface of crankcase when retainer is bolted in position.

Oil seal upper half can be pulled
out, and a new seal inserted from below after removing oil pan, retainer
for lower seal and loosening main
bearing caps.

FLYWHEEL
All Models

63. The flywheel can be removed
after separating engine from transmission as outlined in the clutch section. The flywheel is retained by six
equally spaced bolts and nuts or cap
screws, and can be installed in any
of six positions. When installing flywheel, turn crankshaft until No. 1

piston is at TDC; then install flywheel with DC timing mark at 9
o'clock position as shown in Fig. MM-
815.

To install a new flywheel ring
gear, heat same to approximately 500
deg. F. and install gear on flywheel
with beveled edge of teeth facing
front of engine.

OIL PAN
All Models

64. To remove the oil pan on all
four cylinder engines, first remove
the oil filter element and filter can
from oil pan. Working through filter
opening in side of oil pan remove the
two inside cap screws retaining oil
pan to crankcase at rear of engine. On
all models remove the remaining cap
screws retaining oil pan to crankcase
and timing gear case and remove pan.
On four wheel drive models, it will
be necessary to support front of tractor and remove front drive unit as
an assembly.

When reassembling, UB Special and
UTS Special tractors make certain that
oil line fits down into hole in oil pan.

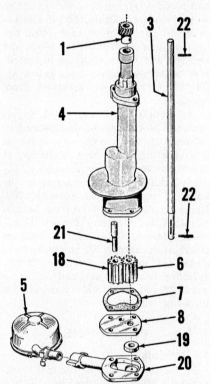

Fig. MM816—Exploded view of oil pump
used on series UB Special and UTS Special
tractors.

  1. Drive shaft pinion
  3. Drive shaft
  4. Pump body
  5. Intake screen
  6. Drive gear
  7. Gasket
  8. Pump cover
  18. Idler gear
  19. Thrust-collar
  20. Adaptor
  21. Idler gear shaft
  22. Roll pins

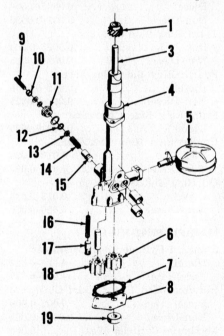

Fig. MM817—Exploded view of oil pump
used on models 5-Star, M5, M504, M602,
M604 and M670.

  1. Drive shaft
     pinion
  3. Drive shaft
  4. Pump body
  5. Intake screen
  6. Drive gear
  7. Gasket
  8. Pump cover
  9. Adjusting screw
  10. Locknut
  11. Regulator cover
  12. Snap ring
  13. Spring retainer
  14. Regulator spring
  15. Regulator valve
  16. By-pass spring
  17. By-pass valve
  18. Idler gear
  19. Thrust-collar

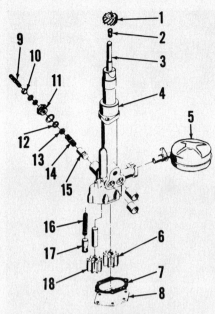

Fig. MM818—Exploded view of oil pump used on model M670 Super.

1. Drive shaft pinion
2. Tachometer drive sleeve
3. Drive shaft
4. Pump body
5. Intake screen
6. Drive gear
7. Gasket
8. Pump cover
9. Adjusting screw
10. Locknut
11. Regulator cover
12. Snap ring
13. Spring retainer
14. Regulator spring
15. Regulator valve
16. By-pass spring
17. By-pass valve
18. Idler gear

OIL PUMP

All Models

65. The gear type oil pump, shown in Figs. MM816, MM817 or MM818, can be removed after removing oil pan. To disassemble pump, remove oil strainer adaptor (20) and thrust collar (19), on pumps so equipped. Bump roll pin from drive shaft pinion (1) and remove pinion. Remove pump cover (8), then withdraw drive shaft (3) and gears (6 and 18). On pumps so

equipped, remove bypass valve (17), by-pass spring (16), pressure regulator valve (15) and regulator spring (14).

Check pump drive shaft and its mating surface for wear. The recommended diametral clearance between gears and pump body is 0.003-0.005. End clearance between pump body gears and pump cover (8) should be 0.001-0.006 and is controlled by shim gaskets (7).

RELIEF VALVE

Series UB Special-UTS Special

66. The piston type pressure relief valve is located in the regulator housing on the left side of engine crankcase as shown in Fig. MM819. To adjust the pressure, loosen lock-nut and turn adjusting screw (P) to obtain the recommended 25 psi pressure at rated engine speed.

Series 5 Star-M5-M504-M602-M604-M670-M670 Super

67. The piston type pressure relief valve is located in the oil pump body as shown in Figs. MM817 and MM818. To adjust the pressure loosen the locknut on adjusting screw (P—Fig. MM820) and turn the screw to obtain the recommended 25-30 psi for model 5-Star; 25-35 psi for models M5, M504, M602 and M604; and 30-35 psi for models M670 and M670 Super, at rated engine speed.

CARBURETOR

(EXCEPT LP-GAS)

All Models

68. Idling mixture adjustment is controlled by the needle valve (2—MM821) nearest to the carburetor flange. Turning adjustment in to the right (clockwise) richens the mixture. Approximate setting is two turns open. Power mixture adjustment is controlled by the other needle valve (1). Turning adjustment in to the right (clockwise) leans the mixture. Approximate setting is two turns open. Float setting is ¼-inch. Calibration data are follows:

Marvel-Schebler TSX624
  Repair kit 286-1087
  Gasket set 16-594
  Inlet needle and seat 233-543
  Idle jet 49-101L
  Nozzle 47-221
  Economizer jet 49-219
  Main needle assembly 43-620
Marvel-Schebler TSX 693
  Repair kit 286-1149
  Gasket set 16-594
  Inlet needle and seat 233-543
  Idle jet 49-101L
  Nozzle 47-221
  Economizer jet 49-219
  Main needle assembly 43-620
Marvel-Schebler TSX795
  Repair kit 286-1300
  Gasket set 16-594
  Inlet needle and seat 233-595
  Idle jet 49-101L
  Nozzle 47-221
  Economizer jet 49-219
  Main needle assembly 43-725
Marvel-Schebler TSX901
  Repair kit 286-1475
  Gasket set 16-641
  Inlet needle and seat 233-595
  Idle jet 49-101L
  Nozzle 47-221
  Economizer jet 49-283
  Main needle assembly 43-725

Fig. MM819—Recommended oil pressure of 25 psi on series UB Special and UTS Special, is obtained by turning adjusting screw (P).

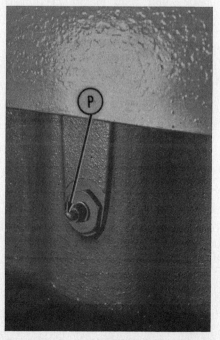

Fig. MM820—Left side of oil pan showing location of oil pressure regulating screw (P) on all models except UB Special and UTS Special.

Fig. MM821 — View showing adjustment screws on Marvel-Schebler TSX carburetor.

1. Main fuel mixture needle
2. Idle mixture needle
3. Idle speed stop screw

LP-GAS SYSTEM

Minneapolis-Moline tractors are available with factory installed LP-Gas systems using Ensign equipment. These systems are designed to operate with the fuel supply tank not more than 80% filled.

The UB Special-UTS Special tractors are equipped with an Ensign No. 7593 Kgl carburetor, an Ensign model R regulator and a No. 8628 pre-set gas economizer. 5-Star tractors are equipped with an Ensign No. C-3971 carburetor and an Ensign Model W vaporizer regulator. M5, M504, M602 and M604 tractors are equipped with an Ensign No. 9152 carburetor and an Ensign Model R regulator. M670 and M670 Super tractors are equipped with an Ensign Model CBX carburetor and Ensign Model RDH regulator.

It is important when starting LP-Gas tractors to open the vapor valve on the supply tank SLOWLY; if opened too fast, the fuel supply to the regulator will be shut off. Too rapid opening of vapor or liquid valves may cause freezing.

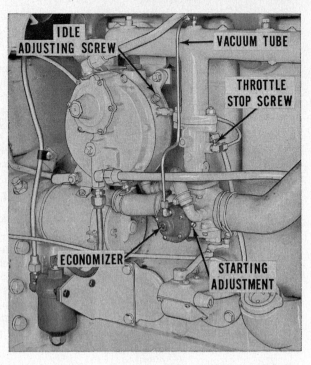

Fig. MM822 — Typical L-P gas equipment installation. The unit has a preset economizer.

CARBURETOR ADJUSTMENTS

Series UB Special-UTS Special

69. Stop screws (See Fig. MM822) on carburetor throttle should be adjusted to provide an engine low idle speed of 450 rpm.

Initial adjustment for the starting screw is one full turn open.

Immediately after engine is started and with throttle open and choke closed, rotate the starting screw until the highest engine speed is obtained.

With the choke open, engine warm and the throttle stop screw set, rotate the idle adjusting screw until the best idle is obtained.

The Kgl carburetor used on series UB Special-UTS Special is equipped with a preset gas economizer shown exploded in Fig. MM823. This economizer provides automatic control of the partial or light load mixture. The richer mixture needed for maximum power is adjusted by varying the depth to which the entire economizer body is screwed into the fuel passage of the carburetor. The economizer body thus becomes the load screw. High manifold vacuum overcomes the diaphragm spring and moves the restricted plunger into the fuel passage; thus, leaning the mixture and providing economizer action. When the manifold vacuum falls below 4-6 inches Hg., the spring retracts the plunger causing a richer maximum power mixture.

With the idle mixture properly adjusted, disconnect the vacuum line (Fig. MM822) from economizer body and plug the line. With the engine running at the recommended high idle speed of 1430 rpm, loosen the locknut (5—Fig. MM823) on economizer body and turn the entire economizer unit until maximum rpm is obtained. Note this position; rotate the entire economizer unit counterclockwise until rpm begins to fall and note this position. Set the unit at the mid-point of these two positions and tighten the locknut. Reconnect vacuum line.

Load adjustment can be adjusted with an exhaust gas analyzer; proceed as follows: Disconnect vacuum line from economizer and plug the line. With the throttle wide open, load the engine to obtain an engine speed of 650-1300 rpm. Turn the entire economizer unit to give a reading of 12.8 on the analyzer gasoline scale or 14.3 on an analyzer with an LPG scale. Reconnect vacuum line.

5 Star-M5-M504-M602-M604-M670-M670 Super

NOTE: The following instructions apply specifically to the Model "R" regulator and Model 9152 carburetor used on M5, M504, M602 and M604 tractors. Although slight differences in construction will be noted, these same instructions apply to the units used on 5-Star, M670 and M670 Super models.

70. The recommended slow idle speed is 400-450 rpm for 5-Star models, 600 rpm for M670 and M670 Super and 450-500 rpm for other models. To adjust the slow idle speed, first allow the engine to reach the normal operating temperature, adjust the idle mixture, and turn the idle stop screw on throttle shaft to provide the recommended slow idle speed.

Initial adjustment for the starting screw (3—Fig. MM824) is ½-¾ turn open for 5-Star tractors or 1½ turns open for other models.

Immediately after engine is started and with throttle open and choke closed, adjust starting screw until the highest engine speed is obtained, then open the screw (enrich the mixture) until the engine speed drops slightly, and lock in place.

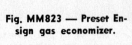

Fig. MM823 — Preset Ensign gas economizer.

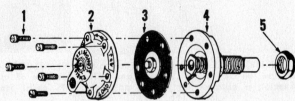

Fig. MM824 — View showing adjustment screws on model CBX Ensign LP-Gas carburetor. Idle mixture screw is on the regulator.

1. Idle speed stop screw
2. Load mixture screw
3. Starting adjustment screw

Initial idle mixture adjusting screw setting is 1½ turns open for 5-Star tractors or 1 turn open for other models.

Idle and load mixture adjustments should be made with the engine at operating temperature and running on liquid fuel. Turn the idle adjusting screw (on regulator) until the best idle is obtained.

Initial load adjustment is 4 turns open for 5-Star tractors or 3½ turns open for other models.

Load mixture adjustment should be made with the engine at operating temperature and running on liquid fuel. Load adjustment must be made with the throttle and governor in a wide open position and the engine under load. These conditions can be met in the shop by either loading the tractor by dynamometer, or removing and grounding all except one of the spark plug wires.

Fig. MM825—Pressure gage installed in Ensign, Model W regulator of the type used on 5-Star tractor.

With the above conditions met, turn the load adjusting screw (2—Fig. MM-824) out until the engine reaches the highest operating rpm; then, turn the load adjusting screw in until the engine speed just starts to drop. Now turn the screw out exactly ½ turn and lock in place.

TROUBLE SHOOTING

All Models

71. Trouble in engine operation due to the fuel supply system usually results from four principal causes as follows:

a. Improper adjustment of carburetor or regulator.
b. Plugged fuel lines, passages or filter.
c. System leaks in lines, valves or diaphragms.
d. Damaged or worn component parts.

To locate trouble in the LP-Gas fuel system, shut off the vapor and liquid withdrawal valves and run engine until all fuel is exhausted and engine stops. Connect a low reading pressure gage to the plug opening in regulator housing as shown in Fig. MM825 on 5-Star tractors equipped with Model "W" regulator, at plug (22—Fig. MM827) on tractors equipped with Model "R" regulator and (R—Fig. MM830) on models M670 and M670 Super tractors equipped with Model RDH regulator. Slowly open the liquid withdrawal valve and start the tractor. Pressure should read 3½-5 lbs. for the Model "W" regulator, 4-5 lbs. for the Model "R" regulator or 9-11 lbs. for the Model RDH regulator, with the engine running. Stop the engine, leaving the withdrawal valve open. If the pressure increases after the engine is stopped, a leak in the high pressure valve is indicated, and the unit should be overhauled as outlined in paragraph 73. An operating pressure higher or lower than the indicated reading would indicate improper adjustment, or worn or damaged parts. Remove and overhaul the unit as outlined in paragraph 73. No pressure at the gage would indicate a plugged high pressure line or filter, or an inoperative withdrawal or regulator valve. Service the filter and lines as outlined in paragraph 72, or the regulator as outlined in paragraph 73. If the regulator unit is cold and shows moisture or frost after standing, it is an indication that either the high or low pressure regulating valve is leaking or improperly adjusted.

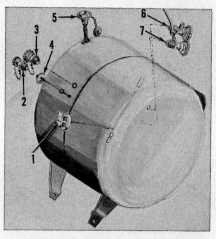

Fig. MM826 — Exploded view of LP-Gas fuel tank and valves used on M5 tractor. Other units are similar.

1. Fuel gage
2. Vapor return valve
3. Filler valve
4. Bleeder valve
5. Safety relief
6. Vapor withdrawal valve
7. Liquid withdrawal valve

If engine does not idle properly with the idle adjusting screw in any position, a leak can be suspected in one of the valves or gaskets. This can usually be traced to the low pressure valve, since any impurities in the fuel are deposited on the valve seat after the fuel is vaporized. If the idle gas mixture is too lean when the idle adjusting screw is opened 3 or 4 turns, the trouble is usually due to a restricted idle line or leakage in the idle line connections. Poor idling as well as poor engine performance under load can be caused by a restricted or plugged balance line on units so equipped.

If there is any indication of liquid fuel entering the carburetor, the circulation of warm water through the regulator has been impaired.

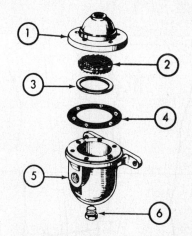

Fig. MM826A—Exploded view of LP-Gas fuel filter.

1. Cover
2. Filter
3. Retainer
4. Gasket
5. Bowl
6. Drain plug

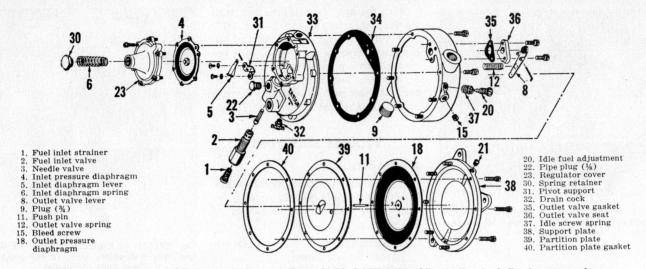

1. Fuel inlet strainer
2. Fuel inlet valve
3. Needle valve
4. Inlet pressure diaphragm
5. Inlet diaphragm lever
6. Inlet diaphragm spring
8. Outlet valve lever
9. Plug (¾)
11. Push pin
12. Outlet valve spring
15. Bleed screw
18. Outlet pressure
    diaphragm

20. Idle fuel adjustment
22. Pipe plug (⅛)
23. Regulator cover
30. Spring retainer
31. Pivot support
32. Drain cock
35. Outlet valve gasket
36. Outlet valve seat
37. Idle screw spring
38. Support plate
39. Partition plate
40. Partition plate gasket

Fig. MM827—Exploded view of Ensign model R regulating unit. Model W. unit, while smaller, is similar in construction.

FUEL TANK, FUEL FILTER AND LINES

72. The pressure tank is fitted with fuel filler (3—Fig. MM826), vapor return (2), pressure relief (5), bleeder (4), and liquid (7) and vapor (6) withdrawal valves which can only be serviced as complete assemblies. Before renewal is attempted on any of these units, drive the tractor to an open area and allow the engine to run until the fuel is exhausted; then, open bleeder valve and allow any remaining pressure to escape. Fuel gage (1) can only be renewed if the fuel tank is completely empty. The safety relief valve (5) is set to open at 312 psi pressure to protect the tank against excessive pressures. U-L regulations in most states prohibit any welding or repair on LP-Gas containers and the tank must be renewed or returned to the tank manufacturer for repair in the event of damage.

Fuel lines can safely be renewed at any time without emptying tank if liquid and vapor withdrawal valves are closed and the engine run until all fuel is exhausted from the lines.

The fuel filter contains a renewable type element (2—Fig. 826A) which may be removed and cleaned in a suitable solvent if in good condition. Thoroughly air-dry the element before reinstalling in the filter body.

R&R AND OVERHAUL

All Models

73. VAPORIZER-REGULATOR. To remove the regulator unit, first close the withdrawal valves and allow the engine to run until the fuel is exhausted. Drain the radiator and disconnect the water, fuel and balance lines from the unit, then unbolt and remove the unit from the tractor. Refer to Fig. MM827 or MM831, and completely disassemble the regulator. Thoroughly wash all parts and blow out all passages with clean, compressed air, carefully inspect each

part and renew any that are worn or damaged. Always use new gaskets when reassembling the regulator.

When reassembling Model R or Model W regulator, install the low pressure valve assembly and valve spring. Install the retaining screws loosely. Center the end of valve lever

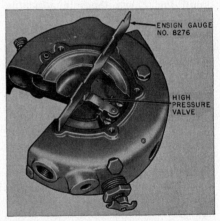

Fig. MM829 — Cutaway view of Ensign Model W regulator showing method of adjustment using Ensign gage. See text.

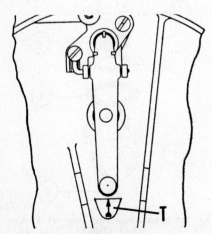

Fig. MM828—Location of post or boss with stamped arrow for the purpose of setting the low pressure valve lever.

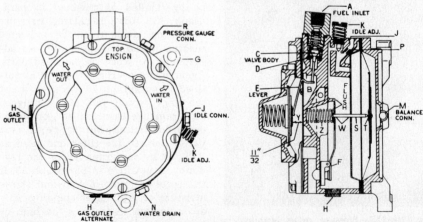

Fig. MM830—Sectional view of Ensign model RDH regulator used on models M670 and M670 Super LP-Gas equipped tractors.

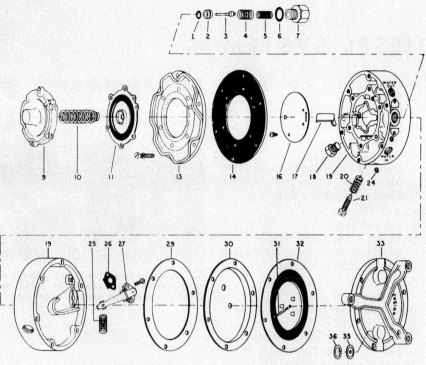

Fig. MM831—Exploded view of Ensign model RDH regulator.

1. "O" ring	9. Cover	19. Body	29. Gasket
2. Valve seat	10. Spring	20. Spring	30. Plate
3. High pressure valve	11. High pressure diaphragm	21. Idle screw	31. Push pin
4. Spring	13. Cover	24. Bleed screw	32. Low pressure diaphragm
5. Valve spring	14. Gasket	25. Valve spring	33. Support plate
6. Gasket	16. Plate	26. Gasket	35. Snap ring
7. Valve retainer	17. Valve lever	27. Low pressure valve	36. Vent valve

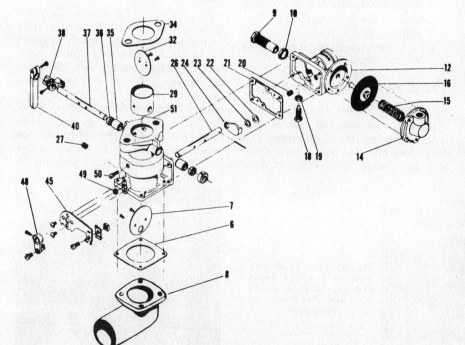

Fig. MM832—Exploded view of Ensign model CBX carburetor used on models M670 and M670 Super LP-Gas equipped tractors.

6. Gasket	16. Diaphragm	24. Valve lever	37. Throttle shaft
7. Choke disc	18. Starting adjusting screw	26. Choke shaft	38. Throttle stop
8. Air intake elbow	19. Locknut	27. Balance bleed screw	40. Throttle lever
9. Load adjusting screw	20. Economizer orifice	29. Venturi	45. Support
10. Locknut	21. Gasket	32. Throttle disc	48. Choke lever
12. Economizer body	22. Washer	34. Gasket	49. Seal
14. Cover	23. Spring washer	35. Bushing	50. Venturi retaining screw
15. Spring		36. Seal	51. Carburetor body

with arrow on post (T—Fig. MM828) then tighten retaining screws to hold lever in position. The top of the low pressure lever should be flush with the top of the post. If it is not, bend the lever as required, being careful not to damage the valve seat. Reinstall the inlet strainer, partition plate and low pressure diaphragm, making certain that the diaphragm push pin is properly located on the valve lever. Reinstall the back cover plate, install high pressure valve assembly then measure the distance of the inlet diaphragm lever below the diaphragm surface of regulator body as shown in Fig. MM829. This dimension, when measured with Ensign gage No. 8276, or a suitable depth gage should be ½-inch when the inlet valve is firmly shut. If the distance is more, or less, than ½-inch bend the lever until the correct setting is obtained. Reinstall diaphragm and regulator cover, mount the assembled regulator on the tractor and reconnect water, fuel and balance lines.

When reassembling Model RDH regulator, make certain that the valve levers are set to the dimensions as follows. The high pressure lever (E—Fig. MM830) should be set at approximately 11/32-inch from top of lever to face of plate. (See Y). Bend lever if necessary to obtain this dimension. When installing the low pressure valve (27—Fig. MM831) and spring (25), center the low pressure lever with the push pin hole in center of partition plate (30). A rib is provided in the recess of body (19) for the purpose of setting the low pressure lever height. The top of the lever, when valve is seated, should be flush with top of this rib. Bend lever if necessary to obtain this setting. Reinstall the assembled regulator on the tractor and reconnect, water, fuel and balance lines.

74. CARBURETOR. To remove the carburetor, close the withdrawal valves and run the engine until the fuel is exhausted. Disconnect the fuel and balance lines, air cleaner hose and throttle and choke levers, then unbolt and remove carburetor unit.

Completely disassemble the carburetor and clean the parts in a suitable solvent. Blow out the drilled passages with clean compressed air, examine the parts and renew any which are damaged or worn. Always use new gaskets when reassembling the carburetor.

Reinstall the assembled carburetor and adjust same as outlined in paragraph 69 or 70.

DIESEL SYSTEM

All Diesel Models

The diesel fuel system consists of three basic units: the fuel filters, injection pump and injection nozzles. When servicing any unit associated with the fuel system, the maintenance of absolute cleanliness is of utmost importance. Of equal importance is the avoidance of nicks or burrs on any of the working parts.

Probably the most important precaution that service personnel can impart to owners of diesel powered tractors, is to urge them to use an approved fuel that is absolutely clean and free from foreign material. Because of the extreme pressures involved in the operation of pump and injectors, the working parts must be hand fitted with utmost care. While the filtering system will easily remove the larger particles of foreign material the greater danger exists in the presence of water or fine dust particles which might pass through an overloaded filter system. Proper care in fuel handling will pay big dividends in better service and performance.

TROUBLE-SHOOTING

All Models

75. QUICK CHECKS-UNITS ON TRACTOR. If the diesel engines does not start or does not run properly, and the diesel fuel system is suspected as the source of trouble, refer to the following list of troubles and their possible causes. Many of the troubles are self-explanatory; however, if the difficulty points to the fuel filters, injection pump and/or injection nozzles, refer to the appropriate following paragraphs.

1. Sudden Stopping of Engine
   a. Lack of fuel
   b. Clogged fuel filter and/or lines
   c. Faulty injection pump
2. Lack of Power
   a. Inferior fuel
   b. Clogged fuel filters and/or lines
   c. Improper injection pump timing
   d. Faulty injection pump
3. Engine Hard to Start
   a. Inferior fuel
   b. Clogged fuel filters and/or lines
   c. Improper injection pump timing
   d. Faulty injection pump
4. Irregular Engine Operation
   a. Inferior fuel
   b. Clogged fuel filters and/or lines
   c. Faulty nozzle
   d. Improper injection pump timing
   e. Faulty injection pump
5. Engine Knocks
   a. Inferior fuel
   b. Improper injection pump timing
   c. Faulty nozzle
6. Excessive Smoking
   a. Inferior fuel
   b. Improper injection pump timing
   c. Faulty nozzle
   d. Improperly adjusted smoke stop
7. Excessive Fuel Consumption
   a. Inferior fuel
   b. Improper injection pump timing
   c. Faulty nozzle

FUEL FILTERS AND BLEEDING

All Diesel Models

76. The fuel filtering system consists of various types of screen and renewable element type filters. Refer to Figs. MM833, MM834 and MM835.

Fig. MM834—Fuel filters and associated parts used on models M5, M504, M602 and M604 equipped with Roosa-Master fuel system.

1. Bleed screws
P. Drain plugs
V. Shut-off valve

77. CIRCUIT DESCRIPTION AND MAINTENANCE. With the fuel shut off at valve (V-Fig. MM833 or MM-834) or at valve (3—Fig. MM835), open petcock or drain plugs and drain off any accumulation of water and dirt. This should be done daily before tractor is operated.

On models with Bosch injection system, fuel flows by force of gravity to the primary filter which contains a fine mesh screen that filters water from the fuel. After each 60 hours of operation, the filter bowl should be removed and the screen thoroughly cleaned with diesel fuel. From the primary filter, the fuel flows through the renewable element type secondary filter. It is recommended that this secondary filter element be

Fig. MM833 — Left side view of typical diesel tractor engine using American Bosch injection equipment.

P. Drain plug
V. Shut-off valve
FF. Final filter
PF. Primary filter
SF. Secondary filter
TP. Transfer pump
PRV. Pressure relief valve
1-5. Bleed points

Fig. MM835—Fuel filters and associated parts used on models M670 and M670 Super equipped with Roosa-Master fuel system.

1. Bleed screws
2. Drain plugs
3. Shut-off valve

renewed after each 90 days of operation. After flowing through the secondary filter, the fuel passes through the positive displacement, gear type transfer pump to the renewable element type final filter and on to the injection pump. The filtering system is equipped with a pressure relief valve located at the inlet side of the final fuel filter. If the final filtering element becomes clogged, the valve will release, the fuel will be by-passed back to the transfer pump and the engine will die from lack of fuel. The final filtering element should be renewed only when it becomes clogged.

On models with Roosa-Master system, a much greater volume of fuel is pumped than is actually burned; the excess serving as a coolant and lubricant for the injection pump then returning to fuel tank. All models are equipped with two filters as shown in Figs. MM834 and MM835.

78. **BLEEDING.** It is necessary to bleed the fuel system whenever the fuel flow is interrupted or air has been allowed to enter the system.

To bleed the system on models equipped with Bosch system, refer to Fig. MM833 and proceed as follows: Open the shut-off valve (V) and remove bleed plug (1) at top of primary filter. Reinstall the plug when the fuel flows free of air. Remove bleed plug (2) from top of secondary filter. Reinstall plug when the fuel flows free of air. Remove bleed plug (3) from the final filter, turn the engine over with starting motor until the fuel flows free of air and install the bleed plug. Loosen the cap nut (4) on the check valve at front of in-

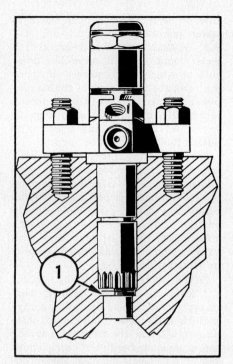

Fig. MM837 — Sectional view showing a typical installation of an American Bosch injection nozzle. Whenever the nozzle has been removed, always renew the copper gasket (1).

jection pump, rotate the engine until air is removed and tighten the nut. At this time, the engine will start, but if it does not run evenly, loosen the high presure line fittings (5) at each nozzle to bleed out any air.

On models equipped with Roosa-Master system, refer to Figs. MM834 and MM835. Open bleed screw (1) on rear filter until all air is exhausted, then close the bleed screw. Repeat the procedure with bleed screw on front filter. The injection pump is self-bleeding. Pressure line connections at the injectors may be loosened while engine is turned with starter or at slow idle, if engine does not run evenly.

INJECTION NOZZLES
All Diesel Models

The engine is equipped with pintle nozzles of the "delay," or "throttling" type. The delay nozzle limits the amount of fuel entering the combustion chamber during the start of the injection period, thus improving engine operation at idle speeds.

WARNING: Fuel leaves the injection nozzles with sufficient force to penetrate the skin. When testing, keep your person clear of the nozzle spray.

79. **TESTING AND LOCATING FAULTY NOZZLE.** If the engine does not run properly and the quick checks, outlined in paragraph 75 point to a faulty injection nozzle, locate the faulty nozzle as follows:

If one engine cylinder is misfiring, it is reasonable to suspect a faulty nozzle. Generally, a faulty nozzle can be located by loosening the high pressure line fitting on each nozzle holder in turn, thereby allowing fuel to escape at the union rather than enter the cylinder. As in checking spark plugs in a spark ignition engine, the faulty nozzle is the one which, when its line is loosened, least affects the running of the engine.

If a faulty nozzle is found and considerable time has elapsed since the injectors have been serviced, it is recommended that all injectors be removed and new or reconditioned units be installed, or the nozzles be serviced as outlined in the following paragraphs.

80. **REMOVE AND REINSTALL.** Before loosening any lines, wash the nozzle holder and connections with clean diesel fuel or solvent. After disconnecting the high pressure and leak-off lines, cover open ends of connections with caps to prevent the entrance of dirt or other foreign material. Remove the nozzle holder stud nuts and carefully withdraw the nozzle from cylinder head, being careful not to strike the tip end of the nozzle against any hard surface.

Remove "O" ring (Fig. MM836) and thoroughly clean the nozzle recess in the cylinder head. It is important that the seating surface of recess be free of even the smallest particle of carbon which could cause the nozzle to be cocked and result in blowby of hot gases. No hard or sharp tools should be used for cleaning. A piece of wood dowel or brass stock properly shaped is very effective. Do not reuse the copper ring gasket (1—Fig. MM837);

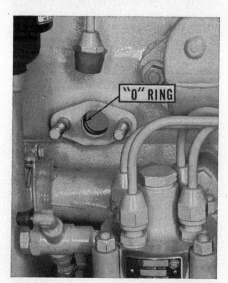

Fig. MM836 — Before installing the injection nozzles, make certain that the "O" ring is in good condition.

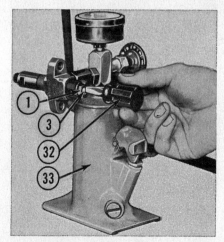

Fig. MM838—Adjusting the nozzle opening pressure, using a nozzle tester.

1. Nut	32. Screw driver
3. Adjusting screw	33. Nozzle tester

always install a new one. If the "O" ring (Fig. MM836) is in good shape, reinstall it and insert the nozzle. Tighten the nozzle holder stud nuts to a torque of 14-16 ft.-lbs.

81. NOZZLE TESTER. A complete job of testing and adjusting the injector requires the use of a special tester such as that shown in Fig. MM838. Only clean approved testing oil should be used in tester tank.

The injector should be tested for spray pattern, seat leakage, back leakage and opening pressure as follows:

82. SPRAY PATTERN. Operate tester handle until oil flows from injector connection, then attach the injector assembly. Close the valve to tester gage and operate tester handle a few quick strokes to purge air from injector and tester pump, and to make sure injector is not plugged or inoperative.

If a straight, solid core of oil flows from nozzle tip without undue pres-

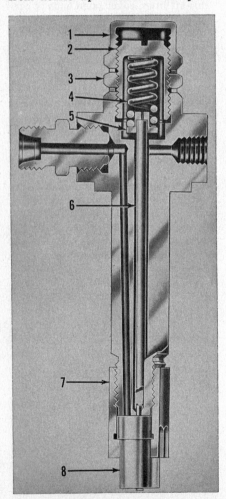

Fig. MM839—Cross sectional view of typical Bosch injector of the type used in MM diesel tractors.

1. Cap nut	5. Spring seat
2. Adjusting screw	6. Spindle
3. Jam nut	7. Holder nut
4. Pressure spring	8. Nozzle assembly

sure on tester handle, open valve to tester gage and remove cap-nut (1—Fig. MM839). Slowly depress the tester handle and observe the pressure at which core emerges. If opening pressure is not within the recommended range of 1800-1850 psi, loosen locknut (3) and turn adjusting cap (2) in or out until opening pressure is within the recommended range.

When opening pressure has been set, again close valve to tester gage and operate tester handle at approximately 100 strokes per minute while examining spray core. Fuel should emerge from nozzle opening in one solid core, in a straight line with injector body, with no branches, splits or atomization.

NOTE: The tester pump cannot duplicate the injection velocity necessary to obtain the operating spray-pattern of the delay type nozzles. Also absent will be the familiar popping sound associated with the nozzle opening of multi-hole nozzles. Under operating velocities, the observed solid core will cross the combustion chamber and enter the energy cell. In addition, a fine conical mist surrounding the core will ignite in the combustion chamber area above the piston. The solid core cannot vary more than 7½ degrees in any direction and still enter the energy cell. While the core is the only spray characteristic which can be observed on the tester, absence of core deviation is of utmost importance.

83. SEAT LEAKAGE. The nozzle valve should not leak at pressures less than 1700 psi. To check for seat leakage, open the valve to tester gage and actuate tester handle slowly until gage pressure approaches 1700 psi. Maintain this pressure for at least 10 seconds, then observe the flat surface of nozzle body and the pintle tip for drops or undue wetness. If drops or wetness appear, the injector must be disassembled and overhauled as outlined in paragraph 86.

84. BACK LEAKAGE. A back leak test will indicate the condition of the internal sealing surfaces of the nozzle assembly. Before checking the back leakage, first check for seat leakage as outlined in paragraph 83, then proceed as follows:

Turn the adjusting screw (2—Fig. MM839) inward until nozzle opening pressure is set at 2350 psi. Release the tester handle and observe the length of time required for gage needle to drop from 2200 psi to 1500 psi. The time should be not less than 6 seconds. A faster drop would indi-

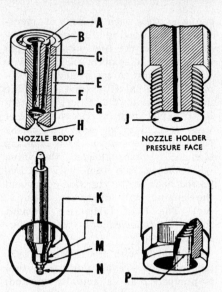

Fig. MM840—Inspect the disassembled injector at the points shown in the above views.

A. Nozzle body pressure face	H. Pintle orifice
B. Nozzle body pressure face	J. Holder pressure face
C. Fuel feed hole	K. Valve cone
D. Shoulder	L. Stem
E. Nozzle trunk	M. Valve seat
F. Fuel gallery	N. Pintle
G. Valve seat	P. Nozzle retaining shoulder

cate wear or scoring between piston surface of nozzle valve or body (8), or improper sealing of pressure face surfaces (A, B and J—Fig. MM840). NOTE: Leakage at tester connections or tester check valve will show up as fast leak back in this test. If all injectors tested fail to pass this test, the tester, rather than the injector, should be suspected.

85. OPENING PRESSURE. To assure peak engine performance, it is recommended that all of the injectors installed in any engine be adjusted as nearly as possible, to equal opening pressures. The recommended opening pressure range is 1800-1850 psi. When a new spring (4—Fig. MM839) is removed from parts stock and installed in an injector assembly, the injection pressure will drop quickly as the spring becomes seated under the constant compression. This rate of pressure drop is approximately 10 per cent. It is recommended that injectors containing new springs be initially set at 2000 psi opening pressure, and injectors with used springs at 1850 psi. After the opening pressure has been adjusted, tighten locknut (3) and reinstall cap nut (1), then recheck opening pressure to make sure adjusting screw has not moved.

86. OVERHAUL. The maintenance of absolute cleanliness in the overhaul of injector assemblies is of utmost importance. Of equal importance is the

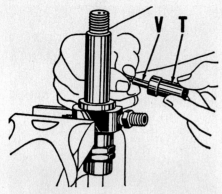

Fig. MM841 — Removing injection nozzle valve (V) from tip (T). If the valve is difficult to remove, soak the assembly in a suitable carbon solvent.

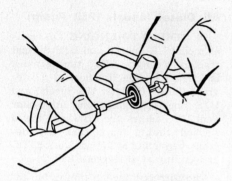

Fig. MM842—Use the special scraper to remove carbon from fuel gallery.

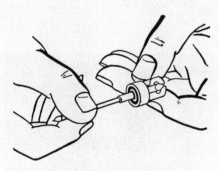

Fig. MM843—Use the brass seat tool to remove carbon from valve seat.

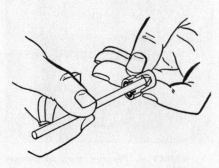

Fig. MM844—Use wooden stick and a small amount of tallow to polish valve seat.

avoidance of nicks or scratches on any of the lapped surfaces. To avoid damage to any of the highly machined parts, only the recommended cleaning kits and oil base carbon solvents should be used in the injector repair sections of the shop. The nozzle valve and body are individualy fit and hand lapped, and these two parts should always be kept together as mated parts.

Before disassembling a set of injectors, cap the pressure line connections with a line nut with the hole soldered shut, or with a special metal cap, and immerse the units in a clean carbon solvent. While the injectors are soaking, clean the work area and remove any accumulation of discarded parts from previous service jobs. Remove the injectors one at a time from the solvent and thoroughly clean the outer surfaces with a brass wire brush. Be extremely careful not to damage the pintle end of nozzle body. Rinse the injector in clean diesel fuel and test the injector as outlined in paragraphs 82 through 85. Never disassemble an injector which can be adjusted and returned to service without disassembly.

If the injector unit must be disassembled, clamp the injector body in a soft jawed vise as shown in Fig. MM841, tightening only tight enough to keep injector from slipping, or use a holding fixture. Remove cap nut (1—Fig. MM839) and back off the adjusting screw (2) until all tension is removed from the spring, then remove the nozzle holder nut (7). Withdraw the nozzle valve (V—Fig. MM-841) from nozzle body (T) with the fingers as shown; or, if valve is stuck, use a special extractor or soak in solvent. NEVER loosen valve by tapping exposed pintle end of valve on a hard surface.

Examine the lapped pressure faces (A, B and J—Fig. MM840) of nozzle body and holder for nicks or scratches, and the piston (larger) portion of nozzle valve for scratches or scoring. Clean the fuel gallery (F) with the special hooked scraper as shown in Fig. MM842, by applying side pressure while the body is rotated. Clean the valve seat with the brass seat tool as shown in Fig. MM843. Polish the seat with the pointed wooden polishing stick and a small amount of tallow as shown in Fig. MM844. Clean the pintle orifice from the inside, using the proper size probe. Polish the nozzle valve seat and pintle with a piece of felt and some tallow, loosening any particle of hardened carbon with a pointed piece of brass stock.

Never use a hard or sharp object such as a knife blade as any scratches will cause distortion of the injection core.

As the parts are cleaned, immerse in clean diesel fuel in a compartmented pan. Insert the nozzle valve into body underneath the fuel level and assemble valve body to nozzle holder while wet. Do not attempt to dry the parts with towels or compressed air because of the danger of dust particles remaining on the pressure faces of nozzle holder and nozzle body. Use a centering sleeve or shim stock when reassembling. To use the sleeve, tighten the holder nut with the fingers while rotating centering sleeve in the opposite direction. When the nut is finger tight remove the sleeve and tighten the holder nut to a torque of approximately 50-55 ft.-lbs. Retest the injector as previously outlined. If injector fails to meet the tests and no leaks because of dust, were found upon disassembly, renew the nozzle assembly and any other parts suspected of being faulty.

INJECTION PUMP

Minneapolis-Moline diesel tractors are equipped with either an American-Bosch single plunger model PSB, American-Bosch multiple plunger model APE or Roosa-Master injection pump.

The following paragraphs will outline ONLY the injection pump service work which can be accomplished without the use of special pump testing equipment. If additional service work is required, the pump should be turned over to a properly equipped diesel service station for overhaul. Inexperienced service personnel should never attempt to overhaul a diesel injection pump.

All Diesel Models (APE Pump)

87. TIMING TO ENGINE. On earlier UB and UTS engines the flywheel is marked with a line and the letters "INJ" at the injection point 27 degrees before top dead center. On later UB and UTS engines, and all 5-Star and M5 engines, the flywheel has a timing mark each 2½ degrees, beginning at 27½ degrees BTDC and ending at 45 degrees BTDC.

The correct injection timing for engines equipped with model APE injection pump is as follows:

UB Special, UTS Special....27° BTDC
5-Star ....29° BTDC
M5 ....40° BTDC

To time the pump to the engine, crank the engine until No. 1 piston

Fig. MM845 — To time the injection pump to the engine, turn flywheel until proper timing mark on flywheel is centered in timing window. Pictured is M5 tractor, others are similar.

is on the compression stroke, and continue cranking until the indicated timing mark is centered in the timing window on the left side of the flywheel housing as shown in Fig. MM-845. Remove the plug from the inspection port in the timing gear housing as shown in Fig. MM846. Timing mark on gear flange should exactly align with mark on pump body as shown. If it does not, but is still visible through the inspection port, proper timing can usually be accomplished after removing timing housing front cover as outlined in paragraph 44. Remove safety wire and loosen the four gear retaining cap screws (T—Fig. MM847), rotate gear on cam gear until pump timing marks are aligned. Tighten retaining cap screws and secure with safety wire. If the timing marks cannot be brought into alignment by rotating the timing gear, the injection pump must be removed and timed as outlined in paragraph 88.

88. REMOVE AND REINSTALL. Before attempting to remove the injection pump, thoroughly wash the pump and connections with clean

Fig. MM846 — Alignment of pump timing marks for diesel engines equipped with Bosch Model APE pump.

diesel fuel. Disconnect the injection lines from the injection pump and the inlet and outlet lines from the transfer pump. Disconnect the remaining lines and control rods. Cap all exposed fuel line connections to prevent the entrance of dirt. Remove the pump mounting cap screws and withdraw the pump.

Before installing the pump, crank the engine until No. 1 piston is on the compression stroke and continue cranking until the proper flywheel timing mark is centered in the timing window on left side of flywheel housing as shown in Fig. MM845. Rotate the injection pump shaft until timing marks on pump body and gear flange are aligned as shown in Fig. MM848, install pump on engine and secure with the mounting cap screws. Remove the plug from the timing port on timing gear housing as shown in Fig. MM846. If the timing marks are not in perfect alignment, remove timing housing front cover as outlined in paragraph 44, loosen timing gear retaining cap screws and rotate timing gear until pump timing marks are aligned.

89. TRANSFER PUMP. Model APE injection pump is equipped with a self-regulating, plunger-type transfer pump which is actuated by the injection pump camshaft. Fig. MM849 shows a phantom view of the transfer pump.

If the pump is not operating properly, the complete pump can be renewed as a unit; or the transfer pump can be disassembled and cleaned. Quite often a thorough cleaning job will restore the pump to its original efficiency.

Fig. MM847—Typical diesel engine timing gear train showing method of adjusting pump timing.

T. Clamping cap screw	2. Adjustable gear
1. Crankshaft gear	3. Camshaft gear
	4. Pump drive gear

Fig. MM848—American Bosch Model APE injection pump showing timing marks properly aligned for installation.

All Diesel Models (PSB Pump)

90. TIMING TO ENGINE. On earlier model UB Special and UTS Special tractors a single "INJ" timing mark is located on the flywheel at 27 degrees BTDC. On later UB Special and UTS Special engines, and all 5-Star and M5 engines the flywheel has a scribed timing mark each 2½ degrees, beginning at 27½ degrees BTDC and ending at 45 degrees BTDC.

The correct injection timing for engines equipped with model PSB injection pump is as follows:

UB Special, UTS Special....27° BTDC
5-Star ....29° BTDC
M5 ....30° BTDC

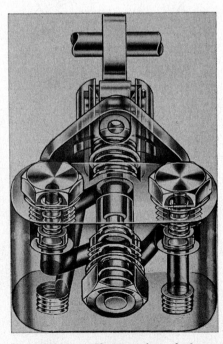

Fig. MM849 — Phantom view of plunger type transfer pump used on model APE injection pump.

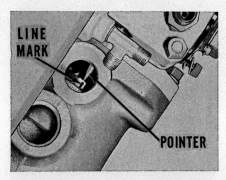

Fig. MM850—Pump drive coupling timing marks on diesel tractors.

To time the pump to the engine, crank the engine until No. 1 piston is coming up on the compression stroke, and continue cranking until the indicated timing mark is centered in the timing window on the left side of the flywheel housing as shown in Fig. MM845. Remove plug on top of injection pump adapter housing as shown in Fig. MM850. The timing mark on the pump coupling flange should be in exact alignment with the timing pointer as shown. If the timing mark is not in alignment, but is less than one drive coupling tooth off, remove timing case front cover as outlined in paragraph 44, remove

safety wire and loosen the gear retaining cap screws (T—Fig. MM847) and shift gear on cam gear until pump timing marks are aligned. Tighten retaining cap screws and secure with safety wire. If the pump timing marks are more than one coupling tooth out of alignment, the pump must be removed and reinstalled as outlined in paragraph 91.

91. REMOVE AND REINSTALL. Before attempting to remove the injection pump, thoroughly wash the pump and connections with clean diesel fuel. Disconnect the injection lines from the pump, inlet and outlet lines from transfer pump, the remaining lines and control rods. Cap all exposed fuel line connections to prevent the entrance of dirt. Remove pump mounting cap screws and withdraw pump from adapter.

Before installing the pump, crank engine until No. 1 piston is coming up on the compression stroke and continue cranking until the proper flywheel timing mark is centered in timing window on flywheel housing as shown in Fig. MM845. Remove the timing window cover (20—Fig. MM-851) and rotate pump shaft until

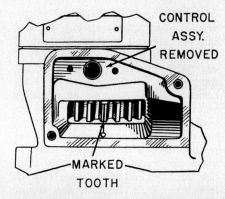

Fig. MM852 — Side view of Bosch model PSB injection pump with timing window cover removed. Notice that the line on one of the gear teeth is in register with pointer on the housing.

marked tooth on plunger drive gear is approximately in the center of timing window as shown in Fig. MM852. With marked tooth visible in window as shown, and timing mark on coupling hub in relation to pointer as shown in Fig. MM853, install pump to adapter and rotate top of pump towards engine until retaining cap screws can be aligned. Start one cap screw and, looking through adapter timing window as shown in Fig. MM850, check for proper alignment of pump timing marks. Note: Marked tooth on plunger drive gear (Fig. MM852) does not need to align with pointer as shown, but must be visible through window. If the timing marks are in alignment, or less than one coupling tooth off, install and tighten mounting cap screws. If the marks are more than one coupling tooth out of alignment, remove and reinstall pump until proper register is obtained.

If the timing marks are not in perfect alignment, but are less than one coupling tooth off, remove timing housing front cover as outlined in paragraph 44; loosen cap screws (T—Fig. MM847) and rotate the drive gear until pump timing marks are aligned.

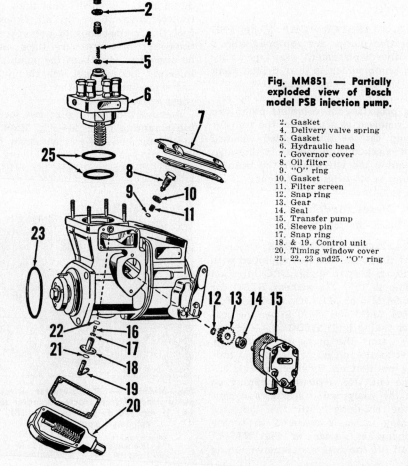

Fig. MM851 — Partially exploded view of Bosch model PSB injection pump.

2. Gasket
4. Delivery valve spring
5. Gasket
6. Hydraulic head
7. Governor cover
8. Oil filter
9. "O" ring
10. Gasket
11. Filter screen
12. Snap ring
13. Gear
14. Seal
15. Transfer pump
16. Sleeve pin
17. Snap ring
18. & 19. Control unit
20. Timing window cover
21, 22, 23 and 25. "O" ring

Fig. MM853—Coupling timing marks in the proper position for installing the injection pump. Notice that line mark is to left of pointer.

92. HYDRAULIC HEAD. The hydraulic head assembly (Fig. MM854) can be renewed without the use of special testing equipment. The head assembly contains all of the precision components which are essential to accurate pumping, distributing, metering and delivery of the fuel. To renew the hydraulic head assembly, first wash the complete injection pump and injection lines with clean fuel oil. Remove the injection lines and disconnect the inlet and outlet lines from the hydraulic head. Remove the timing window cover (20—Fig. MM851) and crank engine until the line mark on the apex of one of the teeth on the pump plunger drive gear is in register with the pointer stamped on the lower face of the timing window hole as shown in Fig. MM852. Remove the two screws and carefully withdraw the control assembly, being careful not to lose plunger sleeve pin (16—Fig. MM851). Remove governor cover (7) and unscrew and remove lube oil filter (8). Remove the hydraulic head retaining stud nuts and carefully withdraw the hydraulic head assembly from the pump housing. Do not use force when attempting to withdraw the hydraulic head. If difficulty is encountered, check to make certain that the plunger drive gear is properly positioned as shown in Fig. MM852.

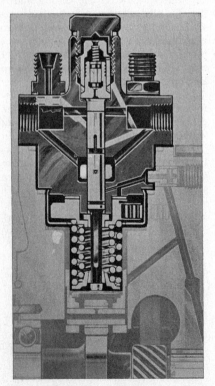

Fig. MM854 — Sectional view of Bosch model PSB injection pump hydraulic head. The complete head assembly can be renewed as a unit.

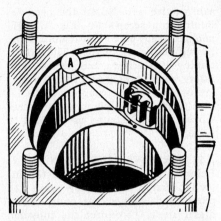

Fig. MM855—When installing a hydraulic head on a model PSB injection pump, make certain that open tooth on quill shaft gear is in register with punch mark in housing as shown at (A).

When installing a new hydraulic head assembly, make certain that the line marked plunger drive gear tooth is in register with the pointer stamped on the lower face of the timing window as shown in Fig. MM852 and that open tooth on quill shaft gear is in register with punch mark in pump housing as shown at (A) in Fig. MM-855. When installing the control sleeve assembly, the plunger sleeve pin (16—Fig. MM851) must be lined up with the slot in the control block. The remainder of the reassembly procedure is evident.

93. TRANSFER PUMP. Model PSB injection pumps are equipped with a positive displacement, gear type transfer pump which is gear driven from the injection pump camshaft.

If the transfer pump is not operating properly, the complete pump can be renewed as a unit; or, the transfer pump can be disassembled, cleaned and checked. Quite often a thorough cleaning job will restore the transfer pump to its original efficiency.

All Diesel Models
(Roosa-Master Pump)

94. TIMING TO ENGINE. The correct timing for tractors equipped with a Roosa-Master Model DBG injection pump is 10° (1¼-inches) BTDC for model M-5 or M504. On models M602, M604, M670 and M670 Super the correct timing is 9° BTDC.

To time the pump to the engine, first locate and mark the correct timing position on flywheel. Crank engine until No. 1 piston is coming up on the compression stroke, and continue cranking until the indicated timing mark is centered in timing window as shown in Fig. MM845. Shut off the fuel and remove timing

Fig. MM856—Roosa-Master pump installation showing timing marks.

window on side of injection pump body. Pump is correctly timed when scribe lines on governor cage and cam ring are aligned as shown at (1—Fig. MM856). If marks are visible but not perfectly aligned, loosen the two stud nuts attaching pump to mounting plate and shift pump body slightly until marks are perfectly aligned.

Reinstall pump timing window and turn on fuel. Injection pump is self bleeding. Injection lines or filter should not require bleeding if pump connections are not broken.

95. REMOVE AND REINSTALL. Before attempting to remove the injection pump, thoroughly wash the pump and connections with clean diesel fuel. Disconnect fuel lines and control rods, then cap all exposed fuel line connections to prevent entrance of dirt. Pressure lines must be disconnected at both the pump and injectors. Loosen fuel line clamps, if necessary, and shift the lines rearward as far as possible.

Remove the four cap screws securing mounting plate (8—Fig. MM857) to adapter housing and withdraw the

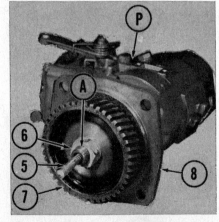

Fig. MM857 — Roosa-Master injection pump removed from tractor. Adapter shaft (A) is serviced as part of pump (P), but numbered parts are not.

A. Adapter shaft	6. Spring
P. Injection pump	7. Pump gear
5. Thrust button	8. Mounting plate

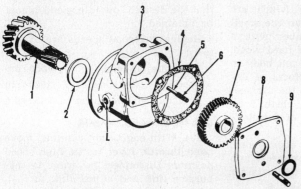

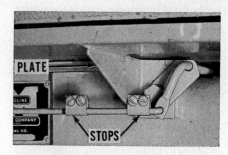

Fig. MM858 — Injection pump adapter housing and associated parts used with Roosa-Master system. Items (5) through (9) are removed with the pump, but must be transferred if pump is renewed. Refer to text.

L. Lube passage
1. Drive gear
2. Thrust washer
3. Adapter housing
4. Gasket
5. Thrust button
6. Spring
7. Pump gear
8. Mounting plate
9. "O" ring

Fig. MM860 — Series "UB Special" diesel governor control rod stops.

pump, mounting plate and drive gear (7) straight to rear out of adapter housing. Be careful not to lose thrust button (5) and spring (6) as pump is removed.

The pump adapter shaft and seals are a part of injection pump. The mounting plate (8—Fig. MM858), drive gear (7) and "O" rings (9) are not a part of the replacement pump and must be transferred if a new pump is installed. DO NOT withdraw adapter shaft and drive gear (7) unless required for service. If adapter shaft must be withdrawn, make sure assembly marks on shaft and rotor are aligned, and that lip of cup-type seal is not turned back during installation.

When installing the pump, make sure that No. 1 piston is on compression stroke and that the correct flywheel timing mark is aligned with timing pointer as outlined in paragraph 94. Remove pump timing window and turn drive shaft until timing marks on cam and governor cage are aligned as shown in Fig. MM856. Turn drive gear backward (clockwise as viewed from front) until governor cage timing mark moves downward approximately 1/16-inch, then install the pump. With mounting plate cap screws installed and flywheel timing marks aligned, pump timing marks should be within 3/32-inch of alignment; if they are not, remove pump, turn drive gear 1 tooth in proper direction and reinstall. If marks are less than one gear tooth out of alignment, tighten mounting plate retaining cap screws, loosen the two stud nuts and shift pump housing slightly until marks are aligned.

Complete the assembly by reversing the disassembly procedure and bleed the system as outlined in paragraph 78.

96. GOVERNOR. Governed speeds are adjusted on test stand and sealed. Speeds should not be adjusted, but should approximate those shown in following table:

High idle—no load
M5-M504 .... 1650 rpm
M602-M604 .... 1650 rpm
M670-M670 Super ...... 1750 rpm
Fully loaded
M5-M504 .... 1500 rpm
M602-M604 .... 1500 rpm
M670-M670 Super ...... 1600 rpm
Low idle
All Models .... 600 rpm

DIESEL GOVERNOR

All Models with Bosch Pump

97. The injection pump is fitted with a mechanical flyweight type governor. For the purposes of this manual, the governor will be considered as an integral part of the injection pump.

While the governors used on model PSB and model APE injection pumps are not interchangeable, adjustment procedure remains the same, and the procedures outlined apply to either pump.

98. ADJUSTMENT. Recommended governed speeds are as follows:
High idle-no load
UB Special-UTS Special..1430 rpm
5-Star .... 1550 rpm
M5 .... 1650 rpm

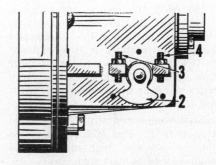

Fig. MM859—High and low speed adjustment screws on Bosch injection pump governor.

2. Adjusting screw stop plate
3. Low speed adjusting screw
4. High speed adjusting screw

Fuly loaded
UB Special-UTS Special..1300 rpm
5-Star .... 1400 rpm
M5 .... 1500 rpm
Low idle
All models .... 600 rpm

The governor should be adjusted, after engine has been run until temperature has reached the normal operating range. To adjust governor, disconnect control rod from governor arm and remove adjusting screw cover as shown in Fig. MM859. With the engine running, move the operating lever stop plate (2) to the high speed position, and with stop plate contacting high speed stop screw (4), turn screw in or out until the recommended high idle engine speed is obtained. Now move stop plate (2) to low speed position and turn low speed adjusting screw (3) in or out to obtain the correct low idle speed. Reinstall adjusting screw cover and connect throttle linkage to governor arm.

On UB Special, refer to Fig. MM860 and loosen the two stops on throttle control rod. Move throttle lever to low and high speed positions and clamp the two stops to the control rod to limit the control rod travel.

ENERGY CELLS

All Diesel Models

99. **R&R AND CLEAN.** The necessity for cleaning the energy cells is usually indicated by excessive exhaust smoke or a drop in fuel economy.

Fig. MM861—Exploded view of diesel engine energy cell.

1. Plug   3. Cell cap
2. Holder   4. Energy cell

Fig. MM862—Using special threaded puller to remove energy cell from diesel engines. Refer to text.

To remove the energy cells, unscrew the retainer plug and remove the cap holder. Grasp the energy cell cap (3—Fig. MM861) with a pair of pliers and withdraw cap from cylinder head. Using a $\frac{15}{16}$-inch NEF-2 puller screwed into energy cell (4), pull cell from head as shown in Fig. MM862.

Clean all parts in a suitable carbon solvent and renew any which are cracked or damaged. Clean the small orifice in the cell chamber with a brass brush or a piece of hard wood. Check seating surface of cell body in cylinder head and mating surfaces of energy cell and cell cap. If the surfaces are rough, they can be cleaned by lapping with a mixture of jeweler's rouge and diesel fuel.

When reinstalling the energy cell, make certain that it fits squarely into cylinder head. Tighten the retainer plug to a torque of 100 ft.-lbs.

ELECTRIC MANIFOLD HEATER
All Models So Equipped

100. The heater unit is equipped with a Champion J-14 single electrode spark plug. The other electrode is attached to a cap screw in the housing. Bend only the electrode attached to the cap screw to obtain an electrode gap of 3/32-inch.

NON-DIESEL GOVERNOR

ADJUSTMENT

101. Before attempting to adjust the governor, warm up the engine and adjust the carburetor as outlined in paragraphs 68, 69 or 70. Also check and eliminate any binding in the throttle or governor linkage.

UB Special-UTS Special

102. With the engine not running, move hand throttle control lever to the high speed position, disconnect

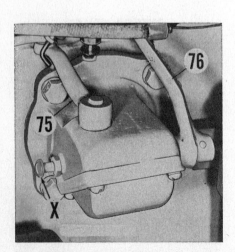

Fig. MM863 — Typical Minneapolis-Moline governor unit installation on UB Spl. and UTS Spl., showing the speed adjusting screw (X).

governor to carburetor link, and adjust link so that with carburetor throttle against high speed stop, link will enter hole in governor control lever (76—Fig. MM863) without moving lever.

Start engine and adjust maximum speed stop screw (X) to obtain the recommended high idle, no load engine speed.

Engine governed speeds are as follows:

High idle, no load......1430 rpm
Loaded engine speed......1300 rpm
Low idle engine speed.... 450 rpm

5-Star Series

103. With the engine not running, move hand throttle control lever to the high speed position, disconnect governor to carburetor link, and adjust link so that with carburetor throttle against high speed stop, link will enter hole in governor arm without moving arm.

Start engine and adjust high speed stop screw (1—Fig. MM864) to obtain the recommended high idle, no load engine speed of 1650 rpm.

The governor should respond quickly to a given load condition without surging. If engine surge is noted, turn surge screw (2) in slightly until surge is eliminated. Care must be taken to

not turn surge screw in far enough that the desired low idle speed cannot be obtained.

Engine governed speeds are as follows:

High idle, no load........1650 rpm
Loaded engine speed......1500 rpm
Low idle engine speed.... 450 rpm

M5-M504-M602-M604

104. With engine not running, move hand throttle lever to the high speed position. Disconnect governor to carburetor link and adjust link so that, with carburetor throttle against high speed stop, link will enter hole in governor arm without moving arm. Reconnect governor to carburetor link and start engine. Move hand throttle lever firmly to the idle position. The idle speed stop screw on the carburetor throttle should override the flexible stop on carburetor, completely closing throttle fly and causing the engine to stop. If it does not, turn idle position adjusting screw (1—Fig MM865) into the governor throttle lever until the engine dies.

After the over-ride idle position has been adjusted, move the hand throttle to the high speed position and, with the engine running turn governed speed adjusting screw (3) in or out of governor fork lever until the correct high idle speed of 1650 rpm is obtained.

On M5, M504 tractors, if the hand throttle lever moves too easily, or will not stay in position, tighten tension adjusting nut (1—Fig. MM866) just enough to provide the desired frictional drag.

Recommended governed engine speed are as follows:

High idle, no load........1650 rpm
Loaded engine speed......1500 rpm
Low idle engine speed.... 475 rpm

Fig. MM864 — Novi governor used on 5-Star tractors, showing (1) High-speed Stop Screw, (2) Surge Screw and (3) Carburetor linkage adjustment.

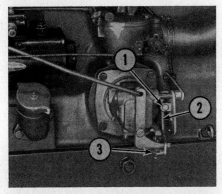

Fig. MM865 — Pierce governor used on many late model tractors showing (1) Low idle speed stop screw, (2) Speed change lever and (3) High speed stop screw.

Fig. MM866 — Throttle lever tension adjusting nut (1), used on M5 tractors.

M670-M670 Super

105. With engine not running, move hand throttle lever to the high speed position. Disconnect the adjusting pin (2—Fig. MM867) from governor fork lever. Raise carburetor linkage rod (3) until carburetor throttle disc is in wide-open position. Loosen locknut and adjust pin (2) up or down as re-

Fig. MM867 — Hoof governor used on models M670 and M670 Super, showing speed adjusting screw (1) and carburetor linkage rod (3).

X. Speed control adjusting screw
75. Speed control hand lever
76. Governor control lever
93. Weight pin
100. Weight shaft
101. Weight
102. Bearing retainer plate
103. Housing bearing
104. Thrust thimble
105. Thimble ball
106. Spindle
107. Spring
108. Speed adjusting lever shaft
110. Control arm shaft bushing
112. Control arm shaft bushing
113. Cover
114. Speed adjusting arm

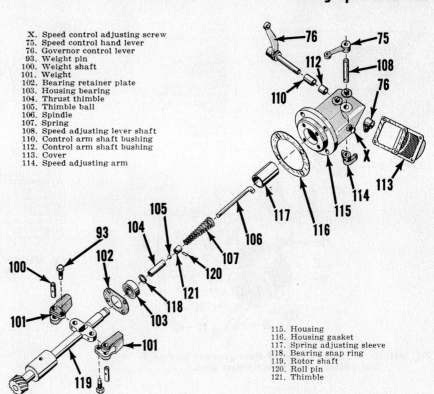

115. Housing
116. Housing gasket
117. Spring adjusting sleeve
118. Bearing snap ring
119. Rotor shaft
120. Roll pin
121. Thimble

Fig. MM868 — Exploded view of governor used on series "UB Special - UTS Special"

quired until pin will enter hole in governor lever. Tighten locknut, start engine and adjust speed screw (1) to obtain the correct governed engine rpm.

Recommended governed engine speeds are as follows:

M670
High idle, no load........1750 rpm
Loaded engine speed......1600 rpm
Low idle engine speed.... 600 rpm

M670 Super
High idle, no load.......1825 rpm
Loaded engine speed.....1600 rpm
Low idle engine speed.... 600 rpm

R&R AND OVERHAUL
UB Special-UTS Special

106. The flyweight governor is mounted to the right side of the engine crankcase and driven by a gear on the engine camshaft. To remove the governor, disconnect linkage, remove the retaining cap screws and withdraw the governor assembly.

To disassemble the governor, unbolt and remove cover (113—Fig. MM868) and bearing retainer plate (102). Refer to Fig. MM869, remove plug from top of governor housing, and, using a suitable punch as shown, drive the pin out of control shaft and lever (76—Fig. MM868). Remove control shaft and lever, bump pin out of speed control lever (75) and shaft (108) and remove lever, shaft and speed adjusting arm (114). Ball (105)

will roll out of governor shaft (119) when spindle (106) and lever (75) is withdrawn. Remove weight pins (93) and withdraw thrust thimble (104) from governor shaft. Remove snap ring (118) and bearing (103). To remove weights (101) remove weight shafts (100).

Control shaft bushings (110 & 112) require final sizing after installation, to provide 0.0005-0.0015 diametral clearance on the shaft. Spring adjusting sleeve (117) should be a close fit in housing, but should not bind.

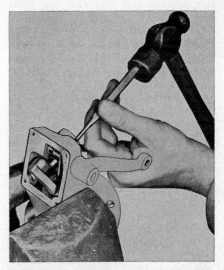

Fig. MM869—Bumping pin out of governor control arm and shaft on series "UB Special-UTS Special".

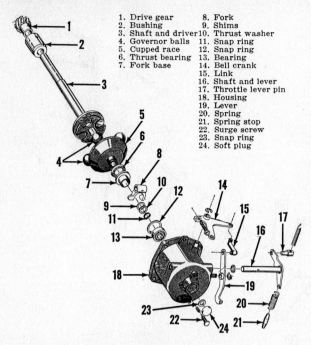

1. Drive gear
2. Bushing
3. Shaft and driver
4. Governor balls
5. Cupped race
6. Thrust bearing
7. Fork base
8. Fork
9. Shims
10. Thrust washer
11. Snap ring
12. Snap ring
13. Bearing
14. Bell crank
15. Link
16. Shaft and lever
17. Throttle lever pin
18. Housing
19. Lever
20. Spring
21. Spring stop
22. Surge screw
23. Snap ring
24. Soft plug

Fig. MM870 — Exploded view of Novi governor used on 5-Star tractors, showing component parts.

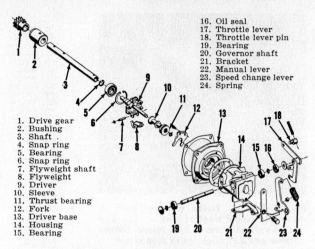

16. Oil seal
17. Throttle lever
18. Throttle lever pin
19. Bearing
20. Governor shaft
21. Bracket
22. Manual lever
23. Speed change lever
24. Spring

1. Drive gear
2. Bushing
3. Shaft
4. Snap ring
5. Bearing
6. Snap ring
7. Flyweight shaft
8. Flyweight
9. Driver
10. Sleeve
11. Thrust bearing
12. Fork
13. Driver base
14. Housing
15. Bearing

Fig. MM871 — Exploded view of Pierce governor used on all M5, M504, M602 and M604 tractors.

Check speed adjusting lever shaft (108) and mating surface in housing for wear. Diametral clearance in excess of 0.007 will require renewal of housing and/or lever shaft. Taper pin holes can be reamed with a No. 10 taper pin reamer for tight fit of pins.

Novi Governor

The Novi governor pictured in Fig. MM-870 is used on all 5-Star tractors.

107. The flyball governor is mounted on the right side of engine and driven by the camshaft.

To disassemble the removed governor, remove soft plug (24—Fig. MM-870), remove snap ring (23) then withdraw shaft and driver assembly from housing (18) and bearing (13). Examine shaft assembly (3) for loose driver, bent or damaged shaft, or grooved wear on the flat ball race. If defects or damage is found, renew the shaft and driver assembly. Examine the balls (4) for rust or flat spots, and the cupped race (5) for channels or wear.

When reassembling, install a sufficient quantity of shims (9) to allow balls to clear case when fully extended. Renew bearing (13) if rough or excessively loose. Insert shaft and driver assembly through bearing and install snap ring (23), then use a new soft plug (24). Examine governor linkage for binding or excessive wear and renew or free as needed.

Pierce Governor

The Pierce governor, pictured in Fig. MM871, is used on all M5, M504, M602 and M604 tractors.

108. The flyweight governor is mounted on the right side of the engine crankcase and is driven by a gear on the engine camshaft. To remove the governor, disconnect linkage, remove the four retaining cap screws and withdraw governor assembly.

To disassemble governor, unbolt and remove the housing (14—Fig. MM871) from the driver base (13). Most of the governor can be examined for wear or damage at this time. Examine the weights (8), weight pins (7) and driver assembly for binding or sloppy fit. To remove the drive shaft sleeve and thrust bearing assembly, remove snap ring at outer end of shaft and withdraw sleeve. Remove snap ring (4) to remove driver from

housing and bearing. Examine governor fork (12) for wear or bending and remainder of governor linkage for binding, wear or damage and renew as indicated.

Hoof Governor

The Hoof governor pictured in Fig. MM872, is used on models M670 and M670 Super tractors.

109. The flyweight governor is mounted on the right side of the engine crankcase and is driven by a gear on the engine camshaft. To remove the governor, disconnect the linkage, remove the four retaining cap screws and withdraw governor assembly.

To disassemble the governor, unbolt and remove housing (1—Fig. MM872) from the driver base (3). Most of the governor can be examined for wear and damage at this time. Check weights (8), weight pins (9) and driver assembly for binding or excessive wear. The balance of disassembly is obvious after an examination of the unit and reference to Fig. MM872.

After assembly and installation are completed, check and adjust engine speed as outlined in paragraph 105.

Fig. MM872 — Exploded view of Hoof governor used on models M670 and M670 Super tractors.

1. Governor housing
2. Rocker shaft lever
3. Driver base
4. Gasket
5. Ball bearing
6. Truarc retainer rings
7. Driver
8. Flyweight
9. Weight pin
10. Retainer
11. Thrust bearing & sleeve
12. Roll pins
13. Extension shaft
14. Bushing
15. Pinion

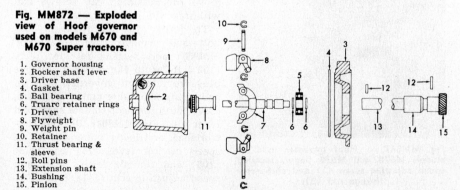

COOLING SYSTEM

RADIATOR

All Models

110. On models UB Special, UTS Special and M670 Super, the upper tank, core and lower tank are of a one-piece construction. On all other models, the upper tank and core unit is detachable from the lower tank which is integral with the steering gear housing.

THERMOSTAT

All Models

111. The thermostat is located in a flanged elbow bolted to front of water outlet manifold on top of engine.

FAN ASSEMBLY

All Models

112. Procedure for removal and/or overhaul of the fan assembly is evident after an examination of the unit and reference to Fig. MM873. The taper roller fan shaft bearings should be adjusted to remove all end play, yet permit shaft to rotate freely.

WATER PUMP

All Models

113. **R&R AND OVERHAUL.** To remove the water pump, drain cooling system an remove hood and grille. Support tractor under engine, then unbolt and slide radiator, front support and axle assembly forward. Remove nuts holding pump to timing gear case and remove pump from tractor.

Remove cover from pump body and drive roll pin out of collar (13—Fig. MM874) and drive shaft. Withdraw impeller, shaft and seal assembly. If seal seating surface in pump body is scored, pitted or rough and cannot be refaced, renew the pump body. If running clearance between pump shaft and bushing (11) is excessive, or if shaft is scored, renew shaft and/or bushing. Ream the bushing after installation, if necessary, to provide a suggested running clearance of 0.0025-0.004.

After collar (13) and roll pin are installed, lay a straight edge across front of pump body and check the clearance between straight edge and impeller. Desired clearance is 0.025-0.035. If clearance is not as specified, it will be necessary to move impeller on the pump shaft.

Before assembling cover to pump, mount pump on engine with gasket and "O" ring in place and check end play of impeller shaft with a straight edge and feelers or with a dial indicator. Desired end play is 0.005-0.010 which can be obtained by varying the number of gaskets between pump body and engine.

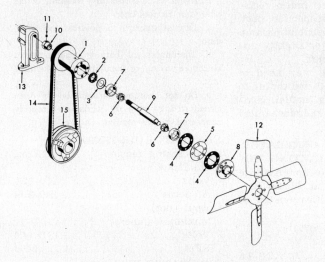

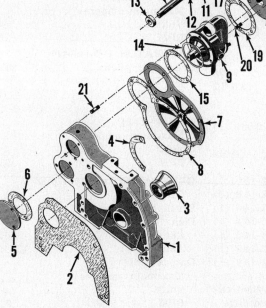

Fig. MM873 — Exploded view of typical fan assembly and components.

1. Fan hub
2. Felt seal
3. Retainer
4. Gasket
5. Shim
6. Bearing cone
7. Bearing cup
8. Cover
9. Shaft
10. Collar
11. Set screw
12. Fan blade
13. Fan bracket
14. Fan belt
15. Pulley

Fig. MM874 — Exploded view of typical gear case and water pump.

1. Gear case
2. Gasket
3. Front oil seal
4. Locking plate
5. Cover
6. Gasket
7. Gear case cover
8. Gasket
9. Water pump
10. Drive shaft
11. Bushing
12. Oil seal
13. Collar
14. Gasket
15. Shim
16. Impeller
17. Impeller seal
18. Cover
19. Gasket
20. Stud
21. Stud

IGNITION AND ELECTRICAL SYSTEM

All Models

114. **DISTRIBUTOR.** Delco-Remy distributors are used on all models except some early M5s, on which Autolite units were optionally available. Specification data are as follows:

Delco-Remy 1112565:

Breaker contact gap............0.022
Breaker arm spring tension
(measured at center of
contact) ....17-21 oz.
Cam angle ....25-34°

Advance data is in distributor degrees and distributor rpm.
Start advance ....0-3.5 @ 225
Intermediate advance ....9-12 @ 525
Maximum advance ....13.5-16.5 @ 700

Delco-Remy 1112629:

Breaker contact gap............0.022

Breaker arm spring tension
(measured at center of
contact) ....17-21 oz.
Cam angle ....25°-34°
Advance data is in distributor degrees and distributor rpm.
Start advance ....0-3.5 @ 225
Intermediate advance .....4-7 @ 325
Intermediate advance ....9-12 @ 525
Maximum advance ...13.5-16.5 @ 700

Delco-Remy 1112660:
Breaker contact gap 0.022
Breaker arm spring tension
(measured at center
of contact) ....17-21 oz.
Cam angle ....31°-34°
Advance data is in distributor degrees and distributor rpm.
Start advance ....0-2 @ 250
Intermediate advance .....2-4 @ 350
Maximum advance ....6-8 @ 900

Delco-Remy 1112661:
Breaker contact gap 0.022
Breaker arm spring tension
(measured at center
of contact) ....17-21 oz.
Cam angle ....31°-34°
Advance data is in distributor degrees and distributor rpm.
Start advance ....0-2.5 @ 300
Intermediate advance .....4-6 @ 450
Maximum advance ......11-13 @ 850

Auto-Lite IBT—4001G:
Breaker contact gap 0.020
Breaker arm spring tension
(measured at center of
contact) ....17-20 oz.
Cam angle ....36°-42°
Advance data is in distributor degrees and distributor rpm.
Start advance ....0-1 @ 210
Intermediate advance ....7 @ 420
Maximum advance ....15 @ 700

115. IGNITION TIMING. To time the ignition it is strongly recommended that a neon timing light be used. Timing procedure is as follows:

Adjust breaker contact gap to setting recommended in paragraph 114 and open inspection cover on flywheel housing. Crank engine until the "DC 1-4" mark on flywheel (DC 1 on some models) is visible in timing hole. Using white paint or chalk, mark a running timing mark on the flywheel rim below the DC mark at the exact distance recommended in the table below. NOTE: Flywheels on most tractor models are marked with scribe lines each 2½ degrees, beginning at 35 degrees BTDC and running to the DC 1 or DC 1-4 mark. These marks may be used to determine the action of distributor advance mechanism, but a painted timing index is still required for accurate setting as the timing marks are not numbered.

UB SPECIAL- UTS SPECIAL	Timing Index BTDC Inches	Degrees
Gasoline	3⅞	..
LP-Gas and Distillate	4⅛	..
5 STAR-M5-M504		
Gasoline	3⅛	25
LP-Gas	2⅞	23
M602-M604		
All		25
M670-M670 Super		
Gasoline (1200 rpm)		11
LP-Gas (1200 rpm)		10

Start engine and on all models except M670 and M670 Super, adjust engine to loaded speed as listed in paragraph 102, 103 or 104. On models M670 and M670 Super, adjust engine speed to 1200 rpm. Then, on all models, use a neon timing light focused on the flywheel rim and observe if the affixed running timing index registers with pointer at inspection port. If it does not, loosen distributor clamp bolt and turn distributor slightly until registration is obtained.

NOTE: Final setting may need to be varied slightly from listed timing to take care of variations in fuel, compression ratio, altitude and mechanical condition of engine.

116. ALTERNATOR, GENERATOR, REGULATOR AND STARTING MOTOR. Both Delco-Remy and Autolite electrical units are used. Model listings and overhaul specifications are as follows:

ALTERNATOR: DR-1100771
Field current @ 80°F.:
Amperes 2.2-2.6
Volts 12.0
Cold output @ specified voltage:
Specified volts 14.0
Amperes at rpm ....21 @ 2000
Amperes at rpm ....30 @ 5000
Rated output hot, amperes 32.0

REGULATOR: DR-1119513
Polarity .... Negative
Field relay:
Air gap 0.015
Point opening............. 0.030
Closing voltage range 3.8-7.2
Voltage regulator:
Air gap
(lower points closed) ..0.067 (1)
Upper point opening
(lower points closed) 0.014
Voltage setting:
65°F. 13.9-15.0 (1)
85°F. 13.8-14.8 (1)
105°F. 13.7-14.6 (1)
125°F. 13.5-14.4 (1)
145°F. 13.4-14.2 (1)
165°F. 13.2-14.0 (1)
185°F. 13.1-13.9 (1)

(1) When bench tested, set air gap at 0.067 as a starting point, then adjust air gap to obtain specified differ-

ence between voltage settings of upper and lower contacts. Operation on lower contacts must be 0.05-0.4 volt lower than on upper contacts. Voltage setting may be increased up to 0.3 volt to correct chronic battery undercharging or decreased up to 0.3 volt to correct battery over-charging. Temperature (ambient) is measured ¼-inch away from regulator cover and adjustment should be made only when regulator is at operating temperature.

PRECAUTIONS: Because certain components of the alternator can be damaged by procedures that will not affect a D. C. generator, the following precautions MUST be observed.

a. When installing batteries or connecting a booster battery, the negative post of battery must be grounded.

b. Never short across any terminal of the alternator or regulator.

c. Do not attempt to polarize the alternator.

d. Disconnect all battery ground straps before removing or installing any electrical unit.

e. Do not operate alternator on an open circuit and be sure all leads are properly connected before starting engine.

GENERATOR DR-1100954:
Brush spring tension..........19 oz.
Field Draw
Volts 12.0
Amperes 2.0-2.14
Output (hot)
Maximum amperes 9-11
Volts 13.8-14.2
RPM 2400

GENERATOR DR-1100314:
Brush spring tension..........28 oz.
Field Draw
Volts 12.0
Amperes 1.5-1.62
Output (Cold)
Maximum amperes 20
Volts 14.0
RPM 2300

GENERATOR DR-1100417:
Brush spring tension .... 28 oz.
Field Draw
Volts 12.0
Amperes 1.58-1.67
Output (Cold)
Maximum amperes 20
Volts 14.0
RPM 2300

GENERATOR DR-1100426 &
DR-1100432:
Brush spring tension........28 oz.
Field Draw
Volts 12.0
Amperes 1.5-1.62
Output (Cold)
Maximum amperes 25
Volts 14.0
RPM 2710

GENERATOR Auto-Lite
GJT-7101:
Brush spring tension........18-36 oz.
Field Draw
  Volts 10.0
  Amperes 2.9-3.3
Output
  Maximum amperes 25
  Volts 15.0
  RPM 2200

REGULATOR Auto-Lite
VBO 6201-L:
Cut-out Relay
  Air gap, inches 0.25
  Point gap, inches .... .015
  Closing voltage
    Range 12.4-13.3
Voltage Regulator
  Air gap, inches .... .050
  Range 14.1-14.7
  Adjust to 14.5

STARTING MOTOR DR-1107356:
Brush spring tension ....40 oz.
No load test
  Volts 11.8
  Amperes (maximum) 72
  Rpm (minimum) 6025

Resistance test
  Volts 3.5
  Amperes (minimum) 295
  Amperes (maximum) 365
STARTING MOTOR DR-1109236:
Brush spring tension........36-40 oz.
No-load test
  Volts 11.7
  Amperes (maximum) 95
  Approximate rpm 8000
Lock test
  Volts 2.8
  Amperes 570
  Torque (Ft.-Lbs.) 20
STARTING MOTOR DR-1113080:
Brush spring tension....48 oz. (min.)
No-load test
  Volts 11.5
  Amperes (maximum) 50
  Approximate rpm 6000
Lock test
  Volts 3.3
  Amperes 500
  Torque (Ft.-Lbs.) 22
STARTING MOTOR DR-1113620:
Brush spring tension....35 oz. (min.)
No-load test
  Volts 11.6

Amperes (maximum) 95
Approximate rpm 8000
Lock test
  Volts 2.2
  Amperes 600
  Torque (Ft.-Lbs.) 20
STARTING MOTOR DR-1113654:
Brush spring tension ....80 oz.
No load test
  Volts 11.6
  Amperes (maximum) 125*
  Rpm (minimum) 5900
Lock test
  Volts 2.35
  Amperes 600
  Torque (Ft.-Lbs.) 17
*Includes Solenoid
STARTING MOTOR AL-MEJ 6001:
Brush spring tension........32-40 oz.
No-load test
  Volts 10.0
  Amperes (maximum) 70
  Approximate rpm 5500
Lock test
  Volts 4.0
  Amperes 630
  Torque (Ft.-Lbs.) 21

ENGINE CLUTCH

ADJUSTMENT

Spring Loaded Type

117. Adjustment to compensate for lining wear is accomplished by adjusting the clutch pedal linkage, NOT by adjusting the position of the clutch release levers. The clutch linkage is properly adjusted when the clutch

pedal has a free travel of 1½ inches. If specified free travel cannot be obtained, renewal or relining of lined plate is indicated.

To adjust the linkage on series UB Special, vary the length of the release rod (X—Fig. MM875) by means of clevis (Y) at front end of rod. On 5-Star models, loosen the locking bolt (2—Fig. MM876) and move adjusting arm (3) down on pedal (1), until the proper adjustment is obtained, then tighten locking bolt (2). On M5, M504, M602, M604, M670 and M670 Super vary the length of release rod (Y—Fig. MM877 by means of adjusting clevis (X).

Series UTS Special Diesel

118. To adjust the clutch, remove inspection cover from clutch housing. Disengage clutch and turn the clutch plate around until the lock clip, Fig. MM878 is accessible. Loosen the retaining cap screw and slide the lock clip out of the notch. Using a bar or large screw driver, turn the clutch back plate clockwise, viewed from rear, to tighten clutch.

Fig. MM875—Typical clutch linkage adjustment for spring loaded type clutches used on series "UB Special" tractors.

Fig. MM876 — Adjust clutch pedal free travel on 5-Star tractors to 1½-inches by loosening locking bolt (2) and shifting pedal (1) on clutch arm (3).

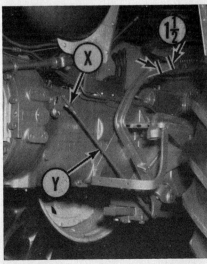

Fig. MM877 — Clutch linkage adjustment for M5 tractors. Models M504, M602, M604, M670 and M670 Super are similar.

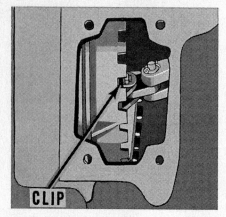

Fig. MM878 — Adjusting the over-center type clutch used on series "UTS Special" diesel tractors. Refer to text.

Fig. MM880 — Front view of transmission housing, showing the removal of clutch release bearing return springs.

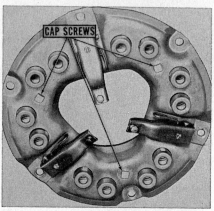

Fig. MM881 — Before removing spring loaded type clutches from flywheel, it is advisable to install three 5/16-inch cap screws as shown, to unload the pressure springs.

The adjustment is satisfactory when some effort is required to push the clutch hand lever over-center and the clutch engages with a definite snap.

Series UTS Special Non-Diesel

119. To adjust the clutch, remove the side cover on the clutch housing. Disengage the clutch; turn the clutch plate until the adjusting lock pin, shown in Fig. MM879, appears. Pull the pin out; this disengages the clutch yoke from the notch in the floating plate. Turn the yoke clockwise until the lock pin engages in the next notch of the floating plate. Engage the clutch with the hand lever. If approximately 75-85 pounds of force is

required to push the lever over center and the clutch snaps into place, the adjustment is complete.

If operation is not satisfactory, repeat the procedure by engaging the lock pin in the next notch of the floating plate until adjustment is sufficient.

NOTE: Less force will be required to fully engage clutch, as clutch plates wear. Readjust the clutch if engagement force drops below 50 pounds when measured at end of lever.

R&R AND OVERHAUL
All Models, Spring Loaded Type

120. To remove the clutch, it is first necessary to detach engine from transmission as outlined in paragraph 124.

The clutch release bearing and collar can be removed after disconnecting the return springs as shown in Fig. MM880.

Unscrew the cap screws retaining the clutch cover assembly to flywheel and remove cover assembly and lined plate. Note: Three 5/16-inch cap screws 1¼ inches long can be installed through the cover plate as shown in Fig. MM881 to unload the pressure springs prior to unbolting the assembly from flywheel. If this procedure is not used, the cover retaining cap screws must be unscrewed evenly to avoid damaging the cover plate.

To disassemble the clutch cover unit, compress the pressure springs by placing the assembly in an arbor press or

by using unloading cap screws as shown in Fig. MM881 until the release lever pins can be removed as shown in Fig. MM882. Remove the assembly from the arbor press or, if unloading cap screws were used, remove them and disassemble the remaining parts.

Inspect all parts and renew any which are damaged or show wear. Friction surface of pressure plate must be smooth, flat and free from cracks and grooves. Cover plate must not be bent, distorted, or excessively worn at drive lug openings. Inspect release lever contact screws, pivot pins and pin holes. Renew the 12 pressure springs if they are distorted, rusted, heat discolored or if they do not test 200-210 lbs. when compressed to a height of $1\frac{13}{16}$ inches.

After the unit is assembled, install and tighten the three cover to pressure plate cap screws (shown in Fig. MM881) until the dimension (A—Fig. MM883) from underside of cover plate to friction face of pressure plate is 1.020 inches. This dimension (A) must be the same all the way around the pressure plate.

With the cap screws (Fig. MM881) still in place (to retain the A setting) turn the release lever adjusting screws (S—Fig. MM883) until the distance (B) between friction face of pressure plate and release bearing contacting surface of each release lever is 2.599-2.629 inches. Dimension (B) must be

Fig. MM879. — Adjusting the over-center type clutch used on series "UTS Special" non-diesel. Pull lock pin out as far as possible; then rotate yoke clockwise (up, when viewed through clutch compartment opening) until lock pin engages in next notch.

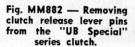

Fig. MM882 — Removing clutch release lever pins from the "UB Special" series clutch.

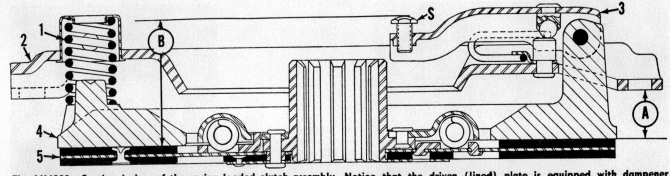

Fig. MM883—Sectional view of the spring loaded clutch assembly. Notice that the driven (lined) plate is equipped with dampener springs on certain models.

A. Position of pressure plate in relation to cover plate which must be maintained when adjusting the release lever height (B).

S. Adjusting screw
1. Pressure spring
2. Cover plate

3. Release lever
4. Pressure plate
5. Driven (lined) plate

identical within 0.005 for all three levers.

After the release levers are adjusted install cover assembly to flywheel and remove the three cover to pressure plate cap screws.

Series UTS Diesel

121. The procedure for removing the clutch is evident after detaching engine from transmission case (refer to paragraph 124). The clutch can then be disassembled as shown in Fig. MM-884. Clean and check all parts for wear. Renew bushings (10) in sleeve (9) if worn, check the cams (12) and cam blocks (4) in pressure plate (3) for wear. Check condition of return springs (17). Check friction surface of pressure plate (3) and renew if warped, grooved or heat checked. Check splines in hub of friction disc (18) and the friction facings. Check threads on adjusting ring (5) and back plate (2) for burrs; clean threads if necessary. Check links and pins for wear.

When reassembling, reverse the disassembly procedure and be sure return springs (17) are properly installed. Before assembling clutch to flywheel, check flywheel for heat checks and reface or renew if necessary. Adjust the clutch as outlined in paragraph 118.

Series UTS Special Non-Diesel

122. To R&R and overhaul the clutch, it is first necessary to detach engine from transmission as outlined in paragraph 124.

Disconnect the clutch actuating linkage by removing the cotter key and pulling the clevis pin out of the shifter fork shaft arm (7—Fig. MM-885). Then pry the lock washer lip away from the clutch shaft nut and remove the nut (2). Disconnect lubrication tube (4) from shifter ring (22).

Remove the clutch assembly from the shaft with a suitable puller. If the

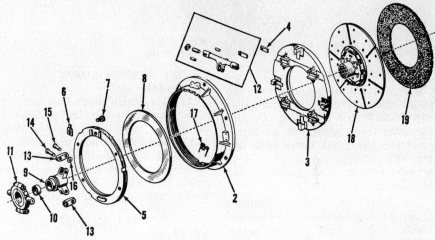

Fig. MM884—Exploded view of clutch used on series "UTS Special" diesel tractors.

2. Back plate
3. Pressure plate
4. Cam blocks
5. Adjusting ring
6. Ring lock clip
7. Lock screw

8. Plate
9. Release sleeve
10. Bushings
11. Shifter ring
12. Cam shaft
13. Link

14. Pin
15. Pin
16. Pin washer
17. Return spring
18. Friction disc
19. Friction linings

clutch shaft Woodruff key catches on the throwout collar, turn the shaft until the key is visible; then use a punch to drive rear of key into keyway (Fig. MM886). The clutch assembly can then be removed easily.

At the rear of the clutch housing is a transmission brake, which stops the transmission gears when the clutch lever is held firmly in rear

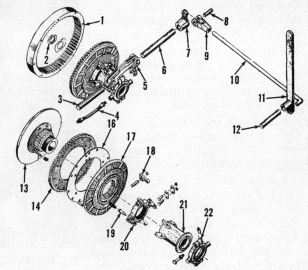

Fig. MM885 — Exploded view of over-center clutch used on series "UTS Special" non-diesel tractors.

1. Clutch drive ring
2. Shaft nut
3. Shaft
4. Lubrication hose
5. Clutch fork
6. Shaft
7. Clutch arm
8. Pin
9. Clevis
10. Rod
11. Clutch lever
12. Lever shaft
13. Back plate
14. Driving plate
16. Lining
17. Floating plate
18. Finger
19. Lock pin
20. Adjusting yoke
21. Sliding sleeve
22. Shifter ring

Fig. MM886 — Clutch shaft key and shifter fork on "UTS Special" non-diesel tractor. Refer to text.

Fig. MM887 — Partially disassembled view of clutch shaft on models with over-center clutch, showing transmission brake and associated parts.

1. Thrust plate
2. Snap ring
3. Spacer
4. Clutch shaft
5. Lube line

(disengaged) position.

If repairs are necessary, remove the clutch shifter fork, thrust washer (3—Fig. MM887) and snap ring (2). Pull the brake thrust plate from the clutch shaft and renew the thrust plate lining. When reassembling use care to prevent getting oil or grease on the new lining.

The shifter ring (22—Fig. MM885) is separated by removing the two connecting bolts. Check the bronze insert in each bearing half for excessive wear and renew if necessary.

To remove the clutch lining, pull the yoke lock pin (19) out of the floating plate notch and unscrew the yoke assembly (20) while holding the lock pin in the disengaged position. Remove the worn clutch plate linings (16) and install new linings. When installing the rivets, alternate rivets so that adjacent rivet heads face in opposite directions. Make certain rivet heads are seated at the bottom of the countersunk holes and are well below the surface of the linings.

When reassembling the clutch, use care to prevent oil or grease spillage on the clutch lining. If the actuating fingers (18), pins or links are worn, they should be renewed.

Reassemble the shifter ring on the clutch and tighten the connecting bolts until a slight drag is felt when the unit is turned.

Reinstall the clutch assembly on the clutch shaft by driving it into position with a heavy mallet. Make certain the clutch keyway in throwout sleeve and clutch hub, lines up with the clutch shaft key. Install the shaft nut (2) and lock it with the lipped lockwasher.

CLUTCH SHAFT
All Models

123. The clutch shaft is a part of main transmission on UB Special and all models with over-center clutch; and a part of "Ampli-Torc" unit or Reverse Shuttle on other models with spring loaded clutch. Refer to appropriate transmission section for overhaul procedures on clutch shaft.

TRACTOR SPLIT
All Models

A general procedure for splitting the tractor is given in the following paragraph. Minor differences in construction are obvious after an examination of the unit.

124. Remove hood and disconnect fuel lines, oil lines, control rods, wires, cables and steering shaft. Block up engine and transmission separately, using a traveling chain hoist or some other device for one section so that it can be moved independently from the óther section. Remove bolts holding engine and main frame to the transmission housing; then move transmission and rear axle unit away from engine and engine frame unit, as shown in Fig. MM888.

Fig. MM888—Typical Minneapolis-Moline tractor split. Notice long pilot studs in transmission housing to facilitate reconnecting the units.

"AMPLI-TORC"

"Ampli-Torc" is a planetary two-speed transmission mechanism installed forward of the regular transmission, and equipped with a mechanically operated multiple disc clutch, enabling the tractor to be operated in a direct or underdrive ratio. Shifting can be done independently of the main engine clutch while the tractor is in motion. "Ampli-Torc" is standard equipment on all 5-Star, M5, M504, M602, M604, M670 and M670 Super series tractors, except some industrial models which have the reverse shuttle unit as an alternate option.

CLUTCH

All Models So Equipped

125. ADJUSTMENT. When the "Ampli-Torc" control lever is pushed forward to the direct (clutch engaged) position, the clutch should lock with a distinct snap, and a reasonably hard push (25-30 lbs. on M670 Super model and 55-60 lbs. on all other models) should be required at the end of the control lever. If less than 35 lbs. on M670 or 14 lbs. on other models is required to engage the clutch, pull lever rearward to underdrive position, remove the small cover plate from the right side of the transmission housing as shown in Fig. MM889 and turn the clutch assembly until the spring loaded lock pin is visible through the cover opening. Depress the lock pin and turn the notched adjusting ring clockwise until pin engages the next notch. Recheck the adjustment and repeat as necessary until the proper adjustment is obtained.

126. REMOVE AND REINSTALL. To remove the Ampli-Torc clutch, first detach (split) the engine from transmission housing as outlined in paragraph 124 and proceed as follows:

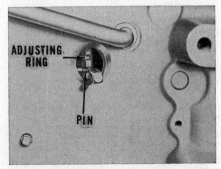

Fig. MM889—To adjust Ampli-Torc clutch, remove cover as shown and turn adjusting ring through opening in housing. See text.

Remove fuel tank, instrument panel, steering support and associated parts from top of transmission case and unbolt and remove planetary top cover. Remove engine clutch release bearing and drive out the pins retaining clutch release fork to the cross shafts. Withdraw fork and shafts. Move the Ampli-Torc control lever to the direct drive position and unbolt and remove the transmission input shaft cover from the front wall of the Ampli-Torc housing. Drive out the two roll pins retaining the shifter forks (31—Fig. MM890) or (21—Fig. MM895) to the control lever and withdraw the lever and forks. Clutch unit and input shaft (34—Fig. MM891) can then be withdrawn from the transmission housing as a unit.

When installing the clutch, reverse the removal procedure, making sure the bronze thrust washer (26—Fig. MM890) or (1—Fig. MM895) is in place before installing the clutch unit. Renew seal (39—Fig. MM891) if its condition is questionable. When installing the cover, use a suitable seal sleeve or shim stock to avoid damaging the seal lip on the input shaft splines. Tighten the cover cap screws securely, mount a dial indicator as shown in Fig. MM892 and check the clutch shaft end play by moving the planetary unit back and forth with a pry bar. If the end play is not between the limits of 0.008 and 0.015, remove the cover and add or remove shims (38—Fig. MM891) as required. Note: On agricultural models of 5-Star series, Ampli-Torc end play is controlled by means of shims located between flange of cover (40), and the transmission housing in the position shown for gasket (41). The proper thickness shim pack in either of the two locations will control the end play. Adjust the Ampli-Torc clutch as outlined in paragraph 125.

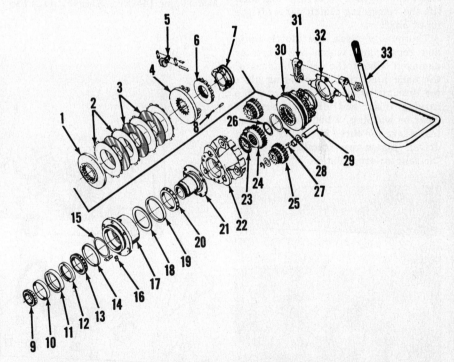

Fig. MM890—Exploded view of Ampli-Torc clutch, gear set and associated parts used on all models except M670 and M670 Super.

1. Back plate	12. Adjusting nut	23. Thrust washer
2. Driving plate	13. Bearing cone	24. Sun gear
3. Driven plate	14. Bearing cup	25. Planet gear
4. Floating plate	15. Washer	26. Thrust washer
5. Lever	16. "Sprag" assy.	27. Bearing
6. Adjusting ring	17. Cam cage	28. Snap ring
7. Sliding sleeve	18. Washer	29. Shaft
8. Lock pin	19. Bearing cup	30. Clutch assembly
9. Bearing cone	20. Bearing cone	31. Fork
10. Bearing cup	21. Hub	32. Shifting ring
11. Spacer	22. Planet carrier	33. Lever

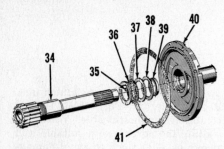

Fig. MM891—Exploded view of input shaft cover, input shaft and associated parts used on tractors equipped with Ampli-Torc transmission.

34. Input shaft
35. Thrust washer
36. Thrust bearing
37. Thrust washer
38. Shim
39. Oil seal
40. Cover
41. Gasket

127. OVERHAUL. With the input shaft and clutch assembly removed as outlined in paragraph 126, remove shim pack (38—Fig. MM891), washer (37), bearing (36) and washer (35) from the shaft. Refer to Figs. MM890 or MM895 and remove pins retaining the throwout levers to the floating clutch plate. Lift off the shifting ring and sliding sleeve. Depress the spring loaded lock pin and completely unscrew the notched adjusting ring, then lift the remaining clutch parts off the input shaft.

Thoroughly clean the clutch parts and renew any which are worn or damaged. Check the friction faces of the back plate and the floating plate for scoring or heat checks, and the driving discs and driven discs for wear or warping. When reassembling, make sure the three internally splined driven plates are installed between the four driving plates.

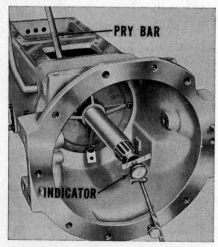

Fig. MM892 — To measure the clutch shaft end play on models equipped with Ampli-Torc, attach a dial indicator as shown and move upper shaft back and forth with pry bar while noting end play.

Fig. MM893 — When reassembling Ampli-Torc planetary assembly, make certain the oil grooves in planet pinions converge on shaft center as shown at (G).

PLANET GEARS, SUN GEARS AND OVER-RUNNING CLUTCH

All Models So Equipped

128. REMOVE AND REINSTALL. To remove the planetary gear cage and over-running clutch, first remove the Ampli-Torc clutch as outlined in paragraph 126, remove the transmission top cover and proceed as follows:

Turn the planet carrier (22—Fig. MM890) or (4—Fig. MM895) until the

Fig. MM894—On all models except M670 and M670 Super, over-running clutch rollers and springs must be properly assembled as shown at (16).

cut-out groove in carrier is aligned with one of the cap screws retaining bearing cage to transmission case wall and remove the cap screw. Continue the procedure until all of the bearing cage cap screws have been removed. Withdraw the planet carrier, bearing cage and cam cage as a unit from the transmission case.

When reinstalling the unit, make sure the oil hole in the cam cage is up, and tighten the bearing cage retaining cap screws securely. Install

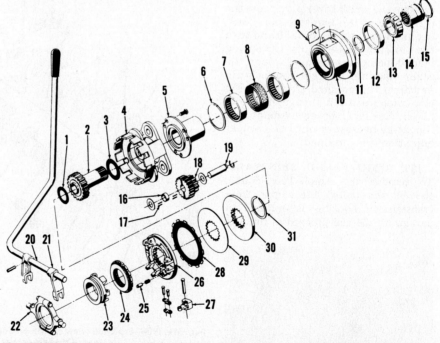

Fig. MM895—Exploded view of Ampli-Torc clutch, gear set and associated parts used on model M670 Super.

1. Thrust washer
2. Sun gear
3. Thrust washer
4. Planet carrier
5. Carrier hub
6. Retaining ring
7. Bearing
8. Over-running clutch
9. Oil deflector
10. Cage
11. Thrust washer
12. Bearing cup
13. Bearing cone
14. Collar
15. Snap ring
16. Spacer
17. Needle rollers
18. Planetary gear
19. Shaft
20. Lever
21. Fork
22. Shifting ring
23. Sleeve
24. Adjusting ring
25. Lock pin
26. Floating plate
27. Lever
28. Driving plate (4 used)
29. Driven plate (3 used)
30. Back plate
31. Snap ring

the Ampli-Torc clutch as outlined in paragraph 126 and adjust the unit as in paragraph 125.

129. **OVERHAUL.** On all models except M670 and M670 Super, proceed as follows: With the planetary gear assembly and over-running clutch removed as outlined in paragraph 128, remove adjusting nut (12—Fig. MM-890) using a suitable spanner wrench, and withdraw cam cage (17) and the carrier bearings from clutch hub (21). Be careful not to lose any of the "sprag" clutch springs (16) and rollers as the two units are separated. Unbolt hub (21) from planet carrier (22). Remove the snap rings from planet gear shafts (29), push out the shafts and withdraw planet gears (25), being careful not to lose the enclosed loose needle bearings (27), spacer washers or spacer. Remove sun gear (24) and thrust washer (23). Clutch hub (21), cam cage (17) and the bearings and spacers (9 through 20) are only available in a complete carrier assembly, however the "sprag" rollers and springs (16) are available and can be renewed if the remainder of the assembly is usable. When assembling the planetary gear assembly,

use a light grease to hold the loose needle bearings in place and align the oil grooves of the three planet gears as shown at (G—Fig. MM893).

Install the "sprag" rollers and springs as shown in Fig. MM894, and, reversing the disassembly procedure install clutch hub (21) into cam cage (17), and bearings. Rotate clutch hub in a clockwise direction as the two units are pushed together, using very little pressure, to avoid losing or damaging the sprag rollers and springs. Reinstall nut (12) and tighten to provide a very slight rotational drag to the tapered roller bearings, then check the over-running clutch assembly to see that it turns freely and does not bind. Stake the nut (12) to clutch hub then reassemble the over-running clutch unit to planet carrier (22). Install the assembled planetary unit as outlined in paragraph 128.

On models M670 and M670 Super, proceed as follows: With the planetary gear assembly and over-running clutch removed as outlined in paragraph 128, separate planet carrier and hub assembly from the over-running clutch cage (10—Fig. MM895). Unbolt and remove hub (5) from planet car-

rier (4), then remove shafts (19) and lift out planetary gears (18) with washers, needle rollers (17) and spacers (16). To service the over-running clutch, remove retaining rings (6) and press bearings (7) and over-running clutch (8) from cage (10). Check all parts and renew as necessary. Planetary gears (18) are available only as a matched set.

When installing the needle rollers (17) in gears (18), use a heavy-bodied, non-fibrous grease to hold rollers in place. Assemble sun gear (2), gears (18) and shafts (19) to carrier (4), making certain that oil grooves are aligned as shown at (G—Fig. MM893). Bolt hub (5—Fig. MM895) to carrier and tighten bolts to a torque of 23 ft.-lbs. Wire each pair of bolts together. Install bearings (7) and over-running clutch (8) in cage (10) and lubricate bearings and clutch with transmission oil. Insert the hub into the over-running clutch assembly by applying a light pressure and rotating hub in a clockwise direction. Install the assembly with lubrication hole in cage to the top and tighten the retaining cap screws to a torque of 23 ft.-lbs.

REVERSE SHUTTLE UNIT

Industrial tractor models in 5-Star series are optionally equipped with a reverse shuttle unit enabling the operator to reverse the direction of travel in any transmission gear. The reverse shuttle unit consists of a planetary reversing unit and a sliding gear shaft which reverses the direction of rotation of the main transmission as well as the differential and final drive.

R&R AND OVERHAUL

Tractors So Equipped

130. To remove the reverse shuttle unit, first split the tractor between the engine and transmission case as outlined in paragraph 124 and proceed as follows. Disconnect clutch release bearing lubrication line and remove release bearing. Drift out the roll pins retaining clutch release fork to cross shafts and remove fork and shafts. Unbolt and remove input shaft cover

(1—Fig. MM896), then disconnect link rod (2—Fig. MM897) from fork shaft (4), drive out the pins retaining fork levers (6) to shaft and remove forks and shaft. Clutch shaft (9), sliding coupling (12), forward gear (14) reverse gear (15) and spur gear (17) may now be withdrawn from the transmission case together with thrust washers (13 and 16). If sliding coupling (12) is to be removed from clutch shaft, first remove detent ball, spring and plug (11), then separate

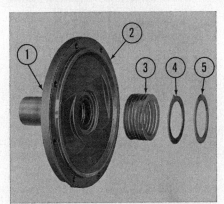

Fig. MM896 — Input shaft cover and associated parts used on tractors equipped with industrial Reverse Shuttle Unit.

1. Cover
2. Gasket
3. Shim pack
4. Tab washer
5. Thrust bearing

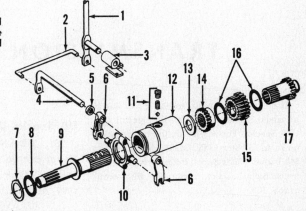

Fig. MM897 — Exploded view of Reverse Shuttle shaft and associated parts.

1. Control lever
2. Link
3. Bracket
4. Shifter shaft
5. Oil seal
6. Shifter fork
7. Tab washer
8. Thrust bearing
9. Input shaft
10. Shifting ring
11. Detent assembly
12. Sliding coupling
13. Thrust washer
14. Forward gear
15. Reverse gear
16. Thrust washers
17. Spur gear

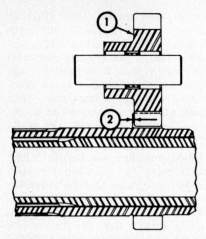

Fig. MM898 — When installing gear cage and spur gear, make sure forward edge of spur gear teeth (2) are 0.020-0.035 forward of narrow pinion (1) in gear cage.

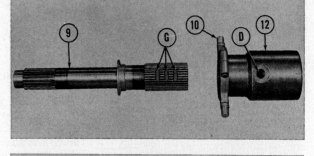

Fig. MM899 — When assembling sliding coupling to input shaft, make sure detent hole (D) aligns with detent grooves (G) in shaft. See Fig. MM897 for legend.

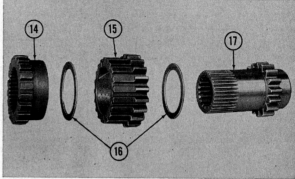

Fig. MM900 — Reverse gear (15) idles on spur gear shaft (17) between the two thrust washers. Forward gear (14) is splined to spur gear shaft at forward end.

Fig. MM901 — To disassemble gear cage, remove set screws (S) and press out shafts retaining wide pinions (1) and narrow pinions (2).

the units. When reassembling, make sure the hole for the detent assembly is centered over the grooves machined in the clutch shaft splines.

Unbolt and remove planetary gear cage from front of transmission case. The four shuttle unit pinions rotate on needle bearings and their shafts are retained in the cage by set screws. See Fig. MM901.

To assemble the unit, reverse the disassembly procedure, tighten the gear cage retaining cap screws to a torque of 25-30 ft.-lbs., and check the end play of the main transmission upper shaft. If the shaft end play exceeds 0.004, adjust as outlined in paragraph 139. Reinstall spur gear (17—Fig. MM897) and check to make sure that front edge of spur gear teeth is 0.020-0.035 forward of the teeth of the narrow pinions as shown in Fig. MM898. Shims (3—Fig. MM-896) are available in a thickness of 0.006 to obtain the recommended

clutch shaft end play of 0.008-0.012. After the remainder of the unit is installed, measure the end float with a

dial indicator, and add or remove shims to obtain the recommended end play.

TRANSMISSION AND CONNECTIONS

This section applies to the Five Speed transmission used in series UB Special and UTS Special. For service on the transmission used in 5 Star, M5, M504, M602, M604, M670 and M670 Super tractors, refer to the transmission section beginning with paragraph 137.

OVERHAUL
UB Special-UTS Special

131. **TRANSMISSION COVER.** Cover can be removed after removing the fuel tank, instrument panel, battery and battery shelf. Remove cap

screws holding cover to transmission case and lift off cover. Reinstallation is reverse of removal.

132. **SHIFTER RAILS AND FORKS.** Rails and forks can be removed after removing transmission cover, and four cap screws (C—Fig. MM903) retain-

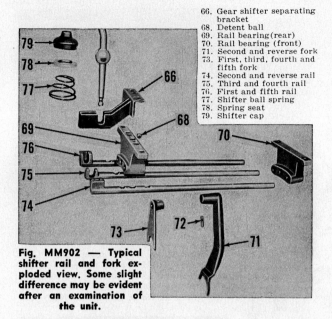

66. Gear shifter separating bracket
68. Detent ball
69. Rail bearing (rear)
70. Rail bearing (front)
71. Second and reverse fork
73. First, third, fourth and fifth fork
74. Second and reverse rail
75. Third and fourth rail
76. First and fifth rail
77. Shifter ball spring
78. Spring seat
79. Shifter cap

Fig. MM902 — Typical shifter rail and fork exploded view. Some slight difference may be evident after an examination of the unit.

ing shifter rail bearings to transmission housing. Detent balls and springs can be removed after removing gear shift separating bracket (66). Roll pins (R) prevent overshifting. Refer also to Fig. MM902 for exploded view of typical shifter mechanism.

133. SLIDING GEAR (CLUTCH) SHAFT. The sliding gear (clutch) shaft (23—Fig. MM905) can be removed after "splitting" the tractor as outlined in paragraph 124, removing clutch (over center type) as in paragraph 121 or 122; and removing shifter rails and forks as in paragraph 132. Remove clutch shaft front bearing housing, then bump shaft forward as shown in Fig. MM906 until bearing (22—Fig. MM905) is free from housing bore. Lift shaft gears out top opening as shaft is removed.

Bearing (22) can be pressed from shaft after removing snap ring (21). To remove gear (24), first remove snap ring (25). Oil seal (20) should be installed in bearing housing (18) with seal lip to rear.

When reassembling, reverse the disassembly procedure. Install bearing housing (18) and gasket (19) with oil slot in housing and drain hole in gasket to the bottom. Use Permatex or other suitable sealant on cap screw threads when installing bearing housing (18).

134. UPPER COUNTERSHAFT. The upper countershaft (38—Fig. MM905) can be removed after removing clutch shaft as outlined in paragraph 133 and the power take-off output shaft unit as in paragraph 174.

Working through clutch compartment, remove front bearing housing (41—Fig. MM907). Working through pto housing opening, bend down tabs on locking plate (30—Fig. MM908) and remove cap screws and retaining plate (31); then, using a long drift, bump upper shaft forward out of housing and rear bearing. Lift the gears (33, 35 and 37—Fig. MM905)

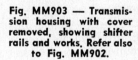

Fig. MM903 — Transmission housing with cover removed, showing shifter rails and works. Refer also to Fig. MM902.

C. Cap screws
R. Roll pins

Fig. MM904 — Transmission input (clutch) shaft with gears installed. Refer to Fig. MM905 for legend.

and spacers (34 and 36) out top opening as shaft is withdrawn from front.

Front bearing (39) will be removed with shaft, and rear bearing (32) will remain in housing, as unit is disassembled. Rear bearing can be bumped from housing wall and front bearing pressed from shaft, if renewal is indicated.

If transmission has been completely disassembled, main drive bevel pinion must be reinstalled as outlined in paragraph 136, before upper countershaft is reinstalled. Reinstall upper countershaft by reversing the disassembly procedure, using Fig. MM909 as a guide for correct installation of gears and spacers.

NOTE: If lower countershaft is in place when reinstalling upper countershaft, place the constant mesh gear (33) in left, rear corner of transmission compartment before positioning double gear (35) on shaft. The gear cannot be installed from above after double gear is in position.

135. LOWER COUNTERSHAFT. The lower countershaft (7—Fig. MM905), can be removed after splitting tractor as outlined in paragraph 124, removing top cover (paragraph 131), shifter rails and forks (paragraph 132), pto output shaft (paragraph 174) and belt pulley unit or transmission

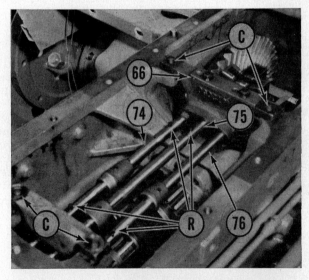

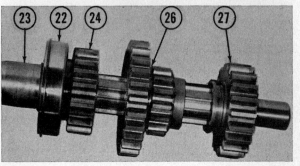

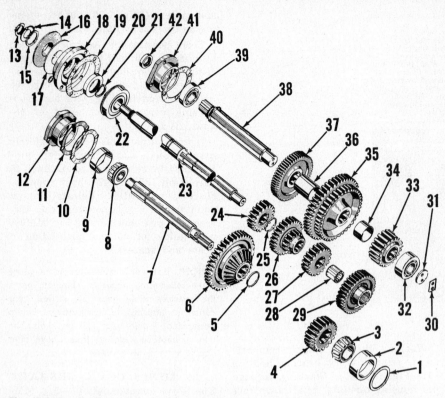

Fig. MM907 — Upper countershaft (38) and bearing (39) can be bumped forward out of housing after removing clutch shaft, front bearing housing (41) and retaining plate as shown in Fig. MM908.

Fig. MM905—Exploded view of transmission gears, shafts and associated parts used on models equipped with over-center clutch. Main drive bevel pinion is not shown.

1. Shim	15. Snap ring	29. Differential drive gear
2. Bearing cup	16. Brake plate	30. Lock clip
3. Bearing cone	17. Brake lining	31. Retaining plate
4. Second-Reverse gear	18. Bearing housing	32. Bearing
5. Snap ring	19. Gasket	33. Constant mesh gear
6. Constant mesh gear	20. Oil seal	34. Spacer
7. Lower countershaft	21. Snap ring	35. Double gear
8. Bearing cone	22. Bearing	36. Spacer
9. Bearing cup	23. Clutch shaft	37. Fourth gear
10. Shim	24. Constant mesh gear	38. Upper countershaft
11. Gasket	25. Snap ring	39. Bearing
12. Bearing housing	26. Double gear	40. Gasket
13. Lock nut	27. Third-Fifth gear	41. Bearing housing
14. Lock washer	28. Pilot bearing	42. Oil seal

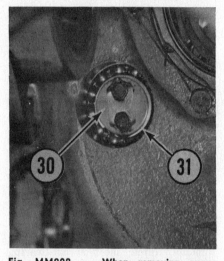

side cover plate. If lower countershaft only, is to be removed, it is not necessary to remove clutch shaft or upper countershaft. Proceed as follows:

Working through front of transmission housing, remove lower countershaft bearing housing (12). Save shim pack (10); shims control bearing preload. Working through belt pulley or side covering opening, unseat snap ring (5) from its groove at rear of constant mesh gear (6) and move snap ring rearward on shaft as shown in Fig. MM910. If a spacer (P—Fig. MM911) is not available, procure a piece of 2⅛-inch heavy

Fig. MM908 — When removing upper countershaft, work through pto output shaft opening, bend down tabs on locking plate (30) and remove cap screws and retaining plate (31). Refer also to Fig. MM907.

walled pipe, 5 7/16-inches long, split the pipe lengthwise and position on shaft as shown, using wire or cord to hold spacer in position. With spacer in position and working through pto out-

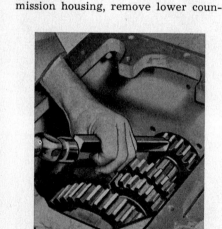

Fig. MM906—Clutch shaft can be bumped forward using a soft drift and hammer as shown, after removing front bearing housing.

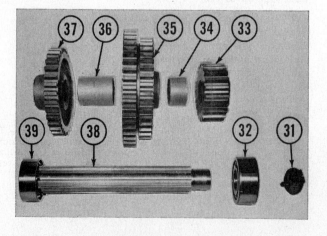

Fig. MM909 — Upper countershaft and associated parts showing proper sequence of assembly. Refer to Fig. MM905 for legend.

Fig. MM910 — When removing lower countershaft, unseat snap ring (5) from groove (G) and move rearward on shaft. Refer to text.

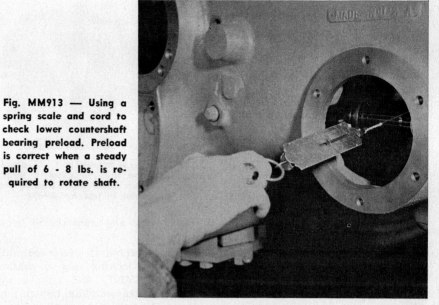

Fig. MM913 — Using a spring scale and cord to check lower countershaft bearing preload. Preload is correct when a steady pull of 6 - 8 lbs. is required to rotate shaft.

Fig. MM911 — A pipe spacer (P) will assist in removing lower countershaft rear bearing cone during shaft removal. Refer to text.

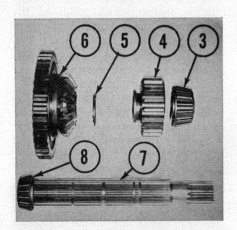

Fig. MM912 — Lower countershaft and associated parts showing proper sequence of assembly. Late parts are shown. Early tractors were similar except for number of splines on shaft and gears. Refer to Fig. MM905 for legend.

put shaft housing opening, bump the lower countershaft forward until rear bearing cone (3—Fig. MM912) is free on shaft. Withdraw shaft through front of housing while lifting gears and bearings out through top opening.

Shims (10—Fig. MM905) control preload of lower countershaft bearings. Shims (1) control backlash of belt pulley bevel gears, if a belt pulley unit is used. Adding or removing shims (1) will affect bearing preload. If rear bearing cup (2) is removed, reinstall using the same number of 0.006 shims (1) as were removed. Lower countershaft bearing preload is correct when 6-8 in.-lbs. of torque is required to rotate the shaft. Preload can be checked using a spring scale and working through side opening as shown in Fig. MM913. Proceed as follows:

Reinstall the shaft and gears by reversing the removal procedure, using Fig. MM912 as a guide. Make sure constant mesh gear (6) is positioned in front of upper countershaft forward gear if upper countershaft is not removed. Bump lower countershaft rearward until rear bearing cone (3) is seated against shaft shoulder, then reinstall front bearing housing using the removed gasket and shim pack or new plastic shims of the same thickness.

NOTE: On late models, plastic shims are color coded and a gasket is not used. Plastic shims can be used on early models. Color code is as follows: Red-0.002; green-0.003; brown-0.010.

To check the rolling torque, first make sure that neither gear is meshed with any other gear in transmission. If clutch shaft has not been removed, it may be necessary to unseat snap ring (25—Fig. MM905) and move gear (24) rearward on clutch shaft. Wrap a light cord around lower countershaft as shown in Fig. MM913, attach a pull scale and check the pull required to KEEP the shaft turning. Pull should be 6 to 8 lbs.; if it is not, add or remove shims (10—Fig. MM905) as required. Use Permatex or similar sealer on cap screw threads when permanently installing front bearing housing (12).

136. **MAIN DRIVE BEVEL PINION AND SHAFT.** Main drive bevel pinion and shaft, differential drive gear and bearing cage assembly (Fig. MM-914) can be removed after splitting tractor as outlined in paragraph 124, removing clutch shaft as in paragraph 133 and upper countershaft as in paragraph 134.

Remove safety wire and cap screws retaining bearing cage (42) to transmission housing wall. A half-moon box-wrench is best suited for this

40. Drive gear
41. Bearing cone
42. Bearing cage
43. Bearing cone
44. Bevel pinion
96. Bearing cup
97. Bearing cup
98. Adjusting nut

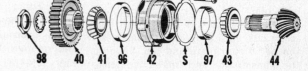

Fig. MM914 — Main drive bevel pinion and associated parts used on UB Special and UTS Special.

Fig. MM915 — To adjust the bearings or disassemble bevel pinion shaft (P), bend down tabs on locking washer (W) and turn nut (N). Refer to text.

Fig. MM916 — A suitable bolt (B), double nutted, can be used to adapt a torque wrench to adjust bevel pinion bearing preload. Refer to text for details.

Fig. MM917—When installing bevel pinion assembly, lube reservoir (R) must be uppermost as shown.

operation. The complete assembly (shaft, gears and bearing) can be withdrawn forward and out of transmission housing.

Pinion (44) and ring gear are available only as matched pairs, and can be identified as such by etched numbers on both pinion and gear. Do not discard shims (S) located between bearing cage and transmission housing.

To disassemble the removed unit, bend down locking tabs on washer (W—Fig. MM915) and remove nut (N). When reassembling, tighten pinion nut (N) to provide a rolling torque of 110-115 inch-lbs. for the shaft bearings. Rolling torque can be checked with a torque wrench, using a suitable bolt (B) as shown in Fig. MM-916, or with a string and pull scale. Bend locking washer (W—Fig. MM-915) as shown, when adjustment is completed.

Reinstall the unit so that lube reservoir (R—Fig. MM917) is uppermost as shown, using the same number of shims (S—Fig. MM914) as were removed, to maintain the correct mesh position.

NOTE: If main drive bevel ring gear and pinion are renewed, mesh position (cone point) must be readjusted as outlined in paragraph 148.

TRANSMISSION

NOTE: This section applies to the five speed gear transmission used on 5-Star, M5, M504, M602, M604, M670 and M670 Super tractors, usually in combination with the "Ampli-Torc" range unit covered in paragraph 125 through 129. For service on the transmission used in UB Special and UTS Special, refer to the transmission section beginning with paragraph 131.

REMOVE AND REINSTALL

5 Star-M5-M504-M602-M604-M670-M670 Super

137. To remove the transmission assembly from tractor, first detach (split) engine from transmission housing as outlined in paragraph 124, and proceed as follows: Disconnect and unclip tubing and wiring from transmission housing. Unbolt and remove both platform assemblies and disconnect brake adjusters and clutch rod so pedals will drop down and clear the pedal stop plate and pin. Support the transmission and final drive housing separately, then unbolt and separate the housings.

OVERHAUL

5 Star-M5-M504-M602-M604-M670-M670 Super

138. **SHIFTER SHAFTS AND FORKS.** To remove the transmission shifter shafts and forks, first drain the hydraulic system, transmission and final drive housings and disconnect the power steering oil lines. Remove both platform assemblies, and disconnect and unclip tubing and wiring from transmission housing. Disconnect brake adjusters and clutch rod so the pedals will drop down and clear the pedal stop plate and pin. Support both halves of tractor separately, then unbolt and split the transmission from the final drive housing.

On all models except M670 and M670 Super, remove the cap screws retaining the transmission top cover to the transmission, lift off the cover and remove the detent springs (21—Fig. MM918) and balls (20) from vertical bores in transmission housing. Slide the shifter shafts forward until the detent ball grooves at front of each shaft are inside the shaft bores in transmission housing. Drift out the roll pins retaining the shifter forks and lugs to the shifter shafts, pull the shifter shafts rearward out of the transmission case and lift out the forks and lugs.

When reassembling, use Fig. MM-918 as guide for proper location of parts and when installing the fork and lug retaining roll pins, slide the shifter shafts forward in the transmission housing bores to provide support for the shafts when the pins are bumped in place.

On models M670 and 670 Super, unbolt and remove the transmission top cover assembly. Position the shifter shafts so that detent ball grooves at rear of shafts are inside the shaft bores in transmission case. Drive out the roll pins retaining the shifter forks and lugs to the shafts. Pull the shifter shafts rearward out of the transmission case and lift out the forks and lugs. CAUTION: Detent balls (18—

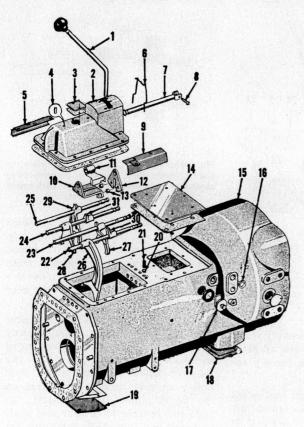

Fig. MM918 — Transmission shifter mechanism, transmission housing and associated parts used on models 5-Star, M5, M504, M602 and M604.

1. Shifter lever
2. Top cover
3. Inspection cover
4. Stop pin
5. Guard
6. Lever spring
7. Shifting rod
8. Pin
9. Guard
10. Quadrant
11. Bracket
12. Quadrant
13. Spacer
14. Planetary cover
15. Transmission housing
16. Plug
17. Adjusting cover
18. Inspection cover
19. Rear cover
20. Detent ball
21. Detent spring
22. Shifter shaft
23. Shifter shaft
24. Shifter shaft
25. Shifter shaft
26. 1st & 5th fork
27. 2nd & 3rd fork
28. 4th speed fork
29. Reverse fork
30. Shifter lug
31. Shifter lug

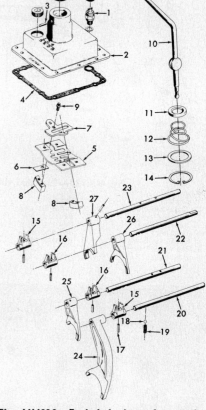

Fig. MM919—Exploded view of transmission shifter mechanism used on models M670 and M670 Super.

1. Neutral start switch	16. Short lug
2. Top cover	17. Roll pin
3. Pin	18. Detent ball
4. Gasket	19. Detent spring
5. Guide plate	20. 1st & 5th shifter shaft
6. Lock plate	21. 2nd & 4th shifter shaft
7. Upper guide	22. 3rd shifter shaft
8. Lower guide	23. Reverse shifter shaft
9. Bolt	24. 1st & 5th fork
10. Shift lever	25. 2nd & 4th fork
11. Spring retainer	26. 3rd fork
12. Spring	27. Reverse fork
13. Spring retainer	
14. Snap ring	
15. Long lug	

Fig. MM919) and springs (19) are located under each shifter shaft in the vertical bores in transmission housing. When withdrawing each shaft, use care to prevent ball and spring from flying out or falling into the gear case.

When reassembling, use Fig. MM919 as a guide for proper location of parts. When installing the fork and lug retaining roll pins, make certain the detent ball grooves are inside the shaft bores in transmission case. This will provide the proper support for the shafts when the roll pins are bumped into place.

139. SLIDING GEAR (UPPER) SHAFT. To remove the sliding gear shaft (6—Fig. MM920 or MM926), first remove the transmission assembly from tractor as outlined in paragraph 137, then remove the transmission case top covers and the shifter shafts and forks. Remove the Ampli-Torc clutch as outlined in paragraph 126 and the planetary gear unit and over-running clutch as in paragraph 128, or the Reverse Shuttle unit as outlined in paragraph 130.

On all models, remove lock clip (1 —Fig. MM920 or MM926) then unscrew and remove the sliding gear shaft bearing adjustment nut (2). Refer also to Fig. MM921. Using a drift punch against the rear bearing inner race as shown in Fig. MM922,

bump the bearing rearward. Turn the shaft and again bump the bearing cone rearward. Continue this procedure until the bearing cup and cone are removed. Move the sliding gear shaft assembly toward right side of transmission case as far as possible, remove the reverse idler gear shaft retaining set screw and push the reverse idler gear shaft forward and out of the transmission case. Lift out the reverse idler gear.

Note: It is not absolutely necessary to remove the reverse idler gear to permit removal of the sliding gear shaft, however considerable time will be saved by doing so.

On all models except M670 and M670 Super, using a pair of right angle Tru-Arc snap ring pliers, disengage the snap ring (18—Fig. MM-920) from the groove in front of the bevel pinion (countershaft) third speed gear (20). Move the snap ring and the third speed gear forward on the bevel pinion shaft as far as possible, then lift the sliding gear (upper) shaft and gears out through top opening in transmission housing.

Place the removed unit in a suitable press and remove the front bearing cone. Remove shaft from press and withdraw the second and third sliding gear (10). Remove snap ring (9) and withdraw the third speed gear (7).

Inside diameter of the third speed gear bushing (8) is 2.113-2.114. Diameter of sliding gear shaft at third speed gear location is 2.1100-2.1105. If bushing is worn or if inner teeth of gear are damaged or worn, install a new gear which contains a factory installed bushing reamed to size. The third speed gear bushing (8) is available as a separate replacement part and must be line-bored or honed after installation to provide a bushing to shaft clearance of 0.0025-0.004. Unless precision sizing equipment is available, field installation of the bushing is not recommended.

Note: Although it is possible to remove the fourth and fifth speed gears from the sliding gear shaft, it would be pointless to do so. If the shaft, fourth speed gear and/or fifth speed

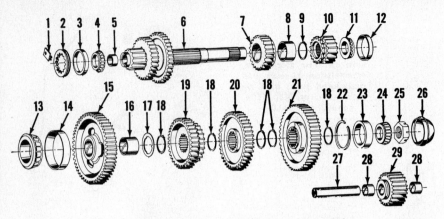

Fig. MM920—Exploded view of sliding gear transmission.

1. Lock	9. Snap ring
2. Adjusting nut	10. 2nd & 3rd gear
3. Bearing cup	11. Bearing cone
4. Bearing cone	12. Bearing cup
5. Bushing	13. Bearing cone
6. Shaft assembly	14. Bearing cup
7. 3rd speed gear	15. 1st speed gear
8. Bushing	16. Bushing

17. Thrust washer	23. Bearing cup
18. Snap rings	24. Bearing cone
19. 4th & 5th speed gear	25. Pinion shaft nut
20. 3rd speed gear	26. Cover
21. 2nd & reverse gear	27. Shaft
22. Snap ring	28. Bushing
	29. Reverse idler gear

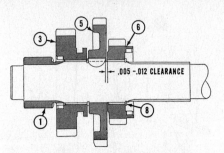

Fig. MM923 — Cross-sectional view of sliding gear shaft showing recommended clearance between gear (6) and fifth speed gear (5). See text.

Fig. MM921 — Rear view of transmission housing showing sliding gear shaft bearing adjusting nut (2) and lock clip (1).

Fig. MM922 — Using a punch to drift the sliding gear shaft rear bearing out of transmission housing.

gear are damaged or excessively worn, it will be necessary to renew all parts which are available as a factory assembled unit only.

If the sliding gear shaft and gears unit are in otherwise good condition, install the third speed gear (7) and its retaining snap ring (9). With the third speed gear contacting the snap ring, use a feeler gage and check the clearance between the shoulder on the third speed gear and the shoulder on the fifth speed gear. Desired clearance is 0.005-0.012 as shown in Fig. MM923. If clearance exceeds 0.012, measure the thickness of the third speed gear (6) and fifth speed gear (5) where they contact shaft (1). If the thickness of the third speed gear (6) is not 0.919-0.922, renew the gear. If the width of the fifth speed gear is not 0.935-0.940, renew the upper shaft and gear assembly.

When reassembling, install the third speed gear and its retaining snap ring. Install the second and third speed sliding gear with the shortest teeth toward the third speed gear. Using a suitable press, install the sliding gear shaft front bearing cone.

Install the assembled sliding gear shaft unit in the transmission housing as shown in Fig. MM924, then move the shaft unit toward right side of the housing. Slide the third speed gear and snap ring back into position on the bevel pinion (countershaft). Install the reverse idler gear and shaft and tighten the shaft retaining set screw until end of screw is flush with the lock nut; then tighten the nut securely.

On models M670 and M670 Super, using a pair of right angle Tru-Arc snap ring pliers, disengage the snap ring from the groove in front of fourth speed gear (20—Fig. MM926) on bevel pinion (counter-shaft). Move the snap ring and fourth speed gear forward on the bevel pinion shaft as far as possible, then lift the sliding gear (upper) shaft and gears out through top opening in transmission housing.

Place the removed unit in a suitable press and remove front bearing cone (11). Remove shaft from press and withdraw the second and fourth sliding gear (10). Remove snap ring (9) and withdraw the fourth speed gear (7).

Inside diameter of the bushing in fourth speed gear (7) is 2.113-2.114. Diameter of sliding gear shaft at fourth speed gear location is 2.1100-2.1105. If bushing is worn or if inner teeth of gear are damaged or worn, install a new gear which contains a factory installed bushing reamed to size. The bushing is available as a separate replacement part and must be line-bored or honed after installation to provide a bushing to shaft clearance of 0.0025-0.004. Unless precision sizing equipment is available, field installation of the bushing is not recommended.

Fig. MM924—Installing the assembled sliding gear shaft in transmission housing.

Note: Although it is possible to remove the third and fifth speed gears from the sliding gear shaft, it would be pointless to do so. If the shaft, third speed gear and/or fifth speed gear are damaged or excessively worn, it will be necessary to renew all parts which are available as a factory assembled unit only.

If the sliding gear shaft and gears are in otherwise good condition, install the fourth speed gear (7) and snap ring (9). Using a feeler gage, check the clearance between the shoulder on fourth speed gear and the shoulder on fifth speed gear. Desired clearance is 0.005-0.012. If clearance exceeds 0.012, renew fourth speed gear and/or fifth speed gear and shaft assembly.

Install the second and fourth sliding gear (10), then using a suitable press, install the sliding shaft front bearing cone (11). Place the assembled sliding gear shaft unit in the transmission housing, then move the shaft assembly toward right side of the housing. Slide fourth speed gear (20)

and snap ring back into position on the bevel pinion (counter-shaft). Install the reverse idler gear and shaft and tighten the shaft retaining set screw until end of screw is flush with locknut; then tighten the locknut securely.

On all models, move the sliding gear shaft over into position and install the rear bearing cone and cup. Install the bearing adjustment nut and turn the nut in until rear face of nut stands out about 3/16-inch from rear face of transmission housing. Install the Ampli-Torc planetary gear unit as outlined in paragraph 128 or the reverse shuttle unit as outlined in paragraph 130.

Tighten the sliding gear shaft bearing adjusting nut to remove all shaft end play. Tap each end of the shaft lightly with a soft driver to be sure bearings are seated and re-tighten the adjusting nut if necessary, to remove all shaft end play. Then, back-off the adjusting nut enough to provide a shaft end play of 0.001-0.004 and install the adjusting nut lock clip and cap screw as shown in Fig. MM-921.

Note: End play can be checked by mounting a dial indicator as shown in Fig. MM925, but be sure the indicator button is contacting the sliding gear shaft and not the adjusting nut.

Install the remaining parts by reversing the removal procedure.

140. **REVERSE IDLER.** The reverse idler gear (29—Fig. MM920 or MM-

926) and shaft (27) can be removed by following the procedure outlined in paragraph 139.

The 1.2420-1.2425 diameter reverse idler gear shaft should have a clearance of 0.0015-0.003 in the reverse idler gear bushing. The bushing and/or shaft are available as separate replacement parts; or, a new idler gear is factory fitted with a bushing. When installing the idler gear and shaft, tighten the retaining set screw until end of screw is flush with the lock nut; then tighten the nut securely. Reinstall the sliding gear (upper) shaft as outlined in paragraph 139.

141. **BEVEL PINION (COUNTER-SHAFT).** To remove the bevel pinion shaft, first remove the sliding gear (upper) shaft as outlined in paragraph 139 and proceed as follows:

Remove cover (26—Fig. MM920 or MM926) and on all models except M670 and M670 Super, remove cotter pin and nut from forward end of shaft. On models M670 and M670 Super, remove the two nuts and lock washer from forward end of shaft. Then on all models, working through top opening in transmission housing, use a pair of right angle Tru-Arc snap ring priers and disengage snap ring from groove in front of the first speed gear (15). Bump the bevel pinion shaft rearward until shaft is out of the front bearing cone (24). Disengage the remaining snap rings from the bevel pinion shaft, withdraw the shaft rear-

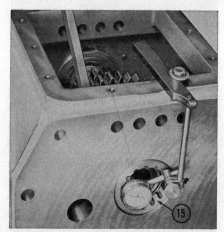

Fig. MM925—Measuring sliding gear shaft for recommended end play of 0.001-0.004. Indicator button must be contacting end of shaft and not the adjusting nut.

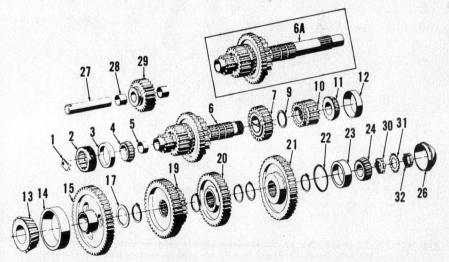

Fig. MM926—Exploded view of sliding gear transmission used on models M670 and M670 Super. Shaft assembly (6A) was used in early production M670 tractors.

1. Lock	10. 2nd & 4th speed gear	19. 3rd & 5th speed gear	27. Reverse shaft
2. Adjusting nut	11. Bearing cone	20. 4th speed gear	28. Bushing
3. Bearing cup	12. Bearing cup	21. 2nd & reverse gear	29. Reverse idler gear
4. Bearing cone	13. Bearing cone	22. Snap ring	30. Nut
5. Bushing	14. Bearing cup	23. Bearing cup	31. Lock washer
6. Shaft assembly	15. 1st speed gear	24. Bearing cone	32. Nut
7. 4th speed gear	17. Thrust washer	26. Cover	
9. Snap ring			

ward and remove gears from above. Rear bearing cone can be removed from shaft and cups can be removed from transmission case at this time.

Inside diameter of the bushing in the first speed gear (15) is 2.0130-2.0135 on models M670 and M670 Super and 2.2535-2.2540 on all other models. If bushing is worn or if inner teeth of gear are damaged or worn, install a new gear which contains a factory installed bushing reamed to size. The first speed gear bushing is available as a separate replacement

part but must be line-bored or honed after installation to provide a bushing to shaft clearance of 0.0035-0.0045. Unless precision sizing equipment is available, field installation of the bushing is not recommended.

The bevel pinion shaft is available only as a matched set with the main drive bevel ring gear. Therefore, if the bevel pinion shaft must be renewed, it will be necessary to remove the differential as outlined in paragraph 149 and install the new mating bevel ring gear.

Install the bevel pinion shaft and gears by reversing the removal procedure and tighten the bearing adjusting nut to remove all shaft end play. Tap each end of the shaft lightly with a soft hammer to be sure the bearings are seated, then retighten the nut to pre-load the bearings. Desired preload is 10-20 inch pounds of rolling torque when checked at bevel pinion (rear) end of shaft.

Install the reverse idler gear and sliding gear (upper) as outlined in paragraph 139.

DIFFERENTIAL AND MAIN DRIVE BEVEL GEARS

NOTE: This section applies to the differential and main drive bevel gears used on series UB Special and UTS Special. For service on main drive bevel gears and differential used on 5 Star, M5, M504, M602, M604, M670 and M670 Super, refer to section beginning with paragraph 149.

DIFFERENTIAL

UB Special-UTS Special

142. BEARING ADJUSTMENT. Differential carrier bearing adjustment is controlled with shims (21—Fig. MM927) inserted between bearing

cages and transmission housing. The same shims also control bevel ring gear and pinion backlash which should be set to the value as etched on individual sets of matched gears.

To adjust differential carrier bearings, first remove transmission top cover. Remove left brake assembly. Remove cap screws holding left bearing cage to transmission housing; then slide cage out far enough to permit removal of required thickness of shims to provide zero end play and yet permit differential unit to rotate without binding. Reinstall bearing cage and check bearing adjustment and backlash. If bearing adjustment is O. K. but backlash is 0.002 greater or less than value stamped on ring gear it will be necessary to adjust backlash by transferring shims from one side to the other until correct backlash is obtained.

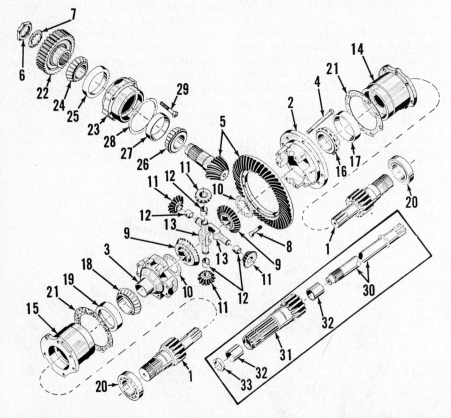

Fig. MM927—Exploded view of differential assembly used on series UB Special and UTS Special tractors. Items 30, 31, 32 and 33 are used on models with live pto only.

1. Differential shaft	11. Pinion	23. Drive shaft cage
2. Right hand differential case	12. Bushing	24. Front bearing cone
	13. Differential pinion shaft	25. Front bearing cup
3. Left hand differential case	14. Right hand bearing cage	26. Rear bearing cone
4. Bolt	15. Left hand bearing cage	27. Rear bearing cup
5. Pinion and ring gear	16. Right hand bearing cone	28. Shim
6. Nut	17. Right hand bearing cup	29. Screw
7. Lock washer	18. Left hand bearing cone	30. Left hand differential shaft
8. Bolt	19. Left hand bearing cup	31. Bull pinion sleeve
9. Side gear	20. Ball bearing	32. Bushing
10. Washer	21. Shim	33. Oil seal
	22. Differential drive gear	

Fig. MM928 — Using a dial indicator (I) to check bevel gear backlash. The correct backlash is etched on gear tooth as shown at (M).

Fig. MM929 — Using a bar and wire to support differential unit for carrier bearing removal. Refer to text.

143. REMOVE AND REINSTALL. The differential unit can be removed after removing transmission housing top cover, rear cover plate or pto output unit and BOTH rear axle shaft and housing assemblies; or, if only the differential or one set of final drive gears are to be serviced, differential case can be split and removed after removing ONE rear axle shaft and housing. Proceed as outlined in the appropriate following paragraphs.

144. BY REMOVING BOTH AXLES. With transmission housing top and rear covers removed, securely block the tractor and remove both rear axle and housing assemblies as outlined in paragraph 161. Remove both brake assemblies and the cap screws retaining differential bearing cages to transmission housing. Support the differential assembly as shown in Fig. MM929. Tilt lower end of each bull gear in turn toward center of transmission housing as shown in Fig. MM930, and remove bull pinion shaft sleeves (S); then, lift out the differential and main drive bevel gear as a unit.

Fig. MM931 — Bull pinion shaft (1) and bearing (20) can be pulled by inserting a suitable pry bar behind brake disc (D).

Assemble by reversing the disassembly procedure, referring to paragraph 146 for tightening torque and other pertinent data.

145. BY SPLITTING DIFFERENTIAL CASE. If supporting tractor with both axles removed is a problem; or when performing service with limited facilities is necessary; the differential unit may be removed by splitting differential case and removing EITHER rear wheel and axle assembly as follows:

With transmission top and rear covers removed, block tractor and remove either wheel, axle and axle housing as outlined in paragraph 161.

Remove both brakes and brake backing plates. Reinstall one brake disc on each bull pinion shaft as shown in Fig. MM931 and, using a bar inserted between brake disc and transmission housing, remove the bull pinions.

Place correlation marks on the differential case halves as shown in Fig. MM932 and remove the cotter pins and retaining nuts. Support the differential as shown in Fig. MM929, tilt the loose bull gear as shown in Fig. MM930, and remove the bull pinion sleeve.

If right axle has been removed, turn the differential unit and withdraw all differential case bolts; then tilt the differential case halves as shown in Fig. MM933 and remove the differential pinions and spider shafts. Differential case halves may then be withdrawn for service on differential, main drive bevel gears or the loose bull gear.

If left axle and housing has been removed, push the case bolts back as far as possible, withdraw differential pinions and spider shafts and lift out the differential case halves.

Reassemble by reversing the disassembly procedure, making sure correlation marks on differential case halves are aligned. Tighten retaining bolts and nuts to a torque of 75 ft.-lbs. and secure with cotter pins. Refer to paragraph 146 for additional assembly data.

146. ASSEMBLY. If differential or main drive bevel gears have been overhauled, adjust carrier bearings and backlash as outlined in paragraph 142. If differential has been removed

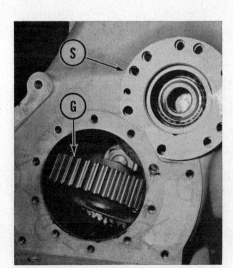

Fig. MM930—Bull gear (G) must be tilted as shown to remove bull pinion shaft sleeve (S). Refer to text.

Fig. MM932 — Removing differential unit by splitting the case. Refer to text for details.

Fig. MM933 — With right axle housing removed, differential case halves will need to be tilted as shown, to remove spider gears and spider.

for bull gear service and adjustments were satisfactory when unit was disassembled, reinstall using the same thickness of shims used before disassembly. Refer to paragraph 136 for bevel pinion renewal and paragraph 148 for adjustment of mesh position, if main drive bevel gears are renewed.

Use Permatex or similar sealant on cap screw threads when reinstalling rear axle housings. Tighten assembly cap screws as outlined in the following table:

Bull Pinion Sleeve (Differential
Carrier) Cap Screws ....75 ft.-lbs.
Brake Backing Plate
Cap Screws ....250 ft.-lbs.
Axle Housing Cap Screws 120 ft.-lbs.

147. **OVERHAUL.** To overhaul the removed differential unit, mark the case halves, if not already done, and remove the retaining cotter pins, castellated nuts and retaining bolts. Refer to Fig. MM927 for an exploded view of typical differential unit.

Examine gears for chipped teeth and all parts for wear, scoring or

other damage. Pinion spider shafts (13) are 0.996-0.997 in diameter and have a recommended diametral clearance of 0.003-0.005 in bushings (12). If clearance exceeds 0.010, renew shafts and/or bushings. Install bushings (12) with oil holes in bushing and pinion aligned and ream bushings to an inside diameter of 1.000-1.001 after installation. Tighten differential case bolts to a torque of 75 ft.-lbs. when reassembling, and secure with cotter pins.

If main drive bevel gears must be renewed, tighten main drive bevel ring gear retaining cap screws to a torque of 110-115 ft.-lbs., install pinion as outlined in paragraph 136 and adjust mesh position as outlined in paragraph 148. Adjust backlash and carrier bearing as outlined in paragraph 142.

BEVEL GEAR MESH ADJUSTMENT
UB Special-UTS Special

148. Mesh position (Cone Point) of the main drive bevel gears is controlled by thickness of shim pack (28—Fig. MM927) located between drive pinion bearing cage and transmission housing.

Main drive bevel gears are available only as a matched set; in addition to the match mark, end of drive pinion contains markings which indicate the relative shim pack thickness for correct mesh position adjustment and edge of ring gear (or both gears) are marked to indicate the correct backlash. Refer to Fig. MM935.

To determine the thickness of shim pack (28) when renewing the gears,

note thickness of removed shim pack and compare mesh position markings (C) on old and new pinion. If the new pinion has a larger plus marking (or smaller minus marking) than the old pinion; REMOVE shims equal in thickness to the difference between the two markings. If new pinon has a smaller plus marking or larger minus marking than old pinion, ADD shims equal in thickness to difference between the two markings. If one pinion has a plus marking and the other a minus marking, add the two markings, then; if new pinion has a plus marking, REMOVE shims equal in thickness to combined reading; or if new pinion has a minus marking, ADD shims. If plus or minus markings are within 0.003 of being identical on the two pinions, use the removed shim pack or one equal in thickness. Shims are 0.006 thick. When mesh position has been changed, backlash must be readjusted as outlined in paragraph 142.

Mesh position can be checked by using the following procedure: With backlash correctly adjusted, apply a coat of Prussian Blue to approximately ten teeth on bevel ring gear and turn ring gear in normal direction of rotation until painted portion passes by the pinion. If heavy tooth contact is indicated at heel (outer) ends of ring gear teeth, ADD one shim to shim pack (28); if heavy tooth contact is indicated at toe (inner) ends, REMOVE one shim. Mesh position is correct when even contact is indicated through ¾-⅞ of length of teeth and slightly toward toe (inner) end. Backlash must be readjusted whenever mesh position is changed.

Fig. MM934 — Using a torque wrench to retighten differential case through bolts. Recommended torque is 75 ft-lbs.

Fig. MM935 — Matched ring gear and pinion are etched with match marks (A), recommended backlash (B) and cone point relative position (C). Cone point is adjusted by means of shims (28).

DIFFERENTIAL AND MAIN DRIVE BEVEL GEARS

NOTE: This section applies to the differential and main drive bevel gears used on Series 5 Star, M5, M504, M602, M604, M670 and M670 Super tractors. For service on main drive bevel gears and differential used on UB Special and UTS Special, refer to section beginning with paragraph 142.

DIFFERENTIAL

5 Star-M5-M504-M602-M604

149. **REMOVE AND REINSTALL.** To remove the differential assembly, drain hydraulic system, transmission and final drive housings and disconnect power steering oil lines. Remove seat, hydraulic reservoir, hydraulic pump, belt pulley and differential case cover. Remove the pto clutch and input shaft as outlined in paragraph 177.

Remove both brake covers. On 5-Star series loosen the chuck screw (CS-Fig. MM936) and pry the speedometer drive gear (G) from the bull pinion sleeve. Remove the brake outer lined discs, both of the brake adjusting bolts and withdraw the actuating plate assemblies and the inner lined discs. Remove the three nuts retaining each of the inner brake plates to the final drive housing and remove the plates, but do not mix or lose the shims located between the brake plates and the housing. Use a double nut arrangement and remove the front stud located in the right brake compartment.

IMPORTANT: Two types of differential assemblies have been used which alter the removal procedure. 5-Star and early M-5

tractors have TWO spider pinion shafts (13—Fig. MM937) which have a $\frac{9}{16}$-inch nib on both ends. The other two shafts (14) have ⅜-inch nibs on outer ends. Late M5, M504, M602 and M604 tractors have ONE shaft with $\frac{9}{16}$-inch nib on outer end; the other three shafts have ⅜-inch nibs. The large nibs identify the shafts which lock the differential cage (8) to cross shaft (10). Disassemble as outlined in the appropriate following paragraph.

150. **EARLY MODELS.** Turn the differential assembly until one of the locking spider pinion shafts is aligned with the previously removed stud hole and, with a long punch carefully tap roll pin (17—Fig. MM937) inward until it is centered in spider pinion shaft (13). CAUTION: Do not tap roll pin too far or it will imbed in differential cage. With roll pin centered, remove the spider pinion shaft by grasping the projecting nib with a pair of vise grips and pulling with a twisting motion. Remove the second locking spider pinion shaft in the same manner; then bump the cross shaft (10) out right side of final drive housing. Pull the bull pinion (5) sharply outward to dislodge bearing cup (3), and lift differential assembly and final drive bevel gear upward out of final drive housing.

151. **LATE MODELS.** Turn the differential assembly until the locking spider pinion shaft is aligned with the previously removed stud hole and, with a long punch drive the retaining pin (17—Fig. MM937) out of differential cage and spider pinion shaft. Grasp the projecting nib with a pair of vise grip pliers and pull pinion shaft from differential cage. Grasp bull pinion (5) and pull sharply outward to dislodge bearing cup (3), then lift differential assembly out top of final drive housing.

152. When reassembling, install the combination bull pinion and differential side gears, then position the differential assembly in the final drive housing and slide the cross shaft into position so that holes in cross shaft register with marked spider gear shaft bores in differential cage. Remove the roll pin from the spider gear shafts, then reinstall spider gear shaft so that tip engages hole in the differential cross shaft. Lock the spider gear shaft in position by driving the roll pin into differential cage and spider gear shaft until end of roll pin is just less than flush with the differential cage. Install other shaft in same manner. Using sealer on the threads, reinstall the stud in the right hand brake compartment, then reinstall the inner brake plates but be sure that the original

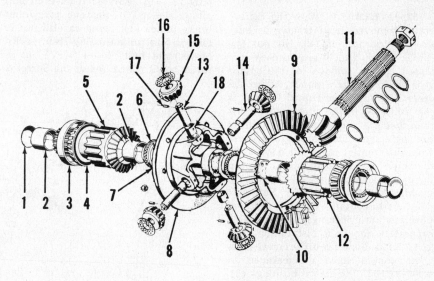

Fig. MM937 — **Exploded view of differential assembly used on 5-Star tractors. Later models are similar.**

1. Plug	7. Spacer	13. Pinion shaft
2. Bushing	8. Differential cage	14. Pinion shaft
3. Bearing cup	9. Bevel gear	15. Spider gear
4. Bearing cone	10. Cross shaft	16. Thrust washer
5. Bull pinion	11. Pinion shaft	17. Roll pin
6. Thrust washer	12. Bull pinion	18. Bushing

Fig. MM936—On 5-Star tractors, speedometer drive gear (G) can be removed from left brake assembly after loosening chuck screw (CS).

shims are installed between each of the brake plates and the final drive housing. If differential carrier bearing play exists, remove an equal thickness of shims from each side of the final drive housing to eliminate all bearing play, but still permit differential to rotate freely without binding.

Observe the main drive bevel pinion and ring gear where the matched set numbers and backlash are stamped. If the backlash between the bevel gears is not as specified, it will be necessary to transfer shims from under one brake plate to the other until the specified backlash value is obtained.

When the differential carrier bearings and bevel gear backlash are properly adjusted, remove the inner brake plates but be careful not to mix or lose any of the shims. Install new seals in the brake plates; then, using a tin sleeve or shim stock to avoid damaging the seal lips, reinstall the brake plates. Using Permatex as a sealer, install a new expansion plug in the right bull pinion shaft sleeve. On 5-Star series, use a new "O" ring, install the speedometer drive gear in the left bull pinion shaft sleeve and tighten the chuck screw. Install the brake lined discs, actuating discs and covers. Note: The single grooved cover spacer should be installed on rear cover bolt.

Install the remaining parts by reversing the removal procedure and adjust the brakes as outlined in paragraph 167.

153. **OVERHAUL.** With the differential removed from tractor as outlined in paragraph 149, lift out the spider gears which are already released by the removal of the spider gear shafts. Using a punch, bump the other roll pin inward until the pin is just centered in the spider gear shaft then, using a pair of pliers, withdraw the spider gear shaft and spider gears from differential cage. The 0.996-0.997 diameter spider gear shafts should have a clearance of 0.003-0.005 in bushing (18—Fig. MM937). New spider gears contain factory installed bushings; or, bushings are available separately for field installation. The 2.117-2.118 diameter differential cross shaft should have a clearance of 0.002-0.004 in the sleeve bushings (2). New sleeves contain factory installed bushings; or, bushings are available separately for field installation. Renew any other damaged parts and reassemble. Note: The locking spider gear shaft or shafts (13) are installed during reinstallation of the differential assembly.

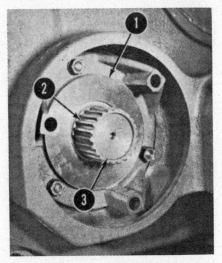

Fig. MM938—M670 and M670 Super bull pinion sleeve with brake removed, showing details of contruction.

1. Inner brake plate
2. Bull pinion sleeve
3. End plug

Install differential as outlined in paragraph 152.

M670-M670 Super

154. **REMOVE AND REINSTALL.** To remove the differential, first drain the hydraulic system and transmission. Remove the hydraulic reservoir, seat and final drive housing top cover. Remove the pto clutch and shaft as outlined in paragraph 177 or 179. Disconnect brake linkage and remove both brake assemblies.

Remove the retaining snap ring and plug (3—Fig. MM938) from each bull pinion sleeve (2). Remove both inner brake plates (1), being careful not to lose or mix the adjusting shim packs. Move right bull pinion sleeve out as far as possible and unseat the Spirolox

retaining ring (16—Fig. MM939). Support the differential assembly from above or by blocking up under bevel ring gear. Bump the differential cross shaft (5) out left side of tractor and lift differential assembly and bull pinion sleeves out top opening.

When reinstalling the differential assembly, note that left bull pinion sleeve (4) has a larger inside diameter than right sleeve (19). Place the bull pinion sleeves and thrust bearings and races in position in housing, then position differential assembly, supporting the assembly from above or by blocking up beneath bevel ring gear. Insert small end of cross shaft in left bull pinion sleeve and as end appears through differential cage hub, place the Spirolox retaining ring (16) over end of shaft. Align the splines as the shaft is inserted and install the retaining ring into groove when shaft is in place.

If carrier bearing preload or bevel gear backlash are not to be adjusted, renew "O" rings and inner and outer oil seals in brake plates. Reinstall brake plates using the removed shim packs and a protector sleeve to prevent damage to oil seal lips. Install the retaining stud nuts and tighten evenly to a torque of 33-37 ft.-lbs. Complete the assembly by reversing the disassembly procedure.

NOTE: If parts are renewed which will alter bearing adjustment or backlash, final drive housing must be separated from transmission to properly adjust bearings. When separating the housings, note the number and color of flange gaskets located between the housings. The gaskets determine the cone point position of the main drive bevel pinion. Refer to paragraph 157.

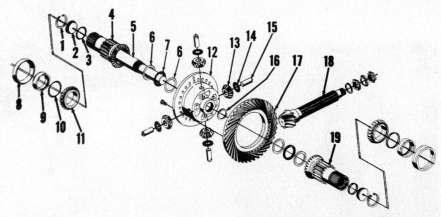

Fig. MM939—Exploded view of differential assembly used on models M670 and M670 Super. Cross shaft (5) is splined to differential cage (12) and is secured in position by a Spirolox retaining ring (16).

1. Snap ring	6. Bearing race	11. Bearing cone
2. Plug	7. Needle thrust bearing	12. Differential cage
3. "O" ring	8. Bearing cup	13. Spider gear
4. Bull pinion sleeve L.H.	9. Collar	14. Thrust washer
5. Cross shaft	10. "O" ring	15. Spider pinion shaft

16. Spirolox retaining ring
17. Ring gear
18. Bevel pinion
19. Bull pinion sleeve R.H.

Three different thickness flange gaskets are used, as follows:

Red 0.002
Green 0.003
Blue 0.005

If adjustment is required, install more than enough shims behind brake plates so that differential has a slight amount of end play. Tighten the brake plate retaining nuts to a torque of 33-37 ft.-lbs. Wrap a cord around a bull pinion in the smooth area between the two sets of teeth and attach a spring scale to end of cord. Check the amount of pull required to keep the differential rolling and record this reading. Next, remove enough shims so that with the brake plate retaining nuts tightened to a torque of 33-37 ft.-lbs., the bearing pre-load will require 8 to 15 pounds more than the previously recorded pull on the spring scale to keep the differential rolling at a constant speed.

Reconnect transmission and final drive housings, using shim gaskets of the same number and color of those removed. Tighten flange cap screws to a torque of 162-178 ft.-lbs.

Adjust bevel gear backlash to 0.010-0.013 by transferring shims from one side to the other, without altering the combined thickness of the two shim packs.

155. OVERHAUL. With the differential removed as outlined in paragraph 154, drive roll pins from spider pinion shafts (15—Fig. MM939) and differential cage (12). Using suitable pliers, withdraw spider shafts and lift out spider gears (13) and thrust washers (14). The 0.996-0.997 diameter spider shafts should have a clearance of 0.003-0.005 in spider gear bushings. New spider gears contain factory installed bushings; or, bushings are available separately for field installations.

If the bushings in bull pinion sleeves (4 and 19) are worn or scored, press new bushings to the position shown in Fig. MM940. Then, bore or hone the bushings to the following sizes: Left hand bull pinion sleeve

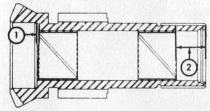

Fig. MM940—Cross sectional view of bull pinion sleeve used on models M670 and M670 Super, showing position of bushings. Dimension (1) is 1/16-inch and dimension (2) is 1 3/4-inch.

bushings, 2.367-2.368; right hand bull pinion sleeve bushings, 2.061-2.062.

If main drive bevel gears are renewed, refer to paragraph 157. Install the assembled differential assembly as outlined in paragraph 154.

MAIN DRIVE BEVEL GEARS
5 Star-M5-M504-M602-M604

156. The main drive bevel pinion and ring gear are available in matched sets only. To renew the bevel pinion, follow the procedure outlined in paragraph 141. To remove the bevel ring gear, first remove the differential as outlined in paragraph 149; then unbolt and remove the bevel ring gear from the differential cage.

Install the new bevel ring gear and tighten the retaining bolts securely. Install the differential and adjust the bevel gear backlash as outlined in paragraph 152.

M670-M670 Super

157. The main drive bevel pinion and ring gear are available in matched sets only. To renew the bevel pinion, follow the procedure outlined in paragraph 141. To renew the bevel ring gear, first remove the differential as outlined in paragraph 154, then unbolt and remove bevel ring gear from differential cage. When installing the bevel ring gear, tighten retaining cap screws to a torque of 85-95 ft.-lbs. and secure with safety wire.

Mesh position (tooth contact) of main bevel gears is controlled by the number and thickness of plastic shim gaskets interposed between transmission and final drive housing. A mounting dimension number from —0.001 to +0.005 is etched on end of pinion.

When renewing a main drive bevel pinion, proceed as follows: Note the mounting dimension number etched on old and new pinions. If numbers are the same, install a shim pack of identical thickness as that removed.

If a +0.001 pinion is used to replace a 0.000 pinion, add 0.001 in plastic shims to the previously installed shim pack.

If a —0.001 pinion is used to replace a 0.000 pinion, remove 0.001 of shims.

If a +0.004 pinion replaces a —0.001 pinion, an additional 0.005 in shims is required.

The plastic shims are color coded as follows:

Red 0.002
Green 0.003
Blue 0.005

If the transmission housing is being renewed, the correct shim pack must be determined as follows: With the main drive bevel pinion installed as

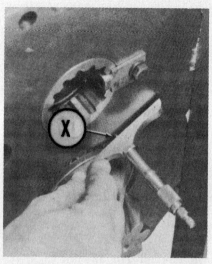

Fig. MM941—View showing distance (X) from transmission case to pinion bearing cone being measured. Refer to text.

outlined in paragraph 141, measure the distance from the surface of the transmission case to the pinion shaft bearing cone as shown in Fig. MM941. This distance minus 0.097 and plus the dimension etched on end of pinion will determine the correct thickness of shim pack to be used.

Assemble the housings using the determined shim pack making sure some backlash exists. Tighten the flange bolts to the recommended torque of 162-178 ft.-lbs. Apply a light coat of Prussian blue on gear teeth and rotate the gear set with no load, in normal direction of rotation. Mesh position is correct when tooth contact pattern is approximately 1/2 to 5/8 the length of the tooth, starting near toe end of tooth as shown in Fig. MM942. If tooth contact pattern is on heel of tooth, add shims between transmission case and differential case. If tooth contact pattern is on toe of tooth, remove shims from between the cases.

Adjust backlash and complete the assembly as outlined in paragraph 154, after mesh position has been properly adjusted.

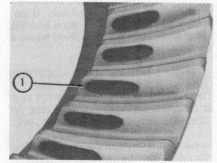

Fig. MM942 — Correct tooth contact pattern starts near toe end of tooth and extends 1/2 to 5/8 the length of the tooth.

FINAL DRIVE AND REAR AXLE

NOTE: This section covers service procedures on final drive bull gears, bull pinions and rear axle units used on UB Special and UTS Special. For service on similar components used on Series 5 Star, M5, M504, M602, M604, M670 and M670 Super tractors, refer to section beginning with paragraph 162.

BULL PINION

UB Special-UTS Special

158. On these models the bull pinion and bearing unit can be withdrawn after removing the brake and brake backing plate, proceed as follows: With brake unit removed, reinstall one brake disc to serve as a fulcrum, and insert a pry bar between brake disc and transmission housing.

To remove the bull pinion, bearing and bull pinion sleeve as an assembly, first remove transmission top cover and rear cover or pto output unit. Remove rear axle and housing assembly as outlined in paragraph 161. Support differential as shown in Fig. MM943. Tilt the loose bull gear to clear the cut-out in bull pinion sleeve, remove brake assembly, brake backing plate and the two remaining bull pinion sleeve retaining cap screws, then remove bull pinion, sleeve and bearing as a unit. Save the differential carrier bearing adjusting shims which are located between sleeve flange and transmission housing.

Reinstall by reversing the removal procedure, using the removed shim pack or one of identical thickness. Tighten bull pinion sleeve retaining cap screws and brake plate retaining cap screws to a torque of 75 ft.-lbs. Adjust the brakes as outlined in paragraph 167.

Fig. MM943 — Using a bar and wire to support differential unit for carrier bearing removal. Refer to text.

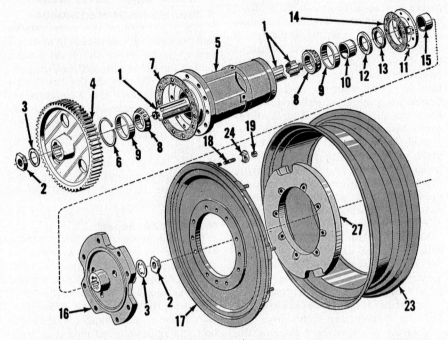

Fig. MM944—Exploded view of rear axle, housing and wheel used on series "UTS Special" tractors. Series "UB Special" are similar.

1. Rear axle	12. Oil seal
2. Axle nut	13. Felt
3. Washer	14. Shim
4. Bull gear	15. Spacer
5. Axle housing	16. Center hub
6. Snap ring	17. Center wheel
7. Gasket	18. Stud
8. Bearing cone	19. Nut
9. Bearing cup	23. Wheel rim
10. Collar	24. Rim clamp
11. Bearing cover	27. Wheel weight

BULL GEARS

UB Special-UTS Special

159. The differential assembly must be removed before either bull gear can be removed. If service is required on only one bull gear, proceed as outlined in paragraph 144.

AXLE SHAFTS AND HOUSINGS

UB Special-UTS Special

160. **BEARING ADJUSTMENT.** Axle bearing play is controlled by shims (14—Fig. MM944) between bearing cap and axle housing. To adjust bearings, support rear of tractor under transmission and remove tire and wheel assembly. Remove bearing cover (11) and vary number of shims (14) between cover and housing to provide zero end play of shaft and yet permit same to rotate without binding.

161. **R&R ASSEMBLY.** Support rear of tractor under transmission and remove tire and wheel assembly. Remove transmission top cover and power take-off unit. Straighten bull gear retaining nut lock and remove bull gear retaining nut (N—Fig. MM945). Remove axle housing to transmission housing retaining bolts and remove axle shaft and housing assembly as a unit, using a hoist or other suitable support.

When reinstalling the unit, position

Fig. MM945 — Axle nut (N) can be loosened and removed through pto output shaft opening in rear of transmission housing.

bull gear on bottom of transmission housing with long hub to inside, engage splines of axle and bull gear; then steady the outer end of axle as unit is raised into position. Differential, carrier bearings and bull pinion sleeves must be installed and adjusted before rear axle and housing is installed.

Use Permatex or other suitable sealant on cap screw threads and tighten cap screws to a torque of 120 ft.-lbs. when installing axle and housing assembly. Tighten bull gear retaining nut to a torque of 450 ft.-lbs. and secure by bending retaining washer. Complete the assembly by reversing the disassembly procedure.

Fig. MM947—View showing special tool used to rotate bull pinion in tightening nut on axle shaft on models M670 and M670 Super.

FINAL DRIVE AND REAR AXLE

NOTE: This section covers service procedures on final drive bull gears, bull pinions and rear axle units used on Series 5 Star, M5, M504, M602, M604, M670 and M670 Super tractors. For service on similar components used on UB Special and UTS Special, refer to section beginning with paragraph 158.

BULL PINION GEARS

5 Star-M5-M504-M602-M604-M670-M670 Super

162. The final drive bull pinion gears are integral with the differential side gears. To remove, overhaul and reinstall the combination differential side gear and bull pinion sleeves, follow the procedure outlined in paragraph 149 through 155.

BULL GEARS

5 Star-M5-M504-M602-M604

163. To remove either bull gear, first remove the pto clutch as outlined in paragraph 177. Unlock and remove nut and driven gear from inner end of the pto output shaft. Support rear of tractor and remove respective fender and wheel and tire unit. Unlock and remove the large nut (1—Fig. MM946) retaining bull gear to inner end of wheel axle shaft and unbolt the axle outer bearing cap from the final drive housing, but be careful not to damage the shims. Bump the wheel axle shaft outward and lift bull gear from final drive housing.

On some tractors, due to inadequate clearance, it may be necessary to remove the brake inner plates and move differential as outlined in paragraph 164 to remove left bull gear.

When reassembling, tighten the gear retaining nut securely and lock the nut in place by bending over a portion of washer (2).

M670-M670 Super

164. To remove either bull gear, first drain final drive housing and hydraulic system. Remove the seat, hydraulic reservoir assembly and the differential cover. On model M670, unbolt and remove hydraulic pump from the rear of final drive housing. Then, on all tractors, remove pto clutch and input shaft as outlined in paragraph 177 or 179.

To remove the right hand bull gear, support rear of tractor, then remove the right fender and wheel and tire unit. Unbolt and remove right brake cover, brake discs and actuator assembly. Straighten bent portion of lock washer and back the axle nut off approximately ¼-inch.

NOTE: The axle nuts are tightened to a torque of 1800-1900 ft.-lbs. A simple tool can be made up and axle nuts can be loosened or tightened by means of the bull pinions. The bull pinion provides a 4 to 1 mechanical advantage, so when holding the axle nut and rotating the bull pinion, only 450-475 ft.-lbs. torque on the pinion is required to tighten the axle nut to 1800-1900 ft.-lbs. To make up the tool, first remove the lining from a brake disc. Weld a 3 inch long section of steel pipe with an inside di-

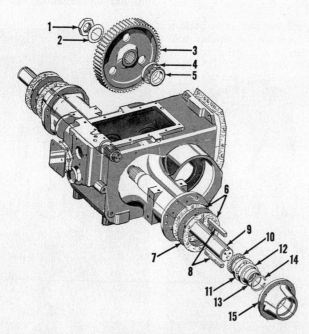

Fig. MM946—Final drive housing, rear axle and associated parts of the type used on 5-Star, M5, M504, M602 and M604. Models M670 and M670 Super are similar.

1. Axle nut	6. Gaskets	11. Bearing cup
2. Lock washer	7. Shim pack	12. Oil seal
3. Bull gear	8. Keys	13. Seal sleeve
4. Bearing cup	9. Axle shaft	14. Snap ring
5. Bearing cone	10. Bearing cone	15. Bearing retainer

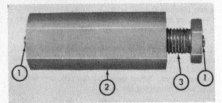

Fig. MM948—View showing an extending tool which can be used to force axle shaft out of bull gear.

1. Pilot
2. Bar stock
3. Cap screw (⅞-inch)

ameter of at least 3½ inches to the disc, centered over the hole in the disc. Weld a handle across end of pipe. Refer to Fig. MM947.

Loosen the cap screws and move axle outer bearing cap out approximately 5/16-inch. The bull gear fits tight on the tapered splines of the axle shaft, so some type of extending tool must be used to force the axle out of the bull gear. An extending tool similar to that shown in Fig. MM948, can be made up by threading a ⅞-inch cap screw into a piece of bar stock.

Extend the tool until axle moves out as far as nut will allow. Remove the tool, nut and lock washer, then remove axle outer bearing cap and shims. Withdraw axle shaft and lift out bull gear.

To remove the left hand bull gear, use the same procedure to remove the left axle as was used to remove the right axle. Then, proceed as follows: Support the ring gear and differential assembly. Remove brake plates and shims from both sides of tractor. The differential assembly can now be moved enough to allow removal of the left hand bull gear.

When reassembling, tighten bull gear retaining nuts to a torque of 1800-1900 ft.-lbs. and lock each nut in place by bending over a portion of lock washer.

WHEEL AXLE SHAFT AND BEARINGS

5 Star-M5-M504-M602-M604-M-670-M670 Super

165. To remove either wheel axle shaft, first remove the respective bull gear as outlined in paragraph 163 or 164, then withdraw the axle shaft from the housing. The procedure for renewing the bearing cups and cones and seal is evident at this time.

When reassembling, tighten the bull gear retaining nut securely and lock the nut in place by bending over a portion of washer (2—Fig. MM946). Install the bearing cap (15) and tighten the retaining cap screws se-

curely to seat the bearings; then, back off the cap screws to relieve any preload on the bearings and using a torque wrench attached to outer end of axle shaft, check the rolling torque required to keep the axle shaft in motion. Then tighten the cap screws to a torque of 80 ft.-lbs. and make a second rolling torque check. If the wheel axle shaft bearings are properly adjusted, the rolling torque reading made with the bearing cap retaining screws tightened will be 30-130 inch pounds greater than the torque reading taken with the screws loose. If bearing pre-load is not as specified, vary the number of shims (7) located between bearing cap (15) and final drive housing.

WHEEL AXLE SHAFT OIL SEAL

5 Star-M5-M504-M602-M604-M670-M670 Super

166. The procedure for removing the oil seal (12—Fig. MM946) is evident after removing the axle shaft bearing cap (15). Removal of the bearing cap can be accomplished after removing the wheel and tire unit and the wheel hub.

BRAKES

ADJUSTMENT

All Models

167. To adjust the disc type brakes, support rear portion of tractor and shorten the brake actuating rods by

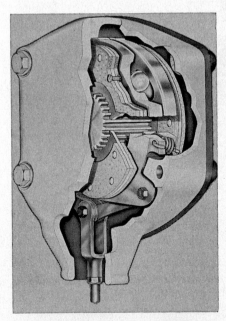

Fig. MM949—Cutaway view of typical disc brake assembly used on all models.

Fig. M950—To adjust the brakes on UB Special and UTS Special models, turn adjusting rod (A) either way until proper adjustment is obtained. See text.

turning the rod (UB Special and UTS Special models, see A—Fig. MM950), or rod nut (other models, see Fig. MM951), until a slight drag is obtained while rotating the rear wheel; then lengthen the rod one-half turn and tighten the jam nut. Both brakes should be free when the pedal is depressed 1½ inches but should lock the wheels when pedal is depressed 2½ inches.

R&R AND OVERHAUL

All Models

168. The brake assembly can be removed from tractor after disconnecting the actuating linkage and removing the retaining cap screws. On

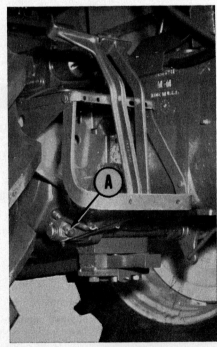

Fig. MM951—To adjust brakes on 5-Star and later series tractors turn rod nut (A) to obtain the recommended adjustment.

UB Special and UTS Special models with live power take-off, it is also necessary to remove the pto clutch and power release mechanism before removing the left brake.

Procedure for overhauling the brakes is evident after an examination of the removed units. When installing the brake housing, make certain that the retaining cap screws are installed in their original position. Install the brake assembly as shown in Fig. MM949.

Refer to paragraph 172 for information concerning the installation of the continuous power take-off clutch and power release mechanism used on UB Special and UTS Special units.

BELT PULLEY

UB Special-UTS Special

169. The belt pulley unit is mounted on side of transmission case and is driven by a bevel gear on the transmission lower countershaft. The procedure for removing, disassembling and overhauling the pulley unit is evident after an examination of the unit and reference to Fig. MM952.

5 Star-M5-M504-M602-M604-M670-M670 Super

170. The belt pulley unit is driven by a bevel gear on the power take-off shaft and is in continuous operation when the engine is running and pto clutch is engaged.

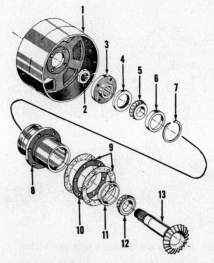

Fig. MM953—Exploded view of belt pulley assembly used on 5-Star, M5, M504, M602, M604, M670 and M670 Super.

1. Pulley	8. Bearing housing
2. Adjusting nut	9. Gaskets
3. Pulley hub	10. Shim pack
4. Oil seal	11. Bearing cup
5. Bearing cone	12. Bearing cone
6. Bearing cup	13. Pulley shaft
7. Snap ring	

To disassemble the belt pulley unit, remove nut (2—Fig. MM953) from pulley end of shaft and withdraw shaft (13) from housing (8). The tapered roller bearing cones (5 and 12), cups (6 and 11) and the oil seal (4) may be renewed at this time. Examine the oil seal seating surface on pulley hub (3) and renew hub if surface is worn or scored. When reassembling, tighten nut (2) to provide a slight rotational drag on the shaft bearings.

When installing the pulley unit, vary the number of shims (10) to provide a backlash of 0.005-0.007 between the driving bevel gears.

Tighten belt pulley housing retaining cap screws evenly to a torque of 52-58 ft.-lbs.

POWER TAKE-OFF

UB Special and UTS Special tractors are equipped with the pto assembly shown in Fig. MM954. The pto assembly is driven by the connecting shaft (21) which is splined to the transmission countershaft. The pto is thus dependent on the transmission main clutch for power. Some models, however, are equipped with the power release mechanism shown in Fig. MM955. This multiple disc clutch interrupts the flow of power to the left bull pinion, thus stopping the forward motion of the tractor without interrupting the power to the pto output shaft, providing a continuous (live) pto.

For service on the power take-off unit used on Series 5 Star, M5, M504, M602, M604, M670 and M670 Super, refer to separate section beginning with paragraph 175.

CLUTCH

Models So Equipped

171. **ADJUSTMENT.** To adjust the disc type power take-off clutch, turn the adjusting nut on clutch rod either way as required to give the clutch control handle a free travel of 2½ inches minimum.

172. **OVERHAUL.** Remove left rear wheel, fender and fender bracket. Remove cover (1—Fig. MM955) from unit; remove screws and withdraw the bearing cage (6). The outboard bearing bronze bushing (7) can be renewed at this time. Remove outer snap ring (2) and withdraw adaptor (3). Remove snap rings (2 and 5) and withdraw the clutch assembly.

The clutch can be disassembled after removing the cover plate cap screws. Inspect all internal parts and renew or recondition any which are questionable. Linings should be renewed if they are warped or worn. Machined surfaces of cover plate, intermediate discs and power plate should be smooth and not scored or grooved. Springs, spring seals, balls and ball inserts must be in good condition and not heat discolored. When

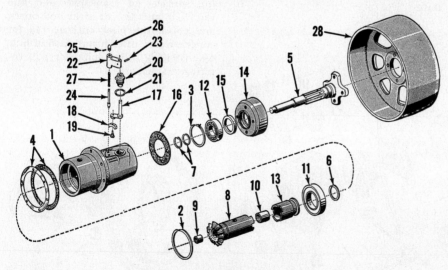

Fig. MM952—Exploded view of belt pulley drive and associated parts used on series UB Special and UTS Special tractors.

1. Housing	8. Bevel pinion	15. Oil seal	22. Lever
2. Snap ring	9. Needle bearing	16. Gasket	23. Roll pin
3. Snap ring	10. Needle bearing	17. Shifting arm	24. Lock pin
4. Shim and gasket	11. Ball bearing	18. Block	25. Roll pin
5. Drive shaft	12. Ball bearing	19. Pin	26. Knob
6. Snap ring	13. Sliding jaw	20. Nut	27. Spring
7. Snap rings	14. Retainer	21. Gasket	28. Belt pulley rim

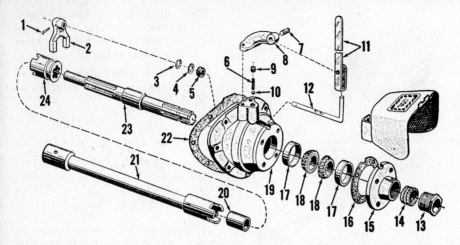

Fig. MM954—Exploded view of pto output shaft. Bearings are adjusted with shims (16).

1. Pin	7. Pin	13. Packing nut	19. Housing
2. Shifter fork	8. Bracket	14. Packing	20. Bushing
3. Snap ring	9. Pipe plug	15. Housing cap	21. Connecting shaft
4. Washer	10. Ball	16. Shims	22. Gasket
5. Seal	11. Lever	17. Bearing cup	23. Splined output shaft
6. Spring	12. Shifter rod	18. Bearing cone	24. Sliding jaw

POWER TAKE-OFF

NOTE: This section refers to the power take-off unit used on Series 5 Star, M5, M504, M602, M604, M670 and M670 Super. For power take-off used on UB Special and UTS Special tractors, refer to section beginning with paragraph 171.

The power take-off system is driven by a splined hub located at the rear of the engine crankshaft and is in continuous operation as long as the engine is running and the pto clutch is engaged.

The occasion for overhauling the complete power take-off system will be infrequent. The subsequent paragraphs will therefore be outlined in the basis of local repairs.

reassembling the clutch, make certain that all parts are in position and properly aligned.

To remove the power release mechanism, remove snap ring (5), remove the three retaining cap screws and disconnect the linkage. Disassemble the unit and renew any questionable parts.

Reassemble the clutch and power release mechanism by reversing the disassembly procedure and adjust the unit as outlined in paragraph 171.

OUTPUT SHAFT
UB Special-UTS Special

173. BEARING ADJUSTMENT. Vary number of shims (16—Fig. MM-954) between housing cap (15) and housing to provide zero end play to PTO shaft and yet permit same to rotate freely.

174. R&R AND DISASSEMBLE. Drain lubricant from transmission housing or raise rear of tractor far enough to prevent loss of lubricant from housing after PTO unit has been removed. Remove cap screws retaining PTO housing to rear of transmission housing and withdraw unit from transmission housing. The need and procedure for further disassembly will be evident by an examination of the parts and reference to Fig. MM954. To reinstall, reverse removal procedure.

DRIVING HUB
5 Star-M5-M504-M602-M604-M670-M670 Super

175. The pto is driven by a hub located at the rear of the engine crankshaft as shown in Fig. MM956. This driving hub (2) also contains the pilot bushing (4) for the main transmission input shaft. The driving hub can be removed after splitting the tractor between the engine and transmission case as outlined in paragraph 124, and removing the clutch assembly and flywheel. When renewing the pto driving hub, make sure the mating surfaces of crankshaft and hub are clean and free of nicks and burrs, and check the pilot bushing (4) for concentricity, after installation of hub, by installing a dial indicator and rotating crankshaft.

Fig. MM955—Exploded view of pto clutch and power release mechanism used on UB Special and UTS Special.

1. Cover	8. Intermediate plate	19. Ball	26. Spring seat
2. Snap ring	10. Power release plate	20. Ball insert	27. Spring
3. Adaptor	11. Ball insert	21. Spacer	28. Thrust bearing
5. Snap ring	12. Ball	22. Cover plate	35. Main housing
6. Bearing cage	13. Backing plate	23. Lined disc	36. Inner oil seal
7. Bearing	18. Housing	25. Power plate	37. Outer oil seal

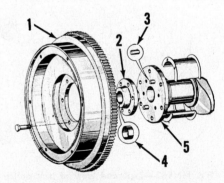

Fig. MM956—Exploded view of crankshaft flywheel assembly showing location of pto driving hub.

1. Flywheel
2. Pto driving hub
3. Dowel
4. Bushing
5. Crankshaft

Fig. MM957 — To adjust pto clutch on 5-Star models, disengage lock pin and turn adjusting ring as shown. Later models are similar.

PTO CLUTCH AND INPUT SHAFT

5 Star-M5-M504-M602-M604-M670-M670 Super

176. **CLUTCH ADJUSTMENT.** The pto clutch should engage with a distinct snap, with 55-65 pounds of pressure required on the engaging lever to lock the clutch in the engaged position. If little effort (35 pound minimum) is required to engage the clutch, the unit must be adjusted as follows:

Fig. MM958 — M5 tractor showing location of pipe plug allowing access to pto clutch adjustment.

Fig. MM959 — View showing location of plug (1) on right side of model M670 final drive housing allowing access to pto clutch adjustment.

On all models equipped with the "Type E" hydraulic system it will first be necessary to drain the hydraulic system and remove the hydraulic lift unit, seat, and cover from the top of the final drive housing. Pull the pto engaging lever to the disengaged (rear) position and turn the clutch assembly until the spring loaded lock pin is visible through the cover opening as shown in Fig. MM957. Depress the lock pin and turn the notched adjusting ring clockwise until pin engages the next notch and recheck the adjustment. Repeat the procedure if necessary, until the proper adjustment is obtained.

Series M5 and later tractors except model M670 Super, equipped with "Tel-O-Flo" hydraulic system are provided with an opening in the final drive cover or final drive housing making clutch adjustment possible without removing the hydraulic lift system. To adjust the clutch on these tractors, remove the plug shown in Fig. MM958 or MM959, turn the pto clutch assembly until the spring loaded locking pin is visible through the plug opening, and proceed as outlined above for the other tractor models.

On model M670 Super, first drain the hydraulic system, then remove tractor seat, hydraulic lift unit and final drive housing top cover. Adjust the clutch using the procedure outlined above for the other tractor models. Then, adjust the pto brake as follows: Disengage the pto clutch, loosen jam nut and back off adjusting nut (1—Fig. MM960) until the band is completely free of the clutch drum. Using a torque wrench, measure the rolling torque of pto output shaft. Tighten the adjusting nut (1) until an ADDITIONAL torque of 22-26 ft.-lbs. (540 rpm output shaft) or 14-16 ft.-lbs. (1000 rpm output shaft) is re-

quired to rotate the output shaft. Tighten the jam nut. Engage clutch and check to see that band is free of drum at this time.

177. **REMOVE AND REINSTALL.** On model M670 Super, refer to paragraph 179; on all other models proceed as follows: To remove the pto clutch and input shaft, first drain the hydraulic system and remove tractor seat, hydraulic lift unit and final drive housing top cover. Unbolt and remove the hydraulic pump and adapter housing from the rear of the final drive housing.

Using a small punch, drive out the two roll pins (RP—Fig. MM962) retaining the clutch forks (20) to the control lever. Withdraw the control lever, forks and throwout yoke. Bend lockwasher (21—Fig. MM962A) away from nut (22) and unscrew the nut as far as possible. After nut (22) has been loosened, remove cotter pin (P) and set screw (25).

NOTE: The hardened and drilled set screw may break if excess leverage or shock load is applied in an attempt to loosen screw, making removal difficult.

Move the clutch assembly forward on the shaft and continue unscrewing the nut until it is free from shaft threads. Turn input shaft 180 degrees, move clutch unit forward and remove the key (2—Fig. MM961) from input shaft, then, using a suitable puller, remove input shaft from rear of final drive housing. Lift out the clutch assembly and clutch cage (16) as the input shaft is withdrawn. If a puller is not available, the shaft can be bumped rearward by using a punch and hammer against the set screw seating surface of shaft or by using a soft faced drift against front end of shaft after splitting tractor at forward end of final drive housing.

178. To reinstall the clutch and input shaft, insert shaft through rear

Fig. MM960—View showing pto clutch and brake used on model M670 Super.

1. PTO brake adjusting nut
2. Lock pin
3. Adjusting ring

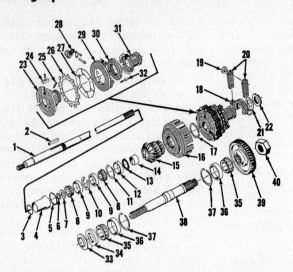

9. Bearing cup
10. Bearing spacer
11. Snap ring
12. Spacer
13. Thrust washer
14. Bushing
15. Driving gear
16. Clutch cage
17. Snap ring
18. Throwout yoke
19. Oil seal
20. Throwout fork
21. Lock washer
22. Adjusting nut
23. Back plate
24. Key
25. Set screw
26. Driven plate
27. Driving plate
28. Lever
29. Floating plate
30. Adjusting ring
31. Sliding sleeve
32. Lock pin
33. Dust shield
34. Oil seal
35. Bearing cone
36. Bearing cup

Fig. MM961 — Exploded view of pto assembly used on 5-Star and later tractors, except M670 Super.

1. Input shaft	5. Gasket	37. Snap ring
2. Key	6. Snap ring	38. Output shaft
3. Gasket	7. Washer	39. Output gear
4. Sleeve	8. Bearing cone	40. Shaft nut

opening in final drive housing and install the thrust washer (13—Fig. MM963). Position the pinion gear and clutch cage assembly over the pto driven gear (39—Fig. MM961) and slide the input shaft forward through the pinion and clutch cage assembly. Position the clutch assembly part way on the input shaft, then install the

Fig. MM962—To remove the pto clutch, first drive out the two roll pins (RP), then remove control lever and clutch forks (20).

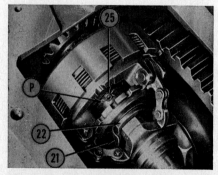

Fig. MM962A — After removing cotter pin (P), set screw (25), bending lock washer (21) and removing nut (22), pto clutch assembly can be slid forward for shaft removal.

lock washer (21) and nut (22) on the shaft so that they are between the sliding sleeve and adjusting ring. Slide the shaft forward making sure that splines in forward end of shaft engage in the internal splines in clutch driving hub, then bump the shaft forward into position.

Insert the key (2—Fig. MM961) in the input shaft, align the clutch keyway and slide the clutch assembly to the rear while tightening the lock nut (22). The fore and aft position of the clutch assembly on the input shaft is adjusted by means of the set screw (25) and nut (22); when the clutch position approaches the recommended clearance of 0.012-0.015 between the thrust washer (13) and drive pinion (15), install and tighten the set screw (25). With a feeler gage, measure the clearance as shown in Fig. MM963A. If the clearance is excessive, loosen the set screw and tighten the lock nut. If insufficient clearance exists, loosen the lock nut and tighten the set screw. When the specified 0.012-0.015 clearance is obtained, lock the adjustments by bending the washer over the flat of the nut and installing the cotter pin in the set screw. Install the clutch throwout forks and shaft and adjust the clutch as outlined in paragraph 176, then install the cover and hydraulic unit.

179. To remove the pto clutch and input shaft from model M670 Super, first drain the hydraulic system and remove tractor seat, hydraulic lift unit and final drive housing top cover. Disengage pto clutch, then remove lock wires and drive spiral pins out of shifting forks (6—Fig. MM964) and

Fig. MM963 — When reassembling pto assembly, be sure thrust washer (13) is in place before installing clutch unit.

brake lever (5). Withdraw the control lever, clutch forks and throwout yoke. Remove jam nut and band adjusting nut, then remove the pto brake assembly. On models equipped with 540 rpm pto, remove cover (42). On models equipped with the dual (540 and 1000 rpm) pto, unbolt and remove rear cover (2—Fig. MM965), idler gear and 540 rpm shaft assembly. Remove pto front plate (4) from final drive housing.

On models equipped with either pto proceed as follows: Bend lock washer (10—Fig. MM964) away from nut (9) and unscrew the nut as far as possible. Remove the over-center link pins and move the sliding sleeve (8) forward. Depress lock pin (13) and back off adjusting ring (11). Remove cotter pin and set screw (17).

NOTE: The hardened and drilled set screw may break if excess leverage or shock load is applied in an attempt to loosen screw, making removal difficult.

Move the clutch assembly forward and continue unscrewing nut until the nut is free from the threads. Rotate the clutch shaft 180 degrees, move clutch hub (18) forward and remove key (33). Using a punch and hammer against set screw seating surface, bump shaft rearward and lift out

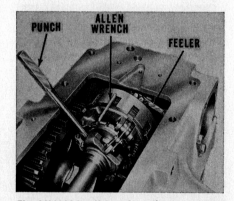

Fig. MM963A—Using the adjusting nut and set screw to obtain correct pto clutch end float. See text for details.

clutch and clutch cage as shaft is withdrawn from rear of final drive housing.

180. To install the clutch and input shaft, insert shaft (34—Fig. MM964) and place the clutch components on the shaft in proper order as shaft moves forward. Engage splines at front end of shaft into flywheel hub and bump shaft into position. Insert key (33) and slide clutch assembly into position while tightening locknut (9). The fore and aft position of the clutch assembly on the input shaft is adjusted by means of the set screw (17) and nut (9). The recommended clearance between gear (22) and thrust washer (23) is 0.012-0.015. If clearance is excessive, loosen the set screw and tighten the nut. If insufficient clearance exists, loosen the nut and tighten the set screw. When the specified 0.012-0.015 clearance is obtained, lock the adjustments by bending the washer over the flat of the nut and installing the cotter pin in the

set screw. Install the pto brake, throwout yoke, forks and shaft. Install rear cover or dual output unit, then adjust pto clutch and brake as outlined in paragraph 176.

181. OVERHAUL. To overhaul the clutch and input shaft on model M670 Super, refer to paragraph 182; on all other models, proceed as follows: With the clutch unit and input shaft removed as outlined in paragraph 177, remove the "C" type bearing spacer (10—Fig. MM961), examine the bearings and cups, and renew as required by removing the snap ring (6) and pressing the bearings from the input shaft. On model 5 Star, the input shaft rear bearings should be adjusted to a clearance of 0.001-0.004 by means of the selective thickness "C" type spacer (10). To adjust, use the thickest spacer which will slip between the bearing cups (9). Spacers are available in thicknesses of 0.120, 0.125, 0.128 and 0.132.

On models M5, M504, M602, M604 and M670, the "C" type spacer is 0.234 thick and the 0.001-0.004 end play is adjusted by selective thickness washer (7). Washers are available in thicknesses of 0.127, 0.132, 0.137, 0.142, 0.147, 0.152, 0.154 and 0.157.

To overhaul the pto clutch unit after it is removed as outlined in paragraph 177, first remove the pins retaining the sliding sleeve (31—Fig. MM961) to the floating plate (29) and lift off the sliding sleeve. Depress the spring-loaded pin (32), completely unscrew the notched adjusting ring (30) and disassemble the floating plate (29), driving plates (27) and driven plates (26) from the back plate (23). Thoroughly clean all parts and renew any which are damaged or worn. The seven driving plates (27) and six driven plates (26) must not be warped or worn. Renew the levers (28), and the connecting pins and links if they are damaged or worn.

The driving gear (15) can be removed from the clutch cage (16) by removing snap ring (17). Normal diametral clearance between the driving gear bushings (14) and input shaft (1) is 0.0025-0.003. Renew the two bushings, driving gear or shaft if clearance is excessive.

182. On model M670 Super, remove clutch and input shaft as outlined in paragraph 179, then remove snap ring (26—Fig. MM964), shim washer (27) and "C" spacer (28). Bearing cups (29) and cones (30) can now be pressed from shaft (34). When reassembling, install the 0.234 thick "C" type spacer between the bearing cups. The recommended 0.001-0.004 bearing end play is adjusted by selective thickness shim washer (27). Washers are available in thicknesses of 0.127, 0.132, 0.137, 0.142, 0.147, 0.152, 0.154 and 0.157.

To overhaul the pto clutch after it is removed as outlined in paragraph 179, separate floating plate (14—Fig. MM964, driving plates (15) and driven plates (16) from clutch hub (18). Clean and check all parts and renew any which are worn or damaged. Make certain that the seven driving plates and six driven plates are not warped or worn. The driving gear (22) can be removed from clutch cage (20) after removing snap ring (19). Normal diametral clearance between the driving gear bushings and input shaft is 0.0025-0.003. Renew the two bushings, driving gear or shaft if clearance is excessive.

Fig. MM964—Exploded view of pto clutch and 540 rpm rear unit used on model M670 Super.

1. PTO brake band	15. Driving plate	29. Bearing cup
2. Brake bracket	16. Driven plate	30. Bearing cone
3. Spring	17. Set screw	31. Snap ring
4. Link	18. Clutch hub	32. Retainer
5. Brake lever	19. Snap ring	33. Key
6. Clutch fork	20. Clutch cage	34. Input shaft
7. Yoke	21. Thrust washer	35. Driven gear
8. Sliding sleeve	22. Driving gear	36. Bearing cone
9. Nut	23. Thrust washer	37. Bearing cup
10. Lock washer	24. Sleeve	38. Snap ring
11. Adjusting ring	25. Gasket	39. Output shaft
12. Lever	26. Snap ring	40. Oil seal
13. Lock pin	27. Shim washer	41. Gasket
14. Floating plate	28. Spacer	42. Cover

PTO OUTPUT SHAFT

5 Star-M5-M504-M602-M604-M-670

183. R&R AND OVERHAUL. To remove the pto output shaft (38—Fig. MM961), first remove the pto clutch and input shaft as outlined in paragraph 177, remove nut (40) and driven gear (39), then bump the output shaft rearward out of the final drive housing. If bearing cups (36) are damaged, drive them from housing using a suitable drift.

When reassembling, be sure that hub end of driven gear (39) is toward rear of tractor; then tighten the retaining nut (40) to provide the desired 3-6 inch pounds rolling torque on the two carrier bearings (35). The pto oil seal (34) should be installed with a suitable driver until the rear face of seal is $\frac{3}{16}$-inch past the rear face of housing. Dust seal (33) is then installed flush with housing.

Install the pto clutch and input shaft as outlined in paragraph 178 and adjust the unit as outlined in paragraph 176.

M670 Super

184. R&R AND OVERHAUL. To remove the pto output shaft (39—Fig. MM964) on models equipped with 540 rpm pto, first remove the pto clutch and input shaft as outlined in paragraph 179. Remove the self-locking nut and bump shaft (39) rearward out of driven gear (35) and bearing cone (36). Bearing cups (37) can now be driven from housing, using a suitable drift.

When reassembling, install the driven gear on output shaft so the long portion of the hub is against the bearing. Tighten the self-locking nut to provide the desired 3-6 inch pounds rolling torque preload on the bearings. Install new oil seal (40) with lip edge to inside. Install the pto clutch and input shaft as outlined in paragraph 180 and adjust the unit as outlined in paragraph 176.

On models equipped with the dual (540 and 1000 rpm) pto, refer to Fig. MM965 and proceed as follows: Unbolt and remove rear cover (2), idler gear and 540 rpm output shaft assembly. Withdraw idler shaft (24), idler gear (22) and thrust washers (21 and 23) from cover. Remove shaft (30), gear (31) with bearing cones (29 and 32) from cover. Bearings and gear can now be removed from 540 rpm output shaft, using a suitable press. Unbolt and remove pto front plate (4) from final drive housing, then remove pto clutch, brake and input

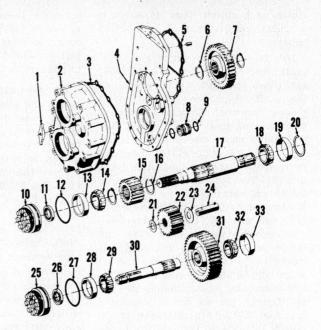

Fig. MM965 — Exploded view of dual pto rear unit used on model M670 Super.

1. Lock
2. Rear cover
3. Gasket
4. Front plate
5. Gasket
6. Snap ring
7. 1000 rpm driving gear
8. Oil tube
9. "O" ring
10. Adjusting nut
11. Oil seal
12. "O" ring
13. Bearing cup
14. Bearing cone
15. 540 rpm driving gear
16. Snap ring
17. 1000 rpm output shaft
18. Bearing cone
19. Bearing cup
20. Snap ring
21. Thrust washer
22. Idler gear
23. Thrust washer
24. Idler shaft
25. Adjusting nut
26. Oil seal
27. "O" ring
28. Bearing cup
29. Bearing cone
30. 540 rpm output shaft
31. 540 rpm driven gear
32. Bearing cone
33. Bearing cup

shaft as outlined in paragraph 179. Remove snap ring from front end of 1000 rpm output shaft and bump shaft rearward out of gear (7). Bearings (14 and 18), snap rings (16) and gear (15) can now be removed. Remove lock (1) and rotate bearing adjusting nuts (10 and 25) until they are removed from inside of cover (2).

When reassembling, renew oil seals, "O" rings and gaskets. Install idler

shaft with roll pin pointing up and tang on thrust washer (23) to the top and away from idler gear. Reinstall all parts by reversing the removal procedure. Adjust pto clutch and brake as outlined in paragraph 176. Using a dial indicator check the end play of each output shaft. Turn adjusting nuts as required until the desired 0.001-0.008 end play is obtained on each shaft. Secure the adjusting nuts with lock (1).

HYDRAULIC LIFT
(Except Tel-O-Flo)

This section covers the hydraulic lift system used on UB Special and UTS Special tractors, and on M5, M504, M602, M604, M670 and M670 Super models equipped with "Type E" hydraulic system. The section covers the hydraulic pump, reservoir, control valve and remote cylinder. For tractors equipped with the three-point hitch "Tel-O-Flo" system, see paragraphs beginning with 206.

CAUTION: Most hydraulic system trouble is caused by dirt or gummy deposits. The dirt may enter the system from the outside or may show up as the result of wear or partial failure of some part of the system. Gummy deposits usually result from inadequate or contaminated fluids or failure to drain and refill the system at the specified intervals. When overhauling any unit of the hydraulic system, the same standards

of care and cleanliness accorded to any diesel or hydraulic units must be observed. Disassembly or service should only be attempted in a clean dust-free shop and the removed assemblies stored and serviced only where good housekeeping is observed.

FILLING AND BLEEDING
All Models

185. It is recommended that the complete hydraulic system be drained at least once a year. Before refilling the system, remove and thoroughly clean the filter screen which is located in the filler plug opening on UB Special and UTS Special tractors, in the top of reservoir on models M5, M504, M602 and M604 and in the side of reservoir on models M670 and M670 Super.

Fig. MM966—Test gage installed in breakaway coupling for checking hydraulic pressure. Refer to text.

Fill the reservoir with MM hydraulic oil, operate the hydraulic jack and power steering several times and refill the reservoir to the level of the filler plug opening. Capacity of the system is approximately 1¾ gallons for UB Special and UTS Special, or 3½ gallons for units with Type E system.

SYSTEM PRESSURE

UB Special-UTS Special

186. Hydraulic system pressure is controlled by a relief valve built into each of the control valve actuating spools. To check the pressure, connect a test gage to breakaway coupling as shown in Fig. MM966 and, with engine running at rated speed, hold control lever in direction to pressurize that port ONLY long enough to note gage pressure. Each line should be tested individually and the pressure recorded for future reference if adjustment is required. With a lifting jack connected to breakaway couplings, actuating lever should remain in raising or lowering position until piston reaches end of stroke, then return to neutral position when relief pressure is attained.

Relief pressure should be 950-1050 psi for each valve. Pressure may be increased not to exceed 1500 psi on tractors equipped with Webster pump only. To adjust the pressure, drain the reservoir and disassemble control valve as outlined in paragraph 195. With valve spools removed, extract cotter pin from spring end of valve spool through-bolt and tighten the castellated nut to increase pressure, or loosen nut to decrease pressure. Make sure valve spools are properly synchronized when reassembling, as outlined in paragraph 195.

Type E. System With Char-Lynn Valve

187. The "Type E" remote system using two Char-Lynn control valves has a pressure relief valve located in each control valve which is set to open at 1450-1550 psi. In addition, the system is equipped with a main relief (by-pass) valve which opens at a pressure of 1600-1800 psi. The purpose of the by-pass valve is to prevent pressure multiplication and possible system damage when both control valves are actuated at the same time. On systems equipped with only one control valve, the by-pass valve is omitted and system pressure is entirely controlled by the pressure valve located in control valve.

To completely check the pressure on dual systems, tee a suitable test gage into the pressure line leading from hydraulic pump to by-pass valve. With hydraulic system at normal operating temperature and engine running at rated speed, momentarily hold BOTH valve levers in an operating position. With oil flow blocked at breakaway couplings, main relief (by-pass) valve should open and gage pressure should read 1600-1800 psi. Remove acorn nut (3—Fig. MM967) and turn the exposed adjusting screw to adjust the by-pass pressure. Hold levers in operating position ONLY long enough to note gage pressure. With by-pass valve properly adjusted, hold EACH valve lever in turn, in an operating position and note the pressure at which the circuit relief valve opens. Pressure should be 1450-1550 psi.; if it is not, remove control valve end cap and turn the exposed relief valve adjusting screw clockwise to increase, or counter-clockwise to de-

crease, pressure. Refer to Fig. MM979 for view of control valve body showing location of relief valve.

Type E. System With Wooster Valve

188. The Wooster control valve used on some tractors with "Type E" system is a sandwich type with a main relief valve adjusted by means of shims after valve is removed; and a separate detent release valve for each spool which can be adjusted without valve removal.

Normal operating pressure is therefore controlled by individual setting of the detent release pressure, and the main relief valve operates in a safety capacity only.

To check the system, connect a test gage to breakaway coupling as shown in Fig. MM966; in series with a lifting jack; or in series with a needle type shut-off valve, the gage and shut-off valve being the preferred combination. With hydraulic fluid at normal operating temperature and engine running at rated speed, close the shut-off valve and momentarily hold operating lever in correct direction to pressurize the gage. Pressure should be 1750-1900 psi. If it is not, remove control valve assembly and overhaul main relief valve as outlined in paragraph 199 before proceeding with the adjustment.

To adjust the detent release pressure, refer to Fig. MM968. Working from behind and below the reservoir, remove valve spool venting cap (1) on spool to be adjusted. With hydrau-

Fig. MM967 — Right side of Type E system reservoir used on tractor with Char-Lynn dual control valves, showing location of by-pass valve.

1. Pressure line   3. Acorn nut
2. By-pass valve   4. Jam nut

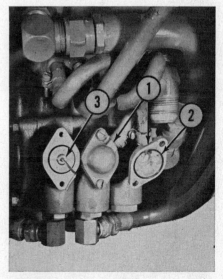

Fig. MM968 — To adjust detent release pressure on Wooster valve, remove venting cap (1) and turn nylock adjusting screw (3) using an Allen wrench. Make sure sealing "O" ring (2) is in good condition when reinstalling venting cap.

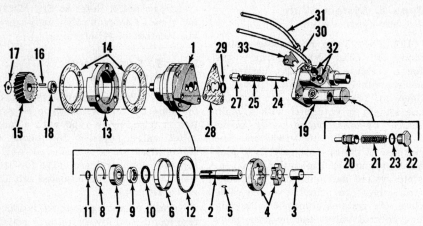

Fig. MM969—Exploded view of Eaton hydraulic pump used on early "UB Special - UTS Special" tractors.

1. Pump body	12. Gasket	22. Valve spring plug
2. Shaft	13. Adaptor	23. "O" ring
3. Bushing	14. Gaskets	24. Relief valve
4. Rotor set	15. Drive gear	25. Relief valve spring
5. Key	16. Key	27. Relief valve seat
6. Bushing	17. Lock washer	28. Gasket
7. Bearing	18. Spacer	29. "O" ring
8. Snap ring	19. Flow control assembly	30. Pressure tube
9. Oil seal	20. Flow control valve	31. Return tube
10. Gasket	21. Flow control valve	32. "O" ring
11. Snap ring	spring	33. Clip

lic fluid at operating temperature and engine running at rated speed, open shut-off valve in test hose and move operating lever to detent position. Slowly close shut-off valve, noting gage pressure at which operating lever snaps back to neutral position. NOTE: If gage pressure does not rise, move operating lever to opposite detent position. Pressure should be 1500-1600 psi; if it is not, turn nyloc adjusting screw (3) using an Allen wrench, until release pressure is correct. Inspect "O" ring (2) and renew if required, before reinstalling venting cap (1). If pressure cannot be satisfactorily adjusted, overhaul the valve as outlined in paragraphs 197 through 201.

Type E. System With Vickers Valve

189. The Vickers control valve used on model M670 Super tractors equipped with Type E system is a two spool unit with a pre-set main relief valve.

The relief valve is non-adjustable and is available only in a relief valve kit which also includes a relief valve plunger and springs.

To check the system relief pressure, connect a test gage to breakaway coupling as shown in Fig. MM966. With hydraulic fluid at operating temperature and engine running at rated speed, move control lever in correct direction to pressurize the gage. Pressure should be 1725-1825 psi. If it is not, remove the control valve and renew the main relief valve as outlined in paragraphs 202 and 203.

PUMP

All Models

190. **REMOVE AND REINSTALL.** On UB Special, UTS Special and M670 Super models, the hydraulic pump is mounted on engine block and is gear driven from engine timing gears. On all other models, the hy-

draulic pump is mounted on rear of final drive housing and coupled to the pto input shaft. Method of removal and installation is evident. Note sequence of hose installation on power steering models before removal, to aid in installation.

Most gear driven models are equipped with shear pins to protect engine timing gears. Examine the shear pins whenever pump is removed, and renew as needed.

191. **OVERHAUL (EATON PUMP).** Some UB Special and UTS Special tractors may be equipped with an Eaton gerotor pump of the type shown exploded in Fig. MM969.

When removing flow control manifold (19) on models equipped with power steering, be careful not to lose relief valve parts (24, 25 and 27) which will be free when manifold is removed.

When disassembling pump body, check for correlation marks on rotor set (4). Marks are to prevent inverting either rotor when pump is reassembled. Bushings (3 and 6) will usually restore pump efficiency if pump parts are not scored. Reassemble by reversing disassembly procedure, turning pump shaft as bolts are tightened, to make sure pump does not bind.

192. **WEBSTER PUMPS.** Webster gear type hydraulic pumps are of two different types. Pumps used on UB Special, UTS Special and 5 Star have fixed wear plates, and field rebuilding is not generally satisfactory. The pump can, however, be disassembled and resealed.

All other models have pressure balanced wear plates as shown in Fig. MM971, and rebuilding is generally satisfactory if normal care is used.

193. **RESEAL (EARLY PUMPS).** To disassemble the unit, unbolt and remove the pump cover and lift out the idler gear and shaft. On some pumps driver gear is retained to drive shaft by a Woodruff key and snap rings. Some models are splined. Remove the drive shaft, seal plate and ball bearing, then thoroughly clean pump parts in a suitable solvent. If parts are badly worn, scored or heat discolored, renew the pump. If parts are suitable for re-use renew all seals and reverse the disassembly procedure. Use a thin coating of shellac between ground surfaces of pump castings and wear plates, being sure excess shellac will not be squeezed into gear area during reassembly. Tighten the $\frac{5}{16}$-inch cap screws to a

Fig. MM970—Exploded view of Webster hydraulic pump used on late series "UB Special - UTS Special" tractors.

1. Pump body	20. Flow control valve
2. Adaptor	21. Flow control valve
3. Gasket	spring
5. Drive gear	22. Plug
6. Sleeve	23. "O" ring
7. Key	24. Relief valve
8. Shear pin	25. Relief valve spring
9. Spacer	27. Valve seat
10. Washer	28. Gasket
11. Bolt	29. "O" ring
12. Flow control valve	33. Flange
assembly	
14. Gasket	

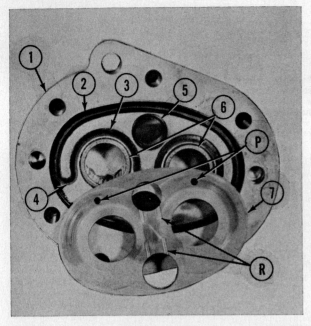

Fig. MM971 — Partially disassembled view of Webster hydraulic pump end housing, wear plate and associated parts.

P. Pressure ports
R. Relief grooves
1. End housing
2. Outer seal
3. Inner seal
4. Back-up ring
5. "O" ring
6. Needle bearings
7. Wear plate

Fig. MM972 — Before removing gears or gear housing on Webster pump, mark the gears as shown at (A) and measure gear to housing clearance. Refer to text.

torque of 9-12 ft.-lbs. and ¼-inch cap screws to a torque of 6-8 ft.-lbs.

194. OVERHAUL (LATE PUMPS). Before disassembling the pump, scribe correlation marks on all housings for alignment during reassembly. Remove the retaining cap screws and lift off the manifold plate and pump rear end plate. Before removing the gears or gear plate, mark the gears as shown at (A—Fig. MM972) and check gear to housing clearance with a feeler gage as shown. If clearance exceeds 0.005, renew the pump. Examine bores of gear housing as shown in Fig. MM-973. If badly scored or heat-discolored, renew the pump.

On most pumps, no attempt should be made to disassemble pumping gears and shafts. Examine ends and sides of gear teeth for scoring, and shaft areas for scoring or wear.

Examine wear plates for wear or deep scoring in gear travel area. Slight marking is normal, and is more pronounced on pressure side. The rear wear plate contains relief slots (R—Fig. MM971).

If gear shafts are worn at bearing area and gears are renewed, the shaft needle bearings should also be renewed on models so equipped. Heating end plates to 200°F. will facilitate removal of blind bearings. Pump end housings are not available separately; if damaged, the pump must be renewed.

Always renew all seals whenever pump is disassembled. Make sure pressure ports (P) in wear plates open into area enclosed by inner pressure seal (3). Bearing areas of end housings are ported to inlet side of pump

to prevent pressure build-up, and return any hydraulic fluid leaking past bearings. Lubricate the parts thoroughly with MM hydraulic fluid or equivalent, when assembling, and tighten the retaining cap screws alternately and evenly to a torque of 190-210 in.-lbs.

If pump binds after assembly, disassemble and determine the cause before installing the pump. Be sure hydraulic lines are connected and reservoir filled before starting tractor engine.

RESERVOIR AND CONTROL VALVE

UB Special-UTS Special

195. The hydraulic unit reservoir contains the system filter, strainer, control linkage and control valves.

The reservoir is the front support for fuel tank and will not need to be removed for hydraulic system service except when thorough cleaning is required.

To remove the reservoir cover containing the control valves for service or adjustment, first drain the system and remove reservoir flange (manifold). Refer to Fig. MM974. Disconnect control rod from cross rod lever on right side of tractor, drive out the retaining pin and remove lever from cross rod (47). Remove the cap screws retaining reservoir cover (49) to reservoir. Cover and valve unit can now be withdrawn. If gasket (61) sticks, bump lever end of cross rod (47) to loosen gasket.

To remove the two control valves (48) for service or adjustment, remove nut from stud (52) and with-

draw cross rod (47) and associated parts. Identify the two valves (48) so they can be reinstalled in same bores if raising and lowering pressures are adjusted to different values, otherwise the valves are fully interchangeable. Component parts of valve spool (48) are not available for service, but spool assembly is available as a service item and individual fitting is not required. Relief pressure of a new valve spool is factory adjusted to the recommended 950-1050 psi relief pressure, and adjustment is not required unless pressures have been altered. Refer to paragraph 186 for adjustment procedure.

Install valve spools in cover (49) by reversing the removal procedure. Both valves must be centered on gear of cross rod (47) with cross rod cam in neutral (center) detent position.

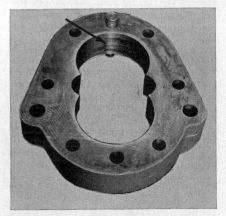

Fig. MM973 — Examine pressure areas of gear housing bore as shown by arrow. Refer to text.

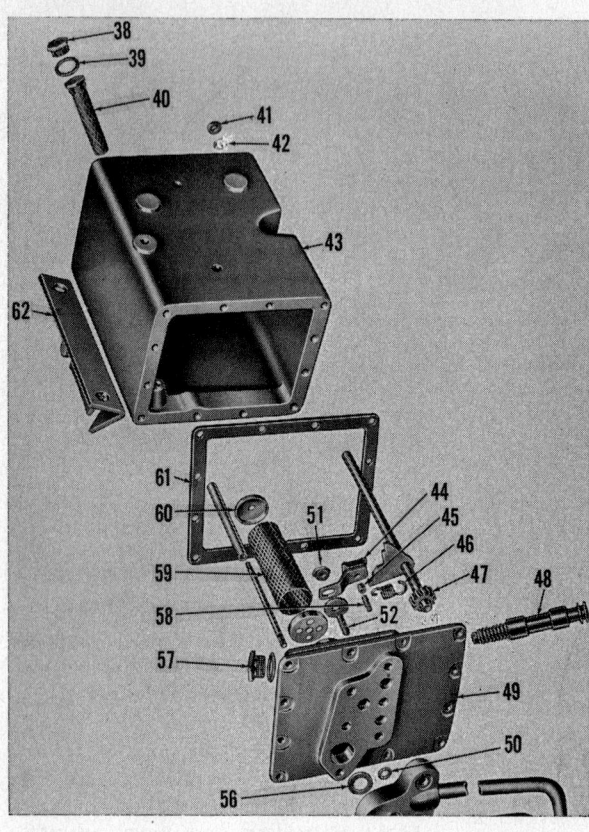

Fig. MM974 — Uni-Matic system reservoir and control valve used on UB Special and UTS Special tractors, showing component parts.

38. Filler plug
39. Gasket
40. Strainer
41. Retainer
42. Seal
43. Reservoir
44. Cam lever
45. Roller
46. Spring
47. Cross rod
48. Control valve
49. Cover
50. "O" ring
51. Eccentric bushing
52. Stud
56. "O" ring
57. End plug
58. Roller shaft
59. Filter screen
60. Retainer
61. Gasket
62. Support

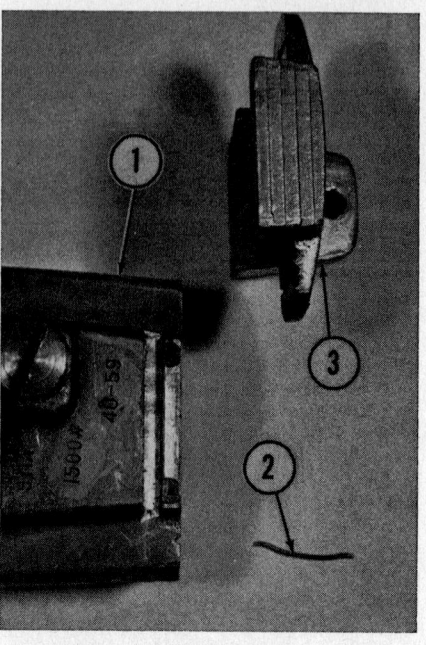

Fig. MM976 — After removing spring-type locking pin (2) on early valve, end cap (3) will slide sideways from housing. On late valve, end cap (3) is retained by screws.

Equalize valves after assembly by turning eccentric bushing (51) until visible ends of both valves are aligned, then tighten stud nut. Rotate cross rod (47) to raising and lowering detent position and check the action, before reinstalling unit in reservoir.

Type E System With Char-Lynn Valve

196. The hydraulic system reservoir is located on the operator's platform underneath the driver's seat. To obtain access to the reservoir or control valves, remove the seat and seat base. One or more Char-Lynn control valves are mounted on the top of the hydraulic system reservoir. To remove the valve (or valves) disconnect the control lever linkage, then unbolt and

remove the valve assemblies. In units where more than one valve is used, the two valves are connected together by a short nipple.

To disassemble the removed valve on early units, refer to Fig. MM975 and, using a small pointed tool, push spring-type locking pin (2) out of housing until it can be grasped with pliers, then remove the pin, and end cap (3) by sliding it sideways off the body. On some valves, end cap is retained by screws. Remove the shuttle valve plug (4), blade spring (5—Fig. MM977) and blade (7), then unscrew and remove the lever end cap (8). On early valves, centering spring and associated parts are located on end of valve spool containing the attaching eye; on late valves, centering

spring is on opposite end of spool. Remove the exposed spring retaining snap ring (10—Fig. MM978) and slide centering spring (11) from the valve spool. Push valve spool (9) into housing far enough to expose the front spool seal (12), remove the seal then withdraw the spool assembly from spring end of valve body as shown in Fig. MM977. Carefully note position of shuttle (13—Fig. MM978) and shuttle spring (14) as valve spool is withdrawn, to insure correct assembly. The shuttle and shuttle spring lie between the two lands at the closed end of the valve spool and contact the edge of shuttle blade (7—Fig. MM977), forming a detent to hold spool in operating position until the hydraulic cylinder reaches the end of its stroke.

Before disturbing the relief valve, make a note of position of relief valve plug (16—Fig. MM979) and count the number of turns required to remove the plug, so that plug can be reinstalled in the same approximate position. Remove the relief valve plug, relief valve and spring (15), and examine the relief valve and seat for wear and damage. The seat (not shown) is threaded into valve body and can be removed with a screw driver of proper size.

Clean the component parts in a suitable solvent and examine for wear or scoring. To assemble the valve proceed as follows: Remove the remaining spring retaining snap ring

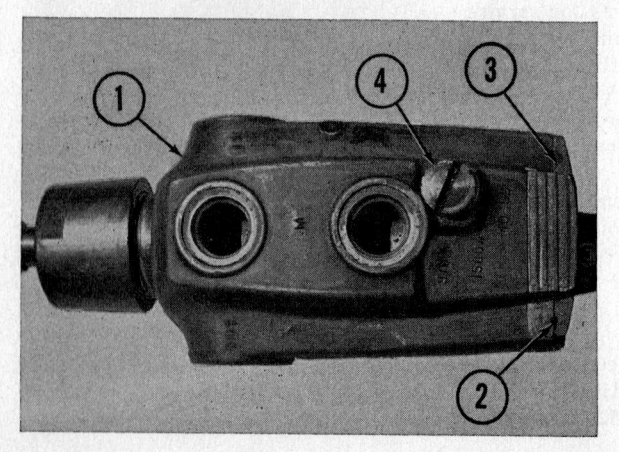

Fig. MM975 — Char-Lynn control valve used on some tractors with Type "E" hydraulic system.

1. Valve body
2. Locking pin
3. End cap
4. Shuttle valve plug

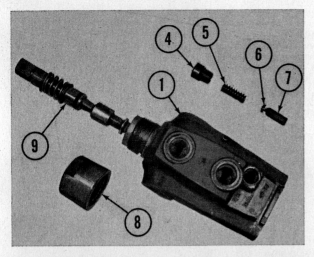

Fig. MM977 — Remove lever end cap (8), shuttle valve plug (4), spring (5) and blade (7), push valve spool through valve to remove inner spool seal, then withdraw spool from spring end as shown.

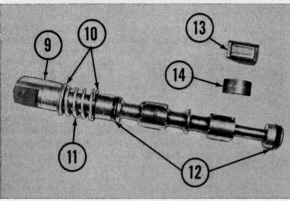

Fig. MM978 — Removed valve spool (9) showing the assembled centering spring (11), retaining snap rings (10) and spool seals (12). Shuttle (13) and shuttle spring (14) lie between the inner two lands of valve spool to hold spool in operating position until cylinder reaches end of stroke. Early valve is shown; centering spring (11) is located on opposite end of spool on some models.

blade (7—Fig. MM977) with narrow edge to shuttle, until blade fits in the retaining groove in valve housing, then install spring (5) and plug (4). Reinstall relief valve (15—Fig. MM-979) and plug (16) if they were removed, and complete the assembly by reversing the disassembly procedure.

Type E System With Wooster Valve

197. **REMOVE AND REINSTALL.** To remove the control valve, first drain the hydraulic system reservoir, disconnect pump pressure and return lines and remove the seat assembly; then unbolt and remove the reservoir and valve assembly from tractor. Remove reservoir front cover retaining bolts, disconnect control levers, and lift off the front cover. Carefully mark the position of control valve on mounting plate to assist in alignment of control levers during assembly. Mark and disconnect hoses from control valve, remove the mounting stud nuts; and lift off the valve.

Reinstall by reversing the removal procedure. Align control valve with previously marked position on mounting plate; or check to be sure control lever links can be installed without binding, before tightening mounting stud nuts.

The fittings contain sealing "O" rings as shown in Fig. MM980. Install and connect fittings as outlined in paragraph 198 to prevent subsequent leakage.

198. **FITTINGS.** The hydraulic fittings have SAE straight tubing threads with "O" ring seals (J.I.C. fittings) as shown in Fig. MM980. DO NOT attempt to install pipe fittings in valve ports.

(10—Fig. MM978) from the valve spool, renew the spool seals (12) with seal lips to center of spool as shown. Lubricate spool with clean hydraulic fluid and carefully insert spring end of spool in valve body. Push spool through valve body until next to last land has just entered body, then assemble shuttle spring (14) in spool with the two spring ends outward. Assemble shuttle (13), either end forward, over spring, then carefully slide the completed assembly into the valve bore until the lip of spool seal (12) contacts valve body. Carefully work the seal lip into the valve bore with a suitable tool, then push spool rearward until end is flush with the end of valve body. Working through the plug hole in top of valve body, turn shuttle (13) until flat surface is parallel to plug hole, then insert shuttle

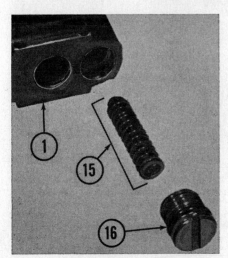

Fig. MM979—Relief valve assembly (15) and plug (16) can be removed after removing end cap (3—Fig. MM976).

Fig. MM980 — Special care must be taken when installing J. I. C. fittings, to be sure "O" ring (4) is not cut causing the fitting to leak. Refer to text.

1. Fitting
2. Jam nut
3. Washer
4. "O" ring

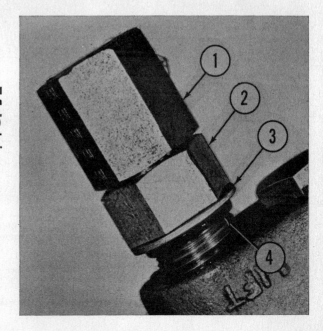

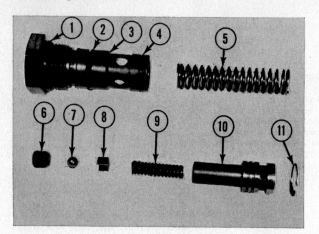

Fig. MM981 — Disassembled view of the main relief valve used in Type E system with Wooster valve.

1. "O" ring
2. "O" ring
3. Cartridge
4. "O" ring
5. Spring
6. Sensing valve seat
7. Valve ball
8. Block
9. Spring
10. Piston
11. Snap ring

Fig. MM983 — On the Wooster valve, adjust detent release pressure to 18-21 lbs. by turning Allen wrench (5).

1. Detent housing
2. Boot
3. Control valve spool
4. Spring scale
5. Allen wrench

The "O" ring (4) is compressed in its groove to form a leak proof seal, by tightening jam nut (2). DO NOT attempt to alter the position of fitting without first loosening jam nut (2) and making sure "O" ring (4) is free in groove. If "O" ring is cut by improper installation or maintenance, leakage will result.

199. MAIN RELIEF VALVE. The main relief valve can be removed for service or adjustment after control valve has been removed as outlined in paragraph 197. The valve (See Fig. MM981) is located in mounting side of inlet cover.

To service the main relief valve, unscrew cartridge (3—Fig. MM982) from cover (C). Check to see that sensing ports (P) in cartridge and cover are open, and that "O" rings (1 & 2) are in satisfactory condition.

Clamp hex head of cartridge (3—Fig. MM981) in a vise, lightly press

down on piston (10) and remove snap ring (11); then withdraw piston (10) and spring (5). Piston must slide freely in cartridge bore.

Using an Allen wrench, remove the threaded pilot valve seat (6), while COUNTING THE TURNS seat is threaded into piston. Remove seat (6), valve ball (7), block (8) and spring (9). Check the block (8) and internal threads in piston (10), to make sure that sharp corners of block are not hanging up in threads in piston, causing erratic action of the valve. If interference is noted, chamfer corners of block or renew the cartridge, using one with fewer threads.

Assemble by reversing the disassembly procedure. If parts have been renewed in valve piston, install pilot valve seat (6) in piston until end of seat protrudes approximately $\frac{1}{16}$-inch

from valve. If parts are not renewed, install seat THE SAME NUMBER OF TURNS used in removing valve; then turn seat in slightly to raise pressure (or out slightly to lower pressure) if other defects were not found while valve was disassembled.

200. CONTROL VALVE. The control valve spool and associated parts can be removed for service without disassembling the valve body housings. Proceed as follows:

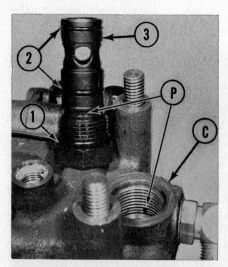

Fig. MM982 — When removing main relief valve cartridge from inlet cover, examine sensing ports (P) to see that they are open.

1. "O" ring
2. "O" rings
3. Cartridge
C. Inlet cover
P. Sensing ports

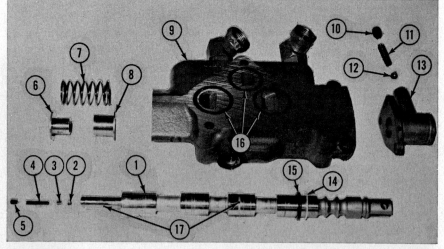

Fig. MM984 — Disassembled view of Wooster control valve body section, showing component parts. Release piston (6) and sleeve (8) move apart by hydraulic pressure entering through valve (2) and internal passages in valve spool, to override detent ball and return the valve to neutral.

1. Valve spool
2. Release valve
3. Block
4. Spring
5. Detent release adjusting screw
6. Release piston
7. Centering spring
8. Centering sleeve
9. Valve body
10. Detent adjusting screw
11. Detent spring
12. Detent ball
13. Detent housing
14. Back-up ring
15. Sealing ring
16. Tetra (quad ring) seals
17. Passage ports

Fig. MM985 — Partially disassembled view of Wooster valve body sections, which are held together with three studs and sealed with tetra seals. Body sections are available separately.

1. Rear cover
2. Valve body
3. Inlet cover

Remove the spool boot (2—Fig. MM983) and venting cap (1—Fig. MM968). Remove detent adjusting screw (10—Fig. MM984), spring (11) and detent ball (12); then unbolt and remove detent housing (13). Depress centering piston (6) and remove the retaining snap ring, then withdraw centering piston, centering spring (7) and centering sleeve (8). Withdraw spool (1) from valve housing. Remove nylock set screw (5) and withdraw detent release valve spring (4), block (3) and valve (2) from end of spool. Check to be sure that drillings (17) in valve are open, that valve and body are not scored, and that valve does not bind. Valve and body are available only as a matched assembly.

Assemble by reversing the disassembly procedure. To renew the tetra (quad ring) seals (16), remove the valve body retaining stud nuts and separate the sections as shown in Fig. MM985.

Adjust detent ball pressure as outlined in paragraph 201, install valve as in paragraph 197, then adjust detent release pressure as in paragraph 188.

201. **DETENT ADJUSTMENT.** To adjust the detent spring pressure, refer to Fig. MM983. With valve mounted and before installing control levers and front cover, push valve spool downward from neutral (center) detent. Attach a spring scale (4) as shown, and measure the pull required to move valve back to neutral position. Adjust the pull to 18-21 lbs. by tightening or loosening detent adjusting screws with Allen wrench (5).

Type E System With Vickers Valve

202. **REMOVE AND REINSTALL.** To remove the control valve, first drain the hydraulic system reservoir, disconnect pump pressure and return lines and remove the seat assembly. Unbolt and remove the reservoir and control valve assembly from tractor. Remove reservoir front cover retaining bolts, disconnect control levers, and lift off the front cover. Identify and disconnect hoses from control valve, remove the mounting bolts, then lift off the valve.

Reinstall by reversing removal procedure. Align control valve so control lever links will not bind and tighten mounting bolts.

The hydraulic fittings have SAE straight tubing threads with "O" ring seals (J.I.C. fittings). DO NOT attempt to install pipe fittings in valve ports.

203. **CONTROL VALVE.** With the control valve removed as outlined in paragraph 202, refer to Fig. MM986 and proceed as follows:

To remove the relief valve (15) and plunger (16), drive out roll pins (20) from both ends of valve body and withdraw plugs (19), plunger, relief valve and springs (14). DO NOT attempt to remove the spring seat in relief valve bore of the control valve body. The relief valve (15), relief valve plunger (16), springs (14), "O" rings (17) and back-up rings (18) are available in a relief valve kit if renewal is indicated.

Fig. MM986—Partially exploded view of Vickers control valve used on model M670 Super tractors equipped with Type E hydraulic system.

1. Valve body	8. "O" ring	14. Spring	20. Roll pin
2. Plug	9. Wiper ring	15. Relief valve	21. Roll pin
3. Centering spring	10. Detent poppet	16. Plunger	22. Load check ball
4. Retainer	11. Poppet spring	17. "O" ring	23. Spring
5. Snap ring	12. "O" ring	18. Back-up ring	24. "O" ring
6. End cap	13. Plug	19. Plug	25. Back-up ring
7. Retaining ring			26. Plug

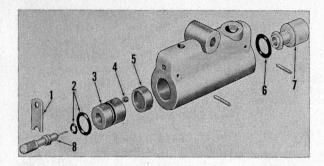

Fig. MM987 — Exploded view of the depth control valve.

1. Lock clip
2. "O" rings
3. Adjusting screw cage
4. Ball seat
5. Piston
6. "O" ring
7. Piston seat
8. Adjusting screw

To remove valve spools, first remove plugs (13), springs (11) and detent poppets (10). NOTE: There are two poppets for each spool. Remove retaining rings (7) and end caps (6), then push spools from valve body. "O" rings (8) and wiper rings (9) can now be removed. Inspect spools and bores in valve body for excessive wear or scoring. If either spool or body is damaged, renew complete valve assembly as the spools or valve body are not available separately.

The control valve is equipped with a load check valve for each spool. To remove the load check valves, remove roll pins (21), then withdraw plugs (26), springs (23) and check balls (22).

Reassemble the components of control valve in reverse order of disassembly, using new "O" rings, back-up rings and wiper rings which are available in a control valve seal kit.

Reinstall control valve as outlined in paragraph 202.

DEPTH CONTROL VALVE
UB Special-UTS Special

204. On some units a depth control valve is used to control the working stroke of the jack. The length of the stroke is adjusted by a knurled thumb screw located at the end of the valve. When the screw is turned all the way in, the valve does not function as a stop and the jack is free to travel a full stroke.

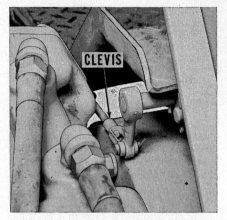

Fig. MM988—Adjusting a typical hydraulic jack control linkage.

The depth control valve is a proportional flow unit. A metered amount of the total fluid volume directed to rod end of lifting jack is fed to adjusting screw side of piston (5—Fig. MM987). The control valve returns to neutral when flat side of piston (5) closes outlet port of piston seat (7). Retracting the piston even a small amount resets the depth control valve piston.

Procedure for removal of valve is obvious. To disassemble valve, remove lock clip (1); drive out the roll pins in each end of housing and withdraw cage (3), piston seat (7) and piston (5).

Piston (5) must be absolutely free in bore of valve body and check ball must be free in cage (3). Renew all "O" rings and any other parts which are worn or damaged. Make sure metering passages in valve body are open and assemble and install by reversing disassembly procedure.

LIFTING JACK (RAM)
All Models So Equipped

205. The lifting jack (ram) is of the double acting type. Refer to Fig. MM990.

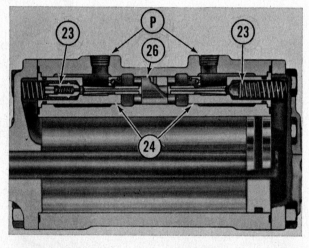

Fig. MM989 — Cross sectional view of lifting jack showing hydraulic circuit locking mechanism. Refer to Fig. MM990 for legend.

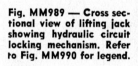

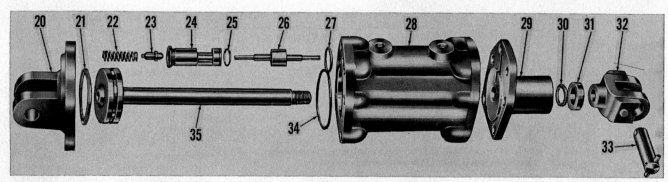

Fig. MM990—Exploded view of a typical Minneapolis-Moline lifting jack assembly.

20. Cylinder head
21. Piston "O" ring
22. Relief spring
23. Relief valve lockout
24. Valve cage (2)
25. Cage "O" ring
26. Push rod and plunger
27. Cap gasket
28. Jack cylinder
29. Bearing cap
30. Rod "O" ring
31. Oil seal
32. Clevis
33. Clevis pin
34. Cap gasket
35. Piston and rod

On UB Special and UTS Special tractors where jack is used on a lifting roll, place the control lever in the number nine position, allowing jack to fully extend. Adjust control linkage at clevis (Fig. MM988) until jack extends 8 inches when measured at piston rod.

The Minneapolis-Moline lifting jack is a locked-circuit cylinder in which a spring loaded check valve traps the fluid in both ends of cylinder when jack is stationary. When pressure fluid enters either port of lifting jack, the opposite check valve is unseated by hydraulic pressure against piston of plunger (26—Fig. MM989), allowing piston rod to move.

Plunger piston must move freely in bore of cylinder (28—Fig. MM990), and push rods must not bind in valve cages (24). Malfunctioning parts may require excessive pressures to actuate the jack, giving the effect of low hydraulic system pressure.

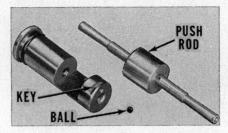

Fig. MM991 — Hydraulic jack valve cage and push rod. The ball is retained in the cage by a key.

To disassemble the removed lifting jack, unbolt and lift off cylinder head (20) and bearing cap (29). Piston and rod assembly (35) will be removed with bearing cap, and disassembly of these components is not required except for renewal of seals or other parts.

Check valves (23) and springs (22) can be lifted out after end plates are removed. Valve cages (24) seat against shoulders of bore in cylinder. Cages are retained by the end plates and are sealed by "O" ring (25). Cages and plunger (26) can be removed after end plates are off.

Check valves (23) have a built-in thermal relief valve which is serviced only by renewing the unit. Check (relief) valves and all "O" rings and seals are available in a repair kit as well as individually.

Clean all parts in a suitable solvent and renew any parts which are worn, scored or otherwise damaged. When reassembling, make sure plunger (26) is absolutely free after installation of plunger and valve cages (24), and that push rods extend through each check valve seat far enough to unseat the valves. Complete the assembly by reversing the disassembly procedure. After assembly, the jack should extend and retract at full throttle with negligible pressure build-up in tractor hydraulic system.

HYDRAULIC LIFT (TEL-O-FLO SYSTEM)

OPERATION

5 Star-M5-M504-M602-M604-M670-M670 Super

206. The Tel-O-Flo system control valve consists of a master valve and three directional valves which control the three-point hitch and two remote cylinders. Proper hydraulic action depends on accurate synchronization of the master control valve with the directional valve being used. Before a raising action can be accomplished with the three-point hitch or single acting remote applications (or any action with double acting remote cylinders), the master control valve must be moved to block the system by-pass opening. At the same time the directional valve must move to open the proper passage to hydraulic system pressure.

Refer to Fig. MM992 for a schematic view of the three-point lift system operation. Hydraulic fluid under pump pressure enters the control valve at (10) and through the master control valve (5) at two points. The passage at the left is connected to the center area of the directional valve (4) by the check valve (6), and around the

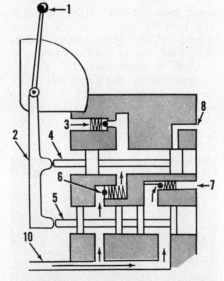

Fig. MM992—Schematic view of "Tel-O-Flo" hydraulic control valve showing oil flow through master control valve and three-point hitch directional valve.

1. Control lever
2. Actuating lever
3. Relief valve
4. Directional valve
5. Master control valve
6. Check valve
7. Regulating valve
8. Ram passage
10. From pump

directional valve to the relief valve (3). This path is never closed, but is always open to pump pressure. The passage on the right leads through the master valve to the regulating valve (7). Oil passing through regulating valve (7) goes through the system filter back to the sump.

When the control lever (1) is moved to the raising position, linkage lever (2) and the two valves (4 and 5) are moved to the right. The land on master valve spool (5) closes passage (7) leading to the sump. At the same time, the directional valve (4) opens passage (8) leading to the lift cylinder. Oil from the pump passes through check valve (6), directional valve (4) and through opened passage (8) to the ram cylinder and a raising action takes place. A mechanical linkage (not pictured) returns the control lever and valves to a neutral position at the completion of the lifting action.

When the control lever is moved to the lowering position the master valve (5) remains stationary allowing oil from the pump to by-pass and the directional valve moves to the left opening passage (8) to the sump

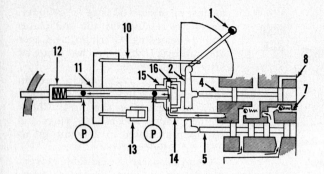

Fig. MM993 — Schematic view of automatic draft control mechanism used on "Tel-O-Flo" system.

10. Draft link
11. Linkage tube
12. Actuating cap
13. Dash pot
14. Supply tube
15. Draft linkage cylinder
16. Linkage piston
P. Actuating ports

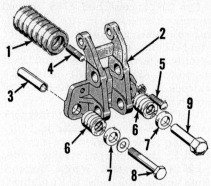

Fig. MM995—Exploded view of draft actuating pivot plate and springs used with "Tel-O-Flo" system.

1. Draft spring
2. Pivot plate
3. Spacer
4. Stud
5. Adjusting bolt
6. Tension springs
7. Spacer washer
8. Retaining bolt
9. Retaining bolt

through the area at the end of the valve spool. The hydraulic fluid trapped in the ram cylinder is then exhausted back to the sump.

Automatic draft action is controlled by a combination of hydraulic and spring pressure as shown in Fig. MM993. Metered oil is fed through line (14) to draft linkage cylinder (15) from the by-pass line in front of regulating valve (7). A pressure of 25-50 psi is maintained in the system by valve (7). The draft linkage cylinder (15) is connected to the draft actuating cap (12) by the hollow linkage tube (11) which contains ports (P) at either end. When the control lever is in the neutral position, port (P) at the front end of the tube is uncovered and the metered oil escapes. When the control lever is moved to the automatic draft position, tube (11) is moved forward by draft link (10) and the front port is closed by the lip of the draft linkage cylinder (15), directional valve (4) is moved into the lowering position and the three point lift lowers into operating position. When the implement enters the ground to the selected depth, the implement draft, acting through the upper link against spring pressure, moves the actuating cap (12) forward to close the rear port in the linkage tube allowing pressure to build up in draft linkage cylinder (15). Piston (16) moves forward under hydraulic pressure to automatically actuate linkage lever (2) and the control valves. The selected implement operating draft is maintained by the automatic metering of the oil in the draft linkage cylinder at the linkage tube rear port.

LUBRICATION AND BLEEDING

207. To check the hydraulic fluid on all models except M670 and M670 Super, remove the cover (1—Fig. MM994) containing the rate and cycle levers (2). Fluid level is correct when filled to within 1-1¼ inches of the top of reservoir. On models M670 and M670 Super, hydraulic fluid level

should be at FULL mark on the dipstick. When draining and refilling the system, start the engine and cycle all operating levers several times to bleed air from the cylinders, then refill to the proper level with all cylinders retracted.

SYSTEM CHECKS AND ADJUSTMENTS

208. Unless the system is inoperative or defect is obvious, the following checks may pinpoint the trouble, eliminating unnecessary tear-down and overhaul.

Before an attempt is made to check the system, check the fluid level as outlined in paragraph 207, start the engine and warm the hydraulic fluid to operating temperature.

209. **PIVOT PLATE SPRINGS.** Spring (6—Fig. MM995) on each side of pivot plate (2) should have 0-$\frac{1}{16}$-inch pre-load. To check the adjustment, loosen the two bolts (8 and 9) and turn the springs to rid the assembly of any accumulated dirt or rust. Continue to turn the spring as the bolt is retightened. The pre-load is correct when the spring can barely be turned with the bolt tight. Four different thicknesses of shim washer (7) are available to adjust the pre-load.

Fig. MM994—To add or check the hyraulic fluid, remove valve cover (1), containing the rate and cycle levers (2).

210. **DRAFT CONTROL BUTTON ADJUSTMENT.** The adjustment of the draft control button determines the length of the secondary lift range on the control lever quadrant. (See Fig. MM996). The adjustment is correct if the length of the secondary lift range is approximately 2 inches on the quadrant as shown.

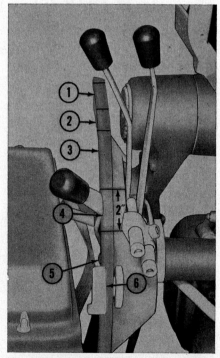

Fig. MM996—Draft control quadrant showing the general location of the different control ranges.

1. Lifting range
2. Neutral
3. Lowering and float range
4. Secondary lift range
5. Automatic draft control range
6. Control lever stop

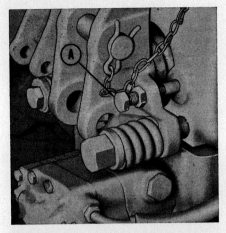

Fig. MM997—To adjust the draft control button, turn adjusting bolt (A) until the length of secondary lift range is approximately two inches.

To make the adjustment, loosen the locknut on the adjusting bolt (A—Fig. MM997) and turn the bolt out until, with the engine running at 1000 rpm, the lift arms will not raise while the control lever is slowly moved through the entire secondary lift range. Now turn the bolt until the lift arms will just raise and the total length of the secondary lift range is approximately ⅛-inch; then, turn the adjusting bolt in 3¾ turns and tighten the locknut.

If the proper adjustment cannot be obtained, it will be necessary to disassemble and check the draft linkage as outlined in paragraph 223.

211. VALVE SYNCHRONIZATION CHECK. To check the synchronization of the master valve with the three-point lift directional valve, remove plug (1—Fig. MM999) from the top of the control valve housing and install a 300 psi pressure gage. Make sure the lift arms are all the way down before removing the plug.

With the engine running at 1500 rpm, and with no load on the lift arms, slowly move the three point

Fig. MM998 — Adjusting dashpot needle valve with socket and extension (A) through plug hole provided in housing.

lift control lever to the raising position. The momentary pressure while the lift arms are raising should be 25-200 psi. If the pressure is not as indicated, disassemble and synchronize the valves as outlined in paragraph 223.

212. DASH POT CHECK AND ADJUSTMENT. The purpose of the dash pot is to restrict or slow the forward movement of the draft linkage tube to allow quick implement penetration before the first draft cycle takes place. To check the dash pot, move the three point lift control lever down the quadrant into the secondary lift range and the rate and cycle levers into the fast position as shown in Fig. MM998. Position the depth stop (S) on the quadrant at the secondary lift position as shown. With the engine running at 1500 rpm, move the control lever to the raise position and allow the lift arms to raise and neutralize the valve. Now move the control lever quickly down the quadrant to the depth stop and check the time required for the lift arms to lower and again start to raise. If the dash pot is correctly adjusted, the lift arms should start to raise 1 to 1½ seconds after the lowering action starts.

To adjust the dash pot needle valve remove the pipe plug in the top of the lift housing and using a ¼-inch hex head socket and extension (A—Fig. MM998), adjust the needle valve through the plug opening. Note: Use care to avoid applying undue pressure to valve. Needle valve or seat may be damaged if pressure is applied when the needle is bottomed.

If the dash pot action is still too fast when needle is bottomed, remove the lift and overhaul the dash pot assembly as outlined in paragraph 221.

213. BACK FLOW VALVE CHECK. The purpose of the back flow valve is to prevent the lift arms from momentarily dropping when the control valve is actuated. To check the valve, place a 120-pound load or light implement on the lift arms and raise the lift until the arms are about halfway up, then manually return the valve to neutral. With the engine running at about 1500 rpm, slowly move the three-point lift control lever to the raising position and note the action of the lift arms. The load should rise to the transport position with no noticeable drop before the raising action begins. If a drop is noted, remove the filter base as outlined in paragraph 221 and, with a pair of pliers remove and service the back flow valve (V—MM999).

Fig. MM999 — Control valve body with filter base removed and back flow valve (V) withdrawn.

1. System pressure port
2. Regulator valve pressure port
6. Back flow valve pressure port

A pressure gage may be used to check the back flow valve for sticking or binding as follows: Remove plug (6) in the side of the control valve housing and install a 0-2000 psi pressure gage. With the engine running at 1500 rpm and the lift arms in a lowered position, move the three-point lift control lever to the raising position and note the pressure gage reading. If the pressure while the arms are raising is more than 250 psi greater than the pressure registered in checking the valve synchronization as outlined in paragraph 211, the back flow valve is sticking or binding and should be removed and serviced.

214. REGULATOR VALVE PRESSURE TEST. The regulator valve supplies the necessary hydraulic pressure to operate the automatic draft control linkage. To check the pressure, remove plug (2—Fig. MM1002) in the top of the control valve housing and

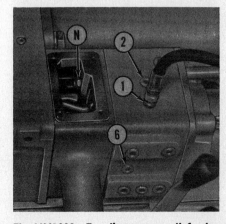

Fig. MM1000—To adjust system relief valve pressure remove valve cover, install gage in system pressure port (1), loosen lock nut (N) and turn pressure adjusting screw in or out as required.

install a 0-300 psi pressure gage. With the hydraulic fluid at operating temperature and the engine running at 1500 rpm, the minimum pressure reading should be at least 25 psi with all of the control valves in the neutral position.

The pressure should not exceed 50 psi. If the pressures are not as indicated, service or renew the valve or spring after removing the filter base as outlined in paragraph 220.

215. RELIEF VALVE PRESSURE. The recommended relief valve pressure is 1550-1650 psi. To check the pressure, remove plug (1—Fig. MM-1000) and install a 0-2000 psi pressure gage. With the engine running at 1500 rpm and the hydraulic fluid at operating temperature, move one of the auxiliary valve levers back to the raising position and hold it just long enough for the relief valve to act, and observe the gage reading. To adjust the pressure, remove the filler plate, loosen the lock nut (N—Fig. MM1000) and turn the adjusting screw in or out until the correct pressure is obtained. To remove the relief valve assembly it is first necessary to remove the control valve housing as outlined in paragraph 220.

216. RATE AND CYCLE CONTROL. A cam at the lower end of the rate lever (4—Fig. MM1001) restricts the movement of the three-point directional control valve to the lowering position, thus controlling the speed of implement drop. The cycle lever (5) has the same effect after

completion of the first draft cycle, thus smoothing the draft response to enable the operator to control the bobbing of the implement.

To check the action of the rate lever, move the lever to the left ("Transport Lock") position and with the engine running at 1000 rpm and a weight or implement on the lower links, move the three-point lift control lever to the raised position. After the system has returned to neutral in the transport position, move the three-point lift control lever to the lowering position. The lift arms should remain in the transport position. The speed of implement drop should progressively increase as the rate lever is moved toward the right (fast position), until a free drop is obtained at the extreme fast setting.

To check the action of the cycle lever, move the rate lever (4) to the fast (right) position and the cycle lever (5) to the extreme left (slow) position. With the engine running at 1000 rpm, move the three-point lift control lever to the raised position. After the system has returned to neutral in the transport position, move the lift control lever to the automatic draft range. The lift arms should lower freely. After the arms have lowered, move the lift control lever to the secondary lift position and allow the lift arms to rise almost to the transport position, then return the control lever to the automatic draft range. The lift arms should remain stationary or fall very slowly. As the cycle lever (5) is moved toward the right the speed of drop should progressively increase until a free drop is obtained at the extreme right (fast) position. The lowering speed of the cycle lever setting will never exceed the speed selected by the rate lever setting.

No adjustments are provided for the rate and cycle levers. If the correct action is not obtained, remove the filler plate and examine the eccentric shafts and the draft control linkage for wear or damage.

217. AUXILIARY VALVE SYNCHRONIZATION CHECK. To use the auxiliary control valves for the operation of single or double acting remote cylinders it is necessary that the cylinder hoses be connected to the correct ports in the control valve housing as follows:

To use the center lever (2—Fig. MM1001) with a single acting cylinder, connect the hose to port (4—Fig. MM1002.

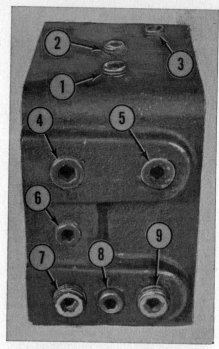

Fig. MM1002—Control valve body showing port location and use.

1. System pressure port.
2. Regulating valve pressure port (System by-pass port).
3. Three-point lift synchronizing port.
4. Jack tapping for single or double acting remote cylinders (center lever).
5. Jack tapping for double acting remote cylinder (center lever).
6. Back flow valve pressure port.
7. Jack tapping for double acting remote cylinder (inner lever).
8. Valve body plug.
9. Jack tapping for single or double acting remote cylinder (inner lever).

Fig. MM1001—Operators platform showing hydraulic system controls.

1. Three-point lift control lever
2. & 3. Auxiliary valve control levers
4. Rate control lever
5. Cycle control lever
6. Auxiliary valve stop screws

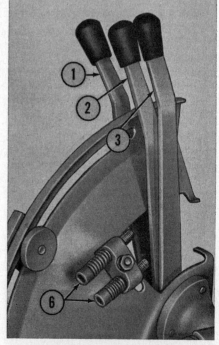

Fig. MM1003—Control valve quadrant and levers.

1. Three-point lift control lever.
2. Auxiliary valve center control lever.
3. Auxiliary valve inner control lever.
6. Auxiliary valve lowering stop screws.

To use the inner control lever (3—Fig. MM1001) with a single acting cylinder, connect the hose to port (9—Fig. MM1002).

To use the center control lever (2—Fig. MM1001) with a double acting cylinder, connect the two hoses to ports (4 and 5—Fig. MM1002).

To use the inner control lever (3—Fig. MM1001) with a double acting cylinder, connect the two hoses to ports (7 and 9—Fig. MM1002).

To check the synchronization of the auxiliary control valves with the master control valve, remove the plug in port (1—Fig. MM1002) and install a 0-2000 psi pressure gage. Remove any attached remote cylinders and hoses and plug ports (4, 5, 7 & 9). With the engine running at 1500 rpm move each of the two auxiliary valve control levers (2 and 3—Fig. MM1001) fully to the rear while noting the gage pressure. The pressure should be equal and at the relief valve pressure. A pressure lower than relief valve pressure would indicate that the master control valve is not fully closing, and will need to be synchronized as outlined in paragraph 223.

Move each of the two auxiliary valves forward against the stop screws

(6—Fig. MM1001) and note the gage reading. If the reading is not the relief valve pressure, back out the stop screw until relief pressure is obtained. If the relief valve pressure cannot be obtained, the valves will need to be synchronized as outlined in paragraph 223.

After performing the checks outlined above, connect a hose between ports (4 and 5—Fig. MM1002) and move the center control lever fully to the rear while noting the gage reading. The pressure should be not more than 200 psi. A pressure greater than 200 psi would indicate that the directional valve is not fully opening and the valves will need to be synchronized as outlined in paragraph 223. Repeat the test with the center control lever in the forward position against stop screw (6—Fig. MM1001). Remove the hose connecting ports (4 and 5—Fig. MM1002), install hose between ports (7 and 9) and repeat the tests using the inner control lever.

To adjust the auxiliary control valves for use with single acting cylinders, remove the jumper hoses and reinstall the port plugs. Leave the pressure gage installed in port (1—Fig. MM1002). Turn the stop screw

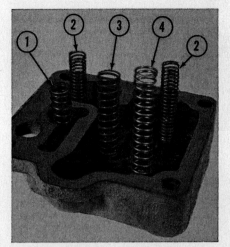

Fig. MM1005—Filter base showing correct installation of valve springs.

1. Regulating valve spring.
2. Auxiliary valve springs.
3. Master valve spring.
4. Three-point lift valve spring.

(6—Fig. MM1003), which contacts the auxiliary lever to be used, fully into the stop housing. Move the auxiliary control lever forward until it contacts the stop screw, then back screw out until the pressure just begins to rise. After attaching the cylinder to the implement the stop screw may need to be turned, slightly to adjust the speed of drop, but under no conditions should the screw be backed out enough to raise the gage pressure above 200 psi or labor the engine.

HYDRAULIC PUMP

Series 5 Star-M5-M504-M602-M604-M670-M670 Super

218. REMOVE AND REINSTALL. On all models except M670 Super, the hydraulic pump is mounted on the rear of the final drive housing and driven by the pto input shaft. Hydraulic fluid to and from the pump on early models is ported through the pump and final drive castings, sealed by "O" ring and pump mounting gasket. On late models, external connections and lines are used.

On model M670 Super, the hydraulic pump is mounted on left side of engine and is driven from the engine timing gears.

To remove the hydraulic pump it is first necessary to drain the hydraulic system by removing the drain plug located at the right rear corner of the hydraulic housing, then unbolt and remove pump. When reinstalling, always renew the gasket and "O" ring.

219. OVERHAUL. Disassembly and the recommended overhaul of the Webster, gear type pump is given in paragraphs 192 through 194.

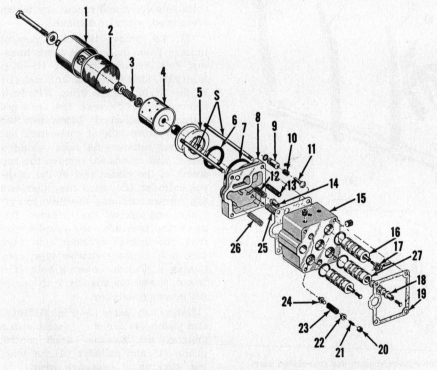

Fig. MM1004—Exploded view of control valve and filter base assembly.

1. Filter cover	11. Back flow valve	20. Lock nut
2. Filter screen	12. Spring	21. Adjusting screw
3. Spring	13. Spring	22. Spring seat
4. Cartrige	14. Regulating valve	23. Spring
5. Screen base	15. Valve body	24. Pressure relief
6. Screen seal	16. Valve sleeve &	valve
7. Filter seal	spool assembly	25. Spring
8. Filter base	17. Adjusting yoke	26. Spring
9. Valve plug	18. Master spool	27. Master valve
10. Spring	19. Gasket	sleeve

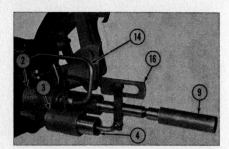

Fig. MM1006 — When control valve and lever housing is removed, unit will contain draft control linkage as shown. See Fig. MM1010 for legend.

CONTROL VALVE

220. R&R AND OVERHAUL. Refer to Figs. MM1004, MM1007 and MM-1019. To remove the control valve assembly it is first necessary to drain and remove the lift housing as outlined in paragraph 224. Remove the four nuts on studs (S—Fig. MM1004) and slide the filter base (8) forward on the studs. Remove the bolt securing the tube clamp (2—Fig. MM1019) to ram cylinder (3) and slide the cylinder tube (1) out of control valve

and cylinder, then remove filter base (8—Fig. MM1004) with filter attached. Do not lose the five springs (Fig. MM1005) between filter base and valve housing. Withdraw the control lever housing (1—Fig. MM1007) and valve housing (15—Fig. MM1004) from lift housing studs (S). The removed unit will contain the draft control mechanism shown in Fig. MM-1006. If the unit is removed for adjustment only, keep valve body (15—Fig. MM1004) and control lever housing (1—Fig. 1007) together.

If overhaul or inspection is indicated, withdraw valve body (15—Fig. MM1004) from control lever housing by pulling straight out. The two auxiliary directional valves (3—Fig. MM-1008) will be withdrawn from valve body as the two units are separated. Withdraw the master control valve (2) and the three-point lift directional valve (1) from valve body. The three directional valves and their sleeves are interchangeable and are available only as a matched set consisting of valve and sleeve. The master control valve (18—Fig. MM1004) and sleeve

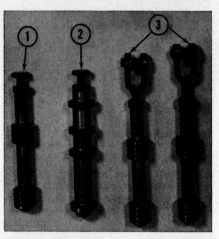

Fig. MM1008—Except for adjusting screw, three-point directional valve spool (1) and auxiliary directional spools are identical and are available only with matched spool sleeve. Master control spool (2) is serviced separately.

(27) are available individually. Keep the valve spools identified so that they can be reinstalled in their original sleeves, and keep the matched sets together if the sleeves are removed from valve body. Withdraw the relief valve (24), regulating valve (14) and back pressure valve (11) from valve body, together with their springs and retainer. Clean all parts in a suitable solvent and renew any which are scored, worn or damaged.

221. To remove the draft control linkage from the control lever housing, first remove the bolt (B—Fig. MM1009) connecting the link rod (L) to the draft linkage tube. Withdraw linkage tube (T), with the dash pot piston (P) attached. Disconnect the draft pressure tube at connecting nut (N) and remove the tube. Using a socket and extension, remove the cap screw at the closed end of the dashpot cylinder (C), then the other two cap screws retaining the linkage cylinder, and lift off the cylinder. Remove the pressure tube adapter (A) from the linkage cylinder and make sure it is of the restricter type, containing a 1/8-inch metering hole. If it is not, renew the adapter with one of the proper restriction.

Dashpot cylinder (3—Fig. MM1010) and piston (4) are only available in a matched set. Examine draft control piston (1) and cylinder (2) for scoring, sticking or excessive wear.

No further disassembly of control lever housing will be necessary if examination reveals no broken or damaged parts. Examine closely the contact ends of the adjusting screws in the auxiliary control valve operating levers (24 and 26—Fig. MM1007). If

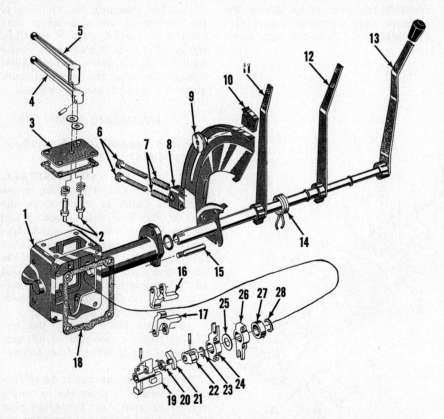

Fig. MM1007—Exploded view of control valve lever housing and associated parts.

1. Lever housing	11. Inner auxiliary lever	18. Gasket
2. Rate & cycle cams	12. Center auxiliary lever	19. Draft control lever
3. Valve cover	13. Three-point control lever	20. Spring
4. Cycle lever	14. Centering spring	21. Cycle pawl
5. Rate lever	15. Spring anchor	22. Detent cam
6. Stop screws	16. Spool control fork	23. Snap ring
7. Springs	17. Spool control fork	24. Actuating lever
8. Stop block		25. Washer
9. Stop nut		26. Actuating lever
10. Adjustable stop		27. Spacer
		28. Thrust shim

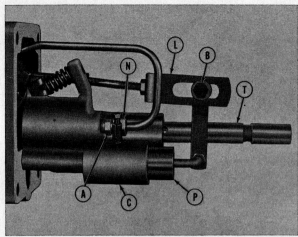

Fig. MM1009 — To remove draft control linkage from lever housing, first remove bolt (B) and slide the linkage tube (T) and dashpot piston (P) from housing. Disconnect nut (N) and remove fluid supply tube and unbolt and remove linkage cylinder. One attaching cap screw is located inside dashpot cylinder (C).

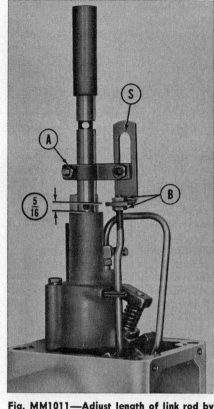

Fig. MM1011—Adjust length of link rod by adjusting nuts (B) until upper edge of tube port is 5/16-inch from edge of cylinder as shown. Tube must be free to fall in slot (S) of its own weight.

the contact ends show appreciable wear renew the adjusting screws, using the special hardened screws supplied by the manufacturer.

Reassemble the control valve assembly by reversing the disassembly procedure. Leave the locknuts on the adjusting yokes of the auxiliary directional valve spools (3—Fig. MM1008) loose during assembly for adjustment as outlined in paragraph 222.

222. **CONTROL VALVE ADJUSTMENT.** After the control valve assembly has been removed for adjustment or reassembled after overhaul, stand the unit on a bench with the linkage tube in a vertical position as shown in Fig. MM1011. Grasp the tube and move it upward to the upper end of slot (S), then release the tube. The asembly should fall slowly to the bottom of the slot of its own weight. If it does not, realign the dashpot linkage with the two locknuts (A), or control rod linkage at (B) until a free drop is obtained. With the linkage tube in the bottom of the slot as shown, measure the distance between the upper edge of the lower port and the edge of the cylinder housing. This distance should be $\frac{5}{16}$-inch as shown. If the adjustment is incorrect, loosen one of the rod adjusting nuts (B) and tighten the other until the proper adjustment is obtained. After making the adjustment, recheck the linkage tube for binding as outlined above and correct as needed.

223. **VALVE SYNCHRONIZATION.** To synchronize the control valves, bolt the valve body and lever housing together with two bolts as shown in Fig. MM1012. If not previously done, loosen locknuts on auxiliary valve adjusting yokes before bolting the housings together. Use flat washers underneath the nuts to prevent damage to the machined surfaces. The regular gasket

between the housings must be in place. Remove the two port plugs (2 and 3—Fig. MM1017). With the three-point lift directional valve lever in the neutral position and the spool held back against the lever, the middle annular groove should be centered in port (3) as shown at (1—Fig. MM1013). If it is not, withdraw the direction valve from the front of the valve body, loosen the locknut and turn the adjusting screw (2) in or out as needed to properly align the valve. After the three-point lift directional valve has been properly centered in the neutral position, move the control lever slowly toward the raising position while applying pressure on the front end of the valve until the rear edge of the front land opens the port ⅖—½ of the port width as shown at (2—Fig. MM1014). At this time the front edge of the second land on the master control valve should just close

port (2—Fig. MM1017) as shown at (3—Fig. MM1014). If the adjustment of the master control valve is incorrect, remove the valve, loosen the lock nut and turn the adjusting screw (4) in or out as required. Recheck both adjustments a second time after the lock nuts have been tightened.

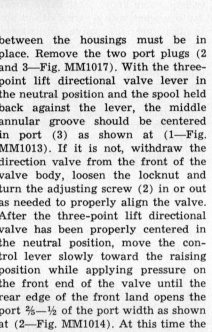

Fig. MM1010—Exploded view of draft linkage.

1. Draft piston
2. Linkage cylinder
3. Dashpot cylinder
4. Dashpot piston
5. Piston seal
6. Dashpot link
7. Linkage tube
8. Spring
9. Actuating cap
10. Detent assembly
11. Adjusting screw
12. Link rod
13. Adapter
14. Pressure tube
15. Tube clamp
16. Adjusting bar

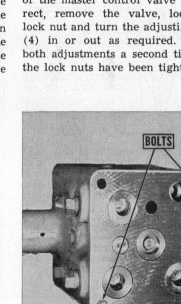

Fig. MM1012 — To synchronize the control valves, bolt lever housing and valve body together as shown. Gasket must be in place and flat washers used under nuts to prevent damage to machined faces.

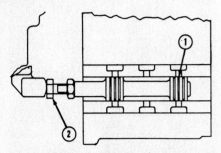

Fig. MM1013 — With three-point control lever in neutral position, groove of spool land must be in center of port as shown at (1). Adjust by removing spool and turning adjusting screw (2).

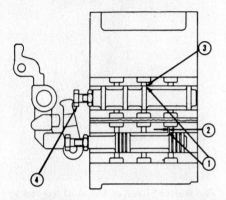

Fig. MM1014—Move control lever toward raising position until directional valve opens port 2/5 to 1/2 width of port (2). Valves are synchronized if land of master valve just closes port (3). Adjustment is made on master spool at (4).

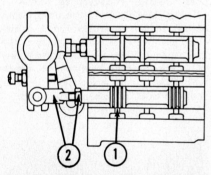

Fig. MM1015—With auxiliary control levers in neutral position, middle groove of directional valve must center in port as shown at (1). Adjust by turning valve on adjusting yoke (2).

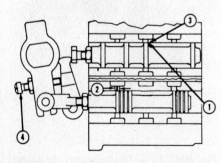

Fig. MM1016 — When auxiliary valve is moved either direction until port is opened 2/5 to 1/2 port width (2), land (1) of master valve must just close port (3).

To synchronize the two auxiliary valve spools with the master control valve, proceed as follows: Remove the plugs in ports (4 and 9—Fig. MM1017) for viewing the adjustment of the two directional valves. Leave port (2) unplugged for checking the setting of the master control valve. With the auxiliary valve control levers in the neutral position, check and center the middle groove of the spool lands visible through ports (4 and 9). See Fig. MM1015. Note: If the adjusting yoke lock nuts were loosened when the valve was removed or assembled, adjustment can be made by turning the valve spool through the open front end of valve body. Most valve spools are equipped with a screw driver slot in the end for valve adjustment. Valves not so equipped can usually be turned with eraser end of a pencil or other friction tool. After the directional spools are properly centered, loosen the two bolts securing valve body to lever housing, separate the two units slightly and tighten the adjusting yoke lock nuts; then, tighten the securing bolts and recheck adjustment. After the directional spools are properly centered, move the center lever rearward until the front edge of rear land opens port (4—Fig. MM1017) 2/5-1/2 of port width. Clamp the control lever to quadrant with directional valve in this position. Apply

pressure on the front end of the master control valve, loosen the lock nut on adjusting screw (3—Fig. MM1018) and turn the adjusting screw in or out until the front edge of the second land just closes port (2—Fig. MM1017). Move center lever forward until rear edge of rear land of directional spool opens port (4) 2/5-1/2 of port width. (Auxiliary lever stop screw (6—Fig. MM1007) may need to be backed out.) Clamp the lever in this position and adjust the master control valve, using adjusting screw (1—Fig. MM1018) to adjust the master valve. Synchronize the inner auxiliary valve lever (lower spool) in the same manner, using port (9—Fig. MM1017) to view the directional valve and adjusting screws (2 and 4—Fig. MM1018) to adjust master valve. Recheck all adjustments after tightening the lock nuts.

RESERVOIR, ROCKSHAFT AND RAM CYLINDER

224. **R&R AND OVERHAUL.** To remove the system reservoir, drain the system by removing drain plug (17—Fig. MM1019), remove seat and disconnect the three-point hitch lift rods. Disconnect power steering return line

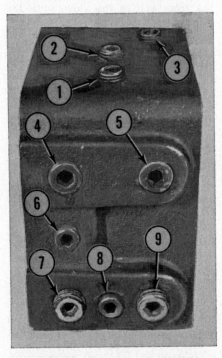

Fig. MM1017—To synchronize the control valves, master valve must be viewed through port (2), three-point directional valve through port (3) and the two auxiliary directional valves through ports (4 and 7).

Fig. MM1018—Master valve spool is synchronized with auxiliary valves by means of the four adjusting screws in actuating levers as shown.

1. Center lever (rearward)
2. Inner lever (forward)
3. Center lever (forward)
4. Inner lever (rearward)

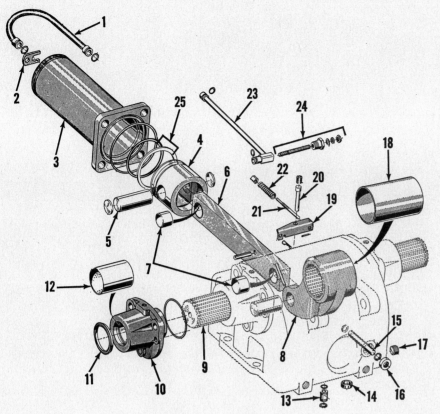

Fig. MM1019 — Exploded view of System housing showing ram cylinder, rockshaft and associated parts used on early models. Late models are similar.

1. Pressure tube	9. Rockshaft	14. Seal
2. Tube clip	10. Rockshaft housing	15. Actuating plunger
3. Ram cylinder	11. Oil seal	16. Oil seal
4. Ram piston	12. Rockshaft bushing	17. Drain plug
5. Piston pin	13. Pump pressure tube	18. Spacer
6. Connecting rod		19. Rocker arm
7. Rod bushings		20. Pivot pin
8. Ram arm		

21. Valve centering pin
22. Spring
23. Pressure tube
24. Retaining screw
25. Piston seal

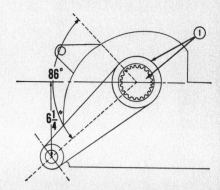

Fig. MM1020 — To properly position lift arms on rockshaft, with lift in lowered position install arm so that distance between centerline of shaft and pin hole is 6¼-inches as shown. Punch mark arm and shaft at (1) for proper reinstallation.

clamp (2) and withdraw from ram cylinder (3). Cylinder can be removed from ram piston (4) by removing the four cap screws securing it to reservoir housing and withdrawing cylinder. The procedure for further disassembly is evident. The lifting arms are retained on the rockshaft by snap rings, lift arms and shaft are not equipped with master splines. Before removing the lift arms, be sure to mark their location on the shaft splines as shown at (1—Fig. MM1020). If it is suspected that the lifting arms are incorrectly installed, move the arms to the extreme lowered position and measure the distance between center line of rockshaft and center of hole in lifting arm as shown in Fig. MM1020. This distance should be 6¼-inches. Rotational arc of rockshaft is 86 degrees.

from reservoir. Attach a hoist to reservoir and remove by lifting it straight up to avoid damage to the pressure

tube (13) and "O" rings. Unbolt and remove filter housing to free valve end of cylinder tube (1) remove tube

NOTES

NOTES

MINNEAPOLIS-MOLINE

Minneapolis-Moline Models

■ G-VI ■ G-705 ■ G-706 ■ G-707 ■ G-708 ■ G-900 ■ G-950

■ G-1000 ■ G-1000 Vista ■ G-1050 ■ G-1350

Massey-Ferguson ■ MF95 (after SN 17300000) ■ MF97

Previously contained in I & T Shop Service Manual No. MM-19

SHOP MANUAL
MINNEAPOLIS-MOLINE

SERIES

G VI	G708	G1000
G705	G900	G1000 Vista
G706	G950	G1050
G707		G1350

(Also Covers MASSEY-FERGUSON)
MODELS

MF-95 (After Ser. No. 17300000)
MF-97

IDENTIFICATION

Tractor serial number is stamped on a plate which is riveted to side of transmission housing.

Engine serial number is stamped on a plate which is riveted to side of crankcase.

INDEX (By Starting Paragraph)

CONDENSED SERVICE DATA

	G VI MF95	G705 G706 G707 G708 MF97	G900 G950	G1000 G1000 Vista G1050	G1350
GENERAL					
Engine Make	M-M	M-M	M-M	M-M	M-M
Number of Cylinders	6	6	6	6	6
Bore & Stroke—Inches (Non-Diesel) . .	4-1/4x5	4-5/8x5	4-1/4x5	4-5/8x5	4-5/8x5
Bore & Stroke—Inches (Diesel)	4-1/4x5	4-5/8x5	4-3/8x5	4-5/8x5	4-3/4x5-1/2
Displacement—Cu. In. (Non-Diesel) . .	425	504	425	504	504
Displacement—Cu. In. (Diesel)	425	504	451	504	585
Cylinders Sleeved	No	No	No	No	No
Main Bearings, Number of	4	4	4	4	4
TUNE-UP					
Firing Order	1-5-3-6-2-4	1-5-3-6-2-4	1-5-3-6-2-4	1-5-3-6-2-4	1-5-3-6-2-4
Valve Tappet Gap—Inlet (Cold)					
Diesel	0.012	0.012	0.015	0.015	0.010
Non-Diesel	0.012	0.012	0.012	0.012	0.010
Valve Tappet Gap—Exhaust (Cold)					
Diesel	0.020	0.020	0.022	0.022	0.020
Non-Diesel	0.022	0.022	0.028	0.028	0.028
Compression @ Cranking Speed (PSI)					
Gasoline	———	———	130-155	140-170	———
LPG	170-195	150-175	170-195	185-215	185-215
Diesel	440-460	440-460	440-460	440-460	440-460

NOTE: Average compression when equipped with standard, sea level—4000 ft. head. Refer to paragraph 63.

	G VI MF95	G705-G708 MF97	G900 G950	G1000 G1050	G1350
Ignition Distributor Make	Delco-Remy	Delco-Remy	Delco-Remy	Delco-Remy	Delco-Remy
Breaker Contact Gap	0.022	0.022	0.021	0.021	0.021
Ignition Timing					
Gasoline	———	———	13° @ 1200	12° @ 1200	———
LP-Gas	24° @ 1500	25° @ 1600	16° @ 1200	15° @ 1500	17° @ 1500
Injection Timing (APE pump)	42° BTDC	———	———	———	———
Injection Timing (PSB pump)	30° BTDC	———	———	———	———
Injection Timing (Roosa-Master)	11° BTDC	11° BTDC	2° BTDC	See Para. 132	4° ATDC
Timing Mark Location	Flywheel	Flywheel	Flywheel	Flywheel	Flywheel
Spark Plug Electrode Gap:					
LP-Gas	0.014-0.016	0.014-0.016	0.014-0.016	0.014-0.016	0.014-0.016
Gasoline	———	———	0.024-0.026	0.024-0.026	———
Carburetor Make (Gasoline)	———	———	Marvel-Schebler	Marvel-Schebler	———
Carburetor Make (LP-Gas)	Ensign	Century	Century	Century	Century
Engine Low Idle RPM (Non-Diesel) . .	475	600	600	600	600
Engine Low Idle RPM (Diesel)	600	600	600	600	700
Engine High Idle RPM (Non-Diesel) . .	1650	1720	2040	2050	2400
Engine High Idle RPM (Diesel)	1625	1710	1950	1950	2335
Engine Loaded RPM (Non-Diesel) . . .	1500	1600	1800	1800	2200
Engine Loaded RPM (Diesel)	1500	1600	1800	1800	2200
SIZES—CAPACITIES—CLEARANCES (Clearances in Thousandths)					
Crankshaft Journal Diameter					
(Non-Diesel)	2.9110-2.9120	2.9110-2.9120	2.9110-2.9120	2.9110-2.9120	2.9110-2.9120
Crankshaft Journal Diameter (Diesel) .	2.9110-2.9120	2.9110-2.9120	2.9110-2.9120	2.9110-2.9120	3.4980-3.4990
Crankpin Diameter (Non-Diesel) . . .	2.5770-2.5775	2.9115-2.9120	2.9115-2.9120	2.9115-2.9120	2.9115-2.9120
Crankpin Diameter (Diesel)	2.9115-2.9120	2.9115-2.9120	2.9115-2.9120	2.9115-2.9120	3.4980-3.4990
Camshaft Journal Diameter:					
No. 1 (Front)	3.3380-3.3390	3.3380-3.3390	3.3380-3.3390	3.3380-3.3390	3.3380-3.3390
No. 2	3.3075-3.3085	3.3075-3.3085	3.3075-3.3085	3.3075-3.3085	3.3075-3.3085
No. 3	3.2750-3.2760	3.2750-3.2760	3.2750-3.2760	3.2750-3.2760	3.2750-3.2760
No. 4	1.9960-1.9970	1.9960-1.9970	1.9960-1.9970	1.9960-1.9970	1.9960-1.9970
Main Bearings, Diameter Clearance					
Non-Diesel	1.4-4.4	1.4-4.4	1.4-4.4	1.4-4.4	1.4-4.4
Diesel	1.4-4.4	1.4-4.4	1.4-4.4	1.4-4.4	3.3-5.3
Rod Bearing, Diameter Clearance					
Non-Diesel	0.9-3.0	0.9-3.0	1.4-3.9	1.4-3.9	1.4-3.9
Diesel	0.9-3.0	0.9-3.0	1.4-3.9	1.4-3.9	2.3-5.3
Cooling System—Gallons					
Non-Diesel	12.5	12.5	7.5	7.5	7.5
Diesel	12.5	12.5	8.25	8.25	8.25
Crankcase Oil—Quarts (Including Filter)					
Non-Diesel	15	14	13	13	15
Diesel	15	14	13	13	16
Transmission and Differential—Gals. . .	13	13	22	22	22

FRONT SYSTEMS

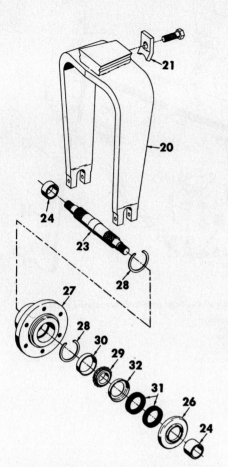

Fig. 1—Type "N" front axle and associated parts.

20. Wheel fork	28. Snap ring
21. Clamp	29. Bearing cone
23. Axle shaft	30. Bearing cup
24. Spacer	31. Felt seals
26. Dust shield	32. Felt seal retainer
27. Wheel hub	

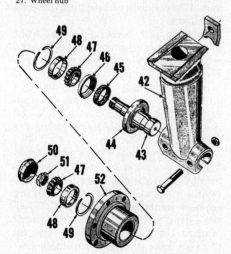

Fig. 2—Type "U" front axle and associated parts.

43. Spindle	48. Bearing cup
44. Dust seal	49. Snap ring
45. Felt seal	50. Cap
46. Seal retainer	51. Nut
47. Bearing cone	52. Wheel hub

Minneapolis-Moline models G900, G1000 and G1000 Vista are optionally equipped with a Type "N" fork mounted single wheel tricycle; Type "U" dual wheel tricycle; Type "E" adjustable wide axle; or the "I" beam heavy duty non-adjustable axle.

Models G950, G1050 and G1350 may be equipped with the Type "E" adjustable wide axle or the "I" beam heavy duty non-adjustable axle.

Models G VI, G705, G707, MF95 and MF97 are equipped with the "I" beam heavy duty non-adjustable axle.

Models G706 and G708 are standard equipped with a front drive axle. Models MF97, G VI, G900, G1000 and G1000 Vista may be optionally equipped with a front drive axle. Refer to appropriate paragraphs in FRONT DRIVE AXLE section for overhaul procedures.

WHEEL FORK OR PEDESTAL
Models G900-G1000-G1000 Vista

1. An exploded view of the tricycle type front end components is shown in Figs. 1 and 2. The procedure for removing and overhauling the compo-

nents is conventional. Front wheel bearings should be adjusted to remove all free play without binding.

STEERING KNUCKLES
All Axle Type Models Except 4-Wheel Drive

2. The procedure for removing the steering knuckles is evident after an examination of the unit and reference to Figs. 3 and 4.

On all models with heavy duty, non-adjustable axle shown in Fig. 3, steering knuckle pin (2) should have a recommended clearance of 0.001-0.005 in knuckle bushings (13). Renew any parts that are excessively worn.

On the Type "E" adjustable front axle shown in Fig. 4, steering spindles (18) should have a recommended 0.002-0.006 clearance in the spindle bushings (6).

Bushings will not require final sizing if carefully installed with a suitable piloted arbor.

Thrust bearings (18-Fig. 3 or 17-Fig. 4) must be installed with the lettering towards the top of spindle.

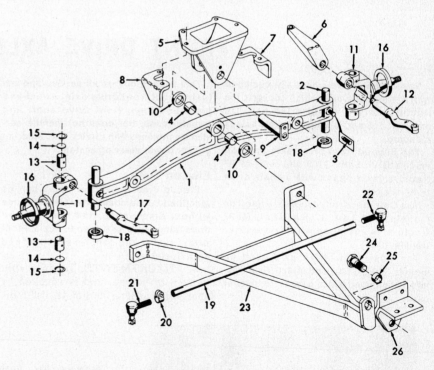

Fig. 3—Exploded view of typical "I" beam heavy duty, non-adjustable front axle.

1. Axle member	10. Spacer	18. Thrust bearing
2. Knuckle pin	11. Steering knuckle	19. Tie rod
3. Set screw	12. Tie rod arm R.H.	20. Clamp
4. Pivot bushing	13. Bushing	21. Tie rod end L.H.
5. Axle support	14. Plug	22. Tie rod end R.H.
6. Steering arm	15. Retaining ring	23. Axle stabilizer
7. Pivot stop R.H.	16. Dust shield	24. Pivot bolt
8. Pivot stop L.H.	17. Tie rod arm L.H.	25. Bushing
9. Pivot pin		26. Rear support

TIE-RODS, DRAG LINK AND TOE-IN
All Axle Type Models Except 4-Wheel Drive

3. On all models, automotive type tie-rod and drag link ends are used. When reassembling, adjust tie-rod length to provide toe-in of ¼-inch.

On models equipped with Type "E" adjustable front axle, adjust both tie-rods equally so that full left and full right turning radius of the tractor will be the same.

AXLE PIVOT PINS AND BUSHINGS
All Axle Type Models Except 4-Wheel Drive

4. Axle main (center) member is fitted with a renewable bushing (or bushings) for the pivot pin. Bushings are pre-sized and will not require reaming if carefully installed. On Type "E" adjustable axle types, the pivot pin should have a clearance of 0.003-0.007 in the bushings.

On heavy duty, non-adjustable axle models, renew bushings and/or pivot pin if clearance exceeds 0.031 (1/32-inch).

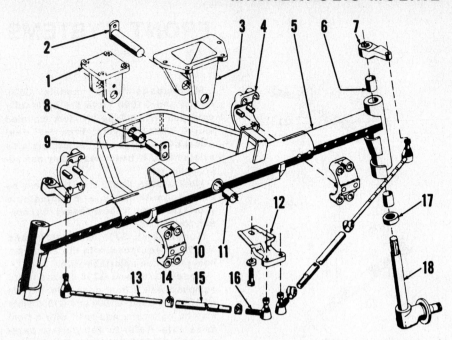

Fig. 4–Exploded view of typical Type "E" adjustable front axle and associated parts.

1. Rear support
2. Axle pivot pin
3. Axle support
4. Extension clamp
5. Axle extension
6. Bushing
7. Steering arm
8. Pivot bushing
9. Pivot pin
10. Axle center member
11. Pivot bushing
12. Center steering arm
13. Tie rod
14. Clamp
15. Tie rod tube
16. Tie rod end
17. Thrust bearing
18. Spindle (steering knuckle)

FRONT DRIVE AXLE

Some models are optionally equipped with a front drive axle which converts the tractor into a 4-wheel drive unit. On models G706 and G708, front drive axle is standard.

The Elwood front drive axle used on models G VI, Early G706 and Early MF97 tractors, is equipped with a chain drive transfer case.

The Coleman front drive axle used on models G708, Late G706 and Late MF97 tractors, is equipped with a gear drive transfer case.

The Ross front drive axle used on models G900, G1000 and G1000 Vista tractors, is equipped with a gear drive transfer case.

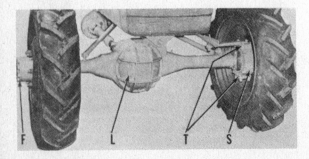

Fig. 5–Elwood type front drive axle.

F. Drive flange
L. Level plug
S. Steering support
T. Trunnions

This section covers all service and adjustment of front drive axle, wheel and pivot bearings, front drive shaft and transfer case, but does not include service on transmission driving unit, steering gear or power steering system.

Elwood Type

Elwood type front drive axles can be identified by the chain drive transfer case without disconnect, and the exposed drive flange hub as shown in Fig. 5. Front wheel caster and camber are fixed and not adjustable.

5. ADJUSTMENTS. Toe-in should be 1/16 to ⅛-inch, and is adjusted by shortening or lengthening the tie-rod.

Wheel bearings are adjusted to a slight rotational drag with no end play, by tightening or loosening the spindle adjusting nuts. To check and/or adjust wheel bearings, proceed as follows:

Support axle housing so that front tire is clear of ground and unbolt and remove front wheel drive flange (F—Fig. 5). Bend down locking tabs and remove outer adjusting nut using a suitable punch and hammer; then remove tab washer and adjust the bearings. Reassemble by reversing the disassembly procedure.

The tapered roller type pivot bearings are adjusted by means of shims located between upper and lower pivot bearing trunnions (T) and steering support housing (S). Because of possible drag or binding, any adjustment is approximate only, without removal of drive axle and joint assembly (9—Fig. 6) and steering support seal (15). Proceed as follows:

Support the tractor and remove front wheel and drive flange (1). Remove screws retaining steering spindle (3) to steering support (7) and

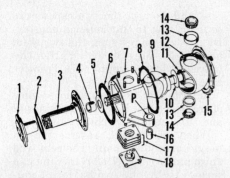

Fig. 6–Exploded view of steering support, drive axle and associated parts used on Elwood front drive unit.

1. Drive flange	11. Oil seal
2. Gasket	12. Axle housing
3. Spindle	13. Bearing cup
4. Bushing	14. Bearing cone
5. Thrust washer	15. Seal assy.
6. Gasket	16. Bushing
7. Steering support	17. Shim pack
8. Gasket	18. Trunnion
9. Shaft & U-joint	P. Tie rod pivot boss
10. Washer	

remove spindle, drive hub and spindle bearings as a unit. Withdraw axle shaft and joint assembly (9). Disconnect tie-rod from steering support and unbolt seal assembly (15). On left unit, disconnect drag link or steering cylinder connecting rod. Attach a pull scale to tie-rod pivot boss (P) and measure the turning effort with force applied parallel to front axle housing. Pivot bearing adjustment is correct when a steady pull of 12-15 lbs. is required to turn the support.

Transfer case drive chain tension should be adjusted to remove all slack without applying tension to chain and sprockets. To check the adjustment, disconnect front drive shaft from rear yoke (1—Fig. 10) and remove cap screws from eccentric housings (2 and 15). Using suitable spanner wrenches, turn the eccentric housings an equal amount until backlash at rear yoke (1) is reduced to a minimum. Reinstall retaining cap screws and front drive shaft. Check and refill transfer case to level of filler plug with SAE 90 Multipurpose lubricant.

6. OVERHAUL. Overhaul of the front drive axle can logically be divided into three operations; overhaul of drive hub and spindle unit, overhaul of main drive bevel gears and differential and overhaul of transfer case. All operations can be performed without removing front drive axle housing from tractor, refer to the appropriate following paragraphs.

7. DRIVE HUB AND SPINDLE. To disassemble either front drive hub and spindle unit, first suitably support the tractor and remove front wheel and tire unit and drive flange (1—Fig. 6). If drive hub, spindle or spindle bearings are to be serviced, remove adjusting nuts (19—Fig. 7), lockwasher (20), washer (21), the wheel spindle bearings and hub (24).

Spindle (3—Fig. 6) may be removed without disturbing drive hub or spindle bearings if their condition is satisfactory. Withdraw axle shaft and joint assembly (9) after spindle has been removed. Component parts of axle shaft and joint are not serviced separately: therefore, disassembly of the joint is not recommended. Bushing (4) in spindle (3) is available for service and can be renewed at this time.

Unbolt spindle support seal (15), tie-rod and upper pivot bearing trunnion (18), being careful not to lose or damage shim pack (17). Tilt upper end of steering support (7) outward until clear of upper bearing cone (14), then remove steering support, lower trunnion and lower pivot bearing cone from axle housing. Upper bearing cone (14) can now be lifted out, and cups (13) can be removed from axle housing (12) if renewal is indicated.

Inspect all parts and renew if condition is questionable. Pivot bearing shims (17) are available in thicknesses of 0.002, 0.005, 0.010 and 0.032, and total shim requirements should be approximately equally divided between upper and lower trunnions. Assemble by reversing the disassembly procedure. Install steering support using a sufficient quantity of shims (17) until a turning effort of 12-15 lbs. is required to turn support before installing drive axle or support seal (15). Turning effort should be measured at tie-rod pivot boss (P) parallel to axle. After unit is reassembled, remove upper plug from axle housing pivot ball (12) and fill joint with approximately 4 lbs. of chassis lubricant.

8. MAIN DRIVE BEVEL GEARS & DIFFERENTIAL. To remove the differential carrier unit, first drain front drive housing, suitably support front of tractor and remove both front wheels. Remove both front wheel drive flanges (1—Fig. 6) and remove the tie-rod. Unbolt both spindles (3) from steering supports (7) and remove spindles and assembled wheel hubs. Withdraw axle shafts (9). Remove front drive shaft and universal joint assembly.

Remove stud nuts securing carrier unit (12—Fig. 8) to axle housing, carefully balance unit on a rolling floor jack and roll the assembly out from underneath the tractor.

Cut safety wires and remove bearing caps (15 and 16), bearing adjusters (17 and 29), bearing cups (18 and 28) and the differential unit. Differential carrier bearing cones (19 and 27) can be renewed at this time if renewal is indicated.

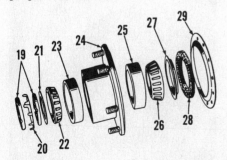

Fig. 7–Exploded view of drive hub, bearings and associated parts used on Elwood front drive unit.

19. Adjusting nuts	
20. Tab washer	25. Bearing cup
21. Washer	26. Bearing cone
22. Bearing cone	27. Retainer
23. Bearing cup	28. Seal
24. Drive hub	29. Retainer

Fig. 8–Exploded view of main drive bevel gears, differential and differential carrier assembly used on Elwood front drive unit.

1. Nut	
2. Washer	
3. Drive yoke	
4. Retainer	
5. Gasket	
6. Packing	
7. Oil seal	
8. Pinion bearing	
9. Drive pinion	
10. Pilot bearing	
11. Snap ring	
12. Carrier	
13. Thrust screw	
14. Locknut	
15. Cap	
16. Cap	
17. Adjuster	
18. Bearing cup	
19. Bearing cone	
20. Case half	
21. Thrust washer	
22. Axle gear	
23. Spider	
24. Spider pinions	
25. Case half	
26. Bevel ring gear	
27. Bearing cone	
28. Bearing cup	
29. Adjuster	

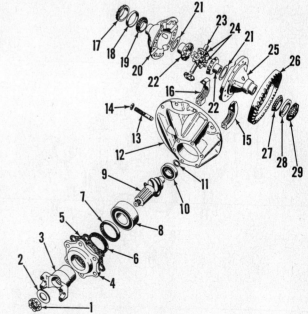

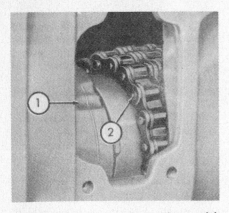

Fig. 9–Transfer case coupling used on models equipped with Elwood type front drive axle.

1. Housing groove   2. Master link pin

Remove the cap screws retaining pinion bearing retainer (4) and bump the drive pinion (9), bearings and associated parts from carrier housing. Pilot bearing (10) is retained to pinion shaft by snap ring (11). To disassemble the pinion, clamp drive shaft yoke (3) in a vise and remove shaft nut (1) and washer (2), then withdraw the yoke and retainer (4). Remove bearing (8) using a suitable puller.

Ring gear and pinion are available only as a matched set. Cone point (mesh position) of bevel gears is fixed and not adjustable.

Separate the differential case halves and examine axle gears, spider pinions, spider and thrust washers, renewing any parts which are worn, scored or otherwise damaged. Spider and spider pinions are serviced only as a matched set.

Assemble and install drive pinion and associated parts by reversing the disassembly procedure; then, before reinstalling the differential unit,

loosen lock nut (14) and back out thrust screw (13) several turns. Install the assembled differential unit, bearing cups (18 and 28) and adjusters (17 and 29), then install carrier caps (15 and 16) in their original positions, making sure adjuster threads to not bind as cap screws are tightened.

Turn the adjusters (17 and 29) until all carrier bearing end play is removed, making sure some backlash exists between bevel gears and that clearance exists between bevel gear (26) and thrust screw (13). After ALL end play is eliminated with minimum preload, adjust backlash to 0.008-0.011 when measured with a dial indicator. With backlash correctly adjusted, turn thrust screw (13) into housing until it contacts rear face of ring gear, back screw out ¼ to ½-turn and secure with locknut (14).

Assemble by reversing the disassembly procedure. Fill differential housing to level of lower plug (L—Fig. 5), with SAE 90 EP, multipurpose gear lubricant.

9. TRANSFER CASE. The transfer case is driven by the extended upper transmission countershaft and connected by coupling (37—Fig. 10) as shown in Fig. 9.

To remove the unit, first remove front drive shaft and transmission clutch adjusting cover on left side of transmission housing. Jack up one rear wheel and with transmission in neutral, turn rear wheel until coupling chain master link pin (2—Fig. 9) is aligned with groove (1) in housing; then remove pin and coupling chain.

Working from beneath the tractor, remove transmission housing lower cover sheet, suitably support transfer

case and remove the two cap screws securing case to transmission housing. Do not lose or intermix the two shim packs (33—Fig. 10) which align the halves of drive coupling (37). Transfer case can now be removed.

Refer to Fig. 10 for an exploded view of transfer case. Eccentric housings (2 and 15) control drive chain tension.

When reinstalling, reverse the removal procedure using the removed shim packs (33). With retaining cap screws tight, the two halves of coupling (37) must be in perfect alignment. Vary the thickness of shim packs, if necessary, to obtain correct alignment.

Coleman Type

American Coleman type drive axles can be identified by the front drive disconnect, stub housings bolted to ends of differential center housing, and the outboard type wheel universal joints shown in Fig. 11. Front wheel caster and camber are fixed and not adjustable.

10. **ADJUSTMENT.** Toe-in should be 1/16 to ⅛-inch, and is adjusted by shortening or lengthening the tie-rod.

Wheel bearings are adjusted to a slight rotational drag with no end play, by adding or removing shims behind the drive hub retaining clamp plate. To check and/or adjust wheel bearings, proceed as follows:

Support the axle housing and remove wheel cover and wheel. Remove the safety wire, drive axle flange bolts and drive axle as shown in Fig. 12. Move power yoke (2) out of the way, bend tabs on lock plates (7—Fig. 14) and remove retaining cap screws and clamp plate (8); then add or remove

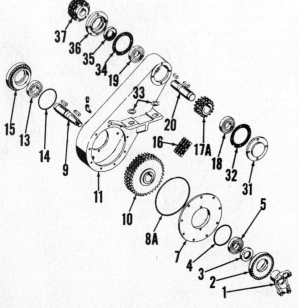

Fig. 10–Exploded view of chain drive transfer case used on models equipped with Elwood type front drive axle.

1. Yoke
2. Eccentric housing
3. Oil seal
4. "O" ring
5. Bearing
7. Cover
8A. "O" ring
9. Output shaft
10. Output sprocket
11. Housing
13. Bearing
14. "O" ring
15. Eccentric housing
16. Drive chain
17A. Drive sprocket
18. Bearing
19. Bearing
20. Input shaft
31. Bearing cup
32. Gasket
33. Shims
34. Gasket
35. Oil seal
36. Bearing housing
37. Coupling

Fig. 11–Coleman type front drive wheel with cover removed, showing components of outboard universal joint.

1. Drive axle
2. Power yoke
3. Compensating ring
4. Drive hub
5. Plug

Fig. 12—Full floating drive axle (1) can be withdrawn after detaching flange from power yoke (2).

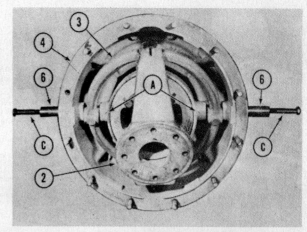

Fig. 13–Power yoke and compensating ring can be removed as a unit after removing wheel cover, wheel, drive axle and the two plugs (5–Fig. 11). Drive pins (6) are internally threaded for pulling. Roll pins (A) fit slots in inner end of drive pins to prevent rotation in drive hub (4). The ⅓-inch NC cap screws (C) are used for pulling drive pins only.

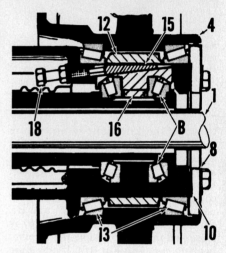

shims (10) as required. Shims are available in thicknesses of 0.002, 0.005 and 0.010. Reassemble by reversing the disassembly procedure.

The tapered roller type pivot bearings are adjusted by a tapered wedge (15—Fig. 15) and adjusting screw (18). Adjustment is correct when a steady pull of approximately 12 lbs. is required at steering arm, to move the steering spindle (11—Fig. 16). Make the adjustment as follows:

Remove wheel cover, wheel and driving axle as outlined for wheel bearing adjustment; then disconnect drag link from steering arm. Loosen locknut on spindle adjusting screw and turn adjusting screw clockwise into spindle to tighten pivot bearings. Adjustment may be checked with a spring scale as shown in Fig. 22. NOTE: If adjustment must be loosened instead of tightened, drive hub and spindle must be partially disassembled as outlined in paragraph 12, and inspection of pivot bearings is advised.

11. **OVERHAUL.** Overhaul of the front drive axle is logically divided into three operations; overhaul of drive hub and spindle unit, overhaul of main drive bevel gears and differential, and overhaul of transfer case. All operations can be performed without removing front drive axle housing from tractor. Refer to the appropriate following paragraphs:

12. **DRIVE HUB AND SPINDLE.** To disassemble either front drive hub and spindle unit, suitably support axle housing and remove wheel cover and wheel. Remove lock wire retaining axle flange cap screws, remove the cap screws and carefully withdraw drive axle (1—Fig. 12) to keep from damaging axle inner oil seal. Remove the two pipe plugs (5—Fig. 11) which retain drive pins (6—Fig. 13). Thread a ⅜-inch NC cap screw (C) into end of

drive pin (6) and remove pins by pulling straight out. NOTE: Slotted inner ends of drive pins fit over dowels (A), which prevent pins from rotating during operation or removal.

Lift out power yoke (2) and compensating ring (3). Compensating ring contains oilite bushings which are renewable.

Bend down tabs on lock plates (7—Fig. 14), and remove the cap screws, lock plates, clamp plate (8) and adjusting shims (10). Remove drive hub (4) carefully, to avoid dropping outer wheel bearing cone as hub is removed.

To remove clamp ring (12—Fig. 16), inner wheel bearing (13) or steering spindle (11), back out the spindle bearing adjusting screw (18—Fig. 15) several turns. Using a pin punch or similar tool and a hammer, drive the adjusting wedge (15—Fig. 17) against point of adjusting screw. If clamp ring binds, two knockout holes are provided in spindle flange, for removal of inner wheel bearing cone (13). Refer to Fig. 18. Using a pin punch and working

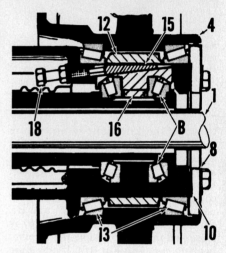

Fig. 15–Cross-sectional view of wheel hub and associated parts, showing method of adjusting spindle bearings. Refer to text for procedure.

B. Pivot bearings
4. Drive hub
8. Clamp plate
10. Shims
12. Clamp ring
13. Wheel bearings
15. Adjusting wedge
16. Bearing cap
18. Adjusting screw

Fig. 14–Wheel hub (4) can be removed after removing power yoke as shown in Fig. 13, then removing clamp plate (8). Wheel bearings are adjusted by shims (10).

4. Drive hub   9. Seal
7. Lock plates   10. Bearing adjusting
8. Clamp plate   shims

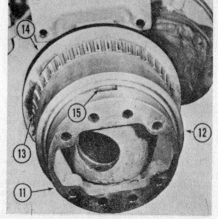

Fig. 16–Before clamp ring or inner wheel bearing can be removed, adjusting wedge (15) must be loosened; refer to text.

11. Steering spindle
12. Clamp ring
13. Wheel bearing
14. Seal
15. Adjusting wedge

Fig. 17—Steering spindle with clamp ring removed showing details of construction. Drillings (P & R) are knockout holes for removal of spindle bearings.

11. Steering spindle	15. Adjusting wedge
13. Wheel bearing	16. Bearing cap
14. Seal	17. Housing stub

Fig. 19—View of Coleman drive axle showing attachment of ball stud and steering arm. Spindle boot (19) may not be used on all models.

4. Drive hub
5. Plug
11. Steering spindle
17. Housing stub
19. Spindle boot
21. Boot clamp
22. Steering arm
23. Ball stud bracket

through the knockout holes, clamp ring and bearing cone can be removed at same time. IMPORTANT: Before attempting to remove clamp ring and bearing cone in this manner, first completely remove the spindle bearing adjusting screw (18—Fig. 15) and BE SURE that adjusting wedge (15) is loose and pushed to end of slot in pivot bearing cap (16—Fig. 18). If adjusting wedge is dragged outward with clamp ring or bearing cone, outer end of slot may be covered before wedging action locks the assembly, making removal extremely difficult.

Fig. 18—To check for pivot bearing wear, reinstall clamp ring and tighten adjusting screw until adjusting wedge (15) is tight; then measure distance (M) from outer end of wedge to end of slot. If distance (M) is less than 1⅜-inches, pivot bearings must either be renewed or shimmed beneath lower bearing cone.

M. 1⅜-inches minimum
P. Knockout holes
11. Steering spindle
14. Seal
15. Adjusting wedge
16. Bearing cap
18. Adjusting screw

If clamp ring can be easily removed, lift out adjusting wedge (15) before drifting off inner wheel bearing cone.

To remove wheel spindle after inner wheel bearing cone has been removed, first remove boot retainers (21—Fig. 19) if so equipped, and double back the boot (19). Insert a slim punch in knockout hole (R—Fig. 17) and tap lower pivot bearing cup out of housing stub (17). Lift off pivot bearing cap (16 —Fig. 18) and upper pivot bearing cone; then remove spindle, lower bearing cone and lower bearing cup as a unit.

Clean all parts in a suitable solvent and renew any which are damaged or worn. Seals (9—Fig. 14 and 14—Fig. 16) are available only in a kit which contains both seals for one wheel.

When assembling the spindle, place lower pivot bearing cup over cone and position spindle over housing stub (17 —Fig. 20). Place a solid wooden support beneath spindle as shown in Fig. 21, and lower full weight of tractor on support, making sure lower pivot bearing cup is properly aligned with bore in housing stub; then, use a heavy hammer and drift (D), to seat lower bearing cup into stub bore.

If pivot bearings show considerable wear, but are to be re-used, completely remove adjusting screw (18—Fig. 18). Install pivot bearing cup (16) and adjusting wedge (15); then install clamp ring, omitting inner wheel bearing cone. Move clamp ring toward inner side of spindle until approximately 1½ inches of bearing cap (16) extends beyond outer edge of clamp ring. Using a long pin punch and working through adjusting screw hole, tap adjusting

wedge (15) outward in slot until wedge is tight; then measure the distance (M) between outer end of adjusting wedge and extreme outer end of slot. The distance (M) should be at least 1⅜ inches. If distance is less than specified, remove the spindle and renew the bearings; or place 0.012 of shims beneath lower pivot bearing cone inner race, for each ⅛-inch distance (M) must be increased.

Complete the assembly by reversing the disassembly procedure. Before installing drive hub, tighten pivot bearing adjusting screw until a steady pull of 12 lbs. is required to maintain turning motion when tested with a spring scale as shown in Fig. 22.

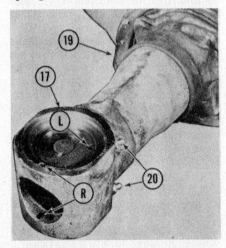

Fig. 20—Stripped axle housing stub showing details of construction. Grease fittings (20) open to pivot bearing lube passages in upper and lower pivot bearing areas.

L. Lube passage
R. Knockout holes
17. Housing stub
19. Spindle boot
20. Lube fittings

Fig. 21–Weight of tractor should be used to assist in spindle pivot bearing installation. Refer to text for procedure.

D. Drift
11. Steering spindle
17. Housing stub

Fig. 23–Front drive differential and carrier assembly removed from axle housing. Refer to Fig. 24 for legend.

13. MAIN DRIVE BEVEL GEARS & DIFFERENTIAL. To remove the differential carrier unit, first drain front drive housing and disconnect tie-rod at one end. Remove front drive shaft and universal joint assembly. Remove both front wheel covers and unbolt and remove both drive axle shafts. NOTE: As wheel covers are removed, reinstall two stud nuts on either wheel, to support wheel discs.

Remove stud nuts securing carrier unit to axle housing, carefully balance unit on a rolling floor jack and roll the assembly out from underneath the tractor.

Cut safety wires and remove bearing caps (5 and 7—Fig. 24), bearing adjusters (10 and 23), bearing cups (11 and 22), and the differential unit. Differential carrier bearing cones (12 and 21) can be renewed at this time if renewal is indicated.

Unbolt and remove seal retainer (37), bearing carrier (30), pinion (25) and associated parts, being sure to lay aside and save shim pack (28) as pinion assembly is removed. The shim pack controls mesh position (cone

point) of main drive bevel gears.

To disassemble pinion shaft unit, remove castellated nut, flat washer and yoke (38), then press pinion shaft and front bearing cone (26) forward out of bearing carrier (30) and rear bearing cone (34). Withdraw spacer (32) from pinion and remove front bearing cone (26) with a suitable puller. DO NOT unstake and remove pilot bearing (24) unless renewal of pinion or bearing is indicated. NOTE: If pilot bearing or pinion must be renewed, stake the installed pilot bearing in at least 4 places.

When disassembling the differential unit, match-mark the differential case halves, remove case retaining cap screws; then separate case and remove spider, pinions, axle gears and thrust washers. If bevel ring gear is to be renewed, drill and press out the rivets to prevent damage to the salvaged part.

Clean all parts and inspect for wear, scoring, chipped teeth or other damage, and renew as necessary. Ring gear and pinion are available only as a matched set; all other parts are available individually.

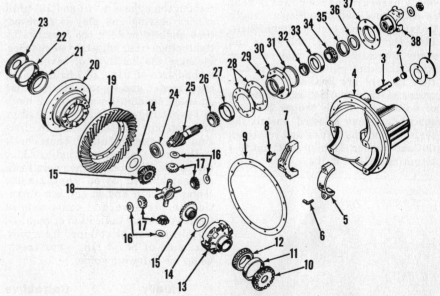

Fig. 24–Exploded view of differential, drive gears and carrier assembly used on the Coleman front drive axle.

1. Cover plate	14. Thrust washer	27. Bearing cup
2. Pipe plug	15. Axle gear	28. Cone point adj. shims
3. Oil distributor	16. Thrust washers	29. Dowel
4. Differential carrier	17. Spider pinions	30. Bearing carrier
5. Bearing cap	18. Differential spider	31. Cork gasket
6. Lock	19. Bevel ring gear	32. Spacer
7. Bearing cap	20. Case half	33. Bearing cup
8. Lock	21. Bearing cone	34. Bearing cone
9. Gasket	22. Bearing cup	35. Oil seal
10. Adjuster	23. Adjuster	36. Felt seal
11. Bearing cup	24. Pilot bearing	37. Seal retainer
12. Bearing cone	25. Bevel pinion	38. Drive yoke
13. Case half	26. Bearing cone	

Fig. 22–Using a spring scale to check pivot bearing adjustment. Refer to text.

S. Spring scale
22. Steering arm

Fig. 25—Inside view of front drive axle housing, showing location of axle inner oil seal (S).

Fig. 27—Partially disassembled view of front drive transfer case. Shift detent ball and spring are located in internal drilling (D) which is closed by pipe plug located in the approximate area indicated by (P).

7. Bearing cap   15. Roll pin
13. Output gear   16. Output shaft
14. Shifter fork   17. Bellcrank

Fig. 28—Input gear is splined in pinion gear and retained by snap ring (9). Bearing (12) consists of loose rollers contained in a cage.

1. Input gear   10. Snap ring
2. Pinion gear   11. Outer collar
9. Snap ring   12. Bearing

The thickness of spacer (32) controls the pre-load of pinion shaft carrier bearings, which should be adjusted to provide a rolling torque of 15-35 inch-lbs. Oil seal (35), felt seal (36) and retainer (37) should be omitted from the assembly when preload is checked. To avoid the necessity of completely assembling pinion and carrier unit when checking and adjusting pre-load, proceed as follows:

Install front bearing cone (26) on pinion and bearing cups (27 and 33) in carrier. Install the removed spacer (32) and rear bearing cone (34); then secure a pipe spacer of proper size to apply pressure to inner race of rear bearing cone, and of sufficient length to extend beyond end of pinion shaft. Place the unit in a suitable press and apply approximately 15 tons pressure while checking rolling torque of carrier. Spacers are available in thicknesses of 0.513 to 0.543 in increments of 0.003. After the proper bearing spacer has been selected, install the seals, pinion shaft yoke and retaining nut and washer. Tighten shaft nut to a torque of 325-450 ft.-lbs.

Fig. 26—Front drive transfer case used on models equipped with Coleman or Ross type front drive axles.

1. Input gear   5. Housing
2. Pinion gear   6. Drive yoke
3. Roll pin   7. Bearing cap
4. Input shaft

Cone point (mesh position) of main drive bevel gears is controlled by thickness of shim pack (28). If used bevel gears are reinstalled, both cone point and backlash should remain as nearly as possible, unchanged from previous settings. If new bevel gears are installed, the tooth contact pattern must be checked and the gears adjusted to provide the proper tooth contact. Proceed as follows:

Reassemble by reversing the disassembly procedure, using the removed shim pack (28) as a starting point. With clearance between the gears, tighten the adjusters (10 and 23) until carrier bearing end play is removed; then slightly preload the bearings by tightening either adjuster two notches. Measure the backlash of bevel gears and adjust to 0.010-0.012 by loosening one adjuster and tightening the other an equal amount. Paint 10 or 12 teeth of bevel ring gear with red lead or prussian blue and turn pinion in direction of normal rotation; then check tooth contact pattern as indicated by the paint. The point of heaviest tooth contact should be on approximate center of teeth and in the same position on pressure and coast side of teeth. A general indication of required adjustment can be obtained from pressure side of bevel ring gear teeth, using the following guide:

Heavy Contact Pattern	Corrective Action
Heel (Outer) Ends	Decrease Backlash
Toe (Inner) Ends	Increase Backlash
High (Tips) Contact	Remove Shims
Low (Root) Contact	Add Shims

After adjustment is completed, backlash should be within the extreme limits of 0.006-0.016. Mesh position

adjusting shims (28) are available in thicknesses of 0.005, 0.010, 0.020 and 0.030.

Before reinstalling the differential carrier assembly, check the axle oil seals (S—Fig. 25) and renew if their condition is questionable. Assemble the tractor by reversing the disassembly procedure. Fill differential housing to level of filler plug with 19 pints of SAE 90 EP transmission oil.

14. TRANSFER CASE. The gear-type transfer case can be detached from transmission housing after draining the unit and disconnecting shift link and front drive shaft. Lay aside and save the plastic mounting shim pack as case housing is removed. The shim pack controls the clearance between input gear (1—Fig. 26) and mating gear in transmission housing.

To disassemble the removed transfer case, drive out the roll pin (3) and push input shaft (4) either way out of input cluster gear and case. Drive the roll pin (15—Fig. 27) out of shifter fork (14), disconnect shifter bellcrank (17) or cable, and withdraw the shifter shaft.

NOTE: A detent ball and spring is located in a bore (D) which is closed with a plug (P), located on opposite side of shifter shaft bore. Detent assembly will be released as shaft is withdrawn.

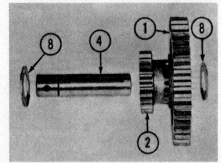

Fig. 29—Input shaft thrust washers (8) have formed tabs to prevent rotation in housing.

1. Input gear   4. Input shaft
2. Pinion gear   8. Thrust washers

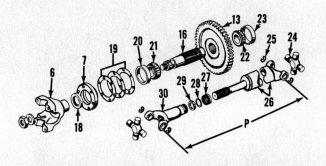

Fig. 30—Exploded view of output shaft, front drive shaft and associated parts.

6. Yoke
7. Bearing cap
13. Output gear
16. Output shaft
18. Oil seal
19. Shims
20. Bearing cup
21. Bearing cone
22. Bearing cone
23. Bearing cup
24. Joint kit
25. Snap ring
26. Drive shaft
27. Dust cap
28. Steel washer
29. Cork washer
30. Shaft sleeve

Shifter Fork (14) can be lifted out after removal of shifter shaft. Remove the screws retaining output shaft bearing cap (7) and use a slide hammer or other means to remove shaft assembly from gear (13) and rear bearing cone (22—Fig. 30).

Input gear (1—Fig. 28) can be removed from pinion gear (2) after expanding and removing snap ring (9). The two gear bearings (12) consist of a cage and loose rollers which are only available as an assembly. The bearings, outer collars (11) and center spacer can be withdrawn after removing either of the retaining snap rings (10).

When assembling the transfer case, vary the thickness of shim pack (19—Fig. 30) to apply a slight pre-load to shaft bearings (21 and 22). Shims (19) are available in thicknesses of 0.002, 0.003 and 0.010.

Install shifter fork (14—Fig. 27), remove plug (P); and install and depress detent spring and ball in its bore using a punch or similar tool, before inserting shifter shaft. Complete the assembly by reversing the disassembly procedure.

Use the removed mounting-shim pack, or install a shim pack of correct thickness to provide a minimum gear backlash without binding, when installing transfer case assembly. The plastic mounting shims are color coded as follows:

Red 0.002
Green 0.003
Brown 0.010

Adjust shifter linkage after installation, so that shifter shaft moves fully into detent notch in both the engaged and disengaged positions.

If front drive shaft is disassembled, reassemble so that universal joints are in register as shown at (P-Fig. 30).

Ross Type

Ross type front drive axles can be identified by the planetary front wheel hubs and by the two steering cylinders attached to front axle differential housing. Front wheel toe-in, caster and camber are non-adjustable.

15. **R&R AND OVERHAUL.** Complete front drive axle assembly can be removed from tractor as follows: Disconnect front drive shaft universal joint from yoke on drive pinion shaft. Remove cylinder shield, then unpin both steering cylinders from axle housing and spindle supports and secure cylinders to front frame. Unbolt axle from oscillating stabilizer frame, raise front of tractor and roll complete axle and wheels assembly forward from tractor.

NOTE: A rolling floor jack can be placed under differential carrier to prevent axle from tilting rearward as unit is removed.

If necessary, wheels and tie rod can now be removed and procedure for doing so is obvious. Ball studs are renewable in tie rod.

Overhaul of front drive axle assembly will be outlined as four operations; planet spider assembly, hub assembly, spindle support assembly and the differential and carrier assembly. All operations except differential and carrier overhaul can be accomplished without removing front drive axle from tractor. Both outer ends of axle are identical, therefore, only one outer end will be discussed.

16. **PLANET SPIDER.** To overhaul the planet spider assembly, support outer end of axle and remove tire and wheel assembly. Remove breather valve from center of planet spider, remove plug from hub and drain hub and planet spider assembly. Unbolt planet spider from wheel hub and using two of the removed cap screws in the jack screw holes in planet spider, force planet spider from wheel hub.

With the assembly removed, remove the three pinion shaft lock pins (4—Fig. 31) by driving them toward center of unit. Remove pinion shafts (6) and expansion plugs (7) by driving pinion shafts toward outside of planet spider (5). Discard the expansion plugs. Remove planet pinions (2), needle rollers (3) and thrust washers (1).

Clean and inspect all parts and renew as necessary. Pay particular attention to needle rollers and thrust washers.

When reassembling, use heavy grease to hold needle rollers (34 in each pinion) in inner bore of pinions. Make certain that tangs on thrust washers are in the slots provided for them and that holes in pinion shafts and mounting boss are aligned. Install lock pins (4) and new expansion plugs (7).

Coat mating surfaces of planet spider and wheel hub with Permatex No. 2 or equivalent sealer and install planet spider in wheel hub. Tighten retaining cap screws to a torque of 52-57 ft.-lbs. Fill hub with approximately 5 pints of SAE 90 SCL type lubricant. Check oil level by rotating hub to position filler plug opening at horizontal (half-full) position. Install tire and wheel.

17. **HUB ASSEMBLY.** To overhaul the wheel hub assembly, first remove planet spider assembly as outlined in paragraph 16. Then, remove snap ring (8—Fig. 32) and sun gear (7) from outer end of axle shaft. Straighten tabs on spindle nut lock washer (5) and remove nut (6) and lock washer. Loosen, but do not remove, spindle inner nut (4). Unbolt dirt shield (13) and spindle (12) from spindle support (8—Fig. 33) and remove wheel hub and spindle assembly.

Place hub assembly on bench with spindle nut on top side and block up under wheel hub flange so spindle will be free to drop several inches. Remove spindle inner nut (4—Fig. 32) and thrust washer (3). Place a wood block on end of spindle and bump spindle from internal hub (1). Lift internal hub and gear assembly (1 and 2) with bearing cone (20) from wheel hub (17). Take care not to drop bearing (20) as it is a loose fit on hub (1).

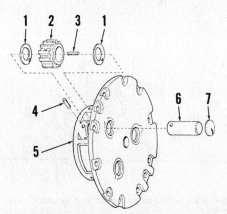

Fig. 31—Exploded view of planet spider assembly used on Ross front drive axle.

1. Thrust washers
2. Planet pinion
3. Needle rollers (34 each pinion)
4. Lock pin
5. Planet spider
6. Pinion shaft
7. Expansion plug

Complete removal of spindle (12) from wheel hub. All bearings, seals and dirt shield can now be removed and renewed if necessary, and procedure for doing so is obvious. Thrust washer and oil seal (5 and 6—Fig. 33) and bushing (11—Fig. 32) in inner bore of spindle (12) can also be renewed at this time.

When reassembling, install bearing cups (16 and 19) in wheel hub (17). Place inner bearing cone (15) in bearing cup (16) and install oil seal (14) in hub with lip of seal towards bearing. Install dirt shield on spindle (12), then using caution not to damage oil seal, install spindle in wheel hub. Hold spindle in position and turn unit over so threaded end of spindle is up. Place outer bearing (20) over end of spindle and into bearing cup (19). Start bearing hub of internal gear hub (1) into outer bearing cone, and if necessary, tap gear lightly with a soft faced hammer to position. Install thrust washer (3) and spindle inner nut (4) and tighten nut finger tight. Coat mating surfaces of spindle and spindle support with Permatex No. 2 or equivalent sealer and bolt dirt shield and spindle to spindle support. Tighten cap screws to a torque of 80-85 ft.-lbs.

Adjust spindle inner nut (4) as required until a pull of 33-38 pounds on a spring scale attached to a wheel mounting bolt is required to keep hub rotating. Install lock washer (5) and outer nut (6). Tighten outer nut and recheck hub rolling torque. When bearing adjustment is correct, bend tabs on lock washer to secure both nuts. Install sun gear (7) and snap ring (8) on outer end of axle shaft.

Install planet spider and fill hub with lubricant as outlined in paragraph 16. Install tire and wheel assembly.

18. **SPINDLE SUPPORT.** The spindle support can be serviced after planet spider and wheel hub assemblies have been removed as outlined in paragraphs 16 and 17. However, if service is required only on the spindle support, the planet spider, wheel hub and axle shaft can be removed as an assembly as follows:

Raise outer end of axle housing and remove tire and wheel assembly. Attach a hoist to wheel mounting bolt on hub, then unbolt spindle from spindle support and pull complete hub assembly and axle shaft from axle housing. Do not allow weight of hub assembly to be supported by axle shaft as damage to oil seal in axle housing outer end will result.

With complete hub and axle shaft

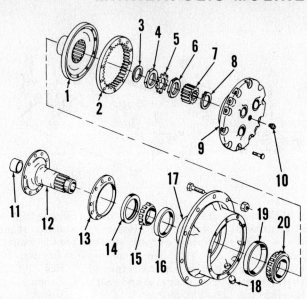

Fig. 32—Exploded view of wheel hub and related parts used on Ross front drive axle.

1. Internal hub
2. Hub gear
3. Thrust washer
4. Spindle nut (inner)
5. Lock washer
6. Spindle nut (outer)
7. Sun gear
8. Snap ring
9. Planet spider assy.
10. Breather valve
11. Bushing
12. Spindle
13. Dirt shield
14. Oil seal
15. Bearing cone
16. Bearing cup
17. Wheel hub
18. Plug
19. Bearing cup
20. Bearing cone

assembly removed, disconnect tie rod and power steering cylinder from spindle support. Unbolt seal retainer from inner side of spindle support and

separate retainers, seals and gasket from support.

NOTE: At this time it is desirable to remove the grease from the cavity

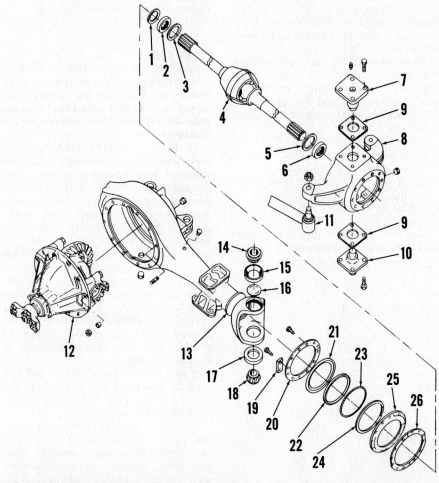

Fig. 33—Exploded view showing spindle support, bearings, seals and axle shaft and universal joint assembly.

1. Seal washer	7. Trunnion (upper)	13. Axle housing	20. Seal retainer ring
2. Oil seal	8. Spindle support	14. Bearing cone	21. Dust seal retainer
3. Thrust washer	9. Shims	15. Bearing cup	22. Dust seal
4. Axle shaft and "U" joint assy.	10. Trunnion (lower,	16. Grease retainer	23. Seal spring
5. Thrust washer	11. Tie rod	17. Bearing cup	24. Oil seal
6. Oil seal	12. Differential carrier assembly	18. Bearing cone	25. Oil seal retainer
		19. Stop plate	26. Gasket

formed by the spindle support and outer end of axle housing.

Remove upper trunnion (7—Fig. 33), pull top of spindle support outward and remove spindle support from axle housing. Keep any shims present under top trunnion tied to the trunnion for use during reassembly. Remove upper trunnion bearing (14) from axle housing. Remove lower trunnion (10), shims (9) and bearing (18) from spindle support. Both trunnion bearing cups (15 and 17) and upper bearing grease retainer (16) can now be removed. If necessary to remove axle shaft thrust washer (3), oil seal (2) and oil seal washer (1) from axle housing outer end, a slide hammer puller can be used.

Clean and inspect all parts and renew as necessary. It is recommended that all seals be renewed during assembly.

To reassemble spindle support, proceed as follows: Install axle shaft seal washer and oil seal with lip toward inside and be sure oil seal is bottomed. Install axle shaft thrust washer. Install seal components (20 thru 25) and gasket (26) over end of axle housing. Make certain that bevel on inside diameter of rubber dust seal (22) and felt oil seal (24) is toward bell of axle outer end. Install grease retainer (16) with cup side down and upper bearing cup (15) in the upper trunnion bearing bore. Bolt the lower trunnion (10) to spindle support using the original shims and tighten the cap screws to a torque of 80-85 ft.-lbs. Place lower trunnion bearing (18) over lower trunnion. Install lower bearing cup (17) in

axle housing. Place upper bearing (14) in upper bearing cup, then while tipping upper side of spindle support slightly outward, position spindle support over end of axle housing. Install upper trunnion and original shims. Tighten trunnion retaining cap screws to a torque of 80-85 ft.-lbs.

Before attaching tie rod, power steering cylinder or seal assembly to spindle support, check adjustment of trunnion bearings as follows: Connect a spring scale to tie rod hole in spindle support and check the effort required to turn the spindle support. This effort should be 12-18 pounds on the scale. If adjustment is required, vary the thickness of shim packs (9). Keep shim pack thickness equal on upper and lower trunnions. Shims are available in thicknesses of 0.003 (green), 0.005 (blue) and 0.010 (brown).

Install seal assembly on spindle support, attach power steering cylinder and tie rod. Tighten tie rod stud nut to a torque of 165 ft.-lbs.

Place approximately four pounds of No. 1 EP Lithium Soap base grease in the cavity of spindle support and pack universal joint on axle shaft. Coat mating surfaces of spindle and spindle support with Permatex No. 2 or equivalent sealer and install the wheel hub and axle shaft assembly on the spindle support. Tighten attaching cap screws to a torque of 80-85 ft.-lbs. Install tire and wheel assembly. Lubricate upper trunnion bearing with GP No. 2 Wheel Bearing Grease.

19. **DIFFERENTIAL & CARRIER.** To remove the differential and carrier assembly, support front of tractor and remove front tire and wheel assemblies. Drain differential housing. Remove cylinder shield, then unpin steering cylinders from axle housing and spindle supports and secure cylinders to front frame. Disconnect front drive shaft universal joint. Attach a hoist to wheel mounting bolt on hub, then unbolt spindle from spindle support and withdraw complete hub and axle shaft assembly from axle housing. Repeat operation for opposite side.

Place a floor jack under front axle, unbolt axle from oscillating stabilizer frame and lower axle assembly from tractor. Position axle assembly on supports with pinion shaft yoke up. Disconnect one end of tie rod and swing it out of the way. Remove nuts securing differential carrier to axle housing and remove carrier assembly. Mark carrier bearing caps (10—Fig. 34) so they can be reinstalled in their original positions, then remove cotter pins and adjusting nut lock pins (9).

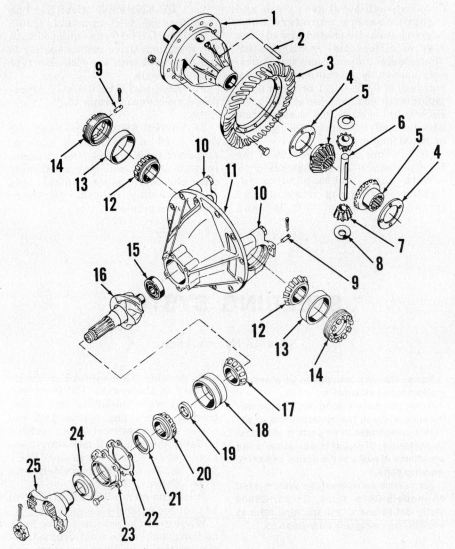

Fig. 34—Exploded view of differential carrier assembly used on Ross front drive axle.

1. Differential cage	9. Lock pins	18. Bearing cup
2. Lock pin	10. Bearing caps	19. Spacer
3. Bevel ring gear	11. Carrier	20. Bearing cone
4. Thrust washer	12. Carrier bearings	21. Oil seal
5. Axle gears	13. Bearing cups	22. Gasket
6. Shaft	14. Bearing adjusters	23. Retainer
7. Differential pinion	15. Pilot bearing	24. Dust shield
8. Thrust washer	16. Bevel pinion	25. Yoke
	17. Bearing cone	

Cut lock wires and remove bearing caps (10). Lift differential from carrier and keep bearing cups (13) identified with their bearing cones (12). Bearing cones can now be removed from differential cage, if necessary. Unbolt and remove bevel ring gear (3). Drive differential pinion shaft lock pin (2) from cage and remove shaft (6), differential pinions (7), thrust washers (8), axle gears (5) and thrust washers (4).

Remove cotter pin and nut from pinion shaft (16), then using a puller, remove yoke (25) and dust shield (24). Unbolt and remove retainer (23) with oil seal (21) and gasket (22). Withdraw bevel pinion and bearings from carrier. Use a split bearing puller to support bearing cone (17) and press pinion shaft from bearings. Save bearing spacer (19) and any spacer shims that are present. Press pinion shaft from bearing (15).

Clean and inspect all parts. Pay particular attention to bearings, bearing cups and thrust washers. If any of the axle gears (5) or differential pinions (7) are damaged or excessively worn, renew all gears (5 and 7), thrust washers (4 and 8) and shaft (6). Bevel pinion shaft (16) and bevel ring gear (3) are available only as a matched set.

When reassembling, install bearing (15) on pinion shaft (16) and stake in place each 90 degrees. Use a piece of pipe the same size as inner race of bearing cone (17) and press bearing into position on pinion shaft. Place bearing spacer (19) and any spacer shims which were present during disassembly over pinion shaft, then position double bearing cup (18) on bearing (17). Install bearing cone (20). Renew oil seal (21) in retainer (23). Place new gasket (22) and retainer (23) over pinion shaft. Check and if necessary, renew dust shield (24). Position yoke (25) so it will not obstruct cotter pin hole in pinion shaft, slide retainer and oil seal on yoke sealing surface, then press yoke on pinion shaft. Install yoke retaining nut, clamp yoke in a vise and tighten nut to a torque of 300 ft.-lbs. Clamp bearing cup (18) in a soft jawed vise only tight enough to prevent rotation. Then, with oil seal retainer (23) free from bearing, attach in inch-pound torque wrench to yoke retaining nut and check rolling torque (bearing preload). Rolling torque should be 13-23 in.-lbs.

If rolling torque is not as specified, it will be necessary to disassemble the unit and vary the thickness of spacer (19) and/or shims as required. A spacer and shim kit is available under MM part No. 10P3669.

With pinion shaft assembled and rolling torque (bearing preload) correct, install pinion shaft assembly into carrier. Install seal retainer and tighten cap screws to a torque of 15 ft.-lbs. Install cotter pin to lock yoke retaining nut in place.

Place axle gears (5), differential pinions (7) and thrust washers (4 and 8) in cage (1) and install shaft (6). Secure shaft in position with lock pin (2). Install bevel ring gear and tighten nuts to a torque of 75-85 ft.-lbs. Press carrier bearings (12) on cage. Place bearing cups (13) over bearings and install differential assembly in carrier. Position bearing adjusters (14) in carrier and install bearing caps (10). Tighten bearing cap retaining cap screws until caps are snug but BE SURE threads of caps and adjusters are in register. Maintain some clearance between bevel gear teeth and tighten bearing adjusters until bearing cups are seated and all end play of differential is eliminated. Mount a dial indicator and shift differential assembly as required to obtain a backlash of 0.008-0.011 between bevel pinion shaft gear and bevel ring gear. Differential is shifted by loosening one adjuster and tightening the opposite an equal amount.

NOTE: Fore and aft position of the bevel pinion shaft is not adjustable.

With gear backlash adjusted, tighten bearing cap retaining cap screws to a torque of 65 ft.-lbs. and secure with lock wire. Install adjuster lock pins (9) and cotter pins. If lock pins will not enter slots in adjusters after backlash adjustment has been made, tighten rather than loosen the adjusters. Recheck gear backlash.

Coat mating surfaces of carrier and axle housing with Permatex No. 2 or equivalent sealer. Install carrier assembly and tighten retaining nuts to a torque of 35-40 ft.-lbs. Tighten tie rod stud nut to a torque of 165 ft.-lbs. When joining spindles to spindle supports, coat mating surfaces with Permatex No. 2 or equivalent sealer and tighten retaining cap screws to a torque of 80-85 ft.-lbs.

When reassembly is completed, fill differential housing to level plug opening with SAE 90 SCL type lubricant. Capacity is 16 pints.

20. TRANSFER CASE. The transfer case used on models G900, G1000 and G1000 Vista equipped with the Ross front drive axle is similar to the unit used with the Coleman type front drive axle.

For R&R and OVERHAUL procedures, refer to paragraph 14.

21. DRIVE SHAFT. The front axle drive shaft is conventional. Removal and overhaul is obvious after an examination of the unit. Universal joint cross and bearings are available only as an assembly. All other parts are available separately.

STEERING SYSTEM

(Except Hydrostatic)

Power steering is supplied as standard equipment on all models.

Note: When working on the power steering system, the maintenance of absolute cleanliness of all parts is of utmost importance. Of equal importance is the avoidance of nicks and burrs on any of the working parts.

For service on Hydrostatic system used on models G900, G950, G1000, G1000 Vista, G1050 and G1350 tractors, refer to section beginning with paragraph 35.

FILLING AND BLEEDING
G VI-G705-G706-G707-G708-MF95-MF97

22. The regular tractor hydraulic system reservoir is the source of fluid supply to the power steering system.

Only genuine MM hydraulic oil should be used in the system. Fill the reservoir only when the lifting jack is contracted. After filling, operate jack and power steering several times; recheck oil level and add oil if necessary. Reservoir should be filled to the "Full" mark on the dipstick on models with Type "E" hydraulic system.

It is recommended that hydraulic oil be changed at least once each year.

Whenever the oil lines have been disconnected or the fluid drained, reconnect the lines, fill the reservoir and cycle the power steering and the hydraulic lift system several times to bleed air from the system; then, refill the reservoir to the proper level. Capacity of the system is approximately 3 gallons.

TROUBLE-SHOOTING
G VI-G705-G706-G707-G708-MF95-MF97

23. Some of the troubles which may be encountered in the operation of the power steering system and their possible causes are listed below. The procedure for correcting most of the troubles is evident; for those not readily remedied, refer to the appropriate subsequent paragraphs.

1. Hard Steering
   a. Linkage damaged, worn or misaligned
   b. Insufficient fluid in reservoir
   c. Low pump pressure
   d. Sticking control valve spool
   e. Faulty flow control valve
   f. Faulty cylinder
2. Power Assistance in One Direction Only
   a. Sticking control valve spool
   b. Damaged cylinder
3. Erratic Steering Control
   a. Linkage damaged, worn or misaligned
   b. Sticking control valve spool
   c. Air in system
4. Noisy Operation or "Shimmy"
   a. Linkage damaged, worn or misaligned
   b. Faulty relief valve
   c. Air in system
   d. Insufficient fluid in reservoir
   e. Ball stud adjusting plug too loose

OPERATING PRESSURE, RELIEF VALVE, FLOW CONTROL VALVE
G VI-G705-G706-G707-G708-MF95-MF97

24. Working fluid for the hydraulic power steering system is supplied by the same pump which powers the hydraulic lift system. Placed between the pump and the remainder of the system is a flow control and relief valve mechanism which is mounted on the rear

face of the hydraulic pump. The small metering hole in the end of the flow control piston passes a pre-determined amount of fluid to the power steering system; but, since the pump supplies considerably more fluid than is required by the steering system, pressure builds up in front of the piston and moves the piston, against spring pressure, until the ports which supply oil to the hydraulic system are uncovered. The power steering system, therefore, receives priority and the fluid requirements of the power steering system are satisfied before any oil flows to the hydraulic lift system.

25. **SYSTEM PRESSURE TEST.** A pressure test of the power steering circuit will disclose whether the pump, relief valve or some other unit in the system is malfunctioning. To make such a test, proceed as follows: Tee a pressure gage into pressure line leading to power steering control valve. Start and run engine until hydraulic fluid is at normal operating temperature. Then, with engine running at fast idle speed, turn front wheels either way against their stop. Hold steering wheel against stop only long enough to observe gage pressure, which should be 950-1050 psi.

Note: On models with steering stops located on steering gear support as shown in Fig. 44, install a shut-off valve along with gage in pressure line. Make sure gage is located between pump and shut-off valve. With engine running at rated speed, close shut off valve ONLY long enough to record gage reading.

If gage reading is less than 950 psi, check and/or adjust the relief valve pressure as outlined in paragraph 26. If the gage reading is still less than 950 psi, a faulty hydraulic pump is indicated.

Refer to Figs. 35 and 36 for exploded views of flow control and relief valve located on hydraulic system pump.

26. **OVERHAUL.** Power steering flow control and relief valves can, in all cases, be removed for inspection or adjustment of relief pressure without removing hydraulic pump from tractor. However, the valve housing must be removed for service on flow control valve.

On all models, housing must be renewed if relief valve seat is damaged. On some G VI and MF95 tractors, pressure is adjusted by turning screw (6—Fig. 35); on all other models, shims are available for adjusting relief pressure.

Refer to the appropriate exploded view when removing or installing flow

control valve and spring. Make sure valve slides freely in bore, and that valve and bore are free of deep scratches or scoring, and that spring is not distorted.

PUMP
G VI-G705-G706-G707-G708-MF95-MF97

27. The hydraulic pump supplies fluid to both the power steering system and the hydraulic lift system.

Refer to paragraph 234 through 237 for overhaul data on hydraulic pumps.

CONTROL VALVE
G VI-G705-G706-G707-G708-MF95-MF97

28. **R&R AND OVERHAUL.** To remove the control valve, first identify and remove pressure and return lines to power steering cylinder and remove nut at rear end of piston rod. Remove the nut securing drag link (7—Fig. 37) to the actuating stud (4—Fig. 38) and disconnect front end of drag link. Loosen the lock nut securing the cylinder end cap (3—Fig. 37) to the steering rod and remove complete cylinder assembly from tractor.

NOTE: The same standards of care and cleanliness required for all hydraulic or diesel injection equipment must be observed when performing any service on the power steering control valve. Cylinder and control valve must only be disassembled in a clean shop on a clean bench.

To remove the control valve, unstake and remove cylinder end cap (33—Fig. 38), remove seal clamp and stud seal. Remove lock pin (32) and adjusting plug (31). Push ball stud (4) into cylinder and out open end.

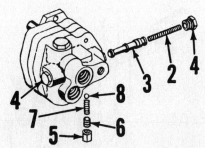

Fig. 35—Webster hydraulic pump used on some G VI and MF95 tractors, showing power steering flow control and relief valves. On this pump both ends of flow control valve bore are plugged.

2. Spring	5. Cap
3. Flow control valve spool	6. Adjusting screw
	7. Spring
4. Plug	8. Relief valve

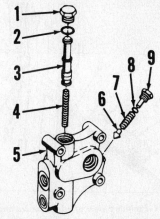

Fig. 36—Exploded view of flow control and relief valve assemblies used on some G VI and MF95 tractors and all MF97, G705, G706, G707 and G708 tractors.

1. Plug	5. Housing
2. "O" ring	6. Relief valve
3. Flow control valve spool	7. Spring
4. Spring	8. Adjusting shims
	9. Plug

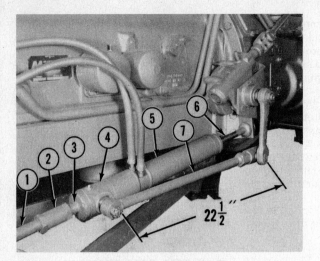

Reassemble by reversing the disassembly procedure. Tighten flexure rod nut (6) to a torque of 10-12 ft.-lbs. When reinstalling control valve in cylinder, notice that seating face of cylinder contains five holes, the center hole being a locating hole for dowel (18). Make sure dowel enters the locating hole and that the four pressure ports are aligned.

When installing ball stud (4), the two retaining balls (24) must be in the two holes in socket shell (23) and in the retaining slot in ball stud (4). Tighten adjusting plug (31) securely, back off to nearest lock point and install lock pin (32). Install end cap (33), tighten to a torque of 50-60 ft.-lbs. and stake in place.

Reinstall cylinder on tractor by reversing the removal procedure. Adjust the linkage as outlined in paragraph 33, then fill and bleed system as outlined in paragraph 22.

Fig. 37—Power steering control valve and cylinder assembly used on early G VI and MF95 tractors. Other models are similar. On early G VI and MF95, adjust drag link to 22 1/2 inches as shown.

1. Steering rod
2. Coupling
3. End cap
4. Valve shield
5. Steering cylinder
6. Piston rod
7. Drag link

Washer (30), spring (29) and outer seat (26) will be removed with ball stud, and retaining balls (24) and inner seat (26) can now be removed. Unscrew grease fitting (5) and withdraw ball socket (28); then withdraw valve assembly as a unit.

To disassemble the valve, reinstall ball seats (26), and stud (4) and adjusting plug (31) in socket shell (23) and tighten adjusting plug securely to prevent flexure rod (25) from turning. Then, remove rod nut (6), centering spring (13) and associated parts. Valve can then be completely disassembled.

Valve spool (21) should only be withdrawn or installed from end of valve housing (20) opposite dowel (18), to prevent cutting "O" ring (22) on internal shoulders of valve housing bore. Also, prevent spool from sliding out dowel end of housing during assembly.

Examine valve housing and spool for excessive wear or scoring. Control valve spool and valve housing are serviced only as an assembly and must be renewed as a unit if worn or scored. Renew all "O" rings when valve is disassembled.

STEERING CYLINDER
G VI-G705-G706-G707-G708-MF95-MF97

The steering cylinder is a sealed unit. Except for linkage and control valve service outlined in paragraph 28, the only service possible is seal renewal covered in the following paragraph.

29. **R&R CYLINDER SHAFT SEAL.** To remove the steering cylinder shaft seal when the cylinder is on the tractor, fully extend the cylinder by turning the wheels to the left. Remove shaft nut (12—Fig. 39) from rear end of shaft, then, with the engine running and cylinder supported, retract cylinder piston by turning steering wheel to the right to actuate the control valve.

Remove anchor cushion and retainer from end of piston rod and carefully remove any dirt, paint or burrs from the exposed portion of the rod. Remove

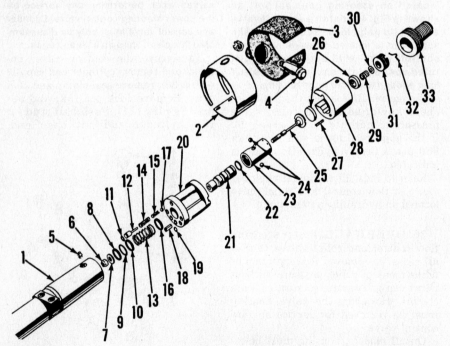

Fig. 38—Exploded view of control valve end of Ross power steering cylinder. Refer also to Fig. 39.

1. Cylinder	12. Body plug	23. Socket shell
2. Seal clamp	13. Centering spring	24. Balls
3. Stud seal	14. Spring	25. Flexure rod
4. Ball stud	15. Spring	26. Ball seat
5. Fitting	16. Washer	27. Roll pin
6. Rod nut	17. Check ball	28. Ball socket
7. Washer	18. Roll pin	29. Spring
8. Washer	19. "O" ring	30. Washer
9. "O" ring	20. Valve housing	31. Adjusting plug
10. Washer	21. Spool	32. Lock pin
11. "O" ring	22. "O" ring	33. End cap

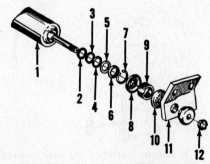

Fig. 39—Exploded view of Ross power steering cylinder seals. Refer also to Fig. 38.

1. Cylinder	7. Snap ring
2. "O" ring	8. Cushion retainer
3. Back-up ring	9. Rubber cushion
4. Washer	10. Frame
5. Washer	11. Bracket
6. Wiper seal	12. Rod nut

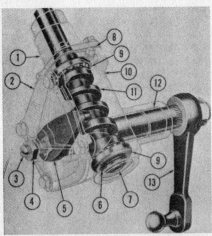

Fig. 40–Phantom view of Ross steering gear used on early G VI and MF95 tractors.

1. Upper cover	8. Shim pack
2. Side cover	9. Worm bearing
3. Adjusting screw	10. Sector housing
4. Lock nut	11. Worm shaft
5. Lever shaft	12. Bushing
6. Snap ring	13. Steering arm
7. Lower plug	

snap ring (7) from end of cylinder, and with a pointed tool, extract dust seal (6), washers (4 and 5), back-up ring (3) and "O" ring (2) from the cylinder.

Extend the cylinder piston and examine the shaft for scoring or bends. If the shaft cannot be smoothed with crocus cloth, if it is bent or excessively loose in cylinder bearing, the complete cylinder must be renewed.

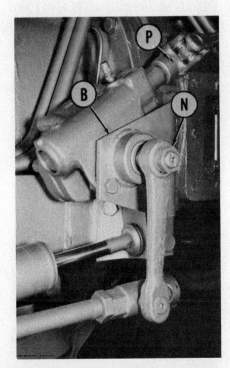

Fig. 41–To remove the steering gear assembly on early G VI and MF95 tractors, remove nut (N) and pull steering arm. Drive out roll pin (P) and remove "U" joint. Unbolt bracket (B) and lift off steering gear.

If the cylinder is found to be serviceable, lubricate the new seals and reinstall in the cylinder by reversing the removal procedure.

STEERING GEAR UNIT
Early G VI-MF95

Early models G VI and MF95 were equipped with the Ross steering gear shown in Fig. 40. Refer to paragraph 32 for the Saginaw unit used on later production G VI and MF95 tractors.

30. **ADJUSTMENT.** To adjust the worm shaft end play, it is first necessary to remove the unit as outlined in paragraph 31. The worm shaft bearings should be adjusted to provide a slight rotational drag, by adding or removing shims (8—Fig. 40) under the upper cover (1).

To adjust the backlash between the worm shaft and lever stud, loosen the lock nut (4) and turn the adjusting screw (3) into the side cover until, with the wheels in a straight ahead position, all backlash is removed but no binding occurs when the wheels are turned.

31. **R&R AND OVERHAUL.** To remove the steering sector, remove the nut (N—Fig. 41) retaining the steering arm to the lever shaft and remove steering arm. Drive roll pin (P) from lower universal joint yoke and remove yoke from worm shaft. Remove the cap screws retaining the sector bracket to flywheel housing and lift the sector and bracket from tractor. Remove the three cap screws retaining sector housing to the mounting bracket and separate the sector and bracket. Remove the four cap screws retaining the sector side cover (2—Fig. 40) to housing, remove the side cover and withdraw the lever shaft (5). The two lever shaft bushings (12) and shaft seal can be renewed at this time. To remove the worm shaft and bearings, remove the cap screws retaining the upper cover and withdraw the cover and shim pack (8), then withdraw the worm shaft (11) and bearings (9) from the housing. Renew the bearings if they are damaged or loose, and adjust bearing preload to provide a slight rotational drag, by means of shims (8).

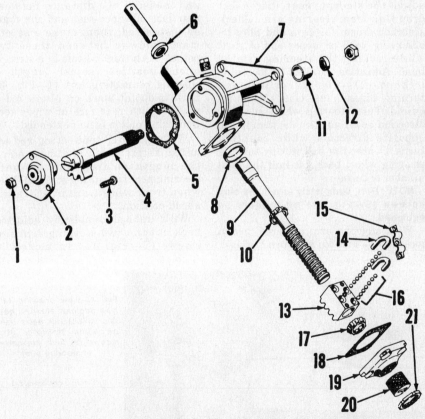

Fig. 42–Exploded view of early type Saginaw steering gear used on some models.

1. Locknut	8. Bearing cup	15. Guide clamp
2. Side cover	9. Worm shaft	16. Steel balls
3. Adjusting screw	10. Bearing cone	17. Bearing cone
4. Sector shaft	11. Bushing	18. Gasket
5. Gasket	12. Oil seal	19. Adjusting cover
6. Seal	13. Ball nut	20. Adjuster
7. Housing	14. Ball guide	21. Locknut

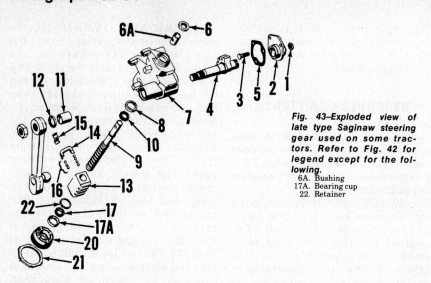

Fig. 43—Exploded view of late type Saginaw steering gear used on some tractors. Refer to Fig. 42 for legend except for the following.
6A. Bushing
17A. Bearing cup
22. Retainer

equipped, until they contact steering arm just before axle stops touch.

34. R&R AND OVERHAUL. To remove the steering gear unit, drive out the roll pin retaining universal joint to upper end of worm shaft and disconnect drag link from steering arm. Remove bolts securing steering gear brackets to crankcase and side frame and lift off steering gear and brackets as a unit.

Remove the nut securing steering arm to sector shaft. Center punchmark steering arm and sector shaft splines so that arm can be reinstalled in same position; then remove steering arm using a suitable puller. Unbolt and remove mounting brackets.

Remove any paint, rust and dirt from exposed end of sector shaft (4—Fig. 42 or 43) and remove any burrs with a file or stone. Remove the three cap screws retaining side cover (2) and remove sector shaft and associated parts by tapping on exposed end of shaft with a soft hammer. Remove nut (1) and thread adjusting screw (3) through side cover to separate shaft and cover. Be careful not to lose shims located on head of adjusting screw.

Remove any rust, paint, dirt or burrs from exposed end of worm shaft (9). Remove adjusting cover (19—Fig. 42) (Early Type) or adjuster (20—Fig. 43) (Late Type); then withdraw worm shaft and ball nut assembly downward out of housing.

Seals (6 and 12), bushing (11 and 6A) and bearings (8, 10, 17 and 17A) can be renewed at this time. The

Late G VI-MF95-All G705-G706-G707-G708-MF97

Some tractors are equipped with a Saginaw steering gear of the type shown in Fig. 42. Most G705, G706 and MF97 and all G707 and G708 tractors use the Saginaw unit shown in Fig. 43. Refer also to paragraph 30 for Ross steering gear used on some G VI and MF95 tractors.

32. SECTOR ADJUSTMENT. To adjust the steering gear, disconnect drag link from steering arm. Check steering worm for zero end play by observing yoke on upper end of shaft while rocking the steering arm by hand. Adjust as required by loosening locknut (21—Fig. 42 or 43) and turning adjuster (20) clockwise as required. Turn steering wheel in either direction as far as possible, then in the opposite direction while counting turns. Center the ball nut by turning steering wheel back one-half the total number of turns.

NOTE: First, completely turn in the stop screws (S—Fig. 44) on models so equipped.

With steering arm centered, loosen locknut (1—Fig. 45) and turn backlash

adjusting screw (3) clockwise until a very slight, noticeable drag is felt as sector gear passes over the midpoint.

33. LINKAGE ADJUSTMENT. To adjust the steering linkage, proceed as follows: Disconnect steering cylinder rod from steering spindle and fully retract the piston. With a wax pencil, mark piston rod at a point just behind the wiper seal. Fully extend piston and measure the distance between rear face of wiper seal and the mark on piston rod; then, make a second mark midway between these two points. With front wheels in a straight ahead position, adjust length of steering connecting link (1—Fig. 46) until midpoint mark on piston rod is aligned with rear face of wiper seal, indicating piston is half extended.

With cylinder connecting rod adjusted as previously outlined, adjust the length of drag link (5) until steering arm is pointing straight down when front wheels are in a straight ahead position.

With linkage completely adjusted, back out the two steering arm stop screws (S—Fig. 44) on models so

Fig. 44—View showing late type Saginaw steering gear and associated parts used on some tractors. Stop screws (S) limit movement of steering arm.

1. Steering connecting rod
2. Drag link

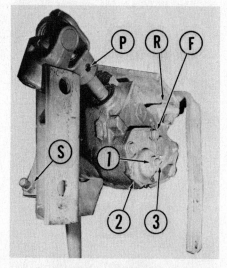

Fig. 45—Late type Saginaw steering gear viewed from engine side, showing details of adjustment. Refer to text.

F. Fill plug
P. Roll pin
R. Shims
S. Stop screw
1. Locknut
2. Side cover
3. Adjusting screw

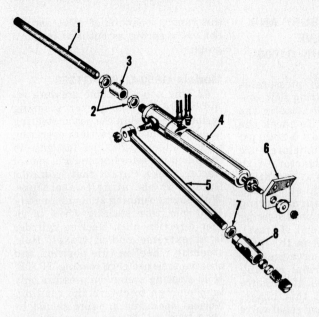

Fig. 46—View showing steering cylinder and associated parts used on G VI, MF95, MF97, G705, G706, G707 and G708 tractors.

1. Connecting link
2. Locknuts
3. Coupling
4. Cylinder
5. Drag link
6. Bracket
7. Jam nut
8. Tie rod end

bushing inside cover (2) is only available as an assembly with the cover.

Remove the ball guide clamp (15) and ball guides (14); then pour out and save the loose balls (16). Early type units (Fig. 42) have 60 balls; late type units (Fig. 43) have 54. Examine worm and ball block for scoring or other damage and check for broken or chipped balls (16).

To reassemble the ball nut, insert shaft in ball block and place the assembly on a bench with ball passage openings up. Divide the balls into two equal groups of 30 balls (early units) or 27 balls (late units) and starting with any ball passage hole, feed balls one at a time into hole until ball passage is full. Fill the second ball passage in the same manner, using the other group of balls. When both ball passages are full and balls appear at all four passage holes, use heavy bodied grease to position the remaining balls for each group in ball guides (14); position the guides on ball block and secure with clamp (15). After completing assembly of ball nut, check to be sure worm shaft turns freely and smoothly in ball block. Reinstall worm shaft and bearings in housing by reversing the disassembly procedure. Before installing sector and shaft, hold ball nut from turning and tighten adjuster (20—Fig. 42 or 43) until all shaft end play is removed and a slight rotational drag is present when shaft is turned. Tighten jam nut (21) to secure the adjustment.

Before assembling sector shaft and side cover, insert head of adjusting screw (3) in slot of sector shaft (4), using the removed shim; then measure clearance of head in slot with a feeler gage. If clearance is greater than 0.002, select a thicker shim from adjusting kit (Part No. 35P546) to obtain the specified 0.002 clearance. Center the two middle teeth of ball block (13) in sector shaft opening and insert sector shaft, making sure the center tooth on shaft enters the space between the two middle teeth on ball block. Back out the adjusting screw (3) enough to assure clearance, and securely tighten the side cover cap screws. Then, turn adjusting screw clockwise until a noticeable drag is felt as sector shaft passes mid-position. Fill gear housing to level of filler plug with Mild E. P., SAE 90 gear lubricant.

HYDROSTATIC STEERING SYSTEM

Models G900, G950, G1000, G1000 Vista, G1050 and G1350 tractors are equipped with hydrostatic steering which has no mechanical linkage between the steering control and the steering cylinder.

OPERATION
Models G900-G1000

35. The pressurized oil for the power steering system is furnished by a belt driven pump which is mounted on right side of engine. The oil is pumped to the Hydramotor unit and if system is in neutral position, the oil flows through the control valve and returns to the reservoir. However, when steering wheel is turned, the control valve is shifted and the oil is directed to the metering unit of the Hydramotor. This unit displaces a given amount of oil which is directed back through the control valve and delivered to one end of the steering cylinder. The return oil from the opposite end of the steering cylinder flows through the control valve and back to the reservoir.

A check ball which is seated by pump pressure when the supply pump is operating, unseats to allow oil to recirculate between the Hydramotor and steering cylinder to provide manual steering when the supply pump is not operating.

Model G1000 Vista

36. Pressurized oil for the steering system is furnished by a belt driven pump which is mounted on right side of engine. The oil is pumped to the steering control (pilot) valve. When steering is not in use, the oil flows through the control (pilot) valve and back to the reservoir. When steering wheel is turned, the steering motor (hand pump) delivers enough pressure to one end of control valve to shift the spring centered spool. This allows the pressurized oil to be directed to the steering cylinder. Return oil from the cylinder flows through the control valve and back to the reservoir.

The recirculating check ball in the control (pilot) valve is seated by pump pressure when the supply pump is operating. When supply pump is not operating (engine stopped) and steering pressure is applied to the steering wheel, the steering motor (hand pump) pumps oil through the control valve and to the steering cylinder. The return oil from steering cylinder flows through the unseated recirculating valve and back to the steering motor (hand pump) instead of back to the reservoir.

Models G950-G1050-G1350

37. Pressurized oil for the steering system is furnished by a belt driven pump which is mounted on right side

of engine. The oil is pumped to the steering motor and if system is in neutral position, the oil flows through the control valve portion of steering motor and back to the reservoir. When steering wheel is turned, the pressurized oil is directed to the steering cylinder. Return oil from opposite end of steering cylinder flows back through steering motor and to the reservoir.

The recirculating check ball in steering motor is seated by pump pressure when the supply pump is operating. When supply pump is not operating (engine stopped) and steering pressure is applied to steering wheel, the steering motor acts as a hand pump and pumps oil to the steering cylinder. Return oil from steering cylinder flows through the unseated recirculating valve and is directed to intake side of hand pump instead of back to the reservoir.

LUBRICATION AND BLEEDING
Models G900-G1000-G1000 Vista

38. MM Hydraulic fluid, or equivalent, is used as the operating fluid. The reservoir is a part of the supply pump and the system capacity is approximately 2 quarts.

The power steering system is self-bleeding. If any part of the system has been disassembled and units are dry, fill the reservoir and cycle the system through full range of travel several times. Then, refill reservoir to the full mark.

Models G950-G1050-G1350

39. The reservoir containing the fluid supply for the hydraulic lift system and power steering is accessible by removing the front hood section. Use MM hydraulic fluid and maintain fluid level at the "F" mark on dipstick attached to filler cap. Hydraulic fluid filter is located in the reservoir, under the top cover. It is recommended that hydraulic fluid filter be renewed after each 300 hours of operation and that hydraulic fluid be renewed each 600 hours of operation or once a year, whichever occurs first. Reservoir capacity is approximately 9 gallons.

To bleed the air from the hydraulic system, connect a by-pass hose to one set of remote control valve couplers. Place the remote valve lever in raise position and start engine. Operate engine for at least two minutes while raising and lowering hitch and rotating steering from stop to stop several times. Stop engine, remove by-pass hose and recheck hydraulic fluid level.

OPERATING PRESSURE AND RELIEF VALVE
Early G900-G1000-Early G1000 Vista

40. The system relief pressure is controlled by a fixed-setting flow control and relief valve located in the power steering pump. To check the operating pressure, tee a 0-2000 psi pressure gage in the pump pressure line on right side of tractor. With power steering system at operating temperature, run tractor at approximately 1000 rpm and turn steering wheel in either direction until steering cylinder is at extreme end of travel. Hold the steering wheel in this position long enough to observe pressure gage reading. The normal reading should be 1250-1275 psi. If pressure reading is not within this range, renew the flow control and relief valve assembly as outlined in paragraph 44.

Late G900-Late G1000 Vista

41. The power steering system relief pressure is controlled by a fixed-setting relief valve located in the power steering pump. To check the system operating pressure, tee a 0-2000 psi test gage in the pump pressure line on right side of tractor. Start engine and allow power steering fluid to reach operating temperature. With engine operating at approximately 1500 rpm, turn steering wheel in either direction until steering cylinder is at extreme end of travel. Hold steering wheel in this position long enough to observe pressure gage reading. Normal operating pressure should be 1450-1500 psi. If pressure reading is not within

this range, renew relief valve and relief valve spring as outlined in paragraph 47.

Models G950-G1050-G1350

42. The non-adjustable pressure relief valve for the power steering system is located in the power steering pump. To check the system operating pressure, tee a 0-2000 psi test gage in the pump pressure line on right side of tractor. Make certain that hydraulic fluid is at operating temperature. With engine running at approximately 1500 rpm, turn steering wheel in either direction until steering cylinder is at extreme end of travel. Hold steering wheel in this position and observe pressure gage reading. NOTE: Hold steering system on pressure only long enough to obtain the reading. Normal operating pressure should be 1650-1700 psi. If pressure reading is not within this range, renew relief valve and relief valve spring as outlined in paragraph 50.

POWER STEERING PUMP
Early G900-G1000-Early G1000 Vista

43. **REMOVE AND REINSTALL.** To remove the power steering pump, disconnect the pressure line and return line and allow reservoir to drain. Remove the belt shield, then unbolt and remove the pump and mounting bracket as a unit.

Install by reversing the removal procedure. Turn the belt tension adjusting screw to provide approximately ¼-inch belt deflection when 10 pounds

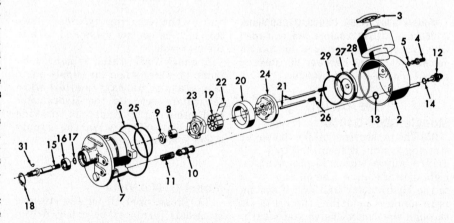

Fig. 47–Exploded view of the Saginaw power steering pump assembly used on early G900 and G1000 Vista and all G1000 tractors.

2. Reservoir	11. Spring	21. Dowel pin
3. Filler cap	12. Pressure fitting	22. Vane (10 used)
4. Mounting stud	13. "O" ring	23. Thrust plate
5. "O" ring	14. "O" ring	24. Pressure plate
6. "O" ring	15. Drive shaft	25. "O" ring
7. Pump housing	16. Bearing	26. Pressure spring
8. Needle bearing	17. Snap ring	27. End plate
9. Oil seal	18. Snap ring	28. Snap ring
10. Flow control &	19. Rotor	29. "O" ring
relief valve	20. Pump ring	31. Woodruff key

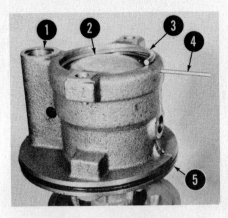

Fig. 48–Pumping elements are retained in body by snap ring (3) and end plate (2). "O" ring (5) seals the formed steel reservoir.

1. Pump body assembly	3. Snap ring
2. End plate	4. Punch
	5. "O" ring

of pressure is applied to belt at midpoint between pulleys. Tighten mounting bolts, then fill and bleed system as outlined in paragraph 38.

44. R&R RELIEF VALVE. The combination flow control and relief valve (10—Fig. 47) can be renewed without removing the power steering pump. To renew the valve, disconnect the pressure line, remove pressure line fitting (12) and withdraw the valve. Relief pressure is pre-set, and no attempt should be made to disassemble or overhaul the valve.

45. PUMP OVERHAUL. To disassemble the removed power steering pump, refer to Fig. 47. Remove the mounting bracket, mounting stud (4) and pressure line fitting (12). Withdraw the flow control and relief valve (10) and valve spring (11), then remove the reservoir (2).

Secure pump body in a vise and turn retaining snap ring (3—Fig. 48) if nec-

essary, until one end is located over the small hole in housing at snap ring groove. Insert a small punch (4) into hole as shown, unseat and remove snap ring (3) and end plate (2).

NOTE: The two pressure springs (26 —Fig. 47) fit over dowel pins (21) and are compressed to apply pressure to the pressure plate. Do not lose the springs when end plate (27) is removed.

Remove the pressure plate (24), cam ring (20), rotor (19) with vanes (22) and thrust plate (23). Note the direction of rotation (arrow on cam ring) for aid in correct reassembly.

Remove the pulley retaining nut and drive pulley, then after first removing snap ring (18), withdraw the drive shaft (15) with bearing (16). Needle bearing (8) and oil seal (9) can now be removed from pump housing (7).

Examine rotor (19) for wear in vane slots and cam ring (20) for ridging or scoring in vane contact area. Examine vane area of thrust plate (23) and pressure plate (24) for wear. Check the vanes (22) for nicks and wear.

Reassemble the pump by reversing the disassembly procedure using Fig. 47 as a guide. Renew all "O" rings and oil seal (9), and any worn or otherwise damaged parts. Reinstall pump as outlined in paragraph 43, then fill and bleed system as outlined in paragraph 38.

Late G900-Late G1000 Vista
46. REMOVE AND REINSTALL. To remove the power steering pump, disconnect the pressure line and return line and allow reservoir to drain. Remove belt shield, loosen belt adjuster on fan bracket and remove drive

belts from pump drive pulley. Remove pulley retaining nut and drive pulley, then unbolt and remove pump assembly from mounting bracket.

Reinstall by reversing the removal procedure. Adjust tension of drive belts until a pressure of 10 pounds, applied midway between fan pulley and crankshaft pulley, will deflect belts ½-inch. Fill and bleed power steering system as outlined in paragraph 38.

47. R&R RELIEF VALVE. The power steering pressure relief valve (2 —Fig. 49) can be removed without removing the power steering pump. To renew the relief valve, drain reservoir, drive out retaining pin, remove plug (4) with "O" ring (3), then withdraw relief valve and spring (1). After reassembling, fill and bleed power steering system as outlined in paragraph 38.

48. PUMP OVERHAUL. To disassemble the removed pump, refer to Fig. 49 and proceed as follows: Remove cover (29), then remove stud (27) and two cap screws which secure baffles (25 and 26), reinforcing plate (24) and reservoir (23) to rear housing (6) and remove reservoir.

Clamp front housing (15) in a vise with pump shaft pointing downward. Remove the four cap screws and carefully remove rear housing (6) and pressure plate spring (7). Note direction of rotation (arrow on eccentric ring) for aid in correct reassembly. Remove pressure plate (8), eccentric ring (10), rotor (11) and vanes (12). Remove front housing assembly from vise. Remove snap ring (21) and pull pump shaft and bearing assembly from front of housing (15). Remove snap ring (18), bearing (19) and washer (20) from pump shaft (22). Shaft seal (17) and bearing (16) can now be removed from front housing. Remove plug (4), relief valve (2) and spring (1) from rear housing.

Thoroughly clean all parts and inspect rotor (11) for wear in vane slots and eccentric ring (10) for scoring or ridging in vane contact area. Inspect vane contact area of pressure plate (8) and front housing (15) for wear. Check the vanes (12) for nicks and wear. A service kit consisting of rotor, vanes and eccentric ring is available. A seal kit consisting of shaft seal, gaskets and all "O" rings is also available.

Inspect pump shaft and bearings for wear or other damage and renew as necessary. Reassemble pump by reversing the disassembly procedure.

Reinstall pump as outlined in paragraph 46, then fill and bleed system as in paragraph 38.

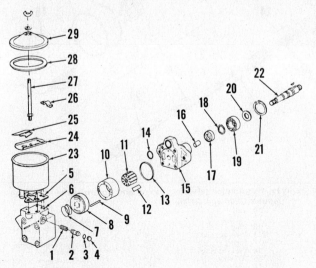

Fig. 49–Exploded view of Vickers power steering pump and reservoir assembly used on late G900 and G1000 Vista tractors.

1. Relief valve spring
2. Relief valve
3. "O" ring
4. Plug
5. Gasket
6. Rear housing
7. Spring
8. Pressure plate
9. Dowel pin (2 used)
10. Eccentric ring
11. Rotor
12. Vanes
13. "O" ring
14. "O" ring
15. Front housing
16. Bearing
17. Seal
18. Snap ring
19. Bearing
20. Washer
21. Snap ring
22. Pump shaft
23. Reservoir
24. Plate
25. Return line baffle
26. Pressure return baffle
27. Stud
28. Gasket
29. Cover

Models G950-G1050-G1350

49. REMOVE AND REINSTALL.
To remove the power steering pump, first drain the hydraulic reservoir (approximately 9 gallons). Remove belt shield, loosen belt adjuster and remove power steering pump drive belt. Disconnect the pressure line, return line and pump drain line. Unbolt and remove pump assembly.

Reinstall pump by reversing the removal procedure. Adjust pump drive belt tension until a pressure of 10 pounds, applied midway between pump pulley and crankshaft pulley, will deflect belt ½-inch. Fill and bleed the hydraulic system as outlined in paragraph 39.

50. R&R RELIEF VALVE. The power steering pressure relief valve (2—Fig. 50) can be removed without removing the power steering pump. To renew the relief valve, first drain the hydraulic reservoir, then drive out retaining pin, remove plug (4) with "O" ring (3) and withdraw relief valve and spring (1). After reassembling, fill and bleed hydraulic system as outlined in paragraph 39.

51. PUMP OVERHAUL. To disassemble the removed pump, remove pump drive pulley, then unbolt and remove manifold (30—Fig. 50).

NOTE: The balance of overhaul procedure for this pump is the same as outlined for the pump in paragraph 48 after its reservoir is removed.

After pump is reassembled, reinstall as outlined in paragraph 49 and fill and bleed hydraulic system as in paragraph 39.

STEERING MOTORS AND CONTROL VALVES
Models G900-G1000 (Saginaw Hydramotor)

52. REMOVE AND REINSTALL.
To remove the power steering Hydramotor, first disconnect battery ground strap, then remove the rear side panels and hood. Disconnect the fuel lines and remove fuel tank. Using a suitable puller, remove the steering wheel. Do not hammer on the attached puller as the Hydramotor will be damaged. Unbolt the Hydramotor cover and lift cover sufficiently to expose the hydraulic lines, then identify and disconnect the lines. Remove the four Hydramotor mounting bolts and carefully withdraw the Hydramotor assembly.

Reinstall the unit by reversing the removal procedure, then fill and bleed system as outlined in paragraph 38.

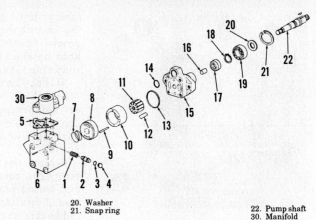

Fig. 50—Exploded view of Vickers power steering pump assembly used on G950, G1050 and G1350 tractors.

1. Relief valve spring
2. Relief valve
3. "O" ring
4. Plug
5. Gasket
6. Rear housing
7. Spring
8. Pressure plate
9. Dowel pin (2 used)
10. Eccentric ring
11. Rotor
12. Vanes
13. "O" ring
14. "O" ring
15. Front housing
16. Bearing
17. Seal
18. Snap ring
19. Bearing
20. Washer
21. Snap ring
22. Pump shaft
30. Manifold

53. OVERHAUL. To disassemble the removed Hydramotor, refer to Fig. 51 and remove cover retaining ring (17). To remove the retaining ring, drive a ⅛-inch punch into hole provided in cover (16) to unseat end of ring from groove. With punch under the ring, use screwdriver to pry ring from cover. See Fig. 52.

Place the housing assembly in a vise so that steering shaft is pointing downward. Usually, spring (13—Fig. 51) will push cover from the housing assembly. If binding condition exists, it may be necessary to bump cover loose by tapping around edge of cover with a soft faced mallet.

Remove pressure plate spring (13), then lift off pressure plate (9). Remove dowel pins (24), then using suitable snap ring pliers and screwdriver, remove snap ring (7) from torsion shaft (29). Discard snap ring (7) as a new snap ring must be used when reassembling. Pull pump ring and rotor assembly (6) off torsion shaft (29). Tap end of shaft (28) with a soft faced mallet until bearing support (2) can be removed, then carefully withdraw actuator assembly from housing (22). NOTE: It is recommended that the actuator assembly not be disassembled as it is a factory balanced unit.

Housing (22) and actuator assembly, which includes spring (23), spool (25) actuator (26), shaft (28) and torsion shaft (29) are not serviced separately. If these parts are serviceable, needle

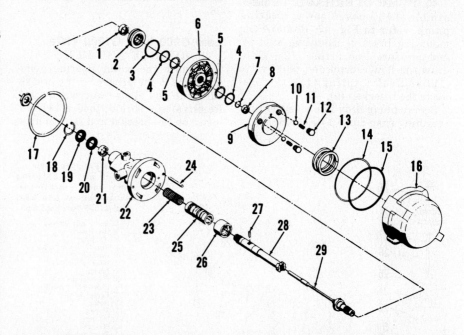

Fig. 51—Exploded view of the Saginaw Hydramotor (steering motor and control valve) used on models G900 and G1000.

1. Needle bearing
2. Bearing support
3. "O" ring
4. "O" ring
5. Rotor seal
6. Rotor and ring assembly
7. Snap ring
8. Needle bearing
9. Pressure plate
10. Ball
11. Spring
12. Plug
13. Pressure plate spring
14. Back-up ring
15. "O" ring
16. Cover
17. Retaining ring
18. Snap ring
19. Dust seal
20. Oil seal
21. Needle bearing
22. Housing
23. Valve spool spring
24. Dowel pin
25. Valve spool
26. Actuator
27. Pin
28. Shaft
29. Torsion shaft

bearing (21) and seals (19 and 20) can be renewed as necessary. Install new needle bearing (21) by pressing on lettered side of bearing cage only until bearing cage is flush with counterbore.

Needle bearings (1 and 8) in bearing support (2) and pressure plate (9) may be renewed if support and/or plate are otherwise serviceable. Install new bearings by pressing only on lettered

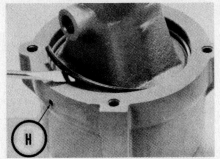

Fig. 52–Drive a 1/8-inch punch into hole (H) to unseat retaining ring, then pry ring out with screwdriver.

Fig.53–All vane springs must be engaged behind the rotor vanes. Springs can be pried into position with screwdriver as shown.

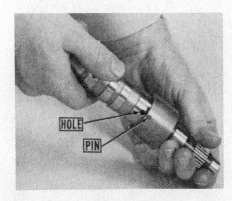

Fig. 54–Pin in actuator sleeve must be engaged in hole in end of spool before actuator assembly is installed.

side of bearing cage. Remove plugs (12) and withdraw springs (11) and check balls (10). Inspect the ball seats and balls for excessive wear. Renew parts as necessary.

Rotor, ring, vanes and vane springs are serviced only as a complete assembly (6); however, the unit may be disassembled for cleaning and inspection. Reassemble by placing rotor in ring on flat surface. Insert vanes (rounded side out) in rotor slots aligned with large diameter of ring, turn rotor ¼-turn and insert remaining vanes. Hook the vane springs behind each vane with screwdriver as shown in Fig. 53; be sure that vane springs are in proper place on both sides of rotor.

To reassemble Hydramotor unit, place housing, with needle bearing, seals and snap ring installed, in a vise with flat (bottom) side up. Check to be sure that pin in actuator is engaged in valve spool; if spool can be pulled away from actuator as shown in Fig. 54, push spool back into actuator and engage pin into hole in spool. Carefully insert actuator assembly into bore of housing. Install bearing support (2—Fig. 51), with bearing (1), "O" rings with Teflon rotor seal, over end of shaft and carefully push the assembly in flush with housing. Place the pump ring and rotor assembly on shaft and housing with chamfered outer edge of pump ring away from housing. Install a new rotor retaining snap ring (7) and insert the dowel pins through pump ring and into housing. Stick the "O" ring and Teflon rotor seal into pressure plate with heavy grease, then install pressure plate on shaft, pump ring and rotor assembly and the dowel pins. Place pressure plate spring (13) on pressure plate. Install new "O" ring (15) and back-up ring (14) in groove in cover, then install cover over the assembled steering unit. To install the cover retaining ring, it is recommended that the unit be placed in an arbor press and the housing be pushed into the cover by a sleeve.

CAUTION: **Do not** push against end of shaft (28). Place retaining ring over housing before placing unit in press. Carefully apply pressure on housing with sleeve until flange on housing is below retaining ring groove in cover. Note that lug on housing must enter slot in cover. If housing binds in cover, **do not** apply heavy pressure; remove unit from press and bump cover loose with mallet. When housing has been pushed sufficiently into cover, install retaining ring in groove with end gap near hole in cover.

G1000 Vista (Ross)

54. R&R STEERING MOTOR. To remove the power steering motor, first disconnect battery ground strap, then remove the rear hood. Remove steering wheel height adjusting knob, steering wheel retaining nut and steering wheel. Unscrew the tilt adjusting lever. Unbolt and raise instrument panel. Identify and disconnect hydraulic hoses from steering motor. Immediately plug and cap openings. Remove pivot bolts and withdraw steering motor assembly.

Refer to Fig. 55 and rotate column jacket (3) to align tilt lock pin (8) with removal hole in end of slot. Remove tilt lock pin and slide column jacket assembly from tilt housing (7). Unbolt tilt housing from steering motor (16) and withdraw steering motor and telescopic shaft assembly (9 thru 16) from tilt housing. Remove snap ring (14) and pin (15) and separate steering motor from sleeve (13). Further disassembly of the tilt and telescopic unit is

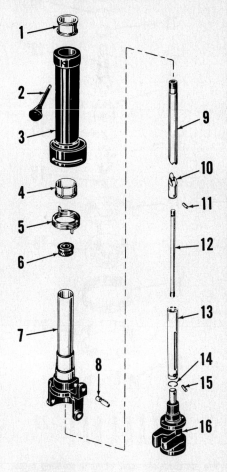

Fig. 55–Exploded view of the tilt and telescopic steering column used on model G1000 Vista.

1. Upper bushing	9. Tube
2. Tilt lever	10. Tube lock
3. Column jacket	11. Pin
4. Lower bushing	12. Lock rod
5. Spring	13. Sleeve
6. Seal	14. Snap ring
7. Tilt housing	15. Pin
8. Tilt lock pin	16. Steering motor

obvious after an examination of the unit and reference to Fig. 55.

Reassemble by reversing disassembly procedure. Reinstall the assembly and fill and bleed power steering system as outlined in paragraph 38.

55. OVERHAUL STEERING MOTOR. To disassemble the removed steering motor, refer to Fig. 56 and clamp unit in a soft jawed vise with

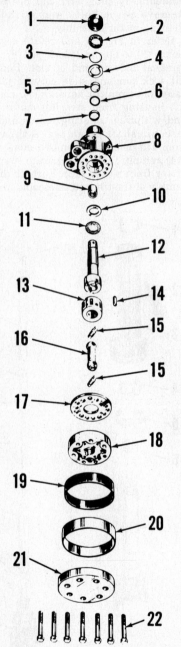

Fig. 56—Exploded view of Ross steering motor used on model G1000 Vista.

1. Dirt shield	12. Shaft
2. Felt seal	13. Commutator
3. Retaining ring	14. Commutator pin
4. Washer	15. Link pins
5. Nylon spacer	16. Rotor drive link
6. Back-up ring	17. Spacer plate
7. Seal	18. Stator-Rotor set
8. Body	19. Seal
9. Needle bearing	20. Seal retainer
10. Bearing race	21. End plate
11. Thrust bearing	22. Cap screws

end plate (21) on top side. Remove end plate cap screws (22) and lift off end plate.

NOTE: Lapped surfaces of end plate (21), stator-rotor set (18), spacer plate (17) and body (8) must be protected from scratching, burring or any other damage as sealing of these parts depends only on their finish and flatness.

Remove seal retainer (20), seal (19) stator-rotor assembly (18) and spacer (17) from body. Remove commutator (13) and drive link (16), with link pins (15) and commutator pin (14). Remove body from vise, remove dirt shield (1) and felt seal (2), smooth any burrs which may be present on input shaft (12), then withdraw input shaft from body. Remove bearing race (10) and thrust bearing (11) from input shaft. Remove retaining ring (3), washer (4), nylon spacer (5), back-up ring (6) and seal (7). Do not remove needle bearing (9) unless renewal is required. If it should be necessary to renew needle bearing, press same out of commutator end of body.

Clean all parts in a suitable solvent and if necessary, remove paint from outer edges of body, spacer and end plate by passing these parts lightly over crocus cloth placed on a perfectly flat surface. Do not attempt to dress out any scratches or other defects since these sealing surfaces are lapped to within 0.0002 of being flat.

Inspect commutator and body for scoring and undue wear. Bear in mind that burnish marks may show, or discolorations from oil residue may be present on commutator after unit has been in service for some time. These can be ignored providing they do not interfere with free rotation of commutator in body.

Check fit of commutator pin (14) in the commutator. Pin should be a snug fit and if bent, or worn until diameter at contacting points is less than 0.2485, renew pin.

Measure inside diameter of input shaft bore in body and outside diameter of input shaft. If body bore is 0.006 or more larger than shaft diameter, renew shaft and/or body and commutator. Body and commutator are not available separately.

Check thrust bearing and race (10 and 11) for excessive wear or other damage and renew if necessary.

Inspect stator, rotor, vanes and vane springs for scoring, excessive wear or other damage. Place stator on lapped surface of end plate and place rotor in stator. Install vanes (V—Fig. 57) and vane springs (S) in rotor. NOTE: Arched back of springs must contact vanes. Position lobe of rotor in valley of stator as shown at (X—Fig. 58).

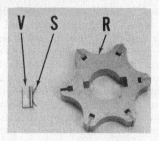

Fig. 57—When installing vanes (V) and springs (S) in rotor (R), arched back of spring contacts vane.

Center opposite lobe on crown of stator, then using two feeler gages, measure clearance (C) between rotor lobes and stator. If clearance is more than 0.006, renew stator-rotor assembly. Use a micrometer and measure width (thickness) of stator and rotor. If stator is 0.002 or more wider (thicker) than rotor, renew the assembly. Stator, rotor, vanes and springs are available only as an assembly.

Check end plate (21—Fig. 56) and spacer (17) for wear, scoring and flatness. Do not confuse the polish pattern on end plate and spacer with wear. This pattern, which results from rotor rotation, is normal.

When reassembling, use all new seals and back-up ring. All parts, except those noted below, are installed dry. Reassemble as follows: If needle bearing (9) was removed, lubricate with power steering fluid and install from commutator end of body. Press bearing into bore until inside end is 3 13/16 to 3 7/8 inches from face of body as shown in Fig. 59. Lubricate thrust bearing and race and install on input shaft, then install shaft and bearing assembly in body. Install a link pin in one end of drive link, then install drive link in input shaft by engaging flats on link pin with slots in input

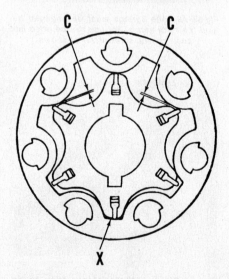

Fig. 58—With rotor positioned as shown, clearances (C) must not exceed 0.006. Refer to text.

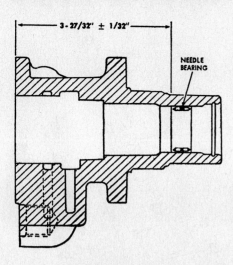

Fig. 59–When installing needle bearing in body, install same to dimension shown.

shaft. Use a small amount of grease to hold commutator pin in commutator, then install commutator and pin in body while engaging pin in one of the long slots in input shaft. Commutator is correctly installed when edge of commutator is slightly below sealing surface of body.

Clamp body in a soft jawed vise with input shaft pointing downward. Place spacer on body and align screw holes with those in body. Place link pin in exposed end of drive link and install rotor while engaging flats of link pin with slots in rotor. Position stator over rotor and align screw holes in stator with those in spacer and body. Install vanes and vane springs in slots in

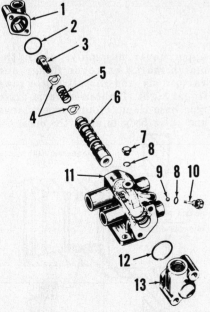

Fig. 60–Exploded view of the Ross control valve used on G1000 Vista tractors.

1. End cap	7. Plug
2. "O" ring	8. "O" rings
3. Centering screw	9. Steel ball
4. Centering spring washers	10. Plug & pin assy.
5. Centering spring	11. Valve body
6. Valve spool	12. "O" ring
	13. End cap

rotor. Install seal (19—Fig. 56) in seal retainer (20), then install seal and retainer over stator. Install end plate, align screw holes and install cap screws. Tighten cap screws evenly to a torque of 18-22 ft.-lbs.

NOTE: If input shaft does not turn evenly after cap screws are tightened, loosen screws and retighten them again. However, bear in mind that unit was assembled dry and some drag is normal. If stickiness or binding cannot be eliminated, disassemble unit and check for foreign material or burrs which could be causing interference.

Lubricate input shaft seal (7) and install seal, back-up ring (6), nylon spacer (5), washer (4) and retaining ring (3). Install felt seal (2) and dirt shield (1).

Turn unit on side with ports upward. Fill unit with power steering fluid and rotate input shaft slowly until interior is thoroughly lubricated. Drain excess fluid and plug ports.

56. R&R CONTROL (PILOT) VALVE. To remove the control (pilot) valve, first drain power steering system. Identify and disconnect the six hydraulic lines from control valve. Unbolt and remove the valve.

Reinstall control valve by reversing removal procedure. Fill and bleed power steering system as outlined in paragraph 38.

57. OVERHAUL CONTROL VALVE. With control valve removed, disassemble as follows: Refer to Fig. 60 and remove end caps (1 and 13) with 'O' rings (2 and 12). Pull spool and centering assembly from valve body (11). Place a punch or small rod in hole of centering spring screw (3) and remove screw, centering spring (5) and centering spring washers (4). Remove plug (10), "O" ring (8) and recirculating ball (9).

Clean all parts in suitable solvent and inspect. Valve spool and spool bore in body should be free of scratches, scoring or excessive wear. Spool should be a snug fit in its bore and should move freely with no visible side play. If spool or spool bore is defective, renew complete valve assembly, as spool (6) and valve body (11) are not available separately.

Reassembly is the reverse of disassembly and the following points should be observed. Lubricate all parts with power steering fluid prior to assembly. Install spool assembly in valve body so that centering spring is at end opposite recirculating valve. Measure distance between "O" ring sealing surface of recirculating valve plug and end of roll pin. This distance

should be 15/16-inch and if necessary, obtain this distance by adjusting roll pin in or out of plug. Tighten end cap retaining cap screws to a torque of 186 in.-lbs.

Models G950-G1050-G1350 (Ross)

58. REMOVE AND REINSTALL. To remove the power steering motor and control valve assembly, disconnect battery ground strap and remove the rear hood. Drain hydraulic supply reservoir. Remove steering wheel retaining nut, then using a suitable puller, remove the steering wheel. Unbolt and raise instrument panel front support. Identify and disconnect the four hydraulic lines from steering motor. Plug and cap openings to prevent entrance of dirt in system. Unbolt and remove the steering motor assembly.

Reinstall by reversing the removal procedure, then refill reservoir and bleed hydraulic system as outlined in paragraph 39.

59. OVERHAUL. To disassemble the removed steering motor and control valve assembly, refer to Fig. 61 and proceed as follows: Install a fitting in one of the four ports in valve body (25), then clamp fitting in a vise so that input shaft (17) is pointing downward. Remove cap screws (39) and remove end cover (38).

NOTE: Lapped surfaces of end cover (38), commutator set (33 and 34), manifold (32), stator-rotor set (31), spacer (w9) and valve body (25) must be protected from scratching, burring or any other damage as sealing of these parts depends on their finish and flatness.

Remove seal retainer (35) and seal (36), then carefully remove washer (37), commutator set (33 and 34) and manifold (32). Grasp spacer (29) and lift off the spacer, drive link (30) and stator-rotor set (31) as an assembly. Separate spacer and drive link from stator-rotor set.

Remove unit from vise, then clamp fitting in vise so that input shaft is pointing upward. Remove water and dirt seal (2) and felt seal (3). Place a light mark on flange of upper cover (9) and valve body (25) for aid in reassembly. Unbolt upper cover from valve body, then grasp input shaft and remove input shaft, upper cover and valve spool assembly. Remove and discard seal ring (10). Slide upper cover assembly from input shaft and remove teflon spacer (16). Remove shims (12) from cavity in upper cover or from face of thrust washer (14) and note number of shims for aid in reassembly. Remove snap ring (4), stepped washer

(5), brass washer (6), teflon washer (7) and seal (8). Retain stepped washer (5) and snap ring (4) for reassembly. Do not remove needle bearing (11) unless renewal is required.

Remove snap ring (13), thrust washers (14) and thrust bearing (15) from input shaft. Drive out pin (18) and withdraw torsion bar (21) and spacer (20). Place end of valve spool on top of bench and rotate input shaft until drive ring (19) falls free, then rotate input shaft clockwise until actuator ball (23) is disengaged from helical groove in input shaft. Withdraw input shaft and remove actuator ball. Do not remove actuator ball retaining spring (24) unless renewal is required.

Remove plug (28) and recirculating ball (26) from valve body.

Thoroughly clean all parts in a suitable solvent, visually inspect parts and renew any showing excessive wear, scoring or other damage.

If needle bearing (11) must be renewed, press same out toward flanged end of cover. Press new bearing in from flanged end of cover to the dimension shown in Fig. 62. Press only on numbered end of bearing, using a piloted mandrel.

Using a micrometer, measure thickness of the commutator ring (33—Fig. 61) and commutator (34). If commutator ring is 0.0015 or more thicker than commutator, renew the matched set.

Place the stator-rotor set (31) on the lapped surface of end cover (38). Make certain that vanes and vane springs are installed correctly in slots of the rotor. NOTE: Arched back of springs must contact vanes. (See inset X-Fig. 61). Position lobe of rotor in valley of stator as shown at (V—Fig. 63). Center opposite lobe on crown of stator, then using two feeler gages, measure clearance (C) between rotor lobes and stator. If clearance is more than 0.006, renew stator-rotor assembly. Using a micrometer, measure thickness of stator and rotor. If stator is 0.002 or more thicker than rotor, renew the assembly. Stator, rotor, vanes and vane springs are available only as an assembly.

Before reassembling, wash all parts in clean solvent and air dry. All parts, unless otherwise indicated, are installed dry. Install recirculating ball (26—Fig. 61) and plug (28) with new "O" ring (27) in valve body and tighten plug to a torque of 10-14 ft.-lbs. Clamp fitting (installed in valve body port) in a vise so that top end of valve body is facing upward. Install thrust washer (14), thrust bearing (15), second thrust washer (14) and snap ring (13) on input shaft (17). If

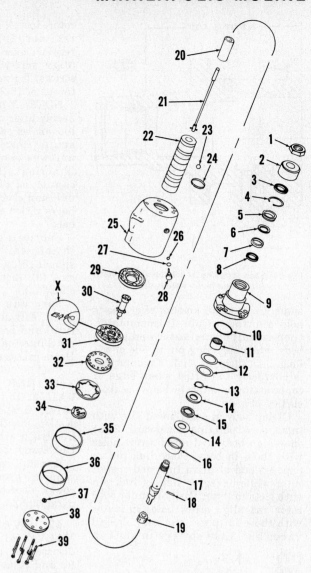

Fig.61–Exploded view of Ross steering motor and control valve assembly used on models G950, G1050 and G1350. Inset "X" shows vane and vane spring used in slot on each rotor lobe.

1. Nut
2. Water & dirt seal
3. Felt seal
4. Snap ring
5. Stepped washer
6. Brass washer
7. Teflon washer
8. Seal
9. Cover (upper)
10. Seal ring
11. Needle bearing
12. Shims
13. Snap ring
14. Thrust washers
15. Thrust bearing
16. Teflon spacer
17. Input shaft
18. Pin
19. Drive ring
20. Spacer
21. Torsion bar
22. Valve spool
23. Actuator ball
24. Retaining spring
25. Valve body
26. Recirculating ball
27. "O" ring
28. Plug
29. Spacer plate
30. Drive link
31. Stator-Rotor set
32. Manifold
33. Commutator ring
34. Commutator
35. Seal retainer
36. Seal
37. Washer
38. End cover
39. Cap screws

actuator ball retaining ring (24) was removed install new retaining ring. Place actuator ball (23) in its seat inside valve spool (22). Insert input shaft into valve spool, engaging the helix and actuator ball with a counterclockwise motion. Use the mid-section of torsion bar (21) as a gage between end of valve spool and thrust washer, then place the assembly in a vertical position with end of input shaft resting on a bench. Insert drive ring (19) into valve spool until drive ring is engaged on input shaft spline. Remove torsion bar gage. Install spacer (20) on torsion bar and insert the assembly into valve spool. Align cross-holes in torsion bar and input shaft and install pin (18). Pin must be pressed into shaft until end of pin is about 1/32-inch below flush. Place spacer (16) over spool and install spool assembly into valve body. Position original shims (12) on thrust washer (14), lubricate new seal ring (10), place seal ring in upper cover (9) and install

upper cover assembly. Align the match marks on cover flange and valve body and install cap screws finger tight. Tighten a worm drive type hose clamp around cover flange and valve body to align the outer di-

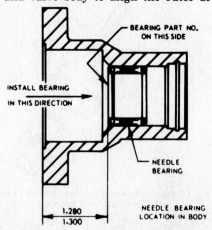

Fig. 62–When installing needle bearing in upper cover, press bearing in to dimension shown.

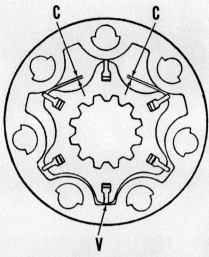

Fig. 63—With rotor positioned in stator as shown, clearances (C) must not exceed 0.006. Refer to test.

ameters, then tighten cap screws to a torque of 18-22 ft.-lbs.

NOTE: If either input shaft (17) or upper cover (9) or both have been renewed, the following procedure for shimming must be used. With upper cover installed (with original shims) as outlined above, invert unit in vise so that input shaft is pointing downward. Grasp input shaft, pull downward and prevent it from rotating. Engage drive link (30) splines in valve spool and rotate drive link until end of spool is flush with end of valve body. Remove drive link and check alignment of drive link slot to torsion bar pin. Install drive link until its slot engages torsion bar pin. Check relationship of spool end to body end. If end of spool is within 0.0025 of being flush with end of body, no additional shimming is required. If not within 0.0025 of being flush, remove cover and add or remove shims (12) as necessary. Reinstall cover and recheck spool to valve body position.

With drive link installed, place spacer plate (29) on valve body with plain side up. Install stator-rotor set over drive link splines and align cap screw holes. Make certain vanes and vane springs are properly installed. Install manifold (32) with circular slotted side up and align cap screw holes with stator, spacer and valve body. Install commutator ring (33) with slotted side up, then install commutator (34) over drive link end making certain that link end is engaged in the smallest elongated hole in commutator. Install seal (36) and retainer (35). Apply a few drops of hydraulic fluid on commutator. Use a small amount of grease to stick washer (37) in position over pin on end cover (38). Install end cover making

sure that pin engages center hole in commutator. Align holes and install cap screws (39). Alternately and progressively tighten cap screws while rotating input shaft. Final tightening should be 18-22 ft.-lbs. torque.

Relocate the unit in vise so input shaft is up. Lubricate new seal (8) and carefully work seal over shaft and into bore with lip toward inside. Install new teflon washer (7), brass washer (6) and stepped washer (5) with flat side up. Install snap ring (4) with rounded edge inward. Place new felt seal (3) and water and dirt seal (2) over input shaft.

Remove unit from vise and remove fitting from port. Turn unit on its side with hose ports upward. Pour clean hydraulic fluid into inlet port, rotate input shaft until fluid appears at outlet port, then plug all ports.

STEERING CYLINDER, SECTOR GEAR AND SHAFT
Early G900-G1000-Early G1000 Vista

60. R&R AND OVERHAUL. To remove the steering piston or cylinder sleeves, first drain cooling system, then remove hood, grille and front side panels. Suitably support the tractor and remove the front axle assembly. Drain the steering gear housing. Unbolt and remove the radiator and radiator support. Disconnect the power steering lines from the piston end covers and remove breather from top of housing. Remove cap screws securing steering gear housing to side rails and slide housing forward and out of rails. Place the housing on a bench with the vertical shaft flange facing upward.

Turn the vertical shaft to the straight ahead position. Mark the vertical shaft in relation to the bearing housing and the bearing housing to steering gear housing so the sector gear and piston can be properly indexed when reassembling. Remove the piston end covers and measure the distance from end of piston to end of each sleeve. Record these dimensions for aid in reassembly. NOTE: The distance from right hand end of piston to sleeve end is greater than that on the left side.

On early production tractors, unbolt and remove the piston guide from front of steering gear housing. Remove the four hex head cap screws and two 12-point cap screws from sector gear

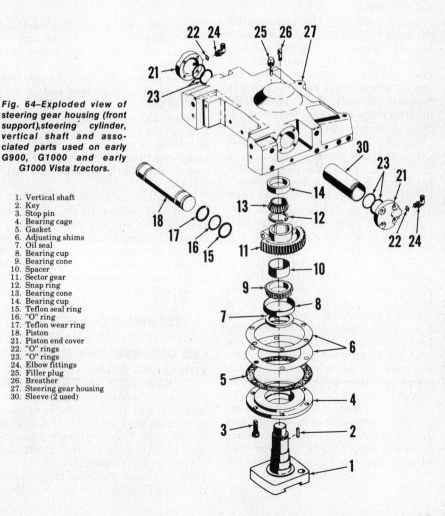

Fig. 64—Exploded view of steering gear housing (front support), steering cylinder, vertical shaft and associated parts used on early G900, G1000 and early G1000 Vista tractors.

1. Vertical shaft
2. Key
3. Stop pin
4. Bearing cage
5. Gasket
6. Adjusting shims
7. Oil seal
8. Bearing cup
9. Bearing cone
10. Spacer
11. Sector gear
12. Snap ring
13. Bearing cone
14. Bearing cup
15. Teflon seal ring
16. "O" ring
17. Teflon wear ring
18. Piston
21. Piston end cover
22. "O" rings
23. "O" rings
24. Elbow fittings
25. Filler plug
26. Breather
27. Steering gear housing
30. Sleeve (2 used)

bearing cage (4—Fig. 64). Note that the 12-point cap screws were in the area traveled by the stop pin (3). Withdraw the vertical shaft and sector gear assembly from steering gear housing. Piston (18) and cylinder sleeves (30) can now be removed. Discard all "O" rings, seal rings and wear rings.

To disassemble the vertical shaft assembly, remove bearing cone (13) using a suitable knife edge puller. Remove snap ring (12), loosen clamp bolt and remove sector gear (11), key (2) and spacer (10). Press vertical shaft (1) out of bearing cage (4) and renew seal (7) before reassembling. Bearing cups (8 and 14) should be renewed if bearing cones (9 and 13) are renewed.

Reassemble the vertical shaft, bearings and sector gear by reversing the disassembly procedure, but do not install in steering housing at this time.

Install cylinder sleeves (30) in housing (27). Coat new "O" rings (16) with Lubriplate and install the "O" rings in the outer grooves at each end of piston. Install Teflon seal rings (15) in same grooves on "O" rings. NOTE: Heat the new Teflon seal rings in hot water (110-120 degrees) for a few minutes to make them more pliable. Stretch seal rings to install them over end of piston.

Before installing the piston, place the wear rings (17) in their grooves in piston to check the wear ring end gap. With the wear rings held firmly in their grooves all the way around the piston, there must be a ⅛-inch gap between the ends. If not, remove the necessary material from end of ring to obtain the proper gap.

Remove wear rings, lubricate seal ring and insert piston in sleeve. Push piston in until the wear ring groove is exposed in housing opening as shown in Fig. 65. Install wear rings in their grooves and place a strap-type hose clamp with shim stock around seal ring and wear ring as shown in Fig. 66. Clamp must be loose enough to slide off the rings when piston is pushed into sleeve. NOTE: Install piston end cover over sleeve opposite the side from which piston is being installed to prevent sleeve from being pushed out. Using a wooden hammer handle, bump piston into sleeves until seal rings and wear rings fully enter the sleeves. At this point, remove clamp and shim stock from piston inside of housing.

Move the piston into the sleeves until the dimensions measured and recorded during piston removal are obtained. Install piston guide on front of housing, if so equipped. Use new "O" rings on sleeves and reinstall end covers.

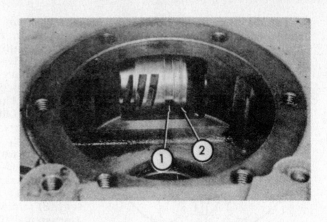

Fig. 65–Install piston with seal ring (2) into sleeve until wear ring groove (1) is positioned as shown.

Fig. 66–View showing a strap-type hose clamp used to hold seal ring and wear ring (1) in position during piston installation. Use shim stock under hose clamp to protect the teflon rings.

Align the marks on the vertical shaft flange and bearing cage and install the vertical shaft and sector gear assembly. Use a new gasket (5—Fig. 64) and sufficient quantity of 0.006 shims (6) to provide zero end play of vertical shaft.

Rotate the vertical shaft to see that stop pin (3) contacts the stops in both directions. If the stop pin fails to contact a stop in one direction, sector gear and piston teeth are not correctly meshed.

Reinstall the steering gear unit on tractor and refill with SAE90 Multipurpose gear oil. The capacity of the housing is approximately 5 pints. The balance of reassembly is the reverse of disassembly procedure. Fill and bleed power steering system as outlined in paragraph 38.

STEERING CYLINDER AND VERTICAL SHAFT
Late G900-G950-Late G1000
Vista-G1050-G1350

61. **R&R AND OVERHAUL.** To remove the power steering cylinder, identify and disconnect hydraulic hoses from steering cylinder and plug or cap lines. Unpin cylinder from anchor bracket and vertical shaft and remove cylinder assembly.

With cylinder removed move piston rod in and out several times to clear fluid from cylinder. Clamp flat end of cylinder tube (26—Fig. 67) in a vise. Remove retaining ring (16) and spacer (17). Bump cylinder head (20) inward and remove retaining ring (18). Pull outward on piston rod (12) and withdraw rod, cylinder head and piston assembly from cylinder tube (26). Remove piston retaining nut, piston (23), cylinder head, retaining rings and spacer from rod.

Clean and inspect all parts for excessive wear, scoring or other damage and renew parts as necessary. Renew all "O" ring seals and back-up rings and reassemble by reversing the disassembly procedure. Reinstall cylinder, then fill and bleed system as in paragraph 39.

To remove the vertical shaft (11—Fig. 67), first remove the hood and grille, then drain cooling system and hydraulic reservoir. Disconnect hydraulic lines and remove the reservoir. Unbolt and remove radiator and disconnect tie rods and steering cylinder from vertical shaft. Remove cover (1), cap screw (2), washer (3) and shims (4). Bump vertical shaft downward out of bearing cone (5) and remove shaft from below. Remove bearing cone (9) and seal (10) from shaft. Bearing cups (6 and 8) can now be removed from front support (vertical shaft housing).

When reassembling, install bearing cups in housing and pack bearing cones with chassis lubricant. Place bearing cone (9) in bearing cup (8), then install new oil seal (10) in housing. Carefully install vertical shaft through oil seal and bearing cone (9), then install upper bearing cone (5). Install shims (4), washer (3) and cap screw (2). Tighten cap screw while rotating vertical shaft. If bearings bind before cap screw is tightened securely, add shims (4) as necessary. If vertical shaft has excessive end play with cap screw tightened securely, remove shims as necessary. Shaft should have zero end play, but should rotate without binding. Shims are available in thicknesses of 0.005 and 0.010. Balance of reassembly is the reverse of disassembly procedure. Fill and bleed hydraulic system as outlined in paragraph 39.

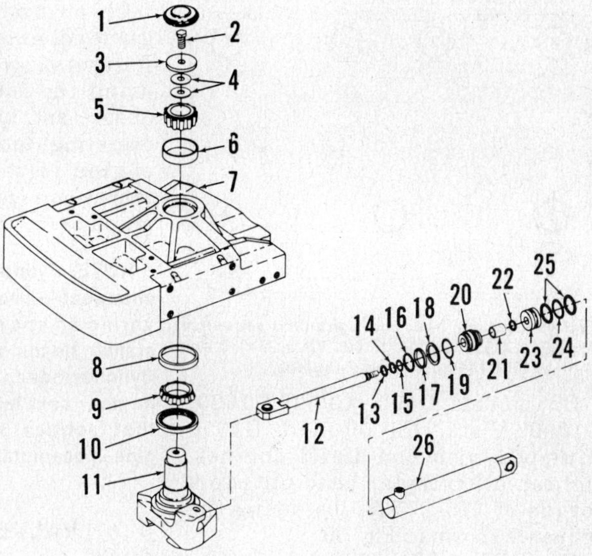

Fig. 67–Exploded view of front support, vertical shaft and steering cylinder used on late G900, G950, late G1000 Vista, G1050 and G1350 tractors.

1. Cover
2. Cap screw
3. Washer
4. Shims (0.005 & 0.010)
5. Bearing cone
6. Bearing cup
7. Front support (vertical shaft housing)
8. Bearing cup
9. Bearing cone
10. Oil seal
11. Vertical shaft
12. Piston rod
13. Wiper ring
14. Back-up ring
15. "O" ring
16. Retaining ring
17. Spacer
18. Retaining ring
19. "O" ring
20. Cylinder head
21. Bushing
22. "O" ring
23. Piston
24. "O" ring
25. Back-up rings
26. Cylinder tube

ENGINE AND COMPONENTS

The six cylinder engines used in all models covered, conform to the same general design, consisting of a one-piece cast crankcase, with cylinder blocks and heads cast in pairs.

Series GVI and MF95 LP-Gas and diesel models, series G900 LP-Gas and gasoline models and series G950 LP-Gas models are equipped with engines having a bore and stroke of 4¼ x 5 inches and a displacement of 425 cubic inches. Series G900 and G950 diesel models are equipped with engines having a bore and stroke of 4⅜ x 5 inches and a displacement of 451 cubic inches.

Series MF97, G705, G706, G707, G708, G1000 Vista and G1050 LP-Gas and diesel models, series G1000 LP-Gas, gasoline and diesel models and series G1350 LP-Gas models are equipped with engines having a bore and stroke of 4⅝ x 5 inches and a displacement of 504 cubic inches. Series G1350 diesel models are equipped with engines having a bore and stroke of 4¾ x 5½ inches and a displacement of 585 cubic inches.

R&R ENGINE WITH CLUTCH
All Models

62. To remove the engine and clutch assembly, first remove hood and drain cooling system. On series G950, G1050 and G1350, drain hydraulic reservoir. On all models, disconnect battery cables, wiring harness and tachometer cable from engine. Disconnect fuel lines and throttle linkage. Disconnect and remove hydraulic lines and power steering lines as necessary. On all models without hydrostatic steering, unbolt steering sector and bracket from side of engine and disconnect steering drag link. Then, on all models except G1000 Vista, block up fuel tank and unbolt and remove fuel tank front support.

Install split stands if available or block up under clutch housing and support engine with a chain hoist. Unbolt frame side rails and engine from clutch housing and separate the tractor halves.

CAUTION: Before removing engine assembly from front frame, block up under front support or front weights to prevent radiator and front frame assembly from tipping forward.

Disconnect radiator hoses and on models so equipped, unbolt axle stabilizer bracket. Unbolt engine from frame at front, then lift engine from frame assembly.

CYLINDER HEAD

63. To remove any cylinder head, first remove hood and drain cooling system. Remove upper radiator hose, water manifold and air cleaner. On non-diesels, disconnect throttle control rod and fuel line from carburetor, and remove exhaust and inlet manifolds. On diesels, disconnect nozzle lines and remove the manifolds. On all models, remove rocker arm cover, oil lines and rocker arms and shaft assembly. Remove cylinder head retaining nuts and lift cylinder head from engine.

When reinstalling cylinder head, tighten inlet and exhaust manifold nuts finger tight to align mounting faces, then tighten cylinder head stud nuts. After cylinder head nuts are tightened to the correct torque, tighten the manifold nuts.

On models G VI and MF95 non-diesel engines, tighten the head nuts to a torque of 125-130 ft.-lbs. on camshaft side and 105-110 ft.-lbs. on exhaust manifold side using the sequence shown in Fig. 68.

On G705, G706, G707, G708 and MF97 non-diesel models, tighten all cylinder head nuts to a torque of 170-175 ft.-lbs. using the sequence shown in Fig. 68.

Fig. 68–Tighten cylinder head nuts on GVI, MF95, MF97, G705, G706, G707 and G708 non-diesel engines in the sequence shown. Rocker arm oil connection is shown at (34).

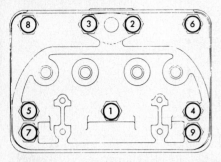

Fig. 69–Cylinder head nut tightening sequence for G900, G950, G1000, G1000 Vista, G1050 and G1350 non-diesel engines.

On models G900, G950, G1000, G1000 Vista, G1050 and G1350 equipped with non-diesel engines, tighten all cylinder head nuts to a torque of 170-175 ft.-lbs. using the sequence shown in Fig. 69.

On G VI and MF95 diesel engines, tighten the ⅝-inch stud nuts to a torque of 125-130 ft.-lbs. on the camshaft side and 105-110 ft.-lbs. on exhaust manifold side and the 9/16-inch stud nuts to a torque of 85-90 ft.-lbs. using the sequence shown in Fig. 70.

On G705, G706, G707, G708, G900, G950, G1000, G1000 Vista, G1050 and MF97 diesel models, tighten all 9/16-inch stud nuts to a torque of 130-135 ft.-lbs.; and all ⅝-inch stud nuts to a torque of 170-175 ft.-lbs., using the sequence shown in Fig. 70.

On G1350 diesel engines, tighten all cylinder head nuts to a torque of 170-175 ft.-lbs. using the sequence shown in Fig. 71.

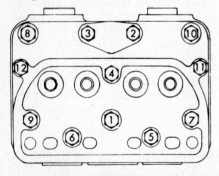

Fig. 70–Cylinder head nut tightening sequence for all diesel models except G1350.

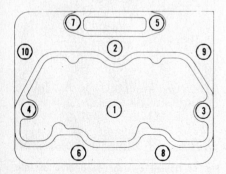

Fig. 71–Cylinder head nut tightening sequence for G1350 diesel engines.

On all models, adjust valve tappet gap (cold) as outlined in paragraph 64. Retighten cylinder head stud nuts using the indicated tightening sequence and torque, after engine is at operating temperature. Then, allow engine to cool and readjust valve tappet gap (cold) as outlined in paragraph 64.

NOTE: Cylinder heads are widely interchangeable and compression ratio can be varied on spark ignition engines by installing heads of a different configuration. Cylinder heads are identified by the part number cast into the head. Make certain that identical heads are used when engine is assembled.

VALVES AND SEATS
All Models

64. On all models except G1350 LP-Gas and diesel engines, cylinder head is fitted with renewable seat inserts for the exhaust valves, while intake valves seat directly in the cylinder head. All G1350 engines are equipped with renewable seat inserts on both intake and exhaust valves. Intake and exhaust valves are not interchangeable. Valves have a face and seat angle of 45 degrees and a desired seat width of 3/32-inch. Valve stem diameter is 0.4335-0.4345.

When installing valves in a diesel cylinder head, make certain that intake valve heads are at least 0.015 below the surface of the cylinder head and are at the same depth within 0.015. The depth of the exhaust valve

heads also must not vary more than 0.015.

To adjust valve tappet gap on all models except G1350 diesel, crank engine until No. 1 piston is at T.D.C. of compression stroke. At this time, adjust tappet gap of the six valves indicated in Fig. 72. Crank engine one revolution to position No. 6 piston at T.D.C. of compression stroke and adjust the tappet gap of the remaining six valves indicated in Fig. 73.

On model G1350 diesel engines, adjust valve tappet gap as follows: Crank engine until No. 1 piston is at T.D.C. of compression stroke. At this time, adjust tappet gap of the six valves indicated in Fig. 74. Crank engine one revolution to position No. 6 piston at T.D.C. of compression stroke and adjust tappet gap of the remaining six valves indicated in Fig. 75.

For greatest accuracy, adjust valve tappet gap when engine is cold and not operating. Valve tappet gap (cold) is as follows:

Series G VI, MF95, MF97, G705, G706, G707, & G708
Non-diesel (static),
   Intake 0.012
   Exhaust 0.022
Diesel (static),
   Intake 0.012
   Exhaust 0.020
Series G900 & G950
Non-diesel (static),
   Intake 0.012
   Exhaust 0.028
Diesel (static)
   Intake 0.015
   Exhaust 0.022

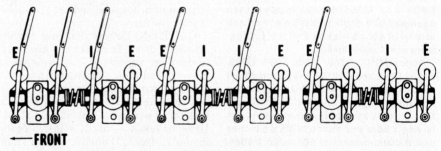

Fig. 72–On all models except G1350 diesel, position No. 1 piston at TDC (compression) and adjust six valves as indicated. Refer to text for correct tappet gap.

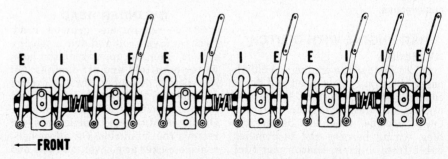

Fig. 73–On all models except G1350 diesel, position No. 6 piston at TDC (compression) and adjust six valves as indicated. Refer to text for correct tappet gap.

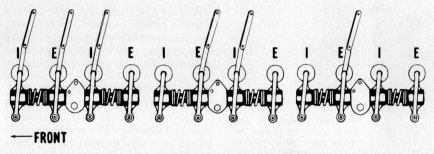

Fig. 74—On model G1350 diesel, position No. 1 piston at TDC (compression) and adjust six valves as indicated. Refer to text for correct tappet gap.

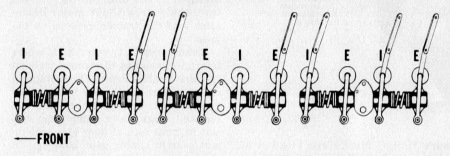

Fig. 75—On model G1350 diesel, position No. 6 piston at TDC (compression) and adjust six valves as indicated. Refer to text for correct tappet gap.

Series G1000, G1000 Vista & G1050
Non-Diesel (static),
   Intake 0.012
   Exhaust 0.028
Diesel (static),
   Intake 0.015
   Exhaust 0.022
Series G1350
Non-diesel (static),
   Intake 0.010
   Exhaust 0.028
Diesel (static)
   Intake 0.010
   Exhaust 0.020
NOTE: Valve arrangement on G1350 diesel engine is intake—exhaust—intake—exhaust, starting at front of each cylinder head. On all other models, valve arrangement is exhaust—intake—intake—exhaust on each cylinder head.

VALVE GUIDES AND SPRINGS
All Models

65. Inlet and exhaust valve guides are interchangeable in all non-diesel models and in model G1350 diesel engines. Ream guides after installation to provide a stem-to-guide clearance of 0.002-0.004 on diesel models and 0.0015-0.0035 on non-diesel models. Inlet and exhaust valve springs are interchangeable in all except gasoline models. On gasoline models, the intake valve springs should test 85-90 lbs. at 2½ inches and the exhaust valve springs should test 85-94 lbs. at 2 3/16 inches. On G900, G950, G1000, G1000 Vista, G1050 and G1350 LP-Gas models, valve springs should test

61-69 lbs. at 2 15/16 inches. On G900, G950, G1000, G1000 Vista and G1050 diesel models, valve springs should test 46-54 lbs. at 2⅞ inches. On G1350 diesel, valve springs should test 56-64 lbs. at 2¼ inches. On all other models, the intake and exhaust valve springs should test 85-90 lbs. at 2½ inches.

On gasoline models, exhaust valves are equipped with positive type valve rotators (Rotocaps). Normal servicing of the valve rotators consists of renewing the units. Rotator action can be considered satisfactory if the valve rotates a slight amount each time the valve opens.

VALVE TAPPETS
(Cam Followers)
All Models

66. The barrel type tappets are supplied in standard size only and should have a clearance of 0.0018-0.0033 in the case bores. Any tappet can be removed after removing either the camshaft or the cylinder block.

ROCKER ARMS
All Models

67. Rocker arms and shaft assembly can be removed after removing hood, valve cover and rocker arm shaft support retaining nuts. On all models except G1350 diesel desired clearance between rocker arm bushing and the 0.9645-0.9670 diameter shaft is 0.001-0.0045. On G1350 diesel, clearance between rocker arm bushing and the 0.996-0.997 diameter shaft should be

0.002-0.004. Bushings are not supplied separately for service; therefore, if clearance between bushing and shaft exceeds 0.008, it will be necessary to renew rocker arms and/or shaft.

On all diesel models except G1350, the end rocker arms for each pair of cylinders are offset on their bushings. When reassembling, make certain that long part of bushings is toward rocker arm shaft supports.

VALVE TIMING
All Models

68. Valves are properly timed when mark "1" on camshaft gear is in mesh with mark "1" on crankshaft gear.

TIMING GEAR COVER
All Models

69. To remove the timing gear cover, remove muffler, air cleaner extension pipe and hood. On models G950, G1050 and G1350, drain and remove hydraulic reservoir. On all models, drain cooling system, disconnect radiator hoses, then unbolt and remove radiator, radiator support and hydraulic oil cooler, if so equipped. On early G900, G1000 and early G1000 Vista, support front of tractor, disconnect hydrostatic steering lines, unbolt and slide front support forward in frame. On late G900 and G1000 Vista and all G950, G1050 and G1350 tractors, disconnect power steering cylinder from vertical shaft, support front of tractor, unbolt front support and slide it forward in frame. On all models, remove fan and water pump.

On all models, using a suitable puller, remove the crankshaft pulley. Remove the timing gear cover retaining cap screws, then remove the timing gear cover.

Camshaft end play is controlled by a thrust screw located in front face of timing gear cover. To adjust, turn screw in until same contacts the camshaft gear retaining cap screw; then, retract screw ¼-turn and lock in place with the lock nut.

TIMING GEARS
All Models

70. The timing gear train consists of the camshaft gear, crankshaft gear and water pump and distributor or injection pump drive gear. On diesel models equipped with Bosch injection pump, an adjustable gear (2—Fig. 76) is bolted to front face of camshaft gear. On non-diesel models or diesel models equipped with Roosa-Master fuel system, the adjustable gear is not used, and distributor drive gear (11—Fig. 78) or injection pump drive gear (1—

Fig. 76–Typical timing gear train used on diesel engines equipped with Bosch pump.

T. Timing adjustment screws
1. Crankshaft gear
2. Adjustable gear
3. Camshaft gear
4. Pump drive gear

Fig. 81) meshes with the camshaft gear. Gears are available in standard size only, if backlash is excessive renew the worn gear or gears.

To remove the timing gears, proceed as outlined in the appropriate following paragraphs.

71. CAMSHAFT GEAR. To remove the camshaft gear, first remove timing gear cover as outlined in paragraph 69. On diesel models equipped with Bosch injection pump, remove injection pump drive shaft and gear as outlined in paragraph 75 and adjustable gear as outlined in paragraph 74. Remove cap screw and washer from front of camshaft, then remove the gear using a suitable puller.

When installing the gear, heat gear to approximately 300°F. and use a longer cap screw if necessary, to draw gear against camshaft shoulder. Make

sure timing marks are aligned as shown in Fig. 77, when gear is installed.

72. CRANKSHAFT GEAR. To remove the crankshaft gear, first remove the camshaft gear as outlined in paragraph 71. If not already off, remove distributor or injection pump and drive housing unit. Unbolt and remove the hydraulic pump from left side of engine. Remove generator or alternator and on models so equipped, remove the belt driven power steering pump.

Remove cap screws retaining timing gear housing to crankcase. Remove the four cap screws securing oil pan to timing gear housing and loosen the remaining oil pan cap screws; then carefully separate oil pan gasket from timing gear housing. Remove timing gear housing.

Remove the crankshaft gear using a suitable puller. Assemble by reversing the disassembly procedure, making sure timing marks are aligned as shown in Fig. 77 when gears are installed.

73. DISTRIBUTOR DRIVE GEAR & HOUSING. Refer to Fig. 78 for exploded view of distributor drive gear and housing. The water pump is driven by a slot in front face of drive gear (11). If only the gear, drive housing and associated parts are to be overhauled, the unit can be removed from the rear without major disassembly of the tractor; proceed as follows.

Remove the distributor and, where interference exists, disconnect tachometer drive cable. Remove the retaining cap screws and withdraw housing and gear from timing gear housing. To reinstall, align water pump tang with slot in front face of gear (11) and insert gear in timing gear housing. Fit thrust washer (9) over shaft of gear and install housing (8).

Complete the assembly by reversing the disassembly procedure. With No. 1 piston on firing stroke, rotor should point toward engine block and slightly to rear when distributor is installed. Time engine as outlined in paragraph 148.

Bushing (7) in housing can be renewed when housing is disassembled. Desired clearance between new bushings and shaft is 0.0007-0.0019.

74. ADJUSTABLE GEAR. The adjustable gear (2—Fig. 76) can be removed after removing timing gear cover as outlined in paragraph 69; and removing the safety wire and timing adjustment screws (T). Slotted holes in gear permit adjustment of injection timing.

When installing gear, check injection pump timing as outlined in paragraph 125 or 128.

Fig. 77–Non-diesel engine timing gear train. Mesh the No. 1 marks on camshaft gear and crankshaft gear as shown at (T). Timing marks are similar on diesel engines.

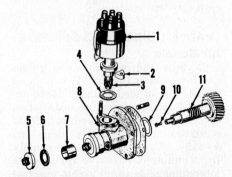

Fig. 78–Exploded view of distributor drive gear and housing used on some models.

1. Distributor
2. Clamp
3. Distributor gear
4. Gasket
5. Tachometer adapter
6. Oil seal
7. Bushing
8. Housing
9. Thrust washer
10. Tachometer drive
11. Drive gear

Fig. 79–Rear view of Bosch PSB injection pump adapter housing with the injection pump removed. Jack screws can be used in holes (H) to facilitate removal of gear (7).

75. INJECTION PUMP DRIVE (BOSCH). On models equipped with APE pump, the double drive gear (4—Fig. 76) can be withdrawn from front after removing timing gear cover as outlined in paragraph 69.

On models equipped with PSB pump, remove timing gear cover as outlined in paragraph 69 and injection pump as outlined in paragraph 129. Remove floating coupling (6—Fig. 79) and, using two fairly long ⅜-inch NC bolts as jack screws, remove coupling gear (7). Remove the Woodruff key and withdraw gear and shaft (4—Fig. 80) forward out of housing. Adapter housing (9) or bushing (5) can be renewed at this time. Ream bushings after installation to provide the recommended 0.0007-0.0019 diametral clearance for the shaft.

Assemble by reversing the disassembly procedure. Install and time injection pump as outlined in paragraph 129.

76. INJECTION PUMP DRIVE (ROOSA-MASTER). Refer to Fig. 81. The injection pump drive gear (1) meshes with the camshaft gear, and the entire drive unit can be removed from rear without removing timing gear cover.

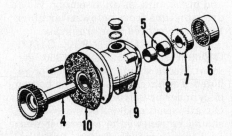

Fig. 80–Bosch PSB injection pump drive mechanism.

4. Pump drive gear	7. Coupling gear
5. Bushings	8. "O" ring
6. Floating coupling	9. Adapter housing

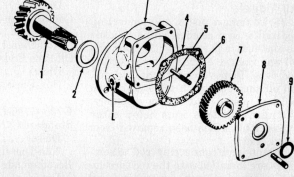

Fig. 81–Exploded view of typical injection pump drive gears, adapter housing and associated parts used on models equipped with Roosa-Master injection pump.

L. Lube passage
1. Drive gear
2. Thrust washer
3. Adapter housing
4. Gasket
5. Thrust button
6. Spring
7. Pump gear
8. Mounting plate
9. "O" ring

To remove the unit, first remove injection pump, adapter (8) and gear (7) as outlined in paragraph 133, being careful not to lose thrust plunger (5) and spring (6) which are inserted in bore of injection pump shaft.

Disconnect the lubrication lines, remove retaining cap screws and lift off housing (3) and gear (1). The gear can be withdrawn from housing bore at this time.

Gears, bushings and housing are pressure lubricated. If shaft bushings must be renewed, make certain that lube hole in bushing aligns with passage hole (L) in housing when bushing is installed. Ream the bushings after installation to provide the recommended 0.0007-0.0019 shaft diametral clearance. Also check to be sure the cup plug in bore of gear shaft (1) is in place and to the rear of the two holes in bearing area of shaft.

To install the injection pump drive unit, align the water pump drive tang with drive slot in front face of gear (1), and install gear and thrust washer (2); then install housing (3) by reversing the removal procedure. Install and time injection pump as outlined in paragraph 133.

CAMSHAFT
All Models

77. To remove the camshaft, first remove the timing gear cover as outlined in paragraph 69. Remove rocker arms and shaft assemblies, push rods, governor, oil pan and oil pump. On diesel models equipped with Bosch injection pump, remove injection pump drive gear as outlined in paragraph 75. Then, on all models, block up cam followers and withdraw camshaft with camshaft gear through front of timing gear case.

On models GVI, G705, G706, G707, G708, MF95 and MF97, the front intermediate, rear intermediate and rear camshaft journals ride directly in machined bores in crankcase. The front journal rides in two renewable bushings. These bushings must be line reamed after installation, to provide the proper shaft to bushing clearance. Recommended camshaft bore clearances for these models are: Front, 0.003-0.005; Second, 0.003-0.005; Third, 0.005-0.007; Rear, 0.002-0.004.

On G1350 LP-Gas and all G900, G950 and G1050 engines, camshaft bushings are used on the front and front intermediate journals. On G1350 diesel and all G1000 and G1000 Vista engines, the camshaft rides in five renewable bushings. Bushings are pre-sized and require no reaming if carefully installed. When installing new bushings, align oil hole in bushings with holes in crankcase and make certain the two rear intermediate bushings are installed with split to the top. Recommended camshaft bearing clearance is 0.003-0.006 on all models except G1350 diesel. Recommended clearance on G1350 diesel is 0.002-0.007.

On all models, camshaft journal sizes are as follows: Front, 3.338-3.339; Second, 3.3075-3.3085; Third, 3.275-3.276; Rear, 1.996-1.997.

When reinstalling camshaft and gear assembly, mesh gears as shown in Fig. 77. After timing gear cover is installed, adjust camshaft end play by turning the adjusting screw (located in case cover) IN until screw contacts cap screw in end of camshaft; then retract the screw ¼-turn and lock in place with the locking nut.

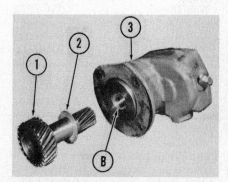

Fig. 82–Roosa-Master injection pump adapter housing with shaft removed. Bushing (B) may be renewed, refer to text for oil passage alignment. Refer to Fig. 81 for legend.

ROD AND PISTON UNITS
All Models

78. To remove piston and connecting rod units, first remove cylinder heads as outlined in paragraph 63. Drain the oil and remove oil pan and connecting rod caps. Remove water manifold and lift off each cylinder block and the two rod and piston units as an assembly. Withdraw pistons from below after cylinder block has been removed from crankcase.

Piston and connecting rod assemblies are installed with the rod correlation marks facing the camshaft on all models except G1350 diesel. On G1350 diesel, rod correlation marks face side opposite from camshaft. Tighten the connecting rod bolts to 70-75 ft.-lbs. torque on all G900 and G950 models, 55-60 ft.-lbs. on G1000, G1000 Vista and G1050 diesel models, 70-75 ft.-lbs. on G1000, G1000 Vista, G1050 and G1350 non-diesel models, 55-60 ft.-lbs. on G1350 diesel and to 80-85 ft.-lbs. torque on all other models.

Connecting rods used in some non-diesel engines are offset at the piston pin end. The long portion of the offset must face the end of each block. Mark new rods and caps on the camshaft side (all models except G1350 diesel; opposite camshaft side on G1350 diesel), corresponding to the cylinder number.

PISTONS AND RINGS
All Models

79. Pistons and rings for models G VI and MF95 non-diesel engines are available in standard size and oversizes of 0.030, 0.063 and 0.094. Pistons and rings for all other engines are available in standard size and oversizes of 0.020, 0.040 and 0.060. Check pistons, cylinders and rings against the values which follow:

G VI—MF95
Standard Cylinder Bore Diameter
  Diesel 4.251-4.252
  Non-Diesel 4.251-4.252
Recommended Piston Skirt Clearance
  Diesel 0.0065-0.0075
  Non-Diesel 0.004-0.005
Maximum Cylinder Wear 0.008
Top Ring Side Clearance
  Diesel 0.0045-0.0065
  Non-Diesel 0.0035-0.005
Second Ring Side Clearance
  Diesel 0.0035-0.0055
  Non-Diesel 0.0035-0.005
Third Ring Side Clearance
  Diesel 0.0025-0.0045
  Non-Diesel 0.0035-0.005
Fourth Ring Side Clearance
  Diesel 0.0020-0.0035
  Non-Diesel 0.0035-0.005

Fifth Ring Side Clearance
  Diesel 0.0020-0.0035
Compression Ring End Gap
  Diesel 0.015-0.020
  Non-Diesel 0.020-0.030
Oil Ring End Gap
  Diesel 0.015-0.020
  Non-Diesel 0.020-0.030

G705-G706-G707-G708-MF97
Standard Cylinder Bore Diameter
  Diesel 4.626-4.627
  Non-Diesel 4.626-4.627
Recommended Piston Skirt Clearance
  Diesel 0.007-0.009
  Non-Diesel 0.0045-0.005
Maximum Cylinder Wear 0.008
Top Ring Side Clearance
  Diesel 0.0045-0.006
  Non-Diesel 0.0035-0.0055
Second Ring Side Clearance
  Diesel 0.0025-0.004
  Non-Diesel 0.0035-0.0055
Third Ring Side Clearance
  Diesel 0.0025-0.004
  Non-Diesel 0.0025-0.0055
Fourth Ring Side Clearance
  Diesel 0.002-0.0035
  Non-Diesel 0.0025-0.0035
Fifth Ring Side Clearance
  Diesel 0.002-0.0035
Compression Ring End Gap
  Diesel 0.013-0.023
  Non-Diesel 0.013-0.025
Oil Ring End Gap
  Diesel 0.013-0.023
  Non-Diesel 0.013-0.025

G900-G950
Standard Cylinder Bore Diameter
  Diesel 4.376-4.3770
  Non-Diesel 4.251-4.252
Recommended Piston Skirt Clearance
  Diesel 0.005-0.007
  Non-Diesel 0.0045-0.0065
Maximum Cylinder Wear
  Bottom of Cylinder 0.003
  Top of Cylinder 0.010
Top Ring Side Clearance
  Diesel 0.0025-0.0045
  Non-Diesel 0.0035-0.005
Second Ring Side Clearance
  Diesel 0.0025-0.0045
  Non-Diesel 0.0035-0.005
Third Ring Side Clearance
  Diesel 0.002-0.004
  Non-Diesel 0.003-0.0045
Fourth Ring Side Clearance
  Diesel 0.0015-0.0035
  Non-Diesel 0.002-0.0035
Compression Ring End Gap
  Diesel 0.015-0.025
  Non-Diesel 0.020-0.030
Oil Ring End Gap
  Diesel 0.010-0.020
  Non-Diesel 0.015-0.025

G1000-G1000 Vista-G1050
Standard Cylinder Bore
  Diameter 4.626-4.627

Recommended Piston Skirt Clearance
  Diesel 0.007-0.009
  Non-Diesel 0.006-0.008
Maximum Cylinder Wear
  Bottom of Cylinder 0.003
  Top of Cylinder 0.010
Piston Ring Side Clearance
  Top Ring 0.0025-0.0045
  Second Ring 0.0025-0.0045
  Third Ring 0.0020-0.0040
  Fourth Ring 0.0010-0.0030
Piston Ring End Gap
  Compression Rings 0.016-0.026
  Oil Ring 0.013-0.023

G1350
Standard Cylinder Bore Diameter
  Diesel 4.752-4.753
  Non-Diesel 4.626-4.627
Recommended Piston Skirt Clearance
  Diesel 0.007-0.009
  Non-Diesel 0.006-0.008
Maximum Cylinder Wear
  Bottom of Cylinder 0.003
  Top of Cylinder 0.010
Top Ring Side Clearance
  Diesel 0.0025-0.0045
  Non-Diesel 0.0025-0.0045
Second Ring Side Clearance
  Diesel 0.0025-0.0045
  Non-Diesel 0.0025-0.0045
Third Ring Side Clearance
  Diesel 0.0020-0.0040
  Non-Diesel 0.0020-0.0040
Fourth Ring Side Clearance
  Diesel 0.0015-0.0035
  Non-Diesel 0.0010-0.0030
Compression Ring End Gap
  Diesel
    Top Ring 0.017-0.027
    2nd & 3rd rings 0.017-0.032
  Non-Diesel 0.016-0.026
Oil Ring End Gap
  Diesel 0.015-0.025
  Non-Diesel 0.013-0.023

CYLINDER BLOCK
All Models

80. To remove any cylinder block, remove hood, rocker arms and shaft assembly, push rods and cylinder head. Drain the oil and remove oil pan. Remove connecting rod bearing caps and lift off this block and two rod and pistol units as an assembly. Withdraw pistons from below after block has been removed from crankcase.

On models G900, G950, G1000, G1000 Vista, G1050 and G1350, cylinder blocks should be renewed or rebored if wear exceeds 0.003 at bottom of cylinder or 0.010 at top of cylinder. On all other models, cylinder blocks should be renewed or rebored if wear or taper exceeds 0.008. Reboring should be done from bottom of block to duplicate factory alignment. Rebore to standard oversizes listed in paragraph 79, or check parts stock for available oversize. Install cylinder heads as outlined in paragraph 63 and adjust valves as outlined in paragraph 64.

PISTON PINS
All Models

81. Piston pins are of the full floating type which are retained in the piston pin bosses by snap rings. The 1.2495-1.2496 diameter pins for non-diesels, 1.8745-1.8746 diameter pins for G1350 diesel or 1.4995-1.4996 diameter pins for all other diesels are available in standard size and oversizes of 0.005 and 0.010.

Install piston pin bushing in rod so that oil hole in bushing registers with oil hole in top end of connecting rod. The bushings must be honed after installation to obtain the correct piston pin clearance of 0.0008-0.0012.

ROD BEARINGS
All Models

82. Connecting rod bearings are of precision type, renewable from below after removing oil pan. When installing new bearing shells, be sure that bearing shell projection engages milled slot in rod and cap, and that rod and cap correlation marks face toward camshaft side of engine on all models except G1350 diesel and opposite camshaft side on G1350 diesel. Bearings are available in 0.002, 0.010, 0.020, 0.030 and 0.040 undersizes as well as standard.

Standard crankpin diameter is 2.5770-2.5775 on G VI and MF95 non-diesel, 3.498-3.499 on G1350 diesel and 2.9115-2.9120 on all other models. Recommended connecting rod bearing diametral clearance is 0.0023-0.0053 for G1350 diesel, 0.0014-0.0039 for G1350 non-diesel and all G900, G950, G1000, G1000 Vista and G1050 engines and 0.0009-0.003 for all other models. Connecting rod side clearance should be 0.008-0.013. Tighten connecting rod cap nuts or cap screws to a torque of 70-75 ft.-lbs. on all G900 and G950 models, 55-60 ft.-lbs. on G1000, G1000 Vista, and G1050 diesel models, 70-75 ft.-lbs on G1000, G1000 Vista, G1050 and G1350 non-diesel models, 55-60 ft.-lbs. on G1350 diesel and 80-85 ft.-lbs. for all other models.

CRANKSHAFT AND BEARINGS
All Models

83. **MAIN BEARINGS.** Crankshaft main bearings are precision, babbitt lined type on models G VI, G705, G706, MF95 and MF97 non-diesels and precision, trimetal type on all other models, which may be renewed from below. Bearing caps are marked "FRONT" and should be installed with markings toward front of engine.

CAUTION: Make certain that main bearing insert with oil hole is installed in the crankcase. Bearings are available in 0.002, 0.010, 0.020, 0.030 and 0.040 undersizes as well as standard.

84. **CRANKSHAFT.** Crankshaft end play is controlled by rear main bearing flange. Recommended end play is 0.008-0.012 for G1350 diesel and 0.006-0.010 for all other models. To remove crankshaft, it is necessary to remove engine, oil pan, timing gear cover, timing gear case, oil pump, flywheel, connecting rod bearing caps and main bearing caps.

Check crankshaft, crankpins and main bearing journals for wear, scoring and out-of-round condition against values listed below.

Crankpin diameter . See paragraph 82
Maximum allowable taper or
out-of-round 0.003
Main journal diameter,
  G1350 diesel 3.498-3.499
  All other models 2.911-2.912
Main bearing oil clearance,
  G1350 diesel 0.0033-0.0053
  All other models 0.0014-0.0044
Main bearing bolt torque (ft.-lbs.) with lubricated threads,
GVI-G705-G706-G707-
G708-MF95-MF97
  Front (non-diesels) 135-145
  Front (diesels) 195-205
  Intermediates and rear
  (non-diesels) 100-105
  Intermediates and rear
  (diesels) 100-105
EARLY G1000
  Front (11/16-inch nuts) 195-205
  Intermediates and rear
  (9/16-inch nuts) 100-105
LATE G1000-G900-G950-G1000
VISTA-G1050
  Front (¾-inch cap screws) 240
  Intermediates and rear
  (⅝-inch cap screws) 140
G1350 NON-DIESEL
  Front (¾-inch cap screws) 240
  Intermediates and rear
  (⅝-inch cap screws) 140
G1350 DIESEL
  Front (¾-inch cap screws) .. 195-205
  Intermediates and rear
  (⅝-inch cap screws) 108-112

CRANKSHAFT OIL SEALS
All Models

85. **FRONT SEAL.** The felt type seal is contained in a metal retainer which is pressed into timing gear case. Procedure for renewing the seal is evident after sliding the radiator, pedestal and front wheels assembly forward and removing the crankshaft pulley. Install seal so that felt insert is toward outside of timing gear case.

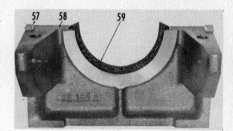

Fig. 83–Typical crankshaft rear oil seal (lower half) and retainer assembly.

  57. Cork seal
  58. Seal retainer
  59. Crankshaft rear oil
     seal

86. **REAR SEAL.** The crankshaft rear oil seal is a two-piece type. The lower half (59—Fig. 83) is contained in a retainer, and the upper half in a groove which is machined in the crankcase.

Lower half of cork or felt seal can be renewed from below after removing oil pan and seal retainer. Allow ends of oil seal to extend 1/32 to 1/16-inch above edge of retainer. Renew side corks (57) before reinstalling the retainer. When reinstalling the retainer, insert a sufficient number of gaskets between mating surfaces of crankcase and seal retainer so that retainer will protrude 0.005 beyond gasket surface of crankcase when retainer is bolted in position.

Oil seal upper half can be pulled out, and a new seal inserted from below after removing oil pan, retainer for lower seal and loosening main bearing caps.

POSITIVE CRANKCASE VENTILATION SYSTEM
All Models So Equipped

87. Model G1350 non-diesel and all models G900, G950, G1000, G1000 Vista and G1050 are equipped with positive crankcase ventilation.

On all models, air is taken in through the breather cap on front rocker arm cover, circulated through the crankcase, and then drawn from the top of center and rear cylinder heads by the venting systems. This air, with any accumulated crankcase fumes, is then taken into the combustion chamber and burned.

Gasoline and LP-Gas models are equipped with a crankcase ventilator valve located on underside of intake manifold. After every 250 hours of engine operation, remove the ventilator valve, then disassemble the valve as shown in Fig. 84. Wash the parts in varnish remover and make sure valve piston (2) slides freely in valve housing (1). Reassemble and reinstall the unit with arrow pointing up. Make certain that tube connec-

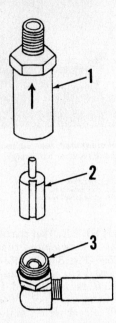

Fig. 84—Exploded view of positive crankcase ventilation valve used on some non-diesel models.

1. Valve housing
2. Valve piston
3. Valve base & connector assembly

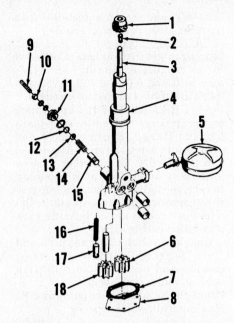

Fig. 85—Exploded view of oil pump used on Models G900, G950, G1000, G1000 Vista and G1050.

1. Drive shaft pinion	10. Lock nut
2. Tachometer drive sleeve	11. Regulator cover
3. Drive shaft	12. Snap ring
4. Pump body	13. Spring retainer
5. Intake screen	14. Regulator spring
6. Pump gear	15. Regulator valve
7. Gasket	16. By-pass spring
8. Pump cover	17. By-pass valve
9. Adjusting screw	18. Idler gear

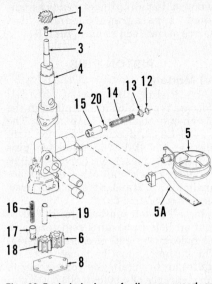

Fig. 86—Exploded view of oil pump used on model G1350.

1. Drive pinion	8. Pump cover
2. Tachometer drive sleeve	12. Snap ring
3. Drive shaft	13. Spring retainer
4. Pump body	14. Regulator spring
5. Intake screen (Non-diesel)	15. Regulator valve
5A. Intake tube (Diesel)	16. By-pass spring
6. Pump gear	17. By-pass valve
	18. Idler gear
	19. Idler gear shaft
	20. Shim

tions at the valve and center and rear rocker arm covers are tight.

On models G900, G950, G1000, G1000 Vista and G1050 diesel tractors, a ventilation tube is installed in the center and rear cylinder heads. A metered bore connects each tube to an intake port in cylinder head.

FLYWHEEL
All Models

88. The flywheel can be removed after separating engine from transmission as outlined in the clutch section. The flywheel is retained by six equally spaced bolts and nuts or cap screws, and can be installed in any of six positions; only one position is right as follows. When installing flywheel, turn crankshaft until No. 1 piston is at TDC; then install flywheel with DC timing mark at 9 o'clock position as viewed from clutch side of flywheel.

To install a new flywheel ring gear, heat same to approximately 500 degrees F. and install on flywheel with beveled edge of teeth facing front of engine.

OIL PAN
All Models

89. To remove the oil pan on models G900, G950, G1000, G1000 Vista, G1050 and G1350, first unbolt and remove the oil filter cover, element and filter can from oil pan. On models G900, G950, G1000, G1000 Vista and G1050, remove the large plug containing oil pressure regulator screw from left side of the oil pan. Unbolt and remove the front axle rear sup-

port, if tractor is equipped with Type E front axle.

On all models, support oil pan with a floor jack, remove cap screws retaining oil pan to crankcase and remove oil pan.

On four wheel drive models, it will be necessary to support front of tractor and remove front drive unit as an assembly.

OIL PUMP
All Models

90. The gear type pump, shown in Figs. 85, 86 and 87, can be removed after removing oil pan.

To disassemble the oil pump used on models G900, G950, G1000, G1000 Vista, G1050 or G1350 (Fig. 85 or 86), remove cotter pin and withdraw intake screen assembly (5) or intake tube (5A). Unbolt and remove cover (8) and idler gear (18). Place the pump in a press in an inverted position. Apply pressure to the shaft (3) and press it out of pump gear (6). Withdraw shaft from pump body (4). Remove snap ring (12) from side of pump body and remove the pressure regulator spring (14) and valve (15). On G1350, note number of shims (20—Fig. 86) removed with regulator valve. To remove the filter by-pass valve, pull the groove pin out far enough to release the valve assembly, and remove piston (17—Fig. 85 or 86) and spring (16)

from bottom of pump.

Check all parts and renew as necessary. The pressure regulator spring (14) free length is 1⅝ inches on models G900, G950, G1000, G1000 Vista and G1050 and 2 21/64 inches on model G1350 and the by-pass valve spring (16) free length is 2 7/16 inches on all models.

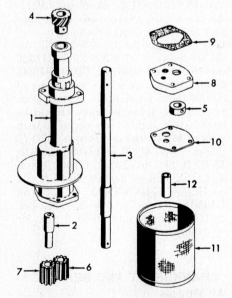

Fig. 87—Exploded view of oil pump used on models GVI, G705, G706, G707, G708, MF95 and MF97.

1. Pump body	7. Idler gear
2. Idler gear shaft	8. Inner cover
3. Drive shaft	9. Gasket
4. Drive pinion	10. Outer plate
5. Thrust collar	11. Intake screen
6. Pump gear	12. Spacer

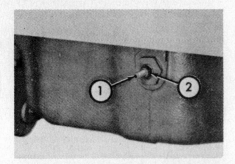

Fig. 88–View showing location of oil pressure regulator adjusting screw on models G900, G950, G1000, G1000 Vista and G1050.

1. Adjusting screw   2. Lock nut

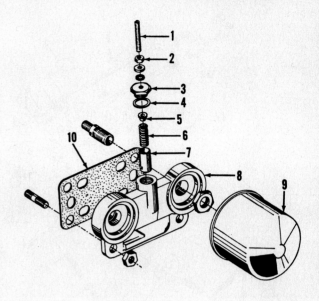

Fig. 89–Oil filter body and pressure regulating valve used on models GVI, G705, G706, G707, G708, MF95 and MF97.

1. Adjusting screw
2. Lock nut
3. Valve cap
4. Gasket
5. Spring seat
6. Valve spring
7. Valve piston
8. Filter body
9. Spin-on filter
10. Gasket

When reassembling, press pump gear (6) on shaft until shaft is flush to 0.010 below face of gear. With all other parts installed, press drive pinion (1) on shaft until pinion is 0.010-0.030 from top of pump body.

To disassemble the oil pump used on models G VI, G705, G706, G707, G708, MF95 and MF97, refer to Fig. 87 and remove strainer screen (11), spacer (12) and outer plate (10). Drive the roll pin out of drive pinion (4) and pull the pinion from shaft (3). Push shaft downward until the roll pin can be driven from thrust collar (5), then remove the thrust collar from shaft. Remove the inner cover (8), pump gear (6), shaft (3) and idler gear (7) from pump body (1).

Check all parts for excessive wear and renew as necessary. Reassemble pump by reversing the disassembly procedure.

OIL PRESSURE REGULATOR
All Models

91. On models G900, G950, G1000, G1000 Vista and G1050, the regulator valve is located in the oil pump as shown in Fig. 85. To adjust the oil pressure regulator, loosen lock nut (2 —Fig. 88) and turn adjusting screw (1) as required to obtain the recommended 40-45 psi oil pressure at engine rated speed, then tighten lock nut.

On models G VI, G705, G706, G707, G708, MF95 and MF97, the regulator valve is located in filter housing on left side of engine as shown at (7—Fig. 89). To adjust oil pressure, loosen lock nut (2) and turn adjusting screw (1) to obtain the recommended 25-35 psi oil pressure at rated engine speed, then tighten lock nut.

On Model G1350 tractors, the oil pressure regulator valve is located in the oil pump as shown in Fig. 86. Oil pressure is adjusted by adding or removing shims (20). NOTE: Engine oil pan must be removed to gain access to the pressure regulator. Installing one additional shim will increase oil pressure approximately 3 psi. Normal engine oil pressure at 2200 rpm is 40-45 psi for LP-Gas engines and 50-55 psi for diesel engines.

GASOLINE FUEL SYSTEM

CARBURETOR
Models G900-G1000

92. **ADJUSTMENT.** Gasoline models G900 and G1000 tractors are equipped with the Marvel-Schebler USX-40 carburetor shown in Fig. 90. To adjust the carburetor, back the idle mixture adjusting needle 1½ to 2 turns off its seat and the power adjusting needle 3 turns off its seat. While holding the throttle shaft assembly in fully closed position, back idle speed stop screw out until it just clears the flexible idle stop. Then, turn the stop screw in 1½ turns against the flexible stop.

Start the engine and allow it to run long enough to reach normal operating temperature. Place the speed control lever in low idle position and adjust idle speed stop screw to obtain an idle speed of 600 rpm. Back idle speed adjusting needle out until engine speed drops from an over-lean mixture, then turn needle in until engine runs smoothly. Readjust idle speed stop screw, if necessary, to maintain correct idle speed. Place the speed control lever in high idle position and turn power adjusting needle in until engine begins to lose speed, then back the needle out ⅛ to ¼-turn.

93. **OVERHAUL.** With carburetor removed, disassemble as follows: Remove throttle plate (5—Fig. 90) and pull throttle shaft (2) from body. Remove retainer (8) and packing (7). Cup (9) need not be removed unless throttle shaft bearings are to be renewed. Remove choke plate (26) and pull choke shaft (20) from body. Remove choke bracket, retainer (34) and packing (33). Remove plug (50) and screen (49). Remove cover (13), then unbolt and remove pump housing (16), diaphragm (18) and spring (19) from cover. Remove float shaft (12), float (11), inlet needle and needle seat (36). Remove plug (45) and nozzle (43). Remove idle jet (42), power adjusting needle (38) and seat (40). Remove plug (48) and minimum fuel jet (47). Remove idle mixture needle (41).

The throttle shaft needle bearings (6) can be removed from the body, if necessary, by using Marvel-Schebler tool M-504 or its equivalent. Refer to Fig. 91. Insert tool through throttle shaft bore, then spread split end of tool with a small screw driver so lips of tool will engage bearing shell and press bearing from its bore. Repeat operation for opposite side.

NOTE: Use a vise as a press to re-

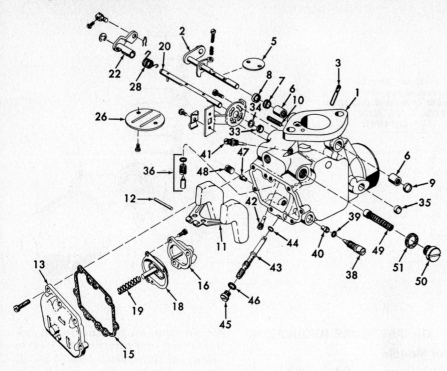

Fig. 90—Exploded view of model USX Marvel-Schebler carburetor used on gasoline models G900 and G1000.

1. Body	11. Float	28. Spring	42. Idle jet
2. Throttle shaft	12. Float shaft	33. Packing	43. Main nozzle
3. Pump discharge jet	13. Bowl cover	34. Retainer	44. Gasket
5. Throttle plate	15. Bowl gasket	35. Choke shaft cup	45. Plug
6. Needle bearings	16. Pump housing	36. Inlet needle and seat	46. Gasket
7. Packing	18. Pump diaphragm	38. Power adjusting	47. Minimum fuel jet
8. Retainer	19. Spring	needle	48. Plug
9. Throttle shaft cup	20. Choke shaft	39. "O" ring	49. Screen
10. Flexible throttle stop	22. Choke lever	40. Power needle seat	50. Plug
	26. Choke plate	41. Idle mixture needle	51. Gasket

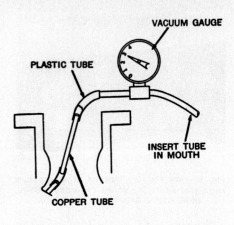

Fig. 92—Use method shown to check model USX carburetor accelerator pump discharge jet. Refer to text.

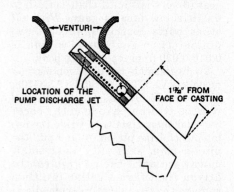

Fig. 93—Accelerator pump discharge jet is installed as shown.

move and install the throttle shaft needle bearings. Bearings are hardened and could break if driven.

The accelerator pump discharge jet (3—Fig. 90) can be checked prior to removal and if satisfactory, jet need not be removed. Check jet operation as follows: Connect a vacuum gage between two short lengths of plastic or rubber tubing. Be sure bowl cover is off, then place one tube end over the end of discharge jet which protrudes into throttle bore. See Fig. 92. Apply vacuum on opposite end of tube assembly and as ball check leaves its seat, note gage reading which should be 3 inches Hg. Ball check leaving seat will be audible. If the jet check ball leaves its seat at less than 3 inches Hg. vacuum, renew the complete discharge jet as follows:

NOTE: If Marvel-Schebler tool M-505 (position tool) is not available, be sure to measure depth that discharge jet is installed in the drilled passage. This depth should be 1 17/32 inches as shown in Fig. 93.

Use a 5/32-inch rod and drive discharge jet out toward throttle bore end of drilled passage. To install new discharge jet, start jet into drilled passage and position slot of discharge end so it is within 5 degrees of being parallel with the centerline of carburetor and deep end of slot is upwards as shown in Fig. 94. Use Marvel-Schebler positioning tool M-505 and drive jet into position. If tool M-505 is not available, use the 5/32-inch rod to drive the jet to the 1 17/32-inch location as shown in Fig. 93.

Clean and inspect all parts. Use compressed air to blow out all passages EXCEPT the pump discharge jet passage. Compressed air can damage discharge jet.

Reassemble by reversing the disassembly procedure and adjust float lever by either adding an additional gasket under inlet needle seat or bending float lever, until float lever is parallel with surface of body mounting flange. Note: Float level can also be

set by removing inlet needle and observing the extreme positions of float travel, then adjusting float until it is midway between these positions when float needle is installed.

Refer to the following table for Marvel-Schebler parts data.

USX-40

Repair kit	286-1494
Gasket set	16-720
Inlet needle and seat	233-607
Pump diaphragm	237-550
Idle jet	49-420
Nozzle	47-A106
Main adjusting needle assy.	43-720
Main needle seat	36-396
Pump discharge jet	49-532
Minimum fuel jet	49-A4

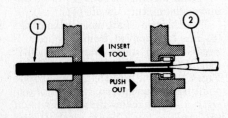

Fig. 91—Use Marvel-Schebler M-504 removal tool (1) and screwdriver (2) as shown to press out throttle shaft bearings from model USX carburetor.

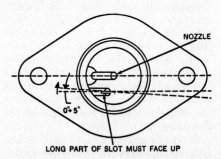

Fig. 94—View showing upper end of model USX carburetor accelerator pump discharge jet after installation.

FUEL PUMP
Early Model G1000

94. Gasoline model G1000 tractors are equipped with a fuel pump located on left side of engine. The diaphragm type fuel pump is driven by an eccentric on engine camshaft that contacts fuel pump rocker arm.

Poor fuel delivery can be caused by worn or improperly seated check valves or by a ruptured diaphragm. If the diaphragm is ruptured, fuel will leak out of the vent hole in pump. The fuel pump should maintain a fuel pressure of 3½-4½ psi at the pump outlet. When operating at capacity, the pump should deliver one pint of fuel in thirty seconds with engine operating at 600 rpm.

G900—Late G1000

95. G900 and late G1000 gasoline models are equipped with Bendix electric fuel pumps. Removal of pump assembly is obvious upon examination of the unit. To disassemble the pump, refer to Fig. 95 and remove cover (12), gasket (13), magnet (14) and filter (15). Remove retainer (16), washer (17), gasket (18), valve (19), spring (20) and plunger (21).

Clean and inspect all parts and renew any showing excessive wear or other damage. Reassembly is the reverse of disassembly procedure.

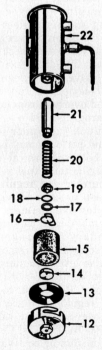

Fig. 95–Exploded view of Bendix electric fuel pump used on G900 and late G1000 gasoline tractors.

12. Cover	18. Gasket
13. Gasket	19. Valve
14. Magnet	20. Spring
15. Filter	21. Plunger
16. Retainer	22. Pump housing
17. Washer	assembly

LP-GAS SYSTEM

Minneapolis-Moline tractors are available with factory installed LP-Gas systems using Ensign and Century equipment. These systems are designed to operate with the fuel tank not more than 80% filled.

G VI and MF95 tractors are equipped with an Ensign No. 9152 carburetor and an Ensign Model R regulator.

G900 and G950 tractors use Century Model 3C 706UD carburetors and Century Model H regulators.

G705, G706, G707, G708, G1000, G1000 Vista, G1050 and MF97 tractors use Century Model 3C 706 UD carburetors and Century Model M5 regulators.

G1350 tractors use Century Model 3C 707UD carburetors and Century Model M5 regulators.

It is important when starting LP-Gas tractors to open the vapor valve on the supply tank SLOWLY; if opened too fast, the fuel supply to the regulator will be shut off. Too rapid opening of vapor or liquid valves may cause freezing.

CARBURETOR ADJUSTMENTS
Series G VI-MF95

96. The recommended slow idle speed is 450-500 rpm. To adjust the slow idle speed, first allow the engine to reach normal operating temperature, adjust the idle mixture, and turn the idle stop screw on throttle shaft to provide recommended slow idle speed.

Initial adjustment for the starting screw (3—Fig. 96) is 1½ turns open.

Immediately after engine is started and with throttle open and choke closed, adjust starting screw until the highest engine speed is obtained.

Then, open the screw (enrich the mixture) until the engine speed drops slightly, and lock in place.

Initial idle mixture adjusting screw setting is 1 turn open.

Idle and load mixture adjustments should be made with the engine at operating temperature and running on liquid fuel. Turn the idle adjusting screw (1—Fig. 96) until the best idle is obtained.

Initial load adjustment is 3½ turns open. Load adjustment must be made with the throttle and governor in wide open position and the engine under load. These conditions can be met in the shop by either loading the tractor with dynamometer, or removing and grounding all except two spark plug wires.

With the above conditions met, turn the load adjusting screw (2—Fig. 96) out until engine reaches the highest operating rpm; then, turn the load adjusting screw in until the engine speed just starts to drop. Now turn the screw out exactly ½-turn and lock in place.

Series G705-G706-G707-G708-G900-G950-G1000-G1000 Vista-G1050-G1350-MF97

97. To make the preliminary adjustments on models G705, G706, G707, G708 and MF97, close the power adjusting screw (3—Fig. 97) completely; then, reopen it according to the fuel being used. Open the screw 2½ turns for butane or 4½ turns for propane and HD-5 LP-Gas.

Fig. 96–View showing location of adjustment screws on Ensign LP-Gas regulator and carburetor used on models GVI and MF95.

P. Pressure plug
1. Idle mixture adjusting screw
2. Load adjusting screw
3. Starting adjusting screw
4. Idle speed stop screw

Models G900, G950, G1000, G1000 Vista, G1050 and G1350 are equipped with high compression heads and must burn only HD-5 LP-Gas. If lower grade fuel is to be used, low compression cylinder heads must be installed. When using HD-5 fuel, close power adjusting screw (3) completely, then back the screw out 6 turns on G900 and G950, 7½ turns on G1000, G1000 Vista and G1050 and 5½ turns on G1350.

On all models, place the speed control lever in slow idle position and adjust idle speed stop screw (2) to obtain an idle speed of 600 rpm. Loosen lock nuts on drag link (4) and rotate drag link barrel to the longest position possible to obtain a smooth idle.

The carburetor is not equipped with a choke valve. Depressing the primer button (1) manually opens the regulator low pressure valve and allows fuel to enter carburetor mixing chamber at 5-9 psi pressure. A hiss should be heard as the primer button is depressed.

Final adjustments must be made with engine at operating temperature and liquid withdrawal valve open to assure adequate fuel supply. Fuel for part-throttle operation is controlled by the metering valve and balanced to the throttle valve by adjusting the length of drag link (4).

To adjust the idle mixture after engine is at operating temperature, loosen locknuts on drag link (4) and turn knurled center section to the point of smoothest idle. Adjust idle speed stop screw (2) to provide a slow idle speed of 600 rpm, then recheck drag link adjustment. Leave drag link as long as possible to still produce a smooth idle.

Turn the power adjusting screw (3) to produce a reading of 12.5-13.5 on

Fig. 97–Location of adjustment points on typical Century carburetor.

1. Primer button
2. Idle speed stop screw
3. Power adjusting screw
4. Idle drag link

gasoline scale of exhaust analyzer, with throttle wide open and engine under full load. If an exhaust gas analyzer is not used, adjust the power mixture screw out until maximum rpm is reached with throttle wide open and engine under load. Turn power adjusting screw in until engine speed starts to drop from too lean a mixture. Then back screw out exactly ½-turn and tighten lock nut.

Recheck idle settings after power mixture has been adjusted and correct as necessary.

TROUBLE SHOOTING
All Models With Ensign Systems

98. Trouble in engine operation due to the fuel supply system usually results from four principal causes, as follows:

a. Improper adjustment of carburetor or regulator.
b. Plugged fuel lines, passages or filter.
c. System leaks in lines, valves or diaphragms.
d. Damaged or worn component parts.

To locate trouble in the LP-Gas fuel system, shut off the vapor and liquid withdrawal valves and run engine until all fuel is exhausted and engine stops. Connect a low reading pressure gage to the pressure plug (P—Fig. 96) opening in regulator. Slowly open the liquid withdrawal valve and start the engine. Pressure gage should read 4-5 psi with the engine operating. Stop the engine, leaving the withdrawal valve open. If the pressure increases after the engine is stopped, a leak in the high pressure valve is indicated, and the unit should be overhauled as outlined in paragraph 102. An operating pressure higher or lower than the indicated reading would indicate improper adjustment, or worn or damaged parts. Remove and overhaul the unit as outlined in paragraph 102. No pressure at the gage would indicate a plugged high pressure line or filter, or an inoperative withdrawal or regulator valve. Service the filter and lines as outlined in paragraph 101, or the regulator as outlined in paragraph 102. If the regulator unit is cold and shows moisture or frost after standing, it is an indication that either the high or low pressure regulating valve is leaking or improperly adjusted.

If engine does not idle properly with the idle adjusting screw in any position, a leak can be suspected in one of the valves or gaskets. This can usually be traced to the low pressure valve, since any impurities in the fuel are deposited on the valve seat after the

fuel is vaporized. If the idle gas mixture is too lean when the idle adjusting screw is opened 3 or 4 turns, the trouble is usually due to a restricted idle line or leakage in the idle line connections. Poor idling as well as poor engine performance under load can be caused by a restricted or plugged balance line.

If there is any indication of liquid fuel entering the carburetor, the circulation of warm water through the regulator has been impaired.

Models G900-G950 With Century System

99. Trouble in this fuel system is normally one of the following conditions: No fuel, too much fuel or freezing.

If engine will not start, due to lack of fuel, close both withdrawal valves on tank and check fuel supply in tank. Remove drain plug from fuel filter. Slowly and momentarily open the liquid withdrawal valve. Fuel should emerge from drain plug opening as a white mist. CAUTION: The escaping fuel can cause severe freezing and damage to unprotected skin. Keep clear of escaping LP-Gas fuel. Repeat the test using the vapor withdrawal valve. If no fuel emerges, trouble is in withdrawal valves or lines. Renew parts as necessary. If fuel emerges with drain plug removed, reinstall drain plug and disconnect fuel inlet line from regulator. Slowly open vapor withdrawal valve and check for fuel at disconnected line. If no fuel is present, close the valve, then clean or renew fuel filter element. If fuel is present, remove and overhaul regulator as outlined in paragraph 104.

If too much fuel (poor idling and poor engine performance) is the trouble, close both withdrawal valves and operate engine until fuel is exhausted from carburetor and regulator. Thoroughly clean exterior of regulator assembly. Remove primer and front cover assembly, then carefully remove the secondary diaphragm. Remove retaining screws, then remove the secondary valve lever assembly. Attach a compressed air hose, with regulated pressure of 130-180 psi, to fuel inlet fitting on regulator. Place a 0-15 psi test gage over secondary valve orifice. See Fig. 98. NOTE: Use Century test gage No. M-508 or equivalent gage fitted with a conical rubber end to seat on secondary valve orifice. With inlet air pressure at 130-180 psi, test gage pressure should be 4-6 psi. If pressure reading is too low, primary valve orifice is clogged or primary valve spring is defective. If pressure reading is too

Fig. 98–On Century model H regulator, primary pressure should be 4-6 psi with inlet pressure of 130-180 psi. Pressure is checked at secondary valve orifice.

high, primary valve seat is defective or dirty, diaphragm is ruptured or valve lever is distorted. If pressure reading is within the 4-6 psi range, the secondary valve seat could be dirty or defective, valve level could be incorrectly set or valve spring could be defective. Renew faulty parts and reassemble regulator as outlined in paragraph 104.

If regulator freezing (with engine operating) is the trouble, check for restricted regulator water lines, low radiator coolant level, defective thermostats or defective water pump. NOTE: The regulator back cover gasket seals coolant passages from expansion areas in back cover. In case of freezing coolant, this gasket is forced into the expansion area which absorbs expansion of the frozen coolant. This prevents damage to vital parts of the regulator. If regulator "freezes up", the assembly should be removed, disassembled and a new back cover gasket installed. Repeated freezing can cause distortion of rear cover which could result in leakage of fuel and coolant. Refer to paragraph 104 for overhaul procedure for regulator.

All Other Models With Century System

100. To locate trouble in the fuel system, shut off the liquid and vapor withdrawal valves and run engine until gas is exhausted from carburetor and regulator. Connect a low reading pressure gage (0-15 psi) in ⅛-inch pipe plug opening as shown in Fig. 99.

With gage installed, open the vapor withdrawal valve and note gage reading which should hold steady within the range of 6-8 psi. Very slightly depress primer button for a few seconds, then release. Gage pressure should drop slightly and then return to original point when primer button is released. If pressure is not as indicated, overhaul regulator as outlined in paragraph 105.

If pressure continues to rise after withdrawal valve is opened; or primer button fully depressed, then released, a leaky primary valve is indicated. Overhaul the regulator as outlined in paragraph 105.

If the regulator becomes noticeably cool to the touch, or frosts over, after standing with engine stopped and withdrawal valve open, secondary valve is leaking or there are external leaks in regulator. Remove and overhaul regulator as outlined in paragraph 105.

If regulator freezing (with engine operating) is the trouble, check for restricted regulator water lines, low radiator coolant level, defective thermostats or defective water pump. NOTE: The regulator back cover gasket seals coolant passages from expansion areas in back cover. In case of freezing coolant, this gasket is forced into the expansion area which absorbs expansion of the frozen coolant. This prevents damage to vital parts of the regulator. If regulator "freezes up", the assembly should be removed, disassembled and a new back cover gasket installed. Repeated freezing can cause distortion of rear cover which could result in leakage of fuel and coolant. Refer to text.

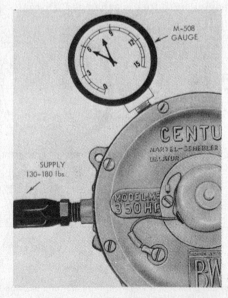

Fig. 99–Century model M5 regulator showing test gage installed. Primary pressure should be 6-8 psi with inlet pressure of 130-180 psi. Refer to text.

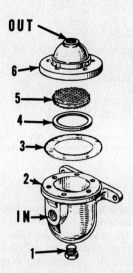

Fig. 100–Exploded view of typical fuel filter used on models equipped with Century LP-Gas system.

1. Drain plug
2. Body
3. Gasket
4. Retainer
5. Filter
6. Cover

paragraph 105 for overhaul procedure for regulator.

If engine will not start and appears to not be getting fuel, close both withdrawal valves and remove drain plug (1—Fig. 100) from fuel filter. Slowly and momentarily open the liquid withdrawal valve. Fuel should emerge from drain plug opening as a white mist and purge the filter trap of any foreign material.

CAUTION: The escaping fuel can cause severe freezing and damage to unprotected skin. Keep clear of escaping LP-Gas fuel.

If no fuel emerges, the trouble is in withdrawal valve or lines, or tank is empty. Repeat the test using the vapor withdrawal valve. Repair or renew the parts found to be malfunctioning.

If fuel emerges with drain plug removed, disassemble the filter and clean or renew filter element (5).

If filter is clean and lines open, tractor should fire when turned with starter while intermittently depressing primer button on regulator.

FUEL TANK, FUEL FILTER AND LINES

101. The pressure tank is fitted with a fuel filler, vapor return, pressure relief valve, 80% bleeder valve, and liquid and vapor withdrawal valves which can only be serviced as complete assemblies. Before renewal is attempted on any of these units, drive the tractor to an open area and allow engine to run until the fuel is exhausted; then, open bleeder valve and allow any remaining pressure to escape. Fuel gage can only be renewed if the fuel tank is completely empty. The safety relief valve is set to open at 312

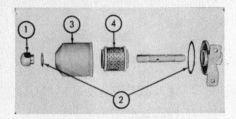

Fig. 101–Exploded view of typical fuel filter used on models equipped with Ensign LP-Gas system.

1. Stud nut   3. Bowl
2. Gaskets   4. Element

psi pressure to protect the tank against excessive pressures. U-L regulations in most states prohibit any welding or repair on LP-Gas containers and the tank must be renewed or returned to the tank manufacturer for repair in the event of damage. Fuel lines can safely be renewed at any time without emptying tank if liquid and vapor withdrawal valves are closed and the engine run until all fuel is exhausted from the lines.

The fuel filter contains a renewable type element (5—Fig. 100 or 4—Fig. 101) which may be removed and cleaned in a suitable solvent if in good condition. Thoroughly air-dry the element before reinstalling in the filter body.

VAPORIZER-REGULATOR AND CARBURETOR
All Models With Ensign System

102. VAPORIZER-REGULATOR OVERHAUL. To remove the regulator unit, first close the withdrawal valves and allow the engine to run until the fuel is exhausted. Drain the cooling system and disconnect the water, fuel and balance lines from the

unit, then unbolt and remove the unit from the tractor. Refer to Fig. 102, and completely disassemble the regulator. Thoroughly wash all parts and blow out all passages with clean, compressed air, carefully inspect each part and renew any that are worn or damaged. Always use new gaskets when reassembling the regulator.

When reassembling the unit, install the low pressure valve assembly and valve spring. Install the retaining screws loosely. Center the end of valve lever with arrow on post (T—Fig. 103) then tighten retaining screws to hold lever in position. The top of the low pressure lever should be flush with the top of post. If it is not, bend the lever as required, being careful not to damage the valve seat. Reinstall the inlet strainer, partition plate and low pressure diaphragm, making certain that the diaphragm push pin is properly located on the valve lever. Reinstall the back cover plate, install high pressure valve assembly, then measure the distance of the inlet diaphragm lever below the diaphragm surface of regulator body. This dimension, when measured with Ensign gage No. 8276, or a suitable depth gage should be ½-inch when the inlet valve is firmly shut. If the distance is more, or less, than ½-inch, bend the lever until the correct setting is obtained. Reinstall diaphragm and regulator cover, mount the assembled regulator on the tractor and reconnect water, fuel and balance lines.

103. CARBURETOR OVERHAUL. To remove the carburetor, close the withdrawal valves and run engine until fuel is exhausted. Discon-

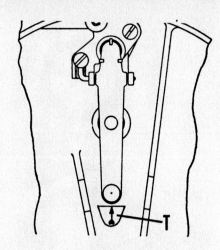

Fig. 103–Location of post or boss with stamped arrow (T) for the purpose of setting the low pressure lever on Ensign model R regulator.

nect the fuel and balance lines, air cleaner hose and throttle and choke levers. Then, unbolt and remove carburetor unit.

Completely disassemble the carburetor and clean the parts in a suitable solvent. Blow out the drilled passages with clean compressed air, examine the parts and renew any which are damaged or worn. Always use new gaskets when reassembling the carburetor.

All Models With Century System

104. MODEL H VAPORIZER—REGULATOR OVERHAUL. To remove the regulator, close withdrawal valves and operate engine until fuel is exhausted. Drain cooling system, then disconnect fuel and coolant lines from regulator. Unbolt and remove regulator assembly.

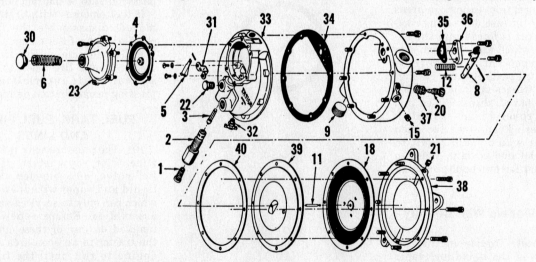

Fig. 102–Exploded view of Ensign model R vaporizer-regulator unit used on models GVI and MF95.

1. Fuel inlet strainer
2. Fuel inlet valve
3. Needle valve
4. Inlet pressure diaphragm
5. Inlet diaphragm lever
6. Inlet diaphragm spring
8. Outlet valve lever
9. Plug (¾)
11. Push pin
12. Outlet valve spring
15. Bleed screw
18. Outlet pressure diaphragm
20. Idle fuel adjustment
22. Plug (⅛)
23. Regulator cover
30. Spring retainer
31. Pivot support
32. Drain cock
35. Outlet valve gasket
36. Outlet valve seat
37. Idle screw spring
38. Support plate
39. Partition plate
40. Partition plate gasket

To disassemble the regulator, refer to Fig. 104 and remove primer assembly (1 thru 4A). Remove front cover (5), secondary diaphragm assembly (6 thru 9) and gasket (10). Remove two screws which retain lever pivot pin (12) and lift out valve lever (11), secondary valve (13) and spring (15). Remove inlet and primary valve assembly (23 thru 28), then remove cover (16), spring (17) and primary diaphragm assembly (18 thru 22). Remove retaining screws, then separate back cover (31) and gasket (30) from body (29). Further disassembly of the primary and secondary valves and diaphragms is obvious after examination of the units and reference to Fig. 104.

Wash metal parts in solvent and dry with compressed air. Renew all gaskets when reassembling. Renew diaphragms (7 and 19) if their condition is questionable and valves (13 and 25) if their sealing surface is damaged. Check back cover and back surface of regulator, using a straight edge, to make certain they are flat. If slightly warped condition exists, lap castings on a surface plate until they are flat. Severely warped parts must be renewed.

To reassemble, lay regulator body (29) with front face down and install new back gasket (30) and back cover (31). NOTE: Do not use sealing compound on any gasket or diaphragm. Tighten back cover screws securely.

When installing new primary diaphragm, assemble diaphragm plate (18) with flanged outer edge toward screw head, diaphragm and gasket assembly (19), damper spring (20), washer (21) and diaphragm link (22). Make certain that legs of damper spring (20) are parallel to any two flat sides of diaphragm link (22) and two square sides of diaphragm. Place diaphragm assembly in position on primary cavity so that legs of damper spring contact sides of slotted opening. To insure proper installation and prevent damage to diaphragm, four aligning pins (Century Part No. M-501) should be used to position diaphragm and cover during assembly. With diaphragm and gasket assembly (19) in position, insert the four aligning pins in screw holes. Place spring (17) on diaphragm and cover (16) over the aligning pins. Press down on cover, remove one aligning pin and install retaining screw before removing the next aligning pin. Tighten all four screws evenly and securely.

Assemble and install inlet and primary valve assembly (23 thru 28), using new gasket (24) and new primary valve (25) if necessary. Make certain that fork on primary lever (26) straddles the diaphragm link (22). Connect a compressed air hose, with regulated pressure of 130-180 psi, to fuel inlet fitting on regulator. Place a 0-15 psi test gage (Century No. M-508) over secondary orifice as shown in Fig. 98. Pressure gage should read 4-6 psi. If pressure creeps upward beyond 6 psi, primary valve is leaking and must be reworked or renewed.

To install a new secondary valve (13 —Fig. 104) on secondary valve lever (11), insert retaining pin (14) through valve and lever. Press face of valve lightly against a clean flat surface and while holding lever firmly, bend upper end of pin sharply over top of lever. Clip bent portion of pin to a length of about ⅛-inch after bending. The valve is self-aligning and should be secured to lever with a minimum of end play, but should not bind. Do not hammer or rivet the retaining pin. Place spring (15) in position, insert pivot pin (12) in lever (11), install the assembly and secure pivot pin with two screws. Open valve and allow it to snap closed several times to align seat with orifice. Using special gage (Century No. 2V-01) or straight edge and steel rule, measure lever height as shown in Fig. 105. Bend secondary lever as necessary to obtain the 5/16-inch distance between lever and machined surface of

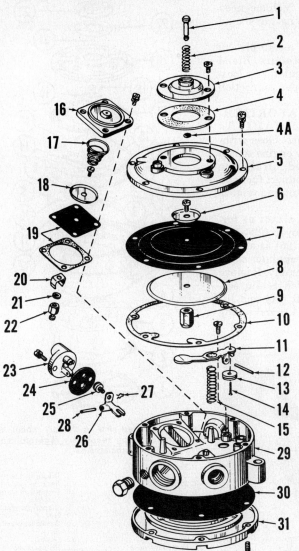

Fig. 104–Exploded view of Century model H regulator.

1. Primer plunger
2. Spring
3. Primer cover
4. Gasket
4A. "O" ring
5. Front cover
6. Diaphragm plate (small)
7. Secondary diaphragm
8. Diaphragm plate (large)
9. Diaphragm button
10. Gasket
11. Secondary valve lever
12. Pivot pin
13. Secondary valve
14. Pin
15. Spring
16. Cover
17. Spring
18. Diaphragm plate
19. Primary diaphragm & gasket assy.
20. Damper spring
21. Washer
22. Diaphragm link
23. Primary valve cover
24. Gasket
25. Primary valve
26. Primary valve lever
27. Retainer
28. Pivot pin
29. Body
30. Gasket
31. Back cover

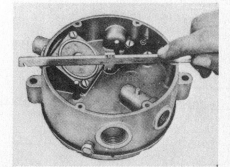

Fig. 105–Checking secondary valve lever height with Century No. 2V-01 gage. Alternate method is to use straight edge and steel rule. Refer to Fig. 106.

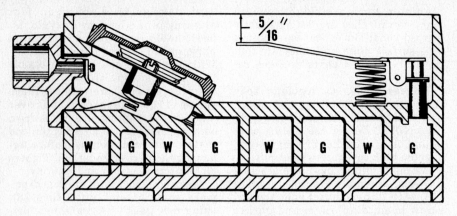

Fig. 106–Cross sectional drawing of regulator body, primary regulator and secondary regulator valve assembly. Distance between machined face of regulator body and secondary valve lever should be 5/16-inch as shown. Hot engine coolant in passages (W) vaporize LP-Gas in passages (G).

regulator body. See Fig. 106. Reconnect air supply to fuel inlet on regulator. Plug one water fitting opening and apply soap bubble to other water opening. Any continuous growth of bubble will indicate internal leakage of back cover gasket. Immerse entire unit in water or check all joints, including secondary valve, with soap solution and correct any leakage noted before proceeding further.

Assemble secondary diaphragm as follows: Place small diaphragm plate (6—Fig. 104) on screw with flanged outer edge of plate toward screw head, secondary diaphragm (7) with dished side away from screw head, large diaphragm plate (8) with flanged outer edge away from diaphragm and screw diaphragm button (9) on exposed screw threads. Tighten securely. Insert three alignment pins (M-501) in alternate holes in front face of regulator body. Place gasket (10) down over the pins so that the two ears on gasket are over the primary cover screws. Install secondary diaphragm over pins so that diaphragm button is contacting valve lever. Place cover (5) on the alignment pins and install three cover retaining screws. Remove pins and install the other three screws. Refer to Fig. 108 and while pulling upward on diaphragm screw with pliers, tighten cover retaining screws securely.

Use new gasket (4—Fig. 104) and

install primer plunger and cover assembly (1, 2, 3 & 4A). Apply air pressure at fuel inlet and check for leakage at vapor outlet port with soap bubble. Any growth in bubble would indicate secondary valve leakage. Depress primer and check for air flow from vapor outlet port. Volume need not be great, but escaping air should be audible.

Reinstall regulator assembly by reversing removal procedure. Bleed any trapped air from regulator by loosening water hose at upper connection on regulator.

105. MODEL M5 VAPORIZER-REGULATOR OVERHAUL. To remove the regulator, first close withdrawal valves and allow engine to run until fuel is exhausted. Drain the cooling system and disconnect fuel and coolant lines. Then, unbolt and remove the assembly.

Disassemble the regulator as follows: Remove primer cover (23—Fig. 109) and primer button (25) as a unit, then remove secondary regulator cover (20) and diaphragm assembly. Remove the two screws (S) which retain secondary valve lever shaft (10) and lift out the lever (9), valve (11) and spring

(6). Compound lever (8) can be removed in the same manner if desired. Remove inlet cover (31—Fig. 110); then remove primary diaphragm cover (40), spring (39) and diaphragm (36). Separate the secondary valve body (5 —Fig. 109), primary valve body (3) and back cover (1) only if leaks are suspected or complete overhaul is indicated.

Wash metal parts in solvent and dry with compressed air. Renew all gaskets when reassembling. Renew diaphragms (17—Fig. 109 or 36—Fig. 110) if their condition is questionable, and valves (11—Fig. 109 or 29—Fig. 110) if sealing surface is damaged. NOTE: Do not use sealing compound on any gasket or diaphragm.

If high pressure diaphragm must be disassembled, make sure that legs of damper spring (34) align with flats of link (32) and any flat side of dia-

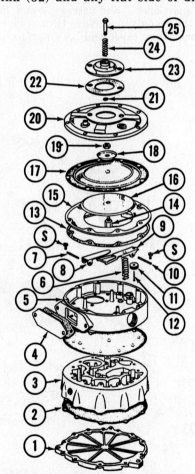

Fig. 109–Exploded view of Century model M5 regulator showing secondary regulator and associated parts.

1. Back cover	14. Diaphragm button
2. Gasket	15. Backing plate
3. Primary body	16. Diaphragm plate
4. Cover	17. Diaphragm
5. Secondary body	18. Diaphragm plate
6. Spring	19. Nut
7. Pivot pin	20. Secondary cover
8. Compound lever	21. Ring
9. Secondary lever	22. Gasket
10. Pivot pin	23. Primer cover
11. Secondary valve	24. Primer spring
12. Pin	25. Primer button
13. Gasket	

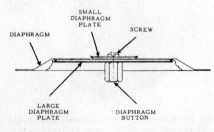

Fig. 107–View showing correct assembly of secondary diaphragm components.

Fig. 108–Pull upward on diaphragm screw with pliers while tightening cover retaining screws.

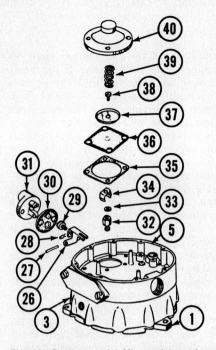

Fig. 110–Century model M5 regulator primary body, primary valve and associated parts.

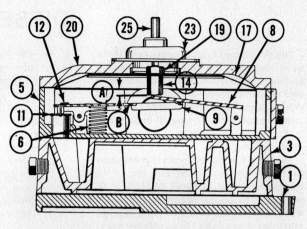

Fig. 111–Cross sectional view of Century model M5 regulator showing details of secondary valve lever adjustment. Distance (A) between diaphragm surface of body (5) and end of compound lever (8) should be 1/8 to 5/32-inch. Adjust by bending secondary valve lever (9) at point shown at (B). Refer to Fig. 109 for legend.

Fig. 112–Using Century gage No. 2V-01 to adjust secondary valve levers. Refer to text.

1. Back cover
3. Primary body
5. Secondary body
26. Primary lever
27. Pivot pin
28. Hairpin retainer
29. Primary valve
30. Gasket
31. Primary cover
32. Diaphragm link
33. Washer
34. Damper spring
35. Gasket
36. Primary diaphragm
37. Diaphragm plate
38. Screw
39. Spring
40. Diaphragm cover

phragm (36). The damper spring legs apply pressure to posts in primary cover and correct positioning is essential. Proper installation is also important. Four aligning pins (Century Part No. M-501) should be used to position diaphragm and cover during assembly. Proceed as follows: Install aligning pins in screw holes in primary valve body (3—Fig. 109). Install a new gasket (35—Fig. 110) over aligning pins. Then, install the assembled diaphragm, making sure the legs of damper spring are in position to contact the round posts in primary cavity. Insert a screw driver or similar flat tool through opening for inlet cover (31) and hold up on diaphragm link (32); then install diaphragm spring (39) and cover (40). Hold diaphragm (36) with the flat tool, press down on cover (40) and remove aligning pins one at a time, installing retaining screw before removing the next aligning pin. Release the pressure on diaphragm link (32) and cover (40) only after all screws are tightened.

To install a new low pressure valve (11—Fig. 109) on secondary valve lever (9), proceed as follows: Insert the retaining pin (12) through valve (11) and lever (9). Press face of valve lightly against a clean, flat surface and while firmly supporting lever, bend upper end of retaining pin

sharply over top edge of lever. Clip bent portion of pin to a length of approximately 1/8-inch after bending. The valve is self-aligned and should be secured to lever with a minimum of end play, but should not bind. Do not hammer or rivet the retaining pin. Install the assembled secondary lever (9), spring (6) and compound lever (8), if removed, by reversing the disassembly procedure.

After levers are installed, the free end of compound lever (8) should be 1/8 to 5/32-inch below gasket surface of secondary valve body (5) as shown at (A—Fig. 111). If adjustment is required, bend secondary lever (9) at (B). DO NOT bend compound lever (8) to obtain the measurement. The setting can be measured with Century gage 2V-01 as shown in Fig. 112, or with a straight edge and rule.

106. **CARBURETOR.** Refer to Fig. 113. The carburetor is simply constructed and overhaul procedures are self-evident. Use a thread sealant when installing reducer bushing in metering valve housing (9) and do not overtighten. Overtightening may distort the housing and cause valve to bind. If metering valve (10) does not move freely, remove lever (7) and plug (12) and push metering valve from housing. Clean the valve and housing bore with an oil base solvent. Coat valve with Lubriplate and reinsert in housing bore. If valve is not now free, chuck lever end of valve in a slow-speed drill and reseat the valve, using tallow or penetrating oil as a lubricant. DO NOT use a lapping compound, or allow valve and housing to become excessively warm. If condition is questionable, renew the parts.

Fig. 113–Exploded view of typical Century carburetor and associated parts.

1. Air horn
2. Bearing
3. Packing
4. Valve lever
5. Idle speed screw
6. Drag link
7. Valve lever
8. Thrust washer
9. Metering valve body
10. Metering valve
11. Spring
12. Valve plug
13. Gasket
14. Carburetor body
15. Throttle valve
16. Throttle shaft
17. Retainer
18. Spray bar
19. Power adjusting screw
20. Jam nut

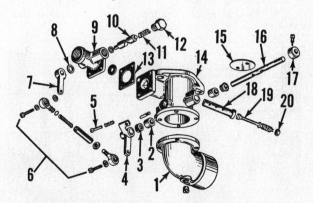

DIESEL SYSTEM

The diesel fuel system consists of three basic units: the fuel filter, injection pump and injection nozzles. When servicing any unit associated with the fuel system, the maintenance of absolute cleanliness is of utmost importance. Of equal importance is the avoidance of nicks or burrs on any of the working parts.

Probably the most important precaution that service personnel can impart to owners of diesel powered tractors, is to urge them to use an approved fuel that is absolutely clean and free from foreign material. Because of the extreme pressures involved in the operation of pump and injectors, the working parts must be hand fitted with utmost care. While the filtering system will easily remove the larger particles of foreign material, the greater danger exists in the presence of water or fine dust particles which might pass through an overloaded filter system. Proper care in fuel handling will pay big dividends in better service and performance.

TROUBLE SHOOTING
All Models

107. **QUICK CHECKS-UNITS ON TRACTOR.** If the diesel engine does not start or does not run properly, and the fuel system is suspected as the source of trouble, refer to the following list of troubles and their possible causes. Many of the troubles are self-explanatory; however, if the difficulty points to the fuel filters, injection pump and/or injection nozzles, refer to the appropriate following paragraphs.

1. Sudden Stopping of Engine
   a. Lack of fuel
   b. Clogged fuel filters and/or lines
   c. Faulty injection pump
2. Lack of Power
   a. Inferior fuel
   b. Clogged fuel filters and/or lines
   c. Improper injection pump timing
   d. Faulty injection pump

3. Engine Hard to Start
   a. Inferior fuel
   b. Clogged fuel filters and/or lines
   c. Improper injection pump timing
   d. Faulty injection pump
4. Irregular Engine Operation
   a. Inferior fuel
   b. Clogged fuel filters and/or lines
   c. Faulty nozzle
   d. Improper injection pump timing
   e. Faulty injection pump
5. Engine Knocks
   a. Inferior fuel
   b. Improper injection pump timing
   c. Faulty nozzle
6. Excessive Smoking
   a. Inferior fuel
   b. Improper injection pump timing
   c. Faulty nozzle
   d. Improperly adjusted smoke stop
7. Excessive Fuel Consumption
   a. Inferior fuel
   b. Improper injection pump timing
   c. Faulty nozzle

FUEL FILTERS AND BLEEDING
All Models

108. The fuel filtering system consists of various types of screen and renewable element type filters. Refer to Figs. 114, 115 and 116.

109. **CIRCUIT DESCRIPTION AND MAINTENANCE.** With the fuel shut off at valve ahead of primary filter, open petcock or drain plugs and drain off any accumulation of water and dirt. This should be done daily before tractor is operated.

On models equipped with Bosch injection system, fuel flows by force of gavity to the primary filter which contains a fine mesh screen that filters

water from the fuel. After each 60 hours of operation, the filter bowl should be removed and the screen thoroughly cleaned with diesel fuel. From the primary filter, the fuel flows through the renewable element type secondary filter. After flowing through the secondary filter, the fuel passes through the positive displacement, gear type transfer pump to the renewable element type final filter and on to the injection pump. The filtering system is equipped with a pressure relief valve located at the inlet side of the final fuel filter. If the final filtering element becomes clogged, the valve will release, the fuel will be by-passed back to the transfer pump and the engine will die from lack of fuel.

On models equipped with Roosa Master system, a much greater volume of fuel is pumped than is actually burned; the excess serving as a coolant and lubricant for the injection

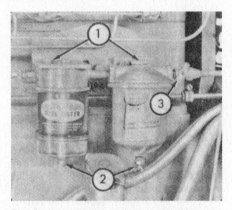

Fig. 115–Fuel filters and associated parts used on G705, G706 and MF97 diesel engines equipped with Roosa Master fuel system.

1. Fuel filter bleed screws
2. Drain plugs
3. Shut-off valve

Fig. 116–Fuel filters and associated parts used on models G707, G708, G900, G950, G1000, G1000 Vista, G1050 and G1350 diesel engines equipped with Roosa Master fuel system.

1. Fuel filter bleed screws
2. Drain plugs
3. Shut-off valve

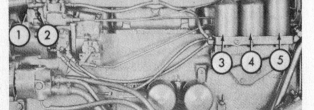

Fig. 114–Left side view of model GVI or MF95 diesel engine using American Bosch injection equipment.

1. Cap nut
2. Check valve
3. Final filter
4. Secondary filter
5. Primary filter

pump then returning to fuel tank. All models are equipped with two renewable element filters as shown in Figs. 115 and 116. The glass sediment bowl at bottom of filters provide visual inspection for the presence of water or dirt. These contaminants can be removed by opening the drain plugs.

109A. **BLEEDING.** It is necessary to bleed the fuel system whenever the fuel flow is interrupted or air has been allowed to enter the system.

To bleed the system on models equipped with Bosch system, refer to Fig. 114 and proceed as follows: Open the shut-off valve ahead of the primary filter and remove bleed plug at top of primary filter (5). Reinstall plug when fuel flows free of air. Remove bleed plug from top of secondary filter (4). Reinstall the plug when fuel flows free of air. Remove bleed plug from top of final filter (3), turn the engine over with starting motor until the fuel flows free of air and reinstall the bleed plug. Loosen the cap nut (1) on the check valve (2) at front of injection pump, rotate engine with starting motor until air is removed and tighten the cap nut. At this time, the engine will start, but if it does not run evenly, loosen the high pressure line fittings at each nozzle to bleed out any air.

On models equipped with Roosa Master system, refer to Figs. 115 and 116. Open bleed screw (1) on rear filter until all air is exhausted, then close the bleed screw. Repeat the procedure with the bleed screw on the front filter. The injection pump is self-bleeding. Pressure line connections at the injectors may be loosened while engine is turned with starter or at slow idle, if engine does not run evenly.

INJECTION NOZZLES

All diesel engines, except G1350 Diesel, are of the indirect injection type and are equipped with Bosch injection nozzles used in conjunction with energy cells.

G1350 Diesel engines are of the direct injection type which do not use energy cells and are equipped with Roosa Master "pencil" type injection nozzles.

WARNING: Fuel leaves the injection nozzles with sufficient force to penetrate the skin. When testing, keep your person clear of the nozzle spray.

All Diesel Models

110. **TESTING AND LOCATING FAULTY NOZZLE.** If the engine does not run properly and the quick checks, outlined in paragraph 107 point to a faulty nozzle, locate the faulty nozzle as follows:

If one engine cylinder is misfiring, it is reasonable to suspect a faulty

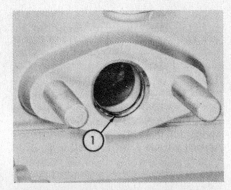

Fig. 117–Renew "O" ring (1) before installing injection nozzle on all indirect injection models.

nozzle. Generally, a faulty nozzle can be located by loosening the high pressure line fitting on each nozzle holder in turn, thereby allowing fuel to escape at the union rather than enter the cylinder. As in checking spark plugs in a spark ignition engine, the faulty nozzle is the one which, when its line is loosened, least affects the running of the engine.

If a faulty nozzle is found and considerable time has elapsed since the injectors have been serviced, it is recommended that all injectors be removed and new or reconditioned units be installed, or the nozzles be serviced as outlined in the following paragraphs.

All Diesel Models Except G1350

111. **REMOVE AND REINSTALL NOZZLES.** Before loosening any lines, wash the nozzle holder and connections with clean diesel fuel or solvent. After disconnecting the high pressure and leak-off lines, cover open ends of connections with caps to prevent the entrance of dirt or other foreign material. Remove the nozzle holder stud nuts and carefully withdraw the nozzle from cylinder head, being careful not to strike the tip end of the nozzle against any hard surface.

Remove "O" ring (1—Fig. 117) and thoroughly clean the nozzle recess in the cylinder head. It is important that the seating surface of recess be free of even the smallest particle of carbon

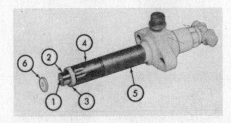

Fig. 118–Typical Bosch injection nozzle used on GVI, G705, G706, G707, G708, MF95, MF97 and early G1000 diesel engines.

1. Pintle	4. Holder nut
2. Valve body	5. Nozzle holder
3. Copper washer	assembly

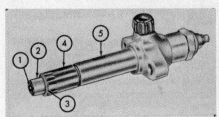

Fig. 119–Typical Bosch injection nozzle used on some G1000 and G1000 Vista and all G900 diesel engines. Refer to paragraph 111 for special information concerning transite washer (3) and asbestos gasket (6).

1. Pintle	4. Holder nut
2. Valve body	5. Nozzle holder
3. Transite washer	6. Asbestos gasket

which could cause the nozzle to be cocked and result in blow-by of hot gases. No hard or sharp tools should be used for cleaning. A piece of wood dowel or brass stock properly shaped is very effective. Do not reuse copper seal ring (3—Fig. 118), transite washer and asbestos gasket (3 and 6—Fig. 119) or heat shield washer (3—Fig. 120).

NOTE: A dimensional change was made on transite washer (3—Fig. 119) and asbestos gasket (6). Early transite washer (0.185-0.190 thick) must be used with early asbestos gasket (0.080-0.085 thick). Late transite washer (0.165-0.170 thick) must be used with late asbestos gasket (0.060-0.065 thick). Do not use an early part and late part on same injection nozzle.

Renew "O" ring seal (1—Fig. 117) and install nozzle assembly. Tighten nozzle holder stud nuts evenly and to a torque of 15 ft.-lbs. on G950 and G1050 and 12 ft.-lbs. on all other indirect injection models.

112. **NOZZLE TEST.** A complete job of testing and adjusting the injector requires the use of a special tester such as that shown in Fig. 121. Only clean approved testing oil should be used in tester tank.

The injector should be tested for spray pattern, seat leakage, back leakage and opening pressure as follows:

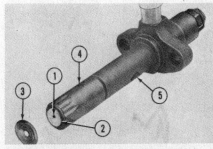

Fig. 120–Typical Bosch injection nozzle used on late G1000 and G1000 Vista and all G950 and G1050 diesel engines.

1. Pintle	4. Holder nut
2. Valve body	5. Nozzle holder
3. Heat shield washer	assembly

113. SPRAY PATTERN. Operate tester handle until oil flows from injector assembly. Close the valve to tester gage and operate tester handle a few quick strokes to purge air from injector and tester pump, and to make sure injector is not plugged or inoperative.

If a straight, solid core of oil flows from nozzle tip without undue pressure on tester handle, open valve to tester gage and remove cap-nut (1—Fig. 122). Slowly depress the tester handle and observe the pressure at which core emerges. If opening pressure is not within the recommended range of 1800-1850 psi, loosen locknut (3) and turn adjusting screw (5) in or out until opening pressure is within the recommended range. Tighten locknut.

When opening pressure has been set, again close valve to tester gage and operate tester handle at approximately 100 strokes per minute while examining spray core. Fuel should emerge from nozzle opening in one solid core, in a straight line with injector body, with no branches, splits or atomization.

NOTE: The tester pump cannot duplicate the injection velocity necessary to obtain the operating spray pattern of the delay type nozzles. Also absent will be the familiar popping sound associated with nozzle opening of multi-hole nozzles. Under operating velocities, the observed solid core will cross the combustion chamber and enter the energy cell. In addition, a fine conical mist surrounding the core will ignite in the combustion chamber area above the piston. The solid core

cannot vary more than 7½ degrees in any direction and still enter the energy cell. While the core is the only spray characteristic which can be observed on the tester, absence of core deviation is of utmost importance.

114. SEAT LEAKAGE. The nozzle valve should not leak at pressures less than 1700 psi. To check for seat leakage, open the valve to tester gage and actuate tester handle slowly until gage pressure approaches 1700 psi. Maintain this pressure for at least 10 seconds, then observe the flat surface of valve body and the pintle tip for drops or undue wetness. If drops or wetness appear, the injector must be disassembled and overhauled as outlined in paragraph 117.

115. BACK LEAKAGE. A back leak test will indicate the condition of the internal sealing surfaces of the nozzle assembly. Before checking the back leakage, first check for seat leakage as outlined in paragraph 114, then proceed as follows:

Turn the adjusting screw (5—Fig. 122) inward until nozzle opening pressure is set at 2350 psi. Release the tester handle and observe the length of time required for gage needle to drop from 2200 psi to 1500 psi. The time should be not less than 6 seconds. A faster drop would indicate wear or

scoring between piston surface of valve pintle (9) and body (10), or improper sealing of pressure face surfaces (A, B and J—Fig. 123).

NOTE: Leakage at tester connections or tester check valve will show up as fast leak back in this test. If all injectors tested fail to pass this test, the tester, rather than the injector, should be suspected.

116. OPENING PRESSURE. To assure peak engine performance, it is recommended that all of the injectors installed in any engine be adjusted as nearly as possible, to equal opening pressures. The recommended opening pressure range is 1800-1850 psi. When a new spring (6—Fig. 122) is removed from parts stock and installed in an injector assembly, the injection pressure will drop quickly as the spring becomes seated under the constant compression. This rate of pressure drop is approximately 10 per cent. It is recommended that injectors containing new springs be initially set at 2000 psi opening pressure, and injectors with used springs at 1850 psi. After the opening pressure has been adjusted, tighten locknut (3) and reinstall cap nut (1), then recheck opening pressure to make sure adjusting screw has not moved.

117. OVERHAUL. The maintenance of absolute cleanliness in the overhaul of injector assemblies is of utmost importance. Of equal importance is the avoidance of nicks or

Fig. 121—Adjusting opening pressure on Bosch injection nozzle (1), using a nozzle tester.

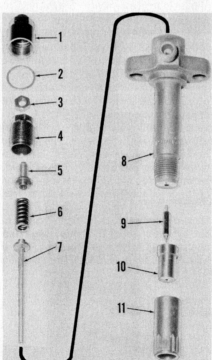

Fig. 122—Exploded view of typical Bosch injection nozzle assembly.

1. Cap nut	
2. Copper gasket	7. Spindle
3. Locknut	8. Nozzle body
4. Spring retainer nut	9. Valve pintle
5. Adjusting screw	10. Valve body
6. Pressure spring	11. Holder nut

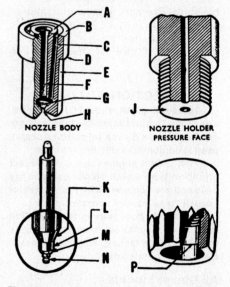

Fig. 123—Inspect disassembled Bosch injector at the points shown in above views.

A. Nozzle body pressure face	H. Pintle orifice
B. Nozzle body pressure face	J. Holder pressure face
C. Fuel feed hole	K. Valve cone
D. Shoulder	L. Stem
E. Nozzle trunk	M. Valve seat
F. Fuel gallery	N. Pintle
G. Valve seat	P. Nozzle retaining shoulder

scratches on any of the lapped surfaces. To avoid any damage to any of the highly machined parts, only the recommended cleaning kits and oil base carbon solvents should be used in the injector repair sections of the shop. The valve pintle (9) and body (10) are individually fit and hand lapped, and these two parts should always be kept together as mated parts.

Before disassembling a set of injectors, cap the pressure and leak-off line connections with a line nut with the hole soldered shut, or with a special metal cap, and immerse the units in a clean carbon solvent. While the injectors are soaking, clean the work area and remove any accumulation of discarded parts from previous service jobs. Remove the injectors one at a time from the solvent and thoroughly clean the outer surfaces with a brass

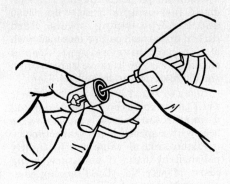

Fig. 124—Use special scraper to remove carbon from fuel gallery.

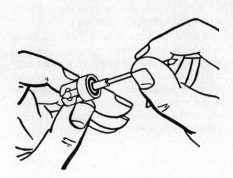

Fig. 125—Use brass seat tool to remove carbon from valve seat.

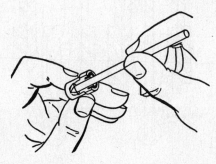

Fig. 126—Use pointed wooden stick and small amount of tallow to polish valve seat.

wire brush. Be extremely careful not to damage the pintle end of the nozzle valve extending out of nozzle body. Rinse the injector in clean diesel fuel and test the injector as outlined in paragraphs 113 through 116. Never disassemble an injector which can be adjusted and returned to service without disassembly.

If the injector unit must be disassembled, clamp the injector body in a soft jawed vise, tightening only enough to keep injector from slipping, or use a holding fixture. Remove cap nut (1—Fig. 122), loosen locknut (3) and back off the adjusting screw (5) until all tension is removed from the spring, then remove the nozzle holder nut (11). Withdraw the valve pintle (9) from valve body (10). If valve is stuck, use a special extractor or soak in solvent. NEVER loosen valve by tapping exposed pintle end of valve on a hard surface.

Examine the lapped pressure faces (A, B and J—Fig. 123) of nozzle body and holder for nicks or scratches, and the piston (larger) portion of valve pintle for scratches or scoring. Clean the fuel gallery (F) with the special hooked scraper as shown in Fig. 124, by applying side pressure while the body is rotated. Clean the valve seat with the brass seat tool as shown in Fig. 125. Polish the seat with the pointed wooden polishing stick and a small amount of tallow as shown in Fig. 126. Clean the pintle orifice from the inside, using the proper size probe. Polish the nozzle valve seat and pintle with a piece of felt and some tallow, loosening any particle of hardened carbon with a pointed piece of brass stock. Never use a hard or sharp object such as a knife blade as any scratches will cause distortion of the injection core.

As the parts are cleaned, immerse in clean diesel fuel in a compartmented pan. Insert the valve pintle into body underneath the fuel level and assemble valve body to nozzle holder

while wet. Do not attempt to dry the parts with towels or compressed air because of the danger of dust particles remaining on the pressure faces of nozzle holder and valve body. Use a centering sleeve or shim stock when reassembling. To use the sleeve, tighten the holder nut with the fingers while rotating centering sleeve in the opposite direction. When the nut is finger tight remove the sleeve and tighten the holder nut to a torque of approximately 55-60 ft.-lbs. Retest the injector as previously outlined. If injector fails to meet the test and no leaks because of dust were found upon disassembly, renew the valve body and pintle assembly and any other parts suspected of being faulty.

G1350 Diesel (Direct Injection)

118. **REMOVE AND REINSTALL NOZZLES.** Before loosening any lines, wash the nozzle holder and connections with clean diesel fuel or solvent. After disconnecting high pressure lines and leak-off hoses, plug or cap all openings to prevent entrance of dirt or other foreign material. Remove nozzle clamp cap screw, clamp and spacer, then withdraw nozzle assembly.

Before reinstalling the injection nozzle, clean nozzle bore in cylinder head and blow out with compressed air. Renew carbon dam seal (1—Fig. 127) and compression seal ring (2) on nozzle assembly. Do not lubricate seal rings.

Using a gentle rotating motion, insert injection nozzle into cylinder head. Install spacer, clamp and cap screw engaging the locating plate on nozzle. Connect high pressure line and tighten connection finger tight. Tighten clamp cap screw to a torque of 20 ft.-lbs. Connect leak-off hoses. Crank engine with starter until fuel emerges from the loosened high pressure line connection, then tighten the connection.

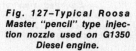

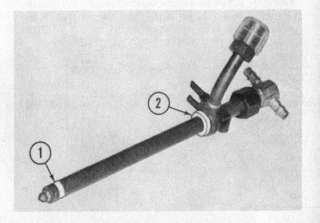

Fig. 127—Typical Roosa Master "pencil" type injection nozzle used on G1350 Diesel engine.

1. Teflon carbon dam seal ring
2. Teflon compression seal ring

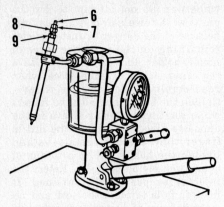

Fig. 128–Roosa Master injection nozzle attached to nozzle tester.

6. Valve lift adjusting   8. Pressure adjusting
   screw   screw
7. Locknut   9. Locknut

119. **NOZZLE TEST.** A complete job of testing and adjusting an injection nozzle requires the use of special test equipment. Only clean approved testing oil should be used in tester tank. Injection nozzle should be tested for opening pressure, seat leakage, back leakage and spray pattern. When tested, the nozzle should open with a sharp popping or buzzing sound and cut off quickly at end of injection with a minimum of seat leakage and a controlled amount of back leakage. Check injection nozzle as outlined in the following paragraphs.

120. OPENING PRESSURE. Before conducting test, operate tester lever until fuel flows from tester output line, then attach injection nozzle as shown in Fig. 128. Unscrew nut (2—Fig. 129) and remove leak-off tee (1). Close the valve to tester gage and pump the tester lever a few quick strokes to be sure nozzle valve is not stuck and that the spray hole is open.

Open valve to tester gage and operate tester lever slowly while observing gage reading. Opening pressure should be 2600 psi, if it is not, adjust opening pressure and valve lift as follows:

Loosen locknut (7—Fig. 129) and back out lift adjusting screw (6) at least two turns to assure against bottoming. Loosen locknut (9) and turn pressure adjusting screw (8) in to in-

crease or out to decrease pressure until specified opening pressure is obtained. Tighten locknut (9). Turn lift adjusting screw (6) in until it bottoms, then back out one turn and tighten locknut (7). Recheck opening pressure.

NOTE: When adjusting a new injection nozzle or an overhauled nozzle with a new pressure spring, set opening pressure at 2800 psi to allow for initial pressure loss as the spring takes a set.

121. SPRAY PATTERN. The injection nozzle tip has a single spray hole which is located 35 degrees from centerline of injection nozzle. The conical shaped spray should be finely atomized and distributed at the 35 degree angle from nozzle tip. If a solid type irregular spray pattern is observed, check for partially clogged or damaged spray hole or an improperly seating nozzle valve. If spray pattern is not satisfactory, disassemble and overhaul injection nozzle as outlined in paragraph 124.

122. VALVE SEAT LEAKAGE. Operate tester slowly to maintain a gage pressure of 2400 psi while examining nozzle tip for fuel accumulation. If nozzle is in good condition, there should be no noticeable accumulation for a period of 10 seconds. However, slight dampness is permissible on a used injection nozzle. If a drop forms or undue wetness appears on nozzle tip, disassemble and overhaul injection nozzle as in paragraph 124.

123. BACK LEAKAGE. Reposition injection nozzle on tester so that nozzle tip is slightly higher than adjusting screw end of nozzle. Operate tester slowly to maintain a gage pressure of 1500 psi. Observe fuel leakage at leak-off area (flat side of valve lift adjusting screw). After the first drop falls, leakage should be at the rate of 3 to 10 drops in 30 seconds. If back leakage is less than specified rate, disassemble and overhaul injection nozzle as in paragraph 124.

124. **OVERHAUL INJECTION NOZZLE.** First clean outside of injection nozzle thoroughly. Place nozzle in a holding fixture and clamp the fix-

ture in a vise. NEVER tighten vise jaws on nozzle body without the fixture. Refer to Fig. 129, unscrew nut (2) and remove leak-off tee (1). Loosen locknut (9) and back out pressure adjusting screw (8) with valve lift adjusting screw (6). Slip nozzle body from fixture, invert the body and remove pressure spring (10), spring seat (11) and valve (12) from body. If valve will not slide from body, use special retractor (Roosa Master No. 16481) to remove the valve.

Nozzle body and valve are a matched set and should never be intermixed. Keep parts for each injection nozzle separate and immerse in clean diesel fuel in compartmented pan as nozzle is disassembled. Remove nut (2) with its "O" ring seal, carbon dam seal ring (5) and compression seal ring (3) from nozzle body.

Clean all parts thoroughly in clean diesel fuel using a brass wire brush and lint-free wiping towels. Hard carbon or varnish can be loosened with a non-corrosive solvent. Use a cleaning wire to remove carbon from the 0.028 diameter spray hole.

Refer to Fig. 130 and use a sac hole drill to clean carbon from the 0.042 diameter sac hole. Clean the valve seat with a special brass seat scraper.

Piston area of valve can be lightly polished by hand if necessary, using Roosa Master No. 16489 lapping compound. Use the special valve retractor to turn valve. Move valve in and out of body slightly while rotating valve but do not apply down pressure while valve is in contact with seat.

Valve and seat are ground to a slight interference angle. Seating areas may be cleaned if necessary, using a small amount of No. 16489 lapping compound, very light pressure and no more than 3 to 5 turns of valve on seat. Thoroughly flush all compound from valve body after polishing.

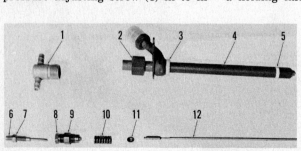

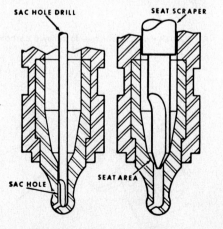

Fig. 129–Exploded view of Roosa Master injection nozzle assembly. An "O" ring seal is used in nut (2).

1. Leak-off tee
2. Nut
3. Teflon compression seal ring
4. Nozzle body
5. Teflon carbon dam seal ring
6. Valve lift adjusting screw
7. Locknut
8. Pressure adjusting screw
9. Locknut
10. Pressure spring
11. Spring seat
12. Valve

Fig. 130–Use special drill to clean sac hole and brass scraper to clean seat area.

Fig. 131–To time Bosch model APE pump to model GVI or MF95 engine, align 42 degree BTDC mark on flywheel (T) with pointer in center of timing window.

Fig. 133–Typical timing gear train of diesel engine equipped with Bosch injection pump.

T. Timing adjustment screws
1. Crankshaft gear
2. Adjustable gear
3. Camshaft gear
4. Pump drive gear

Before reassembling, loosen locknut (7—Fig. 129) and back out lift adjusting screw (6) two turns. Reassemble by reversing disassembly procedure using Fig. 129 as a guide. Adjust opening pressure and valve lift as outlined in paragraph 120 after valve is assembled.

INJECTION PUMP

Minneapolis-Moline diesel tractors are equipped with either an American-Bosch single plunger model PSB, American-Bosch multiple plunger model APE or Roosa-Master injection pump.

The following paragraphs will outline ONLY the injection pump service work which can be accomplished without the use of special pump testing equipment. If additional service work is required, the pump should be turned over to a properly equipped diesel service station for overhaul. Inexperienced service personnel should never attempt to overhaul a diesel injection pump.

Model G VI-MF95 (APE Pump)

125. TIMING TO ENGINE. On models G VI and MF95 engines, the

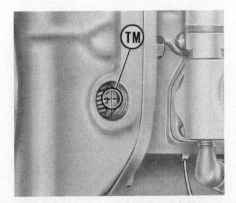

Fig. 132–Alignment of pump timing marks (TM) on diesel engines equipped with Bosch model APE injection pump.

flywheel has a timing mark each 2½ degrees, beginning at 27½ degrees BTDC and ending at 45 degrees BTDC.

The correct timing for engines equipped with APE injection pump is 42 degrees BTDC.

To time the pump to the engine, crank the engine until No. 1 piston is on the compression stroke, and continue cranking until the indicated timing mark is centered in the timing window on the left side of the flywheel housing as shown at (T—Fig. 131). Remove the plug from the inspection port in the timing gear housing as shown in Fig. 132. Timing mark on gear flange should exactly align with mark on pump body as shown. If it does not, but is still visible through the inspection port, proper timing can usually be accomplished after removing timing housing front cover as outlined in paragraph 69. Remove safety wire and loosen the four gear retaining cap screws (T—Fig. 133), rotate gear on cam gear until pump timing marks are aligned. Tighten retaining cap screws and secure with safety wire. If the timing marks cannot be brought into alignment by rotating the timing gear, the pump must be removed and timed as outlined in paragraph 126.

126. REMOVE AND REINSTALL Before attempting to remove the injection pump, thoroughly wash the pump and connections with clean diesel fuel. Disconnect the injection lines from the injection pump and the inlet and outlet lines from the transfer pump. Disconnect the remaining lines and control rods. Cap all exposed fuel line connections to prevent the entrance of dirt. Remove the pump mounting cap

screws and withdraw the pump.

Before installing the pump, crank the engine until No. 1 piston is on the compression stroke and continue cranking until the the proper flywheel timing mark is centered in the timing window on left side of flywheel housing as shown in Fig. 131. Rotate the injection pump shaft until timing marks on pump body and gear flange are aligned as shown in Fig. 134, install pump on engine and secure with the mounting cap screws. Remove the plug from the timing port on timing gear housing as shown in Fig. 132. If timing marks are not in perfect alignment, remove timing gear housing front cover as outlined in paragraph 69, loosen adjustable timing gear retaining cap screws and rotate timing gear until pump timing marks are aligned.

127. TRANSFER PUMP. Model APE injection pump is equipped with a self-regulating, plunger type transfer pump which is actuated by

Fig. 134–American Bosch model APE injection pump showing timing marks properly aligned for installation.

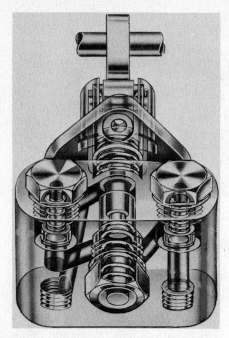

Fig. 135–Phantom view of plunger type transfer pump used on model APE injection pump.

the injection pump camshaft. Fig. 135 shows a phantom view of the transfer pump.

If the pump is not operating properly, the complete pump can be renewed as a unit; or the transfer pump can be disassembled and cleaned. Quite often a thorough cleaning job will restore the pump to its original efficiency.

Model G VI-MF95 (PSB Pump)

128. TIMING TO ENGINE. On models G VI and MF95 engines, the flywheel has a timing mark each 2½ degrees, beginning at 27½ degrees BTDC and ending at 45 degrees BTDC.

The correct injection timing for engines equipped with PSB injection pump is 30 degrees BTDC.

Fig. 136–To time Bosch model PSB injection pump to model GVI or MF95 engine, align 30 degree BTDC mark on flywheel (T) with pointer in center of timing window.

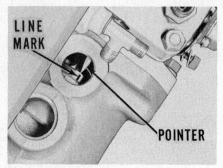

Fig. 137–Bosch model PSB pump drive coupling timing marks.

To time the pump to the engine, crank the engine until No. 1 piston is coming up on the compression stroke, and continue cranking until the indicated timing mark is centered in the timing window on the left side of the flywheel housing as shown at (T—Fig. 136). Remove plug on top of injector pump adapter housing as shown in Fig. 137. The timing mark on the pump coupling flange should be in exact alignment with the timing pointer as shown. If the timing mark is not in alignment, but is less than one drive coupling tooth off, remove timing gear case front cover as outlined in paragraph 69. Remove safety wire and loosen the adjustable gear retaining cap screws (T—Fig. 133). Rotate adjustable gear on cam gear until timing marks are aligned, tighten retaining cap screws and secure with safety wire. If the pump timing marks are more than one coupling tooth out of alignment, the pump must be removed and reinstalled as outlined in paragraph 129.

129. REMOVE AND REINSTALL. Before attempting to remove the injection pump, thoroughly wash the pump and connections with clean diesel fuel. Disconnect the injection lines from the pump, inlet and outlet lines from transfer pump and the remaining lines and control rods. Cap all exposed fuel line connections to prevent the entrance of dirt. Remove pump mounting cap screws and withdraw pump from adapter.

Before installing the pump, crank engine until No. 1 piston is coming up on compression stroke and continue cranking until the proper flywheel timing mark is centered in timing window on flywheel housing as shown in Fig. 136. Remove the pump timing window cover (20—Fig. 138) and rotate pump shaft until marked tooth on plunger drive gear is approximately in the center of timing window as shown in Fig. 139. With marked tooth visible in window as shown, and timing mark on coupling hub in relation to pointer

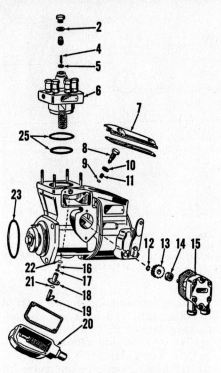

Fig. 138–Partially exploded view of Bosch model PSB injection pump.

2. Gasket	13. Gear
4. Delivery valve spring	14. Seal
5. Gasket	15. Transfer pump
6. Hydraulic head	16. Sleeve pin
7. Governor cover	17. Snap ring
8. Oil filter	18. & 19. Control unit
9. "O" ring	20. Timing window cover
10. Gasket	
11. Filter screen	21., 22., 23. & 25. "O" rings
12. Snap ring	

as shown in Fig. 140, install pump to adapter and rotate top of pump towards engine until retaining cap screws can be aligned. Start one cap screw and looking through adapter timing window as shown in Fig. 137, check for proper alignment of pump timing marks. Note: Marked tooth on plunger drive gear (Fig. 139) does not need to align with pointer as shown, but must be visible through window. If the timing marks are in alignment, or less than one coupling tooth off, install and tighten mounting cap screws. If

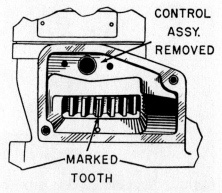

Fig. 139–Side view of Bosch model PSB injection pump with timing window removed. Note that line on one of the gear teeth is in register with pointer on housing.

Fig. 140-Coupling timing marks in proper position for installing model PSB injection pump. Note that line mark is to left of pointer.

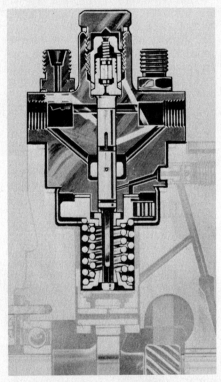

Fig. 141-Sectional view of Bosch model PSB injection pump hydraulic head. Complete head assembly can be renewed as a unit.

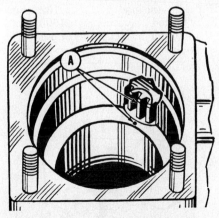

Fig. 142-When installing hydraulic head on model PSB injection pump, make certain that open tooth on quill shaft gear is in register with punch mark in housing as shown at (A).

marks are more than one coupling tooth out of alignment, remove and reinstall pump until proper register is obtained.

If the timing marks are not in perfect alignment, but are less than one tooth off, remove timing gear case front cover as outlined in paragraph 69; loosen cap screws (T—Fig. 133) and rotate the drive gear until pump timing marks are aligned.

130. **HYDRAULIC HEAD.** The hydraulic head assembly (Fig. 141) can be renewed without the use of special testing equipment. The head assembly contains all of the precision components which are essential to accurate pumping, distributing, metering and delivery of the fuel. To renew the hydraulic head assembly, first wash the complete injection pump and injection lines with clean diesel fuel. Remove the injection lines and disconnect the inlet and outlet lines from the hydraulic head. Remove the timing window cover (20—Fig. 138) and crank engine until the line mark on the apex of one of the teeth on the pump plunger drive gear is in register with the pointer stamped on the lower face of the timing window hole as shown in Fig. 139. Remove the two screws and carefully withdraw the control assembly, being careful not to lose plunger sleeve pin (16—Fig 138). Remove governor cover (7) and unscrew and remove lube oil filter (8). Remove the hydraulic head retaining stud nuts and carefully withdraw the hydraulic head assembly from the pump housing. Do not use force when attempting to withdraw the hydraulic head. If difficulty is encountered, check to make certain that the plunger drive gear is properly positioned as shown in Fig. 139.

When installing a new hydraulic head assembly, make certain that the line marked plunger drive gear tooth is in register with the pointer stamped on the lower face of the timing window

as shown in Fig. 139 and that open tooth on quill shaft gear is in register with punch mark in pump housing as shown at (A—Fig. 142). When installing the control sleeve assembly, the plunger sleeve pin (16—Fig. 138) must be lined up with the slot in the control block. The remainder of the reassembly procedure is evident.

131. **TRANSFER PUMP.** Model PSB injection pumps are equipped with a positive displacement, gear type transfer pump (15—Fig. 138) which is gear driven from the injection pump camshaft.

If the transfer pump is not operating properly, the complete pump can be renewed as a unit; or the transfer pump can be disassembled, cleaned and checked. Quite often a thorough cleaning job will restore the transfer pump to its original efficiency.

All Models (Roosa-Master Pump)
132. **TIMING TO ENGINE.** The correct timing for tractors equipped with a Roosa-Master Model DBG injection pump is 11 degrees (1⅛-inches) BTDC for models G VI, MF95, G705, G706, G707, G708 and MF97; 6 degrees BTDC for early models G1000 and G1000 Vista; 2 degrees BTDC for models G1000 after S/N 32701774 and G1000 Vista after S/N 34601435; 2 degrees BTDC for models G900, G950 and G1050; and 4 degrees ATDC for model G1350.

To time the pump to the engine, first locate and mark the correct timing position on flywheel. Crank engine until No. 1 piston is coming up on the compression stroke, and continue cranking until the indicated timing mark is centered in timing window on left side of flywheel housing. Shut off the fuel and remove timing window cover on side of injection pump body. Pump is correctly timed when scribe lines on governor cage and cam ring are aligned as

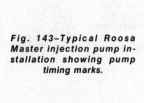

Fig. 143-Typical Roosa Master injection pump installation showing pump timing marks.

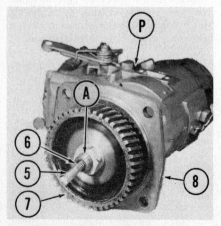

Fig. 144–Left side view of early model diesel engine equipped with Roosa Master injection pump. Later models are similar.

C. Cap screw
S. Stud nuts
T. Timing window cover
3. Adapter housing
8. Mounting plate

3/32-inch of alignment. If they are not, remove pump, turn drive gear 1 tooth in proper direction and reinstall. If marks are less than one gear tooth out of alignment, tighten the mounting plate retaining cap screws, loosen the two stud nuts (S—Fig. 144) and shift pump housing slightly until marks are aligned.

134. GOVERNOR. Governed speeds are adjusted on test stand and sealed. Speeds should not be adjusted, but should approximate those shown in the following table:

High idle—no load
G VI-MF95	1625 rpm
G705-G706-G707-G708 MF97	1710 rpm
G900-G950-G1000-G1000 Vista-G1050	1950 rpm
G1350	2335 rpm

Fully loaded
G VI-MF95	1500 rpm
G705-G706-G707-G708 MF97	1600 rpm
G900-G950-G1000-G1000 Vista-G1050	1800 rpm
G1350	2200 rpm

Low idle
G1350	700 rpm
All Other Models	600 rpm

shown at (1—Fig. 143). If marks are visible but not perfectly aligned, loosen the two stud nuts attaching pump to mounting plate and shift pump body slightly until marks are perfectly aligned.

Reinstall pump timing window and turn on fuel. Injection pump is self-bleeding. Injection lines or filter should not require bleeding if pump connections are not broken.

133. REMOVE AND REINSTALL. Before attempting to remove the injection pump, thoroughly wash the pump and connections with clean diesel fuel. Disconnect fuel lines and control rods, then cap all exposed fuel line connections to prevent entrance of dirt. Pressure lines must be disconnected at both the pump and injectors. Loosen fuel line clamps, if necessary, and shift the lines rearward as far as possible.

Remove the four cap screws securing mounting plate (8—Fig. 144) to adapter housing (3) and withdraw the pump, mounting plate and drive gear (7—Fig. 145) straight to rear out of

adapter housing. Be careful not to lose thrust button (5) and spring (6) as pump is removed.

The pump adapter shaft and seals are a part of injection pump. The mounting plate (8—Fig. 146), drive gear (7) and "O" rings (9) are not a part of the pump and must be transferred if a new pump is installed. DO NOT withdraw adapter shaft and drive gear (7) from pump unless required for service. If adapter shaft must be withdrawn, make sure assembly marks on shaft and rotor are aligned, and that lip of cup-type seal is not turned back during installation.

When installing the pump, make sure that No. 1 piston is on compression stroke and that the correct flywheel timing mark is aligned with timing pointer as outlined in paragraph 132. Remove pump timing window cover (T—Fig. 144) and turn drive shaft until timing marks on cam ring and governor cage are aligned as shown in Fig. 143. Turn drive gear backward (clockwise as viewed from front) until governor cage timing mark moves downward approximately 1/16-inch, then install the pump. With mounting plate cap screws installed and flywheel timing marks aligned, pump timing marks should be within

DIESEL GOVERNOR
Models With Bosch Pump

135. The injection pump is fitted with a mechanical flyweight type governor. For the purposes of this manual, the governor will be considered as an integral part of the injection pump.

While the governors used on model PSB and model APE injection pumps are not interchangeable, adjustment procedure remains the same, and the procedures outlined apply to either pump.

136. ADJUSTMENT. Recommended governed speeds for models G VI and MF95 are as follows:

High idle—no load	1625 rpm
Fully loaded	1500 rpm*
*1300 rpm for belt pulley or pto.	
Low idle	600 rpm

Fig. 145–Roosa Master injection pump removed from tractor. Shaft (A), spring (6) and thrust button (5) are serviced as part of pump (P), but gear (7) and mounting plate (8) are not.

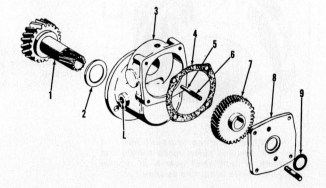

Fig. 146–Exploded view of typical injection pump drive gears, adapter housing and associated parts used on models equipped with Roosa Master injection pump.

L. Lube passage
1. Drive gear
2. Thrust washer
3. Adapter housing
4. Gasket
5. Thrust button
6. Spring
7. Pump gear
8. Mounting plate
9. "O" ring

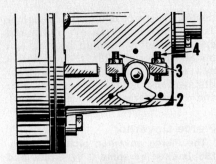

Fig. 147–High and low speed adjusting screws on Bosch injection pump governor.

2. Adjusting screw stop plate
3. Low speed adjusting screw
4. High speed adjusting screw

The governor should be adjusted, after engine has been run until temperature has reached the normal operating range. To adjust the governor, disconnect control rod from governor arm and remove adjusting screw cover as shown in Fig. 147. With the engine running, move the operating lever stop plate (2) to the high speed position, and with stop plate contacting high speed stop screw (4), turn screw in or out until the recommended high idle engine speed is obtained. Now move stop plate (2) to low speed position and turn speed adjusting screw (3) in or out to obtain the correct low idle speed. Reinstall screw cover and connect throttle linkage to governor arm.

Series G VI and MF95 tractors are equipped with an adjustable limit stop as shown in Fig. 148. With the stop (S) in the forward position as shown by dotted lines, the engine speed is limited to the 1300 rpm loaded speed recommended for belt or pto work. To adjust the limit stop, pull stop out and rotate same to the rearward position and loosen the two screws (A) in the slotted holes retaining the stop bracket to the pump body. With the operating lever against the high speed stop screw (4—Fig. 147), move the limit stop in the slotted holes until stop just contacts throttle arm.

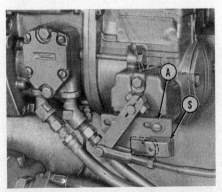

Fig. 148–Diesel governor used on GVI and MF95 tractors showing limit stop adjusting screws (A) and limit stop (S) which turns as shown by broken lines, to establish lower recommended pto governed speed.

Fig. 149–Exploded view of energy cell used on all indirect injection diesel engines.

1. Plug
2. Holder
3. Cell cap
4. Energy cell

Tighten the two screws to secure the limit stop in this position.

ENERGY CELLS
All Indirect Injection Diesel Models

137. **R&R AND CLEAN.** The necessity for cleaning the energy cells is usually indicated by excessive exhaust smoke or a drop in fuel economy. To remove the energy cells, unscrew the retainer plug and remove the cap holder. Grasp the energy cell cap (3—Fig. 149) with a pair of pliers and withdraw cap from cylinder head. Using a 15/16-inch NEF-2 puller

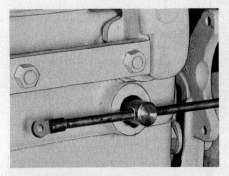

Fig. 150–Using special threaded puller to remove energy cell from indirect injection diesel engine. Refer to text.

screwed into energy cell (4), pull cell from head as shown in Fig. 150.

Clean all parts in a suitable carbon solvent and renew any which are cracked or damaged. Clean the small orifice in the cell chamber with a brass brush or a piece of hard wood. Check seating surface of cell body in cylinder and mating surfaces of energy cell and cell cap. If the surfaces are rough, they can be cleaned by lapping with a mixture of jeweler's rouge and diesel fuel.

When reinstalling the energy cell, make certain that it fits squarely into cylinder head. Tighten the retainer plug to a torque of 100 ft.-lbs.

NON-DIESEL GOVERNOR

ADJUSTMENT
All Models

138. Before attempting to adjust the governor warm up the engine and adjust the carburetor as outlined in paragraphs 92, 96 or 97. Also check and eliminate any binding in the throttle or governor linkage.

With the engine not running, move hand throttle lever to the high speed position. On models G VI, G705, G706, G707, G708, MF95 and MF97, disconnect governor to carburetor link and adjust link so that, with carburetor throttle arm against high speed stop, link will enter hole in governor arm without moving arm. On models G900, G950, G1000, G1000 Vista, G1050 and G1350, adjust the governor to carburetor link so that, with carburetor throttle arm against high speed stop, the adjusting pin on link will be a full hole below the hole in governor arm. It will be necessary to move the governor fork arm down the distance of a full hole in order to insert the adjusting pin in the hole in governor arm.

On all models, start engine and adjust high speed stop screw (1—Figs. 151, 152 and 153) to obtain the recommended high idle, no load engine speed.

Recommended governed engine speeds are as follows:

G VI—MF95
High idle, no load	1650 rpm
Fully loaded	1500 rpm
Low idle	475 rpm

G705-G706-G707-G708-MF97
High idle, no load	1720 rpm
Fully loaded	1600 rpm
Low idle	600 rpm

G900-G950
High idle, no load	2040 rpm
Fully loaded	1800 rpm
Low idle	600 rpm

G1000-G1000Vista-G1050
High idle, no load	2050 rpm
Fully loaded	1800 rpm
Low idle	600 rpm

G1350
High idle, no load	2400 rpm
Fully loaded	2200 rpm
Low idle	600 rpm

R&R AND OVERHAUL
Novi Governor

The Novi governor pictured in Fig. 154 is used on some G VI and MF95 tractors. Other G VI and MF95 LP-Gas tractors use the Pierce governor covered in paragraph 140 and pictured in Fig. 155.

Fig. 151–Novi governor assembly used on some GVI and MF95 tractors, showing high speed stop screw (1), surge screw (2) and carburetor linkage adjustment (3).

Fig. 152–Pierce governor used on some models, showing high speed stop screw (1), speed change lever (2), low idle position screw (3) and carburetor linkage adjusting pin (4).

Fig. 153–Hoof governor used on late model G1000 and all G900, G950, G1000 Vista, G1050 and G1350 tractors, showing high speed stop screw (1), carburetor linkage adjusting pin (2) and linkage rod (3).

139. The flyball governor is mounted on right side of engine and driven by the camshaft. To remove the governor, disconnect linkage, remove the four retaining cap screws and withdraw governor assembly.

To disassemble the removed governor, remove soft plug (24—Fig. 154), remove snap ring (23) then withdraw shaft and driver assembly from housing (18) and bearing (13). Examine shaft assembly (3) for loose driver, bent or damaged shaft, or grooved wear on the flat ball race. If defects or damage is found, renew the shaft and driver assembly. Examine the balls (4) for rust or flat spots, and the cupped race (5) for channels or wear.

When reassembling, install a sufficient quantity of shims (9) to allow balls to clear case when fully ex-

tended. Renew bearing (13) if rough or excessively loose. Insert shaft and driver assembly through bearing and install snap ring (23), then install a new soft plug (24). Examine governor linkage for binding or excessive wear and renew or free as needed.

Pierce Governor

The Pierce governor, pictured in Fig. 155, is used on some G VI, G1000 and MF95 tractors and all G705, G706, G707, G708 and MF97 tractors. Refer to paragraph 139 for the Novi governor used on early G VI and MF95 tractors and paragraph 141 for the Hoof governor used on late production G1000 and all G900, G950, G1000 Vista, G1050 and G1350 tractors.

140. The flyweight governor is mounted on the right side of the engine crankcase and is driven by a gear

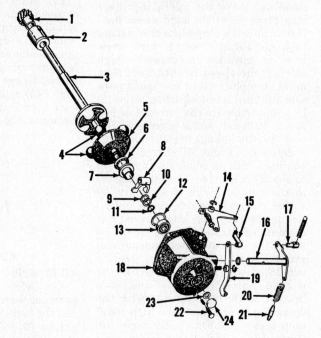

Fig. 154–Exploded view of Novi governor used on some GVI and MF95 tractors.

1. Drive gear
2. Bushing
3. Shaft and driver
4. Governor balls
5. Cupped race
6. Thrust bearing
7. Fork base
8. Fork
9. Shims
10. Thrust washer
11. Snap ring
12. Snap ring
13. Bearing
14. Bell crank
15. Link
16. Shaft and lever
17. Throttle lever pin
18. Housing
19. Lever
20. Spring
21. Spring stop
22. Surge screw
23. Snap ring
24. Soft plug

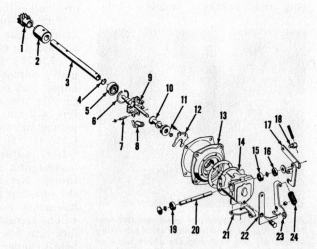

Fig. 155–Exploded view of Pierce governor used on some GVI, G1000 and MF95 tractors and all G705, G706, G707, G708 and MF97 tractors.

1. Drive gear
2. Bushing
3. Shaft
4. Snap ring
5. Bearing
6. Snap ring
7. Flyweight shaft
8. Flyweight
9. Driver
10. Sleeve
11. Thrust bearing
12. Fork
13. Driver base
14. Housing
15. Bearing
16. Oil seal
17. Throttle lever
18. Throttle lever pin
19. Bearing
20. Governor shaft
21. Bracket
22. Manual lever
23. Speed change lever
24. Spring

on the engine camshaft. To remove the governor, disconnect linkage, remove the four retaining cap screws and withdraw governor assembly.

To disassemble the governor, unbolt and remove the housing (14—Fig. 155) from driver base (13). Most of the governor can be examined for wear or damage at this time. Examine the weights (8), weight pins (7) and driver assembly for binding or excessive wear. To remove the drive shaft sleeve and thrust bearing assembly, remove snap ring at outer end of shaft and withdraw sleeve. Remove snap ring (4) to remove driver from housing and bearing. Examine governor fork (12) for wear or bending and remainder of governor linkage for binding, wear or damage and renew as indicated.

Hoof Governor

The Hoof governor, pictured in Fig. 156, is used on late production model G1000 and all G900, G950, G1000 Vista, G1050 and G1350 tractors.

141. The flyweight governor is mounted on the right side of the engine crankcase and is driven by a gear on the engine camshaft. To remove the governor, disconnect linkage, remove the four retaining cap screws and withdraw governor assembly.

To disassemble the removed gover-

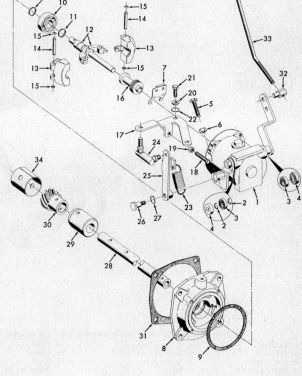

Fig. 156—Exploded view of Hoof governor used on late model G1000 and all G900, G950, G1000 Vista, G1050 and G1350 tractors.

1. Housing & rocker shaft assy.
2. Retainers
3. Bearings
4. Oil seals
5. Idle position screw
6. Locknut
7. Fork
8. Driver base
9. Gasket
10. Bearing
11. Retainers
12. Shaft assembly
13. Flyweights
14. Weight pins
15. Retainers
16. Thrust sleeve & bearing
17. Speed change lever
18. High speed stop screw
19. Locknut
20. Bushing
21. Cap screw
22. Wave washer
23. Governor spring
24. Ball joint link
25. Variable speed lever
26. Shoulder cap screw
27. Wave washer
28. Extension shaft
29. Bushing
30. Drive gear
31. Gasket
32. Adjusting pin
33. Linkage rod
34. Bushing (in crankcase)

nor, unbolt and remove housing (1—Fig. 156) from the driver base (8). Most of the governor can be examined for wear and damage at this time. Check weights (13), weight pins (14) and driver assembly for binding or excessive wear. The balance of disas-

sembly is obvious after an examination of the unit and reference to Fig. 156.

After assembly and installation are completed, check and adjust engine governed speeds as outlined in paragraph 138.

COOLING SYSTEM

RADIATOR
All Models

142. On models G900, G950, G1000, G1000 Vista, G1050 and G1350, the upper tank, core and lower tank are of a one-piece construction. On all other models, the upper tank and core unit is detachable from the cast lower tank which bolts to the front of the one-piece front frame.

THERMOSTAT
All Models

143. The thermostat housing is bolted to the front flange of the water outlet manifold on top of engine. Models G VI and MF95 are equipped with one thermostat while all other models use two thermostats. On all models, the thermostats should open at approximately 170 degrees F.

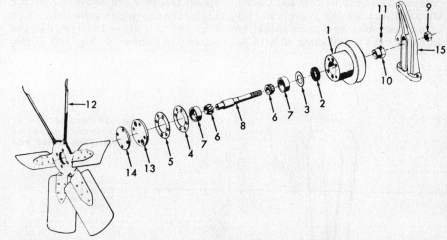

Fig. 157—Exploded view of fan assembly used on models GVI, G705, G706, G707, G708, G900, MF95 and MF97.

1. Fan hub
2. Felt seal
3. Retainer
4. Shim (0.005)
5. Shim (0.015)
6. Bearing cones
7. Bearing cups
8. Shaft
9. Nut
10. Collar
11. Set screw
12. Fan blade
13. Bearing retainer
14. Spacer
15. Fan bracket

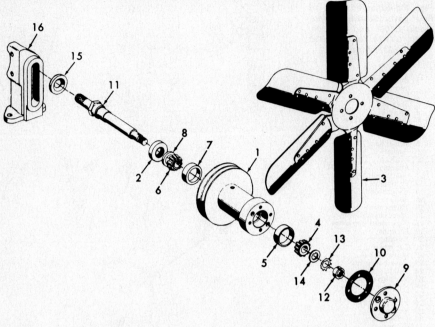

Fig. 158—Exploded view of fan assembly used on models G1000 and G1000 Vista.

1. Fan hub	5. Bearing cup	9. Cover	13. Lock washer
2. Oil seal	6. Bearing cone	10. Gasket	14. Washer
3. Fan blade	7. Bearing cup	11. Shaft	15. Spacer
4. Bearing cone	8. Spacer	12. Adjusting nut	16. Fan bracket

Fig. 160—Exploded view of typical gear case and water pump used on all model GVI, G705, G706, G707, G708, G900, MF95 and MF97 tractors and G1000 and G1000 Vista non-diesel models.

1. Gear case	11. Bushing
2. Gasket	12. Oil seal
3. Crankshaft seal	13. Collar
4. Locking plate	14. Seal ring
5. Cover	15. Shim
6. Gasket	16. Impeller
7. Gear case cover	17. Impeller seal
8. Gasket	18. Cover
9. Water pump	19. Gasket
10. Drive shaft	20. Stud

FAN ASSEMBLY
All Models

144. Procedure for removal and/or overhaul of the fan assembly is evident after an examination of the unit and reference to Figs. 157, 158 and 159.

On all models except G950, G1050 and G1350 the tapered roller fan shaft bearings should be adjusted to obtain the recommended 0.005-0.008 end play.

Fan belts should be adjusted until a deflection of ¾-1 inch is obtained when a force of 10 pounds is applied midway on belt span.

On models G950, G1050 and G1350, fan shaft and bearing is serviced only as an assembly. Fan belts should be adjusted until a deflection of ½ to ¾-

inch is obtained when a force of 10 pounds is applied midway between alternator and fan pulleys.

WATER PUMP
All Models Except G950, G1050 and G1350

145. **R&R AND OVERHAUL.** To remove the water pump, drain cooling system, remove grille and left front side panel, then disconnect the hoses from water pump. Unbolt water pump from timing gear case and remove pump from tractor.

Models G1000 and G1000 Vista diesel tractors are equipped with a high capacity water pump shown in Fig. 161. All other tractors use the water pump shown in Fig. 160. Disas-

sembly procedure is similar for both water pumps.

Remove cover from pump body and press shaft (10—Fig. 160 or 161) out of impeller (16) and pump body.

NOTE: Do not disassemble the shaft and collar as these parts are not serviced individually. Remove impeller seal (17) from impeller or pump body. Inspect all parts and renew any that are pitted, scored or excessively worn. If running clearance between pump shaft and bushing (11) is excessive, or if shaft is scored, renew shaft and/or bushing. New bushings are pre-sized and if carefully installed, need no final reaming.

After reassembling the high capacity water pump shown in Fig. 161, check the clearance between back of impeller and water pump body. To check the clearance, apply sufficient pressure to overcome impeller seal

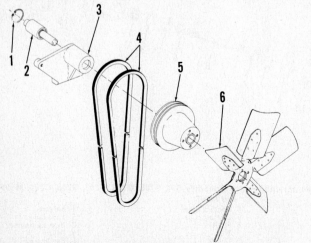

Fig. 159—Exploded view of fan assembly used on models G950, G1050 and G1350.

1. Snap ring
2. Bearing & shaft
3. Fan bracket
4. Fan belts
5. Pulley
6. Fan blade

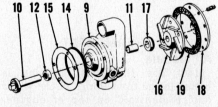

Fig. 161—Exploded view of water pump used on models G1000 and G1000 Vista diesel tractors.

9. Pump body	15. Shim
10. Drive shaft	16. Impeller
11. Bushing	17. Impeller seal
12. Oil seal	18. Cover
14. Seal ring	19. Gasket

spring until impeller contacts pump body. Using a feeler gage, measure the clearance between collar on pump shaft and pump body. Move impeller on shaft as required to obtain the specified 0.025-0.060 clearance.

After reassembling the water pump shown in Fig. 160, check the impeller to pump body clearance as follows: Place a straight edge across the machined front face of water pump body, then using a feeler gage, measure the clearance between straight edge and impeller. Move impeller on pump shaft as required to obtain the specified 0.025-0.035 clearance.

Before assembling cover (18—Fig. 160 or 161) to either type water pump, mount pump on engine with shim (15) and new seal ring (14). Check end play of impeller shaft with a straight edge and feeler gage or with a dial indicator. Desired end play is 0.005-0.010 which can be obtained by varying the number of shims between pump body and engine.

Models G950-G1050-G1350

146. **R&R AND OVERHAUL.** To remove the water pump, drain cooling system and disconnect water lines and

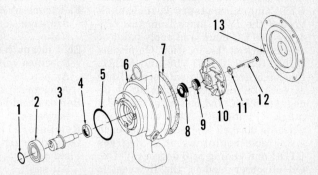

Fig. 162–Exploded view of water pump used on models G950, G1050 and G1350. Cap screw (12) threads into injection pump or distributor drive gear.

1. "O" ring
2. Ball bearing
3. Pump shaft
4. Oil seal
5. Seal ring
6. Pump body
7. Gasket
8. Pump seal
9. Ceramic impeller seal
10. Impeller
11. Washer
12. Cap screw
13. Cover

hoses from pump. Unbolt and remove pump cover (13—Fig. 162), then remove cap screw (12) and washer (11). Unbolt water pump from timing gear case and remove pump from tractor.

To disassemble the pump, remove the three cap screws and washers securing ball bearing (2) to pump body (6). Then, press shaft (3) with bearing from impeller (10) and pump body. Remove oil seal (4) and pump seal (8) from body and ceramic seal (9) from impeller. Clean and inspect all parts and renew any showing excessive wear or other damage.

Renew all seals and reassemble by reversing disassembly procedure. When reinstalling pump, use new seal ring (5) and make certain drive pin in shaft (3) is properly engaged in drive gear. Secure pump to timing gear case, then install cap screw (12) with washer (11). Use new gasket (7) and install cover (13).

Refer to the following torque values when reassembling and reinstalling water pump:
Bearing retaining cap screws . 9 ft.-lbs.
Impeller to drive gear cap
  screw .... 26 ft.-lbs.
Pump mounting stud nuts `. . 25 ft.-lbs.
Pump cover cap screws ..... 14 ft.-lbs.

IGNITION AND ELECTRICAL SYSTEM

DISTRIBUTOR
All Non-Diesel Models

147. Delco-Remy distributors are used on all non-diesel models. Specification data is as follows:
Delco-Remy 1112594
Breaker contact gap 0.022
Breaker arm spring tension
(measured at center of
contact) .... 17-21 oz.
Cam angle .... 31-37°
Advance data is in distributor degrees and distributor rpm.
Start advance ....0-3.5 @ 225
Intermediate advance ..... 4-7 @ 325
Intermediate advance .... 9-12 @ 525
Maximum advance ...13.5-16.5 @ 700
Delco-Remy 1112662
Breaker contact gap 0.021
Breaker arm spring tension
(measured at center of
contact) .... 17-21 oz.
Cam angle .... 31-34°
Advance data is in distributor degrees and distributor rpm.
Start advance ....0-3.5 @ 300
Maximum advance .... 7-9 @ 480
Delco-Remy 1112676
Breaker contact 0.021

Breaker arm spring tension
(measured at center of
contact) .... 17-21 oz.
Cam angle ....31-34°
Advance data is in distributor degrees and distributor rpm.
Start advance ....0-2.5 @ 300
Intermediate advance ..... 4-6 @ 450
Maximum advance ...... 11-13 @ 850
Delco-Remy 1112684
Breaker contact gap 0.021
Breaker arm spring tension
(measured at center of
contact) .... 17-21 oz.
Cam angle ....31-34°
Advance data is in distributor degrees and distributor rpm.
Start advance .... 0.4-2.4 @ 350
Intermediate advance ..... 4-6 @ 600
Maximum advance .... 7-9 @ 950

IGNITION TIMING
All Non-Diesel Models

148. To time the ignition, it is strongly recommended that a neon timing light be used. Timing procedure is as follows:

Adjust breaker contact gap to setting recommended in paragraph 147

and open inspection cover on flywheel housing. Crank engine until the "DC 1-6" mark on flywheel (DC 1 on some models) is visible in timing hole. Using white paint or chalk, mark a running timing mark on flywheel rim below the DC mark at the exact position recommended in the following table.

Timing Index	Degrees BTDC at RPM
G VI-MF95	
LP-Gas .... 24 @ 1500	
G705-G706-G707-G708-MF97	
LP-Gas .... 25 @ 1600	
G900	
Gasoline .... 13 @ 1200	
G900-G950	
LP-Gas .... 16 @ 1200	
G1000-G1000 Vista-G1050	
LP-Gas .... 15 @ 1500	
G1000	
Gasoline .... 12 @ 1200	
G1350	
LP-Gas .... 17 @ 1500	

NOTE: Flywheels on models G VI and MF95 are marked with scribe lines each 2½ degrees, beginning at 45 degrees BTDC and ending at 27½ degrees BTDC. To locate the 24 degree BTDC mark, measure ½-inch back toward the DC 1 mark from the 27½ degree BTDC mark and apply paint or chalk mark at this location. On models G705, G706, G707, 708 and MF97, flywheels are marked with scribe lines at each 2½ degrees, beginning at 35 degrees BTDC and ending at the DC 1 mark. On model G1350 diesel, flywheel is marked with scribe lines each 2 degrees, beginning at 28 degrees BTDC and ending at 6 degrees ATDC. On all other models, the flywheel is marked with scribe lines each 2 degrees, beginning at 30 degrees BTDC and ending at the DC 1-6 mark.

Start engine and adjust engine speed to the correct rpm as given in table above. Use a neon timing light focused on the flywheel rim and observe if the affixed running timing mark registers with pointer at inspection port. If it does not, loosen distributor clamp bolt and turn distributor slightly until registration is obtained.

NOTE: Final setting may need to be varied slightly from listed timing to take care of variations in fuel, compression ratio, altitude and mechanical condition of the engine.

ALTERNATOR & REGULATOR
All Models So Equipped

149. Early model G900, G1000 and G1000 Vista tractors are equipped with Delco-Remy alternators and regulators. Later model G900, G1000 and G1000 Vista and all models G950, G1050 and G1350 tractors are equipped with Motorola alternators and regulators. Refer to appropriate following paragraphs for test specification data:

CAUTION: Because certain components of the alternator can be damaged by procedures that will not affect a D. C. generator, the following precautions MUST be observed.

A. When installing batteries, negative posts must be grounded.

B. When connecting a booster battery, connect negative battery terminals together and positive terminals together.

C. Never short across any terminal of the alternator or regulator.

D. Do not attempt to polarize the alternator.

E. Disconnect battery cables before removing or installing any electrical unit.

F. Do not operate alternator on an open circuit and be sure all leads are properly connected before starting engine.

150. **DELCO-REMY.** Specification data for Delco-Remy alternators and regulator is as follows:

Alternators 1100720 & 1100771
Field current @ 80° F.,
Amperes 2.2-2.6
Volts 12.0
Cold output @ specified voltage,
Specified volts 14.0
Amperes @ rpm ...... 21.0 @ 2000
Amperes @ rpm ...... 30.0 @ 5000
Rated output hot,
Amperes 32.0

Regulator 1119513
Ground Polarity .... Negative
Field relay,
Air gap 0.015
Point opening 0.030
Closing voltage range 3.8-7.2
Voltage regulator,
Air gap
(lower points closed) 0.067 (1)
Upper point opening
(lower points closed) 0.014
Voltage setting,
65° F. 13.9-15.0 (1)
85° F. 13.8-14.8 (1)
105° F. 13.7-14.6 (1)
125° F. 13.5-14.4 (1)
145° F. 13.4-14.2 (1)
165° F. 13.2-14.0 (1)
185° F. 13.1-13.9 (1)

(1) When bench tested, set air gap at 0.067 as a starting point, then adjust air gap to obtain difference between voltage settings of upper and lower contacts. Operation on lower contacts must be 0.05-0.4 volt lower than on upper contacts. Voltage setting may be increased up to 0.3 volt to correct chronic battery under-charging or decreased up to 0.3 volt to correct battery over-charging. Temperature (ambient) is measured ¼-inch away from regulator cover and adjustment should be made only when regulator is at operating temperature.

151. **MOTOROLA.** Specification data for the Motorola alternator and solid state regulator is as follows:
Alternator 8AR2004S
Field current @ 80° F.
Amperes 2.0-2.5
Volts 10.0
Cold output @ specified voltage,
Specified volts 15.0
Amperes @ rpm ...... 32.0 @ 4000
Rated output hot,
Amperes 35.0

Regulator R3-3
Voltage regulation with 10 ampere load:

Ambient Temperature	Output Terminal Voltage
40° F.	14.2-15.0
60° F.	14.1-14.9
80° F.	13.9-14.7
100° F.	13.8-14.6
120° F.	13.6-14.4
140° F.	13.4-14.2
160° F.	13.3-14.1

GENERATOR & REGULATOR
All Models So Equipped

152. Delco-Remy D. C. generators and regulators are used on all model GVI, G705, G706, G707, G708, MF95 and MF97 tractors. Specification data is as follows:

Generator 1100314
Brush spring tension .... 28 oz.
Field draw,
Volts 12.0
Amperes 1.5-1.62
Output cold,
Maximum amperes 20.0
Volts 14.0
Rpm 2300

Generators 1100426 & 1100432
Brush spring tension .... 28 oz.
Field draw,
Volts 12.0
Amperes 1.5-1.62
Output cold,
Maximum amperes 25.0
Volts 14.0
Rpm 2710

Regulator 1118791
Ground Polarity .... Positive
Cut-out relay,
Air gap 0.020
Point gap 0.020
Closing voltage,
Range 11.8-14.0
Adjust to 12.8
Voltage regulator,
Air gap 0.075
Voltage,
Range 14.0-15.0
Adjust to 14.4

Regulator 1119270
Ground Polarity .... Negative
Cut-out relay,
Air gap 0.020
Point gap 0.020
Closing voltage,
Range 11.8-13.5
Adjust to 12.6
Voltage regulator,
Air gap 0.075
Voltage range,
(@ 85° F.) 14.2-15.2
Current regulator,
Air gap 0.075
Current range,
(Amp. @ 85° F.) 24.5-29.0

STARTING MOTORS
All Models

153. Model GVI, G705, G706, G707, G708, G1000, G1350, MF95 and MF97 tractors and some model G900, G950, G1000 Vista and G1050 tractors are equipped with Delco-Remy starting motors. Other model G900, G950, G1000 Vista and G1050 tractors are equipped with Leece-Neville starting

motors. Refer to appropriate following paragraphs for test specifications.

154. DELCO-REMY. Specification data for Delco-Remy starting motors is as follows:

Starting Motor 1107576
Brush spring tension (min.) .... 35 oz.
No load test,
    Volts 9.0
    Amperes (min.) 50*
    Amperes (max.) 80*
    Rpm (min.) 5500
    Rpm (max.) 9000
    *Includes solenoid.

Starting Motor 1113020
Brush spring tension (min.) .... 48 oz.
No load test,
    Volts 11.5
    Amperes (max.) 50
    Rpm (min.) 5000
    Rpm (max.) 7400

Starting Motor 1114036
Brush spring tension (min.) .... 80 oz.

No load test,
    Volts 11.5
    Amperes (min.) 75
    Amperes (max.) 115
    Rpm (min.) 5600
    Rpm (max.) 7600

Starting Motor 1114110
Brush spring tension (min.) .... 80 oz.
No load test,
    Volts 11.0
    Amperes (min.) 115*
    Amperes (max.) 170*
    Rpm (min.) 6300
    Rpm (max.) 9500
    *Includes solenoid.

155. LEECE-NEVILLE. Specification data for Leece-Neville starting motor is as follows:

Starting Motor M001093044
No load test,
    Volts 6.0
    Amperes 100-105
    Rpm 3100

Fig. 163—On models equipped with over center clutch, pull lock pin out as far as possible, then rotate yoke clockwise until lock pin engages in next notch.

ENGINE CLUTCH

ADJUSTMENT
Spring Loaded Type

156. Model G1000, G1000 Vista, G1050 and G1350 tractors are equipped with a spring loaded, 14 inch single plate, dry disc, button type clutch. Models G900 and G950 are equipped with a similar 12 inch spring loaded clutch. Adjustment to compensate for wear is accomplished by adjusting the clutch pedal linkage, NOT by adjusting the position of the clutch release levers.

On all models except G1000 Vista, clutch linkage is properly adjusted when the clutch pedal has a free travel of 1½ inches. Vary the length of the release rod by means of the adjusting clevis. If specified free travel cannot be obtained, renewal of the clutch disc is indicated.

Early model G1000 Vista tractors are equipped with a clutch servo valve in the clutch pedal linkage and a hydraulic clutch assist cylinder on right side of tractor. To adjust the clutch, disconnect the clevis on clutch assist cylinder from arm on clutch shaft (right side). Make certain clutch pedal returns to stop. Adjust length of lower linkage rod attached to arm on clutch shaft (left side) to obtain pedal free travel of 1⅜ inches. Then, adjust stop on assist cylinder to limit the stroke to 1 7/16 inches and adjust clevis on cylinder linkage to provide a clutch shaft arm travel of 1 5/16 inches. With en-

gine operating, actuate clutch pedal several times to check for complete disengagement and engagement of clutch.

Later model G1000 Vista tractors are equipped with standard clutch linkage on left side and mechanical clutch spring assist on right side. To adjust the clutch, disconnect clevis on spring assist unit from arm on clutch shaft (right side). Make sure clutch pedal returns to stop. Adjust length of lower linkage rod attached to arm on clutch shaft (left side) to obtain pedal free travel of 1½ inches. With the spring assist unit in collapsed position, adjust clevis to align pin holes in clevis and clutch shaft arm and insert pin. Actuate clutch pedal several times and check clutch action with engine operating.

NOTE: On all models equipped with clutch operated neutral start switch, adjust switch position so that switch plunger is depressed ⅛-inch when clutch pedal is fully depressed.

Over-Center Type

157. To adjust the twin disc, over-center clutch, used on models GVI, G705, G706, G707, G708, MF95 and MF97, remove the side cover on the clutch housing. Disengage the clutch, then turn the clutch plate until the adjusting lock pin, shown in Fig. 163, appears. Pull the spring loaded pin out; this disengages the clutch yoke

from the notch in the floating plate. Turn the yoke clockwise until the lock pin engages in the next notch of the floating plate. Engage the clutch with the hand lever. If approximately 65-75 pounds of force on models G707 and G708 or 75-85 pounds of force on all other models, is required to push the lever over center and the clutch snaps into place, the adjustment is complete.

If operation is not satisfactory, repeat the procedure by engaging the lock pin in the next notch of the floating plate until adjustment is correct. Normally, the first adjustment is sufficient.

NOTE: Less force will be required to fully engage clutch, as clutch plates wear. Readjust the clutch if engagement force drops below 50 pounds when measured at end of lever.

R&R AND OVERHAUL
Spring Loaded Type

158. To remove the clutch, it is first necessary to detach engine from transmission as outlined in paragraph 164.

The clutch release bearing and collar can be removed after disconnecting the return springs.

Remove the cap screws retaining the clutch cover assembly to flywheel and remove cover assembly and clutch disc. NOTE: Remove the cover retaining cap screws evenly to avoid damaging the cover.

To disassemble the clutch cover unit, compress the pressure springs by placing the assembly in an arbor press

Fig. 164–Install clutch disc as shown using an aligning tool (1) to center the disc on flywheel.

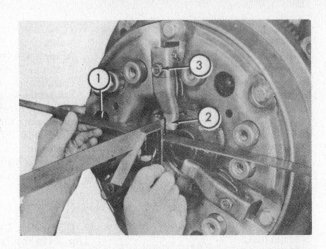

Fig. 165–On models G900 and G950, adjust release lever adjusting screws (3) until contact area (2) of levers is 13/32-inch above cover surface. Use a straight edge (1) across cover.

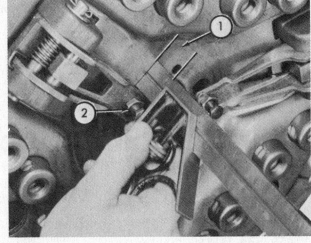

Fig. 166–Adjust lever contact screws (2) until top of each screw is 1.46 inches on models G1000, G1000 Vista and G1050 or 1.70 inches on model G1350 above cover surface, measured as shown at (1).

and applying pressure until the release lever pins can be removed. Remove the assembly from the press and disassemble the remaining parts.

Inspect all parts and renew any which are damaged or show wear. Friction surface of pressure plate must be smooth, flat and free from cracks and grooves. Cover plate must not be bent, distorted or excessively worn at drive lug openings. Inspect release lever contact screws, pivot pins and pin holes. Renew pressure springs if they are distorted, rusted, heat discolored or if they do not test 180-190 lbs. on models G1000, G1000 Vista, G1050 and G1350 or 200-210 lbs. on models G900 and G950 when compressed to a height of 1 13/16 inches.

When reassembling, install the release lever pins so that head of pin is toward direction of clutch rotation.

Position the clutch disc on the flywheel with an old clutch shaft or aligning tool as shown in Fig. 164. Attach the clutch cover assembly to the flywheel and tighten the cap screws to a torque of 22-24 ft.-lbs.

On models G900 and G950, refer to Fig. 165 and place a straight edge (1) across cover between pressure spring cups. Adjust release lever adjusting screws (3) until contact area (2) of levers is 13/32-inch above cover surface. All three levers should be adjusted to equal height (within 0.005).

On models G1000, G1000 Vista, G1050 and G1350, refer to Fig. 166 and adjust release lever contact screws (2) so that top of each screw is 1.46 inches on G1000, G1000 Vista and G1050 or 1.70 inches on G1350 above surface of cover, measured as shown at (1). Dimension (1) must be identical within 0.005 for all three lever screws.

Over Center Type

159. To remove the clutch, it is first necessary to detach engine from trans-

mission as outlined in paragraph 164.

Disconnect the clutch actuating linkage by removing the clevis pin from shifter fork shaft arm (7—Fig. 167). Pry the lock washer lip away from the clutch shaft nut (2) and remove the nut. Disconnect lubrication tube (4) from shifter ring (22).

Remove the clutch assembly from the shaft with a suitable puller. If the clutch shaft Woodruff key catches on the throwout collar, turn the shaft until the key is visible; then use a punch to drive rear of key into keyway. The clutch assembly can then be removed easily.

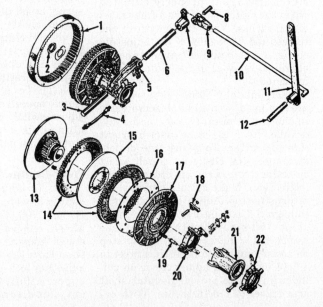

Fig. 167–Exploded view of over center clutch used on model G VI tractors. Other models are similar.

1. Clutch drive ring
2. Shaft nut
3. Shaft
4. Lube hose
5. Clutch fork
6. Shaft
7. Clutch arm
8. Pin
9. Clevis
10. Rod
11. Clutch lever
12. Lever shaft
13. Back plate
14. Driving plates
15. Center plate
16. Lining
17. Floating plate
18. Finger
19. Lock pin
20. Adjusting yoke
21. Sliding sleeve
22. Shifter ring

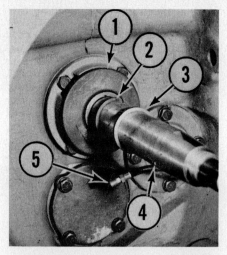

Fig. 168—Partially disassembled view of clutch shaft on models equipped with over center clutch, showing transmission brake and associated parts.

1. Thrust plate
2. Snap ring
3. Thrust washer
4. Clutch shaft
5. Lube line

At the rear of the clutch housing is a transmission brake, which stops the transmission gears when the clutch lever is held firmly in rear (disengaged) position.

If repairs are necessary, remove the clutch shifter fork, thrust washer (3—Fig. 168) and snap ring (2). Pull the brake thrust plate from the clutch shaft and renew the thrust plate lining. When reassembling, use care to prevent getting any oil or grease on the new lining.

The shifter ring (22—Fig. 167) is separated by removing the two connecting bolts. Check the bronze insert in each bearing half for excessive wear and renew if necessary.

To remove the clutch lining, pull the yoke lock pin (19) out of the floating plate notch and unscrew the yoke assembly (20) while holding the lock pin in the disengaged position. Remove the worn clutch plate linings (16) and install new linings. When installing the rivets, alternate rivets so that ad-

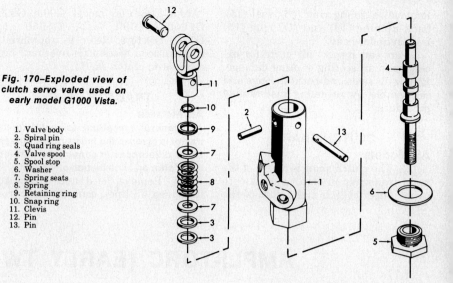

Fig. 170—Exploded view of clutch servo valve used on early model G1000 Vista.

1. Valve body
2. Spiral pin
3. Quad ring seals
4. Valve spool
5. Spool stop
6. Washer
7. Spring seats
8. Spring
9. Retaining ring
10. Snap ring
11. Clevis
12. Pin
13. Pin

jacent rivet heads face in opposite directions. Make certain rivet heads are seated at the bottom of the countersunk holes and are well below the surface of the linings.

When reassembling the clutch, use care to prevent oil or grease spillage on the clutch lining. If actuating fingers (18), pins or links are worn, they should be renewed.

Reassemble the shifter ring on the clutch and tighten the connecting bolts until a slight drag is felt when the unit is turned.

Reinstall the clutch assembly on the clutch shaft by driving it into position with a heavy mallet. Make certain the clutch keyway (A—Fig. 169) in throwout sleeve and clutch hub aligns with the clutch shaft key. Install the shaft nut (2—Fig. 167) and lock it with the lipped lockwasher.

CLUTCH SERVO VALVE AND CYLINDER

Model G1000 Vista

160. **REMOVE AND REINSTALL.** To remove the clutch assist cylinder, unbolt battery holder and swing rear of holder out from tractor. Disconnect hydraulic line from cylinder, then unpin and remove cylinder.

To remove the clutch servo valve, unlatch and remove left hood. Identify and disconnect hydraulic lines from servo valve. Unpin and remove valve assembly. Plug or cap all openings to prevent dirt from entering hydraulic system.

Reinstall units by reversing removal procedure and adjust linkage as outlined in paragraph 156.

161. **OVERHAUL SERVO VALVE.** To disassemble the clutch servo valve, refer to Fig. 170, remove pin (13) and withdraw clevis (11). Remove snap ring (10) from end of valve spool (4). Unscrew spool stop (5) and carefully withdraw spool assembly. Remove retaining ring (9), spring seats (7), spring (8) and quad ring seals (3).

Clean and inspect all parts for excessive wear or other damage. Renew quad ring seals and reassemble by reversing the disassembly procedure.

162. **OVERHAUL ASSIST CYLINDER.** To disassemble the clutch assist cylinder, refer to Fig. 171 and remove retaining ring (10), spacer (11) and retaining ring (9). Remove piston rod, piston and cylinder head as an assembly. Slide cylinder head (8) off the piston rod (5). Remove nut from piston rod, then remove piston (3).

Fig. 169—When reinstalling over center clutch on shaft, make sure key slots are aligned as shown at (A).

Fig. 171—Exploded view of hydraulic clutch assist cylinder used on early model G1000 Vista.

1. Cylinder tube
2. Breather
3. Piston
4. "O" ring
5. Piston rod
6. "O" ring
7. Back-up washers
8. Cylinder head
9. Retaining ring
10. Retaining ring
11. Spacer
12. "O" ring
13. "O" ring
14. Back-up washer
15. Rod seal
16. Retaining ring

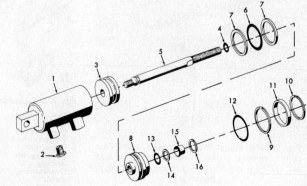

Remove retaining ring (16), seal (15), back-up ring (14) and "O" ring (13) from cylinder head.

Clean and inspect all parts for excessive wear, scoring or other damage. Renew all seals and back-up rings and reassemble by reversing disassembly procedure.

CLUTCH SHAFT
All Models

163. The clutch shaft is a part of the main transmission on all models with over-center clutch and a part of the "Ampli-Torc" on model G900, G950, G1000, G1000 Vista, G1050 and G1350 tractors. Refer to appropriate transmission section for overhaul procedures on clutch shaft.

TRACTOR SPLIT
All Models

A general procedure for splitting the tractor is given in the following paragraph. Minor differences in construction are obvious after an examination of the unit.

164. Remove hood and disconnect fuel lines, oil lines, control rods, wires, cables, steering shaft and hydraulic lines as required. On models where necessary, unbolt fuel tank front support from engine and block up under tank. Block up engine and transmission separately, using a traveling chain hoist or some other device for one section so that it can be moved independently from the other section. Remove bolts holding engine and main frame to the transmission housing; then move transmission and rear axle unit away from engine and engine frame unit.

AMPLI-TORC (EARLY TWO-SPEED)

"Ampli-Torc" is a planetary two-speed transmission mechanism installed forward of the regular transmission, and equipped with a mechanical operated multiple disc clutch, enabling the tractor to be operated in a direct or underdrive ratio. Shifting can be done independently of the main engine clutch while the tractor is in motion. When operating tractor in underdrive, ground speed is reduced and pulling torque is increased by a ratio of approximately 1.9:1.

CLUTCH
Early Model G1000

165. **ADJUSTMENT.** When the Ampli-Torc control lever is pushed forward to the direct (clutch engaged) position, the clutch should lock with a distinct snap, and a reasonably hard push (23 to 30 lbs.) should be required at the end of the control lever. If little effort (less than 14 lbs.) is required to engage the clutch, pull lever rearward to underdrive position, remove the small cover plate from the right side of the transmission housing as shown in Fig. 172 and turn the clutch assembly until the spring loaded lock pin is visible through the opening. Depress the lock pin and turn the notched adjusting ring clockwise until pin engages the next notch. Recheck the adjustment and repeat as necessary until the proper adjustment is obtained.

166. **REMOVE AND REINSTALL.** To remove the Ampli-Torc clutch, first detach (split) the engine from transmission housing as outlined in paragraph 164 and proceed as follows:

Remove fuel tank, instrument panel, steering support and associated parts from top of transmission housing and unbolt and remove planetary top cover. Remove engine clutch release bearing and drive out the pins retaining clutch release fork to the cross shafts. Withdraw fork and shafts. Move the Ampli-Torc control lever to the direct drive position and unbolt and remove the transmission input shaft cover from the front wall of the Ampli-Torc housing. Drive out the two roll pins retaining the shifter forks (21 —Fig. 173) to the control lever and

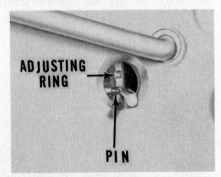

Fig. 172–To adjust the two-speed Ampli-Torc clutch, remove cover as shown, depress lock pin and turn adjusting ring through opening in housing.

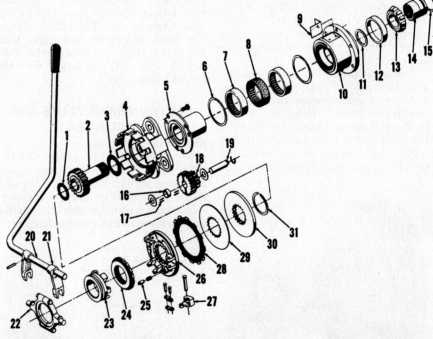

Fig. 173–Exploded view of early two-speed Ampli-Torc clutch, gear set and associated parts used on early model G1000 tractors.

1. Thrust washer	9. Oil deflector	17. Needle rollers	25. Lock pin
2. Sun gear	10. Cage	18. Planetary gear	26. Floating plate
3. Thrust washer	11. Thrust washer	19. Shaft	27. Lever
4. Planet carrier	12. Bearing cup	20. Lever	28. Driving plate (4 used)
5. Carrier hub	13. Bearing cone	21. Fork	29. Driven plate (3 used)
6. Retaining ring	14. Collar	22. Shifting ring	30. Back plate
7. Bearing	15. Snap ring	23. Sleeve	31. Snap ring
8. Over-running clutch	16. Spacer	24. Adjusting ring	

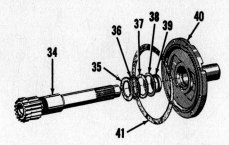

Fig. 174–Exploded view of input shaft cover, input shaft and associated parts used with early two-speed Ampli-Torc.

34. Input shaft	38. Shim
35. Thrust washer	39. Oil seal
36. Thrust bearing	40. Cover
37. Thrust washer	41. Gasket

withdraw the lever and forks. Clutch unit and input shaft (34—Fig. 174) can then be withdrawn from the transmission housing as a unit.

When installing the clutch, reverse the removal procedure, making sure the bronze thrust washer (1—Fig. 173) is in place before installing the clutch unit. Renew seal (39—Fig. 174) if its condition is questionable. When installing the cover, use a suitable seal sleeve or shim stock to avoid damaging the seal lip on the input shaft splines. Tighten the cover cap screws securely, mount a dial indicator at front of housing and check input shaft end play. Add or remove shims (38) as required to obtain the correct end play of 0.008-0.015. Adjust the Ampli-Torc clutch as outlined in paragraph 165.

167. OVERHAUL. With the input shaft and clutch assembly removed as outlined in paragraph 166, remove shim pack (38—Fig. 174), washer (37), bearing (36) and washer (35) from the input shaft. Refer to Fig. 173 and remove pins retaining the throwout levers to the floating clutch plate (26). Lift off the shifting ring and sliding sleeve. Depress the spring loaded lock pin (25) and completely unscrew the notched adjusting ring (24), then lift

the remaining clutch parts from the input shaft. Thoroughly clean the clutch parts and renew any which are worn or damaged. Check the friction faces of the back plate (30) and floating plate (26) for scoring or heat checks, and the driving discs and driven discs for wear or warping. When reassembling, make sure the three internally splined driven plates are installed between the four driving plates.

PLANET GEARS, SUN GEARS AND OVER-RUNNING CLUTCH
Early Model G1000

168. REMOVE AND REINSTALL. To remove the planetary gear cage and over-running clutch, first remove the Ampli-Torc clutch as outlined in paragraph 166 and proceed as follows:

Turn the planet carrier (4—Fig. 173) until the cut-out groove in carrier is aligned with one of the cap screws retaining bearing cage to transmission case wall and remove the cap screw. Continue the procedure until all six cap screws are removed. Withdraw the planet carrier, bearing cage and cam cage as a unit from the transmission case.

When reinstalling the unit, make sure the oil hole in the cam cage is up, and tighten the bearing cage retaining cap screws securely. Install the Ampli-Torc clutch as outlined in paragraph 166 and adjust the unit as outlined in paragraph 165.

169. OVERHAUL. With the planetary gear assembly and over-running clutch removed as outlined in paragraph 168, separate planet carrier and hub assembly from the over-running clutch cage (10—Fig. 173). Unbolt and remove hub (5) from planet carrier (4), then remove shafts (19) and lift out planetary gears (18) with washers,

Fig. 175–When reassembling early two-speed Ampli-Torc planetary unit, make certain the oil grooves in planet pinions converge on shaft center as shown at (G).

needle rollers (17) and spacers (16). To service the over-running clutch, remove retaining rings (6) and press bearings (7) and over-running clutch (8) from cage (10). Check all parts and renew as necessary. Planetary gears (18) are available only as a matched set.

When installing the needle rollers (17) in gears (18), use a heavy-bodied non-fibrous grease to hold rollers in place. Assemble sun gear (2), gears (18) and shafts (19) to carrier (4), making certain that oil grooves are aligned as shown at (G—Fig. 175). Bolt hub (5—Fig. 173) to carrier and tighten bolts to a torque of 23 ft.-lbs. Wire each pair of bolts together. Install bearings (7) and over-running clutch (8) in cage (10) and lubricate bearings and clutch with transmission oil. Insert the hub into the over-running clutch assembly by applying a light pressure and rotating hub in a clockwise direction. Install the assembly with lubrication hole in cage to the top and tighten the retaining cap screws to a torque of 23 ft.-lbs.

AMPLI-TORC (LATE TWO-SPEED)

The late two-speed Ampli-Torc operates similar to the early two-speed unit outlined in previous paragraphs. The late two-speed unit is equipped with a mechanical operated multiple disc clutch. Ampli-Torc shifting can be done independently of the main engine clutch while the tractor is in motion. When operating tractor in underdrive, ground speed is reduced and pulling torque is increased by a ratio of approximately 1.46:1. The late two-speed Ampli-Torc is used on some

G900, G950, G1000, G1000 Vista, G1050 and G1350 tractors.

CLUTCH
All Models With Late Two-Speed Ampli-Torc

170. ADJUSTMENT. When the Ampli-Torc control lever is pushed forward to the direct (clutch engaged) position, the clutch should lock with a distinct snap. A reasonably hard push

(23 to 30 lbs. on models G900, G950, G1000 and G1050, 27 to 33 lbs. on G1000 Vista or 25 to 30 lbs. on G1350) should be required at end of control lever to engage the clutch. If little effort (less than 14 lbs. on models G900, G950, G1000 and G1050, 16 lbs. on G1000 Vista or 20 lbs. on G1350) is required to engage the clutch, pull lever rearward to underdrive position. Remove the small cover plate from right side of transmission housing and

turn engine until the spring loaded
lock pin is visible through the
opening. Depress the lock pin and turn
the notched adjusting ring clockwise
until pin engages the next notch. Recheck the adjustment and repeat as
necessary until the proper adjustment
is obtained.

**171. REMOVE AND REIN-
STALL.** To remove the Ampli-Torc
clutch, first drain Ampli-Torc and
transmission housing, then detach
(split) engine from transmission
housing as outlined in paragraph 164
and proceed as follows: Remove engine
clutch release bearing and drive out
pins retaining clutch release fork and
Ampli-Torc brake cam to the cross
shafts. Withdraw fork and shafts.
Move Ampli-Torc control lever to the
direct drive position. Remove Ampli-
Torc brake adjusting nut (11—Fig.
176), retainer (10) and pressure spring
(9), then unbolt and remove cover (5),
shims (3) and return spring (12).
Loosen but do not remove the lower
left cap screw (as viewed from front)
that attaches brake support (15) to
housing. Remove the three remaining
cap screws and allow brake assembly
to pivot down and to the right. Drive
out the two spiral pins retaining
shifter forks (25—Fig. 177) to control
cross shaft (24) and withdraw cross
shaft and forks. Clutch unit and input
shaft (1—Fig. 176) can now be withdrawn as a unit. Ampli-Torc brake can
now be removed if necessary.

When installing the clutch assembly, reverse the removal procedure,
making sure the bronze thrust washer
(2—Fig. 177) is in place before installing the clutch unit. Install cross
shaft (24) and forks (25). Renew oil
seals (4 and 7—Fig. 176). Install brake
support cap screws with new seals and
tighten cap screws to a torque of 21-24
ft.-lbs. Slide return spring (12) on
brake link (13). When installing cover
(5), use a seal sleeve, shim stock or cellophane tape to prevent damaging oil
seal lips on the input shaft splines and
brake link threads. Tighten cover cap
screws to a torque of 21-24 ft.-lbs.
Mount a dial indicator at front of
housing and check input shaft end
play. Add or remove shims (3) as required to obtain the correct end play of
0.004-0.010. Shims are available in
thicknesses of 0.003, 0.005 and 0.010.
Install engine clutch release cross
shafts, fork, brake cam and release
bearing. Install pressure spring (9)
and retainer (10) on brake link (13)
and start but do not tighten nut (11).
Check the rolling torque on input
shaft with the brake adjusting nut
loose, then tighten adjusting nut until

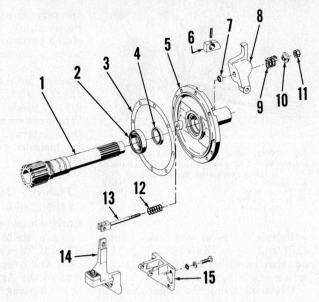

*Fig. 176–Exploded view of
input shaft cover, input
shaft, Ampli-Torc brake and
associated parts used with
late two-speed Ampli-Torc.*

1. Input shaft
2. Bearing
3. Shim (0.003, 0.005 & 0.010)
4. Oil seal
5. Input shaft cover
6. Cam
7. Oil seal
8. Actuating lever
9. Pressure spring
10. Spring retainer
11. Adjusting nut
12. Return spring
13. Brake link
14. Brake shoe
15. Brake support

rolling torque on the shaft is increased
1 to 2 ft.-lbs. Adjust Ampli-Torc clutch
as outlined in paragraph 170.

172. OVERHAUL. With the input
shaft and clutch assembly removed as
outlined in paragraph 171, remove
bearing (2—Fig. 176) from input shaft.
Refer to Fig. 177 and remove pins retaining the throwout levers (31) to
floating plate (32). Lift off the shifting
ring (26) and sleeve (27). Depress lock
pin (29), then unscrew and remove

notched adjusting ring (28). Unbolt
plate (32) from ring gear (36) and separate the balance of the clutch parts.
Clean and inspect all parts and renew
any showing excessive wear or other
damage. Check friction surfaces of
back plate (35) and floating plate (32)
for scoring or heat checks, and the
driving discs and driven discs for wear
or warping. When reassembling, make
certain the seven internally splined
driven plates are installed alternately
with the eight driving plates.

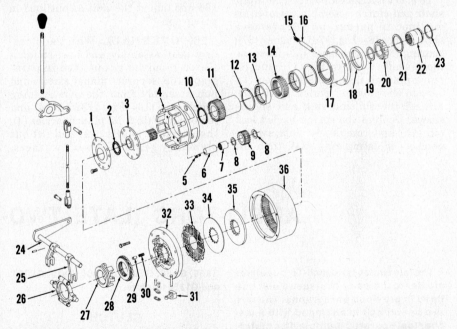

Fig. 177–Exploded view of late two-speed Ampli-Torc clutch, gear set and associated parts.

1. Oil deflector	10. Thrust washer	19. Thrust washer	29. Lock pin
2. Thrust washer	11. Sun gear	20. Bearing cone	30. Spring
3. Output shaft	12. Retaining ring	21. Spacer	31. Lever
4. Carrier	13. Needle bearing	22. Collar	32. Floating plate
5. Special cap screw	14. Over-running	23. Snap ring	33. Driving plate (8
6. Planetary shaft	clutch	24. Cross shaft	used)
7. Needle bearing .	15. Spring	25. Fork	34. Driven plate (7
8. Washers	16. Lube tube	26. Shifting ring	used)
9. Planetary gear	17. Cam cage	27. Sleeve	35. Back plate
(matched set of 3)	18. Bearing cup	28. Adjusting ring	36. Ring gear

PLANET GEARS, SUN GEAR AND OVER-RUNNING CLUTCH
All Models With Late Two-Speed Ampli-Torc

173. REMOVE AND REINSTALL. To remove the planet gears, sun gear and over-running clutch, first remove the Ampli-Torc clutch as outlined in paragraph 171. Carefully withdraw the carrier assembly. Sun gear (11—Fig. 177) may be removed with the carrier or it may remain in the cam cage (17). On models so equipped, remove spring (15) and lube tube (16). Unbolt cam cage (17) from transmission housing and remove the cam cage assembly. When reinstalling, make certain that thrust washers are in correct position. Tighten cam cage retaining cap screws to a torque of 21-24 ft.-lbs. Install Ampli-Torc clutch as outlined in paragraph 171 and adjust the unit as in paragraph 170.

174. OVERHAUL. With the planetary gear assembly and over-running clutch removed as outlined in paragraph 173, remove the lock wire and six cap screws and three special screws (5—Fig. 177). Lift off oil deflector (1) and withdraw output shaft (3) from carrier (4). Planetary shafts (6), bearings (7), washers (8) and gears (9) can now be removed from carrier. Planet gears (9) are serviced only as a matched set of three. Clean and inspect all parts and renew as necessary. When reassembling the carrier assembly, tighten cap screws securely and install lock wires. Bearings (13) and over-running clutch (14) can be pressed from cam cage (17) after retaining rings (12) are removed. Inspect bearings, over-running clutch, sun gear (11) and cam cage for excessive wear or other damage and renew as necessary. Use Fig. 177 as a guide and reassemble by reversing the disassembly procedure.

AMPLI-TORC (THREE-SPEED)

Series G900, G950, G1000, G1000 Vista, G1050 and G1350 may be optionally equipped with a three-speed Ampli-Torc. This unit is equipped with two hydraulically operated clutches and one over-running clutch. In high range, the rear clutch is engaged and the unit operates in direct drive. In intermediate range, the front clutch is engaged and power is transmitted through a reduction gear set. In low range, both clutch packs are disengaged and the drive goes through the over-running clutch, countershaft and a lower reduction gear set. Hydraulic power is supplied by the transmission lube pump located at rear of tractor on pto plate.

PRESSURE CHECKS AND ADJUSTMENTS
All Models With Three-Speed Ampli-Torc

175. To check pump pressure, remove transmission oil pressure sending unit from tee in the line between filter and relief valve. Install a 500 psi test gage. Start engine and operate at rated rpm. With transmission oil at operating temperature, pump pressure should be 280-300 psi. If the pressure is low, check the suction screen in differential housing and clean if necessary. Recheck pump pressure. If the pressure is still low, disconnect relief line (6—Fig. 178), remove connector (5) from valve body and add washers as necessary behind relief valve spring (4) until correct pressure is obtained.

To check high range (direct drive) clutch pressure, refer to Fig. 179 and remove plugs from ports (1) and (2) in transmission housing bottom cover. Install a 500 psi test gage in port (1) and a 50 psi test gage in port (2). With main transmission in neutral position and Ampli-Torc in high range, start engine and operate at rated rpm. At this time, the high pressure gage (port 1) should read 210-250 psi and the low pressure gage (port 2) should read 0-8 psi. Record the readings, stop engine and reverse the test gages. Shift Ampli-Torc to intermediate range. Start engine and operate at rated rpm. High pressure gage (port 2) should read 210-250 psi and low pressure gage (port 1) should read 0-8 psi. In either range, if the engaged clutch pressure reading was below 210 psi, clutch slippage could occur under heavy load. If disengaged clutch pressure reading is above 8 psi, the supposedly disengaged clutch could be partially engaged, resulting in rapid clutch disc wear and possible damage to gear teeth.

Incorrect pressure readings would indicate oil leakage past seal rings on output gear, past "O" rings on manifold or past the spool in control valve.

If pressure in both clutches is correct, tractor should operate properly in high and intermediate ranges.

If high and intermediate ranges are satisfactory and low range does not operate properly, check the over-running clutch as outlined in paragraph 176.

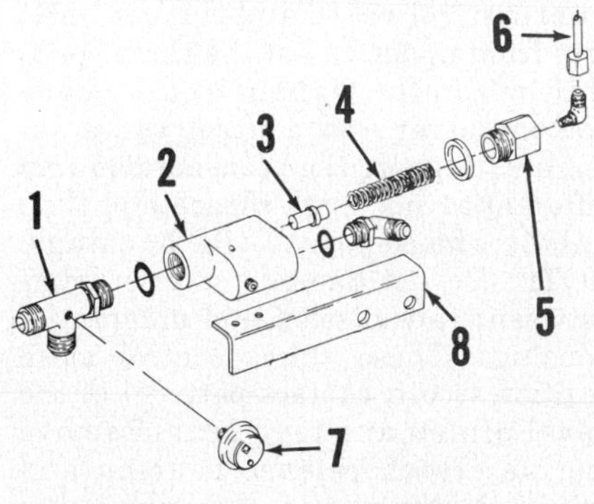

Fig. 178-Exploded view of lube pump relief valve used on models equipped with three-speed Ampli-Torc.

1. Tee
2. Valve body
3. Relief valve
4. Spring
5. Connector
6. Relief line
7. Oil pressure sending unit
8. Relief valve mounting bracket

Fig. 179-To check three-speed Ampli-Torc clutch pressures, remove plugs and install test gages in ports (1) and (2) in transmission housing bottom cover.

1. High range clutch port (toward left side of tractor)
2. Intermediate range clutch port (toward right side of tractor)

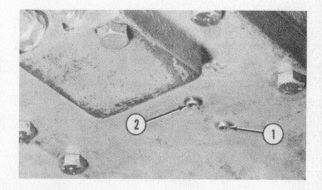

Fig. 180–Side cover removed from tractor with three-speed Ampli-Torc.

1. Adjusting nut
2. Bearing support
3. Lock clip
4. Intermediate reduction gear

OVER-RUNNING CLUTCH
All Models With Three-Speed Ampli-Torc

176. **R&R AND OVERHAUL.** To remove the over-running clutch, first drain the Ampli-Torc section of the transmission housing. Disconnect hydraulic lines from side cover and remove any other interfering parts. Unbolt side cover from transmission housing, then tighten two cap screws into the threaded holes in cover until cover is forced off the dowel pins. Remove side cover assembly. Do not lose spacer shims used behind side cover. To disassemble the unit, remove lock clip (3—Fig. 180) and adjusting nut (1). Cut the lock wire, remove cap screws and pry bearing support (2) off the dowel pins. Refer to Fig. 181 and remove bearing cone (12), adjusting nut (13), lock ring (14) and washer (15). Press low reduction gear and shaft (5) from intermediate reduction gear (1). Remove over-running clutch (4).

Clean and inspect all parts and renew any showing excessive wear or other damage. When reassembling,

install over-running clutch (2—Fig. 182) in intermediate gear (1) so that drag springs on clutch are to the outside. When installing low reduction gear and countershaft assembly in intermediate reduction gear (1—Fig. 181), tighten adjusting nut (13) to obtain a shaft end play of 0.000-0.002. DO NOT pre-load these bearings. Install the countershaft and reduction gear assembly in side cover and tighten bearing support cap screws to a torque of 65-75 ft.-lbs. Wrap a cord around the middle of intermediate reduction gear and attach a spring scale to end of cord. NOTE: Wrap the cord so that clutch locks and turns the low reduction gear and countershaft. Tighten adjusting nut (1—Fig. 180) until a pull of 1⅔ to 3⅓ pounds on the spring scale is required to keep the reduction gears rotating. Secure adjusting nut with lock clip (3) and secure cap screws with wire.

If the Ampli-Torc was fairly quiet during operation before disassembly, install the side cover assembly with the same shim pack that was removed. If the unit had an objectionable whine,

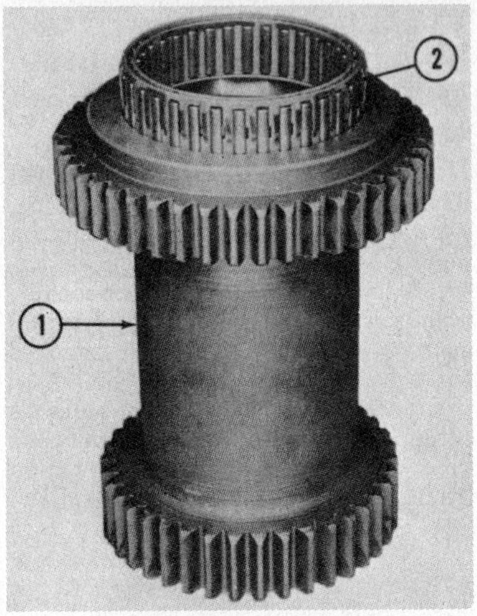

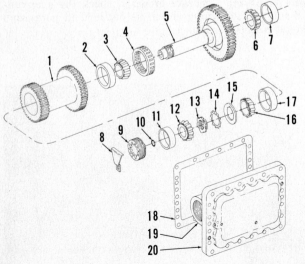

Fig. 182–Install over-running clutch (2) in intermediate reduction gear (1) so the drag springs are to the outside.

gear backlash should be checked and a new shim pack made up. To adjust the gear backlash, remove bottom cover and add or remove shims behind side cover to obtain a gear backlash of 0.008-0.012. Shims are available in thicknesses of 0.003, 0.005 and 0.010.

INPUT SHAFT, GEARS AND HYDRAULIC CLUTCHES
All Models With Three-Speed Ampli-Torc

177. **R&R AND OVERHAUL.** To remove the three-speed unit, first drain the Ampli-Torc, transmission and differential housings, then detach (split) engine from transmission housing as outlined in paragraph 164. Remove fuel tank, platforms, instrument panel, steering motor, steering support and associated parts. Unbolt and remove side cover assembly as in paragraph 176. Disconnect the tubes from control valve and remove shift arm from upper end of the three-speed shifter shaft. Unbolt and remove bottom cover and control valve assembly. Support the transmission and differential housings separately, then unbolt and separate the housings. NOTE: Do not damage or lose shims between transmission and differential housings. These shims control mesh position (tooth contact pattern) of the bevel pinion and ring gear. Remove engine clutch release bearing and drive out pins retaining clutch release fork and Ampli-Torc brake cam to the cross shafts. Withdraw fork and shafts. Remove Ampli-Torc brake adjusting nut (11—Fig. 183), retainer (10) and pressure spring (9), then unbolt and remove cover (5), shims (3)

Fig. 181–Exploded view of side cover assembly used on three-speed Ampli-Torc.

1. Intermediate reduction gear
2. Bearing cup
3. Bearing cone
4. Over-running clutch
5. Low reduction gear and shaft
6. Bearing cone
7. Bearing cup
8. Lock clip
9. Adjusting nut
10. Seal ring
11. Bearing cup
12. Bearing cone
13. Adjusting nut
14. Lock ring
15. Washer
16. Bearing cone
17. Bearing cup
18. Shim (0.003, 0.005 & 0.010)
19. Bearing support
20. Side cover

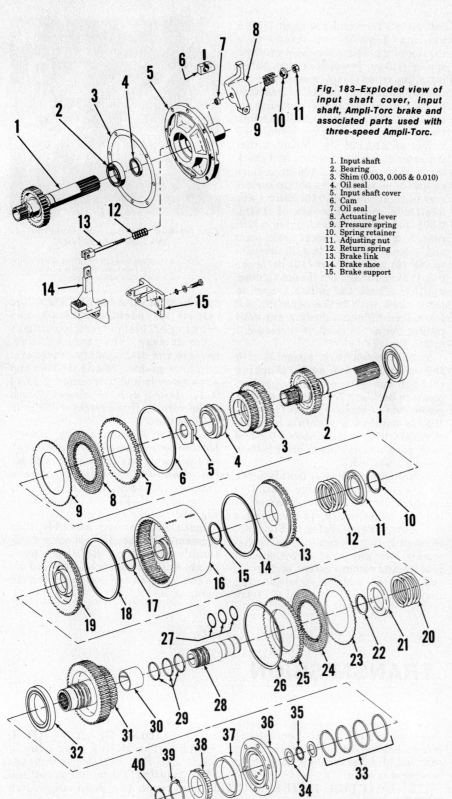

Fig. 183—Exploded view of input shaft cover, input shaft, Ampli-Torc brake and associated parts used with three-speed Ampli-Torc.

1. Input shaft
2. Bearing
3. Shim (0.003, 0.005 & 0.010)
4. Oil seal
5. Input shaft cover
6. Cam
7. Oil seal
8. Actuating lever
9. Pressure spring
10. Spring retainer
11. Adjusting nut
12. Return spring
13. Brake link
14. Brake shoe
15. Brake support

and return spring (12). Remove cap screws securing brake support (15) to housing, then remove brake assembly. Carefully withdraw input shaft and three-speed clutch assembly. Remove input shaft assembly from clutch assembly. Unscrew nut (5—Fig. 184) and remove bearing (4) and intermediate drive gear (3) from input shaft (2). Remove retaining ring (6) and lift out back-up plate (7), friction plates (8) and backing plates (9). Support clutch housing (16) in a press and apply pressure to spring retainer (11). Remove snap ring (10), release press and remove retainer (11), spring (12) and piston (13). NOTE: It may be necessary to bump end of housing (16) on a flat surface to remove piston. Withdraw manifold (28) then remove rear clutch (19 thru 26) in same manner as front clutch.

To remove output gear (31), unbolt and remove main transmission shift tower. Working through transmission top opening, remove snap ring (39) and withdraw output gear. Unbolt and remove adapter assembly (36).

Clean and inspect all parts and renew any showing excessive wear or other damage. Install adapter (36) in housing and tighten cap screws to a torque of 22-24 ft.-lbs. NOTE: Leave upper left cap screw out as this hole acts as a ventilator for the compartments. If new bushing (30) is installed in output gear, ream bushing after installation to 2.122-2.123. Loosen adjusting nut at rear of transmission top shaft and move shaft rearward. Place snap rings (39 and 40) and bearing cone (38) on end of shaft. Install new seal rings (33) on output gear, then install output gear in adapter. Secure with snap rings (39 and 40). Adjust nut at rear of transmission top shaft until a rolling torque of 5-10 inch-lbs. greater than with bearings loose, is obtained.

Using new seal rings (14, 15, 17 and 18) reinstall pistons (13 and 19) by reversing removal procedure. Make certain that screen in piston is installed at 90° from oil port in clutch housing. Reinstall clutch packs and retaining rings. Install bearing assembly (4) and intermediate drive gear (3) on input shaft (2) and tighten nut (5) to 250 ft.-lbs. torque. Align punch mark on input shaft gear and blank tooth on input shaft with punch mark on clutch housing splined hub and slide the two units together. Install new "O" rings (27) and seal rings (29) on manifold (28). Align oil holes in manifold with punch mark on clutch housing hub and insert the manifold. Using a small amount of

Fig. 184—Exploded view of input shaft, gears and hydraulic clutches used on three-speed Ampli-Torc.

1. Ball bearing	11. Spring retainer	21. Spring retainer	31. Output gear
2. Input shaft	12. Piston spring	22. Snap ring	32. Roller Bearing
3. Intermediate drive gear	13. Piston	23. Backing plate	33. Seal rings
4. Bearing	14. Seal ring (outer)	24. Friction plate	34. Thrust washers
5. Nut	15. Seal ring (inner)	25. Back-up plate	35. Thrust bearing
6. Retaining ring	16. Clutch housing	26. Retaining ring	36. Adapter
7. Back-up plate	17. Seal ring (inner)	27. "O" ring seals	37. Bearing cup
8. Friction plate	18. Seal ring (outer)	28. Manifold	38. Bearing cone
9. Backing plate	19. Piston	29. Seal rings	39. Snap ring
10. Snap ring	20. Piston spring	30. Bushing	40. Snap ring

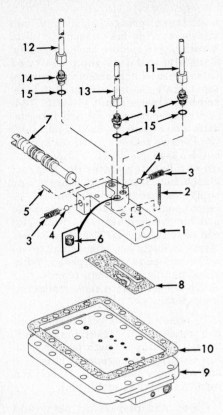

Fig. 185—Exploded view of three-speed Ampli-Torc control valve.

1. Valve body	9. Bottom cover
2. Spiral pin (2 used)	10. Gasket
3. Detent springs	11. Tube
4. Steel balls	(intermediate)
5. Roll pin (2 used)	12. Tube (high)
6. Restrictor (0.062)	13. Tube (lube)
7. Valve spool	14. Connectors
8. Gasket	15. "O" rings

grease to hold them in place, install thrust bearing assembly (34 and 35) into bore of output gear. Install the clutch and input shaft assembly.

Install new oil seals (4 and 7—Fig. 183) in cover (5). Using new seal rings,

bolt Ampli-Torc brake support (15) in position. Tighten cap screws to a torque of 22-24 ft.-lbs. Slide return spring (12) on brake link (13). When installing cover (5) use a seal protector sleeve, shim stock or cellophane tape to prevent damaging oil seal lips on the input shaft splines and brake link threads. Tighten cover cap screws to a torque of 22-24 ft.-lbs. Mount a dial indicator at front of housing and check input shaft end play. Add or remove shims (3) as required to obtain correct end play of 0.004-0.010. Shims are available in thicknesses of 0.003, 0.005 and 0.010. Install engine clutch release cross shafts, fork, brake cam and release bearing. Install pressure spring (9) and retainer (10) on brake link (13) and start, but do not tighten, nut (11). Check the rolling torque on input shaft with brake adjusting nut loose, then tighten adjusting nut until rolling torque on shaft is increased 1 to 2 ft.-lbs.

Install the side cover assembly with the original shim pack. Working through the bottom cover opening, measure backlash between Ampli-Torc gears. Add or remove shims (18—Fig. 181) as required to obtain a backlash of 0.008-0.012. Remove side cover and shim pack and lay aside until bottom cover is installed.

Before bottom cover is installed, the Ampli-Torc control valve should be cleaned, inspected and repaired or renewed as necessary. To disassemble the control valve, refer to Fig. 185, then unbolt and remove valve assembly from cover (9). Drive out roll pins (5) and remove detent springs (3) and balls (4). Remove spiral pins (2), then withdraw valve spool (7) from

Fig. 186—View showing tube installation on three-speed Ampli-Torc.

11. Intermediate tube to front hole in adapter
12. High range tube to center hole in adapter
13. Lube line to rear hole in adapter

detent end of valve body (1). Clean and inspect all parts and renew any showing excessive wear, scoring or other damage. When reassembling, reverse the disassembly procedure. Use new gasket (8) and tighten cap screws evenly and to a torque of 12-14 ft.-lbs. Install new "O" rings (15) and make certain that restrictor (6) is in the lube port.

Using new gasket (10), install bottom cover assembly. Tighten cap screws evenly and to a torque of 55 ft.-lbs. Connect the tubes between adapter (36—Fig. 184) and control valve body (1—Fig. 185) as shown in Fig. 186.

Reinstall side cover assembly, then reassemble tractor by reversing disassembly procedure. Refill compartments with proper lubricant and recheck pressures as outlined in paragraph 175.

TRANSMISSION

This section applies to the Five Speed transmission used in all model G VI, G705, G706, G707, G708, MF95 and MF97 tractors. For service on the transmission used in model G900, G950, G1000, G1000 Vista, G1050 and G1350 tractors, refer to the transmission section beginning with paragraph 184.

OVERHAUL
Models G VI-G705-G706-G707-G708-MF95-MF97

178. **TRANSMISSION COVER.** Cover can be removed after removing the fuel tank, instrument panel, bat-

tery and battery shelf. Remove cap screws holding cover to transmission case and lift off cover. Reinstallation is reverse of removal.

179. **SHIFTER RAILS AND FORKS.** Rails and forks can be removed after removing transmission cover, and four cap screws (C—Fig. 188) retaining shifter rail bearings to transmission housing. Detent balls and springs can be removed after removing gear shift separating bracket (66). Roll pins (R) prevent overshifting. Refer also to Fig. 187 for exploded view of typical shifter mechanism.

180. **SLIDING GEAR (CLUTCH) SHAFT.** The sliding gear (clutch) shaft (23—Fig. 190) can be removed after "splitting" the tractor as outlined in paragraph 164, removing clutch (over-center type) as in paragraph 159; and removing shifter rails and forks as in paragraph 179. Remove clutch shaft front bearing housing, then bump shaft forward as shown in Fig. 191 until bearing (22—Fig. 190) is free from housing bore. Lift gears out top opening as shaft is removed.

Bearing (22) can be pressed from shaft after removing snap ring (21). To remove gear (24), first remove snap ring (25). Oil seal (20) should be installed in bearing housing (18) with seal lip to rear.

When reassembling, reverse the disassembly procedure. Install bearing housing (18) and gasket (19) with oil slot in housing and drain hole in gasket to the bottom. Use Permatex or other suitable sealant on cap screw threads when installing bearing housing (18).

181. UPPER COUNTERSHAFT. The upper countershaft (38—Fig. 190) can be removed after removing clutch shaft as outlined in paragraph 180 and the power take-off output shaft unit as in paragraph 216.

Working through clutch compartment, remove front bearing housing (41—Fig. 192). Working through pto housing opening, bend down tabs on locking plate (30—Fig. 193) and remove cap screws and retaining plate (31); then, using a long drift, bump upper shaft forward out of housing and rear bearing. Lift the gears (33, 35 and 37—Fig. 190) and spacers (34 and 36) out top opening as shaft is withdrawn from front.

Front bearing (39) will be removed with shaft, and rear bearing (32) will remain in housing, as unit is disassembled. Rear bearing can be bumped from housing wall and front bearing pressed from shaft, if renewal is indicated.

If transmission has been completely disassembled, main drive bevel pinion must be reinstalled as outlined in paragraph 183, before upper countershaft is reinstalled. Reinstall upper countershaft by reversing the disassembly procedure, using Fig. 194 as a guide for correct installation of gears and spacers.

NOTE: If lower countershaft is in place when reinstalling upper countershaft, place the constant mesh gear (33) in left, rear corner of transmission compartment before positioning double gear (35) on shaft. The gear cannot be installed from above after double gear is in position.

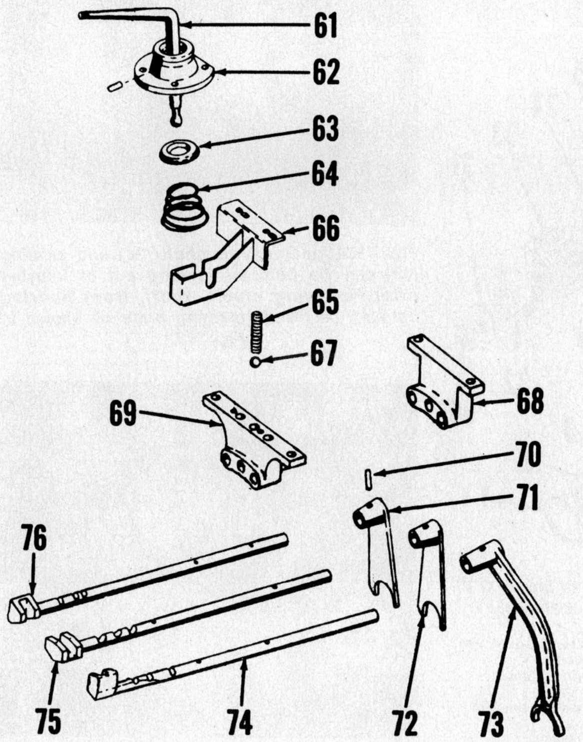

182. LOWER COUNTERSHAFT. The lower countershaft (7—Fig. 190), can be removed after splitting tractor as outlined in paragraph 164, removing top cover (paragraph 178), shifter rails and forks (paragraph 179), pto output shaft (paragraph 216) and belt pulley unit or transmission side cover plate. If lower countershaft only, is to be removed, it is not necessary to remove clutch shaft or upper countershaft. Proceed as follows:

Working through front of transmission housing, remove lower countershaft bearing housing (12). Save shim pack (10); shims control bearing preload. Working through belt pulley or side cover opening, unseat snap ring (5) from its groove at rear of constant mesh gear (6) and move snap ring rearward on shaft. If a spacer (P—Fig. 195) is not available, procure a piece of 2⅛-inch heavy walled pipe, 5 7/16-inches long, split the pipe lengthwise and position on shaft as shown, using wire or cord to hold spacer in position. With spacer in position and working through pto output shaft housing opening, bump the lower countershaft forward until rear bearing cone (3—Fig. 196) is free on shaft. Withdraw

Fig. 187–Exploded view of typical transmission shifter mechanism used on models G VI, G705, G706, G707, G708, MF95 and MF97.

61. Shift lever
62. Housing
63. Spring seat
64. Spring
65. Detent spring
66. Separating bracket
67. Detent ball
68. Rail bearing (front)
69. Rail bearing (rear)
70. Roll pin
71. Third and fifth fork
72. First and fourth fork
73. Second and reverse fork
74. Second and reverse rail
75. First and fourth rail
76. Third and fifth rail

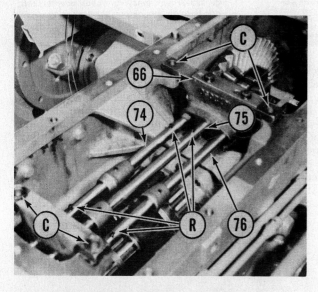

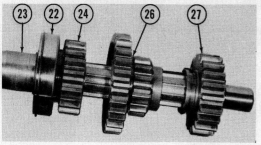

Fig. 188–Transmission housing with cover removed, showing shifter rails and forks. Refer also to Fig. 187.

C. Cap screws
R. Roll pins

Fig. 189–Transmission input (clutch) shaft with gears installed. Refer to Fig. 190 for legend.

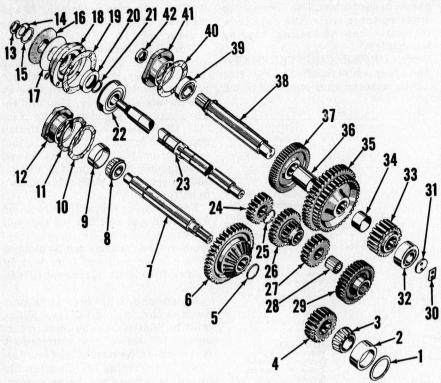

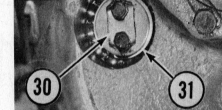

Fig. 192–Upper countershaft (38) and bearing (39) can be bumped forward out of housing after removing clutch shaft, front bearing housing (41) and retaining plate as shown in Fig. 193.

Fig. 190–Exploded view of transmission gears, shafts and associated parts used on all model G VI, G705, G706, G707, G708, MF95 and MF97 tractors. Main drive bevel pinion is not shown.

1. Shim	14. Lock washer	29. Differential drive gear
2. Bearing cup	15. Snap ring	30. Lock clip
3. Bearing cone	16. Brake plate	31. Retaining plate
4. Second-Reverse gear	17. Brake lining	32. Bearing
5. Snap ring	18. Bearing housing	33. Constant mesh gear
6. Constant mesh gear	19. Gasket	34. Spacer
7. Lower countershaft	20. Oil seal	35. Double gear
8. Bearing cone	21. Snap ring	36. Spacer
9. Bearing cup	22. Bearing	37. Fourth gear
10. & 11. Shims	23. Clutch shaft	38. Upper countershaft
12. Bearing housing	24. Constant mesh gear	39. Bearing
13. Lock nut	25. Snap ring	40. Gasket
	26. Double gear	41. Bearing housing
	27. Third-Fifth gear	42. Oil seal
	28. Pilot bearing	

Fig. 193–When removing upper countershaft, work through pto output shaft opening, bend down tabs on locking plate (30) and remove cap screws and retaining plate (31). Refer also to Fig. 192.

shaft through front of housing while lifting gears and bearings out through top opening.

Shims (10—Fig. 190) control pre-load of lower countershaft bearings.

Shims (1) control backlash of belt pulley bevel gears, if a belt pulley unit is used. Adding or removing shims (1) will affect bearing pre-load. If rear bearing cup (2) is removed, reinstall using the same number of 0.006 shims (1) as were removed. Lower countershaft bearing pre-load is correct when 6-8 in.-lbs. of torque is required to rotate the shaft. Pre-load can be checked using a spring scale and working

through side opening as shown in Fig. 197. Proceed as follows:

Reinstall the shaft and gears by reversing the removal procedure, using Fig. 196 as a guide. Make sure constant mesh gear (6) is positioned in front of upper countershaft forward gear if upper countershaft is not removed. Bump lower countershaft rearward until rear bearing cone (3) is seated against shaft shoulder, then

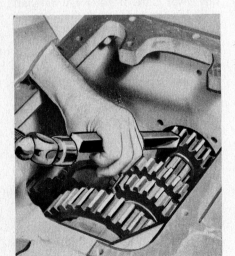

Fig. 191–Clutch shaft can be bumped forward using a soft drift and hammer as shown, after removing front bearing housing.

Fig. 194–Upper countershaft and associated parts showing proper sequence of assembly. Shaft (38) is splined at front end and extends through bearing housing on models equipped with Elwood front drive unit. Refer to Fig. 190 for legend.

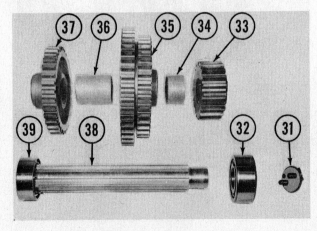

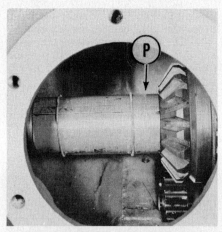

Fig. 195–A pipe spacer (P) will assist in removing lower countershaft rear bearing cone during shaft removal. Refer to text.

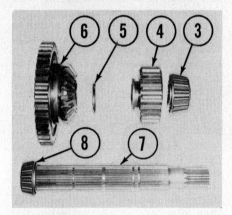

Fig. 196–Lower countershaft and associated parts showing proper sequence of assembly. Refer to Fig. 190 for legend.

reinstall front bearing housing using the removed gasket and shim pack or new plastic shims of the same thickness.

NOTE: On late models, plastic shims are color coded and a gasket is not used. Plastic shims can be used on early models. Color code is as follows: Red-0.002; green-0.003; brown-0.010.

To check the rolling torque, first make sure that neither gear is meshed with any other gear in transmission. If clutch shaft has not been removed, it may be necessary to unseat snap ring (25—Fig. 190) and move gear (24) rearward on clutch shaft. Wrap a light cord around lower countershaft as shown in Fig. 197, attach a pull scale and check the pull required to KEEP the shaft turning. Pull should be 6 to 8 lbs.; if it is not, add or remove shims (10—Fig. 190) as required. Use Permatex or similar sealer on cap screw threads when permanently installing front bearing housing (12).

183. MAIN DRIVE BEVEL PINION AND SHAFT. Main drive bevel pinion and shaft, differential drive gear and bearing cage assembly (Fig. 198) can be removed after splitting tractor as outlined in paragraph 164, removing clutch shaft as in paragraph 180 and upper countershaft as in paragraph 181.

Remove safety wire and cap screws retaining bearing cage (42) to transmission housing wall. A half-moon box-wrench is best suited for this operation. The complete assembly (shaft,

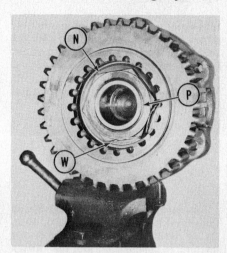

Fig. 199–To adjust bearings or disassemble bevel pinion shaft (P), bend down tabs on locking washer (W) and turn nut (N).

gears and bearing) can be withdrawn forward and out of transmission housing.

Pinion (44) and ring gear are available only as matched pairs, and can be identified as such by etched numbers on both pinion and gear. Do not discard shims (S) located between bearing cage and transmission housing.

To disassemble the removed unit, bend down locking tabs on washer (W —Fig. 199) and remove nut (N). When

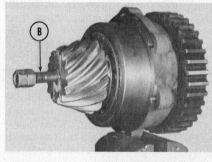

Fig. 200–A suitable bolt (B), double nutted, can be used to adapt a torque wrench to adjust bevel pinion bearing pre-load. Refer to text for details.

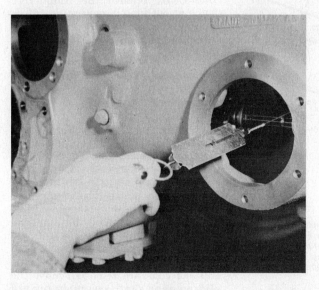

Fig. 197–Using a spring scale and cord to check lower countershaft bearing pre-load. Pre-load is correct when a steady pull of 6-8 lbs. is required to rotate shaft.

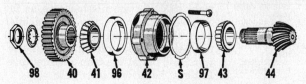

40. Drive gear	
41. Bearing cone	
42. Bearing cage	
43. Bearing cone	
44. Bevel pinion	
96. Bearing cup	
97. Bearing cup	
98. Adjusting nut	

Fig. 198–Main drive bevel pinion and associated parts used on models G VI, G705, G706, G707, G708, MF95 and MF97.

Fig. 201–When installing bevel pinion assembly, lube reservoir (R) must be at top as shown.

reassembling, tighten pinion nut (N) to provide a rolling torque of 110-115 inch-lbs. for the shaft bearings. Rolling torque can be checked with a torque wrench, using a suitable bolt (B) as shown in Fig. 200, or with a string and pull scale. Bend locking washer (W—Fig. 199) as shown, when adjustment is completed.

Reinstall the unit so that lube reservoir (R—Fig. 201) is uppermost as shown, using the same number of shims (S—Fig. 198) as were removed, to maintain the correct mesh position.

NOTE: If main drive bevel ring gear and pinion are renewed, mesh position (cone point) must be readjusted as outlined in paragraph 195.

TRANSMISSION

This section applies to the Five Speed transmission used in model G900, G950, G1000, G1000 Vista, G1050 and G1350 tractors, in combination with the "Ampli-Torc" range unit covered in paragraphs 165 through 177. For service on the transmission used in all earlier models, refer to transmission section beginning with paragraph 178.

REMOVE AND REINSTALL
Models G900-G950-G1000-G1000 Vista-G1050-G1350

184. To remove the transmission assembly from tractor, first drain the Ampli-Torc, transmission and differential housings, then detach (split) engine from transmission housing as outlined in paragraph 164, and proceed as follows: Remove batteries, fuel tank, platforms, instrument panel, steering motor, steering support and associated parts. Disconnect hydraulic lines, electrical wiring, clutch, brake and Ampli-Torc linkage as necessary. Support the transmission and differential housings separately, then unbolt and separate the housings. NOTE: Do not damage or lose shims between transmission and differential housings. These shims control the mesh position (tooth contact) of the bevel pinion and ring gear.

OVERHAUL
Models G900-G950-G1000-G1000 Vista-G1050-G1350

185. SHIFTER SHAFTS AND FORKS. To remove the transmission shifter shafts and forks, first drain the hydraulic system, transmission and differential housing. On G1000 Vista, remove the fuel tank. Then on all models, remove batteries and platform assemblies, and disconnect and unclip tubing and wiring from transmission housing. Support both halves of tractor separately, then unbolt and split the transmission from the differential housing.

Place the shift lever in neutral position, then unbolt and remove transmission top cover assembly. Position the shifter shafts so that detent ball grooves at rear of shafts are inside the shaft bores in transmission case. Drive out the roll pins retaining the shifter forks and lugs to the shafts. Pull the shifter shaft rearward out of the transmission case and lift out the forks and lugs. CAUTION: Detent balls (16—Fig. 202) and detent springs (15) are located under each shifter shaft in the vertical bores in transmission housing. When withdrawing each shaft, use care to prevent ball and spring from flying out or falling into the gear case.

When reassembling, use Fig. 202 as a guide for proper location of parts. When installing the fork and lug retaining roll pins, make certain the detent ball grooves are inside the shaft bores in transmission. This will provide the proper support for the shafts when the roll pins are bumped into place.

186. SLIDING GEAR (UPPER) SHAFT. To remove the sliding gear shaft (7 or 7A—Fig. 204), first remove the transmission assembly from tractor as outlined in paragraph 184, then remove the transmission top cover and the shifter shafts and forks.

On models equipped with two-speed Ampli-Torc, remove the Ampli-Torc clutch as outlined in paragraph 166 or 171 and the planetary gear unit and over-running clutch as in paragraph 168 or 173.

On models equipped with three-speed Ampli-Torc, remove the over-running clutch assembly as in paragraph 176 and the input shaft, gears and hydraulic clutches as in paragraph 177.

Remove lock clip (1—Fig. 204), then unscrew and remove the sliding gear shaft bearing adjustment nut (2). Using a drift punch against the rear bearing inner race as shown in Fig. 205, bump the bearing (6—Fig. 204) rearward. Turn the shaft and again bump the bearing cone rearward. Continue this procedure until the bearing cup and cone are removed. Move the sliding gear shaft assembly toward right side of transmission case as far as possible, remove the reverse idler gear shaft retaining set screw and push the reverse idler gear shaft forward and out of the transmission case. Lift out the reverse idler gear.

Using a suitable pair of snap ring pliers, disengage the snap ring from the groove in front of fourth speed

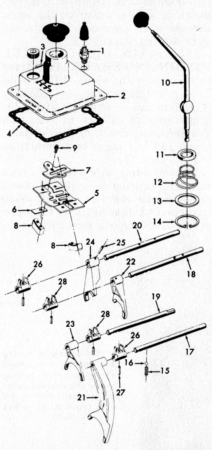

Fig. 202–Exploded view of typical transmission shifter mechanism. Refer to Fig. 203 for shift lever and linkage used on G1000 Vista. Neutral start switch (1) was installed in cover (2) on early G900 and G1000 tractors.

1. Neutral start switch	16. Detent ball
2. Top cover	17. 1st & 5th shifter shaft
3. Pin	18. 2nd & 4th shifter shaft
4. Gasket	19. 3rd shifter shaft
5. Guide plate	20. Reverse shifter shaft
6. Lock plate	21. 1st & 5th fork
7. Upper guide	22. 2nd & 4th fork
8. Lower guide	23. 3rd fork
9. Bolt	24. Reverse fork
10. Shift lever	25. Long lug
11. Spring retainer	26. Long lug
12. Spring	27. Spiral pin
13. Spring retainer	28. Short lug
14. Snap ring	
15. Detent spring	

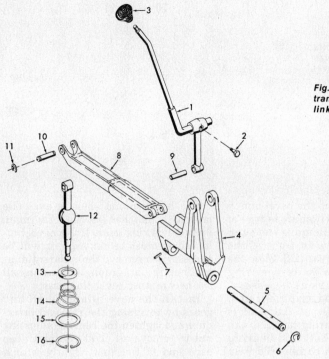

Fig. 203—Exploded view of transmission shift lever and linkage used on G1000 Vista tractors.

1. Shift handle
2. Shoulder bolt
3. Knob
4. Pivot yoke
5. Pivot pin
6. "E" ring
7. Spiral pin
8. Shift link
9. Pin
10. Pin
11. "E" ring
12. Shift lever
13. Spring retainer
14. Spring
15. Spring retainer
16. Snap ring

gear (21—Fig. 204) on bevel pinion (countershaft). Move the snap ring and fourth speed gear forward on the bevel pinion shaft as far as possible, then lift the sliding gear (upper) shaft and gears out through top opening in transmission housing.

NOTE: Special snap ring pliers (Part No. 10T25064), designed for these snap rings, are available from the Minneapolis-Moline parts department.

Remove the second and fourth gear (10), snap ring (9) and withdraw the fourth speed gear (8).

Inside diameter of the bushing in fourth speed gear (8) is 2.1125-2.1135. If bushing is worn or if inner teeth of

gear are worn or damaged, install a new gear which contains a factory installed bushing reamed to size. The bushing is available as a separate renewable part and must be honed after installation to provide a bushing to shaft clearance of 0.0025-0.004. Unless precision sizing equipment is available, field installation of the bushing is not recommended.

NOTE: Although it is possible to remove the third and fifth speed gears from the sliding gear shaft, it would be pointless to do so. If the shaft, third speed gear and/or fifth speed gear are damaged or excessively worn, it will be necessary to renew all parts which are available only as a factory assembled unit.

If the sliding gear shaft and gears are in good condition, install the fourth speed gear (8), snap ring (9) and second and fourth sliding gear (10). Place the assembled sliding gear shaft unit in the transmission housing, then move the shaft assembly toward right side of the housing. Install the reverse idler gear and shaft, tighten shaft retaining set screw until end of screw is flush with locknut, then tighten the locknut securely. Slide fourth speed gear (21) and its retaining snap ring back into position on the bevel pinion (countershaft).

Install bearing cone (6) and cup (5) at the rear of the shaft, then install bearing adjusting nut (2) with bushing (3). Turn adjusting nut in two or three threads at this time. On two-speed Ampli-Torc models, install the Ampli-Torc cam cage with oil hole to top and oil deflector on the top cap screw. On three-speed Ampli-Torc models, install adapter and Ampli-Torc output gear. Tighten the cap screws evenly to a torque of 23 ft.-lbs.

With the bearing adjusting nut (2) loose and all gears in neutral position, wrap a cord around shaft between

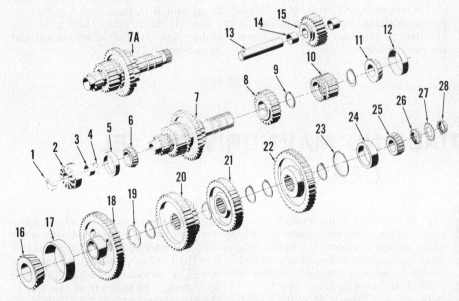

Fig. 204—Exploded view of sliding gear transmission. Shaft assembly (7A) is used with two-speed Ampli-Torc and shaft assembly (7) is used with three-speed Ampli-Torc.

1. Lock clip
2. Adjusting nut
3. Bushing
4. Retaining ring
5. Bearing cup
6. Bearing cone
7. Upper shaft assembly
8. 4th speed gear
9. Retaining ring
10. 2nd & 4th speed gear
11. Bearing cone
12. Bearing cup
13. Reverse idler shaft
14. Bushing
15. Reverse idler gear
16. Bearing cone
17. Bearing cup
18. 1st speed gear
19. Thrust washer
20. 3rd & 5th speed gear
21. 4th speed gear
22. 2nd & reverse gear
23. Snap ring
24. Bearing cup
25. Bearing cone
26. Adjusting nut
27. Lock washer
28. Lock nut

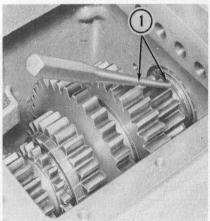

Fig. 205—Using a punch to drift the sliding gear shaft rear bearing out of transmission housing.

gears (8) and (10). Attach a spring scale and check the pounds pull required to rotate the shaft assembly. Record this no-pre-load reading. Tighten the bearing adjusting nut to obtain a bearing pre-load of 5-10 pounds greater than the previously recorded no-pre-load reading. Install lock clip (1).

Install the remaining parts by reversing the removal procedure.

187. REVERSE IDLER. The reverse idler gear (15—Fig. 204) and shaft (13) can be removed by following the procedure outlined in paragraph 186.

The inside diameter of the reverse idler gear bushings should be 1.244-1.245. The bushings and idler shaft are available as separate replacement parts; or, a new idler gear is factory fitted with bushings reamed to size. If new bushings are installed in a reverse idler gear, they must be honed after installation to provide a clearance of 0.0015-0.003 on the idler shaft.

When installing the idler gear and shaft, tighten the retaining set screw until top of screw is flush with lock nut; then tighten nut securely. Reinstall the sliding gear shaft as outlined in paragraph 186.

188. BEVEL PINION (COUNTERSHAFT). To remove the bevel pinion shaft, first remove the sliding gear (upper) shaft as outlined in paragraph 186 and proceed as follows:

Refer to Fig. 204 and remove the two nuts and lock washer from forward end of shaft. Using a pair of suitable snap ring pliers, disengage snap ring from groove in front of the first

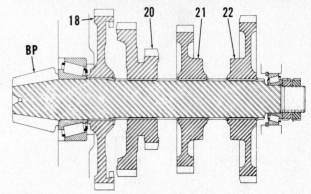

Fig. 206—Cross sectional view showing correct installation of gears on bevel pinion shaft (BP).

18. 1st speed gear
20. 3rd & 5th speed gear
21. 4th speed gear
22. 2nd & reverse gear

speed gear (18). Bump the bevel pinion shaft rearward until shaft is free of bearing cone (25). Remove the snap ring from the groove in front of the second and reverse gear (22). Slide the bevel pinion shaft to the rear, moving gears and snap rings as necessary. Remove the gears and snap rings from the transmission case as the shaft is withdrawn. Rear bearing cone (16) can be removed from shaft and bearing cups (17 and 24) can be removed from the transmission case at this time.

Inside diameter of the bushing in the first speed gear (18) is 2.2740-2.2745. If bushing is worn or if inner teeth of gear are damaged or worn, install a new gear which contains a factory installed bushing reamed to size. The first speed gear bushing is available as a separate replacement part but must be honed after installation to provide a bushing to shaft clearance of 0.0035-0.0045. Unless precision sizing equipment is available, field installation of the bushing is not recommended.

The bevel pinion shaft is available only as a matched set with the main drive bevel ring gear. If the bevel pinion shaft must be renewed, it will be necessary to remove the differential as outlined in paragraph 196 and install the new mating bevel ring gear.

Install the bevel pinion shaft and gears by reversing the removal procedure and tighten the bearing adjusting nut to remove all shaft end play. Tap each end of the shaft lightly with a soft hammer to be sure the bearings are seated. Wrap a cord around the shaft between gears (20 and 21). Attach a spring scale to the cord and check the pounds pull required to rotate the shaft. Adjust nut (26) as required until a pull of 10-14 pounds on the scale will keep the shaft turning. Install lock washer (27) and nut (28). Tighten the outer nut (28) to a torque of 50-60 ft.-lbs., then bend lock washer tangs over both nuts.

Install the reverse idler gear and sliding gear (upper) shaft as outined in paragraph 186.

DIFFERENTIAL AND MAIN DRIVE BEVEL GEARS

This section applies to the differential and main drive bevel gears used in models G VI, G705, G706, G707, G708, MF95 and MF97. For service on differential and main drive bevel gears used in models G900, G950, G1000, G1000 Vista, G1050 and G1350, refer to section beginning with paragraph 196.

DIFFERENTIAL
Models G VI-G705-G706-G707-G708-MF95-MF97
189. BEARING ADJUSTMENT. Differential carrier bearing adjustment is controlled with shims (21—

Fig. 207) inserted between bearing cages and transmission housing. The same shims also control bevel ring gear and pinion backlash which should be set to the value as etched on individual sets of matched gears.

To adjust differential carrier bearings, first remove transmission top cover. Remove left brake assembly. Remove cap screws holding left bearing cage to transmission housing; then slide cage out far enough to permit removal of required thickness of shims to provide zero end play and yet permit differential unit to rotate without binding. Reinstall bearing

cage and check bearing adjustment and backlash. If bearing adjustment is O.K. but backlash is 0.002 greater or less than value stamped on ring gear, it will be necessary to adjust backlash by transferring shims from one side to the other until correct backlash is obtained.

After the backlash has been adjusted and before top cover has been installed, adjust the overload block as follows: Loosen jam nuts on adjusting screws (A—Fig. 209), and turn the screws either way as required to obtain a clearance of 0.002 between block (B) and ring gear. Check clear-

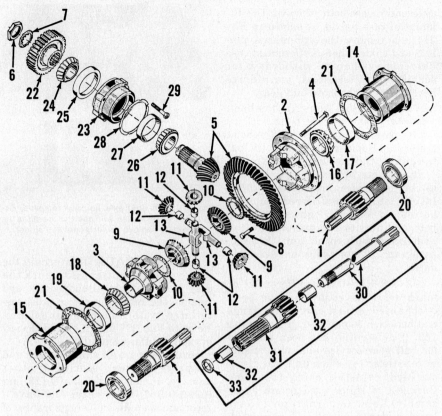

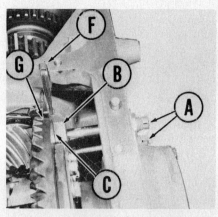

Fig. 209–Overload block (B) must be adjusted to a clearance of 0.002.

A. Adjusting screws
B. Overload block
C. Clearance (0.002)
F. Feeler gage
G. Bevel ring gear

Fig. 207–Exploded view of differential assembly used on models G VI, G705, G706, G707, G708, MF95 and MF97. Items 30, 31, 32 and 33 are used on models equipped with continuous type pto.

1. Differential shaft	12. Bushing	23. Drive shaft cage
2. Differential case R. H.	13. Differential pinion shaft	24. Bearing cone
3. Differential case L. H.	14. Bearing cage R. H.	25. Bearing cup
4. Bolt	15. Bearing cage L. H.	26. Bearing cone
5. Pinion and ring gear	16. Bearing cone	27. Bearing cup
6. Nut	17. Bearing cup	28. Shim
7. Lock washer	18. Bearing cone	29. Cap screw
8. Bolt	19. Bearing cup	30. Left hand differential shaft
9. Side gear	20. Ball bearing	31. Bull pinion sleeve
10. Washer	21. Shim	32. Bushing
11. Differential pinion gear	22. Differential drive gear	33. Oil seal

Fig. 210–Using a bar and wire to support differential unit for carrier bearing removal.

ance at top and bottom to make sure block is parallel to ring gear.

190. **REMOVE AND REINSTALL.** The differential unit can be removed after removing transmission housing top cover, rear cover plate or pto unit and BOTH rear axle shaft and housing assemblies; or, if only the differential or one set of final drive gears are to be serviced, differential case can be split and removed after removing ONE rear axle shaft and housing. Proceed as outlined in the appropriate following paragraphs.

191. BY REMOVING BOTH AXLES. With transmission housing top and rear covers removed, securely block the tractor and remove both rear axle and housing assemblies as outlined in paragraph 202. Remove both brake assemblies and the cap screws retaining differential bearing cages to transmission housing. Support the differential assembly as shown in Fig. 210. Tilt lower end of each bull gear in turn toward center of transmission housing as shown in Fig. 211, and remove bull pinion shaft sleeves (S); then, lift out the differential and main drive bevel gear as a unit.

Assemble by reversing the disassembly procedure, referring to paragraph 193 for tightening torques and other pertinent data.

192. BY SPLITTING DIFFERENTIAL CASE. If supporting tractor with both axles removed is a problem; or when performing service with limited facilities is necessary; the differential unit may be removed by splitting differential case and removing EITHER rear wheel and axle assembly as follows:

With transmission top and rear covers removed, block tractor and remove either wheel, axle and axle

Fig. 208–Using a dial indicator (I) to check bevel gear backlash. The correct backlash is etched on gear tooth as shown at (M).

Fig. 211–Bull gear (G) must be tilted as shown to remove bull pinion shaft sleeve (S).

Fig. 212—Bull pinion shaft (1) and bearing (20) can be pulled by inserting a suitable pry bar behind brake disc (D).

housing as outlined in paragraph 202. Remove both brakes and brake backing plates. Reinstall one brake disc on each bull pinion shaft as shown in Fig. 212 and, using a bar inserted between brake disc and transmission housing, remove the bull pinions.

Place correlation marks on the differential case halves as shown in Fig. 213 and remove the cotter pins and retaining nuts. Support the differential as shown in Fig. 210, tilt the loose bull gear as shown in Fig. 211, and remove the bull pinion sleeve. Remove overload block and adjusting screws and loosen the opposite bull pinion sleeve.

If right axle has been removed, turn the differential unit and withdraw all

differential case bolts; then tilt the differential case halves as shown in Fig. 214 and remove the differential pinions and spider shaft. Differential case halves may then be withdrawn for service on differential, main drive bevel gears or the loose bull gear.

If left axle and housing has been removed, push the case bolts back as far as possible, withdraw differential pinions and spider shafts and lift out the differential case halves.

Reassemble by reversing the disassembly procedure, making sure correlation marks on differential case halves are aligned. Tighten retaining bolts and nuts to a torque of 75 ft.-lbs. and secure with cotter pins. Refer to paragraph 193 for additional assembly data.

193. ASSEMBLY. If differential or main drive bevel gears have been overhauled, adjust carrier bearings and backlash as outlined in paragraph 189. If differential has been removed for bull gear service and adjustments were satisfactory when unit was disassembled, reinstall using the same thickness of shims used before disassembly. Refer to paragraph 183 for bevel pinion renewal and paragraph 195 for adjustment of mesh position, if main drive bevel gears are renewed.

Use Permatex or similar sealant on cap screw threads when reinstalling rear axle housings. Tighten assembly cap screws as outlined in the following table:

Bull Pinion Sleeve (Differential
  Carrier) Cap Screws ...... 75 ft.-lbs.
Brake Backing Plate Cap Screws
  ½-inch .... 90-95 ft.-lbs.
  ¾-inch .... 250-ft.-lbs.
Axle Housing Cap Screws .. 120 ft.-lbs.

Fig. 214—With right axle housing removed, differential case halves will need to be tilted as shown, to remove spider gears and spider.

194. OVERHAUL. To overhaul the removed differential unit, mark the case halves, if not already done, and remove the retaining cotter pins, castellated nuts and retaining bolts. Refer to Fig. 207 for an exploded view of typical differential unit.

Examine gears for chipped teeth and all parts for wear, scoring or other damage. Pinion spider shafts (13) are 0.996-0.997 in diameter and have a recommended diametral clearance of 0.003-0.005 in bushings (12). If clearance exceeds 0.010, renew shafts and/or bushings. Install bushings (12) with oil holes in bushing and pinion aligned and ream bushings to an inside diameter of 1.000-1.001 after installation. Tighten differential case bolts to a torque of 75 ft.-lbs. when reassembling, and secure with cotter pins.

If main drive bevel gears must be renewed, tighten main drive bevel ring gear retaining cap screws to a torque of 110-115 ft.-lbs., install pinion as outlined in paragraph 183 and adjust mesh position as outlined in paragraph 195. Adjust backlash and carrier bearings as outlined in paragraph 189.

Fig. 213—Removing differential unit by splitting the case. Refer to text for details.

C. Correlation marks

Fig. 215—Using a torque wrench to retighten differential case through bolts. Recommended torque is 75 ft.-lbs.

BEVEL GEAR MESH ADJUSTMENT
Models G VI-G705-G706-G707-G708-MF95-MF97

195. Mesh position (Cone Point) of the main drive bevel gears is controlled by thickness of shim pack (28—Fig. 207) located between drive pinion bearing cage and transmission housing.

Main drive bevel gears are available only as a matched set; in addition to the match mark, end of drive pinion contains markings which indicate the relative shim pack thickness for correct mesh position adjustment and edge of ring gear (or both gears) are marked to indicate the correct backlash. Refer to Fig. 216.

To determine the thickness of shim pack (28) when renewing the gears note thickness of removed shim pack and compare mesh position markings (C) on old and new pinion. If the new pinion has a larger plus marking (or smaller minus marking) than the old pinion; REMOVE shims equal in thickness to the difference between the two markings. If new pinion has a smaller plus marking or larger minus marking than old pinion, ADD shims equal in thickness to difference between the two markings. If one pinion has a plus marking and the other a minus marking, add the two markings, then; if new pinion has a plus marking, REMOVE shims equal in

Fig. 216–Matched ring gear and pinion are etched with match marks (A), recommended backlash (B) and cone point relative position (C). Cone point (mesh position) is adjusted by means of shims (28).

thickness to combined reading; or if new pinion has a minus marking, ADD shims. If plus or minus markings are within 0.003 of being identical on the two pinions, use the removed shim pack or one equal in thickness. Shims are 0.006 thick. When mesh position has been changed, backlash must be readjusted as outlined in paragraph 189.

Mesh position can be checked by using the following procedure: With backlash correctly adjusted, apply a coat of Prussian Blue to approximately ten teeth on bevel ring gear and turn ring gear in normal direction of rotation until painted portion passes by the pinion. If heavy tooth contact is indicated at heel (outer) ends of ring gear teeth, ADD one shim to shim pack (28); if heavy tooth contact is indicated at toe (inner) ends, REMOVE one shim. Mesh position is correct when even contact is indicated through ¾-⅞ of length of teeth and slightly toward toe (inner) end. Backlash must be readjusted whenever mesh position is changed.

DIFFERENTIAL AND MAIN DRIVE BEVEL GEARS

This section applies to the differential and main drive bevel gears used in model G900, G950, G1000, G1000 Vista, G1050 and G1350 tractors. For service on differential and main drive bevel gears used in all earlier models, refer to section beginning with paragraph 189.

assembly. On models G950, G1050 and G1350, remove the hitch rockshaft assembly. Then, on all models, support tractor under transmission and differential housings and remove rear

wheels. Remove the pto clutch and input shaft as outlined in paragraph 220. Remove brake covers, and on G900 and G1000 tractors, disconnect and remove clutch and brake pedals,

DIFFERENTIAL
Models G900-G950-G1000-G1000 Vista-G1050-G1350

196. **REMOVE AND REINSTALL.** To remove the differential assembly, drain hydraulic system, transmission and differential housing. On model G1000 Vista, remove the fuel tank. On all models, remove batteries and rear fenders, then unbolt and remove the seat and platform assemblies. On models G900, G1000 and G1000 Vista, disconnect hydraulic lines and remove hydraulic reservoir

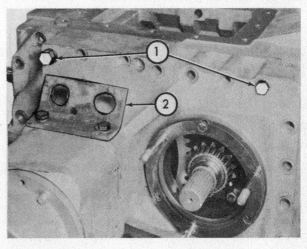

Fig. 217–When removing final drive housing, attach hoist to front hole in lifting bracket (2) before removing cap screws shown at (1).

Fig. 218–To check differential carrier bearing pre-load, wrap a cord around cage (2) in the area shown at (1). Attach a spring scale and check the amount of pull required to keep the differential rolling. Scale reading for correct pre-load will be 1½ to 2½ pounds.

then on all models remove brake discs, actuator assemblies and brake housings. NOTE: Keep each shim pack with its respective brake housing. These shims control bull pinion shaft bearing adjustment.

Remove all cap screws securing each final drive housing to differential housing except those shown at (1— Fig. 217). Bolt a lifting bracket to final drive housing, attach a chain hoist to the front hole in bracket (2), remove cap screws (1) and remove final drive housing assembly. Using the same procedure, remove the opposite final drive housing. Withdraw both bull pinion shafts.

Attach a suitable lift or hoist to the differential housing, unbolt differential housing from transmission housing and separate the housings. NOTE: Do not damage or lose shim pack removed from between the housings. These shims determine the cone point (mesh position) of the main drive bevel pinion.

Support the differential assembly from above or by blocking up under bevel ring gear. Unbolt and remove bearing cage and its shim pack from each side of differential housing. Identify each bearing cage and shim pack so they can be reinstalled in their original position. Remove the ring gear and differential cage assembly through front opening in differential housing on models G900, G1000 and G1000 Vista or through top opening on models G950, G1050 and G1350.

When reinstalling the differential assembly, place the bevel ring gear and differential cage assembly in position in differential housing and install bearing cages with the original shim packs. Tighten cap screws to a torque of 105-115 ft.-lbs. NOTE: Do not use lock washers on bolts in area of the

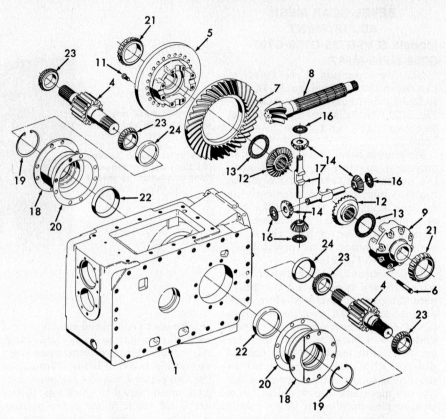

Fig. 219–Exploded view of differential assembly used on models G900 and G1000.

1. Differential housing	11. Cap screw	18. Bearing cage
4. Bull pinion	12. Bevel side gear	19. Snap ring
5. Differential cage	13. Thrust washer	20. Shim (0.002, 0.003 and 0.010)
6. Cap screw	14. Differential pinions	21. Bearing cone
7. Ring gear	16. Thrust washer	22. Bearing cup
8. Bevel pinion	17. Pinion shaft	23. Bearing cone
9. Cage cap		24. Bearing cup

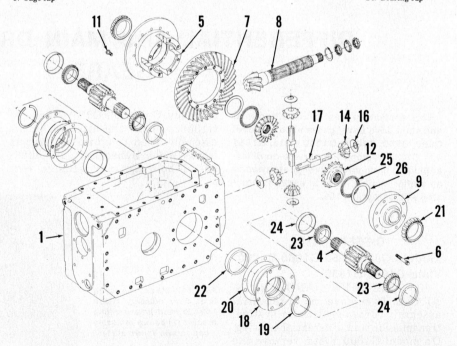

Fig. 220–Exploded view of differential assembly used on models G950, G1000 Vista, G1050 and G1350.

1. Differential housing	8. Bevel pinion	16. Thrust cup washers	21. Bearing cone
4. Bull pinion	9. Cage end cap	17. Pinion shafts	22. Bearing cup
5. Differential cage	11. Cap screw	18. Bearing cage	23. Bearing cone
6. Cap screw	12. Bevel side gears	19. Snap ring	24. Bearing cup
7. Ring gear	14. Differential pinions	20. Shims (0.002, 0.003 & 0.010)	25. Thrust needle bearing
			26. Bearing race

Fig. 221–View showing distance from transmission case to face of pinion bearing cone being measured. Refer to text.

thin flange on the bearing cages: Wrap a cord around the differential cage cap (2—Fig. 218) in the area shown at (1). Attach a spring scale and check the amount of pull required to keep the differential rolling. Add or remove shims (20—Fig. 219 or 220) as required until a scale reading of 1½-2½ pounds pull is required to keep the differential rolling at a constant speed. Shims are available in 0.002, 0.003 and 0.010 thicknesses.

Reconnect transmission and differential housing using the original shim pack between the housings. Tighten the flange cap screws to a torque of 310-320 ft.-lbs.

Adjust bevel gear backlash by transferring shims (20—Fig. 219 or 220) from one side to the other, without altering the combined thickness of the two shim packs. On early production model G1000 tractors, backlash should be 0.010-0.013. On late production G1000 and all G900, G950, G1000 Vista, G1050 and G1350 tractors, the correct backlash is etched on the ring gear.

Reinstall the final drive units as outlined in paragraph 203, then install and adjust pto clutch as outlined in paragraph 218.

Install the remaining parts by reversing the removal procedure.

197. **OVERHAUL.** With the differential assembly removed as outlined in paragraph 196, place correlation marks on differential cage (5—Fig. 219 or 220) and cage cap (9). Remove cap screws (6) and lift off cage cap (9). Side gears (12), differential pinions (14), thrust washers (16), pinion shafts (17) and thrust washers (13—Fig. 219) or thrust bearings (25 and 26—Fig. 220) can now be removed from differential cage.

Inspect all parts and renew any that are worn or otherwise damaged. When

reassembling, tighten cap screws (6—Fig. 219 or 220) to a torque of 75-85 ft.-lbs., then install safety wire to prevent them from working loose.

If main drive bevel ring gear is to be renewed, refer to paragraph 198.

MAIN DRIVE BEVEL GEARS
Models G900-G950-G1000-G1000 Vista-G1050-G1350

198. The main drive bevel pinion (8—Fig. 219 or 220) and ring gear (7) are available in matched sets only. To renew the bevel pinion, follow the procedure outlined in paragraph 188. To renew the bevel ring gear, first remove the differential assembly as outlined in paragraph 196, then unbolt and remove bevel ring gear from differential cage (5).

When installing the bevel ring gear, tighten retaining cap screws to a torque of 85-95 ft.-lbs. and on early models G900, G1000 and G1000 Vista secure with safety wire. Late models G900, G1000 and G1000 Vista and all models G950, G1050 and G1350 are equipped with self-locking cap screws.

Install the assembled differential in the differential housing and adjust carrier bearing pre-load as outlined in paragraph 196.

Mesh position (cone point) of main drive bevel gears is controlled by shims interposed between transmission and differential housings. A mounting dimension number from −0.001 to +0.005 is etched on end of pinion. Using a gage as shown in Fig. 221, measure the distance from transmission case to the face of pinion bearing cone. This distance minus 0.097 and plus the mounting dimension etched on end of pinion will determine the correct thickness of shim pack to be used. Shims are available in 0.010, 0.012, 0.016 and 0.020 thick-

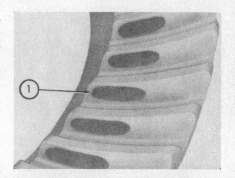

Fig. 222–Correct tooth contact pattern (1) starts near toe end of tooth and extends ½ to ⅝ the length of the tooth.

nesses. Select a shim pack within 0.002 of the determined thickness.

Assemble the housings, using the determined shim pack, making sure some backlash exists. Tighten cap screws securing differential housing to transmission housing to a torque of 310-320 ft.-lbs. Check bevel gear backlash and adjust, if necessary, as outlined in paragraph 196.

After the above adjustments are completed, check the tooth contact pattern as follows: Apply a light coat of Prussian blue on bevel ring gear teeth and rotate the gear set in normal direction of rotation. Mesh position is correct when tooth contact pattern is approximately ½ to ⅝ the length of the tooth, starting near toe end of tooth as shown in Fig. 222. If tooth contact pattern is on heel of tooth, add shims between transmission and differential housings. If tooth contact pattern is on toe of tooth, reduce the shim pack between the housings. If shim pack thickness is altered to obtain the correct tooth pattern (mesh position), readjust backlash, then install final drive units as outlined in paragraph 203.

Install the remaining parts by reversing the removal procedure.

FINAL DRIVE AND REAR AXLE

This section covers service procedures on final drive bull gears, bull pinions and rear axle units used on models G VI, G705, G706, G707, G708, MF95 and MF97. For service on similar components used on model G900, G950, G1000, G1000 Vista, G1050 and G1350 tractors, refer to section beginning with paragraph 203.

BULL PINION
Models G VI-G705-G706-G707-G708-MF95-MF97

199. To remove either bull pinion, first remove the brake assembly and

brake back plate. Reinstall one brake disc on bull pinion to serve as a fulcrum, then insert a pry bar between brake disc and transmission housing and remove bull pinion and bearing.

To remove the bull pinion, bearing and bull pinion sleeve as an assembly, first remove transmission top cover and rear cover or pto output unit. Remove rear axle and housing assembly as outlined in paragraph 202. Support differential from above, using wire and a bar across top opening. Tilt the loose bull gear to clear the cut-out in bull pinion sleeve, remove brake

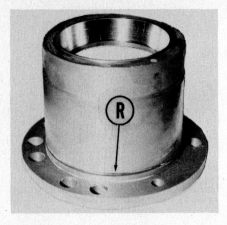

Fig. 223–On some models, bull pinion shaft sleeve is sealed by "O" ring (R). On earlier models, fabric shims must be used in differential carrier bearing adjusting shim pack.

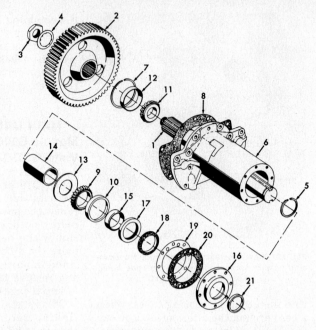

Fig. 226–Exploded view of rear axle assembly used on models G VI, G705, G706, G707, G708, MF95 and MF97.

1. Rear axle
2. Bull gear
3. Axle nut
4. Washer
5. Snap ring
6. Axle housing
7. Snap ring
8. Gasket
9. Bearing cone
10. Bearing cup
11. Bearing cone
12. Bearing cup
13. Grease retainer
14. Sleeve
15. Collar
16. Bearing cover
17. Oil seal
18. Felt
19. Shim
20. Gasket
21. Spacer

assembly, brake back plate and the two remaining bull pinion sleeve retaining cap screws, then remove bull pinion, bearing and bull pinion sleeve as a unit. Save the differential carrier bearing adjusting shims which are located between sleeve flange and transmission housing.

Fig. 224–Brake back plate on some models contains an "O" ring (R) as well as shaft seal (S). Earlier models use a gasket seal.

Fig. 225–Use seal sleeve (S) when installing brake back plate and seal assembly.

Reinstall by reversing the removal procedure, using the removed shim pack or one of identical thickness. On models so equipped, check the sealing "O" ring (R—Fig. 223) and renew if its condition is questionable. Tighten bull pinion sleeve retaining cap screws to a torque of 75 ft.-lbs. and brake plate retaining cap screws to a torque of 90-95 ft.-lbs. (½-inch cap screws) or 250 ft.-lbs. (¾-inch cap screws). Adjust the brakes as outlined in paragraph 207.

BULL GEARS
Models G VI-G705-G706-G707-G708-MF95-MF97

200. The differential assembly must be removed before either bull gear can be removed. If service is required on only one bull gear, proceed as outlined in paragraph 192; if both bull gears must be removed, proceed as outlined in paragraph 191.

AXLE SHAFTS AND HOUSINGS
Models G VI-G705-G706-G707-G708-MF95-MF97

201. **BEARING ADJUSTMENT.** Axle bearing end play is controlled by shims (19—Fig. 226) between bearing cap and axle housing. To adjust bearings, support rear of tractor and remove tire and wheel assembly. Remove bearing cover (16) and vary number of shims (19) between cover and housing to provide zero end play of shaft and yet permit same to rotate without binding.

202. **R&R ASSEMBLY.** Support rear of tractor under transmission and remove wheel and tire assembly. Remove transmission top cover and power take-off unit. Straighten bull gear retaining nut lock and remove

bull gear retaining nut (N—Fig. 227). Remove axle housing to transmission housing retaining bolts and remove axle shaft and housing assembly as a unit, using a hoist or other suitable support.

When reinstalling the unit, position bull gear on bottom of transmission housing with long hub to inside, engage splines of axle and bull gear; then steady the outer end of axle as unit is raised into position. Differential, carrier bearings and bull pinion sleeves must be installed and adjusted before rear axle and housing is installed.

Use Permatex or other suitable sealant on cap screw threads and tighten cap screws to a torque of 120 ft.-lbs. when installing axle and housing assembly. Tighten bull gear retaining nut to a torque of 450 ft.-lbs. and secure by bending retaining washer. Complete the assembly by reversing the disassembly procedure.

Fig. 227–Axle nut (N) can be loosened and removed through pto output shaft opening in rear of transmission housing.

FINAL DRIVE AND REAR AXLE

This section covers service procedures on final drive bull gears, bull pinions and rear axle units used on model G900, G950, G1000, G1000 Vista, G1050 and G1350 tractors. For service on similar components used on all earlier models, refer to section beginning with paragraph 199.

REMOVE AND REINSTALL
Models G900-G950-G1000-G1000 Vista-G1050-G1350

203. To remove either final drive assembly, first drain differential housing, then support rear of tractor and remove battery, fender and wheel and tire assembly. Unbolt and remove brake and brake housing. Remove hitch or drawbar lower support and clutch or brake pedals as necessary.

NOTE: To remove the left final drive, on tractors equipped with pto, remove the hydraulic reservoir and pto control lever on models G900 and G1000; rockshaft assembly, pto cover and pto control lever on models G950, G1050 and G1350; and disconnect pto shift linkage on model G1000 Vista.

Bolt a lifting bracket to final drive housing as shown in Fig. 217, attach a chain hoist to the front hole in lifting bracket, then unbolt and remove final drive housing assembly. Withdraw bull pinion shaft with bearings.

Reinstall by reversing removal procedure and adjust bull pinion bearings and axle bearings as outlined in paragraph 204 on models G900, G950, G1000, G1000 Vista and G1050 or paragraph 205 on model G1350.

OVERHAUL
Models G900-G950-G1000-G1000 Vista-G1050

204. With the final drive removed as outlined in paragraph 203, unbolt and remove bearing cap (13—Fig. 228) and shims (16). Withdraw axle shaft and bull gear assembly from housing (5). Using a suitable puller, remove bearing cone (10) from inner end of axle shaft. Press or drive axle shaft from spacer (4) and bull gear (2). Remove axle outer bearing cone (8) and collar (12). Inspect all parts and renew any that are excessively worn or otherwise damaged.

When reassembling, coat the inside diameter of collar (12) with Bore-tite or similar sealant before installing collar on the axle shaft. When renewing oil seal (14) in bearing cap (13), coat outside diameter of seal with Bore-tite or similar sealant and press seal firmly in place with lip edge toward inside. Install new seals in brake housing. NOTE: The smaller seal acts as a dust seal and must be installed with lip edge to the outside. The larger (oil) seal must have lip edge to the inside.

Reinstall the final drive assembly by reversing the disassembly procedure, using a new gasket (7). Tighten the final drive housing retaining cap screws to a torque of 200 ft.-lbs.

Install the brake housing using the original shim pack and a new "O" ring. Tighten the 12-point cap screws evenly to a torque of 160-180 ft.-lbs. Attach a dial indicator and check bull pinion shaft end play. Add or remove shims behind brake housing as required to obtain 0.001-0.003 end play.

To adjust the axle shaft bearing preload, tighten the bearing cap retaining cap screws securely to seat the bearings; then, back off the cap screws to relieve any pre-load on the bearings.

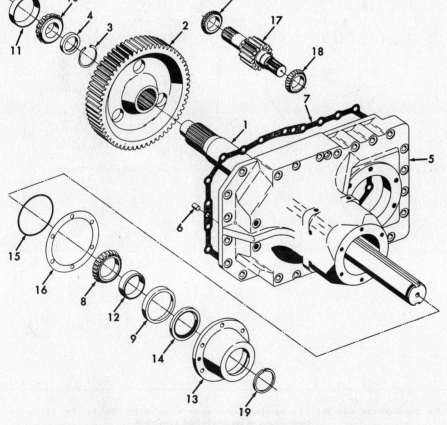

Fig. 228–Exploded view of final drive assembly used on models G900, G950, G1000, G1000 Vista and G1050.

1. Axle shaft	6. Dowel pin	11. Bearing cup
2. Bull gear	7. Gasket	12. Collar
3. Snap ring	8. Bearing cone	13. Bearing cap
4. Spacer	9. Bearing cup	14. Oil seal
5. Housing	10. Bearing cone	15. "O" ring

16. Shim (0.002, 0.003 and 0.010)
17. Bull pinion
18. Bearing cone
19. Snap ring

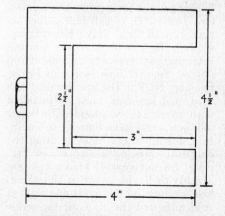

Fig. 229–Special tool for attaching torque wrench to rear axle shaft can be made from ¾-inch plate, using the dimensions shown. Weld a nut on end as shown.

Attach a torque wrench to end of axle shaft. NOTE: A tool can be made from ¾-inch plate, using dimensions shown in Fig. 229, for use in attaching torque wrench to axle shaft. Check and record rolling torque required to keep the axle shaft in motion. Tighten bearing cap retaining cap screws to a torque of 75-85 ft.-lbs. and make a second rolling torque check. If the bearing pre-load is correct, the second rolling torque reading (with cap screws tightened) will be 35 to 40 in.-lbs. greater than the previously recorded no-pre-load reading. If bearing pre-load is not as specified, add or remove shims (16 —Fig. 228) as required to obtain the correct bearing pre-load.

Complete the balance of reassembly and adjust brakes as outlined in paragraph 206 or 207.

Model G1350

205. To overhaul either final drive and planetary hub assembly, first remove wheel and tire assembly, then remove plug (25—Fig. 231) and drain the planetary housing (24). Unbolt and remove cover (20), then remove snap ring (18), drive gear (17) and snap ring (16). Unbolt spindle (29) from adapter (23—Fig. 230), remove planetary hub assembly and lay it aside for later disassembly.

Remove the balance of final drive assembly as outlined in paragraph 203. With final drive removed, unbolt and remove adapter (23—Fig. 230) and shims (16). Withdraw axle shaft and bull gear assembly from housing (5). Using a suitable puller, remove bearing cone (10) from inner end of axle shaft. Press or drive axle shaft (1) from spacer (4) and bull gear (2). Remove axle outer bearing cone (8). Inspect all parts and renew any that are excessively worn or otherwise damaged.

Reinstall bull gear, axle shaft and bearings in housing (5), then using new gasket (7), install bull pinion assembly and final drive housing assembly. Tighten final drive housing retaining cap screws to a torque of 200 ft.-lbs. Install new seals in brake housing. NOTE: The smaller seal acts as a dust seal and must be installed with lip edge to the outside. The larger (oil) seal must have lip edge to the inside. Install brake housing using the original shim pack and a new "O" ring. Do not install brake disc assembly or brake cover at this time. Use washers on the studs and tighten stud nuts and the 12-point cap screw securely. Attach a dial indicator and check bull pinion shaft end play. Add or remove shims behind brake housing as required to obtain 0.001-0.003 end

play. Shims are available in thicknesses of 0.002, 0.003, 0.010 and 0.031. Install balance of brake assembly.

To adjust the axle shaft bearing preload, install adapter (23) with new oil seal (14), original shim pack (16) and new "O" ring (15). Tighten adapter retaining cap screws securely to seat the bearings, then back off the cap screws to relieve any pre-load on the bearings. Attach a torque wrench to end of axle shaft. Check and record rolling torque required to keep the axle shaft rotating. Tighten adapter retaining cap screws to a torque of 75-85 ft.-lbs. and make a second rolling torque check. If bearing pre-load is correct, the second rolling torque reading (with cap screws tightened) will be 35-40 in.-lbs. greater than the previously recorded no-pre-load reading. If bearing pre-load is not as specified, add or remove shims (16) as required to obtain the correct bearing pre-load. Shims are available in thicknesses of 0.002, 0.003 and 0.010.

To disassemble the planetary reduction hub, refer to Fig. 231, then unbolt and remove carrier (13) from housing (24). Drive pinion shafts (15) out toward outside of carrier (13) and remove planetary pinions (11), washers (9), needle rollers (10) and spacers (12). Do not lose retaining balls (14). Remove lock nut (7), lock ring (6) and adjusting nut (5), then separate spindle (29) and ring gear assembly from housing (24). Remove oil seal (28), inner bearing (27) and bearing cups (26 and 23) from housing (24). Remove outer bearing (22) from ring gear hub (3). Cut lock wires, then unbolt and remove the six plates (2) from ring gear assembly. Separate ring gear (4) from hub (3).

Clean and inspect all parts and renew any showing excessive wear or other damage.

To reassemble the unit, proceed as follows: Install bearing cups (23 and 26) in housing (24). Place inner bearing cone (27) in bearing cup (26)

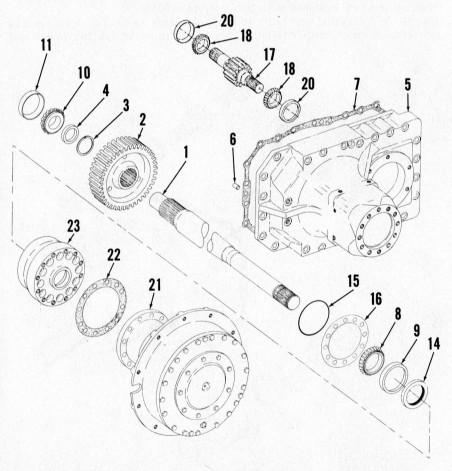

Fig. 230–Exploded view of final drive assembly used on model G1350. Refer to Fig. 231 for exploded view of planetary hub assembly.

1. Axle shaft		17. Bull pinion
2. Bull gear		18. Bearing cone
3. Retaining ring	9. Bearing cup	20. Bearing cup
4. Spacer	10. Bearing cone	21. Planetary
5. Housing	11. Bearing cup	reduction hub
6. Dowel pin	14. Oil seal	assembly
7. Gasket	15. "O" ring	22. Gasket
8. Bearing cone	16. Shim (0.002, 0.003 & 0.010)	23. Adapter

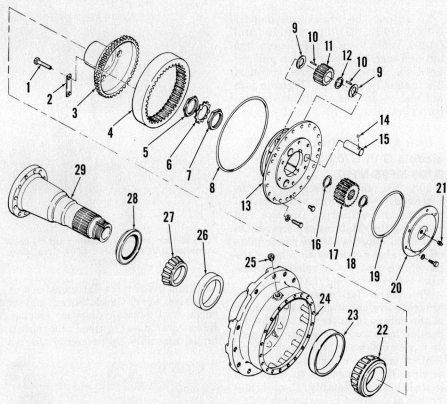

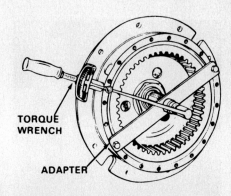

Fig. 232—Torque wrench attached to special adapter bar is used to check pre-load (rolling torque) of planetary hub bearings.

Fig. 231—Exploded view of planetary reduction hub assembly used on model G1350.

1. Cap screw	11. Planetary pinion	20. Cover
2. Plate	12. Spacer	21. Breather
3. Ring gear hub	13. Carrier	22. Bearing cone
4. Ring gear	14. Steel ball	23. Bearing cup
5. Adjusting nut	15. Shaft	24. Planetary housing
6. Lock ring	16. Snap ring	25. Drain plug
7. Lock nut	17. Drive gear	26. Bearing cup
8. "O" ring	18. Snap ring	27. Bearing cone
9. Washer	19. "O" ring	28. Oil seal
10. Needle roller		29. Spindle

and install new oil seal (28) with lip toward bearing. Press outer bearing cone (22) on ring gear hub (3). Place hub in ring gear (4) and secure plates (2) with cap screws (1). Secure cap screws in pairs with lock wire. Stand spindle (29) on flange end, place housing (24) over spindle, then install

ring gear and hub assembly. Install adjusting nut (5) and tighten nut until a rolling torque of 7 to 12 ft.-lbs. (new bearings) or 3 to 5 ft.-lbs. (used bearings) is obtained. NOTE: An adapter bar for attaching torque wrench to housing (Fig. 232) can be made up using the dimensions shown in Fig.

233. Install lock ring (6—Fig. 231) and lock nut (7). Using a small amount of grease, install needle rollers (10) and spacers (12) in planetary pinions (11), then install pinions and washers (9) in carrier (13). Insert pinion shafts (15) and when retaining balls are fully seated, stake face of carrier to secure shafts. Place new "O" ring (8) around carrier and install carrier assembly in housing (24). Use new gasket (22—Fig. 230) and bolt planetary hub assembly (21) to adapter (23). Install snap ring (16—Fig. 231), drive gear (17) and snap ring (18), then install cover (20) with new "O" ring (19).

Complete the balance of assembly and fill transmission, differential and planetary reduction hub to correct level with proper lubricant.

BRAKES

Brakes used on all models are double disc, self energizing type and are splined to the outer end of the bull pinion shafts. On model G1000 Vista, brakes are hydraulically operated. On all other models, brakes are operated through mechanical linkage.

ADJUSTMENT
Model G1000 Vista

206. To adjust the hydraulic brakes on model G1000 Vista, first remove rear hood, then disconnect master cylinder links (2—Fig. 234) from brake pedals. Loosen jam nuts and adjust screws (1) until pedals are even. Tighten jam nuts. Adjust length of both master cylinder links (2) until pedals have approximately ⅛-inch free travel. Secure linkage and install

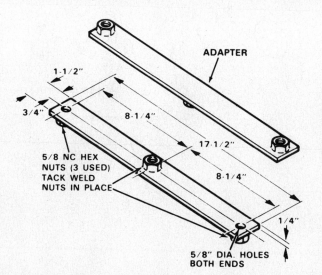

ADAPTER

1-1/2"

3/4"

8-1/4"

17-1/2"

8-1/4"

1/4"

5/8 NC HEX
NUTS (3 USED)
TACK WELD
NUTS IN PLACE

5/8" DIA. HOLES
BOTH ENDS

Fig. 233—Special adapter bar for attaching torque wrench to planetary housing can be made up using the dimensions shown.

Fig. 234—On model G1000 Vista, remove rear hood for access to brake pedal stop screws (1) and master cylinder links (2).

hood. Refer to Fig. 235, loosen jam nut and adjust stop screw (2) under brake arm to prevent the arm from cutting into the rubber cover on brake cylinder. Tighten jam nut. Then, loosen jam nut on pull rod (4) and turn adjusting nut (3) until brake pedal has a full travel of 2¼ inches. Tighten the jam nut and repeat the adjustment on opposite brake.

All Other Models

207. To adjust the brakes on models G VI, G705, G706, G707, G708, MF95 and MF97, refer to Fig. 236, loosen jam nuts and turn adjusting rod (1) as necessary to obtain correct pedal free travel. Correct pedal free travel is 1¾-inches on models G VI and MF95 and ¾-inch on models G705, G706, G707, G708 and MF97. Tighten jam nuts and repeat the adjustment on opposite brake.

To adjust the brakes on models G900, G950, G1000, G1050 and G1350, refer to Fig. 237, loosen jam nut and turn adjusting nut on pull rod until the correct pedal free travel of 2½ inches is obtained. Tighten jam nut and repeat the adjustment on opposite brake.

R&R AND OVERHAUL BRAKE Models G VI-G705-G706-G707-G708-MF95-MF97

208. The brake assembly can be removed from tractor after disconnecting the actuating linkage and removing the retaining cap screws. On models equipped with live power take-off it is also necessary to remove the pto clutch and power release mechanism before removing the left brake.

Procedure for overhauling the brakes is evident after an examination of the removed units. Check the actuating balls and grooves for flat spots or excessive wear and check lining contact surfaces of actuator discs for scoring. Renew parts as required and install brake assembly, then adjust brakes as outlined in paragraph 207.

Refer to paragraph 214 for information concerning the installation of the continuous power take-off clutch and power release mechanism.

Models G900-G950-G1000-G1000 Vista-G1050-G1350

209. To remove the brake assembly, first remove the brake cover, then disconnect the pull rod from the clevis. Withdraw the outer brake disc, actuator assembly and inner brake disc from brake housing. Disconnect the actuator springs and separate the actuator discs. Inspect the actuating

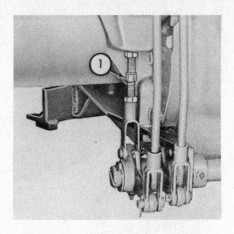

Fig. 236—View of brake adjusting rod (1) used on models G VI, G705, G706, G707, G708, MF95 and MF97.

balls and grooves for flat spots, rust or excessive wear. Check lining contact surfaces of actuator discs for scoring. Renew parts as required and install brake assembly by reversing the re-

Fig. 237—View of brake adjuster (2) used on G950, G1050 and G1350. Additional adjustment can be made at linkage clevis (1). Brake adjuster (2) is similar on G900 and G1000 tractors.

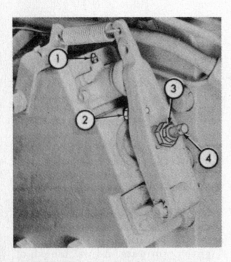

Fig. 235—View of brake on right side of model G1000 Vista showing adjusting points.

1. Bleed screw
2. Stop screw
3. Adjusting nut
4. Pull rod

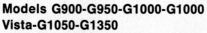

Fig. 238—Exploded view of typical disc brake assembly.

1. Shim
2. "O" ring seal
3. Oil seal
4. Dust seal
5. Brake housing
6. Brake disc
7. Actuating disc
8. Steel ball (5 used)
9. Extension spring
10. Cover
11. Torque sleeve
12. Plain link
13. Yoke link
14. Clevis
15. Pull rod
16. Dust boot
17. Adjusting nut

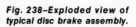
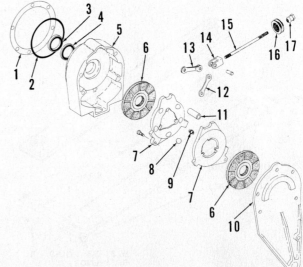

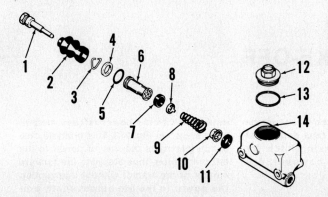

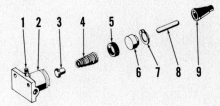

Fig. 239–Exploded view of master cylinder used on G1000 Vista brake system.

1. Push rod
2. Rubber boot
3. Lock ring
4. Stop ring
5. Seal ring
6. Piston
7. Cup
8. Spring seat
9. Spring
10. Check valve
11. Valve seal
12. Filler cap
13. Gasket
14. Body

Fig. 240–Exploded view of brake cylinder used on model G1000 Vista.

1. Bleed screw
2. Body
3. Piston stop
4. Return spring
5. Cup
6. Piston
7. Retaining ring
8. Push rod
9. Rubber boot

moval procedure. Tighten the cover retaining nuts to a torque of 160-180 ft.-lbs. Adjust brakes as outlined in paragraph 206 or 207.

R&R AND OVERHAUL MASTER CYLINDERS
Model G1000 Vista

210. To remove either master cylinder, raise hood half and remove rear hood section. Disconnect brake line, unpin clevis from pedal, remove the two mounting bolts and lift out master cylinder.

To disassemble the master cylinder, refer to Fig. 239, remove cap (12) and dump fluid from reservoir. Remove push rod (1), boot (2), retaining ring (3), stop ring (4), piston and seal ring (5 and 6), cup (7), spring and seat (8 and 9), check valve (10) and valve seal (11).

Clean all parts and inspect piston and body bore for excessive wear, scoring or other damage. The master cylinder bore can be honed as long as the diameter is not increased to where more than 0.007 clearance exists between piston and bore. If the bore is badly scored or does not clean up within limits, renew complete master cylinder assembly. A repair kit is available to service the master cylinder.

Lubricate internal parts and reassemble master cylinder by reversing the disassembly procedure. Fill reservoir and install cap (12) with new gasket (13). Move push rod in and out a few times to fill bore of master cylinder.

Reinstall master cylinder, then bleed air from brake system as follows: Make certain that master cylinder is filled to within ½-inch from the filler opening. Pump brake pedal until pressure is built up in brake line. While holding pedal down, loosen bleed screw on brake cylinder and allow air to flow from system. Close bleed screw, then release pedal. Repeat this bleeding procedure until bubble free

fluid flows from bleed screw. Refill reservoir to correct level (½-inch from filler opening). Check brake adjustment as outlined in paragraph 206.

R&R AND OVERHAUL BRAKE CYLINDER
Model G1000 Vista

211. To remove either brake cylinder, remove brake arm return spring, disconnect park brake cable and back off brake adjuster nut. Disconnect brake line, then unbolt and remove brake cylinder.

To disassemble the cylinder refer to Fig. 240 and remove rubber boot (9) and push rod (8). Remove retaining ring (7), piston (6), cup (5), piston return spring (4) and piston stop (3). Bleed screw (1) can also be removed.

Clean and inspect all parts and renew any showing excessive wear, scoring or other damage.

If condition of cylinder is satisfactory, renew cup (5) and reassemble cylinder. Reinstall cylinder, bleed air from system as outlined in paragraph 210 and adjust brake as in paragraph 206.

BELT PULLEY

Models G VI-G705-G706-G707-G708-MF95-MF97

212. The belt pulley unit is mounted on side of transmission case and is driven by a bevel gear on the trans-

mission lower countershaft. The procedure for removing, disassembling and overhauling the belt pulley unit is evident after an examination of the unit and reference to Fig. 241.

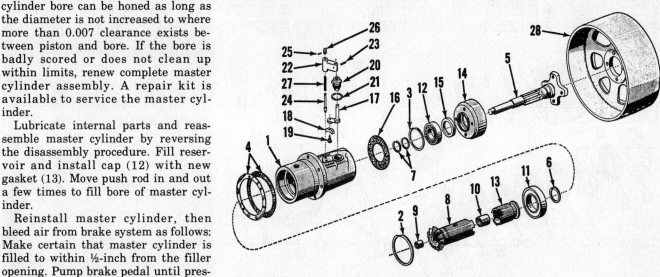

Fig. 241–Exploded view of belt pulley drive used on model G VI, G705, G706, G707, G708, MF95 and MF97.

1. Housing
2. Snap ring
3. Snap ring
4. Shim and gasket
5. Drive shaft
6. Snap ring
7. Snap rings
8. Bevel pinion
9. Needle bearing
10. Needle bearing
11. Ball bearing
12. Ball bearing
13. Sliding jaw
14. Retainer
15. Oil seal
16. Gasket
17. Shifting arm
18. Block
19. Pin
20. Nut
21. Gasket
22. Lever
23. Roll pin
24. Lock pin
25. Roll pin
26. Knob
27. Spring
28. Belt pulley

POWER TAKE-OFF

Models G VI, G705, G706, G707, G708, MF95 and MF97 are equipped with the pto assembly shown in Fig. 242. The pto assembly is driven by the connecting shaft (28) which is splined to the transmission countershaft. The pto is thus dependent on the transmission main clutch for power. Some models, however, are equipped with the power release mechanism shown in Fig. 243. This multiple disc clutch interrupts the flow of power to the left bull pinion, thus stopping the forward motion of the tractor without interrupting the power to the pto output shaft, providing a continuous (live) pto.

For service on the power take-off unit used on models G900, G950, G1000, G1000 Vista, G1050 and G1350, refer to separate section beginning with paragraph 217.

CLUTCH
Models So Equipped

213. **ADJUSTMENT.** To adjust the disc type power take-off clutch, turn the adjusting nut on clutch rod (A—Fig. 244) either way as required to give the clutch control handle a free travel of 2½ inches minimum.

214. **OVERHAUL.** Remove left rear wheel, fender and fender bracket. Remove cover from unit; remove screws (S—Fig. 245) and withdraw the bearing cage. The outboard bearing bronze bushing (7) can be renewed at this time. Remove outer snap ring (2—Fig. 243) and withdraw adapter (3). Remove snap rings (2 and 5) and withdraw the clutch assembly.

The clutch can be disassembled after removing the cover plate cap screws. Inspect all internal parts and renew or recondition any which are question-

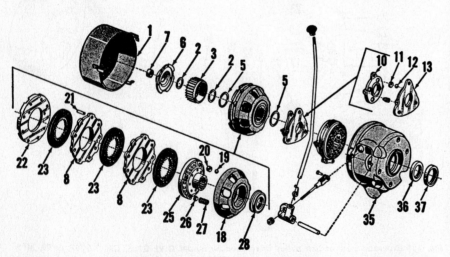

Fig. 242—Exploded view of pto output shaft assembly used on models G VI, G705, G706, G707, G708, MF95 and MF97. Items 13, 14 and 15 are used on some early models.

1. Shift fork	8. Detent ball	15. Packing nut	22. Bearing cone
2. Snap ring	9. Cross bar	16. Bracket	23. Bearing cup
3. Retainer	10. Link	17. Shim	24. Housing
4. Felt seal	11. Lever	18. Oil seal	25. Output shaft
5. Gasket	12. Shift rod	19. Bearing cap	26. Sliding jaw
6. Plug	13. Bearing cap	20. Bearing cup	27. Bushing
7. Spring	14. Packing	21. Bearing cone	28. Shaft

Fig. 243—Exploded view of pto clutch and power release mechanism used on some models.

1. Cover	8. Intermediate plate	19. Ball	26. Spring seat
2. Snap ring	10. Power release plate	20. Ball insert	27. Spring
3. Adapter	11. Ball insert	21. Spacer	28. Thrust bearing
5. Snap ring	12. Ball	22. Cover plate	35. Main housing
6. Bearing cage	13. Backing plate	23. Lined disc	36. Inner oil seal
7. Bearing	18. Housing	25. Power plate	37. Outer oil seal

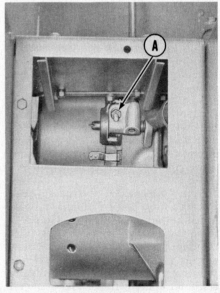

Fig. 244—View showing location of power release clutch adjustment (A) on model G VI tractor. Other tractors are similar.

Fig. 245–Power release mechanism used on model G VI tractors to interrupt power at left bull pinion shaft and provide continuous pto. Other tractors are similar. See Fig. 243 for legend.

able. Linings should be renewed if they are warped or worn. Machined surfaces of cover plate, intermediate discs and power plate should be smooth and not scored or grooved. Springs, spring seats, balls and ball inserts must be in good condition and not heat discolored. When reassembling the clutch, make certain that all parts are in position and properly aligned.

To remove the power release mechanism, remove snap ring (5), remove the three retaining cap screws and disconnect the linkage. Disassemble the unit and renew any questionable parts.

Reassemble the clutch and power release mechanism by reversing the disassembly procedure and adjust the unit as outlined in paragraph 213.

OUTPUT SHAFT
Models So Equipped
215. **BEARING ADJUSTMENT.** Vary number of shims (17—Fig. 242) between bearing cap and housing to provide zero end play to PTO shaft and yet permit same to rotate freely.

216. **R&R AND DISASSEMBLE.** Drain lubricant from transmission housing or raise rear of tractor far enough to prevent loss of lubricant from housing after PTO unit has been removed. Remove cap screws retaining PTO housing to rear of transmission and withdraw unit from transmission housing. The need and procedure for further disassembly will be evident by an examination of the parts and reference to Fig. 242. To reinstall, reverse removal procedure.

POWER TAKE-OFF

This section covers service procedures on the power take-off used on model G900, G950, G1000, G1000 Vista, G1050 and G1350 tractors. For power take-off used on all earlier models, refer to section beginning with paragraph 213.

The power take-off system is driven by a splined hub located at the rear of the engine crankshaft and is in continuous operation as long as the engine is running and the pto clutch is engaged.

The occasion for overhauling the complete power take-off system will be infrequent. The subsequent paragraphs will therefore be outlined on the basis of local repairs.

DRIVING HUB
Models G900-G950-G1000-G1000 Vista-G1050-G1350
217. **REMOVE AND REINSTALL.** To remove the driving hub (3—Fig. 246), first detach engine from transmission as outlined in paragraph 164. Remove clutch assembly as outlined in paragraph 158, then unbolt

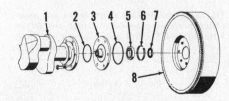

Fig. 246–On models G900, G950, G1000, G1000 Vista, G1050 and G1350, pto driving hub (3) is located at rear of crankshaft.

1. Crankshaft
2. "O" ring
3. Driving hub
4. "O" ring
5. Ball bearing
6. Tolerance ring
7. Oil seal
8. Flywheel

and remove flywheel following the procedure given in paragraph 88.

When reassembling, renew "O" rings (2 and 4) and seal (7) in flywheel. Install flywheel as outlined in paragraph 88. The balance of reassembly is the reverse of disassembly procedure.

PTO CLUTCH, BRAKE AND INPUT SHAFT
Models G900-G950-G1000-G1000 Vista-G1050-G1350
218. **CLUTCH ADJUSTMENT.** The pto clutch should engage with a distinct snap, with 45-50 pounds of pressure required on the engaging lever to lock the clutch in the engaged position. If little effort (25 pound minimum) is required to engage the clutch, the unit must be adjusted as follows: On model G1000, drain the hydraulic system, then remove tractor seat, hydraulic reservoir assembly and differential housing top cover. On models G900 and G1000 Vista, drain the differential housing and remove bottom cover. On models G950 and G1050 remove seat assembly and the cover on top of differential cover. On model G1350, remove seat assembly and access plug in differential cover. Pull pto engaging lever to the disengaged (rear) position and turn engine until the lock pin (1—Fig. 247) is accessible through the opening. Depress the lock pin and turn the notched adjusting ring (2) until lock pin engages the next notch and recheck the adjust-

ment. Repeat the procedure if necessary until the proper adjustment is obtained.

219. **BRAKE ADJUSTMENT.** To adjust the pto brake, it is first necessary to remove the fuel tank, tractor seat, hydraulic reservoir assembly and differential top cover on G1000 Vista, tractor seat, hydraulic reservoir assembly and differential top cover on G900 and G1000, or tractor seat, hitch rockshaft assembly and differential top cover on G950, G1050 and G1350 tractors.

On models G900, G1000 and G1000 Vista, adjust length of spring (4—Fig. 249) to 1⅝ inches (between washers). Lubricate the clutch plates (14 and 15 —Fig. 248) and brake band groove in the clutch cage (18). Disengage pto clutch and attach torque wrench to 1000 rpm output shaft. Adjust tension on brake band (19) until 14-16 ft.-lbs. is required to keep the 1000 rpm shaft rotating. Engage pto clutch and check

Fig. 247–Depress lock pin (1) and turn adjusting ring (2) to adjust pto clutch.

to see that brake band is free of drum at this time.

On models G950, G1050 and G1350, adjust length of spring (4—Fig. 248) to 1⅛ inches (between washers). Hold control lever all the way to the rear and adjust nuts on brake band (19) until there is 0.010-0.015 clearance between each of the spring coils. Attach a torque wrench to the 1000 rpm output shaft. With control lever held all the way to the rear, rolling torque on the 1000 rpm shaft should be 40-60 ft.-lbs. When pto clutch is engaged, brake band should be free.

220. **R&R AND OVERHAUL.** To remove the pto clutch, brake and input shaft, first drain the differential housing, then proceed as follows: On model G1000 Vista, remove fuel tank, seat, hydraulic reservoir and differential top cover. On G900 and G1000, remove tractor seat, hydraulic reservoir assembly and differential top cover. On models G950, G1050 and G1350, remove tractor seat, hitch rockshaft assembly and differential top cover.

On all models, disengage pto clutch, remove safety wires and drive spiral

pins out of shift fork (6—Fig. 248 or 249) and brake lever (30) if so equipped. Withdraw control lever shaft (35) on G1000 Vista or control lever and shaft (5) on all other models. Lift out fork (6) and yoke (7). Disconnect brake band (19) and remove pto brake assembly.

Remove the lube pump as outlined in paragraph 223 or 225. Unbolt and remove rear cover (2—Fig. 250), idler gear (22) and the 540 rpm output shaft assembly. Remove front plate (4), suction tube assembly and oil return tube (8).

Working through the rear opening, remove snap ring (24—Fig. 248). Disconnect linkage between sliding sleeve (9) and floating plate (13), then move sliding sleeve forward on input shaft. Unseat snap ring (8) from its groove and slide it forward on shaft. Depress lock pin (11) and remove adjusting ring (10) from threaded portion of clutch hub (16). Remove input shaft (1) with bearing (23) through rear opening. Remove clutch parts from top as input shaft is withdrawn. Remove snap ring (28) and bump pto drive

gear (22) with bearing (26) from differential housing. Needle bearing (20) can be removed at this time.

Clean and inspect all parts and renew any showing excessive wear or other damage. Make certain oil passages in input shaft are clean.

Reassemble by reversing disassembly procedure and adjust pto clutch and brake as outlined in paragraphs 218 and 219.

PTO OUTPUT SHAFTS
Models G900-G950-G1000-G1000 Vista-G1050-G1350

221. **R&R AND OVERHAUL.** To remove the pto output shafts, refer to Fig. 250 and proceed as follows: Drain the differential housing, then unbolt and remove rear cover (2) with idler gear and 540 rpm output shaft assembly. Withdraw idler shaft (24), idler gear (22) and thrust washers (21 and 23) from cover. Remove 540 rpm shaft (30), gear (31) with bearing cones (29 and 32) from cover. Bearings and gear can now be removed from

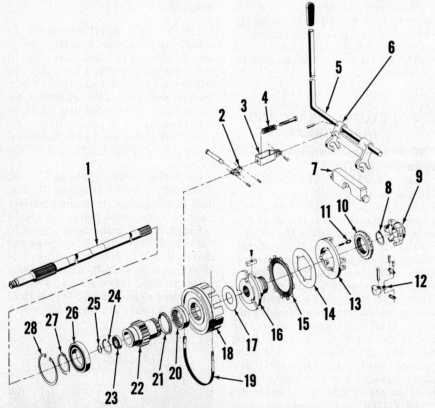

Fig. 248—Exploded view of pto clutch and brake used on models G950, G1050 and G1350. Pto clutch used on models G900, G1000 and G1000 Vista is similar. Refer also to Fig. 249.

1. Input shaft
2. Brake link
3. Spring bracket
4. Spring
5. Control lever
6. Clutch fork
7. Yoke
8. Snap ring
9. Sliding sleeve
10. Adjusting ring
11. Lock pin
12. Lever
13. Floating plate
14. Driving plate (7 used)
15. Driven plate (8 used)
16. Clutch hub
17. Thrust washer
18. Clutch cage
19. Pto brake band
20. Needle bearing
21. Spacer
22. Pto drive gear
23. Ball bearing
24. Snap ring
25. Snap ring
26. Ball bearing
27. Snap ring
28. Snap ring

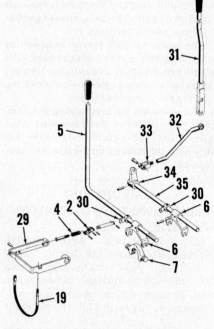

Fig. 249—Exploded view of pto brake and associated parts used on G900, G1000 and G1000 Vista tractors. Control lever, linkage and shaft (items 31 thru 35 are used on model G1000 Vista).

2. Brake link
4. Spring
5. Control lever
6. Clutch fork
7. Yoke
19. Pto brake band
29. Brake bracket
30. Brake lever
31. Control lever
32. Link
33. Clevis
34. Lever
35. Shaft

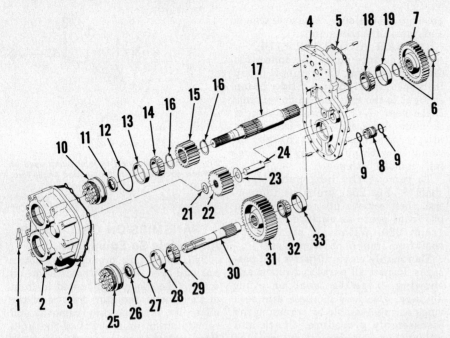

Fig. 250–Exploded view of dual speed pto rear unit used on G900, G950, G1000, G1000 Vista, G1050 and G1350.

1. Lock	9. "O" ring	26. Oil seal
2. Rear cover	10. Adjusting nut	27. "O" ring
3. Gasket	11. Oil seal	28. Bearing cup
4. Front plate	12. "O" ring	29. Bearing cone
5. Gasket	13. Bearing cup	30. 540 rpm output
6. Snap ring	14. Bearing cone	shaft
7. 1000 rpm driving	15. 540 rpm driving	31. 540 rpm driven
gear	gear	gear
8. Oil tube	16. Snap ring	32. Bearing cone
	17. 1000 rpm output	33. Bearing cup
	shaft	
	18. Bearing cone	
	19. Bearing cup	
	21. Thrust washer	
	22. Idler gear	
	23. Thrust washer	
	24. Idler shaft	
	25. Adjusting nut	

540 rpm output shaft, using a suitable press.

Remove the lube pump as outlined in paragraph 223 or 225. On G1000 Vista, remove fuel tank, seat, hydraulic reservoir assembly and differential top cover. On G900 and G1000, remove tractor seat, hydraulic reservoir assembly and differential housing top cover. On G950, G1050 and G1350, remove tractor seat, hitch rockshaft assembly and differential cover. Remove front plate (4), then remove pto input shaft and clutch as outlined in paragraph 220.

Remove snap ring from front end of 1000 rpm output shaft and bump shaft rearward out of gear (7). Bearings (14 and 18), snap rings and gear (15) can now be removed. Remove lock (1) and rotate bearing adjusting nuts (10 and 25) until they are removed from inside of cover (2).

When reassembling, renew oil seals, "O" rings and gaskets. Install idler shaft with roll pin pointing up and tang on thrust washer (23) to the top away from idler gear. Reinstall all parts by reversing the removal procedure. Adjust pto clutch and brake as outlined in paragraphs 218 and 219. Using a dial indicator, check the end play of each output shaft. Turn adjusting nuts (10 and 25) as required until the desired 0.001-0.008 end play is obtained on each shaft. Secure the adjusting nuts with lock (1).

LUBE PUMP
All Models With Two-Speed Ampli-Torc

222. PRESSURE TEST AND ADJUSTMENT. To check and adjust the lube pump oil pressure, remove sending unit from tee in pressure line and install a test gage. With the transmission oil warm and engine operating at 1800 rpm, gage should show a reading of 30-35 psi. If not, loosen lock nut (8—Fig. 251) and turn adjusting

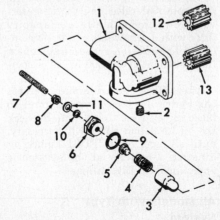

Fig. 251–Exploded view of the lube pump used on models equipped with two-speed Ampli-Torc.

1. Body	
2. Plug	8. Lock nut
3. Relief valve	9. Gasket
4. Spring	10. Lead washer or "O" ring
5. Spring seat	11. Washer
6. Cover	12. Idler gear
7. Adjusting screw	13. Drive gear

screw (7) as required to obtain the specified pressure. Tighten lock nut, remove test gage and reinstall sending unit.

223. R&R AND OVERHAUL. To remove the lube pump, remove the cap screws retaining pump to the pto front plate and slide pump straight to the rear and off dowel pins. Drive gear (13—Fig. 251) will remain on pump drive shaft on tractor while idler gear (12) will be removed with pump body (1). Carefully remove both gears.

Loosen lock nut (8), back out adjusting screw (7), then remove cover (6) with gasket (9). Spring seat (5), relief valve spring (4) and relief valve (3) can now be removed.

To remove the lube pump drive shaft (2—Fig. 252), drain the differential, then remove pto rear cover and pto front plate as outlined in paragraph 220. Withdraw pump drive shaft from front of pto front plate.

Clean all parts and passages thoroughly and check the condition of all components, including the drive shaft bushing in pto front plate. Renew parts as necessary and reassemble by reversing the disassembly procedure. Adjust pressure as outlined in paragraph 222.

All Models With Three-Speed Ampli-Torc

224. PRESSURE TEST AND ADJUSTMENT. To check the lube pump oil pressure, remove transmission oil pressure sending unit (7—Fig. 253) from tee in the line between filter and relief valve. Install a 500 psi test gage. Start engine and operate at rated rpm. With transmission oil at operating temperature, lube pump oil

Fig. 252.–View showing lube pump drive shaft being removed.

1. Pump suction tube
2. Pump drive shaft
3. Pto oil return tube

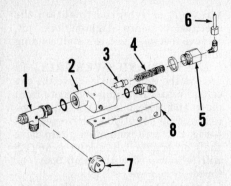

Fig. 253—Exploded view of lube pump relief valve assembly used on models equipped with three-speed Ampli-Torc.

1. Tee	6. Relief line
2. Valve body	7. Oil pressure
3. Relief valve	sending unit
4. Spring	8. Relief valve
5. Connector	mounting bracket

pressure should be 280-300 psi. If pressure is low, disconnect relief line (6), remove connector (5) from valve body and add washers as necessary behind relief valve spring (4) until correct

pressure is obtained. Remove test gage and reinstall sending unit.

225. **R&R AND OVERHAUL.** To remove the lube pump, disconnect the oil pressure line, then unbolt pump from pto front plate. Slide pump straight to the rear and off dowel pins. Drive gear (7—Fig. 254) will remain on pump drive shaft on tractor while idler gear (4) and shaft (5) may be removed with pump body (1). Carefully remove both gears.

To remove the lube pump drive shaft (2—Fig. 252), drain the differential, then remove pto rear cover and pto front plate as outlined in paragraph 220. Withdraw pump drive shaft from front of pto front plate.

Thoroughly clean all parts and passages. Inspect all parts and renew any showing excessive wear or other damage. Use new gaskets and seal rings and reassemble by reversing the disassembly procedure. Check and adjust transmission oil pressure as outlined in paragraph 224.

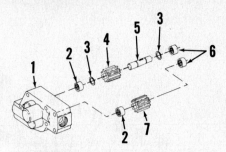

Fig. 254—Exploded view of lube pump used on models equipped with three-speed Ampli-Torc.

1. Body	
2. Needle bearings	5. Idler gear shaft
3. Retaining rings	6. Needle bearings
4. Idler gear	7. Drive gear

TRANSMISSION OIL COOLER
All Models So Equipped

226. Most late production tractors are equipped with a transmission oil cooler. The cooler is mounted in front of the tractor radiator. Service of the oil cooler involves only removal and reinstallation or renewal of the unit. Removal of the oil cooler is obvious after an examination of the unit.

HYDRAULIC LIFT (TYPES E, F & G)

This section covers the "Type E" hydraulic lift system used on models G VI, G705, G706, G707, G708, MF95 and MF97, the "Type F" hydraulic lift system used on models G900, G1000 and G1000 Vista and the "Type G" hydraulic lift system used on models G950, G1050 and G1350. The section covers the hydraulic pump, reservoir, control valve and remote cylinder.

For model G900, G1000 and G1000 Vista tractors equipped with the three-point hitch "Tel-O-Flo" system, refer to section beginning with paragraph 255.

For all models equipped with closed center three-point hitch system, refer to section beginning with paragraph 275.

FILLING AND BLEEDING
All Models With Type "E"
System

227. It is recommended that the complete hydraulic system be drained at least once a year. Before refilling the system, remove and thoroughly clean the filter screen or renew filter element.

Fill the reservoir with MM hydraulic oil, operate the hydraulic jack and power steering several times and refill the reservoir to the "FULL" mark on the dipstick.

Capacity of the system is approximately 3 gallons.

All Models With Type "F"
System

228. Under normal operating conditions, it is recommended that the hydraulic reservoir be drained and refilled with new MM hydraulic oil every 600 hours of operation or at least once a year. A suction screen located inside reservoir (at bottom of tank) filters the oil as it leaves the reservoir. Oil returning to the reservoir flows through a large capacity filter with a renewable paper element. Clean the suction screen and renew filter element every 300 hours of operation.

After filling the reservoir, operate the hydraulic jack several times to bleed the air from the system. Recheck the oil level and add oil if necessary, until oil level is at "FULL" mark on dipstick. Capacity of the system is approximately 15½ gallons.

All Models With Type "G"
System

229. Under normal operating conditions, it is recommended that the hydraulic reservoir be drained and refilled with new MM hydraulic oil every 600 hours of operation or at least once a year. The hydraulic oil filter is located in the reservoir under

the top cover. Filter element should be renewed each 300 hours of operation.

After filling the reservoir, connect a by-pass hose to one set of remote control couplers. Place remote valve lever in raise position and start engine. Operate engine at 1500 rpm for at least two minutes while rotating steering from stop to stop several times. Stop engine, remove by-pass hose and recheck hydraulic fluid level. Add oil if necessary, until oil level is at "F" mark on dipstick. Capacity of the system is approximately 9 gallons.

SYSTEM PRESSURE
Type E System With
Char-Lynn Valve

230. The "Type E" remote system using two Char-Lynn control valves has a pressure relief valve located in each control valve which is set to open at 1450-1550 psi. In addition, the system is equipped with a main relief (by-pass) valve which opens at a pressure of 1600-1800 psi. The purpose of the by-pass valve is to prevent pressure multiplication and possible system damage when both control valves are actuated at the same time. On systems equipped with only one control valve, the by-pass valve is omitted and system pressure is en-

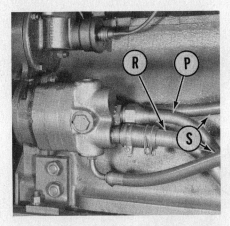

Fig. 255—Engine mounted Webster hydraulic pump on model G VI tractor, showing hydraulic hose connections.

P. Pressure tube
R. Return tube
S. Power steering hoses

tirely controlled by the pressure valve located in control valve.

To completely check the pressure on dual systems, tee a suitable test gage into the pressure line (P—Fig. 255) leading from hydraulic pump to by-pass valve. With hydraulic system at normal operating temperature and engine running at rated speed, momentarily hold BOTH valve levers in an operating position. With oil flow blocked at breakaway couplings, main relief (by-pass) valve should open and gage pressure should read 1600-1800 psi. Turn adjusting screw (A—Fig. 256) or remove acorn nut (3—Fig. 257) and turn the exposed adjusting screw to adjust the by-pass pressure. Hold levers in operating position ONLY long enough to note gage pressure. With by-pass valve properly adjusted, hold EACH valve lever in turn, in an operating position and note the pressure at which the circuit relief valve opens. Pressure should be 1450-1550 psi; if it is not, remove control valve end cap and turn the exposed relief valve adjusting screw clockwise to increase, or counterclockwise to decrease, pressure. Refer to Fig. 269 for view of control valve body showing location of relief valve.

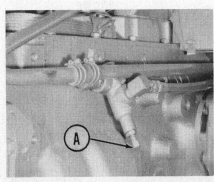

Fig. 256—Left side of model G VI final drive housing showing location of hydraulic system by-pass relief valve adjusting screw (A).

Type E System With Wooster Valve

231. The Wooster control valve used on some tractors with Type E system is a sandwich type with a main relief valve adjusted by means of shims after valve is removed; and a separate detent release valve for each spool which can be adjusted without valve removal.

Normal operating pressure is therefore controlled by individual setting of the detent release pressure, and the main relief valve operates in a safety capacity only.

To check the system, connect a test gage to breakaway coupling as shown in Fig. 258; in series with a lifting jack; or in series with a needle type shut-off valve. The gage and shut-off valve is the preferred combination. With hydraulic fluid at normal operating temperature and engine running at rated speed, close the shut-off valve and move and momentarily hold operating lever in correct direction to pressurize the gage. Pressure should be 1750-1850 psi. If it is not, remove control valve assembly and overhaul main relief valve as outlined in paragraph 242 before proceeding with the adjustment.

To adjust the detent release pressure, refer to Fig. 259. Working from behind and below the reservoir, remove valve spool venting cap (1) on spool to be adjusted. With hydraulic fluid at operating temperature and engine running at rated speed, open shut-off valve in test hose and move operating lever to detent position. Slowly close shut-off valve, noting gage pressure at which operating lever snaps back to neutral position. NOTE: If gage pressure does not rise, move operating lever to opposite detent posi-

Fig. 257—Right side of Type E system reservoir used on some models with Char-Lynn dual control valves, showing location of by-pass valve.

1. Pressure line
2. By-pass valve
3. Acorn nut
4. Jam nut

Fig. 258—Test gage installed in breakaway coupling for checking hydraulic pressure. Refer to text.

tion. Pressure should be 1475-1550 psi; if it is not, turn nyloc adjusting screw (3) using an Allen wrench, until release pressure is correct. Inspect "O" ring (2) and renew if required, before reinstalling venting cap (1). If pressure cannot be satisfactorily adjusted, overhaul the valve as outlined in paragraphs 240 through 244.

Type F System With Vickers Valve

232. The "Type F" remote system is equipped with a two-spool Vickers control valve which has a pre-set main relief valve. The relief valve is non-adjustable and is available only in a relief valve kit which also includes a relief valve plunger and springs.

An additional two-spool control valve can be installed in conjunction with the first valve. When installing a

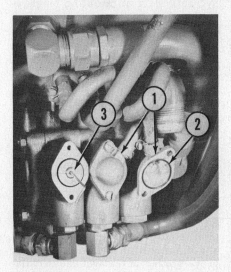

Fig. 259—To adjust detent release pressure on Wooster valve, remove venting cap (1) and turn nyloc adjusting screw (3) using an Allen wrench. Make sure sealing "O" ring (2) is in good condition when reinstalling venting cap.

second valve unit, a ⅜-inch plug must be installed in the power beyond port of the first valve to provide proper oil flow to the second valve.

To check the system relief pressure, connect a test gage to a breakaway coupling which is connected to the first control valve. With hydraulic fluid at operating temperature and engine operating at 1500 rpm, move control lever to pressurize the line to which the gage is attached. Hold the control lever in detent position and note the pressure reading on the gage. The correct relief valve pressure of the first valve should be 1725-1825 psi. If the system is equipped with an additional remote valve, attach test gage to a breakaway coupling of this valve. With engine operating at 1500 rpm, check the relief valve pressure of the second remote valve. The correct relief valve pressure should be 1500-1600 psi.

If relief valve pressures are not within the ranges specified, remove the control valves and renew the relief valves as outlined in paragraphs 245 and 246.

Type G System With Gresen Valve

233. The Gresen control valve used on tractors equipped with Type G system is a sandwich type and is usually used in a stack of two or three. The shim adjustable relief valve for the system is located in the inlet and outlet end block. To check the system relief pressure, connect a test gage to a breakaway coupling which is connected to the first control valve. With hydraulic fluid at operating temperature and engine operating at 1800 rpm, move control lever to pressurize the line to which the test gage is attached. Hold control lever in detent position and note the pressure reading on gage. Correct relief valve pressure should be 1750 psi. If not, remove relief valve cap (35—Fig. 277) and spring (31), then add or remove shims (30) as necessary to obtain the specified relief pressure.

PUMP

All Models

234. **REMOVE AND REINSTALL.** On all models, the hydraulic pump is mounted on left side of engine and is gear driven from engine timing gears. Method of removal and installation is evident. Note sequence of hose installation on power steering models G VI, G705, G706, G707, G708, MF95 and MF97, before removal, to aid in installation.

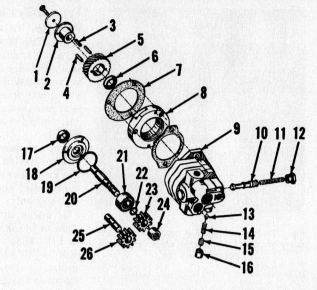

Fig. 260–Exploded view of early Webster hydraulic pump used on model G VI and MF95 tractors.

1. Washer
2. Driving sleeve
3. Key
4. Shear pins
5. Drive gear
6. Spacer
7. Gasket
8. Adapter
9. Pump assembly
10. Flow control valve
11. Spring
12. Valve plug
13. Steering relief valve
14. Spring
15. Adjusting screw
16. Plug
17. Oil seal
18. Seal retainer
19. Gasket
20. Pump shaft
21. Bearing
22. Snap ring
23. Driven gear
24. Needle bearing
25. Idler shaft
26. Idler gear

After pump is installed, fill and bleed system as outlined in paragraph 227, 228 or 229.

235. **WEBSTER PUMPS.** Webster gear type pumps are of two different types. Pumps used on early G VI and MF95 tractors have fixed wear plates, and field rebuilding is not generally satisfactory. The pump can, however be disassembled and resealed. Refer to Fig. 260 and paragraph 236.

Webster pumps used on other models, have pressure balanced wear plates (21 and 25—Fig. 261), and rebuilding is generally satisfactory if normal care is used.

236. **RESEAL (EARLY PUMPS).** To disassemble the unit, unbolt and remove the pump cover and lift out the idler gear and shaft (25 and 26—Fig. 260). On some pumps, the drive gear is retained to the drive shaft by a Woodruff key and snap rings. On other pumps, the drive shaft and gear are splined. Remove the drive shaft (20), seal plate (18) and ball bearing (21),

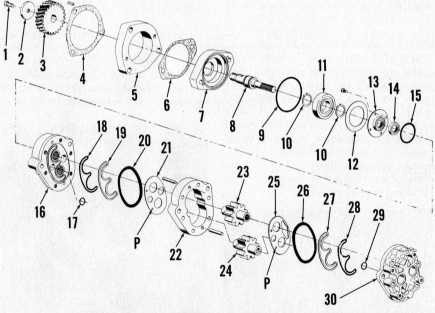

Fig. 261–Exploded view of late type Webster hydraulic pump.

1. Cap screw (L.H. thread)
2. Washer
3. Pump drive gear
4. Gasket
5. Adapter
6. Gasket
7. Bearing housing
8. Drive shaft
9. "O" ring
10. Snap rings
11. Ball bearing
12. Thrust washer
13. Seal retainer
14. Oil seal
15. "O" ring
16. Front body
17. "O" ring
18. Inner seal ring
19. Back-up ring
20. Outer seal ring
21. Front wear plate
22. Gear housing
23. Drive gear
24. Idler gear
25. Rear wear plate
26. Outer seal ring
27. Back-up ring
28. Inner seal ring
29. "O" ring
30. Rear cover

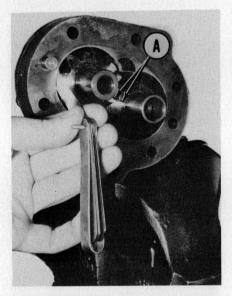

Fig. 262–Before removing gears or gear housing on late Webster pump, mark the gears as shown at (A) and measure gear to housing clearance. Refer to text.

then clean pump parts in a suitable solvent. If parts are badly worn, scored or heat discolored, renew the pump. If parts are suitable for re-use, renew all seals and reverse the disassembly procedure. Use a thin coating of shellac between ground surfaces of pump castings and wear plates, being sure excess shellac will not be squeezed into gear area during reassembly. Tighten the 5/16-inch cap screws to a torque of 9-12 ft.-lbs. and ¼-inch cap screws to a torque of 6-8 ft.-lbs.

237. OVERHAUL (LATE PUMPS). Before disassembling the pump, scribe correlation marks on all housings for alignment during reassembly. Remove the retaining cap screws and lift off the manifold plate and pump rear cover (30—Fig. 261). Before removing gears or gear housing, mark the gears as shown at (A—Fig. 262) and check gear to housing clearance with a feeler gage as shown. If clearance exceeds 0.005, renew the pump. Examine bores

Fig. 263–Examine pressure areas of gear housing bore as shown by arrow. Refer to text.

of gear housing as shown in Fig. 263. If badly scored or heat discolored, renew the pump. Check gears and wear plates for excessive wear or scoring. Slight marking on wear plates is normal, and is more pronounced on pressure side.

If gear shafts are worn at bearing area and gears are renewed, the shaft needle bearings should also be renewed on models so equipped. Heating end plates to 200° F. will facilitate removal of blind bearings. Pump end housings are available separately with new needle bearings installed.

Always renew all seals whenever pump is disassembled. Make sure small pressure ports (P—Fig. 261) in wear plate open into area enclosed by inner pressure seals (18 and 28). Bearing areas of end housings are ported to inlet side of pump to prevent pressure build-up, and return any hydraulic fluid leaking past bearings. Lubricate the parts thoroughly with MM hydraulic fluid when reassembling, and tighten the retaining cap screws alternately and evenly to a torque of 16-18 ft.-lbs.

If pump binds after assembly, disassemble and determine the cause before installing the pump. Be sure hydraulic lines are connected and reservoir filled before starting tractor engine.

238. VICKERS PUMP. To disassemble the pump, first remove the drive gear retaining cap screw and washer from pump shaft and remove the gear (27—Fig. 264), using a suit-

able puller. NOTE: Cap screw (29) has left hand thread. Unbolt and remove valve plate (1) and gasket (4). Place one hand over open end of pump, tip pump over and allow rotor assembly to slide out of pump housing (17). Use care to prevent cylinder block (9) from separating from pistons during removal.

NOTE: Individual components of the rotor assembly are not available separately. If any part of the rotor assembly shows excessive wear or damage, use a new rotor kit (MM Part No. 10P3036) when reassembling the pump.

Remove snap ring (25) and bump drive shaft (21) with bearing (23) out front of housing. Swashplate (15) can now be removed from rear of pump housing and washer (20) and seal (19) can be removed from front of housing.

Clean all parts in a suitable solvent. If needle bearing (3) is worn or damaged, renew the valve plate (1) and bearing assembly.

When reassembling, lubricate the parts with clean hydraulic oil and reverse the disassembly procedure. Tighten the valve plate retaining cap screws alternately to a torque of 25-35 ft.-lbs.

When reinstalling the pump on tractor, connect the pressure and suction lines. Fill the pump housing with clean hydraulic oil through the drain line port, then connect the drain line. Fill hydraulic reservoir to proper level. Start tractor engine and operate

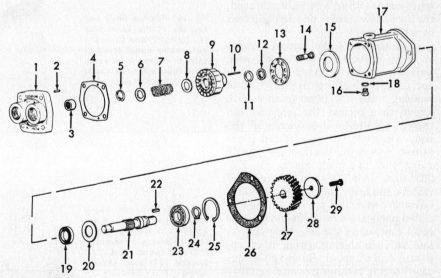

Fig. 264–Exploded view of Vickers piston type hydraulic pump used on model G1000 and some G1000 Vista tractors.

1. Valve plate	11. Washer	21. Drive shaft
2. Dowel pin	12. Spherical washer	22. Key
3. Needle bearing	13. Plate	23. Ball bearing
4. Gasket	14. Piston	24. Snap ring
5. Snap ring	15. Swashplate	25. Snap ring
6. Lift limiter	16. Plug	26. Gasket
7. Spring	17. Pump housing	27. Drive gear
8. Spring guide	18. "O" ring	28. Washer
9. Cylinder block	19. Seal	29. Cap screw (L.H. thread)
10. Pin	20. Washer	

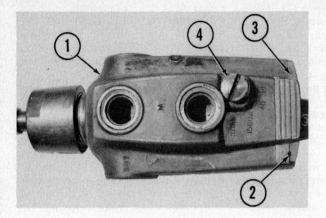

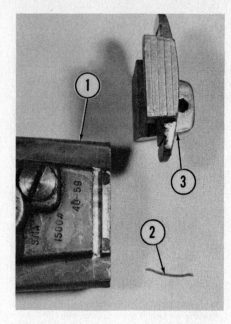

Fig. 265–Char-Lynn control valve used on some tractors equipped with Type E hydraulic systems.

1. Valve body
2. Locking pin
3. End cap
4. Shuttle valve plug

at slow idle. Loosen the pressure line connection to allow air to escape until pump is primed. Retighten connection, check hydraulic fluid level in reservoir and add oil as necessary to maintain oil level at the "FULL" mark on dipstick.

RESERVOIR AND CONTROL VALVE
Type E System With Char-Lynn Valve

239. The hydraulic system reservoir is located on the operator's platform underneath the driver's seat. To obtain access to the reservoir or control valves, remove the seat and seat base. One or more Char-Lynn control valves are mounted on the top of the hydraulic system reservoir. To remove the valve (or valves) disconnect the control lever linkage, then unbolt and remove the valve assemblies. In units where more than one valve is used, the two valves are connected together by a short nipple.

To disassemble the removed valve on early units, refer to Fig. 265 and, using a small pointed tool, push spring-type locking pin (2) out of housing until it can be grasped with pliers, then remove the pin, and end cap (3) by sliding it sideways off the body. On some valves, end cap is retained by screws. Remove the shuttle valve plug (4), blade spring (5—Fig. 267) and blade (7), then unscrew and remove the lever end cap (8). On early valves, centering spring and associated parts are located on end of valve spool containing the attaching eye; on late valve centering spring is on opposite end of spool. Remove the exposed spring retaining snap ring (10—Fig. 268) and slide centering spring (11) from the valve spool. Push valve spool (9) into housing far enough to expose the front spool seal (12), remove the seal then withdraw the spool assembly from spring end of valve body as shown in Fig. 267. Carefully note position of shuttle (13—Fig. 268)

and shuttle spring (14) as valve spool is withdrawn, to insure correct assembly. The shuttle and shuttle spring lie between the two lands at the closed end of the valve spool and contact the edge of shuttle blade (7—Fig. 267), forming a detent to hold spool in operating position until the hydraulic cylinder reaches the end of its stroke.

Before disturbing the relief valve, make a note of position of relief valve plug (16—Fig. 269) and count the number of turns required to remove the plug, so that plug can be reinstalled in the same approximate position. Remove the relief valve plug, relief valve and spring (15), and examine the relief valve and seat for wear and damage. The seat (not

Fig. 266–After removing spring type locking pin (2) on early valve, end cap (3) will slide sideways from housing. On late valve, end cap (3) is retained by screws.

shown) is threaded into valve body and can be removed with a screw driver of proper size.

Clean the component parts in a suitable solvent and examine for wear or scoring. To assemble the valve proceed as follows: Remove the remaining

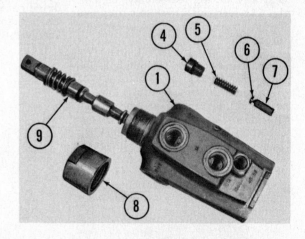

Fig. 267–Remove lever end cap (8), shuttle valve plug (4), spring (5) and blade (7), push valve spool through valve to remove inner spool seal, then withdraw spool from spring end as shown.

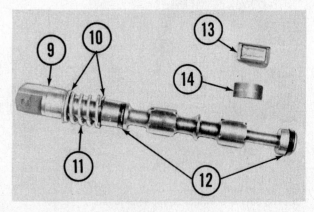

Fig. 268–Removed valve spool (9) showing the assembled centering spring (11), retaining snap rings (10) and spool seals (12). Shuttle (13) and shuttle spring (14) lie between the inner two lands of valve spool to hold spool in operating position until cylinder reaches end of stroke. Early valve is shown; centering spring (11) is located on opposite end of spool on some models.

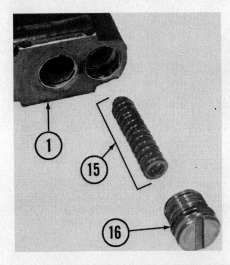

Fig. 269—Relief valve assembly (15) and plug (16) can be removed after removing end cap (3 —Fig. 266).

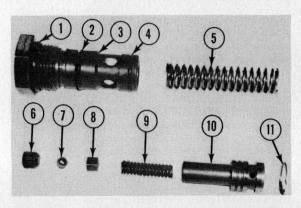

Fig. 271—Disassembled view of the main relief valve used in Type E system with Wooster valve.

1. "O" ring
2. "O" ring
3. Cartridge
4. "O" ring
5. Spring
6. Sensing valve seat
7. Valve ball
8. Block
9. Spring
10. Piston
11. Snap ring

spring retaining snap ring (10—Fig. 268) from the valve spool, renew the spool seals (12) with seal lips to center of spool as shown. Lubricate spool with clean hydraulic fluid and carefully insert spring end of spool in valve body. Push spool through valve body until next to last land has just entered body, then assemble shuttle spring (14) in spool with the two spring ends outward. Assemble shuttle (13), either end forward, over spring, then carefully slide the completed assembly into the valve bore until the lip of spool seal (12) contacts valve body. Carefully work the seal lip into the valve bore with a suitable tool, then push spool rearward until end is flush with the end of valve body. Working through the plug hole in top of valve body, turn shuttle (13) until flat surface is parallel to plug hole, then insert shuttle blade (7—Fig. 267) with narrow edge to shuttle, until blade fits in the retaining groove in valve housing, then install spring (5) and plug

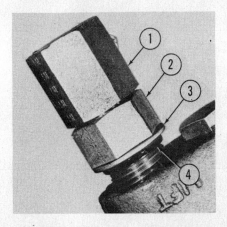

Fig. 270—Special care must be taken when installing J.I.C. fittings, to be sure "O" ring (4) is not cut causing the fitting to leak.

1. Fitting   3. Washer
2. Jam nut   4. "O" ring

(4). Reinstall relief valve (15—Fig. 269) and plug (16) if they were removed, and complete the assembly by reversing the disassembly procedure.

Type E System With Wooster Valve

240. **REMOVE AND REINSTALL.** To remove the control valve, first drain the hydraulic system reservoir, disconnect pump pressure and return lines and remove the seat assembly; then unbolt and remove the reservoir and valve assembly from tractor. Remove reservoir front cover retaining bolts, disconnect control levers, and lift off the front cover. Carefully mark the position of control valve on mounting plate to assist in alignment of control levers during assembly. Mark and disconnect hoses from control valve, remove the mounting stud nuts; and lift off the valve.

Reinstall by reversing the removal procedure. Align control valve with previously marked position on mounting plate; or check to be sure control level links can be installed without binding, before tightening mounting stud nuts.

The fittings contain sealing "O" rings as shown in Fig. 270. Install and connect fittings as outlined in paragraph 241 to prevent subsequent leakage.

241. **FITTINGS.** The hydraulic fittings have SAE straight tubing threads with "O" ring seals (J.I.C. fittings) as shown in Fig. 270. DO NOT attempt to install pipe fittings in valve ports.

The "O" ring (4) is compressed in its groove to form a leak proof seal, by tightening jam nut (2). DO NOT attempt to alter the position of fitting without first loosening jam nut (2) and making sure "O" ring (4) is free in groove. If "O" ring is cut by improper installation or maintenance, leakage will result.

242. **MAIN RELIEF VALVE.** The main relief valve can be removed for

service or adjustment after control valve has been removed as outlined in paragraph 240. The valve (See Fig. 271) is located in mounting side of inlet cover.

To service the main relief valve, unscrew cartridge (3—Fig. 272) from cover (C). Check to see that sensing ports (P) in cartridge and cover are open, and that "O" rings (1 & 2) are in satisfactory condition.

Clamp hex head of cartridge (3—Fig. 271) in a vise, lightly press down on piston (10) and remove snap ring (11); then withdraw piston (10) and spring (5). Piston must slide freely in cartridge bore.

Using an Allen wrench, remove the threaded pilot valve seat (6), while COUNTING THE TURNS seat is threaded into piston. Remove seat (6), valve ball (7), block (8) and spring (9). Check the block (8) and internal threads in piston (10), to make sure that sharp corners of block are not hanging up in threads in piston, causing erratic action of the valve. If interference is noted, chamfer corners of block or renew the cartridge, using one with fewer threads.

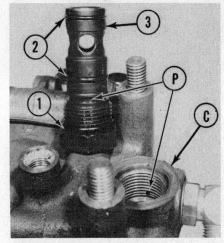

Fig. 272—When removing main relief valve cartridge from inlet cover, examine sensing ports (P) to see that they are open.

1. "O" ring
2. "O" ring
3. Cartridge
c. Inlet cover
p. Sensing ports

Assemble by reversing the disassembly procedure. If parts have been renewed in valve piston, install pilot valve seat (6) in piston until end of seat protrudes approximately 1/16-inch from valve. If parts are not renewed install seat THE SAME NUMBER OF TURNS used in removing valve; then turn seat in slightly to raise pressure (or out slightly to lower pressure) if other defects were not found while valve was disassembled.

243. **CONTROL VALVE.** The control valve spool and associated parts can be removed for service without disassembling the valve body housings. Proceed as follows:

Remove the spool boot (2—Fig. 273) and venting cap (1—Fig. 259). Remove detent adjusting screw (10—Fig. 274), spring (11) and detent ball (12); then unbolt and remove detent housing (13). Depress centering piston (6) and remove the retaining snap ring, then withdraw centering piston, centering spring (7) and centering sleeve (8). Withdraw spool (1) from valve housing. Remove nylock set screw (5) and withdraw detent release valve spring (4), block (3) and valve (2) from end of spool. Check to be sure that drillings (17) in valve are open, that valve and body are not scored, and that valve does not bind. Valve and body are available only as a matched assembly.

Assemble by reversing the disassembly procedure. To renew the tetra (quad ring) seals (16), remove the

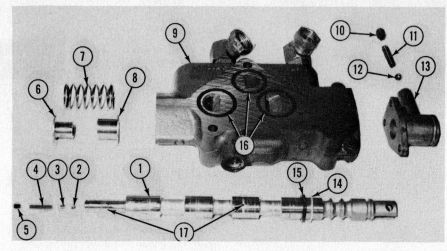

Fig. 274–Disassembled view of Wooster control valve body section. Release piston (6) and sleeve (8) move apart by hydraulic pressure entering through valve (2) and internal passages in valve spool, to override detent ball and return valve to neutral.

1. Valve spool	7. Centering spring	12. Detent ball
2. Release valve	8. Centering sleeve	13. Detent housing
3. Block	9. Valve body	14. Back-up ring
4. Spring	10. Detent adjusting	15. Sealing ring
5. Detent release	screw	16. Tetra (quad ring)
adjusting screw	11. Detent spring	seals
6. Release piston		17. Passage ports

valve body retaining stud nuts and separate the sections as shown in Fig. 275.

Adjust detent ball pressure as outlined in paragraph 244, install valve as in paragraph 240, then adjust detent release pressure as in paragraph 231.

244. **DETENT ADJUSTMENT.** To adjust the detent spring pressure, refer to Fig. 273. With valve mounted and before installing control levers and front cover, push valve spool downward from neutral (center) detent. Attach a spring scale (4) as shown, and measure the pull required to move valve back to neutral position. Adjust the pull to 18-21 lbs. by tightening or loosening detent adjusting screws with Allen wrench (5).

Type F System With Vickers Valve

245. **REMOVE AND REINSTALL.** To remove the control valve, first drain the hydraulic reservoir, then unbolt and remove seat assembly. Remove the 16 cap screws and stat-o-seals that secure the cover to reservoir and tip the cover assembly backward. Disconnect the main oil supply line from the control valve. Remove cap screws from hinge brackets on either side of cover and lift cover assembly from reservoir.

Remove the four oil tubes between the control valve and cover and the oil return tube between control valve and filter. If a second (optional) control valve is installed, disconnect oil tube from power beyond port of first valve.

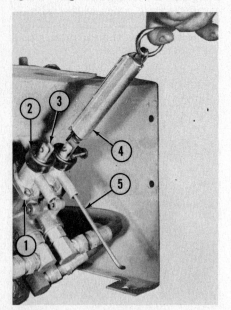

Fig. 273–On the Wooster valve, adjust detent spring pressure by turning Allen wrench (5) until a pull of 18-21 lbs. is required to center the spool.

1. Detent housing	
2. Boot	
3. Control valve spool	4. Spring scale
	5. Allen wrench

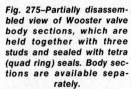

Fig. 275–Partially disassembled view of Wooster valve body sections, which are held together with three studs and sealed with tetra (quad ring) seals. Body sections are available separately.

1. Rear cover
2. Valve body
3. Inlet cover

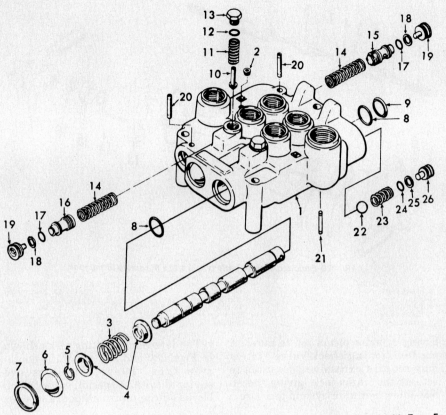

Fig. 276–Partially exploded view of Vickers control valve used on models equipped with Type F hydraulic system.

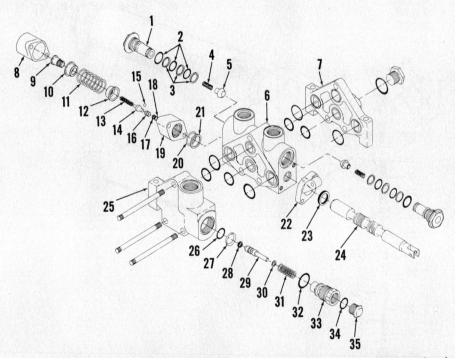

Fig. 277–Exploded view of Gresen control valve and associated parts used on models equipped with Type G hydraulic system. Usually two or three control valve sections are used.

1. Plug
2. "O" rings
3. Back-up rings
4. Spring
5. Load check valve
6. Valve body
7. End cover
8. End cap
9. Spool end
10. Spring seat
11. Centering spring
12. Spring seat
13. Detent spring
14. Spring follower
15. Detent ball (4 used)
16. Piston
17. Back-up ring
18. "O" ring
19. Detent adapter
20. "O" ring
21. Quad ring
22. Lever bracket
23. Quad ring
24. Valve spool
25. Inlet & Outlet end block
26. "O" ring
27. Back-up ring
28. Seal ring
29. Relief valve piston
30. Shim (0.010, 0.020 & 0.040)
31. Spring
32. "O" ring
33. Relief valve body
34. "O" ring
35. Relief valve cap

Disconnect lever linkage, remove the three mounting bolts and lift valve from cover.

Reinstall control valve by reversing removal procedure. The hydraulic fittings have SAE straight tubing threads with "O" ring seals (J.I.C. fittings). DO NOT attempt to install pipe fittings in valve ports.

Clean the reservoir and suction screen and renew the return oil filter element. Fill and bleed system as outlined in paragraph 228.

246. CONTROL VALVE. With the control valve removed as outlined in paragraph 245, refer to Fig. 276 and proceed as follows:

To remove the relief valve (15) and plunger (16), drive out roll pins (20) from both ends of valve body and withdraw plugs (19), plunger, relief valve and springs (14). DO NOT attempt to remove the spring seat in relief valve bore of the control valve body. The relief valve (15), relief valve plunger (16), springs (14), "O" rings (17) and back-up rings (18) are available in a relief valve kit if renewal is indicated.

CAUTION: If first control valve is being overhauled, use relief valve kit MM Part No. 10R1194 which is preset to maintain a relief pressure of 1725-1825 psi. Relief valve kit MM Part No. 10R1232 must be used when overhauling the second (optional) control valve. The second control valve relief pressure is 1500-1600 psi.

To remove valve spools, first remove plugs (13), springs (11) and detent poppets (10). NOTE: There are two poppets for each spool. Remove retaining rings (7) and end caps (6), then push spools from valve body. "O" rings (8) and wiper rings (9) can now be removed. Inspect spools and bores in valve body for excessive wear or scoring. If either spool or body is damaged, renew complete valve assembly as the spools or valve body are not available separately.

The control valve is equipped with a load check valve for each spool. To remove the load check valves, remove roll pins (21), then withdraw plugs (26), springs (23) and check balls (22).

Reassemble the components of control valve in reverse order of disassembly, using new "O" rings, back-up rings and wiper rings which are available in a control valve seal kit.

Type G System with Gresen Valve

247. REMOVE AND REINSTALL. To remove the control valve assembly, first drain the hydraulic system. Unbolt and remove valve cover. Disconnect pressure and return lines from the inlet and outlet end block (25—Fig. 277), then disconnect hydraulic hoses between control valve and remote coupler bracket. Remove three bolts securing valve assembly to mounting bracket, then lift valve assembly from tractor.

Reinstall control valve assembly by reversing the removal procedure. Clean the reservoir and renew the filter, then fill and bleed system as outlined in paragraph 229.

248. **MAIN RELIEF VALVE.** To remove the relief valve assembly, first remove the control valve cover, then proceed as follows: Refer to Fig. 277 and remove relief valve cap (35) and spring (31). Unscrew relief valve body (33) and carefully withdraw relief valve assembly. Remove relief valve piston (29) from body. Do not lose shims (30).

Renew the seal rings and reinstall the relief valve assembly by reversing the removal procedure. Check and adjust relief valve pressure as outlined in paragraph 233.

249. **CONTROL VALVE.** With the control valve assembly removed as outlined in paragraph 247, refer to Fig. 277 and disassemble as follows: Remove the three stud nuts and separate the control valve sections. Remove control valve lever, then remove any paint, rust or burrs from end of spool (24). Unbolt and remove lever bracket (22) and quad ring (23). Remove the cap screws securing end cap (8) and detent adapter (19) to valve body. Withdraw spool assembly from valve body. Unscrew spool end (9) and separate centering spring and detent assemblies from valve spool. Remove plugs (1) with "O" rings (2) and back-up rings (3), springs (4) and load check valves (5).

Clean and inspect all parts and renew any showing excessive wear or other damage. Valve spool (24) and valve body (6) are available only as a matched set.

Renew all "O" rings, back-up rings and quad rings, then using Fig. 277 as a guide, reassemble by reversing the disassembly procedure.

REMOTE LIFTING JACK
All Models So Equipped

250. The early remote lifting jacks shown in Figs. 278 and 279 are of the locked-circuit cylinder type in which a spring loaded check valve traps the fluid in both ends of cylinder when jack is stationary. When pressure fluid enters either port of lifting jack, the opposite check valve is unseated by hydraulic pressure against the check valve actuating piston of plunger, al-

lowing cylinder piston rod to move. A malfunctioning check valve system may require excessive pressures to actuate the lifting jack, giving the effect of low hydraulic system pressure.

The late remote lifting jacks shown in Figs. 280 and 281 are of the depth-stop type. These cylinders are equipped with a special valve which blocks off the return oil port and stops

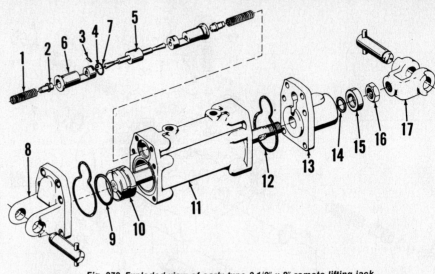

Fig. 278–Exploded view of early type 3 1/2" x 8" remote lifting jack.

1. Check valve spring	6. Valve cage	12. Gasket
2. Check valve	7. "O" ring	13. Bearing cap
3. Key	8. Cylinder head	14. "O" ring
4. Ball	9. "O" ring	15. Seal
5. Check valve actuator	10. Piston and rod	16. Lock nut
	11. Cylinder	17. Rod clevis

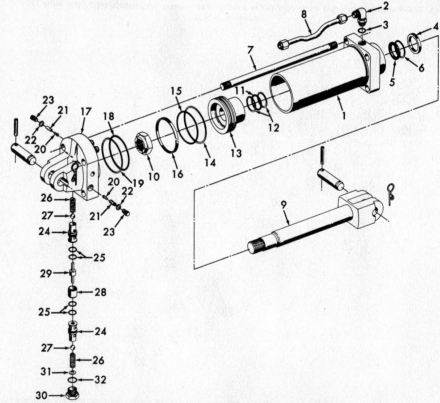

Fig. 279–Exploded view of early type 4" x 8" remote lifting jack.

1. Cylinder	12. Back-up rings	23. Screw
2. Elbow	13. Piston	24. Cage
3. "O" ring	14. Piston seal ring	25. "O" ring
4. Wiper ring	15. "O" ring	26. Spring
5. Seal	16. Wear strip	27. Check ball
6. Back-up ring	17. End cap	28. Actuator sleeve
7. Stud	18. "O" ring	29. Check valve actuator
8. Oil tube	19. Back-up ring	30. Plug
9. Rod	20. Relief valve	31. Gasket
10. Nut	21. Relief spring	32. "O" ring
11. "O" ring	22. Gasket	

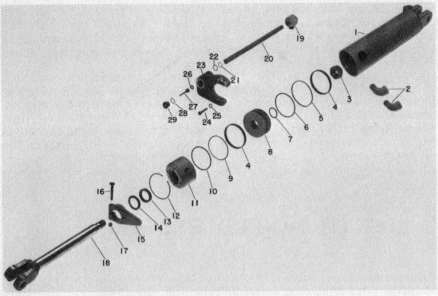

Fig. 280–Exploded view of late type 3 1/2''×8'' remote lifting jack.

1. Cylinder barrel	11. Bearing	20. Tube
2. Elbow fittings	12. Retaining ring	21. Back-up washer
3. Nut	13. Oil seal	22. "O" ring
4. Wear rings	14. Wiper ring	23. Valve housing
5. Teflon ring	15. Stop arm	24. Cap screw
6. "O" ring	16. Bolt	25. Washer
7. "O" ring	17. Nut	26. Seal ring
8. Piston	18. Piston rod	27. Valve
9. "O" ring	19. Elbow	28. "O" ring
10. Back-up ring		29. Guide

cylinder retraction at any pre-set position.

Refer to appropriate following paragraphs for overhaul information.

251. OVERHAUL (3½"x8" EARLY TYPE). To disassemble the 3½"x8" early type lifting jack, refer to Fig. 278 and proceed as follows:

Unbolt and lift off cylinder head (8)

and bearing cap (13). Piston and rod assembly (10) will be removed with bearing cap. Remove clevis (17) and lock nut (16), then withdraw piston and rod from bearing cap. Seal (15) and "O" ring (14) can now be removed from bearing cap.

Remove check valve springs (1), check valves (2) and valve cages (6)

Fig. 281–Exploded view of late type 4''×8'' remote lifting jack.

1. Plug	17. Piston
2. "O" ring	18. "O" ring
3. Back-up ring	19. Wear ring
4. "O" ring	20. "O" ring
5. Spring	21. Teflon ring
6. Seal ring	22. "O" ring
7. Valve	23. Back-up ring
8. Spacer	24. Bearing
9. "O" ring	25. Retaining ring
10. Seal retainer	26. "O" ring
11. "O" ring	27. Valve
12. Wiper ring	28. Wiper ring
13. Cylinder barrel	29. End plate
14. Spring	30. Stop arm
15. Push rod	31. Piston rod
16. Nut	

from each end of cylinder (11), then remove check valve actuator (5). Check valves (2) have a built-in thermal relief valve which is serviced only by renewing the unit. Check valves and all "O" rings and seals are available in a repair kit as well as individually.

Clean all parts in a suitable solvent and renew any parts which are worn, scored or otherwise damaged. When reassembling, make sure check valve actuator (5) is absolutely free after installation of actuator and both valve cages (6), and that actuator push rods will extend through each check valve seat far enough to unseat the check valves. Complete the assembly by reversing the disassembly procedure. After assembly, the jack should extend and retract at full throttle with negligible pressure build-up in tractor hydraulic system.

252. OVERHAUL (4"x8" EARLY TYPE). To disassemble the 4"x8" early type lifting jack, refer to Fig. 279 and proceed as follows:

Remove oil tube (8), then unbolt and remove cylinder end cap (17). Clamp clevis end of rod (9) in a vise, remove nut (10) and piston (13), and remove rod (9) from cylinder (1). Wiper ring (4), seal (5) and back-up ring (6) can now be removed from cylinder.

Remove plug (30), then withdraw check valve assemblies, actuator (29) and sleeve (28). Remove screws (23), relief valve springs (21) and relief valves (20) from each side of cylinder end cap (17).

Clean all parts in a suitable solvent and renew any parts which are worn, scored or otherwise damaged. When reassembling, use all new "O" rings, back-up rings, seals and wear strip.

After assembly, the jack should extend and retract at full throttle with negligible pressure build-up in tractor hydraulic system.

253. OVERHAUL (3½"x8" LATE TYPE). To disassemble the 3½"x8" late type lifting jack, refer to Fig. 280 and proceed as follows:

Loosen nut (17) and slide stop arm (15) to yoke end of piston rod (18). Remove cap screws (24) retaining valve housing (23) to bearing (11) and withdraw valve housing from end of tube (20). Unscrew guide (29) and remove valve (27).

Push bearing (11) into cylinder barrel (1) far enough to allow removal of retaining ring (12), then bump bearing from cylinder barrel with piston (8) by working piston rod in and out.

Remove nut (3), piston (8) and bearing (11) from piston rod. Clean and inspect all parts and renew any showing excessive wear or other damage. When reassembling use all new "O" rings, back-up rings, seals and wear rings. Oil seal (13) is installed with lip to inside and wiper ring (14) is installed with lip to the outside. The balance of reassembly is the reverse of disassembly procedure.

254. OVERHAUL (4"x8" LATE TYPE). To disassemble the 4"x8" late type lifting jack, refer to Fig. 281 and proceed as follows:

Loosen clamp bolt and slide stop arm (30) to yoke end of piston rod (31). Remove cap screws securing end plate (29) to bearing (24) and remove the plate. Push bearing (24) into cylinder barrel (13) far enough to allow removal of retaining ring (25). With retaining ring removed, pull outward on piston rod until piston (17) bumps the bearing from cylinder barrel. Remove nut (16) and withdraw piston rod from piston and bearing.

Unscrew plug (1) then remove spring (5), valve (7), spacer (8) and seal retainer (10). If necessary, drive out roll pins to remove spring (14) and push rod (15).

Clean and inspect all parts and renew any showing excessive wear or other damage. When reassembling, use all new "o" rings, back-up rings, wear ring and seals. Using Fig. 281 as a guide, reassemble by reversing the disassembly procedure.

HYDRAULIC LIFT (TEL-O-FLO SYSTEM)

This section covers the "Tel-O-Flo" hydraulic system used on some G900, G1000 and G1000 Vista tractors.

For models G900, G950, G1000 Vista, G1050 and G1350 equipped with the closed center hydraulic system, refer to section beginning with paragraph 275.

For models equipped with "Types E, F or G" hydraulic systems, refer to section beginning with paragraph 227.

OPERATION
Models G900-G1000-G1000 Vista

255. The Tel-O-Flo system control valve consists of a master valve and three directional valves which control the three-point hitch and two remote cylinders. Proper hydraulic action depends on accurate synchronization of the master control valve with the directional valve being used. Before a raising action can be accomplished with the three-point hitch or single acting remote applications (or any action with double acting remote cylinders), the master control valve must be moved to block the system by-pass opening. At the same time the directional valve must move to open the proper passage to hydraulic system pressure.

Refer to Fig. 282 for a schematic view of the three-point lift system operation. Hydraulic fluid under pump pressure enters the control valve at (9) and through the master control valve (5) at two points. The passage at the left is connected to the center area of the directional valve (4) by the check valve (6), and around the directional valve to the relief valve (3). This path is never closed, but is always open to pump pressure. The passage on the right leads through the master valve to the regulating valve (7). Oil passing through regulating valve (7) goes through the system filter back to the sump.

When the control lever (1) is moved to the raising position, linkage lever (2) and the two valves (4 and 5) are moved to the right. The land on master valve spool (5) closes passage (7) leading to the sump. At the same time, the directional valve (4) opens

passage (8) leading to the lift cylinder. Oil from the pump passes through check valve (6), directional valve (4) and through opened passage (8) to the ram cylinder and a raising action takes place. A mechanical linkage (not pictured) returns the control lever and valves to a neutral position at the completion of the lifting action.

When the control lever is moved to the lowering position the master valve (5) remains stationary allowing oil from the pump to bypass and the directional valve moves to the left opening passage (8) to the sump through the area at the end of the valve spool. The hydraulic fluid trapped in the ram cylinder is then exhausted back to the sump.

Automatic draft action is controlled by a combination of hydraulic and spring pressure as shown in Fig. 283. Metered oil is fed through line (14) to draft linkage cylinder (15) from the bypass line in front of regulating valve (7). A pressure of 25-140 psi is maintained in the system by valve (7). The draft linkage cylinder (15) is connected to the draft actuating cap (12) by the hollow linkage tube (11) which contains ports (P) at either end. When the control lever (1) is in the neutral position, port (P) at the front end of the tube is uncovered and the metered oil escapes. When the control lever is moved to the automatic draft position,

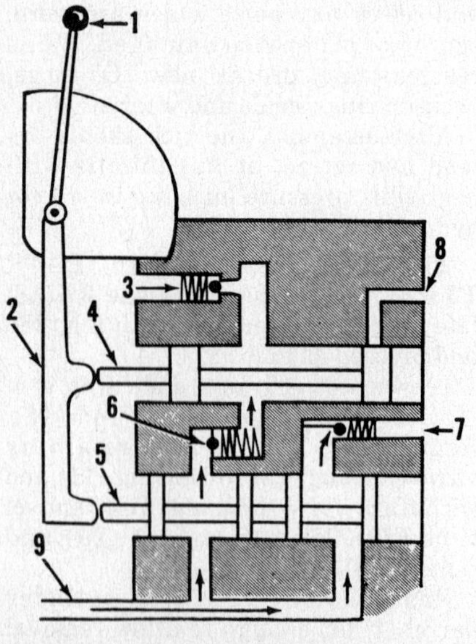

Fig. 282—Schematic view of "Tel-O-Flo" hydraulic control valve showing oil flow through master control valve and three-point hitch directional valve.

1. Control lever	6. Back flow check valve
2. Actuating lever	7. Regulating valve
3. Relief valve	8. Ram passage
4. Directional valve	9. Oil passage from pump
5. Master control valve	

Fig. 283—Schematic view of automatic draft control mechanism used on "Tel-O-Flo" system.

10. Draft link
11. Linkage tube
12. Actuating cap
13. Dash pot
14. Supply tube
15. Draft linkage cylinder
16. Linkage piston
P. Actuating ports

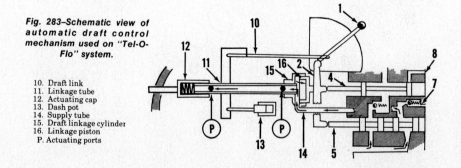

Fig. 284—View showing location of suction filter (1) used on models G900, G1000 and G1000 Vista and high pressure filter (2) used on models G1000 and G1000 Vista, equipped with "Tel-O-Flo" system.

tube (11) is moved forward by draft link (10) and the front port is closed by the lip of the draft linkage cylinder (15), directional valve (4) is moved into the lowering position and the three point lift lowers into operating position. When the implement enters the ground to the selected depth, the implement draft, acting through the upper link against spring pressure, moves the actuating cap (12) forward to close the rear port in the linkage tube allowing pressure to build up in draft linkage cylinder (15). Piston (16) moves forward under hydraulic pressure to automatically actuate linkage lever (2) and the control valves. The selected implement operating draft is maintained by the automatic metering of the oil in the draft linkage cylinder at the linkage tube rear port.

LUBRICATION AND BLEEDING
Models G900-G1000-G1000 Vista

256. Under normal operating conditions, it is recommended that the "Tel-O-Flo" hydraulic system be drained and refilled with new MM hydraulic oil every 600 hours of operation or at least once a year. Clean the screen in suction filter (1—Fig. 284) and renew the element in high pressure filter (2) on models so equipped every 300 hours of operation.

Fig. 286—To adjust draft control button (3), loosen locknut (2) and turn adjusting bolt (1) until length of temporary lift range is approximately two inches.

After filling the reservoir, start the engine and cycle all hydraulic control levers several times to bleed all the air from system. Add oil as required to maintain oil level at "FULL" mark on dipstick. Capacity of the system is approximately 5 gallons.

SYSTEM CHECKS AND ADJUSTMENTS
Models G900-G1000-G1000 Vista

257. Unless the system is inoperative or defect is obvious, the following checks may pinpoint the trouble, eliminating unnecessary tear-down and overhaul.

Before an attempt is made to check the system, check the fluid level as outlined in paragraph 256, start the engine and warm the hydraulic fluid to operating temperature.

Note: On tractors equipped with the "Tel-O-Flo" depth limit control (see paragraph 273), place depth limit control lever in the extreme deep (forward) position while checking and adjusting the following components.

258. **PIVOT PLATE SPRINGS.** Spring (2—Fig. 285) on each side of pivot plate must have a pre-load of 0 to 1/16-inch to provide proper draft control of rear mounted implements.

To adjust the spring pre-load, loosen locknuts (3) and turn bolts (1) as required until springs can just be turned by hand. Then, tighten bolts an additional ¼-turn and secure with locknuts.

259. **DRAFT CONTROL BUTTON ADJUSTMENT.** The adjustment of the draft control button determines the length of the temporary lift range on the control lever quadrant. The adjustment is correct if the length of the temporary lift range is approximately 2 inches on the quadrant.

To adjust the position of the draft control button (3—Fig. 286), loosen locknut (2) and turn adjusting bolt (1) out until, with the engine running at 1500 rpm, the lift arms will not raise while the control lever is slowly moved through entire temporary lift range. Now turn the bolt in until the lift arms will just raise and total length of the temporary lift range is approximately ⅛-inch. Then, turn bolt in 1¾ turns and tighten locknut. The length of the temporary lift range on the quadrant should now be approximately 2 inches.

If proper adjustment cannot be obtained, it will be necessary to disassemble and check the draft linkage as outlined in paragraph 270.

260. **DRAFT CONTROL SENSITIVITY.** To check the sensitivity of the lift, first make certain that the draft control button is properly adjusted as outlined in paragraph 259. Start tractor engine and operate at 1500 rpm. Move the 3-point hitch control lever to the minimum draft position (just below temporary lift range). Force a 0.030 feeler gage between the draft control button and end of ad-

Fig. 285—Pivot plate springs (2) must have a pre-load of 0 to 1/16-inch. Refer to text.

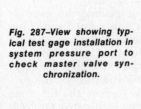

Fig. 287—View showing typical test gage installation in system pressure port to check master valve synchronization.

justing bolt. With feeler gage in place, lift arms should raise.

If lift arms do not raise, first check the pressure setting of the regulator valve as outlined in paragraph 264. If regulator valve pressure is within the 25-140 psi range, disassemble lift and check all components of the draft control assembly.

261. VALVE SYNCHRONIZATION CHECK. To check the synchronization of the master valve with the three-point lift directional valve, first lower lift arms to the extreme lower position. Then, install test gage in right hand port in top of control valve housing as shown in Fig. 287.

With engine operating at 1500 rpm, and no load on lift arms, slowly move the three-point lift control lever toward "UP" position. The momentary pressure while lift arms are raising should be 0-50 psi. If pressure reading is above 50 psi, disassemble and synchronize the valves as outlined in paragraph 271.

262. DASH POT CHECK AND ADJUSTMENT. The purpose of the dash pot is to restrict or slow the forward movement of the draft linkage tube to allow quick implement penetration before the first draft cycle takes place. To check the dash pot, first attach an implement to the three-point hitch, then move the three-point lift control lever down the quadrant into the temporary lift range and the rate and cycle levers into the fast position. Position the depth stop on quadrant at the lower part of temporary lift range. With the engine running at 1500 rpm, move the control lever to the raise position and allow hitch to raise implement to the fully raised position and neutralize the valve. Now move the control lever quickly down the quadrant to the depth stop and check the time required for the lift arms to lower and again start to raise. If the dash pot is correctly adjusted, the lift arms should start to raise 1 to 1½ seconds after lowering action starts.

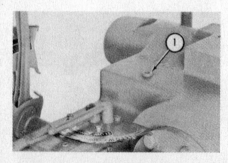

Fig. 288–Remove plug (1) and using a 1/4-inch head socket and extension, adjust dash pot needle valve through the plug opening.

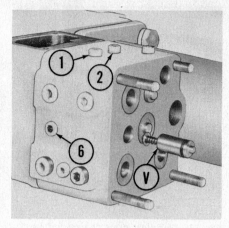

Fig. 289–Control valve body with front cover removed and back flow valve (V) withdrawn.

1. System pressure port
2. Regulator valve pressure port
6. Back flow valve pressure port

To adjust the dash pot needle valve, remove the pipe plug (1—Fig. 288) from top of lift housing and using a ¼-inch hex head socket and extension, adjust the needle valve through plug opening. NOTE: Use care to avoid applying undue pressure to valve. Needle valve or seat may be damaged if pressure is applied when needle is bottomed.

If dash pot action is still too fast when needle is bottomed, remove the lift and overhaul the dash pot assembly as outlined in paragraph 269.

263. BACK FLOW VALVE CHECK. The purpose of the back flow valve is to prevent the lift arms from momentarily dropping when the control valve is actuated. To check the valve, place a 120-pound load or light implement on the lift arms and raise the lift until the arms are about halfway up, then manually return the valve to neutral. With the engine running at 1500 rpm, slowly move the three-point lift control lever to the raising position and note the action of the lift arms. The load should raise to transport position with no noticeable drop before raising action begins. If a drop is noted, remove the control valve front cover as outlined in paragraph 269 and remove and service the back flow valve (V—Fig. 289).

A pressure gage may be used to check the back flow valve for sticking or binding as follows: Remove plug (6) in the side of control valve housing and install a 0-2000 psi pressure gage. With the engine running at full governed speed, no load on the lift arms and the lift arms in lowered position, move the three-point lift control lever to the raising position and note the pressure gage reading. If the pressure, while the arms are raising, is more than 250 psi greater than the pressure

registered in checking the valve synchronization as outlined in paragraph 261, the back flow valve is sticking or binding and should be removed and serviced.

264. REGULATOR VALVE PRESSURE. The regulator valve supplies the necessary hydraulic pressure to operate the automatic draft control linkage. To check the pressure, remove plug (2—Fig. 289) in the top of control valve housing and install a 0-200 psi pressure gage. With the hydraulic fluid at operating temperature and the engine running at 1500 rpm, the minimum pressure reading should be at least 25 psi with all control valves in neutral position. The maximum pressure should not exceed 140 psi. If the pressure is not within the specified range, service or renew the valve or spring after removing the control valve front cover as outlined in paragraph 269.

265. RELIEF VALVE PRESSURE The recommended relief valve pressure is 1675-1725 psi. To check the pressure, remove plug (1—Fig. 290) and install a 0-2000 psi pressure gage. With the engine running at 1500 rpm and the hydraulic fluid at operating temperature, move one of the auxiliary valve levers back to the raising position and hold it just long enough for the relief valve to act, and observe the gage reading. To adjust the pressure, remove top cover, loosen locknut (N—Fig. 290) and turn the adjusting screw in or out until the correct pressure is obtained. To remove the relief valve assembly, it is first necessary to remove the control valve housing as outlined in paragraph 269.

266. RATE AND CYCLE CONTROL. A cam at the lower end of the rate lever (3—Fig. 291) restricts the

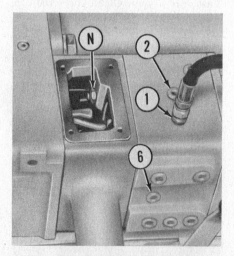

Fig. 290–To adjust system relief valve pressure, remove valve cover, install test gage in system pressure port (1), loosen locknut (N) and turn pressure adjusting screw in or out as required.

movement of the three-point directional control valve in the lowering position, thus controlling the speed of implement drop. The cycle lever (2) has the same effect after completion of the first draft cycle, thus smoothing the draft response to enable the operator to control the bobbing of the implement.

To check the action of the rate lever (3), move the lever to the (Transport Lock) position and with the engine running at 1500 rpm and a weight or implement on the lower links, move the three-point lift control lever to the raise position. After the system has returned to neutral in transport position, move the three-point lift control lever to the lowering position. The lift arms should remain in the transport position. The speed of implement drop should progressively increase as the rate lever is moved toward the fast position, until a free drop is obtained at the extreme fast setting.

To check the action of the cycle lever, move the rate lever (3) to the fast position and the cycle lever (2) to the extreme slow position. With the engine running at 1500 rpm, move the three-point control lever to the raise position. After the system has returned to neutral in the transport position, move the lift control lever to the automatic draft range. The lift arms should lower freely. After the arms have lowered, move the lift control lever to the temporary lift position and allow arms to raise almost to transport position. Then, return the control lever to the automatic draft range. The lift arms should remain stationary or fall very slowly. As the cycle lever (2) is moved toward the fast position, the speed of drop should progressively increase until a free drop is obtained at the extreme fast position. The lowering speed of the cycle lever setting will never exceed the speed selected by the rate lever setting.

267. AUXILIARY VALVE SYNCHRONIZATION CHECK. To use the auxiliary control valves for the operation of single or double acting remote cylinders, it is necessary that the cylinder hoses be connected to the correct ports in the control valve housing as follows:

To use the center control lever with a single acting cylinder, connect the hose to port (4—Fig. 292).

To use the inner control lever with a single acting cylinder, connect the hose to port (9).

To use the center control lever with a double acting cylinder, connect the two hoses to ports (4 and 5).

To use the inner control lever with a double acting cylinder, connect the two hoses to ports (7 and 9).

To check the synchronization of the auxiliary control valves with the master control valve, remove the plug in port (1) and install a 0-2000 psi pressure gage. Remove any attached remote cylinders and hoses and install plugs in ports (4, 5, 7 and 9). With the engine running at 1500 rpm, move each of the two auxiliary valve control levers fully to the rear while noting the gage pressure. The pressure should be equal and at the relief valve pressure (1675-1725 psi). A pressure reading lower than relief valve pressure would indicate that the master control valve is not fully closing, and will need to be synchronized as outlined in paragraph 271.

Move each of the two auxiliary valve levers forward against the stop screws and note the gage reading. If the reading is not the relief valve pressure (1675-1725), back out the stop screw until relief pressure is obtained. If the relief valve pressure cannot be obtained, the valves will need to be synchronized as outlined in paragraph 271.

After performing the checks outlined above, connect a hose between ports (4 and 5—Fig. 292) and move center control lever fully to the rear while noting gage reading. The pressure should be not more than 160 psi. A pressure greater than 160 psi would indicate that the directional valve is not fully opening and valves will need to be synchronized as outlined in paragraph 271. Repeat the test with the center control lever in the forward position against the stop screw. Remove hose connecting ports (4 and 5) and install plugs in ports. Install hose between ports (7 and 9) and repeat tests using the inner control lever.

To adjust the auxiliary control valves for use with single acting cylinders, remove the jumper hoses and reinstall the port plugs. Leave the pressure gage installed in port (1—Fig. 292). Turn the stop screw, which contacts the auxiliary lever to be used, fully into the stop housing. Move the auxiliary control lever forward until it contacts the stop screw, then back screw out until the pressure just begins to increase. After attaching the cylinder to an implement, the stop screw may need to be turned slightly to adjust the speed of drop, but under

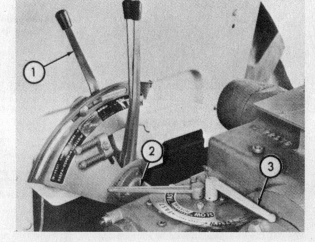

Fig. 291—View showing location of rate and cycle control levers on models G900 and G1000 tractors equipped with "Tel-O-Flo" system.

1. Three-point lift control lever
2. Cycle control lever
3. Rate control lever

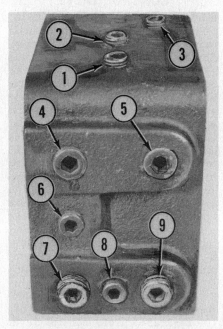

Fig. 292–Control valve body showing location of ports.

1. System pressure port
2. Regulating valve pressure port
3. Three-point lift synchronizing port
4. Jack tapping for single or double acting remote cylinder (center lever)
5. Jack tapping for double acting remote cylinder (center lever)
6. Back flow valve pressure port
7. Jack tapping for double acting remote cylinder (inner lever)
8. Valve body plug
9. Jack tapping for single or double acting remote cylinder (inner lever)

Fig. 293–Control valve front cover showing correct position of valve springs.

1. Regulator valve spring
2. Auxiliary valve springs
3. Master valve spring
4. Three point lift valve spring

Fig. 295–Exploded view of control valve assembly.

1. "O" ring
2. Valve guide
3. Spring
4. Back flow valve
5. Auxiliary valve spring
6. Regulator valve spring
7. Regulator valve
8. Gasket
9. Valve body
10. "O" ring
11. Valve sleeve and spool assembly
12. Adjusting yoke
13. Gasket
14. Master valve spool
15. Master valve sleeve
16. Locknut
17. Adjusting screw
18. Spring seat
19. Relief valve spring
20. Pressure relief valve
21. Three-point lift valve spring
22. Master valve spring
23. Valve front cover

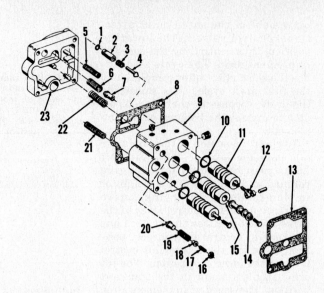

no conditions should the screw be backed out enough to raise the gage pressure above 160 psi.

HYDRAULIC PUMP
Models G900-G1000-G1000 Vista

268. **R&R AND OVERHAUL.** The hydraulic pump is mounted on left side of engine and is gear driven from engine timing gears. To remove the hydraulic pump first drain the "Tel-O-Flo" hydraulic system, then disconnect the pressure, suction and pump drain lines. Unbolt and remove the pump.

Disassembly and the recommended overhaul procedure of the Vickers, piston type pump used on early G1000 Vista and all G1000 tractors equipped with "Tel-O-Flo" system is given in paragraph 238. Overhaul procedure of the Webster gear type pump used on late G1000 Vista and all G900 tractors equipped with "Tel-O-Flo" system is given in paragraph 237.

When reinstalling the pump on tractor, connect the pressure and suction lines. Fill the pump housing with clean hydraulic oil through the drain line port, then connect the drain line.

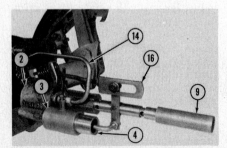

Fig. 294–When control valve and lever housing is removed, unit will contain draft control linkage as shown. See Fig. 298 for legend.

Fill hydraulic reservoir to proper level. Start tractor engine and operate at slow idle. Loosen the pressure line connection to allow air to escape until pump is fully primed. Retighten connection, check hydraulic fluid level in reservoir and add oil as necessary to maintain oil level at the "FULL" mark on dipstick.

CONTROL VALVE
Models G900-G1000-G1000 Vista

269. **R&R AND OVERHAUL.** To remove the control valve assembly, first drain and remove the lift housing as outlined in paragraph 272. Disconnect the oil lines from control valve and remove top cover with the rate and cycle levers. Remove the stud nuts and carefully remove the end cover. CAUTION: Note the position of each of the five springs when removing the cover. These springs must be installed in their original position during reassembly. See Fig. 293. Withdraw the control lever housing and valve housing from the lift housing. The removed unit will contain the draft control mechanism shown in Fig. 294. If the unit is removed for adjustment only, keep valve body and control lever housing together.

To disassemble the valve body, proceed as follows: Withdraw valve body (9—Fig. 295) from control lever housing by pulling straight out. The two auxiliary directional valve spools (3—Fig. 296) will be withdrawn from valve body as the two units are separated. Withdraw the master control valve spool (2) and the three-point lift directional valve spool (1) from valve body. The three direction valves and their sleeves are interchangeable and are available only as a matched set

consisting of valve spool and sleeve. The master control valve spool (14—Fig. 295) and sleeve (15) are available individually. Keep the valve spools identified so they can be reinstalled in their original sleeves, and keep the matched sets together if the sleeves are removed from valve body. Withdraw the relief valve (20), regulator valve (7) and back flow valve (4) from valve body, together with their springs and guide. Clean all parts in a suitable solvent and renew any which are scored, worn or damaged.

To remove the draft control linkage from the control lever housing, first remove bolt (B—Fig. 299) connecting link rod (L) to the draft linkage tube. Withdraw linkage tube (T), with the dash pot piston (P) attached. Disconnect draft pressure tube at connecting nut (N) and remove the tube. Using a socket and extension, remove the cap screw at the closed end of dash pot cyl-

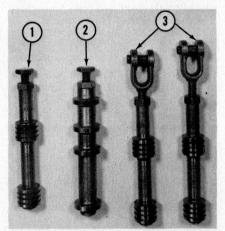

Fig. 296–Except for adjusting screw, three-point directional valve spool (1) and auxiliary directional spools (3) are identical and are available only with matched spool sleeve. Master control spool (2) is serviced separately.

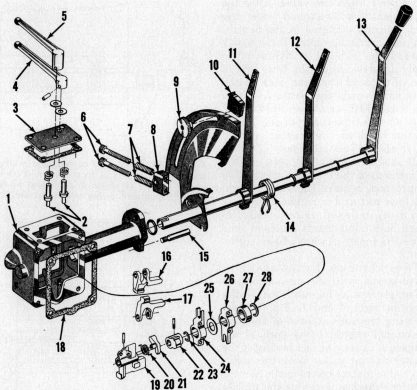

Fig. 297—Exploded view of control lever housing and associated parts used on G900 and G1000 tractors equipped with "Tel-O-Flo" system. Model G1000 Vista is similar.

1. Lever housing
2. Rate & cycle cams
3. Valve cover
4. Cycle lever
5. Rate lever
6. Stop screws
7. Springs
8. Stop block
9. Stop nut
10. Adjustable stop
11. Inner auxiliary lever
12. Center auxiliary lever
13. Three-point control lever
14. Centering spring
15. Spring anchor
16. Spool control fork
17. Spool control fork
18. Gasket
19. Draft control lever
20. Spring
21. Cycle pawl
22. Detent cam
23. Snap ring
24. Actuating lever
25. Washer
26. Actuating lever
27. Spacer
28. Thrust shim

inder (C), then the other two cap screws retaining the linkage cylinder, and lift off the cylinder. Remove pressure tube adapter (A) from the linkage cylinder and make sure it is of the restricter type, containing a ⅛-inch metering hole. If it is not, renew the adapter with one of the proper restriction.

Dash pot cylinder (3—Fig. 298) and piston (4) are only available in a matched set. Examine draft control piston (1) and cylinder (2) for scoring, sticking or excessive wear.

No further disassembly of control lever housing will be necessary if examination reveals no broken or

damaged parts. Examine closely the contact ends of adjusting screws in auxiliary control valve operating levers (24 and 26—Fig. 297). If contact ends show appreciable wear, renew the adjusting screws, using the special hardened screws supplied by the manufacturer.

Reassemble the control valve assembly by reversing the disassembly procedure. Leave the locknuts on the adjusting yokes of the auxiliary directional valve spools (3—Fig. 296) loose during assembly for adjustment as outlined in paragraph 270.

270. **CONTROL VALVE ADJUSTMENT.** After the control valve assembly has been removed for adjustment or reassembled after overhaul, stand the unit on a bench with the linkage tube in a vertical position as shown in Fig. 300. Grasp tube and move it upward to the upper end of slot (S), then release the tube. The assembly should fall slowly to the bottom of the slot of its own weight. If it does not, realign the dash pot linkage with the two locknuts (A), or control rod linkage at (B) until a free drop is obtained. With the linkage tube in bottom of slot as shown, measure the distance between upper edge of lower port and edge of cylinder housing. This distance should be 5/16-inch as shown. If the adjustment is incorrect, loosen one rod adjusting nut (B) and tighten the other until the proper distance is obtained. After making the adjustment, recheck the linkage tube for binding as outlined above and correct as needed.

271. VALVE SYNCHRONIZATION. To synchronize the control valves, bolt the valve body and lever housing together with two bolts as shown in Fig. 301. If not previously done, loosen locknuts on auxiliary valve adjusting yokes before bolting the housings together. Use flat washers underneath the nuts to pre-

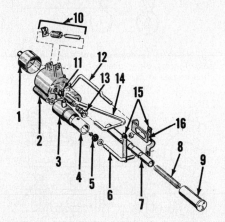

Fig. 298—Exploded view of draft control linkage.

1. Draft piston
2. Linkage cylinder
3. Dash pot cylinder
4. Dash pot piston
5. Piston seal
6. Dash pot link
7. Linkage tube
8. Spring
9. Actuating cap
10. Detent assembly
11. Adjusting screw
12. Link rod
13. Adapter
14. Pressure tube
15. Tube clamp
16. Adjusting bar

Fig. 299—To remove draft control linkage from lever housing, first remove bolt (B) and slide the linkage tube (T) and dash pot piston (P) from housing. Disconnect nut (N), remove fluid supply tube, then unbolt and remove linkage cylinder. One attaching cap screw is located inside dash pot cylinder (C).

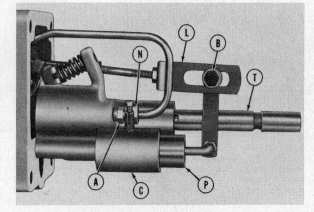

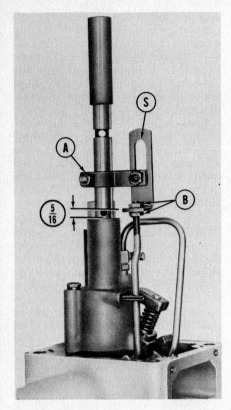

Fig. 300—Adjust length of link rod by adjusting nuts (B) until upper edge of tube port is 5/16-inch from edge of cylinder as shown. Tube must be free to fall in slot (S) of its own weight.

vent damage to the machined surfaces. The regular gasket between the housings must be in place. Remove the two port plugs (2 and 3—Fig. 302). With the three-point lift directional valve lever in the neutral position and the spool held back against the lever, the middle annular groove should be centered in port (3) as shown at (1—Fig. 303). If it is not, withdraw the direction valve from the front of the valve body, loosen the locknut and turn the adjusting screw (2) in or out as needed

Fig. 301—To synchronize the control valves, bolt lever housing and valve body together as shown. Gasket must be in place and flat washers used under nuts to prevent damage to machined surfaces.

to properly align the valve. After the three-point lift directional valve has been properly centered in the neutral position, move the control lever slowly toward the raising position while applying pressure on the front end of the valve until the rear edge of the front land opens the port 2/5—1/2 of the port width as shown at (2—Fig. 304). At this time the front edge of the second land on the master control valve should just close port (2—Fig. 302) as shown at (3—Fig. 304). If the adjustment of the master control valve is incorrect, remove the valve, loosen the lock nut and turn the adjusting screw (4) in or out as required. Recheck both adjustments a second time after the lock nuts have been tightened.

To synchronize the two auxiliary valve spools with the master control valve, proceed as follows: Remove the plugs in ports (4 and 7—Fig. 302) for viewing the adjustment of the two directional valves. Leave port (2) unplugged for checking the setting of the master control valve. With the auxiliary valve control levers in the neutral position, check and center the middle groove of the spool lands visible through ports (4 and 7). See Fig. 305. Note: If the adjusting yoke lock nuts were loosened when the valve was removed or assembled, adjustment can be made by turning the valve spool through the open front end of valve body. Most valve spools are equipped with a screw driver slot in the end for valve adjustment. Valves not so

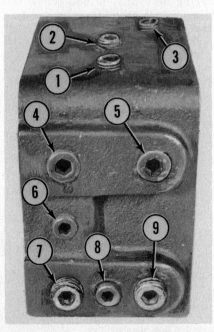

Fig. 302—When synchronizing the control valves, master valve must be viewed through port (2), three-point lift directional valve through port (3) and the two auxiliary directional valves through ports (4 and 7).

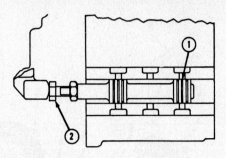

Fig. 303—With three-point control lever in neutral position, groove of spool land must be in center of port as shown at (1). Adjust by removing spool and turning adjusting screw (2).

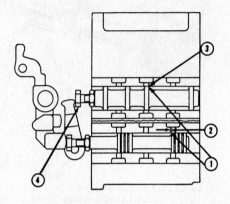

Fig. 304—Move control lever toward raising position until directional valve opens port 2/5 to 1/2 width of port (2). Valves are synchronized if land on master valve just closes port (3). Adjustment is made on master spool at (4).

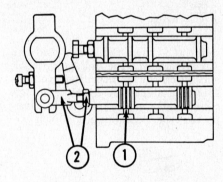

Fig. 305—With auxiliary control levers in neutral position, middle groove of directional valve must center in port as shown at (1). Adjust by turning valve on adjusting yoke (2).

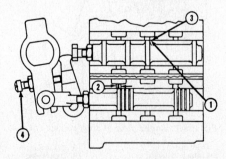

Fig. 306—When auxiliary valve is moved either direction until port is opened 2/5 to 1/2 port width (2), land (1) of master valve must just close port (3).

Fig. 307—Master valve spool is synchronized with auxiliary valves by means of the four adjusting screws in actuating levers as shown.

1. Center lever (rearward)
2. Inner lever (forward)
3. Center lever (forward)
4. Inner lever (rearward)

equipped can usually be turned with eraser end of a pencil or other friction tool. After the directional spools are properly centered, loosen the two bolts securing valve body to lever housing, separate the two units slightly and tighten the adjusting yoke lock nuts; then, tighten the securing bolts and recheck adjustment. After the directional spools are properly centered, move the center lever rearward until the front edge of rear land opens port (4—Fig. 302) 2/5-1/2 of port width. Clamp the control lever to quadrant with directional valve in this position. Apply pressure on the front end of master control valve, loosen the lock

nut on adjusting screw (3—Fig. 307) and turn the adjusting screw in or out until the front edge of the second land just closes port (2—Fig. 302). Move center lever forward until rear edge of rear land of directional spool opens port (4) 2/5-1/2 of port width. (Auxiliary lever stop screw (6—Fig. 297) may need to be backed out.) Clamp the lever in this position and adjust the master control valve, using adjusting screw (1—Fig. 307) to adjust the master valve. Synchronize the inner auxiliary valve lever (lower spool) in the same manner, using port (7—Fig. 302) to view the directional valve and adjusting screws (2 and 4—Fig. 307) to adjust master valve. Recheck all adjustments after tightening the lock nuts.

When either one or both auxiliary valve levers are in the full up or down position, the three-point lift directional spool must be held by the interlock lever in a position that fully covers the port to the three-point lift cylinder. This locks the oil in the lift cylinder so the lift arms cannot drop when the auxiliary valves are opened. The three-point directional spool should fully cover and overlap the port a minimum of 1/32-inch each way. The hook on lower end of interlock lever may have to be bent slightly to accomplish this.

RESERVOIR, ROCKSHAFT AND RAM CYLINDER
Models G900-G1000-G1000 Vista

272. **R&R AND OVERHAUL.** To remove the system reservoir, drain the system, remove seat assembly and on model G1000 Vista, remove or unbolt and block up fuel tank. Then, on all models, disconnect the three-point hitch lift rods. Disconnect the hydraulic pump drain line, suction hose

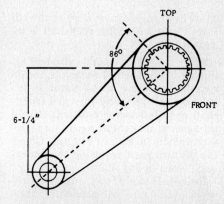

Fig. 309—To properly position lift arms on rockshaft, place lift in lowered position and install arm so that distance between centerline of shaft and pin hole is 6 1/4-inches as shown. Rotation arc of rockshaft is 86 degrees.

and pressure line. Unbolt reservoir from differential housing, attach a suitable hoist and remove lift assembly from tractor.

Move lift arms to the full down position and place the lift assembly on its side. Drive out the roll pin and push link pin in one side to allow piston link to be removed from the rockshaft arm (14—Fig. 308). Remove the six cap screws securing cylinder assembly to reservoir, then withdraw cylinder assembly. Loosen set screws in cylinder nut (3) and punch mark the nut and cylinder so that nut can be retightened in the same position during reassembly. Remove nut and withdraw piston assembly from cylinder. Examine piston (4) and cylinder (1) for scoring or excessive wear. When reassembling cylinder, renew all "O" rings, seal ring and wear rings. Kick-out bolt (5) should be adjusted so that distance from top of bolt head to end of piston is 7/8-inch.

To remove the rockshaft, first remove both lift arms, then drive rockshaft out left side of reservoir. Rock-

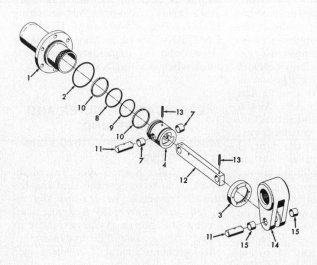

Fig. 308—Exploded view of the three-point lift cylinder used on models G900, G1000 and G1000 Vista tractors equipped with "Tel-O-Flo" system.

1. Cylinder
2. "O" ring
3. Nut
4. Piston
5. Kick-out bolt
6. Locknut
7. Bushing
8. Piston seal ring
9. "O" ring
10. Wear ring
11. Pin
12. Piston link
13. Roll pin
14. Rockshaft arm
15. Bushing

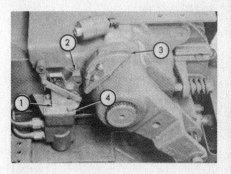

Fig. 310—View showing depth limit control valve on left side of model G1000 with "Tel-O-Flo" system. Valve is located on right side of models G900 and G1000 Vista equipped with "Tel-O-Flo".

1. Actuator bracket
2. Actuator
3. Cam
4. Cap screws

shaft bushings can now be renewed. Install new seals after rockshaft is installed.

After rockshaft and cylinder assembly is installed in reservoir, rotate rockshaft to position the piston in lift cylinder all the way forward (rockshaft in fully lowered position). Install lift arms so that chisel marks on reservoir and lift arms are aligned. Check the lift arm position, using the dimension shown in Fig. 309.

Reinstall the lift assembly by reversing the removal procedure, then fill and bleed the system as outlined in paragraph 256.

DEPTH LIMIT CONTROL
Models G900-G1000-G1000 Vista

273. **ADJUSTMENT.** To adjust the depth limit control on tractors so equipped, first loosen cap screws (4—Fig. 310) and move actuator bracket (1) forward away from cam (3) as far as slotted holes will allow. Tighten the four cap screws. Attach an implement or weight to the lift arms. Place depth limit lever in "Transport" (rear) position. Start tractor engine and raise lift arms to transport position by moving the three-point lift control lever to "Up" (rear) position. Then, with engine not running, place the three-point lift lever in "Down" position. Lower

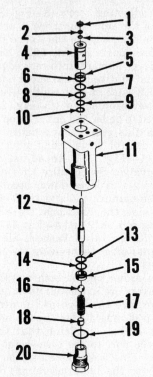

Fig. 311—Exploded view of depth limit control valve used with "Tel-O-Flo" system.

1. Oil seal	11. Valve body
2. Back-up ring	12. Push rod
3. "O" ring	13. Back-up ring
4. Rod end plug	14. "O" ring
5. Back-up ring	15. Ball seat
6. "O" ring	16. Check ball
7. "O" ring	17. Spring
8. Back-up ring	18. Ball stop
9. "O" ring	19. "O" ring
10. Back-up ring	20. Plug

the lift arms by slowly pushing the depth limit lever forward. If lift arms will not lower to their extreme lower position, loosen cap screws and tap actuator bracket (1) toward cam (3) until the lift arms move to the lowest position. Tighten the cap screws.

Check position of actuator bracket in relation to plunger in valve. If necessary, loosen cap screws and shift actuator bracket sideways to obtain a 0.005 minimum clearance between plunger and bracket, then retighten cap screws.

Move depth control lever through full range of travel and secure stops at each end of travel range.

274. **R&R AND OVERHAUL.** To remove the depth control valve, first lower the lift arms and drain the reservoir. Disconnect fluid lines from valve, then unbolt and remove valve.

Disassembly of the valve is obvious after an examination of the unit and reference to Fig. 311. Check all parts for excessive wear or scoring and renew as necessary.

When reassembling, use Fig. 311 as a guide and renew all "O" rings and back-up rings. Oil seal (1) must be installed with lip to outside.

Reinstall by reversing removal procedure, fill and bleed as outlined in paragraph 256 and adjust as outlined in paragraph 273.

HYDRAULIC LIFT (CLOSED CENTER SYSTEM)

This section covers the closed center hydraulic system used on some G900, G950, G1000 Vista, G1050 and G1350 tractors. The section covers the hydraulic pump, reservoir, control valve, rockshaft and lift cylinders.

For models G900, G1000 and G1000 Vista tractors equipped with "Tel-O-Flo" system, refer to section beginning with paragraph 255.

For models equipped with "Types E, F or G" hydraulic systems, refer to section beginning with paragraph 227.

OPERATION
All Models So Equipped

275. The closed center hydraulic system provides for operating the three-point hitch on full draft control, full position control or a combination of both. To operate the hitch in float position, move both the position control and draft control levers to the fully forward position. The pump used in this system is a constant pressure

variable flow axial piston type. A compensator, consisting of a pressure sensitive valve and stroking piston, control the angle of the spring loaded swashplate.

When the position control lever is moved rearward to raise the hitch, line pressure drops momentarily, sensing valve closes, stroking piston retracts and the spring loaded swashplate moves pumping pistons back to a delivery position. The pump delivers as much oil (up to 20 GPM) as is needed through the control valve and to the lift cylinder or cylinders. As the hitch approaches the height determined by the position control lever, feedback linkage moves the control valve spool back to neutral position. Pressure builds to the 2000 psi pre-set pressure, compensator sensing valve opens and a small amount of oil is diverted to the stroking piston. The stroking piston moves the swashplate back to a neutral angle (zero delivery). NOTE: A small amount of oil is

pumped at the zero delivery angle to make up for internal leakage and for pump cooling.

When the engine stops, the load on hitch settles to the ground, regardless of the position of control levers. When engine is started, the hitch immediately raises to a height corresponding to the setting of position control lever. CAUTION: Make certain there is no one around any implement attached to hitch when starting tractor engine.

LUBRICATION, FILTER AND BLEEDING
Models G900-G950-G1000 Vista-G1050-G1350

276. Under normal operating conditions, it is recommended that the hydraulic reservoir be drained and refilled with new MM hydraulic oil every 600 hours of operation or at least once a year. The hydraulic oil filter element should be renewed each

300 hours of operation. On models G900 and G1000 Vista, the hydraulic filter is located on suction line on left side of tractor. On models G950, G1050 and G1350, the filter is located in the reservoir under the top cover.

On models G900 and G1000 Vista, reservoir capacity is approximately 6 gallons. To bleed the air from hydraulic system, connect a by-pass hose to one set of remote valve couplers. Place remote valve lever in raise position and start engine. Operate engine at 1500 rpm for at least two minutes while raising and lowering hitch several times. Stop engine, remove by-pass hose and recheck hydraulic oil level.

On models G950, G1050 and G1350, reservoir capacity is approximately 9 gallons. After filling the reservoir, connect a by-pass hose to one set of remote valve couplers. Place remote valve lever in raise position and start engine. Operate engine at 1500 rpm for at least two minutes while raising and lowering hitch and rotating steering from stop to stop several times. Stop engine, remove by-pass hose and recheck hydraulic oil level.

ADJUSTMENTS
Models G900-G1000 Vista

277. **CONTROL VALVE.** To adjust the control valve, refer to Fig. 312 and proceed as follows: The hitch rate of rise is controlled by needle valve (1). With engine operating at 1800 rpm, adjust needle valve so that hitch will go from fully down to fully up position in 2½ seconds. Backing needle valve out will speed up rate of rise.

Hitch rate of drop is controlled by rotary valve (2). Adjust valve so that hitch will go from fully up to fully down position in 2½ seconds. The slot in end of rotary spool is in line with opening through spool.

The damper valve (3) in the lowering circuit cushions the last few

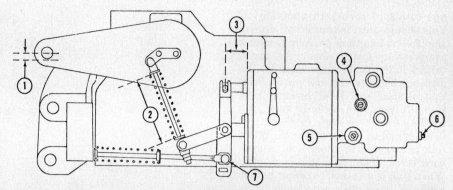

Fig. 313–Adjusting points on closed center lift system used on models G900 and G1000 Vista. Refer to text.

inches of hitch drop to protect both tractor and implement. Recommended adjustment for the needle valve is ¾-turn out from seat. Turning needle valve inward will increase dampening effect. Do not operate lift with damper valve fully seated as this will decrease hitch sensitivity.

278. **CONTROL LINKAGE.** To adjust the control linkage, first adjust the two pivot plate (hitch third link bracket) springs to a pre-load of 0 to 1/16-inch. Refer to Fig. 313 and adjust length of position feedback spring to 5⅝-inches (dimension 2). With engine operating, move position lever to full raise position, then adjust link between position lever and valve so lift arms will stop ½-inch below fully raised position (dimension 1). This will prevent piston from bottoming in lift cylinder. Seal this adjustment with solder. Make certain that draft feedback linkage is in upper slot (7), draft lever is fully rearward against stop and that no load is on hitch third link. Adjust draft feedback linkage to obtain a distance of 1 1/16-inch between lever housing cover and pin (dimension 3). Seal this adjustment with solder. Adjust link between draft lever and control valve until hitch just starts to raise, then seal this adjustment with solder.

Models G950-G1050-G1350

279. **CONTROL VALVE.** To adjust the control valve, refer to Fig. 314 and proceed as follows: Hitch rate of rise is controlled by needle valve (1). With engine operating at 1800 rpm, adjust needle valve so that hitch will go from fully down to fully up position in 1¾ seconds. Backing needle valve out will speed up rate of rise.

Hitch rate of drop is controlled by rotary valve (2). The valve controls the size of opening for return oil from cylinders. Adjust valve to permit hitch to go from fully raised to fully lowered

position in 2½ seconds with average load.

Damper valve (3) in the lowering circuit cushions the last few inches of hitch drop to protect both tractor and implement. Recommended adjustment for the needle valve is ¾-turn out from seat. Turning needle valve inward will increase dampening effect. Do not operate lift with damper valve fully seated as this will decrease hitch sensitivity.

280. **CONTROL LINKAGE.** To adjust the control linkage, make sure there is no load on three-point hitch. Refer to Fig. 315 and check pre-load of draft sensing spring (1). If spring is loose, loosen lock nut and tighten adjusting nut (2) until spring is held snug. Then, tighten adjusting nut an additional ¼-turn and secure with lock nut.

When checking position control linkage, hitch must be in fully lowered position (lift cylinders fully collapsed) and position control lever all the way forward. Check the distance between position feedback clevis pin and lever housing back plate (dimension 3) which should be 2 5/16 inches. If not, adjust length of position feedback link-

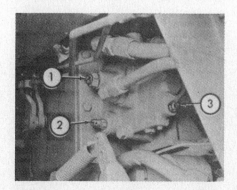

Fig. 312–View showing location of control valve adjustments on models G900 and G1000 Vista.

1. Rate of rise adjustment
2. Rate of drop adjustment
3. Damper adjustment

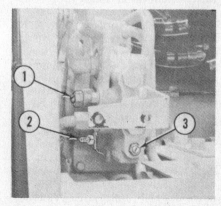

Fig. 314–Location of closed center control valve adjustments on models G950, G1050 and G1350.

1. Rate of rise adjustment
2. Rate of drop adjustment
3. Damper adjustment

age to 6 3/16 inches (dimension 4). This should provide the correct dimension 3. The length of position feedback compression spring should be maintained at 2⅝ inches (dimension 5). The distance between the roll pin in draft control spool and lever housing back plate (dimension 6) will vary, depending on where draft feedback link is attached to feedback lever. When link is attached to upper hole in feedback lever, distance should be ¾-inch. When link is attached to center hole in feedback lever, distance should be ½-inch. NOTE: Upper hole is used for semi-mounted equipment. For fully mounted equipment requiring greater draft sensitivity, use center hole in feedback lever. Approximate length of draft feedback link (dimension 7) should be 4 3/16 inches. The length of draft feedback link compression spring (dimension 8) should be maintained at 2⅛ inches.

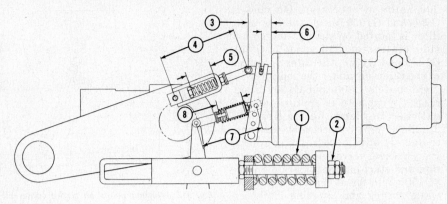

Fig. 315–Adjusting points on closed center lift system used on models G950, G1050 and G1350. Refer to text.

CONTROL VALVE
All Models With Closed Center System

281. **R&R AND OVERHAUL.** To remove the closed center control valve, first drain hydraulic reservoir and disconnect hydraulic lines. Plug or cap all openings to prevent dirt or other foreign material from entering system. Disconnect draft and position feedback linkage and draft and position control lever linkage. Remove mounting bolts, then remove control valve and lever housing assembly. Refer to Figs. 316 and 317, remove pins from rear of shafts (10 and 12), then unbolt and remove housing cover (17). Drive spiral pin from arm (14), then remove levers (6 and 7) with shafts (3 and 5). Unpin and remove lever beams (9 and 11) and shafts (10 and 12). Unbolt valve from lever housing (1).

With control valve removed, refer to Fig. 318 and proceed as follows: Remove plug (25), spring (27), spring seat (28) and check ball (29). Remove plug (1), spring (3) and flow control valve (11). Remove lock nut (19), washer (18) and retaining ring (17), then unbolt and remove spool retainer plate (15). Push plug (14) from bore in valve body. Remove plug (34) and withdraw directional valve spool (21) and spring (20). Loosen jam nuts (8 and 32) and remove rise rate needle valve (7) and damper valve (31). Remove nut (10), Belleville washer (9) and rotary drop rate valve (24).

Clean and inspect all parts for excessive wear or other damage and renew parts as necessary. Directional valve spool (21) and valve body (4) are available only as a matched set.

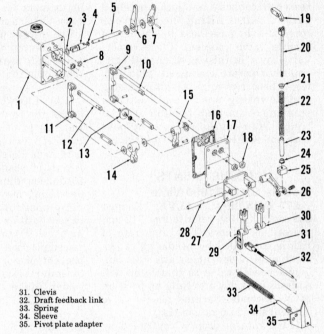

Fig. 316–Exploded view of position, draft and lever housing linkage used on models G900 and G1000 Vista equipped with closed center system.

1. Lever housing.
2. "O" ring
3. Position control shaft
4. "O" ring
5. Draft control shaft
6. Position lever
7. Draft lever
8. Vee packing
9. Position lever beam
10. Position feedback shaft
11. Draft lever beam
12. Draft feedback shaft
13. Directional spool washer
14. Draft arm
15. Position arm
16. Gasket
17. Lever housing cover
18. Oil seals
19. Position feedback arm
20. Feedback link
21. Spring seat
22. Spring
23. Sleeve
24. Spring seat
25. Block
26. Position feedback yoke
27. Bracket
28. Shaft
29. Draft feedback lever
30. Position feedback lever
31. Clevis
32. Draft feedback link
33. Spring
34. Sleeve
35. Pivot plate adapter

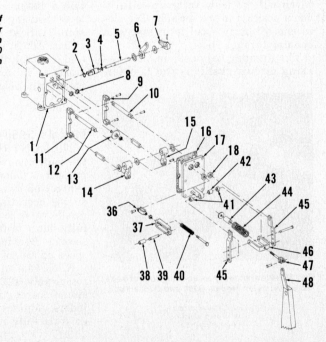

Fig. 317–Exploded view of position, draft and lever housing linkage used on G950, G1050 and G1350 tractors equipped with closed center system.

1. Lever housing
2. "O" ring
3. Draft control shaft
4. "O" ring
5. Position control shaft
6. Draft lever
7. Position lever
8. Vee packing
9. Draft lever beam
10. Draft feedback shaft
11. Position lever beam
12. Position feedback shaft
13. Directional spool washer
14. Position arm
15. Draft arm
16. Gasket
17. Lever housing cover
18. Oil seals
36. Clevis
37. Position feedback link
38. Spacer
39. Stud
40. Spring
41. Spacers
42. Bushing
43. Spacer
44. Spring
45. Draft feedback lever
46. Draft feedback link
47. Feedback rod
48. Hitch draft arm

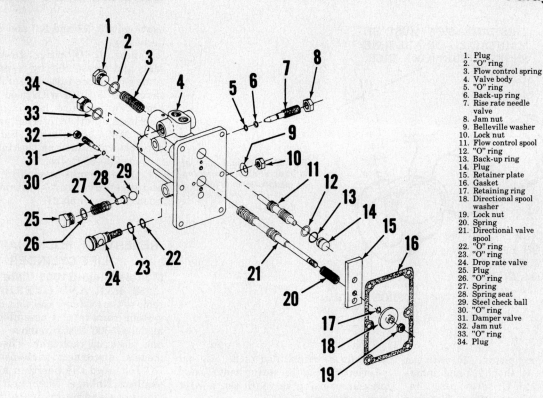

1. Plug
2. "O" ring
3. Flow control spring
4. Valve body
5. "O" ring
6. Back-up ring
7. Rise rate needle valve
8. Jam nut
9. Belleville washer
10. Lock nut
11. Flow control spool
12. "O" ring
13. Back-up ring
14. Plug
15. Retainer plate
16. Gasket
17. Retaining ring
18. Directional spool washer
19. Lock nut
20. Spring
21. Directional valve spool
22. "O" ring
23. "O" ring
24. Drop rate valve
25. Plug
26. "O" ring
27. Spring
28. Spring seat
29. Steel check ball
30. "O" ring
31. Damper valve
32. Jam nut
33. "O" ring
34. Plug

Fig. 318—Exploded view of control valve assembly used on all models equipped with closed center system.

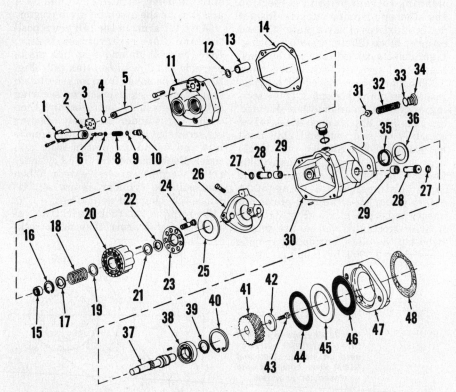

Fig. 319—Exploded view of typical Vickers hydraulic pump used on models with closed center system.

1. Compensator body	13. Piston	25. Thrust plate
2. "O" ring	14. Gasket	26. Swashplate
3. Gasket	15. Needle bearing	27. "O" ring
4. Snap ring	16. Snap ring	28. Trunnion
5. Piston tube	17. Limit washer	29. Needle bearing
6. Sensing valve	18. Spring	30. Pump housing
7. Spring seat	19. Thrust washer	31. Spring seat
8. Spring	20. Cylinder block	32. Spring
9. "O" ring	21. Washer	33. "O" ring
10. Plug	22. Spherical washer	34. Plug
11. Pump end valve plate	23. Slipper shoe plate	35. Oil seal
12. Spacer	24. Piston (9 used)	36. Washer

37. Pump shaft
38. Bearing
39. Snap ring
40. Snap ring
41. Drive gear
42. Washer
43. Cap screw (L.H. thread)
44. Gasket
45. Spacer
46. Gasket
47. Adapter
48. Gasket

Renew all "O" rings, back-up rings, seals and gaskets and reassemble by reversing disassembly procedure. Reinstall valve and lever housing assembly, fill and bleed system as outlined in paragraph 276, then adjust control valve and linkage as outlined in paragraphs 277 through 280.

PUMP
All Models With Closed Center System

282. **R&R AND OVERHAUL.** To remove the pump, drain reservoir, disconnect hydraulic lines and plug or cap all openings to prevent dirt or other foreign material from entering system. Remove cap screws securing pump to adapter (47—Fig. 319) and lift pump assembly from tractor.

To disassemble the pump, first remove left hand thread capscrew (43), washer (42) and drive gear (41). Clamp pump housing (30) in a vise with drive shaft downward. Unbolt compensator body (1) from valve plate (11) and lay compensator aside for later disassembly. Remove cap screws securing valve plate to pump housing, then carefully remove valve plate with piston tube (5), spacer (12) and piston (13). Remove pump from vise, tilt the unit over and remove cylinder block assembly and thrust plate (25). Grasp slipper shoe plate (23) and withdraw

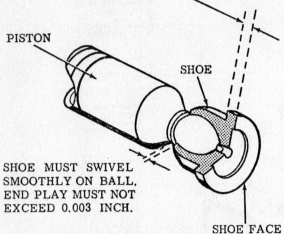

THIS DIMENSION MUST BE MAINTAINED ON ALL NINE SHOES WITHIN 0.001 INCH.

PISTON

SHOE

SHOE MUST SWIVEL SMOOTHLY ON BALL. END PLAY MUST NOT EXCEED 0.003 INCH.

SHOE FACE

Fig. 320–Sectional view of slipper shoe on pumping piston. Refer to text.

bearings (15, 29 and 38) and renew as necessary.

Renew all "O" rings, gaskets and seals and reassemble by reversing the removal procedure. Bearing (38) should be ½ filled with good grade of high temperature bearing grease. Lubricate all other internal parts with clean MM hydraulic oil. Valve plate cap screws should be tightened to a torque of 20-25 ft.-lbs.

Reinstall pump assembly, then fill and bleed hydraulic system as outlined in paragraph 276.

RESERVOIR, ROCKSHAFT AND LIFT CYLINDER
Models G900-G1000 Vista

283. **R&R AND OVERHAUL.** To remove the system reservoir, drain the system, remove seat assembly and on model G1000 Vista, remove or unbolt and block up fuel tank. Then, on all models, disconnect three-point hitch lift rods and the position and draft feedback linkage. Disconnect the suction hose and pump drain line from reservoir. Unbolt reservoir from differential housing, attach a suitable hoist and remove the assembly from tractor.

Move lift arms to the full down position and place reservoir on its side. Drive out roll pin and push link pin to one side to allow piston link (12—Fig. 321) to be removed from rockshaft arm (14). Remove six cap screws securing cylinder assembly to reservoir, then withdraw cylinder assembly. Loosen set screws in cylinder nut (3), remove nut and withdraw piston from cylinder. Examine piston (4) and cylinder (1) for scoring or excessive wear. When reassembling cylinder, renew all "O" rings, seal ring and wear rings.

To remove the rockshaft, first remove both lift arms, then drive rock-

the nine pumping pistons (24) with the plate. Remove washer (21) and spherical washer (22). Unscrew plug (34) and remove spring (32) and spring seat (31). Remove the two clamping cap screws from swashplate (26). Thread a ¼-inch N.C. cap screw into trunnion (28) and pull trunnion from housing. Remove opposite trunnion in same manner, then lift out swashplate (26). Remove snap ring (40) and bump shaft (37)· and bearing (38) from housing. Bearing can be pressed from shaft after snap ring (39) is removed. Remove washer (36) and oil seal (35) from pump housing.

To disassemble the cylinder block assembly, place the unit in a press and apply pressure to limit washer (17). Remove snap ring (16) release press and remove spring (18) and washers from cylinder block.

When disassembling the compensator unit, count the number of turns necessary to remove plug (10) so that

plug can be reinstalled in its original position. Spring (8), spring seat (7) and pressure sensing valve (6) can now be removed from body (1).

Clean all parts in mineral oil cleaning solvent prior to inspection and after any lapping of parts. Inspect mating surfaces of valve plate (11) and cylinder block (20) for wear or scoring. Light defects can be removed by hand lapping. However, not more than 0.0004 should be removed by lapping. Inspect pumping pistons (24) for scoring, excessive wear or other damage. See Fig. 320. Slipper shoe must swivel smoothly on ball, but end play must not exceed 0.003. Slipper shoe thickness must not vary more than 0.001 for all nine pistons. If necessary, hand lap the slipper shoes using 400A emery paper on a lapping plate. Inspect thrust plate (25—Fig. 319) for wear or scoring. If defects are minor, hand lap the plate, but do not remove more than 0.0004 by lapping. Check

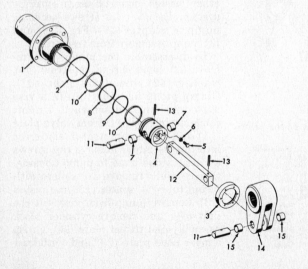

Fig. 321–Exploded view of three-point lift cylinder used on models G900 and G1000 Vista equipped with closed center system.

1. Cylinder
2. "O" ring
3. Nut
4. Piston
7. Bushing
8. Piston seal ring
9. "O" ring
10. Wear ring
11. Pin
12. Piston link
13. Roll pin
14. Rockshaft arm
15. Bushing

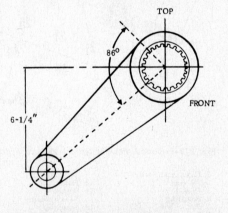

TOP

86°

FRONT

6-1/4"

Fig. 322–To properly position lift arms on rockshaft on models G900 and G1000 Vista, place lift in lowered position and install arms so that distance between center-line of shaft and pin hole is 6 1/4 inches as shown. Rotation arc of rockshaft is approximately 86 degrees.

shaft out left side of reservoir. Rockshaft bushings can now be renewed. Install new seals after rockshaft is installed.

After rockshaft and cylinder assembly are installed in reservoir, rotate rockshaft to place the piston in lift cylinder all the way forward (rockshaft in fully lowered position). Install lift arms so that chisel marks on reservoir and lift arms are aligned. Check lift arm position using the dimension shown in Fig. 322.

Reinstall reservoir assembly by reversing the removal procedure, then fill and bleed the system as outlined in paragraph 276.

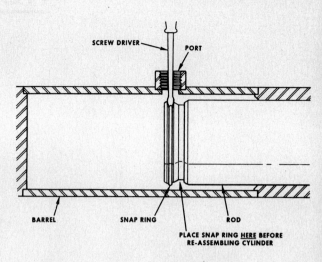

Fig. 324—Use a screw driver to shift snap ring when removing or installing piston rod. Refer to text.

LIFT CYLINDERS
Models G950-G1050-G1350

284. R&R AND OVERHAUL. To remove either lift cylinder, place hitch in lowered position and support lower hitch links with blocks. Disconnect hydraulic line from cylinder. Unbolt and remove hitch wear plate, remove cylinder pins and remove cylinder from tractor.

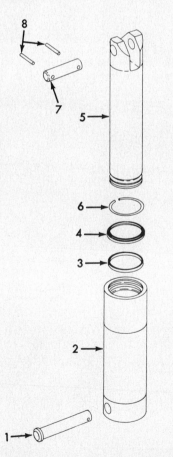

Fig. 323—Exploded view of three-point hitch lift cylinder used on models G950, G1050 and G1350.

1. Pin
2. Cylinder barrel
3. Rod seal
4. Wiper ring
5. Piston rod
6. Snap ring
7. Pin
8. Roll pins

To disassemble the cylinder, remove hydraulic fitting and pull rod (5—Fig. 323) outward until snap ring (6) is aligned with port. Use a screwdriver as shown in Fig. 324, to disengage snap ring from the shallow groove and move it into the deep groove on piston rod. Pull rod from barrel and remove wiper ring (4—Fig. 323) and seal ring (3) from barrel.

Clean and inspect all parts and renew any showing excessive wear or other damage. Reassemble cylinder as follows: Install new seal ring (3) and wiper ring (4) in barrel (2) and lubricate with clean hydraulic oil. Place snap ring (6) in deep groove on piston rod (5), then carefully insert rod assembly through seals and into barrel until snap ring is visible through port. Use screw driver to move snap ring from deep groove into shallow groove on piston rod. If necessary, repeat operation on opposite cylinder.

Reinstall cylinder, then fill and bleed system as outlined in paragraph 276.

ROCKSHAFT
Models G950-G1050-G1350

285. R&R AND OVERHAUL. To remove the rockshaft, first unbolt and remove left rear wheel fender. Block up under lower hitch links, then disconnect upper end of lift rods from lift arms. Unpin upper end of lift cylinders. Remove snap rings from ends of rockshaft and remove left lift arm and cylinder arm. Drive rockshaft out left side of support. Rockshaft bushings can be renewed at this time. When installing bushings, align lube holes in bushings with lube fittings in support.

Reassemble by reversing disassembly procedure. Lift arms, cylinder arms and rockshaft are all equipped with a blind spline to prevent incorrect positioning of arms.

RESERVOIR
Models G950-G1050-G1350

286. The reservoir containing the oil supply for the hydraulic lift system and power steering is accessible by removing the hood nose section. The hydraulic filter is located inside the reservoir. To renew filter element (8—Fig. 325), first drain the reservoir. Remove cover retaining nuts, then remove cover (3), spring (5), by-pass valve (6), seal ring (7), element (8) and element seal (9). Thoroughly clean reservoir and install new element and seal rings by reversing the removal procedure. Inspect filler screen (2) for damage and renew if necessary. Fill reservoir and bleed air from system as outlined in paragraph 276. Capacity is approximately 9 gallons.

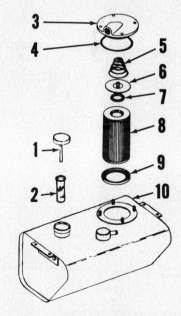

Fig. 325—Exploded view of hydraulic reservoir and filter used on models G950, G1050 and G1350.

1. Dipstick
2. Filler screen
3. Cover
4. Seal ring
5. Spring
6. By-pass valve
7. Seal ring
8. Element
9. Seal ring
10. Reservoir

NOTES

General Torque Recommendations

Use the following torque *recommendations* as a guideline when a specification for a particular fastener is not available. In many cases manufacturers do not provide torque specifications, especially on older models.

Consider fastener condition carefully when referring to either a recommendation or a specification. If fastener reuse is appropriate, select the minimum value to account for fastener stretch. Softer fasteners or those securing softer materials, such as aluminum or cast iron, typically require less torque. In addition, lubricated or unusually long fasteners typically require less torque.

Determine fastener strength by referring to the grade mark on the bolt head. The higher the grade is, the stronger the fastener.

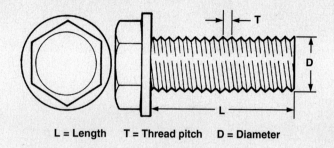

L = Length   T = Thread pitch   D = Diameter

Determine fastener size by measuring the thread diameter (D), fastener length (L) and thread pitch (T).

Size and Pitch	SAE grade 1 or 2 bolts	SAE grade 5 bolts	SAE grade 8 bolts
1/4—20	4-6 ft.-lbs.	6-10 ft.-lbs.	9-14 ft.-lbs.
1/4—28	5-7 ft.-lbs.	7-11 ft.-lbs.	10-16 ft.-lbs.
5/16—18	6-12 ft.-lbs.	8-19 ft.-lbs.	15-29 ft.-lbs.
5/16—24	9-13 ft.-lbs.	15-21 ft.-lbs.	19-33 ft.-lbs.
3/8—16	12-20 ft.-lbs.	19-33 ft.-lbs.	28-47 ft.-lbs.
3/8—24	17-25 ft.-lbs.	26-37 ft.-lbs.	36-53 ft.-lbs.
7/16—14	22-32 ft.-lbs.	31-54 ft.-lbs.	51-78 ft.-lbs.
7/16—20	27-36 ft.-lbs.	40-60 ft.-lbs.	58-84 ft.-lbs.
1/2—13	34-47 ft.-lbs.	56-78 ft.-lbs.	80-119 ft.-lbs.
1/2—20	41-59 ft.-lbs.	64-87 ft.-lbs.	89-129 ft.-lbs.
9/16—12	53-69 ft.-lbs.	69-114 ft.-lbs.	102-169 ft.-lbs.
9/16—18	60-79 ft.-lbs.	78-127 ft.-lbs.	115-185 ft.-lbs.
5/8—11	74-96 ft.-lbs.	112-154 ft.-lbs.	156-230 ft.-lbs.
5/8—18	82-110 ft.-lbs.	127-175 ft.-lbs.	178-287 ft.-lbs.
3/4—10	105-155 ft.-lbs.	165-257 ft.-lbs.	263-380 ft.-lbs.
3/4—16	130-180 ft.-lbs.	196-317 ft.-lbs.	309-448 ft.-lbs.
7/8—9	165-206 ft.-lbs.	290-382 ft.-lbs.	426-600 ft.-lbs.
7/8—14	185-230 ft.-lbs.	342-451 ft.-lbs.	492-665 ft.-lbs.
1—8	225-310 ft.-lbs.	441-587 ft.-lbs.	650-879 ft.-lbs.
1—14	252-345 ft.-lbs.	508-675 ft.-lbs.	742-1032 ft.-lbs.
1 1/8—7	330-480 ft.-lbs.	609-794 ft.-lbs.	860-1430 ft.-lbs.